Speer Reloading Manual #14

Lewiston, Idaho U.S.A.

DISCLAIMER

These loads are for Speer® bullets. Bullets of other makes will not produce the same pressures and velocities and can create an unsafe condition if used with loads shown here.

Because ATK has no control over individual loading practices or the quality of the firearms in which the resulting ammunition may be used, we assume no liability—either expressed or implied—for the use of this load data information and instructional materials.

The data contained herein replaces, supersedes and obsoletes all data previously published by Speer, Omark Industries and Blount International, Inc.

First Printing, April 2007

ISBN 978-0-9791860-0-4

Speer Bullets
P.O. Box 856
Lewiston, ID 83501

PRINTED IN THE U.S.A.

Thanks, AJG

Table of Contents

Table of Contents

Rifle Data

Rifle Data (continued)

Rifle Data (continued)

Chapter 14

Chapter 15

Chapter 16

Chapter 17

Chapter 18

Introduction to the Handgun Data

Handgun Data

Handgun Data (continued)

Handgun Data (continued)

Reference Section

Speer® Trajectory Tables

Glossary of Firearms and Reloading Terms

president's **letter**

In pursuit of perfection

Like many of you, I strive for perfection in all I do. I see this same passion in reloading and the people it attracts. Although there's a nostalgic appeal to the reloading process, the real hook is the drive to create the optimal load. It can be very rewarding when you safely develop a load that exceeds the performance of today's factory offerings. There may be a number of standard calibers and bullets that will do the trick, but there's a real satisfaction in knowing you fine-tuned the case, determined the powder, seated the primer and topped it with your favorite bullet.

If you reload enough you may reduce the cost of your ammunition, but you can't fool your inner self - the true payoff is in loading your unique cartridge and making it the best possible ammunition for your firearm, hunt, or target set. You are a perfectionist when it comes to ammunition.

Reloading is one of our true passions here at Speer®. In an age of automation and mass production, reloading provides an opportunity to make a quality product yourself and then use it with the satisfaction that only comes to those who create. I hope you enjoy this edition of our *Speer Reloading Manual*. It's the largest volume yet, and represents years of fine tuning components and combinations in developing cartridges and loads. I appreciate your support and wish you a safe and rewarding reloading experience!

Mark DeYoung, ATK Senior Vice President; President, ATK Ammunition Systems Group, (center) with his two sons, Curtis, 13 (left) and Scott, 17 (right) with whitetail deer, Albany, Texas.

Mark W. DeYoung,
President, Speer Bullets

Acknowledgements

The research staff at Speer extends our sincere appreciation to those firms and people in the industry who provided both material and technical assistance invaluable to the production of *Speer® Reloading Manual Number 14*:

Hodgdon Powder Company—Ron Reiber, Tom Sheppard, Mike Daly, and George Weber

IMR Powders

Winchester Powders

Western Powders (Ramshot and Accurate Powders)—Bob Rodefer

Kaltron-Pettibone (VihtaVuori Powders)—Bob Trownsell and Jeanne Bolda

Hornady—Dave Emary and Bob Palmer

Remington—David K. Schluckebier

Freedom Arms—Bob Baker

Starline—Bob and Barbara Hayden

M. L. McPherson

John Kort

Paul Coil

From the Editor's Desk

As I wrap up work on the biggest *Speer® Reloading Manual* ever, I am thinking about many things. Twenty years of developing Speer data and presenting it to our loyal customers has given me the honor of making many friends in this industry.

Allan Jones

One of the oldest friendships is with Lane Pearce. In 1994, Lane offered me his technical proofreading assistance and I quickly found how knowledgeable and keen he was in the art of "wordsmithing." He is also one sharp guy when it comes to guns and reloading. Once again, Lane's skills have helped me put together a book that is both a data source and a teaching tool. Lane has now ascended to the position of Reloading Editor for *Shooting Times* Magazine so even more reloaders can benefit from his vast knowledge of our hobby. Lane has also been there to cheer me on when I get buried in work and to share a laugh to raise my spirits. Some people use the term "friend" lightly; when I say Lane is a friend, I mean it in every sense of the word. Thanks, Lane—you're the best.

I'm also looking at the many new cartridges that have been introduced since we wrote *Speer #13*. After 40 years of reloading, I look at each one and consider what it means to me as a reloader and where it fits in the field of existing cartridges. For me the most significant new developments are those that removed the belt from "magnum" cartridges. The belt has served us well but it also creates some problems for handloaders. I support and encourage this trend to beltless cases and hope that it continues.

I'm an admirer of small, efficient cartridges and a number of the new offerings fall into this class. I like the concept behind the 6.8mm Remington, the 338 Federal, the various "short magnums" and others of this class. They all satisfy the ballistician in me.

I also think about a first for *Speer Manuals:* two independent ballistic labs working toward the same goal. In addition to the Speer ballistics lab in Lewiston, our counterparts in the R&D Ballistics lab at Federal Cartridge contributed much in labor and equipment to the data in this manual. We overcame the potential obstacles that a thousand miles between labs can create and had a smooth flow of data between the two ATK facilities. Throwing this much expertise at the *Manual* meant we were able to include more cartridges in a limited time frame.

The last item —and by no means least—is that this is my last *Speer Manual*. After 20 years at Speer, I'm retiring in 2007. I plan to get involved in volunteering to give something back to the Lewiston community that's been so important to my family. I also plan to spend a lot of time getting reacquainted with my guns. When one spends all day writing about reloading and analyzing data, it's easy to let personal reloading take a back seat.

I sincerely hope that you have enjoyed *Speer Manuals 12, 13* and *14* as much I did creating them. Thank you for your continued support.

With warm regards and best wishes,

Allan Jones, Editor

In addition to those in the industry that we acknowledged in the preceding section, I wish to extend my personal "thank you" to the men and women within ATK Ammunition Systems Group who contributed to this project:

Bruce Young—Chief Reloading Manual Ballistician, Lewiston
Paul Westlund—Chief Reloading Manual Ballistician, Federal Cartridge
Steve Moore—Speer Development Engineer and Project Manager
Drew Goodlin and Larry Head—Federal Cartridge Development Engineering
Ben Amonette and Paul Furrier—Alliant Powders
Penney Rudd—Art Director/Graphic Designer
Annalyn Hechtner—Graphic Design Intern
Linda Olin—Tool and Gauge Calibration Technician
Ken Kees—Quality Assurance Manager
Don Preussler—Speer QA Supervisor
Joan Ireland and Judi Trieb—Speer QA Technicians
Ann Bare—CCI QA Technician
Brett Olin—CCI Development Engineer
Rory DesJardin, Dave Imthurn, Kathy Schock, and Donnie Seubert—Engineering Technicians
Tom Hill and Tim Snyder—Speer Production Managers
Doug McCallum—Speer Assistant Supervisor
Su Hill—Senior Buyer, Purchasing
John Ader—R&D Model Shop
Allan Jernigan, Kent Sakamoto, Alan Schufeldt, and John Sager—RCBS

About the Cartridge Drawings

This edition of the *Speer Reloading Manual* features new cartridge drawings that better define the case than the drawings in previous editions.

The big difference from our earlier drawings is the inclusion of *reference dimensions* that permit more accurate determination of diameters at specific reference points. The U.S. firearms industry uses these dimensions to accurately define the taper of the case body. They are labeled "*basic*," and identify the exact distance (measured from the case base) at which critical diameter measurements are made. For most cartridges, there are two "basic" dimensions. The diameters corresponding to these two points define the case taper. Cartridges with a true cylindrical case body have a single diameter call out with the "*cyl*" notation.

Some cartridges like the Norma Magnums and the 9.3mm rifle cartridges do not have U.S. dimensional standards. For non-U.S. cartridges, dimensions are those of the Commission Internationale Permantente (CIP) and follow CIP dimensioning conventions.

Advanced reloaders such as those who are making "wildcat" cases will find the reference dimensions very useful. They assist in the search for appropriate parent cases for wildcats.

Some shooters own custom firearms that were chambered by a custom gunsmith long before the cartridge was standardized. Having reference dimensions can help these reloaders insure that their handloads are right for their gun.

We followed industry cartridge drawing conventions and show the maximum cartridge dimensions.

chapter 1

A Heritage of Innovation

It wasn't by accident that several respected shooting companies came together. The gradual merging of these firms beneath one banner complimented the others' strengths and experience, forming a solid base of innovation, service and expertise for the sports shooter. Today, ATK Ammunition Systems Group offers the most inclusive line of shooting and reloading products in the industry. After you buy a new gun, you can find nearly everything else you need for it in the ATK family of products.

Need ammo? ATK Civil Ammunition makes Federal Premium®, CCI®, Speer®, Fusion®, Blazer® and Estate Cartridge® brands. When you're ready to reload, RCBS® has the tools and equipment you need, and Speer, CCI, Alliant Powder®, and Federal provide a wealth of bullets, primers and propellants to assemble custom-tuned ammunition for your favorite guns.

What about accessories? You're covered. Outers® and Gunslick® make a wide line of gun cleaning equipment and chemicals to keep you firearm in top condition. Shooter's Ridge® has all the gun rests, portable shooting benches and gear bags you need for an effective session at the range. And Ram-Line® makes tough and economical replacement gunstocks for customizing most popular firearm models.

Every shooter needs targets. Champion Targets® has paper targets for rifle and handgun shooting, and clay birds for shotgunners. They also make superb clay bird launchers, paper target holders and reactive steel targets. Even mounting a scope on your favorite shooting iron is easy with ATK. We have three lines of handsome and effective sight mounting systems: Weaver®, Redfield® and Simmons®.

Everything you need to be a better and more confident shooter can be found under the ATK Ammunition Systems Group banner.

Speer®—Component Bullets and World-Class Ammunition

Vernon Speer (1901-1979) was a man whose life was driven by his inventive nature. He was born in Cedar Falls, Iowa, in 1901. Serving in the U.S. Navy during World War I, he became interested in aviation and at age 21, he designed and built an aircraft engine. To prove its worth, he installed it in a biplane and flight-tested it himself. For

Vernon Speer

ten years, Vernon was a tool foreman at the John Deere Company. In 1941, he became chief ground instructor at a flying school in Lincoln, Nebraska. While living there, Vernon began making bullets.

Reloading was an emerging hobby and most components were only available from the major ammunition manufacturers. Traditionally, selection was limited and supplies did not always keep up with demand. Reloaders were expected to cast their own bullets from scrap lead, just as their forebears had done for 100 years. Vernon was quick to realize the need to fill a gap in the system. If he could specialize in component bullets—especially jacketed ones—perhaps there was enough interest among shooters to change an inventor's idea into a business reality.

Things were not good for shooters in general in the 1940's. The war effort made most ammunition products almost impossible to find. One of the basic materials, copper, was pouring into the government arsenals at a staggering rate. Faced with an unacceptable raw material situation, Vernon came up with an ingenious solution.

In spite of the military demands, one scrap material was abundant. Rifle ranges were covered with spent 22-caliber rimfire cases. Vernon designed and built a machine to iron out the rims and draw the cases to the proper dimensions to function as brass jackets for 22-caliber varmint bullets. The system worked and, by word of mouth, shooters discovered a source for the badly-needed jacketed bullets. Soon, he was traveling to salvage as much rimfire brass as possible. For a time, he and Joyce Hornady were business partners selling bullets in boxes marked with both their names.

In 1944, Speer realized his wish to move west. After searching for the proper climate, business environment and, of course, proximity to good hunting he came to Lewiston, Idaho. He started his bullet-making operation in the basement of an old grocery store. He continued to produce 22-caliber bullets and sold his goods in paper bags. The first two years proved that Vernon's plan was financially sound—the Speer® Bullet Company was on its way. Speer bought property on the banks of the Snake River and built a new facility. We still build bullets here today.

With the end of the war, the basic material of bullet jackets—gilding metal—was once again available and Speer could expand his line into other calibers. His son, Ray, joined the firm in 1952 to take on the marketing and sales efforts. This freed Vernon to spend more time on the research and development he loved. Ray developed the original *Speer Reloading Manual* in 1954, the first in a long and valued line of reference materials.

Ray Speer

During this time, many innovations in bullet design and performance rolled out of the bullet works on Snake River Avenue. One of the most famous is the Speer Hot-Cor® hunting bullet. It has long been the workhorse of the line. Speer led the industry in developing high-performance jacketed handgun bullets for hunting and defense. Vernon also realized the advantages of reusable packaging and invested in injection molding equipment to make plastic boxes for his bullets and ammunition. This technology opened the door for plastic training ammunition and shot capsules for handgun cartridges as well.

In 1969, Speer decided to put the world's best handgun bullets into loaded ammunition. Thus was born the famous line of Lawman® centerfire handgun ammunition. Gold Dot® ammunition joined the Speer product family in 1994, loaded with Gold Dot bonded bullets. In a little over a decade, Gold Dot has become the preferred service cartridge for the nation's peace officers. The Gold Dot ammo line includes loads for handgun hunting, plus special loads for short-barreled handguns. These special projectiles allow users of compact pistols and revolvers to achieve ballistics performance on par with that delivered by handguns with longer barrels.

Speer Bullets, Inc. remained a family-owned and operated business until 1975. Today, we still embrace Vernon's vision of the better bullet and work to keep the trust that an interesting and inventive man gained for the bullets that bear his name.

For additional information on Speer bullets, see chapters 3 and 13.

CCI®—The Leader in Rimfire Ammunition®

There was another brother in the Speer family who, like Vernon, had a remarkable talent for things mechanical. Dick Speer (1915-1994) was employed as a machinist at Boeing Aircraft in Seattle. The brothers felt there was another niche in the reloading marketplace that could prove as successful as Speer bullets.

There were several proprietary or specialty cartridges that were reasonably popular but handicapped by an unreliable supply of cartridge cases. Major ammunition makers had discontinued exotic rifle loadings and did not support semi-custom ammunition for Weatherby and Newton rifles. Dick quit his job with Boeing and headed to Lewiston to join his brother. In a small room at the Speer bullet plant he began to produce these special brass cases using an impact extrusion technique.

Dick Speer

Dick originally sold cases under the name "Forged from Solid," and named the company Speer Cartridge Works. Although the extrusion process was sound, the quality of raw brass stock was poor in those early post-war days. The number of acceptable cases that could be made and shipped to customers could not support a successful business.

Dick Speer thought that providing component primers offered greater potential for a viable business. Major ammunition factories were reluctant to cut into their cartridge business by providing a steady and generous supply of centerfire primers to reloaders. Like his brother Vernon, Dick found that limitations of the "big" companies created a niche where an entrepreneur could thrive.

In 1951, Dick hired an explosives chemist from Lithuania, Dr. Victor Jasaitis, to develop the critical chemical components needed for small arms primers. The first shipments fulfilled a government contract for military primers using the proven FA-70 mixture. Later, Dr. Jasaitis developed non-corrosive primer compounds for sporting applications.

Business was good but consumer confusion regarding "Speer Cartridges" and "Speer Bullets" led Dick and his partner, Arvid Nelson, to change the name to Cascade Cartridge, Inc. The now-famous initials CCI became an integral part of the shooting world.

CCI® quickly outgrew its small space in brother Vernon's plant, so Dick sought a new location to expand operations. He bought a 17-acre chicken farm next to the Lewiston Gun Club a mile south of the bullet factory on Snake River Avenue. The farmhouse became the office and ware-house and production began in a tar-paper

Collectors' Item: Original Speer rifle cases.

chicken coop. Soon modern buildings were erected and there was room to expand the product line. When the gun club moved a few years later, Dick purchased the range property for future expansion.

CCI added shotshell primers in 1957 and, two years later, expanded into making rim-fire powerloads for use in powder-actuated industrial fastening tools (informally called "nail guns"). Rimfire sporting ammunition was introduced in 1963 after a two-year development program and it was quickly recognized for its power and accuracy. CCI Mini-Mag® ammunition became *the* premier 22 Long Rifle ammunition.

Dick Speer sold CCI to Omark Industries in 1967. Omark wisely chose to continue development of sport shooting products. CCI became the first element in Omark's Sporting Equipment Division. Today, CCI has the widest selection of rimfire ammuni-tion, including many products unique to the industry.

In 1980, CCI introduced one of its most revolutionary products—Blazer® centerfire handgun ammunition. Blazer uses a special aluminum alloy instead of brass for the cartridge cases. Blazer offers economy previously only available in reloaded ammuni-tion, yet is factory-loaded to industry standards.

When progressive reloading presses became common in the consumer market, CCI saw the need to optimize primer metallurgy and chemistry to stay at the forefront of the market. In 1989, an extensive 36-month development program yielded improved, state-of-the-art primers featuring lower seating forces and greatly improved sensitivity. In addition, the primer cups and anvils were redesigned to provide top-notch feeding in primer transfer systems found in the new progressive reloading equipment.

In 1991, CCI opened a new primer manufacturing facility in Lewiston. This plant gives CCI the latest in explosives chemistry technology and made CCI a major supplier of cannon primers to U.S. military arsenals.

In 1992, CCI-Speer became the first U.S. ammo maker to receive ISO 9001 certification for its quality systems. CCI is committed to providing quality primers and ammunition to the reloading fraternity for years to come. Dick Speer wouldn't have it any other way.

Federal Premium® Ammunition

(Editor's note: Thanks to Dr. Dave Frederickson for his role as "unofficial historian" for Federal Premium. This historical information here drew heavily from materials furnished by Dr. Frederickson)

In 1916, co-founders Harry and Lewis Sherman incorporated the Federal Cartridge and Machine Company and began constructing a facility in Anoka, Minnesota near Minneapolis. The following year, shipment of shotshells began and the company was reorganized as Federal Cartridge Company. Federal selected the trade name "Hi-Power®" for its products.

In 1922, Charles L. Horn took over the leadership of the Anoka facility and soon implemented an innovative plan to better distribute the new line. Horn's plan placed Hi-Power shotshells in non-traditional outlets such as grocery stores, barbershops and filling stations. This move brought Federal both local and national brand recognition and put Federal on the ammunition map alongside much older and larger firms.

In 1924, Federal Cartridge introduced rimfire ammunition. In the 1930's, Federal became among the first in the industry to push for wildlife conservation and responsible hunting practices. In 1941, months before the onset of World War II, Federal Cartridge earned a U.S. Government contract to build and operate the Twin City Ordnance Plant in New Brighton, Minnesota. This facility provided millions of rounds of 30 and 50-caliber ammunition to the war effort.

Federal began making component primers for reloaders in 1951 and, in 1960, introduced color-coding of shotshells for safety and convenience. Two years later, Federal moved into the centerfire ammunition market with a limited line of rifle and handgun ammunition. The company was now a full-service ammunition supplier and the product lines continued to grow.

In 1965, Horn's son, William B. Horn, began an innovative marketing and advertising program to increase the company's visibility. He was elevated to President in 1977, when Federal's line of Premium® ammunition debuted featuring enhanced ballistic performance that continues today.

Expanding once again in 1975, Federal formed a new division in Richmond, Indiana to produce clay targets for shotgun competition. Later, Champion® Targets added paper targets, traps, and reactive targets to their product line.

Federal Cartridge and its sister company, Hoffman Engineering, were acquired in 1985 by a group of investors and members of the Federal and Hoffman management teams; the new company became Federal-Hoffman, Inc. F-H was purchased three years later by Pentair, Inc to become their new Specialty Products Group. This provided new capital for significant plant modernization and upgrades at Anoka that continued into the 1990's.

Federal launched two new lines in 1989 that would complete the evolution of the company from a "look-alike" ammo maker to the leader in high-grade ammunition. The Premium line was expanded to include Safari® and Hydra-Shok®. Safari is a special line for the world's most demanding hunting, with Premium bullets and cartridges not previously available from U.S. suppliers, like the 416 Rigby and the 470 Nitro Express. Hydra-Shok is personal defense and law enforcement handgun ammunition with a unique cavity designed for top terminal performance. In 1996, High Energy rifle loads joined the line, using special propellants that deliver significant ballistic improvements compared to ammunition loaded with conventional propellants.

In 2002, Federal embarked on major rebranding initiative to support consumer research results that emphasized the importance of the Premium name to the company, its history and products. The result was an entirely new logo and positioning the company as the technology leader in the ammunition business.

2004 saw an entirely new brand of rifle ammunition-Fusion®. A joint development effort from Federal and Speer engineers, Fusion features bullets that deliver flat trajectories and optimum wound profiles for deer-sized game. It was followed in 2006 by the first rifle cartridge to bear the Federal name—338 Federal.

RCBS®—The Finest Reloading Equipment in the World

There are a number of remarkable similarities among the founders of the original companies that form the core of ATK Ammunition Systems Group. Like Vernon Speer, Fred Huntington (1912-1998) found that quality reloading components weren't readily available from the major ammo factories. Fred started experimenting in 1943 with handmade die sets to swage rifle bullets in a home workshop. The steel for Huntington's first dies came from scrap automobile axles. The precision bullets that these dies produced were used for varmint shooting, especially the Western rock chuck or marmot, a smaller cousin of the Eastern woodchuck. From this, Huntington named his bullet-forming die the Rock Chuck Bullet Swage—RCBS® for short.

Fred Huntington

Huntington's first shop was in the back of his father's laundry in Oroville, California. Soon the demand for his swage dies outgrew the laundry and he moved the business to his garage. Fred later built permanent quarters on Oro Dam Boulevard. As the RCBS line expanded to include dies for cartridge reloading, presses and other items followed to create a complete line of reloading tools and accessories.

Huntington introduced his first general-purpose reloading press, the "A" model, in 1949. The massive A-2 press followed in 1954 and became the standard by which all other reloading presses were judged. It featured Huntington's patented compound leverage system that provides a greater mechanical advantage for heavy-duty bullet swaging and case-forming operations. The A-2 is a true classic and still eagerly sought by reloaders in the used equipment market.

In 1967, a new compound-leverage press was introduced to offer A-2 performance at a more attractive price. The Rock Chucker™ quickly became the most popular reloading presses in history. Their strength and ease of use have made them the first choice around the world. The Rock Chucker and its successor, the Rock Chucker Supreme, continue today as the cornerstones of the RCBS reloading press line. It is estimated that there are more Rock Chucker presses in use than all other makes and models combined!

Precision reloading presses need precision dies to produce accurate handloaded ammunition. Fred Huntington made reloading dies to the highest standards of fit and finish. One area where other die manufacturers left room for improvement was the bullet seating die. Most seating dies were oversized at the critical point where the bullet rests just before seating begins. They relied on the seating punch to align the bullet. With little or no lateral support, the bullet could tip as seating pressure was applied causing poor bullet-to-case alignment resulting in poor accuracy. Fred designed a seater die with a tight alignment section in the die body to keep the bullet from tipping, thus giving reloaders the accuracy they sought. In addition to dies and presses, RCBS offers more accessories than any other reloading manufacturer. All are designed with one goal in mind: *to help you do it right.*

For the precise engineering that went into all his products, Fred Huntington coined the term "Precisioneered®" that, in a word, clearly states RCBS's commitment to serving the reloading community. This term is still the motto at RCBS today.

In 1976, Huntington sold RCBS to Omark Industries and remained as general manager until his retirement. In the ensuing 30 years, nearly two dozen new or improved press models have been developed and marketed. Other innovations include: the revolutionary APS® strip priming system that eliminates spilled primers; the latest loading system, the Pro 2000®, a robust and advanced progressive press featuring APS priming; and the Grand™ shotshell loader that provides a high-grade option and RCBS innovation for shotgunners.

Fred Huntington once said, "Why not start out with the equipment that you're going to end up with." Today, two-thirds of a century after Fred Huntington started producing reloading equipment in his garage, that's still sound advice.

Alliant Powder®—Technically Superior by Design

Alliant Powder® is the oldest member of the ATK Ammunition Systems Group, dating to 1882. In the 1880's there were two major propellant and explosives makers in the United States: DuPont and Laflin & Rand. The friendly competitors engaged in collaboration and jointly set up several sub-companies. They ultimately controlled two-thirds of the industry through a variety of brands, including Hercules Powder Company (1882).

DuPont's takeover of Laflin & Rand in 1902 gained the attention of government anti-trust officials. In 1912, Dupont was forced to sell a large portion of its holdings following a successful anti-trust suit against the company. In this divestiture, Hercules Powder Company and Atlas Powder Company became independent entities competing against DuPont. As part of the divestiture proceedings Hercules was granted rights to smokeless propellant patents formerly held by Laflin & Rand.

Hercules produced many classes of military and commercial explosives and propellants and related products such as nitrate-based fertilizers. Additional military contracts and the eventual expansion into rocket propulsion technology resulted in the company being renamed Hercules Aerospace.

In 1996, Alliant TechSystems (now ATK) purchased Hercules Aerospace to expand its growing space and defense sectors. The only consumer sector was the reloading powder business, which was renamed Alliant Powder. The new owners wisely continued the tradition of excellence in reloading products and technology that goes back 125 years.

Outers®—The Gunner's Companion

Vernon F. Dale (1900-1976) was a native of Wisconsin and was, by all standards, the classic rugged individualist. Of Irish descent, Dale settled in Onalaska, just outside LaCrosse. After working in a bakery, he bought and operated a garage. At the same time, he managed a pump factory and ran a bus line between Onalaska and LaCrosse.

Dale had a natural prowess for mechanical things. He was a self-taught toolmaker and an avid reader. Like Vernon Speer and Fred Huntington, he was also an active outdoorsman. This led to his developing a specialized gun grease, Gunslick®, that became the first product of the new Outers® Laboratories in the 1930's.

During World War II, Dale produced metal parts for military contracts on government-owned machines. He won a Navy award for excellence in fulfilling the contract and bought the equipment from the government after the war. Dale expanded Outers into a complete gun care company with the addition of cleaning rods, brushes and other gear needed to keep firearms in top condition. He designed special machines to make bore brushes that wouldn't come apart like traditional brushes often did. His superior technique for manufacturing bronze brushes is still in use at Outers today.

Dale also added other chemicals to compliment Gunslick. Gun oil, nitro solvents, gun blue and stock finish kits were soon added to dealers' shelves. He came up with the idea to put all the cleaning gear into a convenient, caliber-specific kit so a single purchase provided the customer exactly what he needed to care for his gun. He also was the first in the shooting industry to develop point-of-sale displays so the products could sell themselves.

Later, he introduced NRA-approved targets, rimfire bullet traps, clay bird traps for skeet and trap shooting, and a line of leather care products. To round out the line, Outers also offered gun cases and cabinets.

Vern Dale passed away in 1976 after a productive life filled with contributions to the shooting sports community. In 1980, the Dale family sold Outers Laboratories to Omark Industries and Outers became the fourth firm to join Omark's growing family. Since then, new products have continued to come from the Outers facility. Today, brands manufactured in the Onalaska facility include Ram-line, Gunslick, Champion and Shooters' Ridge.

Weaver®—In Place. On Target. Since 1930

In the 1930's, telescopic sights on rifles were not common in North America. Typically, the scopes were made in Europe and were very expensive. When typical American sporting rifles cost between $35 and $70, a top-quality German scope might cost two to three times that amount. Mounting these scopes on American rifles often was a nightmare and most of the mounting systems of the time were expensive, over-engineered and, more often than not, downright ugly.

William Ralph Weaver (1905-1975) entered the business world in the late 1920's and, like the other founders of our family of companies, found a situation in the sport shooting industry that needed attention. Bill Weaver believed, with proper engineering, an affordable riflescope could be built in America. He also recognized there must be a better way to mate scopes to rifles. He started by building a few scopes for himself and friends and, like Vernon Speer and Fred Huntington, quickly found enough demand to justify a full-time business.

To make scope mounting easier and more reliable, Weaver developed a line of sturdy mounts and rings for almost every popular rifle found in North America. The design was simple, unobtrusive and affordable. The Weaver base and ring system remains one of the strongest, most economical and popular scope mounts today.

Labor problems and competition forced Bill Weaver to sell his company to Olin Corporation in 1968. Olin continued the Weaver operation until 1984 when foreign competition made the business unprofitable.

Omark's Sporting Equipment Division—who by now owned CCI, Speer, RCBS, and Outers—bought the Weaver mount-making equipment. Because much of the technology used to manufacture mounts was already in place at the Outers Operation in Onalaska, Omark moved the equipment to Wisconsin where Weaver mounts and rings are still made.

Acquisition and Growth—Omark Industries and Blount International

Omark Industries started as the Oregon Saw Chain Company in Portland. As the business grew, Omark expanded its product line to include powder-actuated tools (PAT) for industrial fastening. Concerned that its PAT business would suffer if major ammunition manufacturers cut off sales of powerloads to Omark, the company looked for its own source of loads. They found it in CCI®.

In 1967, Omark bought CCI from Dick Speer. Although Omark was most interested in the powerloads that CCI manufactured, they saw how lucrative the sporting ammunition and component primer business could be. Omark continued to invest in the sporting side of CCI. This solid start in the shooting sports field led them to eventually acquire Speer®, RCBS®, Outers® and Weaver®, forming the Omark Sporting Equipment Division.

Blount International was founded after World War II as a specialty construction company in Alabama. Blount (rhymes with "hunt") wanted to branch out into manufacturing to smooth over seasonal variations in the construction business. In 1985, Blount acquired Omark Industries because of the latter's solid reputation for quality products, efficient manufacturing and profitability.

In 1994 Blount added Ram-Line® to the shooting sports group. Ram-Line makes injection-molded polymer gunstocks and accessories for a variety of popular firearms. Simmons Outdoors, a major player in the sports optics market, was added in 1996 to provide expanded optics capacity. In June 1997, Blount announced its intent to purchase Federal Cartridge Company. The acquisition, added to CCI and Speer, made Blount the largest U.S. ammunition company. Later, Blount acquired the assets of Redfield Optics from creditors and reintroduced their excellent all-steel scope mounting systems.

Alliant TechSystems (ATK)—Building for the Future

Blount International decided to scale back its sphere of influence and focus on its highly successful Oregon Cutting System operations (formerly Omark's Oregon Saw Chain Division). ATK, a major defense and aerospace firm, wanted to expand into the commercial ammunition business. Blount's Sporting Equipment Group had already bundled three superb brands—CCI, Speer, and Federal—plus a number of major shooting accessory companies like Outers and RCBS.

ATK bought the entire Sporting Equipment group in December, 2001. This gave the companies the necessary capital boost to permit increased output and product development. The shooting sports group is known as ATK Ammunition Systems Group.

Later, ATK sold the "glass" part of the optics business—all the riflescopes, binoculars and spotting scopes—to Meade Optical but retained the profitable scope-mounting components represented by Weaver, Simmons, and Redfield. This led to investment in all the facilities and to new brands like Shooter's Ridge (gun rests and accessories), and a new line of rifle ammunition, Fusion®.

It has been a long and eventful journey, one that has teamed the best companies in their respective fields for shared development, improved distribution and market presence. Today, Speer and its sister sporting equipment companies join the high-tech business environment at ATK committed to bringing you the best shooting products for many years to come.

chapter 2

Handloading: A Hobby for a Lifetime

The terms *handloading* and *reloading* are practically synonymous. Handloading is the act of assembling ammunition on a non-commercial basis using simple equipment. Re-loading is the restoration of fired cartridge cases into loaded ammunition. A fired case requires you to perform certain simple operations to restore it to a usable cartridge. As a reloader, you have control over these processes. Reloading ammunition can be a very rewarding part of the shooting sports and one that will enable you to shoot more ammo—and shoot more often.

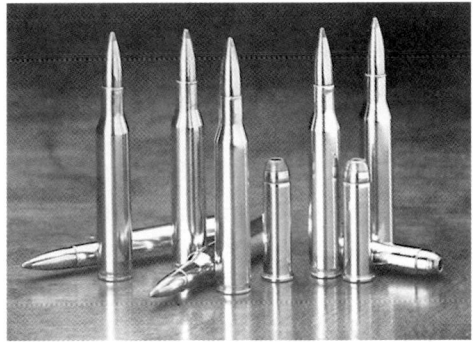

"Tune" your ammunition to match your gun.

Most shooters begin with factory ammunition usually because it's the fastest way to try out that new gun. However, as shooters become more familiar with a new gun, eventually they will consider handloading their own ammunition. Let's look at several factors involved in this decision.

Economy

Saving money is usually the first reason we consider handloading. The cost of factory ammunition will eventually cause many shooters to look for a way to reduce costs in order to shoot more. Most articles written on handloading, especially those of an intro-ductory nature, point out that reloading gives you more shots per dollar.

Usually the costliest component of a cartridge is the brass case, easily accounting for 60-65 percent of the total cost. If you buy and shoot 100 rounds of factory ammunition, you have 100 empty cases with significant retained value. Leaving them on the ground at the range means that you walked away from that investment. A cartridge case can be reused several times before it's no longer suitable for loading. The reloader can use this remaining case life to reduce his cost per shot. If you plan to do even a moderate amount of shooting, the payback time for the hardware investment is relatively short.

The actual saving per shot depends on the cartridge you plan to reload; other than the primer, components for a large-capacity rifle case are more costly than those for lead bullet pistol ammo.

You can expect to save 50 to 65 percent over the cost of factory ammunition when reloading most rifle and handgun cartridges. Most reloaders will tell you that they started reloading to save money but quickly discovered the second reason:

Custom-tuned Ammunition

When the handloader takes his reloaded ammunition to the range, he often finds that it shoots better than the factory ammunition he tried the week before. Factory ammunition is great stuff, meeting industry standards and thoroughly tested. In spite of all this, the fact remains that major ammunition factories must design their ammunition to shoot reasonably well in thousands of different rifles or handguns. With the wide variety of makes and action types available, factory ammunition must fit the shortest action and the tightest chamber of the lot.

Careful loading and testing of reloaded ammunition will point the way to the component combination that will shoot best in *your* firearm. For example, factory ammunition is often loaded to the minimum cartridge length so it will operate through the shortest action. If your rifle has a longer action and/or magazine, you can load up to the maximum industry cartridge length or the length your rifle allows and find that accuracy is greatly improved. Likewise, you may find that your rifle performance is enhanced with a certain bullet weight or style not available in factory loads. Handloading gives you the flexibility to tune ammunition to your rifle or handgun. A wise man once said, "The best ammo maker for your rifle is you." We agree.

Versatility

Soon after discovering the economy and improved accuracy that reloading offers, the shooter discovers how versatile one firearm can become when the broad assortment of bullet styles is explored. There are styles from varmint bullets to big game bullets in most of the larger rifle calibers. In 30-caliber alone, Speer catalogs 31 different bullets weighing from 100 to 200 grains. The same rifle that you load with heavy soft points for deer and elk in the fall can be loaded with light, hollow point bullets to take varmints in the spring. Yet you now have even more control than permitted by bullet selection alone.

Suppose you want to introduce a youngster to your favorite deer rifle but are concerned that recoil may prove too much. The reloader can safely assemble reduced velocity ammunition that will subject the novice shooter to less recoil. Because the rifle has now been "tamed," the novice will be willing to put in more practice time at the range. As the new shooter's skill and recoil tolerance increase, you can gradually increase the powder charge and/or bullet weight to make a load suitable for the type of shooting you and your new shooting partner enjoy. Reduced velocity loading data is included in this manual for many popular cartridges.

Handloading also lets owners of obsolete firearms continue to shoot even when factory ammunition becomes scarce. With care, most cartridge cases will last for many firings. Many military rifle cartridges were never loaded with hunting bullets and you often find only full metal jacket bullet loads when you search for ammunition. The handloader can reload a military cartridge with hunting bullets, greatly extending the usefulness of these veterans. If new cases are not readily available, the experienced handloader can often convert a common, modern case to function in the old rifles through a process known as *case forming*. Often, the reliability of formed brass exceeds that of the original military cases because of the improved quality of modern brass. Case-forming dies for many obsolete cartridges are available through the special order department at RCBS.

Enjoyment

This last benefit of handloading is the hardest to quantify, but it is the area that often means the most to a shooter. Handloading lets you learn all there is to know about your firearm—its likes, dislikes and other factors that give each firearm its own character. The attention to detail and the ability to experiment (within limits, of course) will make you a better and more confident shooter. There is great satisfaction in posting a high score or bagging that big buck with ammo that you have finely tuned to the needs of your firearm.

As you read on in this manual, you will find all the information needed to safely load quality ammunition. With a little care and common sense, reloading can become a rewarding hobby—one that can be shared with your shooting companions, your children and your grandchildren throughout a lifetime.

Speer® Rifle Bullets: Characteristics & Uses

In the years since Vernon Speer first made varmint bullets out of spent 22 rimfire cases, many new styles of Speer® bullets have evolved—from super-accurate match bullets to super-tough hunting bullets for the world's largest game. With so many choices of bullet type and style, the reloader may wonder which bullet to choose for his particular shooting sport. To make the choice easier, we present the following guide to Speer rifle bullets.

Remember that a bullet is intended to efficiently deliver ballistic performance to a target. Your choice of bullet depends on the rifle, the cartridge, and the target. The varmint hunter requires different terminal ballistics than an elk hunter. Speer offers a generous selection of centerfire rifle bullets with distinctly different expansion and penetration characteristics for humanely taking every class of game animal.

HOT-COR®—Category: Standard Big Game

Hot-Cor® is Speer's exclusive and unique bullet-making process. Vernon Speer sought a technology that would enhance the terminal performance of his rifle bullets. At the time Speer embarked on this project, few game bullets could be relied upon to retain their integrity. Even today, many bullets break up during expansion, resulting in limited penetration and the potential for lost game. A visit to a game processing business for a look at their collection of recovered bullets will tell you the problem still exists.

Vernon found that core-jacket separations rather than jacket failures were the primary cause of bullet weight loss on impact. Conventional hunting bullets start with the insertion of a pre-formed lead alloy core into a jacket. Such cores are normally lubricated to allow the bullet assembly equipment to handle them without stoppages. Even if left unlubricated, a coating of lead oxide begins to form on the bullet cores as soon as they leave the core-forming machine. Be it oxide or lubricant, such coatings can allow the core and jacket to slip as normal expansion feeds lead into the mushrooming nose. This slippage leaves a void inside the base of the bullet, reducing the amount of core adhering to the jacket and making core-jacket separations more likely.

Speer attacked this problem and came up with the idea of pouring a molten core into a jacket. Because the core wasn't formed in a separate operation, no lubricant was needed. By pouring the core, no air was trapped between the core and jacket that could cause oxidation. By eliminating the lubricants and oxides, a more secure core-jacket grip was created. Thus Hot-Cor bullets were born.

Expansion testing proved Vernon's design work to be right. Sectioning expanded bullets revealed that the core did not slip in the jacket during mushrooming. An additional benefit is that more core stays in the jacket, and the frontal area, although adequate for traumatizing tissue, isn't so large as to reduce penetration. The portion of the jacket that peels back stays close to the bullet shank, allowing excellent penetration. In laboratory ballistic test media, retained weight is in the 70 to 75 percent range. However, bullets recovered from game often exceed 85 percent retained weight. All Hot-Cor bullets feature a flat base and internally tapered jackets to insure adequate strength for the task.

The classic application for Hot-Cor is the hunting of game animals that are at the upper end of your rifle's ability. For example, if a big whitetail is considered the largest game you want to shoot with a 257 Roberts, then the 120-grain Hot-Cor bullet is the choice for deep penetration over a wide range of shooting angles. As experienced hunters know, good penetration is critical to successful performance on large game.

Speer Hot-Cor bullets are manufactured in four tip configurations—spitzer, semi-spitzer, flat point and round nose—in calibers from 24 (6mm) to 45 for the serious game hunter.

Boat Tail—Category: Standard Big Game

Boat tail bullets differ from standard bullets in the heel profile. The boat tail heel is tapered, usually at an angle of 9 to 13 degrees. Boat tail bullets were first used in the United States in 30-06 military ammunition intended for use in machine guns. The idea was to give a longer effective range to existing cartridges by making the bullet fly farther. Today, all major component manufacturers offer the boat tail design. Originally available only to the reloader, this style is now common in factory rifle ammunition.

The ballistic coefficient (BC) of a bullet is a theoretical measure of a bullet's ability to resist slowing down due to the normal in-flight drag of air flowing around it. The higher the BC, the more easily a bullet slips through the air. A "slippery" bullet reaches the target with higher retained velocity and less drop than one that encounters more drag.

In lay terms, one source of drag comes from the bullet base. Some of the air flowing along the sides of the bullet swirls around and across the base creating disturbed flow. This zone of disturbance creates drag, a force that has the effect of slowing the bullet. If the surface area of the base can be reduced, the effects of base drag is reduced. A boat tail bullet has a smaller base area than a corresponding flat base bullet and, therefore, less drag and greater range.

The BC for a boat tail bullet is higher than the BC for a flat base bullet with the same point shape and weight. The BC can be plugged into popular computer programs such as RCBS.LOAD® to generate drop charts that profile the bullet's flight over a predetermined distance.

In the real world, most hunters will not notice an advantage in the boat tail for shots less than 300 yards. The differences in drop and velocity at these ranges are relatively small, as seen in the example in Table 1 for a 30-06 rifle loaded with 165-grain Speer bullets sighted in for 200 yards. You can see that the differences are trivial at average hunting distances.

So why choose a boat tail bullet? Many reloaders prefer boat tail bullets simply because of the ease of bullet seating that the tapered heel affords. But there is more. At Speer, the introduction of the boat tail design gave the opportunity to offer hunters a different terminal effect. Speer

HOT-COR BC of 0.433	100 yds.	200 yds.	300 yds.	500 yds.
Velocity	2586	2381	2186	1824
Energy	2450	2077	1750	1219
Path, Inches	+1.90	0.00	-8.00	-47.30

30-06 loaded with Speer Hot-Cor 165-gr bullets; Muzzle Vel. = 2800 fps.

BOAT TAIL BC of 0.477	100 yds.	200 yds.	300 yds.	500 yds.
Velocity	2608	2423	2246	1915
Energy	2491	2149	1848	1343
Path, Inches	+1.80	0.00	-7.70	-45.10

30-06 loaded with Speer Boat Tail 165-gr bullets; Muzzle Vel. = 2800 fps.

boat tail bullets are of slightly lighter construction than their comparable Hot-Cor versions and expand somewhat faster. They do not use the Hot-Cor process, so the frontal area of an expanded boat tail bullet is usually larger. Speer boat tail bullets cause greater shock, but penetration is slightly less. They are an excellent choice for lighter species of game animals like pronghorn or for heavy varmints.

In spite of the fact that our boat tail bullets are of lighter construction than our Hot-Cors, they are still substantial hunting tools. Like other Speer hunting bullets, the jacket is tapered to give greater strength in the shank area, preventing the jacket from rolling back too far. In any boat tail design, rolling the bullet jacket all the way to the tapered heel often allows the jacket to separate from the core. The heavy Speer jacket shank resists separation better than many competitors' boat tail bullets.

Speer boat tail bullets are available in calibers from 22 to 375.

TNT® and other Hollow Point Varmint Bullets—Category: Varmint

For the ultimate in explosive expansion on varmints, Speer hollow point rifle bullets are hard to beat. Thin jackets and a generous hollow point opening combine to give quick and reliable expansion over a wide range of velocities.

Contrary to popular belief, hollow point rifle bullets seldom give classic "mushroom" expansion at rifle velocities. The bullets are designed to break up soon after striking the target. Air and fluid trapped in the hollow cavity break off part of the jacket, causing the bullet to instantly yaw. As soon as the bullet tumbles, its self-destructs, creating terrific shock as fragments cause multiple wound tracks.

Varmint bullet penetration is very limited. For this reason, Speer does not recommend hollow point rifle bullets for taking large game. The standard soft point bullet gives deep penetration and more humane kills on larger animals. A light, hollow point bullet may only wound a deer-sized animal or cause extensive damage to edible meat.

On the other hand, this bullet performance is ideal for varmints where quick kills are important and meat damage is not a factor. The classic application is the 22-caliber centerfire cartridges. For cartridges generating velocities up to 3400 ft/sec, the 22-caliber 50-grain TNT® hollow point is exceptional. It has a thin, fluted jacket to provide reliable expansion from cartridges like the 222 and 223 Remington cartridges. Because its design still produces expansion at speeds as low as 1800 ft/sec, it is also an excellent choice for the popular 22-caliber centerfire handguns. For cartridges like the 220 Swift, the 22-250 and 223 WSSM we now offer a 55-grain TNT with slightly heavier construction for the extreme velocities these cartridges generate. We even make a special 33-grain TNT just for the popular 22 Hornet cartridge.

TNT Velocity Limits		
Caliber	Bullet Weight, grs	Max. Velocity, ft/sec
.224"	33, 50	3400
.224"	55	See note below.
.244"	70	3500
.257"	87	3700
.264"	90	3500
.277"	90	3500
.284"	110	3500
.308"	125	3100

These limits assume some degree of barrel wear or roughness. Some barrels may allow higher velocities. NOTE: We have yet to reach a velocity limit for the 22-cal 55 HV TNT in any commercial cartridge.

TNT hollow points are exceptionally accurate, capable of producing ½ minute of angle groups in many factory varmint rifles. One bench rest shooter posted a 5-shot group of 0.152 inch with the 22-caliber 50-grain TNT at 100 yards!

TNT design is also available in 24-caliber (70-grain), 25-caliber (87-grain), 6.5mm (90-grain), 27-caliber (90-grain), 7mm (110-grain), and 30-caliber (125-grain).

To insure complete disruption on impact, TNT bullets are very lightly constructed. Therefore, they have an upper limit for muzzle velocity shown in the accompanying table. For cartridges that exceed the velocity ratings for TNT, we have conventional hollow points in 22, 24, 25, 27, 28 and 30-caliber. They are as accurate as TNT but can tolerate higher velocities. Hollow points let the reloader use his favorite deer rifle for off-season varminting to keep in practice.

Rifling twist rate is now an important factor to varmint shooters. Some military-style rifles chambered for 223 Remington ammunition have 1-in-9 inch or even 1-in-7 inch twist rates, spinning the bullet much faster than the original 1-in-12 inch twist designated for the 223 Remington. This added rotational velocity can be enough to cause a varmint bullet to come apart shortly after leaving the muzzle.

There is a formula that calculates the rotational velocity in revolutions per minute (rpm) of a bullet at the muzzle. For a 55-grain 22-caliber bullet at 3200 ft/sec (typical 223 Remington load), the rotational velocity at the muzzle created by the conventional 1-in-12 inch twist is 192,000 rpm. Although an impressive number, standard varmint bullets can handle it. Shoot the same ammunition from a barrel with a 1-in-7 inch twist and the rotational velocity spikes to 329,000 rpm. Few, if any, varmint bullets can stay in one piece at that rotational speed.

Independent studies by several component bullet companies have shown that a 55-grain 22-caliber bullet must have a muzzle velocity no higher than 2800 ft/sec to hold together in a 1-in-7 inch twist barrel. Even this assumes a barrel in top-notch condition; the critical speed drops for worn, rough, or pitted barrels.

The best way to avoid the problem is to ask about the twist rate before investing in a varmint rifle. Check catalogs or company websites; they often show the twist rate used.

Match Boat Tail Hollow Point—Category: Match

For years, the inherent accuracy of the hollow point design has made these bullets popular with target shooters. Also known as OTM (open tip match), Speer makes match bullets in .224 diameter (52-grain), 7mm (145-grain), and 30-caliber (168-grain). These bullets are suitable for match shooting on paper targets or, in the larger calibers, rifle metallic silhouette shooting.

Precision match shooting must start with precision components. Speer draws match bullet jackets from high-grade gilding metal with constant monitoring of the entire jacket-making process. Final forming is done at low swage pressures to reduce internal stresses. All this care means that Speer match grade bullets will give the kind of accuracy target shooters demand—box after box.

Match hollow point bullets are not recommended for game animals. Expansion patterns of OTM bullets are unpredictable and therefore preclude their use as game bullets.

Trophy Bonded® Bear Claw®—Category: Mission-Critical™ Big Game

In 1985, renowned big game hunter Jack Carter wanted a bullet that gave a large expanded diameter without sacrificing penetration or retained weight. He was also aware that true bonding of a core to the jacket in conventional designs could weaken the jacket to the point of failure; the heat required in bonding would leave a typical thin copper jacket dead-soft, limiting the bullet to low-velocity applications.

Carter solved the problem by starting with a rod of solid copper. He machined a cavity in what would become the front half of the bullet. Into the cavity he inserted a *flux*, the catalyst required for true bonding, and then a lead core. He heated the assembly to 900°F, melting the core and bonding it to the jacket, creating a strong chemical bond.

The solid copper rear shank, although dead-soft after the bonding process remains tougher than any other bullet. It contains no lead so the shank remains more than rigid enough to hold its shape under the toughest impact conditions.

The bonding is so effective that Bear Claw® bullets retain as much as 96 percent of their original weight after expansion. The lead core stays attached to the "petals" on jacket, and the rigid shank retains its cylindrical shape after expansion.

TBBC Expanded Bullet: 96% weight retention

The design also provides a boost to penetration after expansion is complete. After conventional bullets fully mushroom, the center of mass shifts close to the bullet base and causes the bullet to yaw as it slows. This reduces penetration. Bear Claw's "weight-forward after expansion" configuration keeps the center of mass forward, greatly extending the nose-forward penetration zone. A 30-caliber 165-grain Bear Claw will penetrate as deeply as conventional 180 and 200-grain bullets.

Federal Cartridge® chose Bear Claw for its excellent Federal Premium® rifle ammunition. Their needs exceeded Carter's capacity to produce these bullets so an agreement was reached to allow Federal to build the bullets for loaded ammo. Carter continued to sell Bear Claw as components.

Following Carter's death in 2000, component Bear Claws were unavailable. The agreement with his estate was extended to allow Speer Bullets to sell Bear Claw in component form. Today's Bear Claw is more uniform and bonded at a higher temperature than the original versions. Handloaders can still get these superb bullets in diameters from .224 to .474 inch.

Trophy Bonded® Sledgehammer® Solid—Category: Mission-Critical™ Big Game

Sledgehammer® was another of Jack Carter's developments that gave dangerous game hunters a deep-driving companion for the Bear Claw soft point. Like Bear Claw, Sledgehammer was the bullet of choice when Federal needed a great solid for its impressive Cape-Shok® ammunition line.

Sledgehammer has a massive bronze jacket to resist deformation. Backing the jacket is a bonded lead core to keep the bullet compact, an important consideration when loading some cartridges where a case full of propellant is the norm.

Other "solids" have a round tip. However, this ballistic shape can often result in the bullet taking a curved path after it enters the animal. The resulting unpredictable results have no place in dangerous game hunting.

Carter chose a flat point, or "clipped-tip" design for Sledgehammer for greater shock. This nose profile has proved its ability to produce straight-line penetration both by aeroballistic computer modeling and in actual hunting experience.

Sledgehammer solids are available as Speer components in 375, 416, 45, and 470-caliber.

Grand Slam®—Category: Enhanced Big Game

The flagship of the Speer bullet line since 1975, Grand Slam® incorporates a number of high-tech features to ensure top-notch performance on large game animals. Grand Slam starts with a jacket having a heavy shank tapering to a fluted mouth.

Original Grand Slams featured a two-piece core, with the rear core being harder than the front core. However, unavoidable changes to raw materials and processing materials made it harder to maintain the bond between the front and rear cores. Further research showed that the jacket profile was more important to terminal performance. The 24 and 25-caliber Grand Slams always had a one-piece core and they perform admirably.

The Grand Slam jacket has always featured internal fluting at the nose to afford symmetrical expansion over a wide range of velocities. We redesigned the jacket to beef up the shank and made heel folds between the base and sidewalls to create a pocket. Hot-Cor technology inserts a ternary (three-component) lead core at 900°F that flows into the heel pocket for a combination of mechanical and friction grip. These changes improved retained weights in test media by ten percent compared to dual-core Grand Slams and improved accuracy as well.

All Grand Slam bullets have a crimping cannelure for secure seating in rifles producing heavy recoil, and are finished with a long protected-tip ogive so the ballistic coefficients are higher than Mag-Tip®.

In the ever more crowded field of top quality game bullets, Grand Slam still holds its own.

Mag-Tip®—Category: Standard Big Game

Speer Mag-Tip represents an intermediate step between original Hot-Cor hunting bullets and Grand Slam bullets. Developed in the early 1970's, Mag-Tip is still quite popular.

Mag-Tip bullets are manufactured using the Hot-Cor process, but the jacket thickness in the critical shank area is thicker than the same area in an equivalent Hot-Cor bullet. This added material gives Mag-Tip greater strength for high-velocity applications. Mag-Tip also features internal fluting at the jacket opening for reliable initial expansion at lower velocities. Mag-Tip also has a protected point—the jacket is as long as the core. This feature is useful in bolt-action rifles that show a tendency to batter the bullet point in the magazine. Such battering is more prevalent in heavy calibers, but can occur in light calibers depending on the design of the magazine and the weight of the rifle.

These design features of Mag-Tip give it a very wide range of usefulness. Every bullet operates in a "velocity window." There is a lower velocity at which the bullet can no longer expand, and there is an upper velocity beyond which bullet breakup is possible. Mag-Tip's fluted jacket and flat tip provide better expansion at velocities lower than many spitzers, yet the heavy jacket shank allows very high velocities before bullet breakup occurs. In 30-caliber, Mag-Tips are effective in modest velocity cartridges like the 300 Savage yet have the strength to hold up when driven at velocities of 300 Magnum cartridges.

Speer makes Mag-Tip bullets in 7mm, 30, 416, and 45-caliber.

Special Application Bullets—Category: Special Purpose Bullets

Speer's commitment to the reloading community means that there will always be bullets to fit those special needs that do not fall into one of the categories discussed above. For reloaders duplicating military ammunition performance or who need non-deforming bullets for taking fur-bearing game, Speer offers several full metal jacket bullets in 22 and 30-caliber.

As the popularity of some of the old lever action cartridges increased, Speer supported their comeback with new bullets designed specifically for those rifles. For the 218 Bee cartridge, there's a 46-grain flat point. Fans of the 25-20 cartridge now have a 75-grain Hot-Cor flat point, and there is a .312" diameter 100-grain jacketed hollow point designed for the 32-20 cartridge. We also have an excellent flat-point Hot-Cor bullet for the 7-30 Waters cartridge. All these bullets are cannelured in the proper location for smooth feeding in lever action rifles and feature flat points so they can be safely used in tubular magazines.

To add months to the shooting season for fans of 30-caliber cartridges, Speer has two light bullets for off-season practice and varmint hunting. The 100-grain Plinker® was developed as a low-cost practice bullet for all 30-caliber rifles. Its half-jacket design makes sure that the lead core doesn't touch the bore, and the generous exposed lead point means rapid and complete expansion at rifle velocities. The 110-grain Varminter® is a slightly heavier version of the Plinker with less exposed lead and a large hollow point. Both bullets are excellent for reduced-recoil loading, useful in training new centerfire shooters.

Commitment. Skill. Know-how.

As you can see, Speer is committed to the serious hunter and shooter. Continuing research, development and testing have generated a line of rifle bullets that can handle the entire range of game animals from prairie dogs to pachyderms! Over sixty years of experience goes into every bullet, helping the reloader make those great shots.

RCBS

5·0·5 scale

5·0·5 is a Registered TM
of OHAUS CORP.

OUNCE TO GRAIN CONVERSION

1/2	218.8	1 1/4	546.9	2	875.0
5/8	273.4	1 3/8	601.6	2 1/8	929.7
3/4	328.1	1 1/2	666.3	2 1/4	984.4
7/8	382.8	1 5/8	710.9	2 3/8	1039.1
1	437.5	1 3/4	765.6	2 1/2	1093.8
1 1/8	492.2	1 7/8	820.3		

MANUFACTURED BY OHAUS CORPORATION

Modern Cartridges & Their Components

Modern rifle and handgun cartridges, known as *metallic cartridges*, have four components: the cartridge case, the primer, the propellant and the bullet. Knowing the role of each of these will help the novice reloader understand the entire loading process and the importance of each operation required.

The Cartridge Case

The cartridge case is the most critical component of metallic cartridges. In addition to being the convenient envelope that holds all the other components, the case acts as a precision seal to insure that the high-pressure, expanding gases are directed down the barrel and away from the shooter. Another function of the case is to hold the cartridge in a consistent position in the chamber so it cannot shift when the firing pin hits the primer. Without this, ignition would be very unreliable, if not impossible.

Cartridge cases fall into several categories by body shape and head configuration. Regardless of shape or application, each cartridge case has some physical feature to consistently position it in the chamber. The front-to-rear relationship of a cartridge to the firearm's chamber with the action closed is called *headspace*. The Sporting Arms and Ammunition Manufacturers' Institute (SAAMI) establishes dimensional standards, including headspace, for U.S. firearm and ammunition manufacturers. Headspace dimensions must be maintained when handloading ammunition to ensure safety and good performance. However, the case configuration determines how well the handloader can control or affect headspace.

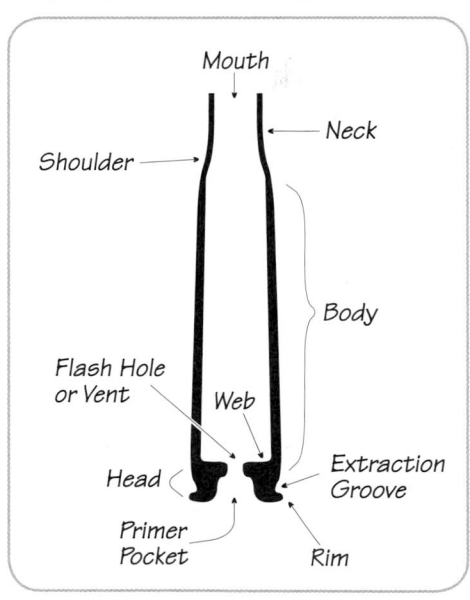

Case Types and Headspace

Most metallic cartridges can be classified by the configuration of their *body* and *head*. Body types include *bottleneck, straight*, and *straight-tapered*. Head types include *rimmed, rimless, belted*, and *rebated rim*. A sub-type of the rimmed case is the *semi-rimmed* case.

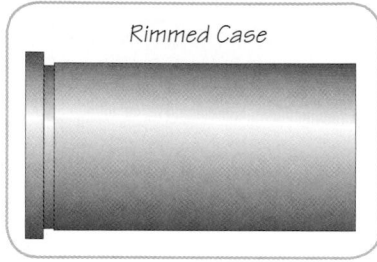

Rimmed Case

Rimmed cases were used for many years following the introduction of "fixed" or self-contained ammunition. The protruding flange at the head limits the forward motion of the cartridge in the chamber so headspace is controlled by the rim thickness. Common examples of rimmed cases are the 30-30 Winchester, the 22 Hornet, and nearly all cartridges designed for revolvers.

Semi-rimmed cases have a protruding rim but it is usually subtle. You may only detect it by running your fingers along the case or taking a measurement with a micrometer or caliper. Semi-rimmed rifle cases are intended to headspace on the shoulder because most examples are bottleneck designs. The 220 Swift is an early semi-rimmed case. The only other modern rifle cartridge in the past four decades to use the semi-rim design is the 225 Winchester. For these cartridges the semi-rim is an accommodation to manufacturing. They share the diameter of a 30-06 rim while the case body is somewhat smaller. This allowed gun makers to manufacture rifles with standard bolt designs. Several pistol cartridges are semi-rimmed (e.g., 25 Auto, 32 Auto and 38 Super Auto) and may use the rim to control headspace.

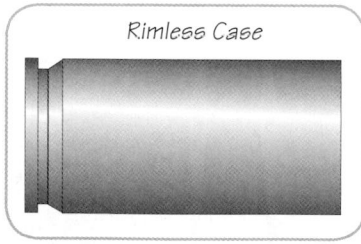

Rimless Case

In modern rifle cartridges, the rimless design is the most common. Rimless is not an entirely correct term. "Flush-rim" would be better but rimless is ingrained in most shooters' lexicon. There is a rim but it is about the same diameter as the case head and is defined by the machining of a shallow extraction groove or cannelure into the case head. This groove also serves to provide an engagement surface so the extractor can capture and withdraw the fired case from the chamber.

Lack of a protruding rim allows the cartridges to stack easily in box magazines and feed smoothly in repeating firearms. With few exceptions, these cartridges are bottle-necked, so the headspace is controlled by the position of the case shoulder. If the case is not bottlenecked, the case mouth controls headspace (ex., the 30 Carbine cartridge).

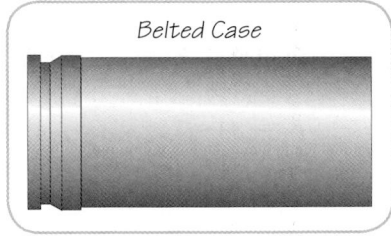

Belted Case

"Belted" cases are a variant of the rimless configuration and are found only in rifle cartridges. They have a raised belt just ahead of the extraction groove. Holland & Holland in England developed this feature for their 400/375 Belted Nitro Express. This cartridge, now obsolete, was technically a bottleneck design but had a shallow sloping shoulder that did not provide sufficient resistance to the firing pin blow. To ensure positive headspace control, the cartridge designers added a raised belt to the case that mated with a corresponding recess in the rifle's chamber. Holland later applied the same concept when developing their ground-breaking 375 H&H Magnum.

Most modern cartridges bearing the "magnum" designation have a belt simply because they were developed from the superb H&H design. The belt is not necessary for headspace control in cases with a more prominent shoulder. Theory says that the case should headspace on the belt; however, accuracy and case life are improved if the reloader adjusts the sizing die so the case and chamber contact at the shoulder. Belts on most modern "magnums" are primarily cosmetic and add little to the strength of the case—contrary to what many people think. They are necessary for proper headspace control only in the original H&H cartridges, the 450 Marlin, the 458 Winchester Magnum and, arguably, the 416 Remington. For many decades, it seemed that any "magnum" cartridge needed a belt. Fortunately, this is changing with the introduction of new non-belted, large-capacity cartridges like the various "short" and "ultra" magnums.

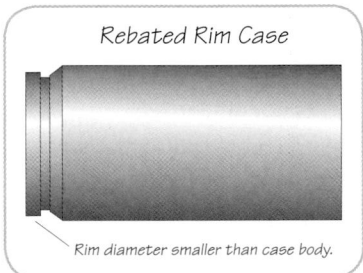

Rebated Rim Case

Rim diameter smaller than case body.

The rebated rim was seldom seen in modern cartridges until recently. The rim is smaller than the case body, allowing additional powder capacity but providing a standard rim diameter to fit existing bolt faces. The most recent rifle cartridges of this type are the Remington Ultra Magnum series, and the Winchester and Remington "short magnums." These cartridges have a 0.532-inch rim that fits a standard "magnum," or H&H bolt face, but have a 0.550 to 0.555-inch major body diameter to maximize powder capacity. In handgun ammunition, the 50 Action Express cartridge has a rebated rim.

The Case as a Safety Feature

As stated earlier, the case's primary function is to seal the breech during firing. It must be flexible enough to seal off the chamber so hot gases are kept away from the shooter.

It must be strong but also resilient; the fired case must spring away from the chamber walls after firing to allow easy extraction.

In rifle applications, cartridge brass (70 percent copper; 30 percent zinc) has the best combination of properties to accomplish this. Reloaders must always remember this: *the modern rifle is capable of containing much greater pressures than the brass case.* The steel alloys in modern rifles may have ultimate strengths ranging up to 160,000 pounds per square inch (psi). The best cartridge case will fail at about half that pressure. Thus, the case becomes the limiting factor in the overall system. Only by following lab-tested reloading data will you remain safely within the capabilities of modern brass cases.

Brass is not the only material used for cartridge cases. In countries lacking native copper resources (or for cost savings), mild steel is commonly used for both cases and bullet jackets. To a point, it is as strong as brass. With proper heat-treatment, steel cases can provide adequate flexibility and springback in new ammunition but are seldom satisfactory for handloading. Running a large magnet through a bin of mixed cases can easily separate steel cases.

CCI® pioneered the use of special aluminum alloys for low-cost handgun cartridge cases. A specific grade of aluminum allows heat-treating to add strength and to ease extraction. However, for reloaders the conventional brass alloy case is the best component.

The handloader needs to be aware of the functions of the case and use special care when reloading. With quality loading equipment and proper handling, a case can be loaded and fired numerous times before its properties degrade to the point that it must be discarded.

Primers

Primers provide the "spark" needed to ignite the propellant and set the bullet in motion. Primers are often given little consideration beyond the fact that they need to be present.

In spite of their simple appearance, modern primers are complex devices resulting from decades of evolution and development. In addition to igniting the propellant, the primer produces a small initial pressure to support propellant ignition and is an integral part of the gas seal system.

Modern priming is a form of *chemical ignition*. Primitive firearms required a glowing match or the mechanical sparking of flint on

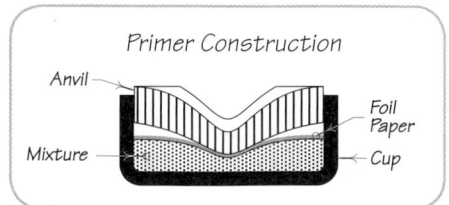

Primer Construction

Anvil

Foil
Paper

Mixture

Cup

steel to ignite the propellant charge. Primers store chemical energy in compounds that, alone or together, produce heat and pressure when activated by impact or *percussion*.

All modern primers contain a small amount of a primary *initiator*, which will react when struck by the firing pin to create a high-velocity pressure wave and heat. The initiator ignites a *fuel* that typically includes traces of powdered aluminum. It adds heat and propels hot particles into the propellant charge. An oxygen source, the *oxidizer*, raises the temperature of the reaction. Priming compounds also contain a *sensitizer* that acts as a booster in the primer by reducing the amount of firing pin energy required. Organic *binders* hold the primer mix together during shipping and handling.

Primer Evolution

In the infancy of chemical ignition, several percussion-sensitive chemicals were tested and used. Eventually, the clear winner was *mercury fulminate*, although other chemicals such as azides were used for a short time before being phased out. Mercuric priming functioned fine for igniting muzzle-loading firearms. However, when copper and copper-alloy cartridge cases were introduced, a problem developed. The vaporized mercury released from the primer attacked the brass and caused the case to become brittle, rendering the cases unsuitable for reloading.

Later, the priming compound's base constituent was changed to *potassium chlorate*. This avoided damage to cartridge brass and yielded a very stable and reliable priming formula. Its negative feature was its residue, which contained chemicals similar to common table salt that caused rust if the firearm was not cleaned promptly with soapy hot water. Because of this characteristic, chlorate primers are referred to as *corrosive*.

Finally a new priming initiator was developed in the late 1920's. *Lead styphnate* was blended with non-corrosive fuels and oxidizers to make a clean, stable priming compound that also met all ballistic requirements. Virtually all American commercial ammunition and component primers have used lead styphnate for over 70 years. However, the U.S. military did not abandon chlorate primers until the 1950's. Lead styphnate primers are referred to as non-corrosive and non-mercuric.

Lead-Free Primers

Because of health concerns potentially caused by shooting in poorly ventilated indoor ranges, primers have been developed recently that contain no lead compounds or other toxic metals. CCI was the first American primer manufacturer to develop and sell "lead-free" primers in factory ammunition. To date, these primers are available only in loaded ammunition. Their unique chemical characteristics require special loading operations and they are suitable only for certain propellant types. It may be some time before lead-free primers are developed to the point that hobby reloaders can use them for all current reloading applications.

Berdan vs. Boxer Primers

Primers were once an integral part of the case. The 22 Long Rifle rimfire cartridge is an excellent example of *inside priming*. Early centerfire cartridges also used inside priming. Ignition components were inserted through the case mouth before charging. Cartridge case evolution and manufacturing challenges forced most arsenals to seek more effective ways to prime a case. Improved cases were of sturdier construction and did not readily accept inside priming systems as did the thin-walled cases they replaced. Developers had to create a separate component that was inserted from the outside of the case; thus the term *outside priming*. An external primer is universal in today's centerfire ammunition.

Berdan (left), and Boxer (right) primer pockets.

Modern rifle/pistol cases and primers have two different configurations of metal parts that date to the 1860's. An American ordnance officer, Hiram Berdan, developed an external cartridge primer consisting a soft metal cup containing primer mix. To compress the primer mix for firing, Berdan incorporated a metal post—the *anvil*—as an integral part of the cartridge case. Located in the center of the primer pocket and aligned with the firing pin, the anvil provides a "pinch point" so the mix receives all the energy of the firing pin impact. Small flash holes on either side of the anvil allow the flame from the primer to pass into the main propellant charge. Because it is a separate component, a spent primer can be removed from the case and a new one inserted. The cartridge case becomes reusable or reloadable. However, extracting a fired Berdan primer is not easy and damage to the case often occurs if the decapping operation is not carefully performed.

At roughly the same time Berdan was developing his priming system, a British ordnance officer, Edward Boxer, was working on a slightly different approach. In the Boxer system, the anvil is not part of the cartridge case but is placed inside the primer itself. The anvil had two or three "legs" that touch the bottom of the primer pocket for positive support, and straddled a single, centered flash hole in the case. This minor change made cases easier to manufacture and had a huge effect on the ability to reload. The spent primer can be easily removed with a small punch with little chance of harming the case.

As things turned out, the American Berdan system was adopted almost worldwide. Fortunately, the United States adopted the English Boxer system gradually between 1860 and 1900. As a result America became the cradle of reloading development and technology. During the last two decades, many foreign cartridge manufacturers have changed to the Boxer system for priming commercial cases.

Because a mixed batch of spent cases—especially military surplus ones—may contain some foreign Berdan cases, the wise reloader will inspect his cases before decapping to insure all the cases are reloadable. The easiest way is to look for headstamps you recognize as major U.S. manufacturers or military arsenals. If you are loading a European military rifle for which no American or Norma cases are available, you must be more diligent in checking for Berdan primers. Any case with a cryptic military headstamp should be considered to be Berdan until inspection proves otherwise.

You can shine a bright penlight into the case mouth and look at the bottom of the case to quickly identify Berdan cases. Two or three small holes that are off-center indicate it is Berdan primed and should be discarded. Look at the center of the case head, too. In making the Berdan anvil, some case manufacturers drive extra material into the anvil by dimpling the inside of the case web. In poor light, you can mistake this for a Boxer flashhole.

Reloading Berdan-primed cases is possible but requires special equipment. Berdan primers are also difficult to find in the United States and often differ from standard U.S. primer diameters. RCBS makes a Berdan decapping tool that cleanly removes old primers if you reload Berdan-primed cases.

In the United States, there are two standard diameters for rifle/pistol primers: .175" and .210". Small pistol primer pockets are the same depth as small rifle pockets. Large rifle primer pockets are deeper than large pistol primer pockets. In each size, separate primers for rifle and handgun applications are manufactured.

Rifle primers must be able to ignite large charges of propellant and withstand higher pressures than pistol primers. To accomplish this, rifle primers have thicker cups and use more priming compound. Handguns generally produce lighter firing pin forces than rifles and, for this reason, pistol primer cups are thinner to ensure adequate sensitivity. Except where noted in this manual, do not load rifle primers in handgun cartridges, or vice versa.

Magnum Primers

A standard primer may not have enough power to reliably ignite the powder charge in certain cartridge/propellant combinations. For these special applications, CCI and

Federal manufacture "magnum" primers. The priming compound in magnum primers is designed to produce a longer, hotter flame to insure proper ignition. As general guidelines, magnum rifle primers are used:

- when loading spherical or "ball" propellants (some exceptions exist).
- when loading large capacity "magnum" cases, especially long ones.
- when the cartridge may be fired at very cold temperatures (below 20° F).

Magnum pistol primers are useful when loading large charges of slow-burning ball propellants such as Winchester 296 or H110. As they developed loads for this manual, our technicians noted those where magnum primers were required. This is indicated in the data pages by an asterisk (*) next to the powder type. CCI® Magnum primers are designated by the number "5" in the middle position of the primer number. For example, a standard CCI large rifle primer is a No. 200. The CCI Magnum version is a No. 250. Federal Magnum primers have "5" in the third position. A Federal 210 is a standard large rifle primer and the 215 is the magnum version.

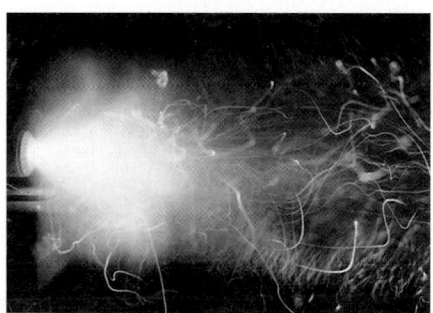

This photo shows the intensity of the primer detonation which is required to effectively ignite the powder.

Propellant manufacturers may state that their propellants do not require magnum primers. This is generally true at maximum safe pressure levels. However, our ballistic testing fully explores propellant behavior over the usable range of charge weights. We often find that a particular propellant works fine with standard primers at the maximum safe pressure. However, it may not consistently ignite with lower charge weights. In the lower pressure regimes typical of "starting loads," we commonly see increased extremes of pressure and velocity. Some ball propellants ignited by standard primers will even produce very short hang-fires—called "click-bangs" for obvious reasons—at start load levels but not at maximum safe pressure. In those cases, we use magnum primers for that propellant to insure consistent performance over the range of charge weights recommended.

Magnum primers should only be used when specified in the loading data. Substituting a magnum primer for a standard primer can increase pressures.

Bench Rest Primers

For critical accuracy requirements, CCI developed the BR2 (large rifle) and BR4 (small rifle) Benchrest primers. CCI Benchrest primers are ballistically equivalent to the CCI

200 and 400, respectively, and use the same reloading data. Benchrest cups and anvils are selected for exceptional uniformity. During the assembly operation, the charger (the operator who meters the primer mix into the cup) is chosen from the most experienced workers. The charger who makes CCI Benchrest primers must have demonstrated a record of consistent charging technique when making other primer products. The BR line runs at a slower pace to provide time for extra inspection.

This care and uniformity means each primer fires just like the one before—and the one after. In small-capacity cases, significant accuracy improvement is often achieved because of the consistent flame characteristics and gas volume produced by these carefully crafted primers.

Federal Premium Gold Medal® primers are also match-grade primers produced with similar care to ensure best performance.

Misfires

The most common cause of misfires in reloaded ammunition is the "high primer;" the reloader fails to fully seat the primer in the case. For proper function and sensitivity, the legs of the anvil must firmly contact the bottom of the primer pocket. CCI and Federal® primers have optimum sensitivity when seated so that the primer is 0.003" to 0.005" below the level of the case head. In this condition, the anvil is properly supported and the ideal thickness of primer mix between the anvil and the cup is established.

When a primer is not fully seated, some of the force of the firing pin drives the primer deeper into the pocket. CCI lab tests show that, if primers are not fully seated, more than 50% additional energy may be required to activate them. Many firearms, especially handguns, do not have this much reserve energy in their ignition systems. In addition to producing misfires, high primers can cause hazardous conditions in semi-automatics. When the bolt or slide closes sharply, it can set off the cartridge before the action is fully locked.

Shooters often attempt to strike a misfired cartridge a second time. Because the first blow usually shatters the priming pellet and upsets the relationship between the various primer parts, the shooter shouldn't be surprised if the cartridge doesn't fire on the second try. If it does fire on the second try, there's about a 98 percent probability that a high primer was the culprit.

It is also possible to create misfires by seating primers too deeply. When this occurs, the anvil stops but the cup continues to encroach. The tip of the anvil presses the primer compound so hard that the material is either pushed off the anvil tip or shatters. Either situation means there is little if any primer mix left between cup and anvil tip.

Primer seating defects can result in misfires.

Misfires can also be caused by excessive headspace. When excessive headspace is present, the cartridge may be too far forward in the chamber and the firing pin can't make solid contact. Excessive headspace can be created in rimless bottleneck cartridges by improper resizing that pushes the shoulder too far back. In rimless cartridges that headspace on the case mouth (like the 45 Auto or 30 Carbine), excessively short cases can produce the same effect. Excessively light firing pin springs, off-center hits and oil contamination can also cause misfires. Very dirty firearms can misfire because excessive residue cushions the impact of the firing pin. In revolvers, a type of wear called *endshake* can cause the cylinder to have excessive front-to-rear motion. This condition results in excessive headspace, and the primer can receive a light hit.

Off-center firing pin strikes are yet another gun problem that can create misfires. This problem is more likely in revolvers with worn timing mechanisms, and in certain locked-breech semi-auto pistols. The industry specification for allowable off-center hits is 0.030 inch. CCI primers are designed with a large "sweet spot" to handle off-center hits. Ultimately, misfires caused by off-center hits can only be truly corrected by repairing the firearm.

CCI's laboratory routinely investigates reports of misfires in reloaded ammunition. Problems are seldom attributed to the primer. Nearly all are caused by reloading errors or a mechanical problem with the firearm.

Slam-fires

A slam-fire occurs when a cartridge discharges in a firearm when the bolt closes without you pulling the trigger. In most cases this phenomenon occurs in military-style semi-automatic rifles using handloaded ammunition. High primers contribute to slam-fires because the closing bolt drives the high primer cup against its anvil. All handloads must be checked for high primers; however, this caution is even more important when shooting military-style, semi-auto rifles.

A slam-fire can occur even when primers are properly seated. Many semi-auto service rifles have no firing pin retractor spring and the firing pin is quite heavy. The inertia of the firing pin may cause it to snap forward as the bolt closes, firing the cartridge. If the bolt is not yet fully locked, the case can rupture, potentially damaging the firing pin and/or injuring the shooter. Military primers are less sensitive than commercial primers to address this potentially hazardous condition.

CCI offers military style primers for 5.56, 7.62, and 50-caliber ammunition. CCI Primers No. 34, No. 41, and No. 35 are commercial versions of our fully DOD-qualified primers for use in U.S. military ammunition. They are available to hobby reloaders as well as commercial accounts.

These special primers minimize the chance of a slam-fire if other factors unexpectedly go out of control. However, no primer can provide 100% protection against slam-fires if the loader doesn't seat the primers deeply enough, or the rifle has a headspace problem or an out-of-spec firing pin.

The No. 34 primer is ballistically equivalent to the CCI 250 Magnum primer, and the No. 41 is equivalent to the CCI 450 Magnum primer. Any load showing a CCI 250 or 450 primer can be assembled with No. 34 and No. 41 primers, respectively.

For an excellent dissertation on slam-fires and their solutions, pick up a copy of *The U.S. 30 Caliber Gas-Operated Service Rifles: A Shop Manual* by Jerry Kuhnhausen, published by Heritage Gun Books (PO Drawer 887, McCall, ID 83638, or on the Internet at www.gunbooks.com).

Primer Storage and Shelf Life

Our technical staff often receives calls from reloaders asking how long primers will last. Shelf life is directly dependent on storage conditions. With proper storage, primers should stay in first-rate condition for decades.

During a primer shortage in 1998-99 (caused by unprecedented levels of ammunition orders), rumors abounded regarding the U.S. Government requiring makers to add "something" to primers to make them "go dead" after two years. That's nonsense; anything added to a primer to make it "go dead" after two years would kill it a few days after manufacture. By the way, CCI was the only primer manufacturer that continued to make and ship an uninterrupted flow of component primers for reloaders during that period.

Ideally, primers should be stored in a cool, dry environment free from wide temperature variations. Dry storage at temperatures up to 100°F should not significantly degrade performance. On the other hand, high humidity, especially when combined with large temperature swings, can degrade primers. Avoid storing primers in a garage or outbuilding without climate control. Be sure to comply with local regulations for primer storage and leave the primers in their original packaging.

Bullets

The evolution of firearms and the bullets they propel are intimately related. Any change in one forced adaptation by the other. Two factors—conical bullets and smokeless propellants—had the greatest influence on this evolutionary process.

Cannons were among the earliest firearms, replacing stone-throwing catapults as instruments for battering castle walls. However, round iron shot suitable for cannon use proved too light for small arms use. A naturally occurring mineral—galena—could be processed with primitive smelting equipment to yield metallic lead. Because lead is very soft and has a low melting point, it is easily shaped. The earliest lead balls may have been pounded or rolled into shape. Iron moulds for casting bullets from molten lead made the process more uniform.

Lead proved to be an excellent material for bullets. Because of its high density, a lead bullet is heavier than an iron bullet of the same diameter and retains velocity better. Round lead balls fired from smooth bores became the standard of the small arms industry until the middle of the 19th century.

Developers wanted to fire even heavier lead bullets without making the firearm larger. The only practical way to accomplish this was to change the projectile shape from round to conical. This doubled or tripled the weight without increasing bullet diameter. However, it soon became obvious that conical projectiles were not stable in flight when fired from a smooth bore. After exiting the barrel, the bullet would begin to tumble and lose accuracy and velocity at an unacceptable rate.

The solution to this problem was to spin-stabilize the bullet. A bullet rotating about its central axis at high speed tends to stay pointed in the direction it started. This is called *gyroscopic stability*. To alter the axis of a rapidly rotating object from its original orientation requires significant force.

You can see this in a simple experiment. Remove a wheel from a small bicycle and hold it by the ends of the axle. Have a helper spin the wheel rapidly, and then try to move the spinning wheel. You can move it but you'll feel strong resistance. Try moving it again after the wheel stops—it's quite easy when the wheel is not turning.

In this experiment, the axle represents the long axis of a bullet. Like the axle that resists your efforts to move it, a spinning bullet tends to stay pointed in the same direction it was pointed when the spin started.

This principle was sound but it took much experimenting to find practical ways to spin the bullet. Ultimately, shallow spiral grooves were cut into the bore of the firearm that forced the bullet to spin. A tight bullet fit was needed to make this system work. In sporting guns, where round balls were still the popular choice, a cloth patch was placed around a round ball to give the proper fit. The patched round ball works so well that it is still in limited use today.

Because these were hunting firearms, the longer-range capability and speed of reloading needed by the military were not factors. The military wanted longer range for volley fire. The complicated loading procedure for a patched ball was not suitable for soldiers in the heat of battle. In muzzleloaders, the heavy fouling generated by black powder quickly clogs the rifling and a tight-fitting projectile cannot be pushed down the bore after only a few shots.

A French officer, Colonel Minié, developed the best solution to remedy this problem in military rifles. His design used an undersized conical bullet with a hollow base. Because the bullet was smaller than the bore, it was easy to push down even heavily fouled barrels. When the powder charge ignited, the hollow base expanded to give a tight seal while permitting excellent accuracy (for those days) and full power. Grooves on the body of the bullet were profiled to scrape out excessive fouling when fired, allowing more shots between cleaning. This type of muzzleloading projectile—called the "minie ball"—is still used today. The basic features of the Minié design are commonly used today in modern revolver ammunition loaded with lead bullets.

Jacketed Bullets

Following the U.S. Civil War, cartridges loaded with black powder and all-lead bullets continued to be state-of-the-art technology until late in the 19th century. Military thinkers knew that the big puff of white smoke that a black powder charge produces pinpointed a shooter's location and reduced battlefield visibility. Emerging smokeless propellant technology promised to correct these problems and make higher velocities possible. Firearms firing smokeless propellant could also shoot longer between cleanings.

However, smokeless propellants produced higher temperatures than black powder and caused severe barrel leading as hot gases melted the unprotected bullet bases. Higher velocities melted the bullet's bearing surface from increased friction. The solution was to put a metal jacket around the lead, opening a new era in bullet design. The soft metal jacket is a logical progression of the cloth patch. It protects the soft lead and provides a surface that the rifling can engage. Old habits are hard to break; you can still hear the word "patch" today referring to a metal jacket, as in "full-patch" bullet, another name for a full metal jacket bullet.

The metal jacket allowed the use of smaller bores and added versatility to bullet designs. Putting the jacket over the front of the bullet creates excellent full-jacketed bullets for military use, target shooting or plinking. Turn the jacket around so that some lead is exposed at the tip and you have an expanding hunting bullet.

During the last 100 years, many metal alloys have been used as jacket materials. Steel, copper and brass are the most common. Because copper is not a native resource for many countries, steel bullet jackets remain quite common outside North and South America, especially in military ammunition. Some U.S. 45 Auto military ammo has been loaded with steel-jacket bullets coated with a copper wash to resist corrosion. With proper processing, mild steel can be made ductile enough to provide reasonable expansion in hunting type bullets.

In spite of this, the best metal for bullet jackets is an alloy of copper and zinc called *gilding metal*. Modern gilding metal bullets for reloading are designed to work well over a wide range of velocities and hunting conditions. Gilding metal has a copper/zinc ratio of 95/5. Another common copper alloy with the somewhat misleading name *commercial bronze* (90% copper, 10% zinc) may also be selected depending on the application.

Selecting the Right Bullet

One of the appeals of reloading is the versatility offered. A wide selection of bullet types in each popular caliber lets you tailor ammunition to your specific need. The two chapters in this manual about Speer rifle and handgun bullets have much more information on our different bullets styles than is appropriate to this chapter.

Before choosing a bullet, you need to consider the type of shooting you want to do and the type of rifle you plan to shoot. Big game hunting and target shooting place different demands on the bullet than does informal plinking or varmint hunting. Different cartridges need different bullets. The 300 Savage may not require the same bullet weight or type for a certain job as a 300 Magnum.

First, look at the range of bullet weights offered in the caliber you plan to shoot. For average game hunting requirements like whitetail and mule deer, the mid-weight bullets are best. For example, Speer makes 30-caliber bullets ranging in weight from 100 to 200 grains. In this case, the mid-weight bullets will weigh 150 to 165 grains. For varmints and light game, go with bullets lighter than this. For heavier game (within the capability of your cartridge) choose heavier bullets. Increased bullet weight normally means more bullet length. Longer bullets usually provide the deep penetration required for taking the largest game that your rifle can handle.

Informal target practice, or "plinking," is quite enjoyable. Some reloaders use up leftover odds and ends of bullet boxes for plinking. If you do this, be sure to verify the bullet weights involved and adjust the powder charges as needed.

Lead Rifle Bullets

In spite of the many advances in jacketed bullet technology, lead rifle bullets are still around and offer the reloader a new field for experimentation. RCBS and other firms sell bullet moulds in a variety of shapes and weights for most popular calibers. The home bullet caster can produce high quality lead bullets using hard alloys that can resist the high pressures and temperatures of centerfire rifles. Bullets cast from a hard alloy such as linotype metal can handle velocities up to 2000 feet per second and, with care, even higher.

In low-pressure cartridges like the 30-30 Winchester or 30-40 Krag, cast bullets can normally be driven almost as fast as jacketed ones of the same weight. Improvements in lead alloys and bullet lubricants have increased the maximum practical cast bullet velocity.

Cast bullets can shoot quite accurately and, with the proper shape, can be used on game. Often, bullet casting is the only source of projectiles for obsolete cartridge. Data for loading cast bullets in certain cartridges is featured in this edition of the *Speer Reloading Manual*.

· · · · ·

Bullet making evolved rapidly in the last half of the 20th century. Today, the rejects from most commercial manufacturers will often beat the accuracy of match bullets from 60 years ago. Modern manufacturing technology provides you bullets of the highest quality. In addition to accuracy, extensive testing has resulted in innovative bullet designs that can deliver the exacting terminal ballistics performance demanded by the modern hunter. Speer continues its commitment to developing bullets to meet the needs of today's shooters.

Ballistic Propellants

Modern firearm propellants are solid chemical compounds that store energy. When confined in a cartridge case, they burn at a rapid and predictable rate to produce expanding gases that push the bullet down the barrel of the firearm at high speed. Like the other components of small arms ammunition, propellants have evolved over the past century into the highly specialized materials that today's handloader can buy.

However, this hasn't always been the case.

Black Powder

For hundreds of years, black powder was the only practical ballistic propellant. Its discovery as a source of stored chemical energy ushered in the firearms era. Black powder is a mechanical mixture of charcoal (carbon), saltpeter (potassium nitrate— an oxidizer) and sulfur. When properly combined, these simple components can be ignited to produce enough heat and gas to drive a bullet down a gun barrel or blast rock from a quarry face. Research indicates that the Chinese were experimenting with saltpeter-based compounds as early as 1000 AD. It wasn't until the 13th century that the western cultures began to use similar compounds for ballistic purposes. When tightly confined, black powder becomes an explosive; with less confinement in a gun system, it behaves as a propellant.

In its original form, mixing the three powdered components together in the prescribed ratios made a crude but usable ballistic propellant. Historical documents indicate that black powder's first military use was for combat engineering. It made possible breeching of walls and gates with *petards*. Petards are containment devices that, when filled with black powder, could be placed with the open end in contact with a barrier to blast through it. Petards did not carry projectiles; they focused the force of an explosion into a small area. They were an early incarnation of the shaped-charge principle and the forebearer of modern explosives used in construction and demolition.

Physically placing petards against your enemy's castle walls was an obvious impediment to becoming an old soldier. People in castles usually greeted enemy combat engineers with a hail of arrows, hot oil, and rocks. Cannons likely evolved from large petards to increase the soldiers' life expectancy. Adding a projectile to a petard allowed chipping away at walls and gates from a safer, standoff position. The black powder employed was still a simple mechanical mixture. The reduction in confinement resulting from moving the open end of a petard from a wall allows the black powder to act as a propelling material.

From a military standpoint, getting primitive black powder to the battle presented a problem. When transported over rough roads and fields, vibration would separate the raw components and weaken the explosive power of the mix. For some time, the raw materials were transported into battle separately and then blended just before loading. More than a few accidents occurred while black powder was blended directly behind an active line of cannons!

A technique known as "corning" eliminated the separation of the three powdered components. The blended mixture was dampened with water, ground and pressed into a cake. Potassium nitrate is water-soluble. When small amounts of moisture were introduced it became a sticky binder. Adding water also made powder manufacture safer because no flammable dust was produced in the blending operation. When the cake dried, it was broken up and sifted to separate the granules by size. The granules were often tumbled with graphite to facilitate handling. It also gives the granules a "glazed" appearance.

By corning the powder, it could be transported without component separation, and the glazing made the powder easier to load in small arms. Corning provided the additional benefit of producing a significant increase in power because the ratio of components was now uniform throughout an entire batch. This power boost caused some older cannons, which functioned perfectly with dry-blended powder, to burst from the additional power of the improved propellant. Corned powder forced cannon makers to develop better techniques and materials. Again we see the intimate relation between the development of ballistic components and the machines that use them.

Corned black powder has remained almost unchanged for over 500 years. This does not mean that black powder was ever the perfect ballistic propellant. It was still inefficient; less than half converts to gas on firing. The remaining solid residue produces the thick white smoke that makes the shooter's position readily apparent in a combat situation. The solids also contributed to heavy barrel fouling. Black powder residue is *hygroscopic*; it absorbs moisture and creates acids that will rapidly rust metal if not removed.

Another factor is black powder's limited energy content. Any significant velocity increase meant adding more black powder, which required a larger cartridge case to hold the charge. Some of the most powerful "buffalo" cartridges developed by Sharps and Winchester used cartridge cases that were 3¼ inches long! These massive cartridges were intended for falling block single-shot rifles where cartridge length was not a major concern. The advent of repeating firearms helped stimulate development of a more efficient fuel that would produce high energy from compact cartridges suitable for repeaters.

Shooters still use black powder today for a variety of reasons. Some hunt with it to actually experience the traditions of our forefathers. Others enjoy the black powder hunting season simply because it extends their time in the field each year. Cartridge rifles such as the Sharps single shots and the 1873 Springfield are commonly used with black powder for Old West-style competitions. It seems primitive weapons and black powder will be with us for a long time to come.

Nitrocellulose-based Propellants

The era of modern propellants began with the discovery of nitrocellulose in 1845-46. Nitrocellulose, also called *guncotton*, is made by the chemical reaction of nitric acid with natural cellulose, usually cotton or wood fiber. The chemical reaction adds oxygen to the cellulose molecules. When ignited, the added oxygen causes the nitrated cellulose to burn rapidly and release much more energy than untreated cellulose. A large volume of gas is created and very little residue remains.

Because it is practically impossible to control the burning rate of raw guncotton, it was not suitable as a small arms propellant. However, it became the basis for continued experimentation in explosives and other fields. It also was used to make the first plastic, celluloid, formed by dissolving guncotton in a strong solvent to form a sticky mass that was shaped and allowed to dry. Solvents used for softening guncotton are called *plasticizers*.

In the 1880's a French chemist, Vielle, found that softening guncotton in a mixture of alcohol and ether concentrated the energy content into a smaller volume. He formed the resulting flexible solid into thin sheets and cut the sheets into small flakes. Once partially dried, the flakes could be loaded into a cartridge. The resulting material burned at a controlled rate that was suitable for firearms use. By changing the granule size, the burning rates could be regulated to support a wide variety of cartridge applications.

Alfred Nobel and Nitroglycerine

After Vielle's discovery made safer nitrocellulose propellants possible, Alfred Nobel found that *nitroglycerine* could also be used to plasticize nitrocellulose. The nitroglycerine increased the energy of the propellant and, because no volatile solvents were used, the resulting propellants were very stable. Combining the work of Vielle and Nobel with different granule configurations gave combinations of performance characteristics that were useful in many types of small arms munitions. These materials fulfilled the need for a high-energy material that delivered significant velocity in the compact cartridges used in repeating firearms.

Propellant powders manufactured with nitrocellulose alone are referred to as *single-base*. Those made with both nitrocellulose and nitroglycerine are called *double-base*. Both types are available to today's handloader.

Deterrent Technology

The development of small-bore service rifles and other military requirements demanded a slower release of energy than could be offered by adjusting granule size alone. Around 1900, chemists discovered that by adding certain chemicals to powder granules, the reaction speed could be further controlled. These chemicals delayed the full combustion of the propellant by a predictable amount, thereby releasing energy over a longer time interval. Different amounts and types of deterrents were used to develop a wide selection of propellants for many small arms applications.

Few shooters realize that the natural color of nitrocellulose is a pale, greenish yellow. The dark gray or black color of finished smokeless propellants is due to the graphite coating applied to facilitate powder handling. In addition to deterrents and graphite, modern smokeless propellants contain other additives to reduce flash and to ensure extended storage life.

Modern Powder Types

Today, propellants are usually classified by their *morphology*, or shape. There are several different shapes:

- **Flake**—Granules are shaped like round discs. The thickness and diameter of the flake determine the burning rate (some flake powders may be perforated to further modify the burning rate). Example: Alliant Bullseye

- **Cylindrical**—Sometimes called "stick" powder. Granules are rod-shaped and may be perforated on the long axis. The length of the grain depends on the application. Examples: Alliant Reloder® 19 or Hodgdon 4831

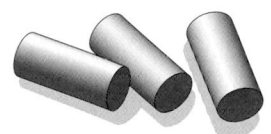

- **Spherical**—In its most basic form, the granules are round balls and most often referred to as "ball powder." However, the granules may be flattened to some degree to control burning rate. Examples: Hodgdon H380, Accurate #9, and Winchester 748

- **Sheet**—Seldom seen outside of Europe, sheet powders are formed by rolling out large sheets of nitrocellulose and allowing them to partially dry. Then the sheets go through a cutter that produces flakes that are square or diamond shaped.

Some people refer to cylindrical propellants as "extruded" but this is not technically correct. Most current propellants start by extruding the gelatinous mass of nitrocellulose through a perforated die plate to form a series of strands. Just beyond the extrusion die is a cutter unit with rotating blades. These blades cut the strands into the desired length. The number of blades, speed of the blade rotation and the rate of extrusion determine the shape.

Ball propellant receives different processing after extrusion. The strands are cut to form short cylinders with the length roughly equal to their diameter. The irregular cylinders are introduced into a fluid-filled shaper and are rounded as they flow through the system. A chemical added to the fluid removes excess moisture from the granules.

The rounded particles pass into a series of progressive evaporators to drive off residual solvents. This process produces dense spheres of single-base nitrocellulose.

After cleaning and sorting by size, the spheres are impregnated with nitroglycerine and treated with deterrents to obtain the desired energy characteristics. If the spheres are to be flattened, this operation is performed before the granules fully harden. To meet ballistic requirements the manufacturer will often blend spherical and flattened granules. Don't be surprised to see both in the same powder sample.

Burning Rates

Modern propellants are classified as flammable solids. Although the shooter hears a single loud explosion, the propellant actually burns at a rapid rate. Releasing energy through controlled burning is called *deflagration*. How "fast" or "slow" this occurs is the *burning rate* of the propellant. Typically, loads for small-capacity cases and/or with light bullets work best with faster powders. Large-capacity cases and/or heavy bullets usually prefer propellants at the slower end of the scale. The primary factors that control burning rates are morphology (shape and size) and deterrents.

Canister propellants are often ranked in order of burning rate. Published burning rate charts are based on propellant behavior measured in a special test device called a *calorimeter bomb*. However, propellants may not maintain those lab relationships when loaded into cartridges. Ranking is not absolute and the way a propellant burns is totally dependent on the conditions of loading. A charge of IMR 3031 in a 300 Savage loaded with a 110-grain bullet will not burn at the same rate when loaded in a 30-06 case with a 150-grain bullet. Never attempt to substitute propellants based on how they are ranked in burning rate tables or charts. These tables are intended as general reference guides but must never be used instead of published reloading data. We do not include a burning rate chart in this manual because we feel it will be misused.

For more information on burning rates, refer to the next chapter, "Velocity, Energy and Pressure."

Propellant Lot Uniformity

Manufacturers of smokeless propellants strive to ensure that each batch of powder is the same as every other batch sold under the same label. However, some minor variations occur. For that reason, you will find loads in this manual that differ from data published in earlier editions of the *Speer® Reloading Manual* or in data from other sources.

Even with the utmost care in manufacturing, variations between powder lots can cause pressure changes. For this reason, we list a *starting load* for each powder/bullet combination. Never begin loading with the maximum charge weight listed. Begin with the start load and work up in small steps toward the maximum, carefully watching for signs of excessive pressure. This method also provides a margin of safety when working up loads to be used in extreme temperature conditions, where pressure changes due to temperature can occur. If you have worked up a near-maximum load with a favorite powder and then load a different lot, drop the charge weight two to five percent to safely reestablish a new maximum load for your current powder lot.

Propellants with Similar Names

Sometimes, different propellants have similar names or numbers. For example, both IMR Powder Company and Hodgdon market 4831 rifle powder. Hodgdon first distributed this propellant as H4831. DuPont (now IMR) introduced a similar propellant in 1973. IMR 4831 typically exhibits a faster burning rate than H4831 and *they are not interchangeable*. On the other hand, IMR 4895 and H4895 are usually so close in performance that the data is often interchangeable. However, we strongly recommend that you follow published loads to the letter.

The reloader must carefully read the label. IMR powder produces two powders—SR4756 and SR4759—having similar names but very different burning rates. Substituting SR4756 for the much slower SR4759 can destroy a firearm.

Pressure Variations with Temperature

The temperature of a cartridge will affect the pressure it generates when it is fired. A load that was safe at 40°F may prove excessive when fired at 100°F. Likewise a load developed at 100°F will likely show a five to ten percent velocity loss when fired at 40°F. Loads in this manual were developed in the temperature range of 68°F to 74°F.

Identification of Reloading Propellants

Reloaders have only one method of positively identifying a propellant powder: *the manufacturer's label on the original container.* No other identification can be considered reliable.

Many commercial propellants have similar physical appearances. However, there may be significant differences in their energy content. A wrong guess as to the type of powder can lead to property damage or serious injury. Any unlabeled powder must be considered defective and discarded. It's a bad case of false economy to save a few dollars on unlabeled bulk powder and risk ruining a fine firearm or injuring yourself and bystanders. Any propellants that inadvertently become mixed must also be discarded. Never attempt to blend powders to get that "special load"—it isn't worth the extreme risk!

Partial Charges of Slow-burning Propellants

Reloaders may have heard that partial charges of slow-burning propellants in certain rifle cartridges can create high pressure—high enough to destroy a rifle and injure the shooter. "Secondary explosion effect," or "SEE," is the term applied to this controversial subject. SEE is typically reported in small-bore, large capacity cartridges such as 7mm and 30-caliber magnums. The term "explosion" is inappropriate. A true explosion will shatter steel into tiny pieces. Most firearm-damaging incidents are actually excessive pressure events causing the cartridge case to fail and release enough gas to bend and break metal gun parts. This does not satisfy the strict definition of explosion.

Like Bigfoot and the Loch Ness Monster, SEE has been reported but never dragged into a lab for proper analysis—at least with sporting cartridges. It has been documented in 20mm cannon ammunition and larger. Testing small arms ammunition in standard pressure barrels shows that pressure drops faster than charge weights. Years ago, Bruce Hodgdon tested H4831 propellant in the 30-06 cartridge by incrementally reducing the charge weight and noting the pressures. At 50 percent of normal maximum charge, pressure fell to around 25 percent of maximum. His results suggest that, if reduced loads are damaging guns, something other than an exotic pressure effect may be the culprit.

There can be a logical mechanism to explain gun damage. In Hodgdon's tests, a 50 percent charge of a slow-burning propellant generated pressures of only 12,000 CUP, the same as the old 32 Long revolver cartridge. Pressure would build to that level slowly and a jacketed bullet could stick in the throat. If it stops just far enough to allow another cartridge to be chambered, you would be pushing twice the normal payload. The stuck bullet would become a plug under these conditions and the next case fired would surely rupture. True detonation is not required to damage a rifle. Escaping gas from a ruptured case can rip off the extractor, break the stock, deform the magazine, and damage the receiver.

If SEE is ever eliminated as a gun damage factor, compelling reasons still exist to avoid substantially reduced charges of slow propellants. Even a ten percent reduction with some propellants can produce an increased variation in pressure and velocity. Although not unsafe, these loads may exhibit poor ballistic performance and are certainly not the quality product that most handloaders strive to create.

Powder Storage

Proper powder storage is similar to that for primers. A cool area is best for long-term storage. Avoid large temperature changes. If you buy several cans at a time, leave the factory seals intact on the others until you need to open one. The original cans are designed for safe transport and storage. Keep all cans tightly sealed with their labels intact. If you buy a bulk container of reloading powder that is too large to conveniently use on the bench, be sure all information from the original label is transferred if you repackage part of the powder in a smaller container. Many reloaders mark the purchase date on each can. Doing this can help you judge your rate of powder usage and allow you to use the oldest stock first.

Never use glass as a storage container. When exposed to light, the "greenhouse effect" will raise temperatures inside the container and degrade the powder. Check cans regularly for signs of deterioration. In many powders, a fine red-brown dust on the granules and the inside of the container indicates this condition. If you see any evidence of deterioration, the propellant should not be used; dispose of it properly.

Most single-base powders have a strong alcohol smell from the solvents used as plasticizers. That is a normal condition while the lack of this smell may indicate that the powder characteristics have changed. However, some people do not have as good a sense of smell as others, so this test is not definitive. On the other hand, a strong, acrid smell that irritates the nose is a sure sign of deterioration and the sample should be scrapped.

Storage of propellant powder is usually regulated by local fire codes. Most localities require an approved storage magazine for quantities over a prescribed minimum. For additional information, contact the National Fire Protection Association, 470 Atlantic Avenue, Boston, MA 02210 (www.nfpa.org). Ask for NFPA Bulletin 495, which contains storage recommendations for both the handloader and commercial distributors. Additional information on powder and primer storage and handling is available from the Sporting Arms and Ammunition Manufacturers' Institute (www.saami.org), Flintlock Ridge Office Center, 11 Mile Hill Road, Newton CT 06470. Item #200 discusses the safe storage of propellants; item #201 concerns primers safety.

Current Modern Propellants

There are many different component powders available to the handloader. They are usually classed by their intended use: rifle, handgun, or shotgun. However, there is some crossover. Some shotshell powders are excellent for pistol and revolver ammunition. Some quick burning rifle powders are very effective for high-velocity handloads in "magnum" revolver cartridges. Whatever the application, be sure to follow published guidelines when loading and never attempt experimentation with untested combinations.

It was once fairly easy to tell the propellant make from its name. IMR propellants all began with "IMR" or "SR." Hodgdon propellants began with "H" and Accurate with

"AA." Today, propellant names are more creative, like Retumbo (Hodgdon), Magpro (Accurate), or Big Game (Ramshot), placing more responsibility on you to be an informed consumer.

IMPORTANT SAFETY INFORMATION: *It is the responsibility of the reloader to first learn about the different propellants available and their characteristics before undertaking the hobby of reloading. This is the only way to avoid confusion over propellants brands, names, types, and applications that could lead to hazardous conditions.*

New propellant products appear faster than reloading manuals are printed. It is easier today to use the Internet to stay abreast of current propellant offerings. Rather than list hundreds of propellants separately as in past manuals, we encourage our readers to learn about the propellant companies and their products directly from company websites or from brochures offered by the respective companies.

Here are the website addresses and conventional contact information for the propellant manufacturers represented in this manual:

Alliant Powder (formerly Hercules):
www.alliantpowder.com
PO Box 6, Radford, VA 24143-0006

Accurate Arms:
www.accuratepowder.com
Western Powders, PO Box 158, Miles City, MT 59301

Hodgdon Powder:
www.hodgdon.com
PO Box 2932, Shawnee Mission, KS 66201

IMR Powders
www.imrpowder.com
c/o Hodgdon, PO Box 2932, Shawnee Mission, KS 66201

Ramshot Powders
www.ramshot.com
Western Powders, PO Box 158, Miles City, MT 59301

VihtaVuori Powders
www.vihtavuori-lapua.com
Kaltron-Pettibone, 1241 Ellis Street, Bensenville, IL 60106

Winchester Powders
www.wwpowder.com
c/o Hodgdon, 6231 Robinson, Shawnee Mission, KS 66202

Studying the excellent product information available from these manufacturers will make you a more informed reloader and, therefore, a safer one.

chapter 5

Velocity, Energy & Pressure

Pressure in a cartridge creates velocity and that creates energy, intertwining these attributes. It is pressure that has the greatest influence on the safety of the reloaded cartridge. Velocity has the major influence on how the bullet behaves in flight and on impact with the target, and energy tells how much work the bullet will do.

Velocity

Velocity is simply the speed of the bullet. Measuring bullet velocity once was a task only attempted by the most sophisticated ballistics labs. Historically, devices to measure velocities have shown an incredible amount of ingenuity, from the simple ballistic pendulum to exotic spinning-disk devices. The shooting industry measures velocity with a *chronograph* (Greek for "time writer," so named because the first units measured only time).

Improved sensing technology and advances in low-cost, solid-state electronics now make accurate chronographs available to the average reloader. Some units sell for less than $100 and are completely portable. They may have an interface that lets you connect the chronograph to a laptop computer on the shooting bench for automated data acquisition.

Modern chronographs determine velocity by accurately measuring the time it takes the bullet to travel the distance between two fixed points. The formula for calculating velocity is:

$$\text{velocity} = \frac{\text{distance}}{\text{time}}$$

If distance is measured in feet and the time in seconds, the result is velocity in *feet per second* (ft/sec). In countries using the metric system, velocity is expressed in meters per second (m/sec).

In the velocity formula for ballistics testing, distance is the spacing between detection units or *screens* of the chronograph. Each modern screen contains a light-sensitive electronic device called a *photocell*. The photocell is so sensitive that it can detect the shadow of a bullet passing over it. Two screens—a start screen and a stop screen—are normal; some models have a third screen to increase detection reliability. When a screen detects the bullet shadow, it transmits an electronic signal to the electronics package of the chronograph; these are the *start* and *stop* signals depending on which screen sends the signal.

Inside the electronics package is an *oscillator*, a precision electronic timer. The oscillator vibrates one million cycles per second or more. A counting circuit logs the number of cycles the oscillator produces between the arrival of the start and stop signals from the screens. Once the counter circuit knows the number of cycles made, the chronograph can look at the screen spacing (distance) and calculate the velocity.

For example, in a chronograph with a 1-million cycle oscillator, the counter circuit logs 2000 cycles between receiving the start and stop signals. 2000 cycles equals 0.002 seconds. The chronograph screens are 5 feet apart. The chronograph uses the velocity formula:

$$\text{velocity} = \frac{\text{distance}}{\text{time}} = \frac{5 \text{ feet}}{0.002 \text{ second}} = 2500 \text{ ft/sec}$$

A microprocessor performs the calculations automatically and the readout on the chronograph quickly displays the results for the user.

For most shooting applications, accuracy is more important than maximum velocity. A gain in velocity of 100 to 200 ft/sec in typical rifle cartridges will seldom be noticeable either to the shooter or the target. Trajectory changes due to slight velocity increases are usually so small at typical hunting ranges as to be of little concern to the hunter. Often, loading for higher velocity only degrades accuracy.

Velocity affects bullet expansion in hunting bullets. At low velocities, a bullet may expand very little. The same bullet fired 500 ft/sec faster will expand normally. It is possible to drive a bullet fast enough to cause the bullet to break up completely.

Bullet velocities are now easier for the hobbyist handloader to measure and we often get calls asking why velocities in the *Speer Manual* are different from those the shooter gets from the same load in his rifle or handgun. The answer is simple: all firearms are different. Variations in rifling dimensions, bore smoothness, chamber dimensions, throat shape, headspace and other factors combine to make each firearm unique. Throw in external factors like temperature, powder lot variation, case construction and primer differences and you can see why there are differences in velocities between seemingly identical firearms. For an excellent discussion and examples of velocity variations, please read the section, "Why Ballisticians Get Gray" immediately following the handgun text section of this manual.

For the *Speer Manual*, we develop the loads in industry test barrels and, whenever possible, report their velocities from popular sporter rifles and handguns with common barrel lengths. This way, velocities are more meaningful to the average reloader than velocities reported from test barrels. Due to the press of testing new cartridges and the time required for sporter velocity determination, you will see more pressure barrel velocities in this edition than in previous ones. However, these are for cartridges whose velocities in sporting firearms are close to the pressure gun. For other cartridges commonly fired in barrel lengths that differ greatly from the pressure barrel, we still use sporting arms. Just keep in mind that your rifle or handgun probably won't produce exactly the same speed as ours, whether we show velocities from a sporting rifle or a pressure barrel.

Energy

Energy is defined as the ability to do work. The energy of an object in motion is called *kinetic energy* (KE). Kinetic energy is expressed in foot-pounds (ft/lbs) in the English system. It is not directly measured; rather, it is calculated from the bullet's *mass* and *velocity*. Any object having mass and velocity has kinetic energy. The general formula for calculating energy is:

$$KE = \frac{mv^2}{2}$$

where *m* is the mass of the bullet and v is the velocity. Mass and weight are not the same. To get the results to come out correctly in ft/lbs, the following formula is used. It contains the necessary conversions to derive English units:

$$KE_{ft/lbs} = \frac{velocity^2_{ft/sec}}{450400} \times bullet\ weight_{grains}$$

For example, the energy of a 150-grain bullet traveling at 2800 ft/sec can be calculated:

$$KE = \frac{2800 \times 2800}{450400} \times 150 = 2611\ ft/lbs$$

The average hunter will normally not worry about the amount of energy his load generates. The only exception is that some states specify a minimum energy for big game hunting, for example 1000 ft/lbs at the muzzle or 500 ft/lbs at 100 yards. Check with your state's game regulations to see if this affects you.

Pressure

Throughout the data pages in this manual, you will find references to pressure. This is the peak pressure generated by the expanding gases as the powder charge burns in a cartridge case. The Small Arms and Ammunition Manufacturers Institute (SAAMI) establishes maximum pressure limits for each cartridge. These pressure standards take into consideration the types of firearms in which each cartridge will be used. Cartridges commonly used in weak actions will have a lower pressure standard than ones used in strong actions.

Pressure does the work to move the bullet through the rifle barrel, giving it the velocity needed to reach the target. If the pressure is not high enough, the bullet could stick in the bore or fail to generate enough velocity to do the intended task. If the pressure is too high, the firearm may be damaged and the shooter injured.

The weak link in a shooting system is the cartridge case. Even though a strong rifle action may have an ultimate yield strength of 160,000 pounds per square inch, the best brass case will withstand only about half that amount. This is the compelling reason to comply with published loading data from reputable bullet and propellant manufacturers. Never exceed recommended loads. As you read on, you will see that accurate and meaningful pressure determination is not something that the typical hobbyist can do.

There are two different methods recognized by the American firearms industry for the accurate assessment of cartridge pressures. In both systems, a heavy barrel with very precise chamber and bore dimensions is mounted in a rigid firing mechanism known as a *universal receiver.*

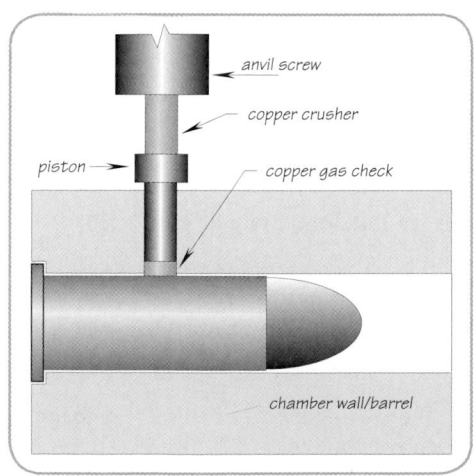

anvil screw

copper crusher

piston →

copper gas check

chamber wall/barrel

Basic layout of crusher-type pressure barrel

Crusher Pressure Measurement

Crusher pressure measurement is the older of the two systems. This system determines pressure by correlating the amount that a cylinder of copper is deformed by exposure to the pressure of the expanding gasses.

The pressure barrel's chamber has a hole in the side, perpendicular to the chamber. After a case is inserted, a soft copper seal—*the gas check*— is placed in the hole and seated against the side of the cartridge to protect the precision steel parts from gas erosion. A

steel piston is placed in the hole and a copper cylinder is placed on top of the piston. A heavy steel yoke with a large anvil screw is then installed and tightened to hold the assembly in place.

The copper cylinders are of known metallurgy and each lot of crushers is calibrated. A *tarage table* is furnished with each crusher lot showing how much pressure is required to compress the crusher a given distance. The greater the pressure, the shorter the copper crusher becomes.

Copper crushers before (left) and after firing.

When setup is complete, the cartridge is fired. Pressure pierces the case at the sensor hole and drives the piston into the copper crusher. The compressed cylinder is then removed and its length measured. The operator finds that length in the tarage table. Beside the length in the table is a number that is the chamber pressure expressed in copper units of pressure (CUP). The test setup must be repeated for each shot.

Crusher testing is slow, but has the advantage of requiring no power source; you could test for pressure on a deserted island as long as you remember to take the tarage table and a micrometer.

Piezoelectric Pressure Measurement

This is a newer system that provides faster readings through the use of electronics. A sensor called a *transducer* is mounted in the chamber wall. It contains a piezoelectric crystal that generates a small electrical charge when compressed. The strength of the electrical signal is directly proportional to the pressure applied to the transducer. When the cartridge fires, the electrical signal is amplified and sent to a processing computer to be converted into a pressure reading in pounds per square inch (psi). Because the sensor does not have

A modern pressure barrel showing the electronic transducer.

to be removed and reset for each shot as in the crusher system, data can be gathered more rapidly. Both transducer and crusher systems were used during the development of the data presented in the *Speer Reloading Manual.*

In Europe, the Commission Internationale Permanente, or CIP, controls cartridge specifications. Transducers are also used but are of a different type than used in North America. Some are mounted at the case mouth instead of against the sidewall of the case. Others read on the case body but require that a drilled case be used. Differences in transducer types and locations can mean that loads developed on the European system may be different than those tested by SAAMI protocols.

Calibration of Pressure Guns

Both the crusher system and the piezoelectric system give raw pressure readings. Because of normal variations from barrel to barrel, each must be calibrated to a common standard if pressure readings are to be accurately compared to established limits.

Reference ammunition is loaded under tight tolerances and then evaluated by several labs to establish the assessed pressure and velocity values. This value is made available to qualified test stations. Before production testing starts, the technician obtains reference ammunition and fires it in his pressure barrel. The raw reading is compared to the assessed value of the reference lot. The difference between the raw number and the assessed reference value is the pressure correction factor. For example, a manufacturer fires reference ammunition in his 30-06 pressure barrel and gets a raw reading of 50,300 CUP. The published value of the reference lot is 48,600 CUP. The manufacturer must adjust his raw reading by subtracting a *correction factor* of 1700 CUP. In this manner, the barrel is "zeroed" against a known standard. A similar correction factor is used for velocity testing.

Reference ammunition is available only in standard calibers recognized by SAAMI. It does not exist for wildcat, obsolete or many foreign cartridges. Therefore it is not possible to get corrected pressure readings for ammunition that is not a standard SAAMI cartridge. Safe working pressures for a particular rifle for a non-SAAMI cartridge must be established by other means that may be less accurate than real lab testing. Remember that gun designers rely on dimensional standards mated with ammunition pressure standards that are based on the two accepted test methods: copper crusher and transducer. When you try to use an alternative system like case head expansion, you may go outside the design parameters of your firearm. Stick with published data.

Primer Appearance

The art of "reading" a fired primer to approximate pressure has received a lot of attention. It is true that excessive pressure might be detected by interpreting the appearance of a fired primer; however, the reloader must be aware of pitfalls that can lead to grossly erroneous conclusions.

Pierced primers are sometimes assumed to be indicative of high pressures. However, most pierced primers are the result of a rough or improperly shaped firing pin. Even

Pierced Primer

a small burr on the tip of a firing pin can cause the primer to pierce. The same result could occur from a well-polished firing pin that is too sharp. When you see a pierced primer, check the condition of the firing pin before making a judgment about the load.

In some firearms, excessive clearance between the firing pin and the breech face can cause the indented portion of the primer to fall out. The case looks like someone drilled a hole in the primer, although the primer retains its radiused edges indicative of normal pressure. A weak firing pin spring can produce similar symptoms. Again, both of these point to a *gun problem* that should be corrected before shooting again. If this type of gas leak continues, the breech face can be eroded.

Primers that back out of the pocket seldom indicate a high-pressure condition. In fact, the opposite is more often true; low pressure is the culprit. All sporting firearms have a certain amount of clearance between the breech face and the cartridge. This allows a little room for powder residue and dirt to accumulate that may prevent a malfunction when the firearm is used under dirty conditions. When a primer fires, it generates its own level of pressure even before the propellant charge fully ignites. This initial pressure causes the primer to back out of the primer pocket until it stops against the breech face. When the propellant charge reaches normal pressure, the cartridge case is driven back until it strikes the breech face reseating the protruding primer. If the operating pressure is low, there isn't enough force to drive the case back and the primer remains backed out.

Flattened primers are another sign often used as an indicator of high pressures. Although a more reliable indicator than pierced or protruding primers, flattened primers can result at normal pressures. The thickness of the primer cup, its shape, metallurgy and the headspace of the firearm can create flattened primers.

Excessive headspace can cause severely flattened primers at safe working pressures because the primer backs out much more than normal before the powder charge ignites. As pressure builds, the primer begins to "balloon" due to a lack of lateral support and, when reseated by the setback of the case, the edges tend to fill the pocket. Primers in the same load fired in a firearm with proper headspace would appear normal. Firearms suspected of having excessive headspace must be inspected and repaired before shooting them further.

A test set up by the Speer® staff clearly shows the folly of trying to read primer flattening as a sign of excess pressure. Three 44 Magnum loads were developed. One was at maximum working pressure, one was 20 percent under maximum and one was 20 percent over maximum. All three loads were fired in a production revolver. In spite of the fact the loads cover a range of 16,000 CUP, no difference was apparent among them based on primer appearance.

Of course, a primer flattened so much that it flows into the radius of the primer pocket, filling it entirely, is definitely a sign of high pressure *if* the firearm is known to have proper headspace. Usually, this condition also results in a stretched primer pocket that will no longer hold a new primer securely. At even higher pressures, the fired primer may fall out when the bolt is opened. At this point, the load is severely over any safe pressure.

Primer extrusion or "cratering" is often incorrectly cited as being signs of excess pressure. Extrusion produces a ridge of metal around the firing pin indent. In most cases,

Cratered Primer

these are not pressure indications but rather gun problems. Extrusion can be due to excessive clearance between the firing pin and firing pin hole in the breech face or due to a weak firing pin spring. Changing from a standard primer to a magnum primer (with appropriate load adjustments, of course) will usually reduce the symptoms, but the best action is to have the gun problem corrected.

Occasionally, a dark, sooty ring may be noticed between the primer and the case. Although it can be caused by high pressure, the presence of this ring on otherwise normal primers indicates a damaged primer pocket that leaked. If the sidewalls of the pocket are badly scratched, the normal sealing action of the primer cannot stop all the gas. Very old primers that have developed age cracks in the sidewalls or a loose primer pocket can also cause primer leaks. If you notice primer leaks, try a different lot of cases or

44 Magnum cartridges fired at (l to r) 31,800 CUP, 39,000 CUP and 47,700 CUP. Note that there are NO visible differences among the three primers, even though one is a 20 percent overload!

primers. When cleaning primer pockets, avoid using tools that gouge the sidewalls of the pocket.

If you notice primer leaks, stop shooting that ammo immediately. Continued firing can cause cosmetic damage to the breech face of the firearm.

Appearance of the Fired Case

Although primers can give false pressure indications, the brass case itself can show symptoms that are absolutely indicative of excess pressure. As normal pressures are passed, a bright mark may appear on the case head at the point where the breech face is cut away for the extractor and/or ejector. As pressures increase, the brass begins to flow into these recesses. Usually the primer pocket will enlarge excessively at this point. If these signs are seen, you have gone far beyond any safe pressures! The next step is a ruptured cartridge case. Remember: the brass case is the weakest part of the system. When it fails, damage to the firearm and injury to the shooter will occur.

Assumptions Concerning Pressures

Like most people, reloaders want to generalize. It is always comforting to have things around us fall into predictable patterns. Unfortunately, theory sometimes collides head-on with reality.

Accurately predicting a pattern requires more technical information than most reloaders possess. Industry ballisticians have an advantage; their experience with component manufacturing and access to standard pressure test equipment expands their knowledge of the little details.

Reloaders recognize certain generalities or assumptions regarding pressure. We assume that adding more powder increases pressure. Likewise, changing to a heavier bullet without adjusting the powder charge is assumed to create more pressure. Often these assumptions are correct. However, interior ballistics is a science that strives to evaluate inexact objects. We don't mean to imply that the manufacturing methods or the people involved are sloppy. Today's ammunition and components are the best ever and the workers making them are highly skilled and strive for excellence regardless of where they work. It is the basic nature of the cartridge and its components that produce any lack of exactness.

Modern propellants are hard to "pigeon-hole". They are remarkable chemicals that provide the shooter with maximum performance and quality. However, their burning characteristics are not constant—they vary depending on the case volume, shape, and the pressure level used.

Powder burning rate charts are ranked based on the performance of the powder in a specific lab test. The heat and pressure production of a propellant sample are measured in a closed, fixed-volume device called a *calorimeter bomb*. When you look at a burning rate chart, the rankings you see are based on this test.

In a cartridge case, these rankings may not be the same. It is precisely this reason that the home reloader, without the benefit of laboratory equipment, must never substitute propellants based on burning rate charts. We found that some powders "flip-flop" their published burning rate positions depending on the cartridge and the pressure level.

Other variables enter the picture when you're talking about a "real world" gun system. One of the big variables is bullet construction. As you have seen, Speer uses several different manufacturing techniques to build its bullets. This gives reloaders access to different types of terminal performance. However, it also means that each bullet style has a unique effect on pressure depending on how much force is required to propel it down the barrel.

Bearing surface is a major player. It is the amount of the bullet shank that is in direct contact with the bore. Speer's .458" 350-grain Hot-Cor® bullet produced lower pressures than a bullet of another make that, although the same weight, had a much longer bearing surface. Speer TNT® varmint bullets are designed with the minimum bearing surface required to maintain accuracy. As a result, the difference in maximum charge weight between the TNT and other Speer hollow points of similar weight can be significant.

The thickness of the bullet jacket has an effect. Thin jackets are more susceptible to in-bore deformation than thicker ones. Thin jackets are pressed against the bore harder, and can raise pressures. When load data is developed for a cartridge, we test all the Speer bullets of the same weight, and develop the data with the bullet that produced the highest pressure. The rigid rear portion of the Trophy Bonded® Bear Claw® bullet is little affected by in-bore deformation, often allowing higher safe charge weights with a Bear Claw than with a conventional jacketed bullet that weighs less.

Remember that bullets of different makes will give different pressures. The variety of jacket alloys, shapes and manufacturing techniques all contribute to pressure changes. The data in this manual was developed and intended for Speer bullets. The data presented may not give the same pressure and velocities if bullets of another make are used.

Primer changes produce different pressures, too. A load developed with brand "A" will seldom develop the same pressure as one developed with brand "B" even though all other components are the same. Cases from different manufacturers have different internal volumes. All these affect the working pressure of the cartridge. Without testing equipment, the reloader cannot know if these changes are up or down.

We are occasionally asked why we don't show pressures for each load. We leave this information in the file cabinet for a very good reason. Some reloaders look at a pressure value and think, "This load is 3000 CUP below the published pressure limit. I can add another grain of powder and be right at the limit."

This is a very bad assumption! It may be that a

The case on the left clearly shows high pressure.

grain more would really be "right at the limit," but it could just as easily produce excessive pressure. In the load development for this manual, we found many instances where adding just one more grain did exactly that—the pressure went well over maximum. Not every cartridge or propellant produces this effect, but lacking standard test equipment, the hobby reloader doesn't know. It cannot be assumed or predicted without accurate lab testing.

Here are some commonly assumed pressure relationships:

- An increase in bullet weight increases pressure, *but not always.*
- A thin bullet jacket causes higher pressure than a thick one, *but not always.*
- A long bearing surface causes higher pressure than a shorter surface, *but not always.*
- Changing from a standard primer to a magnum primer increases pressure, *but not always.*

We could go on with this list, but won't. Look at the last phrase of each of the assumptions. It reads *"...but not always."* This should tell you that assumptions may be wrong. It is for this reason that you may see loads in this and other manuals that don't "track" as bullet weights or types change in the same cartridge.

All of this reinforces two points we've deliberately made in several places in this book:

- Always follow published load data.
- Always begin with the starting loads and work up in small increments toward the maximum, watching for pressure indications at each step.

Safety in Reloading

Reloading is a safe and enjoyable hobby. It requires no special skills beyond the ability to read, understand and follow instructions. Like any human endeavor, reloading has certain safety guidelines that must be followed. By understanding the potential hazards and following well-established guidelines and procedures, the average shooter can satisfy his lifetime need for quality ammunition and never suffer any injury or property damage.

Reloading Safety Rules

WARNING: *Failure to read, observe and practice the following safety rules and guidelines can result in serious personal injury and/or property damage. It is YOUR responsibility—and yours alone—to become familiar with your firearm, the cartridge for which it is chambered, and the components the cartridge requires. That responsibility extends to understanding your firearm and knowing that it is in safe operating condition. Your personal shooting habits must put safety first. Accept this responsibility before using a firearm or reloading ammunition for it.*

General

Reload ammunition only when you can give your full and undivided attention. Allow sufficient time to load ammunition so that you don't rush. Loading at a consistent and leisurely pace is a key part of safe reloading. Never reload while watching television or engaged in conversation. Distraction can lead to serious accidents. Limit your visitors; if they want to talk, stop loading.

Set up your reloading operations in a quiet area where you will not be interrupted. Keep small children out of the loading area, locking the room if necessary. Use your parental discretion with older children who wish to observe and learn. As the old song says, "teach your children well."

Never attempt to reload while under the influence of alcohol or medications. Do not reload when fatigued or ill.

Thoroughly read and understand equipment instructions before using the equipment. All manufacturers of reloading equipment furnish thorough instructions covering the safe operation of their equipment. If you do not have instructions, contact the equipment manufacturer to request a copy before attempting to load ammunition. If there is something you don't understand, ASK THE MANUFACTURER—most have toll-free numbers and/or websites.

Wear approved safety glasses during all reloading operations and while shooting. This is standard practice for any shop, not just reloading rooms. Eye protection reduces the risk of eye injury from flying particles should a reloading mishap occur. Provide safety glasses to others you authorize to be in the loading area. Other than your brain, safety glasses are the most important part of safe shooting and reloading.

Keep your loading area clean and organized. Store all components in their proper places and keep tools clean. Clean up any spilled propellants or primers promptly and completely. Limit the components on your loading bench to just those needed for assembling one load type.

Keep complete records of your reloading activities and load information. Don't trust your memory. Some reloaders use a logbook to track which loads were assembled on a particular day. This system also makes it easy to watch your inventory of components.

Accurately label all ammunition containers. Never try to "guess" at the identity of reloads. Make certain every container of reloads is immediately and properly labeled. Each box of Speer bullets comes with adhesive labels that can be attached to ammo boxes for positive load identification. If in doubt, don't shoot it!

Powder and Primers

Store primers and powder away from heat, open flames and sources of electricity. Do not smoke in your reloading area. Even after powder and primers are stored away, traces of flammable material may remain on equipment, work surfaces, or the floor.

Keep propellant powders only in their original, approved containers with all factory labeling information intact. Do not use any propellant unless its identity is positively known. Scrap any propellant for which you do not have positive, written identification. Purchase propellants only from reputable sources and avoid powders that have been transferred from their original containers or relabeled. Too many fine firearms have been destroyed by propellants sold in a paper bag. Scrap any propellants that become mixed or contaminated.

Keep no more than one canister of propellant on the loading bench at a time to avoid mixing powders. A good layout for the loading area is to have all propellants stored away from the bench except for the one being used. If you move powder from the original canister to another container such as a powder measure, be sure to return the unused portion to the original container immediately after that stage of loading is completed. The longer you delay this important step increases the risk that you lose the identity of that propellant sample. It's a good idea to temporarily attach a sticky note to the outside of the powder measure to clearly show the powder type in use.

Carefully read and follow published load recommendations. Plan your load before you assemble it. Before loading, verify that the data you have before you is for the cartridge you are loading. It is easy to have a reloading manual open to the 300 Weatherby Magnum data instead of the 300 Winchester Magnum.

Never attempt to reload without a reliable powder scale designed for reloading. Even when using an adjustable powder measure, it is absolutely mandatory to use a reloading scale to insure accurate settings. Never guess at a powder weight.

All scales, whether mechanical or electronic, can be affected by drafts. Locate the scale away from vents or open windows. If drafts prove hard to control, a simple windscreen can be made from a cardboard box and placed around the scale.

Make sure the scale is placed on a level surface. Check the zero adjustment before each loading session or whenever the scale is moved to another location. Verify the accuracy of the scale with an RCBS® Scale Weight Check Set once a month or whenever the scale is cleaned, moved or jostled.

Clean the scale often; even small amounts of dust in the bearings of a mechanical scale can result in incorrect readings. Use a soft, non-static brush to remove dust from the bearings.

Do not use any mechanical scale within three (3) feet of a fluorescent light. Under certain conditions, the electro-magnetic field generated by these lights can interfere with the scale's magnetic damping devices, causing spurious readings.

Scales made for other purposes such as kitchen or postal scales must never be used to reload ammunition. They are likely built in weight units not used in reloading. To use the data in this manual, you need a reloading scale that reads in grains (avoirdupois), the standard weight unit for the U.S. ammunition industry. RCBS scales are built to these standards.

Store primers only in their original containers for safety and to insure proper identification. Primer packaging is carefully designed to provide primers with maximum protection from heat or impact. Promptly return unused primers to their original package.

Never store primers in a bulk container. Loose primers randomly oriented in a can, jar, or containers other than the original package can be very hazardous should they detonate. This can cause severe injury and/or property damage.

Never apply excessive force when seating primers. If a primer seems unusually difficult to seat, CEASE LOADING OPERATIONS IMMEDIATELY; do not resume until you determine and correct the cause of the problem.

Never attempt to use primers whose identity is unknown. Unknown primers must be scrapped. Disposal of live primers must be done in accordance with applicable ordinances and regulations in your area. Testing has revealed that soaking primers in oil only desensitizes them to impact by raising the ignition temperature of the chemical mix. This prevents them from firing upon impact, but oil-soaked primers may still detonate if subjected to high temperature such as in a fire.

Primer Tubes

These are commonly used in progressive reloading equipment, or to speed up single-stage reloading. They have special safety requirements.

Never store primers in priming tubes. Exposure to vibration can eventually dislodge some small amount of priming mix from the cups. This is called *dusting* and it can accumulate on the interior walls of the tube increasing the chance of an accident. Use care in filling and handling loaded tubes. Dropping a tube, even if only partially loaded, can result in an explosion.

Periodically check tubes for primer residue. If found, do not use them until they have been cleaned. Look through the tube; residue often appears as rings on the inner surface. Remove the residue by holding tubes under water and gently brushing with a plastic brush, a long pipe cleaner, or small cleaning patch attached to a wire. Make sure cleaned tubes are completely dry before using. Never apply oil to primer tubes because it can contaminate primers or leave a sticky residue that will retain primer dust.

When filling primer tubes, apply no more than five (5) pounds of force to insert primers. You can gauge insertion force by placing the primer tray on a bathroom scale and watching the dial as you press the tube over the primers. If more than five pounds of force is required to insert primers, examine tubes for damage and replace if necessary.

Replace—don't repair—damaged primer tubes. Your repairs may make matters worse and increase the risk of an accident.

Never use a primer feed tube of one make with reloading equipment of a different make. This is an extremely hazardous practice. Even though tubes may appear similar in size, any mismatch of tube and press may cause incorrect primer feeding with the risk of detonating primers. Never attempt to build and use homemade tubes for the same reason.

Safety with Inertial Bullet Pullers

These devices are basically hollow hammers that allow the reloader to disassemble any "mistakes" to salvage components. You place a cartridge in the hollow cavity and lock it in place. Then you strike the puller against a sturdy surface. The case stops but inertial forces (thus the tool's name) cause the heavy bullet to move forward and eventually exit the case. The bullet and propellant are caught in the hollow cavity for recovery.

It is the "strike against a sturdy surface" part that gets some people in trouble. Never try to pull a bullet with one massive blow. Several light blows do the job better with no damage to the bullet, the tool, or your well-being.

Please heed these safety rules for inertial bullet pullers:

- **Always** use short, light blows rather than one massive one.
- **Never** use excessive force to pull bullets.
- **Never** put a rimfire case in an inertial puller. The case holder used on most pullers can pinch the rim and discharge the cartridge.
- **Never** attempt to disassemble a black powder cartridge with an inertial tool.
- **Never** use an inertial tool to pull bullets with high primers. Under certain conditions, the primer cup can suddenly shift to the bottom of the primer pocket and ignite the cartridge.
- **Never** use any tool to pull bullets that you cannot positively identify. This is especially important with military surplus ammo, where explosive or incendiary bullets may exist.
- **Always** wear safety glasses when pulling bullets, just as in any other stage of reloading.

Progressive Reloading Equipment

Progressive reloading equipment has automated features that require more attention and care than do single-stage presses. Before using a progressive reloader, read chapter 10, "Automating the Reloading Process." Safety information for these specialized machines is there.

Loading Data

NOTICE: *The reloading information in this manual is for SPEER bullets. Substituting bullets of other makes may cause excessive pressures. These loads were developed using current standards, equipment and components. They supersede, replace, and make obsolete any reloading data previously published by Speer, Omark Industries, or Blount International, Inc.*

Most of the loads shown in this manual were developed using industry standard pressure testing equipment and techniques. Maximum loads shown do not exceed published industry pressures unless noted otherwise. Certain older cartridges whose pressure limits were originally set relatively low have seen a new popularity because of their reintroduction in modern, strong firearms. Examples are the 6.5x55mm Mauser, 7mm Mauser, 32-20 Winchester, 45-70 and 45 Colt. In these cases the reloading data is clearly identified as being only for modern firearms and the acceptable loading practices for older firearms are specifically discussed.

Because no industry pressure standards exist for wildcat and proprietary cartridges, recommended loads were developed using the technique of monitoring case head expansion. It is especially important to begin with the start load when preparing ammunition for non-standard cartridges.

Never start with a maximum load. Always begin with the minimum charge shown for a bullet/propellant combination. Work up in small increments but do not exceed the listed maximum, carefully watching for any signs of excessive pressure at each step. Even though our maximum loads are within industry specifications, they may function improperly or exhibit pressure signs in a particular firearm, especially a custom or foreign model having non-standard chamber or bore dimensions.

Manufacturers of propellants strive to make every lot uniform when compared with prior lots of the same powder. However, some minor differences do occur. This is another reason to start low and work up toward the maximum. The powder lot that Speer used to develop the data shown is unlikely the same as your lot.

Use only light to moderate loads until your experience increases. New reloaders need a little time to grow accustomed to their equipment and reloading operations. Avoiding maximum loads during this learning period insures an extra safety margin.

Only use lab-tested load data. Reloading manuals like this one are basically "recipe books" for handloaders. However, unlike a cookbook, a reloading manual is not intended to be a "jumping-off point" for wild experimentation. The component combinations shown in loading manuals have been carefully selected and tested for compatibility with the cartridge being reloaded. Going outside these recommendations is an invitation to disaster!

We receive calls and letters asking, "Isn't this data really conservative? Can't I go higher?" The answer to both is emphatically "NO!" The maximum loads are just that—maximum! Do not exceed these levels under any circumstance.

Never mix propellants. To do so is the height of folly! Blending powders to get a particular performance level is extremely hazardous. Stick with standard commercial propellants.

Always reduce loads when changing components. Changing components can affect pressure. First try to match our recipes as closely as possible. If that is not possible and you need to change part of the combination—a different brand of cartridge case, for example—reduce the load to our start load and work back up in steps.

And remember this: Speer makes hundreds of different bullets. We do not have the time to test all the other makes of bullets on the market. The loads published here were developed with SPEER bullets. Bullets of other makes may not produce the same pressures and velocities. Yes, in the past, bullets were all quite similar, but today's hi-tech designs differ considerably by make. When you put a Ford piston in a Chevy engine, you're on your own. Same with reloading—don't call us for data for a bullet that doesn't say SPEER on the box.

Avoid excessive load reduction with slow-burning rifle powders. Over the years, reports have circulated that severely reduced charges of slow-burning rifle powders have caused pressures high enough to damage or even destroy a rifle. Do not load lighter than the start load shown. See the chapter "Modern Cartridges and Their Components" for additional information on this subject.

Static Electricity and the Reloader

Static electricity is a high-voltage, low-current form of energy that builds on surfaces due to friction. For the reloader, static charges can be hazardous under certain conditions.

Of the components we use, primers are most sensitive to static charges. The energy is enough to ignite primer dust in and around priming tools. If you scuff your feet on carpet and then touch a priming tube, the dust can ignite and propagate to all the primers in the tube. The result is a serious explosion. This is the reason to keep those tubes clean!

Static charges prefer low-humidity environments. If you live in an area where low humidity is a common condition, you have probably experienced static effect in other areas. Your heating/cooling system probably dries the air so much that you notice a "shock" when you touch a doorknob. If so, you should take some simple precautions:

Use a humidifier. This raises the relative humidity, reducing static build up. A humidifier can either be a portable unit that you place in your shop or a house-wide system incorporated into the heating/cooling system.

Avoid carpeted reloading areas. This is the prime cause of static energy accidents. In addition to static charges, carpet can hold spilled powder. That alone can cause a fire if some ignition source comes in contact with the carpet.

Clean the reloading area on a schedule. Good housekeeping is a safety measure. Routine cleaning removes residues of primers and propellants that can react to static energy. Clean hard surface counters and floors with a damp rag or mop.

Use an anti-static product. Hard smooth surfaces like laminate bench tops can be wiped with a laundry product called an anti-static dryer sheet. The sheets also reduce static on plastic powder measure hoppers, scale pans, and powder funnels. If you are unable to eliminate carpeting from the area, use an approved spray anti-static product on the carpet to reduce static charge build-up.

Lead Exposure

There has been a growing concern over the toxic effects of metallic lead. At high exposure levels, lead can cause serious physical impairment. Some individuals are more susceptible than others. One person may not discover he has lead poisoning until he has a routine blood test; another may become ill before tests find the problem.

Because certain reloading components must contain lead or lead compounds, it is possible to be exposed during reloading. Primers and bullets contain lead, and lead residue is present in fired cartridge cases. Lead can enter the body in several ways, but the most likely avenues are through the nose and mouth. With very simple precautions, the reloader can avoid the hazards of lead exposure.

Observe good hygiene. Wash hands thoroughly with soap as soon as you finish loading or shooting.

Never eat or drink while reloading or shooting. Residue containing lead can get on your hands. Keep your hands away from your nose and mouth while loading. Eating anything that qualifies as "finger food" means you are ingesting lead.

Avoid breathing dust in the reloading area. Wear a dust mask when working with dry case cleaning media. Lead residue from fired cases builds up in the media with use. When pouring the media in and out of a case cleaner, use a mask to avoid any dust that might escape. Change out your media often to reduce lead accumulation.

Keep the loading area clean. Regular cleaning will prevent the build-up of residues including those containing lead. Clean bench surfaces with a damp cloth. If the area has a hard-surface floor (which it should be), damp mopping is preferable to vacuuming.

Summary

Following these guidelines will help insure that your reloading experiences are always safe. Don't let these safety rules scare you—observing them is simple. Integrate them as part of your reloading routine from the start and you will find that they are not oppressive, and you can enjoy your hobby to the maximum.

chapter 7

From the Loading Bench to the Range:
A Step-by-Step Guide to Reloading Rifle Cartridges

In this chapter, we look at the basic and optional equipment needed for reloading. Then we will explore the steps of loading rifle ammo, starting at the loading bench and ending at the range.

Even if you plan to only reload handgun cartridges, read this rifle information first. There are more similarities than differences and most of the handloading basics are here. chapter 15 deals with specific techniques and equipment used for loading handgun cartridges.

• • • • •

Reloading requires an initial investment in the tools and related equipment needed to safely assemble ammunition. The *minimum* equipment items you must have include:

A quality reloading manual—if you're reading this, you've already made the most important purchase. Safe reloading can be accomplished only after reading and understanding appropriate instructional materials and then using loading data developed in laboratories employing standardized test methods. Never guess at a powder charge. Use only published load data from a reputable reloading component or equipment manufacturer.

A place to load—Set up your reloading equipment in a reasonably quiet area that's well lit and comfortable where you can give your undivided attention. An unheated garage workshop can get very cold in winter and, in humid climates, tools and equipment can rust. For safety, choose a place that can be secured to prevent others—especially children—from tampering with your equipment and components.

A reloading press—the press provides the mechanical advantage required to recondition the cartridge case. The press also holds the next two equipment items—the *reloading dies* and *shell holder*—in perfect alignment. RCBS® makes four single-stage presses from the compact Partner™ press to the powerful Rock Chucker™ Supreme. All RCBS presses include the hardware needed to prime cases. Reloading presses are designed expressly for reloading ammunition and you should never attempt to cut corners by using other tools such as an arbor press or a bench vise as substitutes.

A place to mount the reloading press—although there are some hand-held loading tools on the market, the bench press provides maximum power and precision for full-length resizing and must be firmly mounted for safe and easy use.

Clamping a press directly to a tabletop is an unsafe and unacceptable mounting technique. Clamps can work loose and allow the press to move under pressure. Worse yet, the heavy press can fall to the floor and severely injure your feet and legs.

A sturdy workbench is best. It need not be elaborate and lighter benches can be weighted with bullets or other heavy objects to steady them. The National Reloading Manufacturers Association (NRMA, 1 Centerpoint Drive, Suite 300, Lake Oswego, OR 97035; www.reload-nrma.com) sells plans for an excellent, heavy-duty reloading bench.

NRMA reloading bench; see text for ordering plans

RCBS offers the Accessory Base Plate-2 that is predrilled to accept most RCBS presses and accessories. These heavy metal plates attach to the bench top and allow quick changing of tools. They are especially useful where bench top space is at a premium. If you don't use these base plates, presses should be attached to the bench top with bolts, not wood screws. Wood screws can pull out under heavy loads. Large presses like the RCBS Rock Chucker™ Supreme can be attached with 5/16-inch carriage bolts.

RCBS Accessory Base Plate

If a permanent setup is not possible due to space limitations, portable loading benches are a good alternative. Typically, they include a built-in seat so your weight steadies the workstation. Ready-made portable benches are available from several sources or you can build one from scrap lumber. Most designs can be folded or taken apart for storage in a closet or under a bed.

Reloading dies—normally, you will need only one press to reload metallic ammunition. However, you will need a different set of loading dies for each cartridge that you wish to load. Don't cut corners by trying to load a cartridge in a set of dies intended for another cartridge. Doing so can produce poor-quality ammunition and create a serious safety hazard.

Die sets for bottleneck rifle cartridges like the 30-06 consist of two dies. The sizing die reshapes the brass case to permit easy chambering in standard rifles. This die also insures the case neck is the proper diameter to grip the bullet and ejects the spent primer. The seater die aligns the bullet with the case and pushes it to the desired depth in the case neck. If required, the seater die will crimp the case mouth into the bullet's crimp groove for a firmer grip.

Die sets for straight or straight-taper cases (e.g., the 45-70 and most handgun cartridges) have three dies. The sizing die returns the case body to its proper dimensions. The expander die forms the case mouth to proper size and flares it slightly to make bullet seating easier. The seater die functions just as it does in a bottleneck set with the option of crimping the case mouth if needed.

Like presses, die sets are available with a wide range of features. RCBS standard dies are available in a wide selection of calibers and provide very high quality at a reasonable price. Gold Medal Match Series dies offer interchangeable neck sizing inserts to allow fine-tuning of the case neck grip for precision shooting. The seater die has a free-floating bullet guide with micrometer-type seating depth adjustment. RCBS Competition Dies are premium dies with special features including a precision-alignment bullet seater with a micrometer-type depth adjustment. Cowboy Dies are specially dimensioned to precisely prepare the cases for loading lead bullets required in Cowboy Action Shooting.

Reloading dies, regardless of make or model, are the precision tools that can make your handloaded ammunition perform better than factory ammunition. They should be treated with the same care you would give a fine firearm.

Most modern rifle/pistol dies have the standard 7/8-14 thread used by the reloading industry. Larger die diameters up to 1½ inch may be required in special applications like the 50-caliber BMG cartridge and some large English cartridges. If you plan to load one of these, make sure your press has the ability to handle larger diameter dies. Several RCBS presses have removable die bushings for larger specialty dies.

Shell holder—the shell holder attaches to the ram of the loading press and holds the rim of the cartridge to accurately align the case with the reloading die. Most modern loading presses accept interchangeable shell holders. RCBS shell holders are available in standard rim configurations for all popular cartridges. Many shell holders can be used for more than one cartridge. The data pages in this manual list the RCBS shell holder needed for each cartridge.

Industry standards control the dimensional relation of the shell holder to the sizer die. Even so, the best way to get uniform and safe headspacing with bottleneck cartridges is to use dies and shell holders of the same make.

Powder scale—a reliable and accurate scale is *absolutely mandatory* for safe reloading. A reloading scale must be calibrated in *grains* (1 ounce = 437.5 grains) and be accurate to ±0.1 grain. Reloading scales are furnished with a special pan to facilitate pouring propellant into the case. To avoid any confusion, buy a scale sold by one of the reloading companies.

Some novice reloaders have suffered accidents when trying to use a scale intended for another purpose that is calibrated for grams or ounces. Read and fully under-

Accurate powder weighing is crucial to consistent and safe handloading. (RCBS® ChargeMaster® Combo)

stand the operating instructions for your reloading scale, especially those pertaining to reading and adjusting the poises on mechanical scales. Misreading a scale setting can cause accidents. RCBS markets both mechanical scales and electronic scales specifically designed for reloading.

Case lube and pad—rifle cases must be lubricated before resizing. If not, they will stick in the die and stop the reloading process. A lube pad looks like an ink pad. When a case is rolled on the pad's porous surface, the proper amount of lubricant is applied. Case lube can be applied by hand but may not be uniform. A lube pad is among the least expensive reloading gadgets so why not make things easy on yourself?

There are many materials that are lubricants. Use only those formulated for reloading when preparing cases for sizing. RCBS sells the Case Lube Kit that includes lubricant, pad and brushes for cleaning and lubricating the inside of the case neck. RCBS Case Lube 2 is water-soluble for easy cleanup. For ease of application, there is RCBS Case Slick®, a spray lubricant that delivers very low sizing effort. Owners of progressive presses should consider the excellent RCBS Lube Die that makes automated loading a cleaner experience.

Powder funnel—a powder funnel will save a lot of time and aggravation when pouring propellant from the scale pan to the cartridge case. Funnels designed especially for reloading are available from RCBS and other reloading manufacturers. A key feature of powder funnels is a cupped spout that centers the funnel on the case mouth to eliminate spillage. The RCBS Quick Change Powder Funnel includes inserts for various neck diameters plus a long drop tube to facilitate loading large propellant charges.

Loading block—this item holds cases neatly in rows for easier processing. Proper use of a loading block minimizes the chance of a double charge, minimizes powder spillage and makes inspection easier. The RCBS Universal Case Loading Block handles the new, larger diameter rifle cases as well as short handgun cases.

Case length gauge—This tool measures the various dimensions of a cartridge. It helps you more accurately adjust your loading dies, determine correct cartridge case length, check bullet diameter and measure cartridge overall length.

RCBS® Accessory Kit.

The most convenient case length tool is a *caliper,* either a digital or dial type. Calipers for reloading should be calibrated in inches and be accurate to at least ±0.001 inch. RCBS markets a mechanical Stainless Steel Dial Caliper and an electronic Digital Caliber. Both are precision measuring devices with six-inch capacities. Both digital and dial calipers are superior to older vernier models because they reduce the chance of misreading the results.

· · · · ·

With this basic equipment you are ready to load quality ammunition. However, there are other accessories that can speed up the operation and add convenience.

Powder Measure—a powder measure meters the same volume of propellant time after time, speeding up the propellant charging operation. Measures are available in both fixed cavity and adjustable cavity designs. The RCBS Little Dandy® is a fixed-cavity design primarily intended for handgun use. Little Dandy rotors come predrilled to dispense different volumes of propellant. To change the charge weight, a different rotor is selected. It comes with a chart showing the nominal powder charge for each rotor for a variety of popular propellants.

Adjustable-cavity powder measures are more versatile. The RCBS Quick Change™ and Uniflow® powder measures have adjustable chambers that will consistently meter small propellant charges for handguns to heavy charge weights for rifles. The repeatability of any powder measure is equally dependent on the type of propellant and the operator's technique. Fine-grained ball powders dispense from adjustable powder measures with little or no variation in weight. Large-grained, cylindrical powders may meter less uniformly depending on the shape of the metering cavity in the measure. All RCBS powder measures use a steel-on-steel contact surface and are precision-machined ensuring uniform charges, smooth operation and long life expectancy.

Any mechanical powder measure requires the human factor to be consistent. We strongly encourage new reloaders to do some "dry runs" before using their new measure to charge ammunition. Dispensing and weighing charges will help you develop a style that delivers consistent charges.

For the advanced reloader, an electronic powder measure is a must-have upgrade. The RCBS ChargeMaster Combo combines an electronic dispenser with an electronic scale. All you need to do is to calibrate the unit, enter the desired charge weight on the keypad, and press a button. The unit automatically dispenses and weighs the correct charge.

> **NOTE:** *A mechanical powder measure must be ADJUSTED and the charges verified using an accurate reloading scale. The measure does not replace the scale; it simply makes case charging faster.*

Case trimmer—A case trimmer is a miniature lathe-like device used to accurately trim your cases to a uniform length. Trimming the mouth reduces the overall case length to the proper dimension. New cases from the same lot can vary in length and the wise reloader will trim all new cases to a consistent length. If you are shooting a high-capacity bottleneck rifle cartridge, consider buying a trimmer sooner rather than later. The cases can lengthen quickly and exceed the length of your rifle's chamber causing hard chambering and high pressures.

*RCBS Trim Pro®
power case trimmer*

The RCBS Trim Pro® system represents the ultimate in trimmer evolution. Cases can be quickly moved in and out because of the special quick-change case holder system that replaces the awkward collet holders employed by other trimmers. Both coarse and fine adjustment collars ensure precise length control that's accurate case after case. Trim Pro comes in a standard, manually-driven model and a powered version for high-volume trimming.

Proper case length can also be obtained with a *trim die*. Install the trim die in the press and adjust it like a sizer die. Run a lubed case into the die; if it is too long the mouth will protrude above the top of the die. The excess is removed with a fine-cut file. The top surface of the die is hardened to prevent the file from damaging it. Like most reloading dies, trim dies are cartridge-specific.

Off-press priming— Although you can prime cases on the reloading press, some reloaders choose to perform this operation with separate equipment. The reasons can vary from wanting a better "feel" of the primer entering the case to simply speeding up the process. RCBS offers several off-press priming accessories. The RCBS Universal Hand Priming Tool is a tray-fed, hand-held unit that can be used almost anywhere you want to prime cases. The universal shell holder accepts cases from 32 Auto to 45-70. It also has an important safety feature: an integral gate that separates the primer supply from the insertion operation.

APS® priming is a unique RCBS priming development. CCI® APS primers are packaged in plastic strips that feed into the APS priming tool that makes spilled and contaminated primers a thing of the past. Strips can be linked together for continuous feeding. The RCBS Pro 2000® progressive press and the Piggyback™-3 and -4 progressive conversion units are configured for APS priming. Three stand-alone priming tools are also APS-compatible, including the popular APS Hand Priming Tool with a universal shell holder. Contact RCBS (800-533-5000 or www.rcbs.com) for additional information on this and other off-press priming systems.

APS® Bench Mounted Priming Tool from RCBS

Starting the Reloading Process

You've been to your local gun shop and now have all the components, tools and equipment you need to start loading for that favorite rifle. It's time to look at the steps that will produce your handloaded ammunition. Note that some steps are labeled "optional." Everything else is a "MUST DO!" operation.

Step One—Read the Instructions

Read the equipment instructions and load data manuals carefully and completely. It is important to understand how your hardware works. Time invested in study now will help avoid headaches and safety hazards later. If you fail to understand the instructions, get help. Most equipment makers have toll-free phone numbers or useful tutorials on their websites. RCBS tech support is at 800-533-5000 and on the Internet at www.rcbs.com. Use these resources to insure that you fully understand you equipment before attempting to load.

Understanding your firearm is as critical as understanding the reloading equipment and processes. It is your responsibility, and yours alone, to know your firearm and its characteristics. It is vitally important to know what is "normal" based on firing factory ammunition in order to recognize something abnormal if you have a problem with your handloads.

Step Two—Case Cleaning (optional)

Fired cases can get very dirty. In addition to powder and primer residues, the case can pick up residual oils left in the firearm. When the case falls to the ground it picks up dirt. Cases can become stained or darken with age. Stains won't keep a cartridge from shooting accurately. However, most reloaders take pride in their hobby and usually

Spent primers will corrode and break during decapping if not removed prior to washing the cases.

want the product of their labors to look good. On the other hand, extremely dirty cases will eventually damage loading dies and firearms and should be cleaned before proceeding. Clean cases are also easier to inspect than dirty ones. Cases can be cleaned in two ways—wet or dry.

Wet cleaning involves giving the cases a bath. Cases should be deprimed before wet cleaning to insure thorough drying. The RCBS Universal Decapping Die removes primers without performing any other operations on the case. If cases are washed with primers still in place, trapped moisture can cause spent primers to corrode with the potential for serious decapping problems later.

Washing can be as simple as placing deprimed cases in a bucket and rinsing them with clear, hot water. Dirtier cases may require adding soap. A small quantity of liquid dish washing detergent will help speed cleaning. RCBS sells an excellent Liquid Case Cleaner that removes most stains and rinses cleanly.

For more aggressive washing and stain removal, the RCBS Sidewinder™ Case Tumbler can be used for either wet or dry cleaning. Its large drum holds up to 150 30-06 cases and it comes with Liquid Case Cleaner concentrate for effective case cleaning.

RCBS Sidewinder™ Case Tumbler

Washed cases must be completely dry before reloading. Cases can be placed in the sun or on a stationary rack available for many brands of clothes dryers. About 45 minutes with the dryer set on high heat will dry them nicely. Cases should never be dried in a kitchen oven. Even at the lowest settings, the temperature may reach levels that could dangerously weaken brass.

Dry cleaning of cases is accomplished by the action of mild polishing media that is vibrated or tumbled against the cases. Vibratory cleaners consist of a large bowl attached to a motor-driven base and are available from RCBS. The cases and cleaning media are placed in the bowl and the unit is allowed to run for several hours. Vibratory case cleaners should never be used for wet cleaning unless so specified by the manufacturer.

Tumbling cases means they are placed in a rotating drum that causes the cases and media to fall against and rub each other, providing the friction needed to remove stains and dirt. Tumbling can be performed in the RCBS Sidewinder.

RCBS offers two different types of dry media for case cleaning. Ground walnut hull media charged with a red oxide cleaning agent is best for heavily stained cases. Ground corn cob media is excellent for clean-

RCBS Vibratory Case Cleaner

ing less dirty cases and gives a higher degree of polish. Corn cob media comes with white oxide compound in a separate packet so you can add as much as you need. Plain (untreated) cob is an excellent light cleaning agent for cases that are not very dirty, and will remove case lubricants that are not water-soluble.

Regardless of how you choose to clean cases, the time and effort expended will insure longer case and die life. See the RCBS website for an excellent array of case preparation accessories.

Step Three—Case Inspection

First, individually inspect the cases for obvious defects. If using military surplus cases, this is a good time to run a magnet through them to sort out any steel cases. If you are uncertain of the "pedigree" of the cases, make sure they are Boxer—not Berdan—primed. Shine a strong light into the case mouth and look at the web area. Boxer-primed cases have a single, centered flash hole. Berdan-primed cases normally have two very small flash holes located on either side of center. Unless you have the special depriming equipment to handle Berdan cases, you are better off to discard them.

Any cases with the following defects should be segregated or discarded:

◆ **Mixed calibers**— it is quite easy to get a 270 Winchester case mixed in with 30-06 cases as they are very similar in size and shape. Having the wrong case on the bench will disrupt the loading process and could result in an unsafe cartridge if it were somehow reloaded.

Examples of split case necks.

◆ **Split case mouths.**

◆ **Cracks, splits or holes.**

◆ **Crushed cases**— even though some may look salvageable, the damage may have weakened the case internally and the flaws may not show until the case is fired. Discard any crushed cases.

◆ **Pitted or corroded cases**— cases that have been stored in leather belt loops or exposed to a corrosive environment will be weakened and should never be reloaded.

◆ **Excessive case bulges**— some bulging is normal in fired cases, but you will occasionally find one that seems out of the ordinary. Excessive bulging, especially just above the case head, indicates potential weakening of the case. When resized, the case may be too thin in this critical area and could fail on the next firing. Watch for narrow bright rings close to the web of the case. A certain amount of swelling is normal at this point. However, bright rings associated with normal expansion are generally wider than the narrow bands that indicate excessive stretching. Excessive headspace, excessive

Examples of case body defects.

resizing and high-pressure loads can cause cases to fail at this point.

If you are unsure of the condition of a case, make a probe from a short length of stiff wire with the tip bent about 45 degrees and use it to "feel" the inside of the case above the web. A shallow depression of ridge indicates thinning and a potential for failure. Better yet, use the *case probe* on the RCBS CaseMaster® gauging tool to examine for thinning. If this condition is detected in once-fired factory cases, you should have the rifle's headspace checked by a competent gunsmith. See the next chapter, "Advanced Techniques" for additional information.

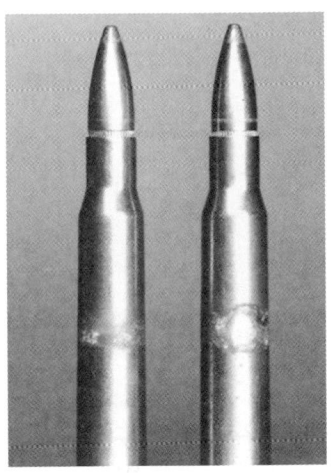

Badly corroded cases must be scrapped.

◆ **Cases with damaged rims**—damaged rims can cause a case to stick in the shell holder or the cartridge may fail to chamber or extract properly in your rifle. Minor rims burrs can be removed using a fine-cut file.

Refer to the photo examples shown here of common case defects. When you find a defective case, crush it with pliers to make sure it doesn't get mixed with good cases and reloaded.

Case thinning due to excessive sizing.

Step Four—Case Lubrication

Cartridge cases *must be lubricated before resizing* to prevent sticking in the sizing die. The only exception is when you size straight-wall or straight-taper handgun cartridges with a carbide sizer die.

For single-stage loading, use a case lube pad with a good reloading lubricant like RCBS Case Lube-2. Other shop lubricants may not work properly under the heavy contact stresses of sizing. Place about a half-teaspoon of lube on the pad and rub it in evenly over the surface of the pad. Allow a few minutes for the lube to soak in.

> **Tech Tip:** *Just bought a new case lube pad? Charge it with lube as soon as you get home, not five minutes before you need it for loading. New pads take longer for the lube to distribute evenly. Overnight is about the right amount of time to condition a new pad.*

Using a pad to lubricate cases before sizing. Always choose a lubricant designed for reloading.

Place about five inspected cases on the pad and lightly roll them so each case has a thin film of lube completely around the body. Avoid getting lube on the shoulder or neck of bottleneck cases. Excess lube trapped at this point can cause hydraulic dents in the case shoulder.

The inside of the case neck can accumulate propellant residue that can make neck expansion and bullet seating more difficult. The inside of the case necks can be lubricated by either lightly dragging the open end of the case across the pad or by rolling a case neck brush on the pad and brushing the inside of the neck. Avoid excessive lube in the neck area. Too much lube can contaminate the propellant powder later. Often, simply dry-brushing the necks is sufficient to let them pass easily over the expander ball.

RCBS also makes Case Slick®, a spray lubricant that greatly reduces sizing forces yet can be applied sparingly. A little Case Slick will go a long way. One of the best ways to apply a spray lube is to place the cases in a large plastic bag. Puff a small amount of spray lube into the bag, aiming at the bag's walls, and roll the bag between your hands. Each case gets just the right amount.

Case lube must be removed before firing the cartridges. Cleaning the lube from the cases immediately after sizing is excellent insurance against getting oil in primers and propellants later in the loading operation. Water-soluble lubes can be removed with a damp cloth. Wiping with a dry cloth can remove other lubes, but tumbling the cases in plain corncob media will remove the lubricant plus gives the cases a nice finish.

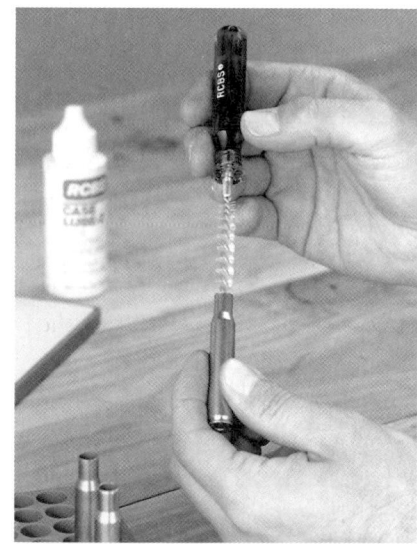

Using the RCBS Neck Brush to lubricate case neck.

Step Five—Full-length Case Sizing and Neck Expansion

Resizing returns the case to the proper dimensions to insure reliable chambering and proper grip of the bullet. Sizing dies for bottleneck cartridges are designed to reduce the neck's internal diameter so it is slightly smaller than the bullet diameter. When the case is withdrawn from the die, an *expander ball* mounted on the decapping spindle is pulled through the case neck, setting the correct diameter for bullet seating. Proper adjustment of the sizing die is critical for reloading accurate and safe ammunition.

> **Tech Tip:** *Clean new dies with solvent before using them to remove preservative oils. If the die has a vent hole in the shoulder area, clear it with a wire or small punch. The first case sized in a new die may require more lubricant than used for normal reloading.*

Install the proper shell holder in the press ram and screw the sizing die into the threaded hole in the top of the press. With the ram at the top of its stroke, turn the die until it touches the shell holder. Release the ram slightly and tighten the die one-quarter turn more, then bring the ram back up. You should feel a slight springing when the ram is fully raised against the die. The die is now properly adjusted for full-length resizing. To prevent the setting from changing while reloading, screw the lock ring down until it touches the press body, and tighten the lock ring's setscrew. *NOTE: Carbide sizing dies for handgun cartridges must be adjusted differently—see the section on loading handgun ammunition.*

Remember that most bottleneck cases headspace on the shoulder. With the proper die setting, the shoulder will not be pushed back past its original position. Pushing the shoulder beyond this point will create excessive headspace. Excessive headspace may degrade accuracy and can cause a case failure when the cartridge is fired. Modern dies and shell holders are engineered to prevent this from happening. However, some people insist on modifying the die or shell holder. This creates a dangerous condition. Never attempt to remove metal from either the sizing die or shell holder. For best results, use dies and shell holders made by the same manufacturer.

Cut-away of RCBS Sizer die.

Most sizing dies have a decapping pin that ejects the spent primer during the sizing operation. The pin should be adjusted so that it protrudes beyond the bottom of the sizing die about one-quarter inch.

Sizer die set for full-length sizing (die touches shell holder).

Once the die is adjusted, place a lubricated case in the shell holder and lower the press handle. The leverage of the press forces the fired case into the die and performs the necessary dimensional changes. The fired primer is ejected at the same time.

As you raise the press handle to remove a bottleneck rifle case from the die, you will notice a slight resistance. This is normal; the case neck is passing over the expander ball. After fully lowering the ram, remove the case from the shell holder. Inspect the case to make sure it is free from dents or mouth damage. Set the case aside in a loading block and size the next lubed case.

Sizer die set for neck-sizing (gap between die and shell holder).

Before going to the next operation, be sure to remove the case lube from the cases.

Check the Case Length Now

Resizing affects case length. The best time to check the case length is after sizing. Measure the cases with a caliper and trim any that are over the maximum length to about 0.010" under the maximum. The maximum case length is noted on the drawing for each cartridge in this manual. Case neck growth is common with high-pressure rifle cartridges. Some cases may never grow; in fact, those that headspace on the case mouth may actually become shorter after repeated firings.

Neck Expansion for Straight-Wall Cases

Sizing straight-wall rifle cases requires the same procedure noted above except that neck expansion is not performed in the sizer die. Neck expansion for these cases requires a separate step and an extra die that comes with the die set. This operation also flares the case mouth in straight-wall cases.

Lower the press handle and screw the expander die into the press until the die body lightly touches the shell holder. Adjust the expander plug until a sized case just touches the plug when the ram is fully raised. Lift the handle to lower the ram slightly and screw the plug down one-quarter turn at a time until the case mouth is slightly flared. Avoid excessive flare to avoid premature mouth splits. Using a bullet you intend to load, check that there is just enough flare to keep it from catching on the edge of the case, yet allow it to freely enter the case about one-sixteenth of an inch.

Step Six—Priming

Before handling primers, make sure your hands are free of case lube and other oils. Contaminated primers can cause misfires or erratic ignition.

How primers are inserted depends on the type of press. Some presses like the Rock Chucker have an attached priming arm that swings under the shell holder. Others like the RCBS Ammo Master single-stage use a special ram priming device mounted in the die station. Primers can also be seated in an off-press unit, either bench-mounted or hand-held.

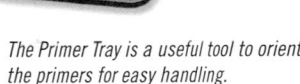

Because priming methods vary with the type of equipment used, carefully read the instructions for your reloading equipment before priming. Regardless of equipment make, there are several universal rules for priming safely and successfully:

The Primer Tray is a useful tool to orient the primers for easy handling.

- Primers must be correctly seated to avoid misfires. "High" primers—those whose anvil legs do not touch the bottom of the pocket—cause about 95 percent of all misfires. CCI primers provide optimum sensitivity when seated .003" to .005" below flush with the anvil legs in contact with the bottom of the pocket. With practice, you will soon recognize how a properly seated primer feels as it is pressed into the pocket.

- Use a slow, even pressure to seat primers. *Never* use a sharp blow. If you feel unexpected resistance, STOP! Carefully remove the case from the shell holder and identify and correct the cause of the problem before proceeding.

- Military surplus cases commonly have crimped-in primers. Before repriming them, be sure that the original crimp is removed completely. The RCBS Primer Pocket Swaging Combo will reform the military primer pocket to one with a smooth, commercial type profile. Failure to remove military primer crimps increases the risk of igniting a primer inadvertently.

- Almost all priming devices have a spring-loaded sleeve around the punch to hold and align the primer. Before priming, make certain that the proper size sleeve and punch is selected. Older reloading equipment may have a cup-shaped primer punch. This type of punch is intended for an obsolete style of primer with a domed base. Unless you have a supply of these older primers, make sure to use a flat primer punch. A punch contoured for domed primers will deform current-production primers and increase the risk of an accident.

♦ Fired cases will have a buildup of primer residue in the bottom of the primer pocket. Excessive residue can make seating the new primer difficult and can cause high primers. This residue can be quickly removed with an RCBS Primer Pocket Brush of the appropriate size.

IMPORTANT Safety Warning!

If you discover a high primer after the cartridge is fully loaded, do not attempt to reseat it. It can ignite and the cartridge will rupture with potentially dangerous results. There is only one way to safely deal with this: pull the bullet and remove the powder charge. Then—and ONLY then—is it safe to reseat the primer.

Step Seven—Charging the Case with Propellant

Proper propellant charging is critical to safe reloading. Never guess at the correct charge weight. Refer to the reloading data furnished by a reputable reloading component or equipment supplier. The loads contained in this manual were developed under laboratory conditions and conform to established pressure limits.

Never start with the maximum listed charge levels. Begin with the listed start load and work the load up in your firearm in small increments. Chances are that you will find an accurate load before reaching the maximum load shown.

Charging must be done only with a reliable and accurate reloading scale. Place the cases to be charged into a loading block. Weigh the desired amount of propellant on the scale and transfer it to a case using a powder funnel. Repeat until all the cases are charged. Before seating bullets, shine a flashlight into *every* case in the loading block to verify the desired powder charge is in each case. All cases should appear to have the same amount of propellant. If you have the slightest doubt about a charge, pour it back into

Use a Loading Block for charging the cases.

the scale pan and verify the weight. *It is critical to charge and inspect all cases before seating bullets.*

Powder Measures

Many reloaders use a powder measure to speed the charging process after a favorite load has been carefully developed and recorded. Most quality measures will meter charges as consistently as you can weigh them. All factory ammunition has metered propellant charges with remarkable charge-to-charge uniformity. Because a powder measure works by volume, it is mandatory that you use a reloading scale to set the measure to throw the desired weight of propellant.

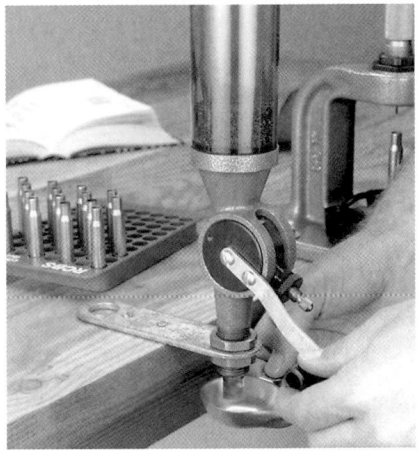

A powder measure like this RCBS Uniflow® permits faster charging of cases.

Pour the proper propellant into the measure's hopper so the hopper is at least half-full. Place the scale pan under the powder measure and operate the handle. Weigh the powder charge and adjust the measure until you reach the proper charge weight. Meter five additional charges to settle the powder and then recheck the weight. Adjust as needed to reach the proper charge weight. Remember that the meter *must be reset* when you change propellant types. Fifty grains of Reloder 19 will not occupy the same volume as a 50-grain charge of Winchester 760.

Always pour more propellant into the hopper than you will need. Many powder measures begin to throw lighter charges if the hopper runs low. For most measures, keeping the level between 1/3 and 2/3 full will ensure consistent weights.

Take a primed case from the loading block, place the mouth in contact with the measure's drop tube and operate the handle. After charging the first case, return it to the loading block at the opposite end from the uncharged cases or, better yet, place the charged case in a second block. Pick up the next empty case and repeat the sequence. Operating the handle with a consistent stroke will insure uniform charge weights. After charging the tenth case, pour the powder back into the scale pan to verify the weight. Continue until all cases are charged.

Large Case Precaution: *The greater the charge weight, the longer it takes to flow from the powder hopper into the metering unit, and from the metering unit to the case. Cycling the handle too fast will stop the powder flow prematurely, resulting in inconsistent and even dangerously low charge weights. A small charge for the tiny 22 Hornet cartridge will drop almost instantaneously while the charge for a 378 Weatherby can take one to two seconds. Allow extra time for a large propellant charge to flow into the case. Develop a rhythm for operating the handle and stick with it.*

Propellant Bridging

Bridging is the "log-jamming" of large propellant granules in the neck of a powder measure and is always a result of inconsistent operation of the measure combined with coarsely granulated propellants. Part of the charge falls into the case but a portion of it remains stuck below the metering unit. When the next case is charged it receives the remainder of the previous charge plus all of another and you have two dangerous cartridges, one with too little powder and another with too much.

You can eliminate bridging by sharply "clicking" the measure handle as you operate it. When you raise the handle, click it against the upper stop. When you lower it, click it against the lower stop. Do this consistently and with a set rhythm.

Bridging can occur in measures with interchangeable spout tips if you leave the 22-caliber tip in place when you start to load a larger case. Be sure that the proper tip is installed before metering charges.

Powder Measures and Maximum Loads

Near-maximum loads should always be weighed. However, you can use a modified procedure combining both metering and weighing that is not as slow as using the scale alone. For near-maximum loads, set the measure to meter about 0.5 grains *under* the desired charge. Throw the charge directly from the powder measure into the scale pan and put the pan on the scale. Use an RCBS Powder Trickler or a small spoon to add a few kernels of powder at a time until the scale shows you have reached the desired charge weight. Using this technique, you have the confidence of

RCBS Powder Trickler allows feeding single granules for accurate charges.

knowing each charge is individually weighed yet the charging goes much faster than when using the scale alone.

Inspect, Inspect, Inspect!

As with any powder charging operation, *look into every case before seating bullets*. Some reloaders have developed the habit of metering a charge into one case and then seating the bullet before going to the next case. This technique is extremely hazardous because it is possible to incorrectly charge and seat a bullet without recognizing that a problem exists. Inspecting all the charged cases in a loading block *before* seating the bullets insures they are uniform and correct.

When using a powder charge that does not fill the case, take extra time in the inspection stage to look for double charges. A strong light source like a penlight will make inspection easier. A double-charge of a fast-burning powder can destroy a fine rifle and injure the shooter or bystanders.

Compressed Powder Charges

Some combinations of powder charges and cases may result in compressing the powder charge when the bullet is seated. This is normal with small, high-pressure cartridges like the 308 Winchester and with many of the larger cases when slow-burning propellants are loaded. Compressed loads in this manual are indicated with the letter "**C**" next to the charge weight.

The new reloader may wonder how he can get so much powder in the case. Slight modifications to the charging technique will help you accomplish this task with minimum effort. Don't dump the entire scale pan at once. Pour the charge slowly onto the upper portion of the funnel while tipping the funnel slightly to one side. This causes the powder to swirl down the funnel, allowing extra time for the charge to settle. This will usually give enough room to easily start the bullet into the case.

You can also facilitate loading compressed charges by using a funnel with a *long drop tube*. Combined with slow pouring, a drop tube allows even more time for the charge to settle. We used long drop tube funnels when developing load data for this manual. The RCBS Quick Change Powder Funnel Kit includes a 4-inch drop tube accessory.

Slow, even pressure on the press handle when seating bullets on compressed charges will prevent damage to the case or bullet. Heavily-compressed charges of fine-grained powders with a boat tail bullet can create problems. A few of the granules can wedge between the tapered bullet heel and the case neck, creating a tiny bulge. In some rifles, this bulge can prevent the cartridge from chambering. If this happens, you must use a different propellant or switch to a flat-base bullet.

Step Eight—Bullet Seating

Before seating a bullet, you need to determine the proper seating depth. The loads listed in this manual show the cartridge overall length (COAL) used by Speer for load development. In most cases, this is under the maximum SAAMI cartridge length specified in industry standards.

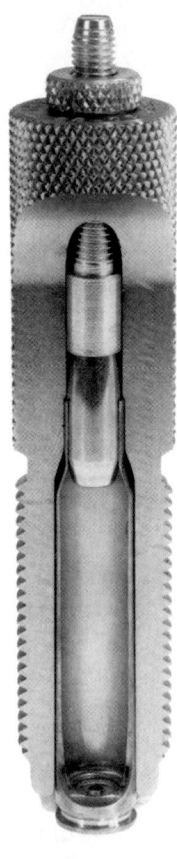

Although the SAAMI maximum COAL should function properly in any factory rifle having the shortest action, your rifle's throat will also affect the COAL. One rifle may have less freebore in the throat than another. Magazine length can also affect the required cartridge length. The bullet itself is also a factor. The ogive (the curvature of the bullet nose) will vary between styles of bullets and affect where the bullet contacts the rifling. A round nose bullet often must be loaded shorter than a spitzer.

For reliable function, ammunition for semi-automatic, slide-action and lever-action rifles should be loaded very close to factory dimensions. Rifles with tubular magazines are often the most sensitive to cartridge length. Bullets intended for tubular magazine rifles have a flat tip for safety. A crimping cannelure ("crimp groove") sets the proper length for that cartridge. COAL for a falling block single-shot rifle such as the Ruger No. 1 is not so critical, and need only to clear the rifling.

Often, best accuracy is obtained when the bullet almost touches the rifling in the chamber throat. However, under no condition should a jacketed bullet contact the rifling before firing. This condition may cause high pressures in an otherwise safe load.

Seating a bullet without crimping: place a charged case (sized and, if needed, trimmed) in the shell holder and raise the ram fully. Screw the seater die into the press until you feel a slight resistance. The case mouth is now lightly touching the crimp shoulder in the die.

Cut-away of RCBS Bullet Seating Die with a bullet and case engaged.

We do not want to crimp this load, so back the die out (up) one turn and tighten the lock ring. Loosen the lock nut on the seating stem and unscrew the stem as far as possible. Remove the empty case. Place a bullet on the mouth of a charged case. If the bullet does not readily stay on the case mouth, support it between your thumb and forefinger. Insert the case head into the shell holder and raise the ram. As the case neck enters the die, let go of the case and give the press handle a full stroke. Slight resistance means the bullet has started into the case. If the bullet has not started to seat, screw the seating stem in and repeat the steps until you feel the bullet start to seat. Lower the ram and measure the cartridge with a caliper. If the bullet needs to go deeper, screw in the stem and repeat. Continue until the proper COAL is obtained. Securing the lock nut on the seating stem will preserve the COAL setting.

Sometimes, a factory cartridge or published loading length is not available. A good way to determine proper seating depth for your rifle is to make a dummy round (no primer or powder) with the bullet you plan

Bullet seating on a single-stage press.

to use. Start a bullet into the sized case but leave it long. Try gently chambering the dummy round in your rifle. If you feel resistance, remove the dummy round and screw the seater stem in (down) one full turn and seat the bullet deeper. Try the round again in your rifle.

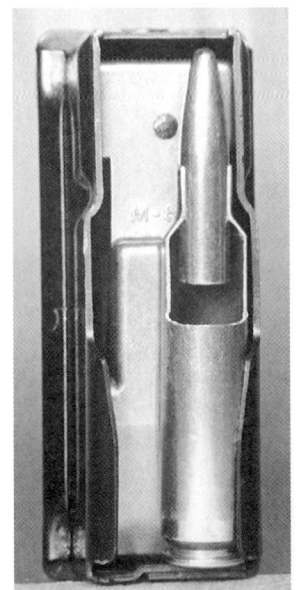

If the cartridge is to fit into a short magazine, longer bullets may take up some of the powder space .

As soon as the action can fully close with only a slight effort, remove the cartridge and rub a dark-colored "whiteboard" marker over the bullet or soot the bullet with a match (dummy rounds only!). Chamber the round and see if the ink or soot has rubbed off at evenly spaced points. If so, this shows that the origin of the rifling is contacting the bullet and the bullet must be seated slightly deeper. Usually, one more full turn of the stem will position the bullet off the rifling yet be close enough for excellent accuracy.

Once the bullet is properly seated, keep this dummy round with your loading dies as a gauge for quickly setting your dies in the future. Mark it to clearly show the bullet weight and style, and for which gun it's for if you have more than one rifle chambered for that cartridge. Different rifles can have different chamber throat dimensions although chambered for the same cartridge. The RCBS Precision Mic™ can also be used to set the seater die. Refer to the instruction sheet for details.

By popular request, we have included the COAL we used for testing each load. Remember—this length is presented as a *guideline*, not *gospel*. It may not be right for your rifle. You alone bear the responsibility to determine and apply the correct COAL for your rifle.

Step Nine—Crimping (optional)

For certain applications, it may be necessary to crimp the bullet after seating. Crimping rolls the edge of the case mouth into a recessed groove in the bullet—the *crimping cannelure.* The groove provides the needed clearance to allow the crimp to form properly without damaging the bullet or the case. Crimping is not needed for most cartridges or firearms but, when appropriate, helps prevent the bullet from moving.

> **Important:** *Bullets to be crimped must have a crimping groove. Crimping a bullet that does not have a crimping groove deforms the jacket and poor accuracy can result. Any gains in interior ballistic uniformity are meaningless if the load is not accurate.*

Crimping is recommended for the following applications:

* Ammunition intended for semi-automatic rifles, particularly the military-style firearms. The normal loading and firing cycle is rather violent and uncrimped bullets may dislodge.

* Ammunition for rifles with tubular magazines. With the cartridges stacked end-to-end, recoil can push the bullets into the cases, causing feeding problems and potentially raising pressures.

* Ammunition for magazine rifles that produce very heavy recoil. Depending on the design of the box magazine, the bullets can unseat when the rifle recoils making the cartridge too long to properly chamber. As you can imagine, this is a very hazardous condition when hunting dangerous game.

Seating die (cut-away) set for no crimp.

Most standard seating dies have the capability to crimp bullets. The die has a tapered shoulder in the neck area of the die that forms the crimp when properly set.

Seating die (cut-away) set for crimping.

Handy Crimping Tips: When seating cannelured bullets that will be crimped, seat the bullet gradually into the case until you can see only the upper edge of the cannelure above the case mouth. This provides the maximum surface area into which the crimp can form to avoid case bulging. You will get the best crimps in case batches that have been trimmed to uniform length.

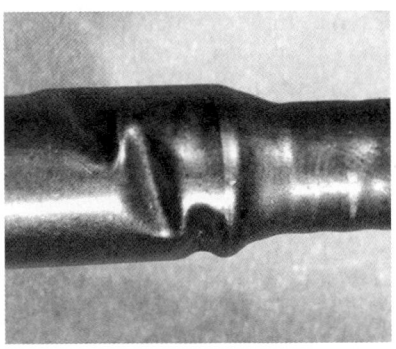

Applying too much crimp ruined this cartridge.

To set the die for crimping, seat a cannelured bullet as described above. Then unscrew the seating stem several full turns. Loosen the lock ring on the die body and make sure the seating die is "backed off" a little, too. With the cartridge in the shell holder and the ram up, screw the die body in until you feel it touch the case. Lower the ram slightly and screw in the die one-quarter to one-half turn. Slowly raise the ram again. You should feel a small resistance as the crimp forms.

Inspect the cartridge. If more crimp is needed, screw in the die body one-eighth to one-quarter turn at a time until you are satisfied with the crimp. Don't adjust in big steps—a little crimp goes a long way! When the crimp is sufficient, set the lock ring on the die body. If you wish to seat and crimp at the same time, replace the cartridge in the press and raise the ram fully. Screw in the seater stem until it stops and secure the lock nut. The die is now correctly set to seat the bullet and apply the desired amount of crimp. Seat bullets as before; the crimp is formed just as the bullet finishes seating. Use care—excessive crimp will bulge the case neck and shoulder. A cartridge with a bulged neck may not chamber and surely looks bad.

Cartridges with very thin case mouths (e.g., 32-20 Winchester; 375 H&H) may be difficult to seat and crimp in one operation without bulging. If this is the case, crimp in a separate step. Seat bullets in all the cases and then unscrew the seater stem fully. Set the crimp as before, but do not lower the seating stem after the crimp is set. Even if the cartridge case is not one of the thin-neck varieties, separating the seating and crimping operations often produces the best-looking crimp.

Step Ten—Another Inspection

Now you have finished cartridges ready for firing. There is one more step you must do before boxing up the ammunition—inspect your work.

Remove any residual lubricant and metal chips at this time. Lay the cartridges on a light colored cloth or towel and look them over while rolling them with your hand. Check for:

- consistent bullet seating depth
- damaged case mouths
- high or deformed primers
- bulged or split necks
- damaged bullets, especially on the tip
- missing crimps (if you planned to crimp)

As you box the ammunition, run your finger across the case head to check once more for high primers. Remember that you must *never* attempt to reseat a high primer in a loaded cartridge. Set them aside for later disassembly and reprocessing.

Hunting ammunition should be checked to see if it feeds and chambers easily in the rifle you plan to use. However, you must follow standard safety procedures. If you must test ammo fit in the shop, disassemble the bolt and remove the firing pin and its spring. If you cannot disassemble the firing mechanism, test the ammunition *only* at an approved shooting facility with the muzzle pointed downrange.

Inspection and testing of your handloads before the big hunt can save you much disappointment, frustration and missed game.

The Final Step—Proper Identification

After the ammo is boxed, record the exact loading information and the date on a label and attach it to the box. Speer bullets come with stick-on labels for this purpose. If you are keeping a logbook, this is the right time to bring it up to date. Proper identification of your handloads is an important step in safe reloading.

You've Now Loaded Your Own Ammo!

The steps listed above sound lengthy when reading them. However, you will find that, as your experience increases, reloading is neither complicated nor time-consuming. This text is written so that the beginning reloader can fully understand

The finished cartridges are now ready for firing.

the operations. Hopefully, some of you experienced reloaders will pick up a few pointers, too. Now it's time to shoot those custom loads.

At the Range

The proof of quality handloads is whether they shoot safely and perform well. Range testing for accuracy and function is required to assess the loads and make sure that they meet your requirements.

Safety at the Range

Always wear safety glasses to protect your eyes. Wear approved hearing protectors to prevent hearing loss. Make sure of your backstop. Understand and follow all of the commandments of gun safety!

Getting Started

While loading, you should have observed the "working up" method. Begin with the starting (minimum) load shown in the *Speer Manual* and load seven to ten rounds. Without changing the seater die settings, increase the charge weight in the next set of cartridges by one-half to one grain depending on the size of the case. Repeat this loading process until you reach the maximum load listed. Mark each batch of cartridges with the powder weight used and place them in separate boxes or, better yet, use a marker to code each group by coloring the primers (just remember to record your color code system!).

A single, five-shot group is seldom adequate to give you an accurate picture of the quality of your ammunition. Even though a load produces a five-shot group of 0.75 inches, you don't know if the next group will be 0.55 inches or 1.75 inches. For an industrial level of statistical confidence, four groups of five shots each is considered minimum. However, the cost of components mounts up quickly. A statistical analysis performed by the CCI-Speer Quality Assurance Section, showed that seven-shot groups gave the highest degree of statistical confidence with the fewest shots.

At the range, start with the lowest charge weight and shoot one seven-shot group or two five-shot groups. You are looking for the load that gives the smallest group size—not the one closest to the bull! Once an accurate load is developed, it is easy to adjust the sights to correct the point of impact relative to the aiming point.

Fire each group on a separate target, or use targets with multiple bullseyes. After completing the series, compare the group sizes to determine which powder charge gave the best accuracy in your rifle. Inspect each case as you remove it from the rifle. If you encounter any pressure signs while shooting a particular load, stop!

Pressure signs indicating you are in the "yellow zone" are sticky bolt opening or bright raised marks on the case head corresponding to extractor and/or ejector cuts in the bolt. You are well into the dangerous "red zone" if headstamp markings are deformed or the primer falls out. If you encounter any of these don't shoot any more of that batch—and surely none from the next higher increment. For whatever reason, your rifle has reached its own maximum.

From these tests, you should be able to find a safe and accurate load. If no groups in the series meet your needs, the next step is to adjust the bullet seating depth. If that doesn't improve accuracy, try a different powder and repeat the process until you are satisfied you have found the "right" load. Eventually, you will find a combination of components that delivers the accuracy and performance you seek.

Accuracy of Ammunition

New reloaders often ask, "What kind of accuracy should I get?" Well, that's a difficult question to answer because there are so many variables. Shooters often find their carefully developed handloads shoot better than factory ammunition in their rifles.

In a bolt-action, sporter-weight deer rifle with typical hunting bullets, 100-yard groups less than 1½ inch are typical with good handloads. Many semi-automatic, slide action, and lever-action rifles will produce larger groups in the range of two to three inches. This accuracy is still quite adequate for most large game at normal ranges. Heavy varmint rifles with hollow point bullets will commonly shoot groups between three-eights and three-quarters of an inch. With the right combination of rifle, components and shooting technique, even smaller groups are quite common.

Shooters' Tips for Effective Testing

Shooter's Ridge Deluxe Range Bench

- Use a shooting bench that allows you to sit comfortably. Many ranges have benches; if not, a portable bench kit can be purchased from Shooters' Ridge® or you can build one yourself. Kits and plans are advertised in most of the popular shooting magazines.

- Support the rifle firmly on sandbags or a shooting rest such as the Shooters' Ridge Zero Kick Shooting Rest. If you use a rest, support the fore-end—not the barrel. For minor elevation adjustments turn the micro windage adjustment knob under the front sand bag with your non-shooting hand. Proper support removes most of the human factor and lets you shoot better groups and enjoy longer test sessions because you are more comfortable.

◆ Don't get kicked! Heavy-caliber rifles can be painful when fired on the bench. Several firms offer recoil-absorbing shoulder pads that slip over your shirt or jacket. High-recoil sandbags are also available that transmit a portion of the recoil to the shooting bench. You can shoot better and longer if your rifle isn't abusing you. Wearing an extra recoil pad doesn't make you look like a novice. It simply indicates that you're more interested in serious shooting than in trying to impress someone!

Shooter's Ridge
Zero Kick Shooting Rest

◆ Position the rifle consistently for each shot. Pull the rifle butt firmly into your shoulder. Varying your grip can affect group size.

◆ Press the trigger consistently. Pace your breathing so you let out your breath just before each shot.

◆ Pace your shots and shoot slowly. Rapid firing heats up the barrel resulting in unpredictable groups.

◆ Don't rush. Plan your shooting sessions and allow sufficient time to shoot at a leisurely rate.

◆ Most importantly—have fun!

chapter 8

Fine-Tuning the Reloading Process:
Advanced Techniques from the Experts' Notebooks

This chapter covers useful techniques for accuracy improvement and more efficient re-loading. These tips have been gathered from the years of reloading experience at Speer® and RCBS®, and from the comments and suggestions of involved shooters willing to share their knowledge.

Loading New Cases

In recent years, the reloader can buy bulk quantities of new, unprimed cases at substantial savings. Even though the loading techniques (other than resizing) are essentially the same, a few simple steps can make loading new brass easier.

Normal case manufacturing and bulk shipping can cause dents in the case mouths. Some dents are deep enough to catch a bullet during seating and damage the case. Denting is more prevalent in cases bought in bulk than those that come in 20-count boxes because cases bang together during shipping.

With new bottleneck cases, you should condition the necks by adjusting the proper sizing die so that it will only size about half of the length of the case neck. When the case is withdrawn from the die, the expander ball will insure that the neck is both the proper diameter and round. Because only a small portion of the case touches the die, lubrication is seldom required and the operation can be done quickly. If you find a case with a severe mouth dent, you may need to straighten it manually with a wooden dowel before running it into the die. Cases with sharp mouth folds should be discarded. A severe fold can weaken the case mouth even if it can be fixed.

For straight-wall cases, whether rifle or handgun, usually running the case into the expander die set for normal flaring will insure round case mouths. However, the case neck tension must be sufficient to hold the bullet you plan to load, especially a jacketed bullet in cartridges usually factory-loaded with lead bullets, e.g., 44 Special and 45 Colt. If the bullets seat too easily, partially size the new cases before flaring. Running the case about halfway into the die usually is enough. Straight cases must be lubricated unless you have a carbide sizer die.

With the case mouths now uniformly round, it's a good time to check the case length. You will probably find that they vary. If you have a Rotary Case Trimmer, set it to the "trim-to" length for the cartridge and trim the cases. This sets a consistent length that can improve accuracy and, if needed, ensure uniform crimping. Remember to use a deburring tool on the case mouths after trimming to give a finished edge inside and out. Deburring makes bullet seating easier and should be performed on all new cases, even if trimming is not required.

While you have everything set up for neck conditioning and trimming, perform this operation on all the cartridges in the batch. Let's say you bought 500 cases. Go ahead and invest the time to trim all the cases even though you don't plan to load all of them right now. The remainder can be stored and you have one less thing to deal with later.

Resizing for Maximum Accuracy and Case Life

Most bottleneck cases headspace on the case shoulder. When fired, the shoulder can change position relative to the base of the case as pressure expands the case to fill the chamber.

Sizing dies for each cartridge are designed to reset the shoulder to near the minimum dimension specified by the U.S. industry association, SAAMI. This insures that the reloaded ammunition will fit any standard factory chamber. However, it is possible to have a rifle with a "long" chamber. Cases fired in this rifle will have the shoulder pushed back too much if the dies are set in the normal manner. Cartridges that fit the chamber closely are usually more accurate than those that don't. Another advantage to fitting the fired case to your chamber is that cases will last longer if the shoulder is not constantly pushed back during sizing and shoved forward at the next firing.

For precise measurement of the relative headspace of your rifle, RCBS offers a device called the Precision Mic™. These tools are individually calibrated for the industry base-to-shoulder length of many standard rifle cartridges. To use the tool, place a factory round or a new, unfired case in the gauge and screw the thimble down until it lightly touches the case. Record this reading and then take a case that has been fired in your rifle and gauge it in the same manner. Compare the two readings. A "zero" reading in the gauge is the minimum length for that particular cartridge. If the new case reads 0.002" and the fired case reads 0.008", then the case shoulder moved forward 0.006". If resizing returns the shoulder to its

RCBS Precision Mic™

original position, the next firing will again stretch the case to fill the chamber, reducing the life of the case. Instead, you can use the Precision Mic reading to set the sizer die to move the shoulder back only 0.002 inches to get a custom fit for that rifle.

This technique is best suited to target or varmint loads in bolt action and single shot rifles. A case sized in this manner will fill the chamber better, last longer and often give better accuracy. For hunting ammunition where reliable function is vitally important, this method of fitting the case to the chamber might cause problems. If dirt or other foreign material gets into the chamber, a tight-fitting cartridge may fail to fully chamber and cause a jam. Cases for semi-automatic, pump-action and lever-action rifles should always be full-length resized for reliable function.

Sizing Belted Cases

The belted case has become synonymous with the word "magnum." The original purpose of the belt was to provide positive headspace control on cartridges like the 300 and 375 H&H Magnums that have very little shoulder. Modern belted magnums like the 7mm Remington Magnum and the 300 Winchester are also bottlenecked but have adequate shoulders for headspace control. The belt is more a cosmetic feature than a design necessity.

To get top accuracy from your belted magnum, use the method described above to assure that the case headspaces on its shoulder instead of the belt. Many rifles will also shoot better when this technique is used and the cases will last longer.

Flash Hole Conditioning

The flash holes in most modern cartridge cases are pierced into the case, not drilled. Excess metal can be pushed up around the inside edge of the hole. In medium to large volume cartridges, the presence of this burr usually has little effect on the performance of hunting ammunition. However, for critical applications like match or varmint ammunition, or in small cases like the 22 Hornet or 222 Remington, an uneven flash hole burr can cause inconsistent ignition from shot to shot.

To provide a uniform flash hole, you can remove the burr with the RCBS Flash Hole Deburring tool and leave a neat beveled edge around the flash hole. The RCBS unit has a caliber-specific pilot that aligns with the neck and centers the trimmer in the case without the need to "fish" for the flash hole. The pilot also features a positive stop so that all cases are uniformly trimmed. The deburring tool shaft can be removed from its handle and mounted on the powered Trim Mate Case Prep Center. Pilots are available in popular sizes from 22 through 45-caliber.

Loading for Semi-Auto and Pump Action Rifles

Rifle cartridges originally designed for bolt-action or single-shot rifles are often used in semiautomatic and pump action rifles. Because these actions lack the mechanical leverage of a manually operated bolt-action, fired cases must be sized to a smaller diameter to permit reliable chambering and extraction. The critical area is the base of the case just above the extractor groove. RCBS offers Small Base sizing dies (in both complete sets and the sizer die only) that are designed to reduce the base of the case slightly more than a standard sizer die. Full-length resizing is recommended for any reloaded ammunition used in semi-automatic and pump-action rifles. Small base dies are also useful for loading ammunition for the Browning Lever Action Rifle. Occasionally, reloading surplus military 30-06 and 7.62mm NATO brass may require using a small base die for the first sizing, even if it is to be used in a bolt action.

Standard dies for cartridges such as the 7.62x39mm and the 30 Carbine originally designed for semi-auto rifles are already a small base design so no special dies are normally required for resizing.

Chapter 11, "Troubleshooting," has additional information about loading for semi-automatic rifles.

Case Neck Turning

Cartridge case manufacturers take great pains to insure that case neck walls are of uniform thickness. Although most modern cases are manufactured to tight tolerances, you may occasionally find a case lot where neck wall thickness varies. Handloaders making one case out of another will more commonly encounter this especially if they have to shorten the parent case. Normal case resizing will not correct a serious condition. Case neck turning is the key to uniform neck thickness.

The new RCBS Hand Case Neck Turner lets you obtain uniform neck thickness with ease. The cutter features a micrometer adjustment that permits .0005" increments; you can "zero" the cutter tip against the pilot and then use the micrometer settings to set a precise neck wall dimension. The Hand Case Neck Turner can be easily configured for either right- or left-hand operation. Interchangeable pilots/mandrels are available in 23 different diameters for most popular cartridges.

RCBS Hand Case Neck Turner

Owners of the RCBS Trim Pro® manual case trimmer can buy the Case Neck Turner Kit from RCBS. This accessory attaches to the trimmer and turns the inside and outside of the neck simultaneously. An optional automatic feed mechanism advances the cutter at a constant rate for clean and even cutting.

By setting the adjustable cutter to lightly contact the highest point of the case neck, any variation in the thickness should be readily apparent. A properly turned case neck should have the cutting action visible only on the high side.

Except for cases you form from another cartridge, neck wall thickness variation will seldom have an adverse effect on hunting ammunition accuracy. Target and varmint shooters are more likely to benefit from case neck conditioning.

Case Forming

Many cartridge cases share similar dimensions. Because of this, a case of one caliber can be used to form a case of another caliber. The case you start with is called the *parent case*. Handloaders normally reform cases for three reasons:

- they wish to reload a cartridge for which factory cases are either hard to find or discontinued. As an example, there are a number of Mauser rifles in circulation chambered for the 7.65mm Argentine Mauser cartridge but only one make of imported brass is available in this country. The Argentine case has a head and body diameter very similar to the 30-06. The longer '06 case can be reformed to make excellent 7.65 Mauser cases with a minimum of special equipment.

- the handloader owns a rifle chambered for a "wildcat" cartridge. A wildcat is a custom cartridge derived by modifying a standard case. Many popular commercial cartridges we shoot today started life as wildcats.

- the handloader has a surplus of one cartridge case but needs cases for another. As long as the two cartridges share certain common dimensions, the desired case dimensions can be achieved with case forming.

Reforming operations are similar to case sizing in most respects, including the need to lubricate the case. For a simple conversion, it is often possible to use standard sizing dies. The 257 Roberts case can be formed from 7mm Mauser brass by running the Mauser cases into a properly adjusted 257 Roberts sizer die. Because the cases are nearly identical except for neck diameter, no other forming is necessary except checking case length and, if necessary, trimming. Often, an existing sizer die for another cartridge can be used as an intermediate step. For example, in forming the 6.5-06

A-Square from 30-06 cases, a 280 Remington full length sizing die can provide an intermediate step between the parent case and the wildcat.

Other case conversions are more complex. If the new case is significantly shorter than the parent case, metal in the newly formed neck may be too thick and neck reaming dies are required. When the neck diameter or case length needs to be changed significantly, it is often necessary to perform the conversion in steps.

Some conversions require *fire-forming*, using the pressure of firing to contour a case to the dimensions of the rifle's chamber. In some wildcats, referred to as "Improved" cartridges, the only difference between the wildcat and the parent case is the body taper and the shoulder angle. For these, simply firing a standard cartridge in the custom rifle often makes the new case. In more complex conversions, fire-forming is usually the last step.

RCBS produces case-forming die sets for many standard and wildcat cartridges. They are designed to provide the proper steps to produce precisely formed cases with minimum loss during reforming. Each set includes complete instructions for the specific conversion. Call or write the RCBS Special Order Department at 800-533-5000 to obtain more information.

Easier Neck Expansion for Bottleneck Cartridges

When set up in the normal manner, the sizer die also expands the case neck just before the case exits the die body. Because the expander ball is near the mouth of the die, you feel the normal resistance of the ball when the press stroke leverage is relatively low. This resistance can be nearly eliminated if you are sizing cases that have already been deprimed in a separate operation (for example, if you deprime cases prior to cleaning).

To do so, loosen the lock nut that holds the expander rod in the guide bushing. Screw the expander rod counterclockwise until the top of the expander ball is roughly even with the shoulder section of the die. Make sure that the ball is not close to the neck of the die or the cases will be damaged. Tighten the lock nut and continue with sizing. With the expander ball in this higher position, the case neck is expanded when press stroke leverage is fairly high and you will hardly feel the expander ball pass through the neck.

Remember that this technique works only with bottleneck cases that have already been deprimed. If you plan to deprime when you size, leave the expander in its normal position. This technique is not necessary if you are using RCBS Competition dies. The expander ball is already at the higher position when the sizer die is adjusted to deprime.

Chamber Casting

Most sporting rifles are built to very consistent tolerances; however it is sometimes useful to know the exact chamber and throat dimensions of your rifle. Although chamber dimensions are relatively uniform in production rifles, throats can vary. Chamber casting is an alternative to buying an expensive bore scope to examine your rifle's throat.

A good chamber cast gives you a "snapshot" of the throat. This part of the barrel is the most stressed during shooting. A rifle with a badly worn throat will usually shoot poorly even though the rest of the barrel looks good. A chamber cast can help you evaluate this hard-to-see area of the barrel.

A chamber cast is made by plugging the bore about an inch ahead of the throat with a cotton patch and pouring a low melting point metal such as Cerrosafe® or a polymer material into the chamber. Chamber casting kits are available from gunsmith supply catalogs. Follow the instructions supplied with the casting material to obtain the most accurate measurement.

Measuring Bore Diameter

It's often helpful to know the exact diameter of your barrel especially when reloading for military surplus firearms. Measuring just inside the muzzle with a caliper seldom gives the true diameter. The most common method is called "slugging" the bore and is most accurate with barrels having an even number of grooves.

To slug the bore, clean the barrel thoroughly and apply a very thin coat of light machine oil. Select a piece of soft lead such as a buckshot pellet or a cast bullet that is just large enough that it cannot be pushed into the bore by hand. Place the lead slug on the muzzle and drive it flush with a non-metal mallet. Then use a short section of hardwood dowel that measures just under bore diameter to drive the bullet in a few inches. This step will usually cause a ring of excess lead to be cut off. This indicates you have a proper fit. Remove the dowel and continue driving the slug with a longer dowel until the slug falls from the chamber. The slug will be engraved by the rifling and can be measured with calipers or a micrometer. Be sure to measure the slug at several places and use the maximum dimension as the effective bore diameter. ***NOTE:*** Never attempt to drive a jacketed bullet through the bore in this manner.

Some barrels have an odd number of rifling grooves. Their diameters are difficult to accurately measure without special gauging equipment.

Determining Twist Rate

In this manual, you will see reference to the rate of rifling twist. All rifled barrels have spiral grooves in the barrel to rotate the bullet at a predetermined rate. You can measure this rate using simple tools. You will need the following items:

- a metal cleaning rod appropriate for your rifle's bore, preferable light-colored and fitted with a rotating handle.
- jag tip and patches of the correct size
- a long straight-edge, such as a yardstick
- a dark-colored, fine-point felt-tip marker that will write on metal

Lay the cleaning rod on the bench and, using the straight edge and marker, draw a long line the full length of the rod parallel to its axis. Place the jag and patch on the rod and start the rod into the barrel from the muzzle. If the patch fits properly, the rod should rotate smoothly. Make sure you see uniform rotation before proceeding. It may be necessary to adjust the position of the patch or change its size to achieve the proper fit.

Stop the rod so that the line you drew is facing up. If the rifle has a front sight, use it for a reference point. In the absence of an existing reference point, you can make a temporary one by placing a bit of masking tape adjacent to the muzzle and making a pencil mark on it. Make a cross mark on the rod with the marker even with the muzzle. Push the rod slowly through the bore while making sure it is rotating smoothly. When the long line returns to the reference point, make another cross mark even with the muzzle, then remove the rod. The distance between the two cross marks is the approximate rate of twist.

Reloading for Cowboy Action Shooting

Cowboy Action Shooting is one of the fastest growing shooting events around. It calls for guns and loads from another era and participants dress to fit the part. Targets are usually reactive steel plates so spectators get to see the hits and keep track of their favorite shooter. Most matches combine rifle, revolver and shotgun stages. The emphasis is on history, fun and, of course, safety.

The Single Action Shooting Society (www.sassnet.com) sets the rules of Cowboy Action Shooting. Revolvers are single-actions, rifles are lever guns, and shotguns are side-by-side doubles, lever-action or pump guns appropriate to the period. Modern reproductions are also permitted.

There are strict performance requirements for ammunition. Revolver ammo must produce velocities under 1000 ft/sec. Revolver cartridges fired in rifles must not exceed 1400 ft/sec. Lead bullets rule the game; in fact, no jacketed or gas check bullets are permitted for match use.

The Challenge

Competitors know that fast repeat shots are easier if the recoil is reduced, so many Cowboy Action shooters load lighter bullets at reduced velocities to get faster runs. It is this very issue that has caused problems for some reloaders.

The 45 Colt, 44-40 Winchester and the 38-40 Winchester cartridges are true veterans of Old West service and were developed as black powder cartridges. Smokeless propellants were not yet invented when these cartridges were released to the shooting world in the 1870's.

Mr. Colt's famous Peacemaker

A powerful black powder cartridge needs a big case to hold as much of the primitive propellant as possible. Modern smokeless propellants can give similar velocities with substantially reduced charges compared to the original black powder loads; smokeless propellants contain more energy per grain of weight. This means that safe smokeless loads typically leave a lot of air space in the case. Then you must consider that these cartridges operate at quite low pressures by today's standards. When you combine light bullets, low pressure and a big case, the reloader and the data developer face some real performance and safety challenges.

The maximum average pressure for the 45 Colt and 38-40 is 14,000 CUP and the 44-40 is 13,000 CUP. When we load a bullet that's significantly lighter than the "standard" bullet weight and try to obtain velocities in the 600 to 700 ft/sec range, the working pressures fall very low. Often, such loads can generate less than 8000 CUP, and shot-to-shot pressure variation may mean that individual shots fall to the 5000 CUP level if the load is inefficient. That's hardly enough gas volume and pressure to overcome the cylinder gap and the friction in the barrel. It's also not enough to make the bullet seal the bore or the case to obturate the chamber. Whatever the technical cause, the result is poor ammo.

Another factor, powder position, also comes into the picture. Standard pressure testing procedures call for the cartridge to be carefully rotated before it is loaded into the test barrel so that the powder charge is at the primer when the cartridge is fired. This doesn't happen in competition shooting. When the revolver is in the holster, the powder is at the bullet. Drawing and pointing the revolver at the target probably won't return the charge to the primer end of the case. Powder-at-bullet will often reduce the pressure even more.

The point is that, in trying to "milk" the system to reduce recoil, the reloader will often create ballistic problems for himself. The least of these worries is a wide variation in velocity that may hurt accuracy. At worst, a bullet may stop in the barrel creating a hazardous bore obstruction.

Reloaders must understand these potential problems and look for ways to minimize or eliminate them. The solutions involve both the gun and the ammo.

The Gun

The problems we're discussing are most evident in revolvers. Before shooting any revolver, measure the barrel/cylinder gap. Industry specs call for a maximum gap of 0.012 inch. Unfortunately, there are many revolvers in use, both originals and replicas, that exceed this value. Realistically, 0.012" is quite generous. For light loads, this gap should be much smaller—close to the minimum dimension that still allows a cylinder to freely rotate when it is dirty. An inexpensive feeler gauge from the auto parts store will let you measure the gap easily. When taking the measurement, make sure the revolver is thoroughly clean and unloaded. Grease and residue can give a false reading. Hold the cylinder firmly to the rear when you measure. That's where it will be when the cartridge reaches peak pressure.

An excessive gap allows too much gas to escape, not leaving enough to push the bullet down the bore. The lighter the load, the more likely that a large gap will cause a bullet to stop in the bore. If you find a large gap, it can only be cured by having a gunsmith set the barrel back one full turn and recut the rear face. We examined a reproduction single-action that had a gap of 0.015" from the factory. The reason we examined it was that it had a bullet lodged in its barrel.

The next item to check is the size of the chamber throats (they're the exit holes in the front of the cylinder). Chamber throats can be easily measured with the inside diameter portion of a dial caliper. Be sure to measure each throat. It's not uncommon, even in high-quality revolvers, for throat diameter to vary in the same cylinder. Oversize chamber throats or undersize bullets let large quantities of gas blow around the bullet before it crosses the critical barrel/cylinder gap. Although hard to change without having a custom cylinder fitted, knowing the throat dimensions ahead of time will allow you to compensate somewhat when assembling ammo for that gun.

The last thing to check is the barrel itself. The grove diameter can be measured by driving a slightly oversize lead bullet (preferably soft) through the bore with a wood dowel. Remember to thoroughly clean and lightly oil the bore before starting. Ideally, the test bullet should be just large enough that a small ring of lead is sheared off as the bullet enters the muzzle. After driving the bullet completely through the bore, measure its largest diameter with a caliper or micrometer. Although this factor is not as critical as the other two, barrel diameter is a good thing to know. If you have 0.451" throats and a 0.454" barrel, don't expect great accuracy.

While you are checking barrel diameter, take a moment to inspect the forcing cone. This is the tapered section at the rear of the barrel where the rifling is cut away to provide a transition zone for the bullet as it enters the rifling. If the maximum size of the cone is smaller than the chamber throat, the bullet will encounter extra resistance that may prove difficult for an overly light load to overcome. The forcing cone should be very smooth for the same reason, particularly if you are sizing bullets to fit the chamber throats. Rough forcing cones are fixed easily if you or your gunsmith has the right tool. As you use the revolver, check the barrel during routine cleaning to make certain that lead fouling isn't building up in the cone. Heavy fouling here can retard the bullet, once again increasing the possibility of a bullet obstructing the barrel.

The Ammunition

It is important to select a bullet that isn't too light for the cartridge. Below is a chart showing the lightest cast lead bullets that we recommend for Cowboy Action cartridges.

Cartridge	Factory Lead Bullet Weight, grs	Recommended Minimum Weight for CAS, gr
32-20 Win.	100	90
38 Special	158	140
38-40 Win.	180	170
44 Russian & Special	246	200
44-40 Win.	200	200
45 Schofield	225-230	200
45 Colt	250-255	220

Choosing bullets lighter than these may cause excessive pressure and velocity variation, making a bullet-in-bore condition possible. In trying many combinations of light loads, the Speer staff found that loading light powder charges with bullets close to factory weight gives more consistent and accurate results than attempting the same with unusually light bullets.

Ideally, a lead bullet's diameter should be no more than 0.001 larger than the largest chamber throat. If this isn't possible (some revolvers have quite generous throats) choose the largest bullet that will fit in the case and still permit it to chamber. A tight bullet fit in the throat area keeps the powder gas behind the bullet. Using a softer bullet alloy can help in oversize throats because the bullet expands to seal the throat when struck by the pressure wave. Hard-cast bullets cannot upset in the throats at modest pressures and gas leaks around them if they are under throat diameter.

Sizing to throat diameter will almost always result in a bullet that is larger than the barrel's groove diameter. Although this can be a problem with jacketed bullets, softer lubricated lead bullets normally swage down quite easily as they enter the barrel's forcing cone.

Proper case sizing and neck expansion insures a good bullet fit. If the bullet is "loose" in the case mouth, the combustion pressure will drop below normal levels. We have encountered some new 44 Special and 45 Colt cases that won't properly grip .429" and .452" cast bullets (respectively) unless the case is partially sized. The expander plug should be at least 0.002" smaller than the bullet you are using. A quick test involves making an uncrimped dummy round with the case and bullet you plan to use. Hold the inert round against the edge of the loading bench and give it a push. If the neck tension is acceptable, the bullet shouldn't slide deeper with reasonable force. If it does slide, then load a larger bullet or neck size the cases if they're new.

Quick-burning propellants provide better results with light loads. They permit loading to modest velocities yet keep the operating pressures in the normal range. Slow-burning powders seldom produce consistent combustion at low pressures, and could contribute to a bullet-in-bore situation. We watched the pressures generated by our start loads rather closely to assure that they were reasonable. For example, the start loads for the 44-40 and 38-40 data in this book are all at least 10,000 CUP in our pressure barrel. Don't try to load below published minimums!

The one exception to the "smokeless loads leave too much airspace" issue is IMR's Trail Boss™ propellant. It is very bulky yet quick-burning. Its uncommon bulk means a safe charge of Trail Boss uses up more case capacity than a conventional propellant. Many of us here feel that Trail Boss may be the right step toward fixing many CAS ammo problems.

For Cowboy Action shooting, it's also acceptable to load these big cases like they were 100 years ago—with a case full of black powder. Modern cases won't hold quite as much black powder as the original ones, but there's no problem of too much air space. The downside is that the gun and cartridge cases must be thoroughly cleaned to eliminate corrosive black powder residues. FFFg granulation is appropriate for loading most revolver cartridges. That big cloud of white smoke at each shot is certainly in keeping with the Old West image of SASS competition. There are several good books out now that cover special techniques for loading black powder.

If you prefer using a conventional smokeless powder, there are a couple of ways to reduce air space. In straight-wall cases, you can deep-seat the bullet—but only with an appropriate reduction in powder charge. Noted reloading researcher M. L. McPherson found that this technique improved both consistency and accuracy with Cowboy loads in the larger cases.

Another approach is to use a case with less capacity, by either shortening the existing case (again with appropriate charge reductions) or choosing one of the "obsolete" cartridges recently resurrected by Black Hills Ammunition Company. These include 38 Colt, 44 Russian and 45 Schofield. They are the same diameter as the 38 Special, 44 Special and 45 Colt, respectively, just shorter. You can buy new, unprimed brass in these calibers from Starline. Loading data for the Russian and Schofield cartridges are shown in this manual.

A firm crimp will also keep pressures up, especially at that critical time before the bullet enters the barrel. When possible, choose a bullet that has a generous crimping groove and apply a heavy roll crimp. With thin-mouth cases like the 32-20, 38-40 and 44-40, you will probably find that crimping needs to be separated from the seating operation to avoid damage to the case. Trimming all cases to uniform length before loading makes crimping easier, too.

Magnum primers should not be used with any reduced loads unless specified in the data. Under some conditions, the increased power of magnum primers can dislodge the bullet from a handgun cartridge before the powder charge reaches working pressures. Without a sustained burn, extreme velocity variations are going to appear.

Rifles Chambered for Pistol Cartridges

The greatest challenge in loading for these rifles comes when reloaders want to shoot the same ammo that they load for their revolvers. Lever-action rifles are very finicky about cartridge length; if the cartridge is too long or too short, it may not cycle in the action. This could present a problem if you use a short case or deep-seated bullets in your revolver loads. Many 44 Magnum carbines will feed 44 Special ammo, but not Russians. Likewise, 45 Colt carbines may not feed Schofield ammo.

You can either load a separate batch of ammo for the rifle, or experiment to find a load in a standard length case that cycles in the rifle yet provides consistency in the revolver. Following these recommendations will go a long way toward assuring safe and reliable performance.

Remember that a light powder charge that can easily push a bullet down a short handgun barrel may not be able to do the same in a longer rifle or carbine barrel. Again, keep the pressure up by using the recommended charge of a fast-burning powder behind a well-lubricated bullet of reasonable weight, firmly crimped in place.

Test Before the Match!

The best way to avoid problems *during* the big match is to test your ammo *before* the big match! Once you've decided on a load, assemble a sample quantity and head to the range to test it. If you have access to a chronograph, first make sure that the loads meet the velocity requirements of SASS. Your revolver or rifle may not give the same numbers our test guns produced.

When you are chronographing the loads, record the velocities to see if they are varying excessively. What's excessive? Although there is no hard specification, most good quality ammo will post an extreme variation (the difference between the highest and lowest velocity, abbreviated "EV") that is from 3 to 6 percent of the average muzzle velocity.

If you don't have a chronograph, listen for "off sounds," that is, something out of the ordinary. If you hear "bang, pop, pop, bang, pop," (or a similar irregular pattern of sounds) the ammo is probably performing inconsistently. A noticeable variation in felt recoil is another "red flag" indicating poor performance.

Where safe to do so, hold the revolver muzzle-down before slowly returning it to horizontal. This puts the powder at the bullet. Fire and mentally note the report and recoil. With ammo from the same batch, do a similar drill. This time, elevate the muzzle to put the powder at the primer. Again, slowly return the gun to horizontal and fire a string. Did the report and recoil seem similar for both tests? Shoot groups during this testing and "read" the target with a critical eye. Vertical stringing of holes in the target says there may be variation problems.

Always do this type of testing slowly to prevent gun damage should a bullet lodge in the bore.

One Man's Opinion

I'm Allan Jones, the "buck stops here" guy for the *Speer® Reloading Manuals* starting with *Number 12*. I wrote most of this manual, directed the testing and interpreted the raw data. Through two careers, first as a forensic firearms examiner in a crime lab and now as development engineer/ballistician for Speer, I've heard lots of facts and plenty of myths about guns and ammunition. As a scientist working in the firearms field, I confirmed facts and investigated myths using the considerable resources available to me. I've investigated firearm accidents and malfunctions to reconstruct the events leading to disaster. I have looked at reports of accidents involving Cowboy Action Shooting with the same resources as I had in the crime lab and in the ballistics lab. I accept this fact:

Some Cowboy Action shooters have experienced blown-up guns.

There are a number of theories circulating why this happens. They range from simple to very complex. I was taught to resolve a problem by looking at the most likely explanations first, only turning toward the less likely explanations if the evidence doesn't satisfactorily support the former. If you've read any Sherlock Holmes stories, you've heard him expound to Dr. Watson:

"After you have explored all the possible explanations, then consider the impossible ones." [Paraphrased, with my apologies to Sir Arthur Conan Doyle.]

I've reviewed several reports of revolver blow-ups and I feel that, for the majority of these, the answer readily falls into the "most likely" category rather than the "least likely" or "impossible" realm.

Here is one likely scenario. A pistol blows up because an earlier event—the deliberate assembly of a low-pressure load—caused a bullet to stick in the forcing cone just far enough to allow the cylinder to rotate. A few seconds later another bullet is fired into the obstructing one. Instead of a 200-grain payload, we now have one weighing 400 grains. The pressure spikes and the gun lets go. Do you see what happened?

> **A low-pressure event was the direct cause of a high-pressure event.**

Another scenario that falls into the "likely" category is that the reloader double-charged a case. Large handgun cases require extra attention to detail when you visually check for double-charges. Two small charges of powder in a 45 Colt case aren't always obvious, even to the experienced reloader. It's also possible to inadvertently seat two lighter bullets in the same 45 Colt case and not see anything abnormal during final inspection.

Take a look at the Cowboy ammo manufactured by one of the largest ammo manufacturers in the U.S. Velocities are reduced but not the bullets weights. The company has made ammunition continuously for over 140 years. That should tell you something about their concern over low-pressure loads.

As a scientist, I was trained in the maxim: *"Never say 'never' and never say 'always'!"*

For these cases of blown-up revolvers, I can't say that some exotic ballistic phenomenon didn't blow up those guns. On the other hand, no one has positively proved that it did either. However, I know many more "likely" causes that can and do produce the same effects. Airspace effects seen in military ordnance and big rifle cases don't necessarily translate to straight-wall pistol cases.

I hold another opinion about Cowboy shooting and its ammo. The sport is intended to recreate the events and the *spirit* of that time. Would a self-respecting cowboy or backwoods man in 1885 carry a 45 Colt revolver with 165-grain bullets loaded to 600 ft/sec when he could get 255-grain bullets launching at 900 ft/sec in the same revolver? I think not.

We need ask ourselves some questions. Are we straying from the spirit of the period for the sake of gamesmanship? Are we trying to substitute technology for practice and skill? From personal experience I can testify that continued practice trumps technology any day. How would you feel if you placed high in a match with "real" ammo when others were milking the system? Even if I came in fourth behind three guys shooting "mouse" loads, I'd feel pretty good about it. How about you?

That's one man's opinion, based on nearly 40 years of personal and professional experience in the field.

Three Cowboys Horsin' Around....

From left to right...John Ader, aka "Yahoo", Model Shop Machinist; Earnest Durham, aka "Slim Pickens", Engineer; and Brett Olin, aka "Sabin Tanner", Engineer, at the 1998 Great Northern Regional CAS Championships.

Brett Olin firing from a "horse" with an original 1887 Winchester. Brett uses black powder exclusively.

chapter 10

Automating the Loading Process
Progressive Reloading Equipment

The last four decades saw tremendous growth in new shooting sports including several handgun sports such as IPSC/USPSA, NRA Action, bowling pin, IDPA, and Cowboy Action Shooting. It's common for top shooters in these events to fire 30,000 to 50,000 rounds annually to maintain proficiency.

Shooters who require large quantities of ammunition eventually reach the point where single-stage reloading can no longer satisfy their needs. The need to maximize practice time and reduce the time spent loading has sparked the development of faster ways to reload ammunition.

Progressive reloading presses accomplish all of the steps performed on a single-stage press. However, the steps are performed on several different cases at the same time. This is possible by providing multiple die stations and a moving shell carrier or shellplate. With each stroke of the handle, a typical progressive press will resize and deprime one case, expand the case neck and seat a new primer in another, charge yet another case with powder and seat the bullet in still another.

This saves time because the tool performs several operations with every stroke of the press handle. Some tools are more automated than others. For example, one tool may advance the cartridges to the next station automatically while others require the operator to manually rotate the shell carrier.

Progressive reloading tools date back to the 1930's. Small-capacity automated loaders were usually marketed to police departments, shooting clubs or small commercial ammo businesses. Star Machine Works built the most popular and durable version of these early tools. It was a robust five-station, manually indexed machine.

The original Star machine was intended to load handgun cartridges and lacked sufficient stroke length for most rifle cartridges. With its rotary shellplate, it represents one of the two distinct designs in progressive loading presses. Most current progressive loaders for the consumer market are *rotary designs*. RCBS®, Dillon and Hornady fall into this category. Other progressive tools employed a *linear design*. The cases move in a straight line from left to right under a rack of dies. The most common are the various models of the C-H Autochamp™ and the RCBS Green Machine™.

Progressive reloaders were once relatively expensive. The Star listed for $850 in 1977 and the C-H and RCBS tools sold for around $500. During the same period, a Colt Government Model pistol cost about $300—the tools were decidedly not for everyone. Complex progressive tools made for high-volume commercial reloaders were even more expensive.

There are many progressive tools on the market today at prices most shooters can afford. Some models can load selected rifle cartridges as well as handgun. Die stations range from three to eight. When counting available die stations, remember one position must hold a powder measure. The shooter has a broad choice of features and options based on his need and budget.

RCBS's leading progressive press is the Pro 2000®. Like the Star machine, it processes several cases at once using a rotary shellplate. Unlike the Star, the Pro 2000 Auto will load rifle cartridges up to 30-06 length, has more dies stations, features a removable die plate and incorporates APS® strip-priming technology for safety and reliability.

RCBS Piggyback™-3 and -4 are unique progressive conversion units. They mount on many RCBS single-stage presses converting them to five-station progressives. The unit can be quickly removed to return the press to single-stage mode. The Piggyback-3 loads cartridges up to 223 Remington length on an original Rock Chucker™, Reloader Special-3 or -5 press. The PB-4 mounted to a Rock Chucker Supreme will load 30-06 length cartridges.

Because of significant design and operational differences among the various makes of progressive presses, we will not attempt to give a complete review of each. For details about the safe operation of your progressive press, consult the instruction manual furnished with it. If it is not available, contact the equipment manufacturer for a copy.

RCBS Piggyback 4

Regardless of the type of progressive press you choose, we strongly recommend that you master the basics of reloading on single-stage equipment before automating the process. In other words, it's smarter to learn to walk before you try to run when loading ammunition. If you understand what's happening in the progressive tool, troubleshooting loading problems will be easier.

Turret Presses

Turret reloading presses, often grouped with true progressive tools, are really enhanced single-stage presses. The lower unit of the typical turret press is much like a single-stage unit with a ram that holds one cartridge at a time. The difference is at the top. Instead of a single die station, the press features a large rotating disk or turret with multiple die stations. Over the years, the number of die stations has hovered between three and seven, with four to six being most common.

RCBS Turret Press

The reason that turret presses get included with progressive presses is that they can be used to perform *semi-progressive loading*. If you have all the dies for one cartridge installed and adjusted, you can perform one operation, index the turret to the next die, perform that operation and continue the sequence until you have a loaded cartridge. It's slower than a true progressive but faster than single-stage loading. That's one way to use a turret press.

The turret press has other benefits that are too often overlooked. Because a complete die set can be left installed and ready to use, you lose no time in changing or adjusting dies. This is very useful when you only need a dozen cartridges or if one or two cartridges make up the majority of your reloading. Let's consider the handgun reloader who loads more 38 Special and 45 Auto than anything else. He can set up a six-station turret press with a full set of both dies preset for each cartridge and quickly begin loading without having to do anything other than changing the shell holder. In this situation, the user will often use the turret press as a single-stage, only rotating the turret to the next die after all cases have been through the previous stage. If you are loading bottleneck rifle cartridges, a six-station turret will let you preset dies for three cartridges, saving much setup time.

Until now, turret presses have changed little and their few disadvantages carried from one design to the next. Heavy-duty resizing is often not possible on traditional turret presses because the turret plate can tip under stress and misalign the die. Some press makers recommend only using their turret model for neck sizing. Many had small-diameter turret pivots that did not maintain concentricity or wore quickly. On-press priming was either awkward or unavailable and some models required special dies or shell holders. The situation has changed—for the better!

RCBS makes an excellent six-station turret press with 21st Century features. It has a heavy-duty, interchangeable turret mounted on a large pivot, a robust cast frame and convenient primer feeding from a protected magazine. It uses standard RCBS dies and shell holders. A heavy pedestal rising from the base snugly supports the turret head under load so the plate remains flat when full-length sizing. Install the optional Case Activated Linkage Kit and a Uniflow powder measure and you have a dedicated and convenient charging station.

Extra turret heads are available to let you keep even more dies set up and ready to load. Switching heads is easy. You can quickly remove the heavy-duty turret nut with the same handle that turns the plate while loading so there is no time lost looking for tools.

The RCBS turret press is a very useful tool and is the highest evolutionary step of this loading tool system that's been with reloaders for decades.

Progressive Loading—Pros and Cons

Progressive reloading tools have their strong points and weak points. Rest assured; the pros far outweigh the cons.

The most obvious benefit is *capacity*—the number of cartridges that can be loaded in a specific period of time. Most progressive reloaders can yield 200 to 400 rounds per hour at a safe and steady pace. A steady pace minimizes the chance for error and will produce reliable and accurate ammunition. Regardless of make and model, trying to load too fast will result in unsafe loading practices and poor or unsafe ammunition.

With care, ammunition loaded on a progressive tool can be every bit as accurate as ammo loaded on single-stage equipment. Because quite a bit of hardware is often linked to the powder measure, progressive presses often damp out slight variations in operator technique resulting in very uniform charge weights with many propellants.

The only real drawback to a properly operated progressive loader is that you have little chance to perform "right now" inspections as you load. A high primer won't be found until the cartridge is fully loaded. You may not be able to inspect each case for a powder charge before seating bullets. With reasonable loading techniques and a couple of handy RCBS accessories, charge inspection is readily available.

The best insurance against a missing or incorrect powder charge is a *powder level detector*. RCBS makes two such items—the Powder Checker™ and the Lock Out Die™. The Powder Checker is a visual powder level indicator that is installed in the die station just past the powder measure. When the press ram reaches the top of its stroke, glance at the Checker. The alignment of a sensor rod with a reference marker tells you if the charge is correct, over, under or missing. The Powder Checker works with any metallic cartridge.

The Lock Out die performs a similar function for straight-wall pistol cases but with a twist. When it detects a charge that is too heavy or light or missing, the Lock Out die halts the ram travel abruptly. The operator is instantly alerted to the problem even if he's not paying attention. Both of these safety devices are best suited to five-station presses—they have the necessary extra die position.

Progressive presses need more maintenance than single-stage presses. As you deprime on a progressive press, primer residue will eventually accumulate under the rotary shellplate and in the primer transport mechanism. You must keep these areas clean to avoid erratic shellplate rotation or priming difficulties. Clean under the plate with a brush or compressed air every time you change plates or at 1000-rounds intervals. Clean up any spilled propellant immediately to eliminate a fire hazard and avoid inter-ruption of normal press operation.

High or tipped primers can also result from a buildup of residue in the primer pocket after several firings. Avoid this problem by periodically depriming the cases off-press with an RCBS Universal Decapping Die. Remove any primer pocket residue before put-ting the cases back through the progressive press. This is also a good time to clean and inspect the cases.

Speed—Claims vs. Reality

Don't become a "speed addict" just because you are loading with progressive equip-ment. Never try to match "advertised" production rates. Such rates are sometimes derived from running the press for a few minutes then multiplying to get an hourly rate. In normal usage you will not safely achieve such rates. Powder hoppers and primer tubes eventually run low and you must stop to refill them. Sometimes you drop a case or bullet that has to be retrieved. Load at a comfortable pace and you will still be far ahead compared to single-stage loading. Speed means nothing if you produce inferior or dangerous ammo.

Operate the equipment so that you complete a cartridge every ten or fifteen seconds. This rate will produce plenty of ammo and the user has adequate time to handle the components and verify that the equipment is working correctly. The equipment must always be operated smoothly. A "jerking" motion can cause irregular powder charges or tipped primers. Cases snap too fast from one station to the next and may lose part of their powder charge. If you're operating the tool too fast, you may not notice some unusual resistance to normal operation that would otherwise alert you to a problem. Poor ammunition or equipment damage may result.

Securely mounting the progressive press to a stable and level surface is MANDATORY. Movement and vibration that would go unnoticed on a single-stage press can cause malfunctions with a progressive. Mount it on a heavy bench and secure with carriage bolts whenever possible.

Sizing Dies in Progressive Loaders

A carbide sizer die is recommended—almost mandatory—to eliminate the need to lube cases when reloading straight-wall handgun cartridges on a progressive press. In addition to greatly speeding up the process, you will avoid handling greasy cases with the same hand that handles bullets. Getting case lube on bullets can cause irregular bullet pulls or contaminate the powder and cause a misfire.

Few hobbyists can afford carbide dies for bottleneck cartridges. The best way to avoid lubrication problems is to use the RCBS Lube Die. It has a reservoir for liquid case lube and automatically meters it onto a felt ring at the mouth of the die. The die, installed in station one, also deprimes the case. The case sizing die with the decapping pin removed is installed in station two. RCBS Lube Dies are available in four sizes to handle most bottleneck rifle cartridges.

Of course, you can spray the cases with RCBS CaseSlick® before putting them into the press. With either method, remember to remove the lube from finished cartridges.

"Interrupted" Progressive Loading

You can interrupt the progressive sequence when loading bottleneck rifle cases to allow lube removal and ensure clean, reliable ammunition. Install a Lube Die in station 1 and the sizer die in station 2. No other dies are used nor are any primers or propellant. Insert the cases normally and start the cycle. Cases are lubed and decapped in the first station and sized in the second. That's all. Continue until all cases are processed and ejected.

To remove the lubricant from the cases, use plain corn cob media in a tumbler or vibratory cleaner to have a clean, dry case. The cases aren't primed so you can even wash off the lube if it is water-soluble like RCBS Case Lube-2. Be sure cases are completely dry before proceeding. Dry cleaning with cob is preferable because it takes only about 10-15 minutes. Washing and drying take longer.

With the cases clean and dry, install a Universal Decapping Die in the first station to knock out any cob residue that's lodged in the flash hole. Install and fill the primer feeder device, fill the powder measure and remember to put an RCBS powder level detector behind it. Finish with the bullet seater die and start loading. Cases get their flash holes cleared, are primed, charged, the charge verified and the bullets seated. Each cartridge ejected into the catch bin is clean and ready to inspect.

Picking the Right Propellant

Progressive presses mechanically move the cartridge cases from station to station and some vibration is bound to occur. Cases filled close to the top with propellant may shake out part of the charge before the bullet is seated. Select a propellant and charge weight that keeps the powder level well below the case mouth.

A number of loads in this and other reloading manuals call for compressed propellant charges. Most progressive tools can handle a little compression without a problem. We recommend you avoid heavily compressed loads when using rotary progressive loaders. Because the case is not directly over the centerline of the ram during bullet seating, abnormal flexing of the shellplate carrier and/or die plate may lead to inconsistent bullet seating depths or upset other operations happening at the same time. Over a long time, the shellplate carrier could be permanently damaged. It's best to assemble heavily compressed loads on single-stage equipment.

When loading large-capacity rifle cases, you must always pause a second or two with the ram at the top of its stroke. This insures that the propellant charge will have adequate time to pass through the powder measure into the case. You will likely need to modify your pacing from one used when loading small-capacity cartridges. The best way to gauge how much time you must allow is to test flow time during set-up. You can use the measure on the progressive press to test in single-stage mode, or use a similar model measure off-press. Operating the press too fast will produce defective ammo with light charges and cause propellant spills.

Safety with the Progressives

Although each manufacturer's design and operation varies, progressive presses share several universal safety guidelines:

- ❖ **Read and understand** all instructions furnished with the equipment. Progressive presses are quite complex compared to single-stage equipment. If you don't understand how it works, call the equipment manufacturer for help. Most have a toll-free number and websites for technical assistance. Use them!

- **Always** wear eye protection when reloading, regardless of the type of equipment being used.

- **Avoid** anything that may distract you when loading. Progressive presses have many things happening at once and require your full attention.

- **Develop the habit** of routinely checking all parts and connections for tightness, alignment and fit. Keep the press clean and lubricate it *only* according to the manufacturer's recommendations. Excessive lubrication is often worse than no lubrication.

- **Never** attempt to modify built-in safety features of any reloading tool.

- **Never** attempt to increase the capacity of primer feeders and powder hoppers beyond their original design.

- **Make certain** that replacement primer tubes are the correct ones for the make and model of your tool. The wrong tube can lead to big problems including a dangerous primer tube detonation. Replace—don't repair—any damaged primer tubes.

- **Don't rush!** Operate the press with a smooth, even stroke of the handle and maintain a steady pace of one finished round every ten or fifteen seconds. Never attempt to load so fast that you cannot keep an eye on all equipment functions. When operating the press for the first time, pay close attention to the feel and sound of the equipment. Knowing what feels and sounds "normal" makes it easier to detect malfunctions that may happen later.

- **Take a break** if you get tired. Extended progressive loading sessions can be physically exerting and operator fatigue can lead to inattentiveness and dangerous mistakes.

- **Never use excessive force.** If you feel something out of the ordinary, *stop loading immediately*! Do not resume until the problem is found, understood and corrected.

- **Develop** a consistent routine for picking up cases and bullets and smoothly coordinate these motions with the stroke of the press handle.

- **Case preparation** is still important when loading on progressive equipment. You still must check cases for defects and proper length before loading them.

• • • • •

Observe these guidelines and you and your progressive reloader will soon be producing an impressive amount of quality ammunition with complete safety.

When All Else Fails: Troubleshooting Techniques

We expect that reloading will go smoothly but occasionally we'll encounter something that isn't according to plan. This section will help you diagnose and fix problems that may occur during the loading process or at the range.

Sizing Problems—Stuck Cases

The most common sizing problem is sticking a case in the sizer die. When you lower the ram, the shell holder pulls the rim off the case and you're out of business. The usual cause for this problem is easy to find—little or no lube on the case. Frictional forces during sizing are very high and without adequate lubrication, the case will seize in the die. Removing a stuck case from the die takes care and special equipment to avoid ruining the die. The stuck case seldom harms the die; improper removal techniques do the damage.

RCBS® makes two tools to handle this problem: the Stuck Case Remover and the Stuck Case Remover 2 kits. The former is used with standard dies and the latter with dies having a removable guide bushing or elevated expander balls. Both units are designed to gently ease a case from the die. The case is lost but not your precision die. If you do not have one of these tools, you can send an RCBS die to their Customer Service department to have a stuck case removed.

Ensuring the case has adequate lube will eliminate this problem. The first case sized in a new die usually requires slightly more lube than subsequent cases. After the first few cases are sized, less lubricant can be used. If you feel a case hesitate as it enters or exits the die, make sure the next

Trouble? A torn rim left this case stuck in the sizer die.

case has enough lubricant before sizing. When using a new die for the first time, flush it with an aerosol solvent such as Outers® Crud Cutter® to remove the shipping preservatives. For bottleneck cartridges, clear any material from the small vent hole in the side of the die with a small wire or punch.

A die that has been damaged by sizing too many gritty cases will become rough enough to increase resizing forces. Stop using the die until it can be repaired or replaced. To avoid this problem, clean those cases before sizing.

Dents in the Case Shoulder

You can have too much of a good thing. Although lubrication is necessary, excessive lube will collect in the shoulder area of the die. When a case is sized, the trapped lubricant can create hydraulic dents in the shoulder. The vent hole normally allows excess lubricant to escape. However, if force is applied rapidly, the excess lube may not vent fast enough. If you find hydraulic dents, first check to see that the vent hole is clear and clean the die. Excess lube on the pad can be removed with a clean shop rag or paper towel. Only the case body—not the shoulder and neck—needs lubrication.

An oil-dented case will usually fire without failing but it may be weakened. Discard the case rather than risk a case failure.

Difficult Sizing

If you notice that you need to exert more force than usual when sizing (even though the case is clean and properly lubed and the die is clean), stop and do the following:

- make sure that you have the correct die installed.
- see if the case is the correct one. A 358 Winchester case is similar in appearance to the 35 Remington but is larger in diameter.
- see if the case was excessively bulged from previous firings. Some surplus military cases that have been fired in machine guns will have more bulge than cases fired in a sporting rifle.
- check the case for major dents.

Special Sizing Dies for Semi-Automatic Rifles

Difficult chambering or extraction can occur in some makes of semi-automatic rifles. Reloading with RCBS Small Base sizing dies usually corrects the problem because the SB die reduces the case diameter slightly more than a standard sizing die.

Headspace Problems—Bottleneck Cases

Headspace for a bottleneck cartridge is controlled by the position of the shoulder. If the case shoulder is pushed back too far during sizing, excessive headspace will result and cause poor accuracy or misfires. In the worst case, a case may rupture and ruin a rifle and/or injure the shooter or bystanders.

Shoulder position can be accurately measured to ±.001" with the RCBS Precision Mic™. See chapter 8 for more information on this tool. Due to the quality of most current reloading dies, over-sizing is rare. However, three factors can cause this:

- the die or shell holder has been modified by removing metal where they meet. Either alteration puts the shoulder of the die too close to the shell holder resulting in excess headspace. Never modify a sizer die or shell holder.

- the sizer die and shell holder are different makes. Although most manufacturers of dies and shell holders use the same reference dimensions, a mismatch can occur. Usually it is small and does not create a safety hazard. Avoid homemade shell holders or mixing different brands of dies and holders—you have no guarantee that they are dimensionally compatible.

- a rifle has a "long" chamber due to excessive headspace. Even though the dies are properly adjusted, the case will fire form to the chamber's longer base-to-shoulder length. Normal sizing pushes the stretched shoulder back, reducing accuracy potential and case life. The Precision Mic will tell you if your rifle has this condition and how much to adjust the die to avoid recreating an excessive headspace condition.

The amount of headspace control afforded by reloading is limited and does not extend to using factory ammo. You should have such a rifle properly repaired rather than risk its falling into the hands of someone who's unaware of the rifle's condition and history.

The problem of over-sizing is more prevalent with belted cases. Review the section on sizing bottleneck cases in chapter 8.

Neck Expansion Problems

If neck expanding seems unusually difficult, remove the spindle assembly and inspect the expander ball. Grit accumulating on top of the ball increases the force needed to expand the neck. Clean it while it's out and verify that the rod is not bent.

Normally, expander balls will process tens of thousands of cartridge cases without showing wear. However, really dirty cases can scratch the working surfaces of the ball. If so, polish the ball lightly or replace it.

It's normal for fired cases to have powder residue on the interior. If the residue is unusually heavy, it can cause hard neck expansion even with a properly adjusted and maintained expander. Case necks should be cleaned thoroughly with an RCBS Case Neck Brush after lightly rolling the brush across your case lube pad. Don't dip the brush in lube—too much lube will contaminate powder.

Priming Difficulties—"Hard" Primer Seating

Difficult primer seating is a fairly common problem. If you encounter this, STOP LOADING UNTIL THE PROBLEM IS CORRECTED. Never force a primer or use sharp blows during any priming operation. Slow, even pressure is mandatory for safety. Here are some things to check:

- **Is the primer the correct size?**
- **Is the primer punch the correct size and shape?**
- **Is the primer punch bent?**
- **On swing-arm primer punches, is the arm free to move fully into position?** A build-up of primer residue on and around the arm and its spring can prevent it from centering under the case. The effect is similar to that of a bent punch—the primer is misaligned and cannot smoothly slip into the case. Clean excess residue from the press regularly.
- **Is the primer pocket clean and undamaged?**
- **Does the case have a crimped pocket?** Completely remove the crimp with an RCBS Primer Pocket Swager.

Primer pocket shape can vary with the brand of case, and even within one brand. If the radius between the sidewall and the bottom of the pocket is too large, it will stop the primer anvil prematurely causing a high primer and misfires. RCBS makes three sizes of its Primer Pocket Uniformer to remove this excess metal leaving a square pocket bottom that greatly improves seating and ignition. The Uniformer fits in the electric Trim Mate™ case prep center but may also be used manually.

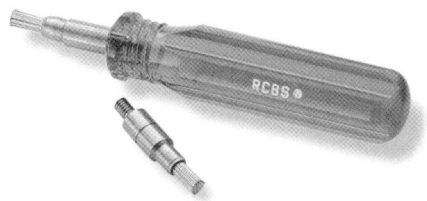

You will eventually encounter some combination of primer and cartridge case that causes excessive priming force. A different combination is the only solution to this problem.

An RCBS Primer Pocket Brush

Primer Feeding in Progressive Reloading Equipment

Progressive reloading presses feed primers through automated devices. A buildup of dirt and residue causes most malfunctions in these priming systems. Progressive equipment must be cleaned regularly to insure safe and smooth operation. Remove the shellplate in rotary-type loaders to clean under it. Keep the primer shuttle and the surrounding area clean. DO NOT USE OIL except as directed by the tool manufacturer.

Check primer feed tubes for residue and damage. Replace any bent or damaged tubes; never attempt to repair them. If the tubes are dirty inside, clean them. Review the section "Powders and Primers" in chapter 6 for instructions on safely cleaning primer tubes.

If the priming mechanism is clean and still doesn't work properly, review your instruction manual to learn the procedure for proper adjustment. If in doubt, contact the equipment manufacturer.

Powder Charging

This critical area of reloading is fortunately one where few problems occur. However, two potential problems can occur that can lead to significant safety problems.

Missing Powder Charge

A missing powder charge will cause a misfire. In small-capacity cases, it is also possible for the primer's output to drive the bullet out of the case and stick it in the bore—a dangerous condition if another cartridge is fired! Careful process control and simply paying attention when reloading will assure you avoid this situation.

If after you have seated the bullet, you suspect that you failed to charge a case, a simple test will help you find out. Place a primed, uncharged case (same brand) and a bullet of the same weight you loaded in the scale pan and record the weight. Then weigh the suspect cartridge. If the suspect cartridge weighs within a few grains of the weight of the bullet and primed case alone, then the charge is missing.

Proper charging practices and inspection will eliminate missing powder charges. Review chapter 7 for the recommended procedures.

Progressive loading equipment reduces the opportunity for inspection compared to single-stage equipment. Review chapter 10 for more information on these tools.

Variable Powder Charges

A charge variation of a few tenths of a grain in a large rifle case may have little effect on accuracy or performance. However, variations of several grains can cause problems.

Accuracy can suffer and charges falling on the high side may cause excessive pressures. These large variations are usually caused by improper powder measure techniques.

Operate the handle in a consistent manner. When throwing large charges of rifle powder, allow enough time for the entire charge to flow through the measure. Check the powder measure routinely to see that all lock screws and fittings are tight.

If you are not using a powder measure and get large variations in hand-weighed charges, make certain that your scale is clean. Dust in the pivots (mechanical scales) can cause erroneous readings. Is the scale level? If you move the scale to another location in the shop, ALWAYS rezero it with the leveling screw. Check the scale with calibrated weights available from RCBS and other manufacturers.

Is the scale affected by drafts? A cardboard deflector placed over a vent or around the scale will eliminate the problem. Mechanical scales must be located at least three feet from fluorescent light fixtures to avoid interference from electromagnetic fields.

Bullet Seating Problems—Hard Bullet Seating

Hard bullet seating can ruin cases for further reloading. Here's a checklist:

- **Are you using the proper diameter bullet?** A 7mm bullet is .007" larger than a 270 Winchester bullet and will also cause dangerous pressures if the cartridge is chambered and fired.

- **Has the case neck been properly sized and expanded?** If you fail to adjust the expander ball properly, the bullet can collapse the case. Expander rods held by collets in some makes of dies can loosen, slide up and not expand the case neck at all.

- **On straight-wall cases, is there enough flare on the case mouth?** Variable flare is often due to non-uniform case lengths.

- **Is the case mouth too sharp?** If loading new cases, you must chamfer the inside of the case mouth to remove burrs, but only after you have made sure the case mouth is round; otherwise, it will be uneven or incomplete.

Bullets Fall into the Case

This is an easy problem to spot and fix. Check the following items:

- **Are you using a bullet of the correct diameter?**
- **Did you fail to properly size the case?**

Lead Bullets that Seat Deeper as Loading Progresses

This is caused by bullet lubricant gradually building up on the seater plug or the crimp shoulder. The build-up pushes each bullet slightly deeper into the case until the seating depth is excessive. In some cartridges this can cause excessive pressure. Remove the seater die and disassemble and clean it thoroughly. A very light coat of oil or release compound will slow future build-up. Remember that too much oil is worse than none at all!

All Speer® lead handgun bullets now feature an improved lubricant that virtually eliminates lube accumulating in the seater die.

Crimping Problems

Never attempt to roll-crimp jacketed bullets that do not have a crimping groove. Doing so will only damage the bullet and degrade accuracy.

If you have trouble crimping bullets that have a crimping groove, look for the following:

* **Is the proper die installed in the press?**

* **Is the seater plug adjusted so that the crimp groove meets the crimp shoulder in the die?** If not, adjust the seating depth accordingly. Attempting to crimp above or below the groove will probably damage both case and bullet.

* **Are the cases trimmed to uniform length?** Variable lengths will cause some cases to be crimped too much and others very little. If cases are trimmed too short, you may not be able to crimp them at all.

* **Are you collapsing the case mouths or shoulders during crimping?** If so, you are applying too much crimp. Adjust the die to apply less crimp. When crimping bullets in cases with thin mouths (32-20, 44-40, 375 H&H, etc.) you will find that seating and crimping in separate operation will minimize this.

"Erasers" for Reloaders

If you discover that you have made a mistake, you will need to take the defective cartridge apart to salvage the components. Just as pencils have erasers to correct mistakes, the reloader has access to a couple of different ways to "erase" his errors. Bullet pullers come in both collet and inertial types.

Collet Bullet Pullers

RCBS sells a collet-type bullet puller that mounts in the die station of a single-stage press. The puller unit usually consists of three parts: the body, a threaded shaft with a handle and a collet. Collets are caliber-specific—you will need a collet for each diameter bullet you need to pull. A 30-caliber collet will work with most standard .308" diameter rifle bullets.

The puller body is screwed into the die station and the collet attached to the handle assembly. Insert the cartridge into the proper shell holder and raise the ram so that the bullet (but not the case mouth) fully enters the collet. Turn the puller handle clockwise until the bullet is firmly gripped. Give the press handle a sharp upward blow to lower the ram and extract the bullet. Turning the handle counter-clockwise releases the pulled bullet from the collet.

The pulled bullet will likely have shallow marks from the collet jaws. Most bullets' performance will not be affected by these marks and can be reused. However, thin-jacketed varmint bullets may be crushed in the process and should be discarded.

Inertial Bullet Pullers

The collet-type puller cannot be used to pull lead bullets or most jacketed handgun bullets and can damage thin-jacketed varmint bullets. In these situations an inertial puller is the answer.

RCBS Inertia Bullet Puller

Inertial pullers look like hammers with hollow heads. The cartridge is placed in a chuck assembly that grips the rim or extractor groove with the cartridge inside the puller body. The assembled unit is struck against a hard surface. The puller and the cartridge case stop but the inertia of the bullet causes it to move forward out of the case.

Bullets removed with the inertial puller are seldom damaged unless excess force is used. The bullet and powder charge are caught in the puller body for reclaiming.

Do not try to pull the bullet with one hard blow. Several light taps will pull the bullet safely and effectively. Heavy blows can break the puller or deform the bullet and may cause the cartridge to discharge.

Here are some safety precautions to follow when using an inertial puller, regardless of make:

* **NEVER** put a rimfire case in an inertial puller.
* **NEVER** attempt to disassemble a black powder cartridge with an inertial puller.
* **NEVER** use an inertial puller to pull bullets from cartridges with high primers. Under certain conditions, the primer can snap hard against the bottom of the pocket and ignite. Use a collet-type puller if possible.
* **NEVER** attempt to disassemble any cartridge whose projectile type cannot be positively identified. Accidents have occurred when someone attempted to pull an explosive military projectile.
* **ALWAYS** use short, light taps instead of one heavy blow to remove the bullet.
* **ALWAYS** wear safety/shooting glasses when pulling bullets, just as in any other stage of reloading.

> **Tech Tip:** *Some factory ammunition, particularly military ammo, has a mouth sealant that effectively "glues" the bullet in place. When disassembling ammunition that may have this seal, run the cartridge into a bullet seating die of the proper size and seat the bullet about .005" to .015" deeper. This normally breaks the seal and makes extraction much easier.*

At the Range

Sometimes problems with reloaded ammunition do not show up until you get to the range. They may be functional problems but can also be accuracy problems.

Misfires

Misfires have been discussed in the section on components but this problem is common enough to warrant additional discussion. By far, the majority of misfire problems are due to a handloading error or a gun problem—not a primer defect.

Handloading Problems

- **Is the cartridge the correct one for the firearm?**

- **Is there propellant in the case?** Weighing the cartridge and comparing it to a primed case and loose bullet of the same type will usually tell you if the charge is missing.

- **Did you fail to remove the old primer from the case?**

- **Is the primer seated below flush?** Failure to do this is the most common cause of misfires in reloaded ammunition. The anvil legs must make contact with the bottom of the cup. CCI primers should be seated between .003" and .005" below flush for optimum sensitivity.

- **Has the primer or ammunition become contaminated with oil or water?**

- **In a bottleneck case, has the shoulder been pushed back too far?** This creates excessive headspace and the firing pin has to reach too far to make solid contact with the primer. Shoulder position can be checked with the RCBS Precision Mic.

- **In a straight-wall rimless case, is the case short?** This also increases headspace. Measure the case length with calipers and check against the minimum case length in the reloading data.

Gun Problems

Gun problems also cause misfires. Firearms-related items to check are:

- **Is the firing pin broken or damaged?** Check to see if the firing pin marked the primer.

- **Is the firing pin spring adequate?** Some after-market spring kits may not have the same energy as the original spring. Original springs may be altered or weaken with age. See that the firing mechanism is properly assembled. Some revolvers have a screw that controls the position and tension of the mainspring. Make sure this screw is fully seated.

- **Is the firing mechanism coated with grease or dirt that can slow the firing pin fall?** This problem will most likely show up in cold weather. A spray solvent like Outers Crud Cutter™ is useful for cleaning grease buildup.

- **Is there a build-up of powder residue or grease in the area of the chamber and breech face?** Residue here can cushion the firing pin blow, especially with rimmed cartridges. Thorough cleaning will usually correct the problem.

◆ **In rifles and semi-auto pistols, is there excessive headspace?** In revolvers, is there excessive front-to-rear play in the cylinder? This condition, *endshake*, is due to normal wear. Excessive headspace or endshake puts the cartridge too far from the firing pin, weakening its blow. Consult a qualified gunsmith to determine if excessive headspace or endshake is present and have it corrected.

The Bolt is Hard to Open

With any ammunition, a "sticky" bolt lift is a BIG DANGER SIGN. The cartridge may have produced excessive pressure causing the brass case to deform and wedge in the chamber. When you get the action open, examine the case for signs of high pressure. DO NOT fire any more loads from that batch.

For safety's sake, always assume the hard bolt opening is signaling excessive pressure. However, having difficulty opening the bolt could also be due to a mechanical problem with the rifle such as a rough or dirty chamber.

Clean and dry the bore and chamber to completely remove grease or oil before each range trip. Cartridge cases are designed to grip the chamber walls at peak pressure and then release when the pressure drops. Oil in the chamber or on the cartridge will cause the case to slip in the chamber at peak pressure and increase the thrust on the bolt. This may cause hard opening at normal pressures. In addition, excessive lubricant can attract and accumulate dirt.

Again, hard opening can be due to several factors; but your first reaction must be to think "DANGER!" and cease firing until the cause is understood and corrected.

Unusual Sounds and/or Recoil

Firearms producing supersonic velocities (over about 1100 ft/sec) make a sharp crack when fired. You probably have a good idea of how your firearm sounds and feels when firing factory ammunition. A soft report or unusually light recoil could indicate a squib load and the danger of a bullet being lodged in the barrel. Before firing any more ammunition, check for a bore obstruction.

If you hear a faint hissing sound following a shot or hear a sound like the opening of a beverage can when you open the bolt, you almost certainly have a bullet stuck in the bore! The bullet has plugged the bore and the residual gases are slowly escaping. Check the bore and clear any obstructions before taking another shot.

Variable reports are a sign of inconsistent propellant charge weights or ignition. These variations usually occur when using a hard-to-ignite propellant with a standard primer or when trying to develop reduced velocity loads in a large case. Either switch to a magnum primer or choose a different propellant.

Double sounds such as a "ker-WHUMP" or a detectable delay after pulling the trigger are also signs of poor ignition. They are relatively common when working up reduced loads in large cases. Normally, switching to a quicker burning propellant will eliminate this problem. We have provided lab-tested reduced loads for many of the rifle cartridges in this manual.

Semi-Automatic Rifles

Even with small-base sizer dies, it is possible to have malfunctions in semi-auto rifles. For best performance in most gas-operated semi-autos, use propellants having a medium burning rate. Slow-burning propellants may create too much gas for the gas system to handle. On the other hand, quick-burning powders may not generate enough gas to operate the action. Reloads should be kept close to factory velocity specifications for reliable functioning.

Light loads or a dirty chamber can cause poor extraction. If you discover that fired cases are covered with tiny dents, powder residue has built up in the chamber. Clean the chamber with a brush. Light loads can also cause poor feeding and extraction because they do not generate enough gas to fully cycle the action. The first round fired may have enough power to eject the fired case but not enough to move the bolt far enough to pick up the next cartridge in the magazine.

Some rifles function best with crimped bullets; others require crimping. Several Speer bullets feature cannelures so that secure crimping can be performed. If a reloader wants to shoot 150-grain bullets in a 30-caliber semi-auto, he can choose the 150-grain Mag-Tip®, which has a crimping cannelure. The crimp has two advantages in this class of rifle. It smoothes the sharp edge at the case mouth and also prevents the bullet from being shoved into the case when it strikes the feed ramp.

Many semi-auto sporters have very light barrels. To effectively evaluate accuracy, allow sufficient time between shots for the barrel to cool. This recommendation also applies to any rifle with a slim barrel profile.

Poor Accuracy

There are many factors that can affect accuracy. We will assume you are shooting from a solid rest and using a firearm that has already demonstrated its ability to produce good groups. Before troubleshooting the ammo, it is a good idea to troubleshoot the gun as follows:

◆ **Is the rifle chambered for the ammunition you're shooting?** Some cartridges will chamber and fire in firearms intended for a different cartridge. If you shoot a 257 Roberts cartridge in a 7mm Mauser rifle, the bullets would not properly contact the rifling and you will see "keyholes" in the target—if they even hit the target! Keyholes are elongated bullet holes caused by a tumbling bullet.

◆ **Are you positioning the firearm on the rest consistently?** Try to make each setup the same.

◆ **Is the barrel touching the rest?** Bench testing requires that the rest contact the rifle's forearm, not the barrel.

◆ **Are the sights firmly attached to the firearm?** Screws can work loose from recoil, allowing the sights to move with each shot.

◆ **Are the screws holding the action in the stock secure?** A loose action screw in a bolt-action rifle can open groups significantly.

◆ **Is the bore fouled with lead or jacket material?** This problem will usually show up later in the shooting session as more residue builds up in the bore.

◆ **Has a wood stock warped due to moisture absorption?** If your rifle and ammo shot well last season but refuse to perform now, a warped stock should be a prime suspect. If this happens, consult a gunsmith to have the situation corrected.

If these factors do not seem to be the problem, then review the things that can directly affect the ammunition:

◆ **Under-ignition**—This is usually caused by using a standard primer when a magnum primer is recommended. The shorter burning time of a standard primer may result in widely varying velocities. On the target, this usually takes the form of vertical stringing of the shots. This condition is more prevalent in cold weather.

◆ **Excessive headspace**—A bottleneck case with the shoulder pushed back too far or a rimless straight case trimmed too short can degrade accuracy.

◆ **Unnecessary crimp**—Have you attempted to crimp a rifle bullet that doesn't have a crimping groove? Group sizes can increase as much as 40 percent because this damages the jacket.

◆ **Mixed cartridge cases**—for critical accuracy testing, your cases should have the same headstamp and preferably be from the same lot. Better yet, weigh the cases and use those that weigh within a grain or two of each other. Near-equal weights can mean near-equal capacity and that's good!

◆ **Excessive lubricant**—Have you removed all traces of sizing lubricant from the cases? If not, they will be inconsistent in the way they grip the chamber at peak pressure.

◆ **Wind conditions**—A strong, gusting crosswind will cause horizontal dispersion of the groups. Light, high-velocity bullets are more subject to wind conditions than heavier, slower bullets. There's not much you can do about this problem. You may have to pack up and try again on a calmer day.

◆ ◆ ◆ ◆ ◆

Ammunition loaded with care and attention will give fine results. More problems arise from cutting corners and rushing the job than from ignorance or inexperience. Reloading is a more rewarding hobby if you relax and take the time to enjoy it.

chapter 12

Exterior Ballistics: Flight Planning for Bullets
Dr. Cristina A. Berisso and Dr. Gregory J. Mushial; GMDR, Inc.

Editor's Note: *Drs. Berisso and Mushial are co-developers of RCBS.LOAD® reloading and ballistic software from RCBS®. We are grateful to them for their excellent work in developing the software. We also appreciate their insightful understanding of the complex subject of exterior ballistics and their willingness to share it with our readers. Information on RCBS.LOAD is presented at the end of this section.*

• • • • •

Ballistics studies the propulsion, motion and impact of projectiles. Ably assisted by progress in mathematics, physics and chemistry, it has evolved to give sound answers to both old and modern problems of warfare. Like so many other endeavors, ballistic research that started for military purposes benefited the civilian community as well. From its origins, ballistics has tried to predict the initial firing conditions that will result in a desired strike and terminal effect. It is obvious that this is an extremely valuable tool for the sports shooter. After all, each of us eventually faces the question, "Am I zeroed right for this shot?"

Ballistics is a very old disciple. When some ancient *homo sapiens* armed with a rock or spear discovered that his "projectile" traveled farther when launched at a slight upward angle, he experienced ballistics in a very basic form. Ballistics itself has a fairly broad domain. It studies the laws of physics and chemistry that govern energy generation and dissipation during firing, forces exerted on the projectile in flight, and the energy dissipation and mechanical effects upon reaching the target. Although these are closely interrelated, modern ballistics is divided in three branches:

- *Internal Ballistics* (also called "interior ballistics") covers the complex phenomena that take place within the gun from the moment the primer ignites to the moment the bullet leaves the barrel. Many physical variables are involved in the process: propellant quantity and burning rate; case and primer characteristics; bullet size, shape, weight and seating depth; pressure/time effects; bore friction; barrel twist and length, etc. These extremely complex systems have been methodically investigated in detail on a large scale by bullet and propellant manufacturers and presented in data manuals for cartridge reloading like the *Speer® Reloading Manual.*

- *External Ballistics* (also called "exterior ballistics") studies the flight of the projectile between exiting the barrel and reaching the target. External ballistics studies and predicts the complete projectile trajectory, or *path*, relative to some frame of reference. The result is usually a firing table with the information on how to release the projectile in order to hit the target as the distance changes. The fundamental information in these tables normally includes the bullet path, i.e., the vertical distance that the projectile rises or falls relative to the line of sight (or LOS), its remaining velocity, and the time of flight (TOF) at different ranges. By knowing the full trajectory of the bullet, the shooter can reasonably predict where the bullet will strike and decide how to "zero" the firearm for best results. By knowing the remaining velocity (and consequently the energy) of the projectile at any point along its path, the shooter can estimate its effectiveness at any distance.

- *Terminal Ballistics* studies the stopping process of the bullet at the target. Penetration, material resistance, energy dissipation, projectile deformation and stability are some of the processes extensively covered by this branch. This is of particular interest for the hunter as it provides information on the most effective bullet for the selected game. For the military weapons engineer, terminal ballistics studies point to the most effective projectiles for use against armor or reinforced bunkers.

A History of External Ballistics

Ballistics research started as a weapons design tool long before gunpowder was introduced in Europe. Early war machines were stone-throwing catapults that evolved through the designer's intuition combined with trial-and-error field tests. If a catapult threw a rock 40 yards farther because the front of the machine was wedged up a few degrees, the catapult builder had applied external ballistics principles whether he knew it or not.

The first true firearms were massive machines that used gunpowder to improve upon catapult launching. Like the catapult, their main object was to launch bulky projectiles that could break through the thick walls of fortified cities allowing foot soldiers and cavalry to enter and deal with the defenders. Field commanders soon realized the anti-personnel attributes of artillery. If a large section of castle wall collapsed on thirty defenders, there were thirty fewer problems for the infantry to face in single combat.

With improvements to metal casting and other industrial disciplines, more portable firearms appeared by the beginning of the 16th century. Guns could be carried to the battlefield and entire armies turned away before they could set siege to cities. Targets were no longer huge, stationary walls but smaller, fast-moving knots of men and equipment. Ballistics research became a necessity for gaining control of the battlefield by using powerful, more accurate guns and smarter tactics. Nations supported research not only in ballistics but also in physics, mathematics and material sciences, knowing that each could assist in finding the answers that their military tacticians needed.

Initial research concentrated on describing and later predicting the trajectory of the projectile. It was first believed that the trajectory was a straight-line path until the velocity was almost zero, at which point the projectile would fall to the ground. Later descriptions involved two straight paths; the bullet rising straight in the direction of the barrel, reaching a maximum altitude and then changing to another straight-line path with the same angle as before but falling towards the target. In the middle 16th century an Italian artillery consultant, Tartaglia, first introduced the concept that the bullet path was a smoothly curved line.

Still, little was known about the real forces governing the motion of bullets. The research conducted by the Italian physicist and astronomer Galileo (about a century after Tartaglia's findings) led to a fundamental contribution to the science of that time: *that falling bodies are subject to a constant acceleration.* This permitted the first mathematical description of the force of gravity acting on the bullet and allowed calculation of the first trajectories.

It took almost another century to understand the importance of aerodynamic forces in describing the bullet path. This came with the British invention of the *ballistic pendulum* that, for the first time, allowed direct measurements of the projectile's *velocity.* The tests performed with the ballistic pendulum showed severe discrepancies with Galileo's trajectory predictions. It was evident that Galileo's simple approach was by no means complete. About the same time, Sir Isaac Newton did experimental research on air resistance to fast-moving objects and published the first description of air drag in 1710. Newton also formulated the fundamental laws of mechanics and the infinitesimal calculus that provided ballisticians (and science in general) with all the necessary tools to analyze and describe a mechanical system.

Bernoulli of Basel first introduced the concept of air drag into ballistics in 1718. Ballistic pendulum tests with faster projectiles started to indicate that Newton's description of air resistance was correct up to 1100 to 1200 feet per second. A large increase in air drag was found for projectile velocities close to the speed of sound.

Until the 1860's, all research was done with round balls; however, elongated projectiles were becoming more popular. Bashford, Professor of the Royal Academy in England, began ballistic research with the new conical projectiles in 1864. To facilitate his research, he developed a new form of chronograph to measure velocities. The Bashford chronograph gave surprisingly accurate results for its day and a series of firing tests began in 1865. Extensive ballistic research was conducted in different European countries by the middle and late 1800's. The most extensive tests were conducted in France (1873-1898) by the Commission d'Experience de Gavre. The work performed by Krupp in Germany and Colonel Mayevski in Russia became the foundations of modern ballistics. In the United States, Colonel James Ingalls of the U.S. Army converted Mayevski's work to English units. Ingalls' ballistic tables were the mainstay for American ballistic research until the early 1960's.

Drag and the Ballistic Coefficient

Once ballisticians realized the importance of air resistance on bullet flight, they focused enormous amounts of effort into studying the phenomenon. Several models were formulated and innumerable experiments were performed in an effort to understand the complex aerodynamic forces. The breakthroughs leading to a serious formulation of the drag took place after the first chronographs appeared and were applied to firing test research.

This research showed that the effect of air resistance on a projectile's motion depended on several measurable factors:

- the projectile's shape and diameter
- its velocity
- air density
- the local velocity of sound

Because the shape of the bullet was a clearly important factor, different projectiles with characteristic shapes were studied in great detail. The designs represented almost every conceivable form: round balls, cylinders, conical nose shapes, and an innumerable array of rounded point (ogival) missiles with different tip profiles. One particular design dominated the studies performed by Krupp in Germany and by the Gavre Commission in France. It was a flat base design whose length was three times its caliber. Its ogival pointed nose had a defining radius twice its caliber.

The Gavre Commission finally formulated the detailed drag function for this bullet in 1898, based on the research done in many countries. This bullet was adopted as the *standard bullet* for ballistic modeling and its well-known drag function was used

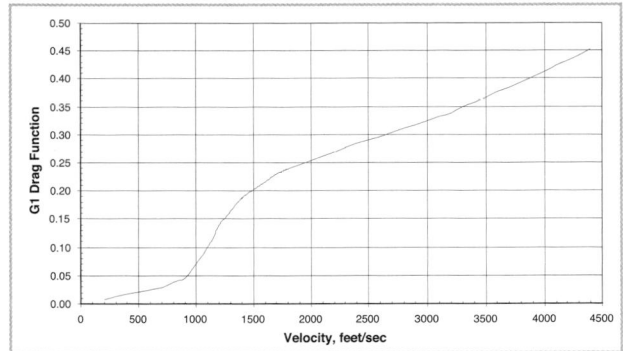

G1 Drag Function for the Standard Bullet

to derive the drag of other bullets by comparison. This research gave rise to the concept of the *ballistic coefficient*, denoted "C" when used in math equations.

The ballistic coefficient is a numerical gauge that compares a bullet's drag deceleration to the "standard bullet." Simply stated, it expresses the ability of the bullet to cut through air. The smaller the ballistic coefficient of a bullet, the greater air resistance it experiences. Drag slows a low BC bullet more than a high BC bullet. Ballistic coefficients are usually obtained under very specific atmospheric conditions to provide a common frame of reference and simplify its usage.

This concept allowed ballisticians to formulate the equations that describe the motion of a projectile using the well-studied standard bullet drag function instead of elaborating a different drag function for each type of projectile. The simple insertion of the ballistic coefficient accounts for the effect of air resistance on the bullet

The ballistic coefficient (C) is defined as the weight (w) of the bullet in pounds divided by the square of its caliber (d) in inches and by a factor related to the shape of the bullet (i):

$$C = \frac{w}{id^2}$$

The ratio of weight to the square of the bullet diameter in the formula above,

$$\frac{w}{d^2}$$

is known as *sectional density* (SD) of the projectile. It is a measure of the weight distribution through the cross-section of the bullet. Using this to simplify the equation for C, it becomes

$$C = \frac{SD}{i}$$

Traditional Firing Tables

The bullet trajectory is a product of the forces acting on it during flight. Forces include those pertaining to the Earth and its rotational motion (gravity, centrifugal and Coriolis forces), and aerodynamic forces produced by the resistance of the air to projectile motion. The equations of motion associated with this mechanical system can be very precise, since many of the above forces are quite well understood. However, the exact solution involves extremely long and complex procedures that are absolutely impractical for routine use.

A workable solution thus requires the simplification of the general equations that involves:

◆ disregarding those forces whose effect will be insignificant compared to the rest,

◆ reducing the bullet model to a point-like mass, and

◆ describing the remaining forces acting on the system by simpler terms.

Under these assumptions, the two basic forces that are taken into account are gravity and the air resistance to bullet motion. For simplicity, it is generally assumed that the gravitational field is constant along the bullet trajectory, and that the atmospheric conditions—temperature, atmospheric pressure, altitude and relative humidity—are standard. In this situation, the bullet path is curved and strictly within the vertical plane defined by the muzzle and the sighting devices fitted the firearm.

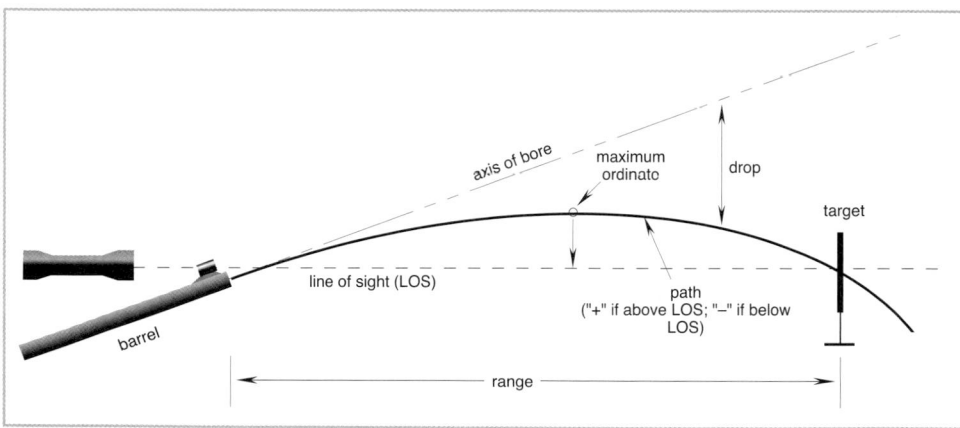

Diagram illustrating trajectory elements and references

In spite of this simplification of the equations that define trajectory, no general solution in terms of elementary functions was available. In the late 1880's an Italian artillery officer, Colonel Siacci, formulated a method for solving equations by approximating the bullet path to a very flat trajectory. Although such method limits considerably the ranges at which it can be applied and constrains the shooting conditions to low-angle firing, it was able to provide the best answers to the ballistic problem. Siacci's method, combined with the mathematical expressions for drag derived from the meticulous work of Mayevski, has been the basic tools used to calculate trajectories for years. It required the arrival of electronic computers for newer methods to evolve.

When using most published firing tables, the user must remember that they have been evaluated for low-angle fire with no wind, and for ballistic coefficients obtained at standard atmospheric conditions. All published ballistic coefficients are really standard ballistic coefficients (C_{std}). They were based on a drag function for atmospheric conditions defined as the *artillery standard* by the U.S. Army Ballistic Research Laboratory at Aberdeen Proving Ground, Maryland. These standard conditions are:

Altitude:	sea level
Temperature (T_{std}):	59° F (15° C)
Pressure (P_{std}):	29.53 inches Hg (750 mm Hg)
Relative Humidity (RH):	78%
Air Density:	0.0751 lbs/foot³ (0.001203 grams/cc)

In order to assemble the proper firing table, the user should first evaluate the *effective* ballistic coefficient (C_{eff}) for the environmental conditions at which the firing actually takes place. If the local atmospheric conditions differ from the standard ones, the published ballistic coefficient (C_{std}) can be corrected for these differences. The adjustments include a factor (F_p) due to pressure (P) differences:

$$F_p = \frac{(P_{local} - P_{std})}{P_{std}}$$

and a factor (F_T) due to temperature (T) differences:

$$F_T = \frac{(T_{local} - T_{std})}{T_{std}}$$

for temperatures in degrees Fahrenheit. Both standard pressure (P) and temperature (T) are not constant values—they vary with altitude (A) as illustrated in the formulas below. The user enters the standard pressure and temperature for the local altitude in the equations for the correction factors given above.

$$T_{std} = 59 - 3.5845 \times 10^{-3} A + 1.1905 \times 10^{-9} A^2$$
$$P_{std} = 29.527 - 1.0755 \times 10^{-3} A + 1.5289 \times 10^{-8} A^2$$

Air density, too, changes with altitude, consequently affecting the drag on the bullet. This is accounted for by the correction factor F_A given by the expression:

$$F_A = 2.7183^{3.02149 \times 10^{-5} A}$$

The ambient *relative humidity* (water content of the air) also affects the air density and thus the drag. Dry air generates higher drag than humid air, slightly affecting the ballistic coefficient adjustment. This correction factor F_{RH} depends on the local pressure, the water content in the air in percent, and the vapor pressure of water at the local ambient temperature. It is in general a value very close to one.

With these factors, the effective ballistic coefficient can be calculated from the equation:

$$C_{eff} = C_{std} (F_A (1 + F_T - F_P) F_{RH})$$

Now the user can generate the proper firing table using this effective ballistic coefficient. Knowing the bullet's velocity, the user can obtain the bullet's time of flight, velocity, energy, and position at different distances from the muzzle, and for different gun zeroing conditions.

The muzzle velocity is absolutely required to calculate the bullet's path. In the past, instruments to measure bullet velocities were complicated and expensive. With modern electronics and computer technology, today's chronographs are priced within easy reach for most shooters. Even the simplest electronic chronographs give an accurate velocity reading. Because different guns can give different muzzle velocities for the same load, knowing the exact velocity from your firearm allows you to accurately predict the trajectory.

Uphill / Downhill Shooting Corrections

Because firing tables result from horizontal firing tests, their values cannot be directly used when estimating shooting that includes an elevation angle. In general terms, since the muzzle is inclined at some angle, the initial (muzzle) velocity of the bullet now has a component in the vertical direction. For level fire, only gravity produces a vertical component. These alter the initial conditions of the equations of motion and the resulting trajectory. If the shooter wants to apply the level firing tables to shooting at an angle θ, the drop ($D_θ$) expected for flat firing (D_{flat}) is corrected by the trigonometric relationship:

$$D_θ = D_{flat} (1-cosθ)$$

where "cosθ" is the cosine of angle θ found in standard trigonometric tables. This arises from the fact that the bullet drop (D_{flat}) in flat firing is always perpendicular to the firing direction, which is not the case for angle shooting (see figure below).

Simply stated, for both uphill and downhill shooting, the bullet strike will be higher than expected for level shooting at the same distance. Thus, the shooter will have to aim lower in these conditions.

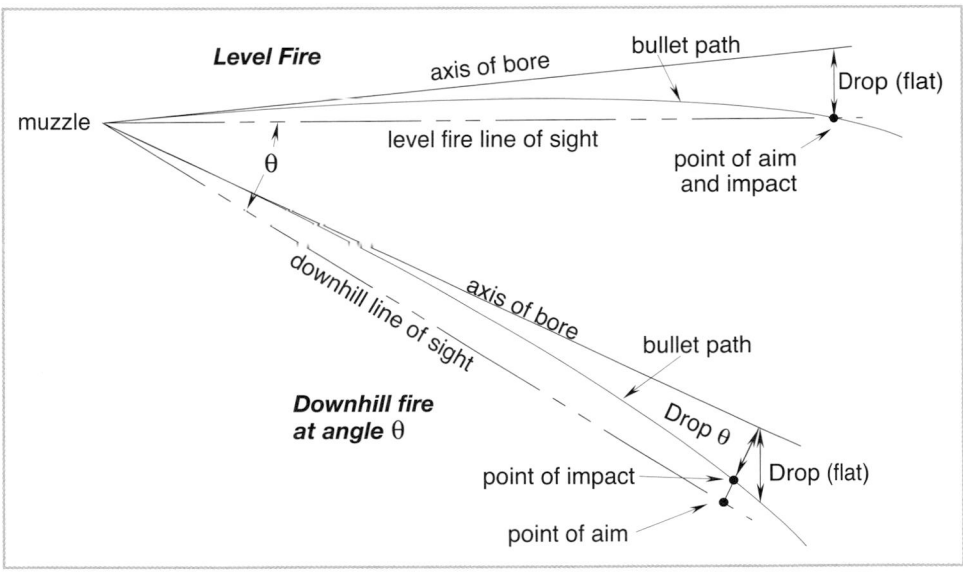

Second order corrections include the effects introduced by the changes in the gravity and air density when the bullet changes altitude in uphill or downhill shooting. Considering the velocity variations associated even with the best ammunition, these effects are small enough to be ignored for hunting and target shooting situations.

Wind Corrections

The drag exerted on a bullet by air resistance is a function of the velocity of the bullet relative to the air. Higher bullet velocity relative to that of the air, produce greater drag. If the bullet travels in moving air—wind—the drag force is different from firing in still air. When the wind blows across the line of fire (cross-wind), the bullet will be drifted from the line of the bore. The actual amount of drift is estimated with the formula given by the *lag-time model*:

$$\text{Drift}_R = V_w \left(\text{TOF} - \frac{R}{V_m} \right)$$

In this expression, TOF is the time of the bullet's flight (in seconds) to a given range R (in feet). V_w is the crosswind velocity and V_m is the muzzle velocity (all velocities are in feet per second). In this formula, drift is expressed in feet; multiply by 12 to convert to inches. There are other factors that affect drift but these are usually considered for artillery applications rather than small arms studies at normal hunting and target shooting distances.

In the presence of head winds, drag on the bullet is increased because the velocity of the bullet relative to the air is larger than when it goes through still air. With head winds, the bullet decelerates faster, reaches the target later with a larger drop and has less remaining velocity than when fired in still air.

Conversely, when tail winds are present, the drag on the bullet is less than in the case of no wind. A bullet at 3000 ft/sec with a 30 ft/sec tail wind has a relative velocity of 3030 ft/sec. The bullet will reach the target earlier, with a higher remaining velocity and will impact higher than in the case of no wind.

The action of wind on the bullet can always be broken into three component vectors at right angles to each other. There are no simple expressions to correct firing table trajectory values for head and tail winds. The best way to estimate their influence on trajectory is by performing numerical integration calculations, easily accomplished today with personal computers.

Point Blank Range

This term is badly misused in popular culture as implying the firearm was nearly touching the target. In classic ballistics, the meaning is much different.

Every game animal has a zone within which a bullet strike has high chances of killing the animal. This is called the *vital zone*, and varies in diameter according to the type of animal. This vital zone determines the target diameter.

Point blank range is a very useful ballistic concept, especially for the hunter. It is the horizontal distance where the bullet will hit within a specified zone, or target diameter, without the shooter having to hold over or under. The target size, weapon's zero range, bullet muzzle velocity and ballistic coefficient are all important factors in determining the point blank range. As the zero range is increased, the point blank range also increases.

However, there comes a point when the bullet path is so arched that the bullet will fly above and below the target diameter for part of its path requiring correction by the shooter. This is the *maximum point blank range* (MPBR). This concept can be visualized by extending an imaginary tube between the prey and the sights of the gun. The diameter of the tube is the diameter of the vital zone, and the tube is centered about the line of sight. Given the sight settings, load and environmental conditions, the MPBR will be the maximum distance along which the shooter can fire with a dead-on hold, and not have the bullet "touch" the imaginary tube at any point.

There is another way to look at MPBR. If the vital zone is 10 inches and the rifle/ammo combination has an MBPR of 290 yards, the bullet drop (below LOS) at 290 yards is five inches and the maximum ordinate (highest rise above LOS) is also five inches.

When you know the MPBR for a particular gun/ammo combination, you can use this information to pick a very effective sight-in distance. Once you decide what target diameter you need (a typical whitetail deer has a vital zone of 10 inches), you can determine the sight-in needed to obtain MPBR. You can hold "dead-on" for any shot out to that distance without having to memorize hold-over or hold-under. Mentally, the hunter has only to remember that he is shooting at a zone, not a point.

The drawback to this technique is that MPBR is hard to derive from classic trajectory tables. Only those tables having a fine resolution—numbers every 5 yards, for example—would give satisfactory accuracy. Most tables, including those in the back of this manual, are constrained to 50 or 100-yard range increments because of space limitations. They cannot contain enough information to accurately pinpoint the MPBR. That's where the power of the modern personal computer enters the scene.

Advantages of Using Computers

Some of the earliest computers, first mechanical and then electronic, were developed to help artillery personnel solve ballistics problems. With fast and inexpensive computers flooding the consumer market, their benefit in solving complex ballistics equations is readily apparent. Problems that were once only handled by large research facilities with powerful mainframe computers can now be solved in seconds by the hobbyist with an inexpensive desktop PC. The first attempts to use computers for solving ballistic problems were centered on the production of basic firing tables. Combining the use of Siacci's approximation method with the computational abilities of early computers made the calculations faster and more reliable.

The big step forward came with the approach of using computers to actually solve the complicated differential equations of motion by the method called Numerical Integration by Finite Intervals. In this approach, no simplifying approximations are required to the equations of motion. As long as the forces acting on the system are well known and described by mathematical terms, the exact solution can be obtained. It is, in fact, the only method available for the accurate solution of most differential equations and, therefore, widely used in science and engineering.

For ballistic calculations, this method divides the bullet's flight into a large number of small time steps. Given the coordinates for the position and velocity of the projectile at the beginning of the first step, the equations allow for the evolution of such coordinates in the small time step. The resulting values for position and velocity at the end of the first step are obtained. The process is then repeated for the second and following steps, using the resulting values from the previous step as input for each subsequent step. Because of the massive number of calculations that result, only the computational power of a computer can solve the problem in an acceptable period of time.

The smaller the step used in the integration, the greater the accuracy of the method (within limits). The task of the computer programmer is twofold:

- finding the point at which a further decrease in the size of the step simply increases the labor (or time) of computation with no significant improvement in precision, while

- identifying the maximum number of steps allowed that produce the desired accuracy, beyond which the result diverges due to error leakage.

In other words, the programmer must stop the calculation from producing divergencies due to accumulated rounding errors. When both of these conditions are met, it is said that the calculation has achieved its *convergency*.

The great advantage of using numerical integration in ballistic calculations is that any environmental or firing condition can be included in the system and be computed exactly. There is no need to use the awkward tables derived from Siacci's method that are valid only for shooting conditions close to level fire. The computer always calculates the exact trajectory for the given set of shooting conditions, whatever they are.

No "corrections" are necessary for uphill or downhill shooting when the path is calculated by integration. The actual bore angle is included in the initial conditions and the exact trajectory is obtained. No corrections due to cross- or tail-winds are needed because the environmental conditions are placed directly into the equations of motion. Gravity can be entered in its real form as a function of altitude. The effect that small alterations to standard shooting have on the bullet path can be observed. For example, slight rotations ("canting") of the gun around the line of sight, small variations in the initial velocity, or the changes in zeroing conditions can be included in the initial conditions. Because the calculations are performed step by step, multi-valued ballistic coefficients (different values for different velocity ranges) are naturally accessed as the velocity of the bullet changes.

Maximum point blank range is easily determined because the computer does what tables cannot—rapidly divide the trajectory into sufficiently small slices to permit accuracy. RCBS.LOAD optimizes the trajectory to fit the target diameter with a single mouse click and tells you exactly where to sight your firearm to achieve MPBR.

As the last topic, let us mention that, with the personal computers that have been on the market in the last 20 years, the computational time required for integrating trajectory calculations is no longer the problem faced by early researchers. A well-optimized program can perform a large number of these calculations in one second. As an example, RCBS.LOAD, working on a consumer PC with a very basic 133 MHz Pentium® processor, completes at least 120 trajectories per second. In other words, with computers whose performance is painfully slow by today's standards, RCBS.LOAD can calculate the entire set of ballistic tables published in the *Speer Reloading Manual* in under a minute.

RCBS.LOAD®—Comprehensive Software for the Serious Shooter

RCBS was one of the first reloading firms to offer ballistics software, dating to the late 1980's. The old program has been replaced by a totally new package, built from the ground up for today's computer-using reloader and shooter.

Traditionally, computer ballistic packages fall into two categories: those that calculate the path of the bullet (external ballistics), and those that catalog the user's own load data. Few packages let you do both and, of those, most don't include a wealth of factory-generated load data. If they do include data, it's usually from a single source. In other words, you had to buy at least two programs and you had few if any analytical tools to help you learn from the stored data.

That changed for the better.

The current RCBS program is RCBS.LOAD. It does sophisticated external ballistics modeling and lets you graph and analyze loading data—either your own or factory data from many sources. It also has a number of useful utilities. Here's a brief overview of the program and what the shooter and reloader can do with it.

Getting Started

RCBS.LOAD quickly installs from a CD with only two mouse clicks. The process is automated and, when complete, lets you launch RCBS.LOAD from the Windows Start menu or by clicking on a desktop icon. When you start the program, you see the main screen showing a cartridge list of over 800 commercial and wildcat cartridges. Load in a database—let's say the *Speer Reloading Manual #13*—and every cartridge contained in that database is highlighted with a "+" sign. Double-click on a marked cartridge and the sources available in the database are listed. Double-click again and the loads from each selected source are now displayed on your monitor. This is handy, but the format is still text-based. With RCBS.LOAD, you can do much more.

Load Data Analysis—The Big Picture

It's been said that a picture is worth a thousand words. Historically, some reloaders have hand-plotted performance data for visual analysis, spending hours with graph paper and pencil. If you routinely do this, you can put that pencil aside.

RCBS.LOAD also lets you view reloading data as a graph on your computer screen. Graphing lets you see how loads relate to each other in picture form. Let's say that you are looking for an efficient load for the 30-30 Winchester cartridge and a 150-grain bullet. The graph utility in RCBS.LOAD initially plots the data with charge weight across the bottom (horizontal axis) and velocity up the side (vertical axis). By the way, you can change the axes to other values if you wish.

Now we have a graph with families of lines representing the propellants used. For many cartridges, it's possible that some of the powders listed are a little too fast or slow for a particular cartridge. The graph quickly shows the powders that give the best velocity for the least charge, generally a good situation considering the cost of component powders today.

RCBS.LOAD always calculates the bullet energy and the IPSC/USPSA power factor (weight times velocity divided by 1000). IPSC shooters have to attain certain power factors for competition. If you're using the printed copy of any manual, you have to manually calculate the PF for each load to find those that "make major." In RCBS. LOAD, all you need do is set the vertical axis to display power factor instead of velocity and find the line that represents the level you need. Any load above that line makes "major." Easy!

For a cartridge where the data source has many bullet weights and powder types, the initial plot will look crowded, of course. If you combine all the standard and optional databases and graph them at one time, there are over 9000 loads for the 30-06 alone! This isn't a problem for RCBS.LOAD.

RCBS.LOAD lets you sort and filter to make graphs easier to read. Sorting is accomplished by displaying multiple panes, or "mini-windows." If you wish, you can set up the graph utility to sort the data by bullet weight, for example. If there are eight bullet weights in the database for the 30-06, selecting this option displays eight smaller panes each showing the powders and charges for their respective bullet weight. Clicking on any one of these small panes zooms it to full size for easy viewing; clicking a second time returns the screen to the original set of small panes.

Filters are provided to limit the bullet weights, powder types and barrel lengths that are displayed. If you want to view all the data for one cartridge using IMR 4350 powder, selecting this filter will let you do just that.

When the graph first opens, the lines (or points) aren't labeled. You can choose up to two labels for the data if you like. This makes the data easier to interpret. Sometimes, you may want to see the original numbers that went into plotting the data. You could go back to the main screen, but RCBS.LOAD lets you see them without leaving the graph. Simply click on any line or point with the right mouse button and a "Loads Specifics" window will pop up on the screen with all the information in the original database that plotted that line.

RCBS.LOAD allows merging two or more databases to form a larger one. Let's say that your most-used manuals are the *Speer #13* and the optional *Hodgdon #26*. Load in one, and then tell the program to overlay the next. RCBS.LOAD will go to work combining the two (a one-time operation whose speed depends on your computer's power). When merging is complete, you simply save the new file with a different name (ex. "My favorite data") and the larger file is always available to you in the database library. The merging happens on a cartridge-by-cartridge basis; that means all the 257 Roberts loads are listed together on the main screen. The original data sources are still clearly identified to avoid confusion.

Exterior Ballistics Horsepower

The power of the personal computer to calculate and model the path of a bullet has been part of many ballistics programs. What sets RCBS.LOAD above the rest is the convenience, sophisticated technology, and options incorporated. RCBS.LOAD does not use the obsolete method of "look-up values" (space-time functions) to calculate trajectories. Instead it uses the actual equations of motion to quickly and precisely describe the trajectory in great detail. All initial conditions that affect trajectory can be entered on the working screen. Wind, elevation, weather, uphill/downhill conditions and even any side-to-side "canting" of the gun can be quickly dialed in. Any changes you enter causes the program to immediately update the trajectory, so it's easy to do "what if" analysis of a trajectory. "What if I switch to a boat tail bullet? What if I'm shooting at 7,000 feet elevation instead of 700?" RCBS.LOAD will answer your "what if" in milliseconds.

With RCBS.LOAD, you can access this function in two different ways. If you are looking at the main screen, simply click on the "Tools" button and select "External Ballistics Calculator" from the menu. We'll call it the "XBC" from here on.

You can also reach the XBC from the Graph Utility. When viewing data in the "full screen" format, right-clicking on a line to bring up the Loads Specifics box and then right-button click again on any of the loads in the Specifics box. The XBC appears, with the bullet and its muzzle velocity already set.

Once in the XBC, clicking the "Standard Bullets" box label toggles it from component bullets (there are over 1600 of them in there) to a list of some 1500 factory loads including popular rimfire cartridges. You don't have to be a reloader to use RCBS.LOAD.

The XBC shows a side view of the bullet's path over the range you select, up to 1000 yards. There's also an axial view that shows a face-on view of the target. This view is useful to see effects of crosswinds or canting the gun.

A very useful feature consists of three interrelated boxes in the XBC header. They are "Zero Distance," "Sight-in Distance," and "Sight-in Vertical Offset." These are especially handy when your shooting range doesn't have enough distance to let you do a long-range sight-in. Let's say you have only a 100-yard shooting range but want to hit dead-on at 275 yards. Set the Sight-in Distance to 100 and the Zero Distance to 275. The Vertical Offset box will tell you exactly how high you need to be at 100 yards for the bullet to intersect the line of sight at 275. Conversely, if you know you are hitting 3.5 inches high at 100 yards, you can dial in these values to find out where you are zeroed.

The XBC also lets you determine maximum point blank range (MPBR) for a given load and target diameter. Once you have the conditions and target diameter entered in the upper portion of the screen, clicking the "Optmz PBR" button will calculate the MPBR in three dimensions.

Trajectory comparisons among different loads or cartridges are also easy because the XBC lets you set up to five trajectories as "reference" points in addition to the current plot. They plot on the screen in numbered patterns so you can see how your load compares.

Using RCBS.LOAD with Your Personal Data

Most reloaders have a file of their favorite loads. It may be in an old notebook or on a collection of 3x5 cards. What if you could organize that collection and analyze it in detail? RCBS.LOAD lets you analyze loads you developed in the same way you analyze loads from factory sources. Included is a "Construct User Data" feature that allows you to enter your data in a format that RCBS.LOAD reads. The entry screen looks like a spreadsheet but actually allows you to convert your data to electronic form without any programming or spreadsheet experience. Included are powerful statistical utilities to analyze any chronograph data you have. Gun type, group size, statistical values and environmental conditions can be entered, too. Once entered, you can use all the program's tools to better understand your loads.

If you have buddies who are also using RCBS.LOAD, you can share your personal databases with them. Simply copy the file you built to a disk or send it as an e-mail attachment.

More Tools

As if the above weren't enough, RCBS.LOAD is packed with other useful tools for the reloader and shooter:

- See a cartridge in the list that you don't recognize? There's an electronic library of dimensioned cartridge drawings that includes hundreds of commercial and wildcat cartridges. Like the Graph Utility, the Cartridge drawing lets you display multiple drawings in separate panes and zoom each to full-screen size with a mouse click. When the drawings are displayed in multiple panes, each drawing is scaled so that it is the proper size in relation to the others.

- A kinetic energy calculator lets you see changes in energy as bullet weights and velocities change. You can set the range of velocities to be viewed and print the graph for reference.

- There's a chart that predicts minimum recommended twist rates. Find the bullet description and the velocity and then look up the optimum rifling twist for that combination.

- Wildcatters will enjoy the Cartridge Designer. Start with a parent cartridge and move shoulders, necks and body tapers and watch the internal capacity be recalculated before your eyes.

- ❖ Also included is a Ballistic Coefficient Calculator. Starting with the muzzle velocity, you can use a downrange velocity, time-of-flight, or bullet drop to estimate the BC.
- ❖ RCBS.LOAD can be connected to a chronograph for direct data input.

Examples of many of these features can be found at the web link at the end of this chapter.

What's Included

The RCBS.LOAD package includes the full program plus databases from the following sources: *Accurate Reloading Manual #2; Alliant® 1998* and *2000 Reloading Reference; Hodgdon 1998* and *2002 Reloading Reference; LaserCast #1; RamShot #22*; the *RCBS Cast Bullet Manual; SomChem 1997; Speer #13; Vectan #4; VihtaVuori 2000 Reloading Reference; Winchester Reloading Reference #15; Winchester 2000 Reloading Reference.* Yes, you could laboriously type in all the data from these sources but why bother—it's free with RCBS.LOAD. Right out of the box, you're ready to analyze all the loads in these sources plus create your own databases. Electronic databases include all the load data from each manual, but not the pictures and text.

There's also a handy index of reloading sources. Load it in just like the other data sources and it shows you places to find published data. The actual data isn't in the index—there isn't room—but you have a road map of where to find the data. It's much like the card catalog at the local public library. Wildcatters will find this to be a very useful search tool when researching for existing load data.

In addition to the features already described, there are several useful reference functions, including a powder burning rate chart, metric equivalents, and industry pressure assignments.

What's Available

Even though the basic package includes a wealth of loading data, you can expand your RCBS.LOAD library even more by purchasing other electronic data sets from RCBS. These include just about every reloading manual, both current and historical, published in the United States in the last four decades, including every *Speer Manual*, even the rare Wildcat versions (numbers 2 and 4).

Of course, you could use the Construct User Data tool to laboriously type in a book you already own, but it might take a month or more if you're a good typist. The charge for the add-on manuals is simply a transcription fee so you can spend your time shooting instead of typing! A list of available add-on databases is in the back of the program's instruction manual and in the web link at the end of this chapter.

What It Takes—System Requirements

In spite of its sophisticated features, RCBS.LOAD system requirement are mild. You need a minimum operating system of Windows 95®, Windows 98® or Windows NT® (v3.51 or higher). Newer versions of Windows including Vista® are completely supported. The minimum recommended processor is a 486DX 66mHz, backed up by 16 MB RAM. All Pentium® processors are supported as well and those from other firms producing Windows-compatible processors. The standard installation needs only 8 MB of hard disk space (up to 20MB if all add-on libraries are installed). Of course, faster processors and more RAM simply mean your RCBS.LOAD use will be that much faster.

RCBS.LOAD also requires a monitor capable of displaying 256 colors at a minimum resolution of 800x600 pixels (a setting of 1024x768 is highly recommended for best viewing and to have all tool buttons available). An Internet connection is optional but recommended to take advantage of electronic software updates.

Keeping it Current

Version 3 of RCBS.LOAD can automatically update itself when new databases and incremental improvements are released. If you have an Internet connection, you can perform the updates without leaving the program.

Learn Even More

Software changes faster than we can print reloading manuals. If you're connected to the Internet, visit **www.gmdr.com/rcbs/rcbs.htm** for the latest information on RCBS. LOAD, including updates, databases, and detailed system requirements.

RCBS.LOAD is available from your RCBS dealer. Add-on electronic manuals (databases) are available from RCBS by calling 800-533-5000.

Windows 95, Windows 98, Windows NT and Vista are registered trademarks of Microsoft, Inc. Pentium is a registered trademark of Intel, Inc.

chapter 13

Black Powder Cartridge Performance: A New Look at an Old Art
By Brett Olin with Allan Jones

Editor's Note: *Brett Olin is a CCI® Development Engineer and a 24-year veteran at CCI-SPEER®. In addition to knowing more about ammo than anyone I know, Brett is a Cowboy Action shooter who uses black powder exclusively in match events. He also shoots long-range black powder competition. Brett is a skilled reloader and gunsmith and a student of military and firearms history. The black powder project was Brett's proposal and he directed the design and execution of all the experiments.*

· · · · ·

We learn by applying modern technology to understand the technology of the past. Egyptian mummies have given up their medical secrets to magnetic resonance imaging (MRI). Modern metallurgists have analyzed hull plates from the *RMS Titanic* wreck with the latest methods available. We did the same thing with cartridges loaded with black powder.

When we replaced our old 45-70 Government copper crusher test barrel with a new electronic transducer barrel, we had the opportunity to study black powder with the latest technology. The 45-70 cartridge made an excellent test subject because it is a standard industry cartridge and commonly used in long-range black powder shooting events. Other cartridges used in that field of competition do not have SAAMI standards and test barrels cannot be calibrated with precision.

Black powder bullets and 45-70 cartridges tested. 421-gr bullet (l) and 524-gr bullet (r).

Copper crusher pressure testing is best described as a low-resolution photograph of the firing event that only captures the instant of maximum pressure. Crusher testing reliably tells you if a load is safe—and that's important—but it yields little about the short-lived firing events inside a cartridge. Modern electronic transducer (XDCR) pressure testing is equivalent to a high-resolution digital motion picture that records pressure from the moment the pressure activates the electronic sensor until the bullet exits the barrel. Modern equipment gave us new insight on black powder's firing cycle.

Rediscovering Black Powder Cartridge Loading

For years, modern reloaders putting black powder in cartridges used the same method as they used for smokeless propellants. They poured in the powder and used the bullet to push until the charge was compressed. Brett Olin remembers his youth when he and his best friend Mark Baker attempted to load black powder 45-70 loads. They weighed out 70 grains of FFg, dumped it into modern cases and packed it by seating 500-grain bullets. Even though the bullet noses were crushed (who knows what the bases looked like!), the young reloaders were still surprised that every bullet keyholed at 50 yards.

Brett and Mark weren't the only ones that had trouble. The overall poor results in using black powder in cartridge firearms kindled interest in learning how the "old guys" did it.

Several people were the key to reinventing technology our 19th Century counterparts used daily. They researched old reloading articles (there were few), found early government arsenal records and drawings, and disassembled old cartridges. They also did a lot of range testing to find what works and what doesn't.

One of the most prolific writers on black powder shooting is Paul A. Matthews. He has written a number of books on cast bullet and black powder shooting. An author search for his name at any of the online booksellers will return an impressive list of Matthews' publications.

RCBS Black Powder Measurer

One of the leading researchers into the black powder 45-70 cartridge was Spencer Wolf who produced an important book on the subject, *Loading Cartridges for the Original 45-70 Springfield Rifle and Carbine*. Using original arsenal documentation he began testing to determine how to most closely duplicate military loadings with modern cases, primers and bullets. His research included bullet design, bullet lubricants, powder compression and priming. Wolf's excellent book is still available through a number of online booksellers, especially those specializing in gun books.

Steve Garbe and Mike Venturino have made huge contributions to the art of black powder cartridge shooting. Both are experienced competitors and have decades of experience between them. They co-authored several technical books including the *Black Powder Cartridge Primer* and publish a periodical, *The Black Powder Cartridge News*. Both publications have black powder load data for a number of cartridges. They also developed a specialized bullet lubricant, SPG™, for black powder. Information on their books and other products is on the SPG website, www.blackpowderspg.com.

Combining all this research and practical testing means we can now assemble black powder cartridges that work in a manner we believe recreates the shooting experiences of the earliest days of the cartridge era. Because of the efforts of these dedicated researchers, the Speer technical staff knew the following factors were important before we began modern pressure testing:

◆ Lead bullets must be cast from soft alloys.

◆ Special black powder bullet lubes must be used.

◆ Lube wads between the powder charge and the bullet base were quite useful.

◆ Special charge compression techniques are required with some black powders for proper combustion. Compressing the charge with the bullet during the seating operation only serves to deform the bullet base.

When we load ammunition using these factors, it shoots well. What we did not know or only partially understood makes another list:

◆ How much pressure does black powder generate in a cartridge?

◆ How does the internal firing cycle compare to smokeless propellants?

◆ What is the effect of powder granulation on pressure? (A number followed by the letter F traditionally expresses granulation or granule size. The smaller the leading number, the larger the granule size: 2F powder is coarser than 3F.)

◆ Do different brands of black powder affect internal ballistics?

◆ Do primers of different types affect performance?

Some of these questions could be at least partially answered using chronographs alone but testing on electronic pressure equipment gives a much larger picture.

Test Conditions

We used a standard set of test conditions to study these questions. It's important to keep certain things constant.

- ◆ **Test Barrel:** Krieger chrome-moly 24-inch barrel made to SAAMI chamber specifications fitted with a PCB Electronics conformal transducer. The barrel was mounted in a Universal Receiver. The bore was swabbed with a slightly damp patch between shots to keep the fouling soft.

- ◆ **Sample Size:** Ten rounds of each sample.

- ◆ **Cases:** New Winchester 45-70 cases from a single lot. A pressure transducer is routinely calibrated for one brand of case but we wanted even better resolution and calibrated the test equipment to one lot of cases.

- ◆ **Bullets:** Most of the testing was done with 524-grain cast lead bullets from Montana Precision Swaging. The version selected was a round-nose design with four lube grooves and a hardness of 9 BHN. They were weight-selected to ±1 percent, the standard industry tolerance for bullet weight. We fired a reduced data set with a 421-grain flat nose bullet, also from Montana Precision Swaging, a four-groove design with the same hardness.

- ◆ **Lubricant:** SPG™

- ◆ **Over-powder Wad:** Cabela's 0.030-inch vegetable fiber wad treated with SPG.

- ◆ **Powder Charging:** We used loads recommended to Brett Olin by Steve Garbe. Powder charge was determined by volume. The amount of bullet shank plus fiber wad that is seated into the case marks the top of the powder column. The bullet does no compressing. The case is filled with the amount of powder that corresponds to this level (whether compressed or not). If a compressed charge is desired, the amount of compression is added to the column height. This is a volumetric measurement and a black powder charger can be set up to produce this. In our experiments the resulting volumes were then converted to weight so as to more precisely repeat the powder charges used in each string. All charges were poured into the case using a long drop tube.

- ◆ **Powder Compression:** We compressed charges according to common practices of competition shooters. GOEX and Elephant powders were die-compressed; the Swiss powders were not. We made a die fitted with a flat-faced punch to allow compression of the powder column before bullet seating.

❖ **Cartridge Conditioning:** All test samples were conditioned for at least one week before firing to allow internal air pressure to equalize.

The Variables

Our variables in the test program were:

❖ **Black Powder Brand and Granulation:** We used: GOEX 2F; GOEX Cartridge; Elephant 2F; Swiss 1½F; and Swiss 2F for every test. GOEX 3F was used in five primer tests but was eliminated from further testing to reduce demand on our limited supply of same-lot cases.

❖ **Primers:** For standard rifle primers, we selected; CCI 200; CCI BR2; Federal 210; Winchester WLR; and Remington 9½ LR. For magnum rifle primers, we selected: CCI 250; Federal 215; Winchester WLRM and Remington 9 ½ LRM. We also tested one standard large pistol primer, the CCI 300. To investigate the question, "Does black powder need a special primer mix," we also tested several experimental CCI primers. Those results are not presented for reasons that will become apparent later.

Answering the Questions

Q: How much pressure does black powder generate in a 45-70 cartridge?

A: With 524-grain bullets and up to six different brands and granulations of black powder, the observed average pressures ranged from a low of 14,498 psi (GOEX Cartridge; CCI 250 primer) to a high of 20,765 psi (GOEX 3F; Federal 210 primer) giving velocities of 1049 and 1152 ft/sec, respectively. Limited testing with 421-grain bullets yielded a range from 11,920 psi (GOEX 2F; CCI 250 primer) to 16,748 psi (Swiss 2F; Federal 210 primer).

To put these pressures in perspective, these are maximum pressures for common modern cartridges:

❖ 32 Automatic: 20,500 psi

❖ 38 Special +P: 20,000 psi

❖ 45 Automatic: 21,000 psi

Q: How does the internal firing cycle compare to smokeless propellants?

A: Transducer testing allows capturing a time-pressure trace that plots the change in pressure with time. Smokeless propellants produce a distinctive trace with a very steep initial pressure rise and a gradual decline as the bullet travels down the barrel. We typically plot all ten traces for one sample on the same chart so any abnormal shots within one sample stand out.

Time-pressure traces for the black powder 45-70 samples were quite similar to smokeless propellant traces. This disputes claims of some pundits that black powder simply explodes, blasting the bullet down the barrel. The traces clearly show that black powders burn progressively and in a manner quite similar to modern propellants.

Q: What is the effect of powder granulation on pressure?

A: Finer granulation increases pressure. Comparing GOEX 2F with GOEX 3F (Table 1) shows a significant pressure increase with the finer 3F granulation and a small increase in velocity even though the charge weight was 2.5 grains less.

Table 1: Effect of Granulation; GOEX Powders					
Powder	Granulation	Bullet	Charge Wt, gr	Velocity, ft/sec	Pressure, psi
GOEX	2F	524-gr MPS	63.5	1053	15425
GOEX	3F	524-gr MPS	61.0	1149	20170
			Change, Percent	9.1	30.7

The other powder brand where we had two granulations was Swiss Black Powder. Swiss has "half-steps" of granulation and we tested 1½F and the slightly finer 2F. The charge weights were the same and the smaller granulation steps made less difference, but the finer 2F gave slightly higher pressures and velocities (Table 2).

Table 2: Effect of Granulation; Swiss Powders					
Powder	Granulation	Bullet	Charge Wt, gr	Velocity, ft/sec	Pressure, psi
Swiss	1-1/2F	500-gr MPS	63.5	1119	19402
Swiss	2F	500-gr MPS	63.5	1145	19972
			Change, Percent	2.3	2.9

Q: Do different brands of black powder affect internal ballistics?

A: The answer is an unqualified "yes." When we completed the most complex test (524-grain bullet with six black powders and up to ten primer types) it was clear that the propellant type had the greatest effect on pressure and velocity. Table 3 shows the "all primers" averages for two bullet weights.

This in no way says that one brand is "better" than another across the board. Instead it shows that the black powder cartridge reloader has a choice of propellants that he can match to the type of shooting he does. For example, if you do not want to use a powder compression die, the two Swiss powders are the ones to choose. If you're comfortable with compression and want maximum velocity, then GOEX 3F takes the prize. It's not much different from selecting a smokeless propellant.

Q: Do primers of different types affect black powder performance?

Discussion: The effect of primer types was the driving force behind this study. We needed to know if CCI should consider creating a special black powder cartridge primer. We knew that black powder competitors have strong primer preferences. Some use pistol primers looking for a "soft" ignition while others feel a magnum primer better ignites heavily compressed charges and the higher flame temperature reduces residue.

The only way to find out was to study how existing primers performed. Remember we also made and tested some special primer compound formulas and tested them along with the ones you can buy today.

A: Of the results of these tests, primers were the biggest surprise. Of course, there were differences but they were too small to be of statistical significance. When you look at Table 3, you see that the last row shows the number of different primers used in obtaining the averages. If the number of primers is 10, that means 100 rounds were tested in 10-shot strings, each string representing a different primer. The all-primer average velocities, pressures and the standard deviations and extreme variations for each powder type are as consistent as 50 percent of the 10-shot groups fired with one primer type. Let's put it another way: as long as you use one kind of black powder and properly

Table 3. All Primer Summary

421-Grain Bullet		
Powder	GOEX 2F	Swiss 2F
Charge Wt, gr	63.0	63.0
Compression	0.100"	none
Velocity, ft/sec	1,095	1,208
Vel. Std. Dev.	11	8
Vel. Ext. Var.	36	27
Pressure, psi	12,412	16,465
Pressure Std. Dev.	627	736
Pressure Ext. Var.	1,843	2,569
No. of Primer Types	5	5

524-Grain Bullet						
Powder	GOEX 2F	GOEX 3F	GOEX Cartridge	Swiss 1-1/2F	Swiss 2F	Elephant 2F
Charge Wt, gr	63.5	61.0	65.0	63.5	63.5	69.0
Compression	0.100"	0.100"	0.100"	none	none	0.100"
Velocity, ft/sec	1,054	1,149	1,058	1,126	1,140	1,079
Vel. Std. Dev.	11	8	10	9	14	9
Vel. Ext. Var.	33	25	34	29	37	29
Pressure, psi	15,257	20,170	14,807	19,208	19,734	15,827
Pressure Std. Dev.	1,004	1,179	656	787	657	819
Pressure Ext. Var.	3,311	3,806	2,133	2,539	1,987	2,672
No. of Primer Types	10	5	10	10	10	10

Table 4: Statistical Averages by Primer Class
45-70 Black Powder Cartridge; 524-Grain Lead Bullet

Standard Rifle Primers		V	P
Fed 210	SD	9	843
	Range	28	2730
CCI 200	SD	11	745
	Range	30	2455
CCI BR2	SD	13	890
	Range	37	2787
Win WLR	SD	10	694
	Range	31	2280
Rem 9-1/2 LR	SD	9	837
	Range	28	2857
Average	SD	10	802
	Range	31	2622
Magnum Rifle Primers		V	P
Fed 215	SD	14	950
	Range	42	3103
CCI 250	SD	9	863
	Range	27	2609
Win WLRM	SD	9	771
	Range	27	2411
Rem 9-1/2	SD	10	859
	Range	34	2782
Average	SD	11	861
	Range	33	2726
Standard Pistol Primer		V	P
CCI 300	SD	12	744
	Range	33	2415

Table 5: Flash Hole Diameter
45-70 Gov't; 524-Grain Bullet 70.0 Grain GOEX 2F with 0.300" Compression; CCI 200 Primer

	Standard Flash Hole	Modified .096" Flash Hole
Ave. Velocity, ft/sec	1067	1065
Vel. Std. Dev.	13	9
Vel. Ext. Range	39	27
Ave. Pressure, psi	15222	15110
Pressure Std. Dev.	1285	1200
Pressure Ext. Range	4639	3646

Based on 10-shot strings

load the cartridge, you can load ten cartridges with a different primer in each and not have any greater shot-to-shot variation than half the tests fired with a single primer type. Table 4 shows a summary by primer type.

The experimental CCI primers we tested showed the same behavior. The bottom line is, at least in the 45-70 cartridge, primer choice is a second-order variable that can be ignored as long as you take care in the other variables. CCI decided there was not enough evidence to support the development of a special black powder cartridge primer.

Although the numerical indicators show little difference among primer types, the time-pressure curves are more revealing. Each curve overlays the ten shots that make up one test string. The numerical indicators don't report *time-to-peak*, the time in microseconds for the charge to reach its maximum pressure but it is readily apparent on time-pressure printouts. The time-to-peak is more uniform with standard rifle primers than with magnum rifle primers across the board. The pair of time-pressure curves presented here shows the magnum primer overlay is clearly more "ragged" than the overlay for standard rifle primers (see illustrations). A more uniform time-to-peak alone is good reason to choose standard primers over magnums when loading 45-70 black powder cartridges.

What about pistol primers? They gave reasonable ballistic results in our limited tests with them including time-to-peak uniformity. However, you must remember that a large rifle primer pocket is deeper than a large pistol pocket and that pistol primers seat

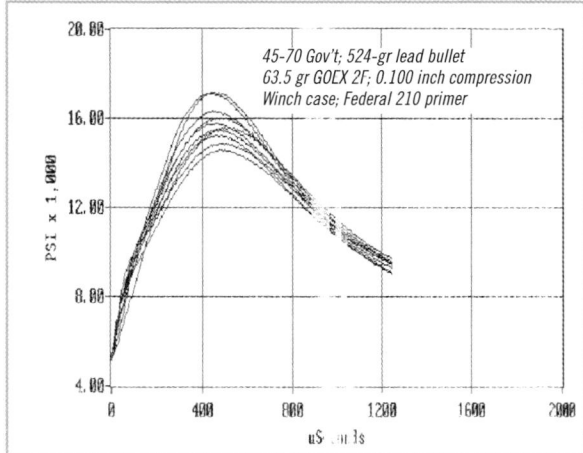

10-shot Overlay Time-pressure Curve—Standard Primer

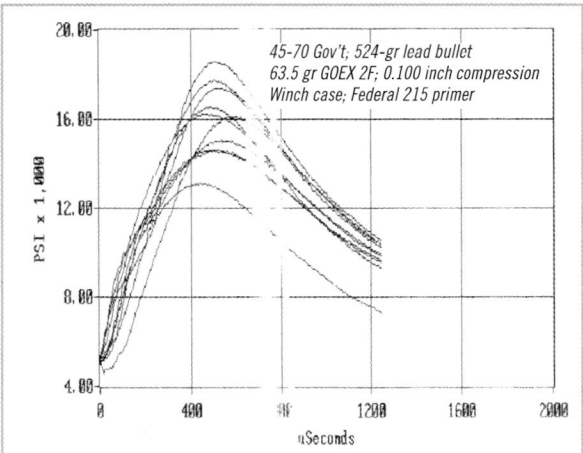

10-shot Overlay Time-pressure Curve—Magnum Primer

too deep in rifle cases. This could lead to misfires in some firearms. That's the last thing you need in a big match.

Other Considerations

One of Spencer Wolf's interesting observations is the flash hole in the 45-70 cartridge case. Original Frankfort Arsenal military cases were Benét-primed and have two flash holes. Modern cases are Boxer-primed and have a single flash hole. Wolf calculated the surface area of the twin flash holes and found it greater than a modern case's single hole. He calculated that you have to ream a modern flash hole to 0.096-inch diameter to match the flash hole area of original Frankfort Arsenal cases.

We thought this was an interesting idea and loaded samples using the 524-grain bullet, 70 grains of GOEX 2F with 0.300-inch compression, and CCI 200 primers. We were by then nearly out of our same-lot cases so could not try more propellants or primers. We had enough cases for two 10-round samples. One sample had a standard flash hole and the other was reamed to 0.096-inch. Table 5 shows the results of this limited test.

The average velocity and pressure are unchanged but the standard deviations and extreme variations are lower (better) for cases with the Wolf-modified flash holes. We're not yet ready to stake our jobs on this but feel that additional work with other powders could lead to a conclusion regarding flash hole modification.

Another variable is the effect of crimp. However, we felt the consistency of the un-crimped rounds in the primer and propellant tests was quite good. Crimping is not required for most competition cartridges as they are loaded singly. We judged that we could find a powder/primer combination in our existing data that would provide more than enough consistency for competition without crimping.

Getting Meaningful Results from Your Testing

We've presented a lot of data here and made some conclusions. Whether or not you reach similar conclusions from your chronograph or accuracy testing largely depends on how well you respect statistics in your testing. If your velocity or accuracy tests lead you to a conclusion based on 3-shot strings per sample, the results are not statistically valid. Your sample size is too small to make a general statement. We used the industry standard for pressure and velocity testing, the 10-shot string. Even 5-shot strings can lead you to erroneous results. In his youth, the *Manual* editor worked up some loads for his pet Ruger 7x57. A load printing five-shot groups under an inch the first day shot nearly two inches a week later from the same rifle and under nearly identical environmental conditions. Why? The first sample was too small.

Take a coin from your pocket and flip it four times. It's quite easy to get three heads and one tail—a 75 percent condition—yet you know that the coin should produce as many heads as tails. Flip the coin twenty times and the heads-to-tails ration will move closer to 1:1. A hundred flips will more it even closer.

Get the "picture?" A computer picture consisting of four giant pixels can't be understood by anyone. Double the pixels and you probably still can't make it out. However, continue to double and at some point the number of pixels (the sample size) is large enough for you to get an idea of what the picture represents.

Here's another example: the entire population of a town is in a large building and you are in a separate room where you can't see the crowd. One at a time people come in to meet you. Of the first five people, three have red hair. Would you conclude that 60 percent of the town is red-headed based on meeting five people out of several thousand? No. Your natural intuition tells you that there aren't that many redheads. You must train your shooting intuition to the same point.

Statistics in data analysis strives to give you a reasonable picture of the whole without using up the whole. Data analysis can only give a representative picture of a group through proper sample size and technique.

Go Make Some Smoke

When speaking of black powder, telling someone to "go blow smoke" is a good thing. We entered this project to learn what today's technology could tell us about a historical product, the black powder cartridge. We don't intend to create a black powder loading manual; Steve Garbe and Mike Venturino plus others have already done that very well. Using ballistic test equipment found only in major ammunition facilities, we've conclusively demonstrated that:

- Black powder generates pressure in the range of several common smokeless powder cartridges.

- Black powder burns progressively.

- Pressure increases as granule size decreases.

- Varying the make and type of propellant can yield significant differences in performance, much as smokeless powder does.

- Varying primers does not create unacceptable ballistic variations but standard rifle primers produce a more uniform time-to-peak than magnum rifle primers.

- Modifying the flash hole shows promise for improved uniformity and deserves further investigation.

• • • • •

We hope that this section gives you some insight into what contributes to black powder performance in a cartridge.

Brett Olin with two target types used in black powder long-range shooting. The bear silhouette is used for 200-yard shooting and the bison target is used beyond 500 yards. Brett's competition rifle is an original Model 1884 "Trap-Door" Springfield.

Black Powder Summary—45-70 Gov't. Cartridge; 524-Grain Bullet								
Primer Brand and Type		**Fed 210**		**Fed 215**		**CCI 200**		**CCI BR2**
Powder		Vfps	Ppsi	Vfps	Ppsi	Vfps	Ppsi	Vfps	Ppsi
Goex 2F 63.5 Grain .100" Compression	Ave	1058	15793	1058	15974	1049	15300	1056	15550
	SD	10	875	19	1667	10	492	11	935
	Range	33	2613	49	5453	27	1717	41	3133
	High	1075	17148	1085	18564	1063	16065	1079	17416
	Low	1042	14535	1036	13111	1036	14348	1038	14283
Goex 3F 61.0 Grain .100" Compression	Ave	1152	20765	1150	20278	1149	20197		
	SD	7	1081	11	1012	7	1051		
	Range	22	3589	33	3621	24	3622	Not Tested	
	High	1163	22885	1166	22140	1157	21892		
	Low	1141	19296	1133	18519	1133	18271		
Goex Cartridge 65.0 Grain .100" Compression	Ave	1059	15277	1056	14609	1055	14772	1057	14967
	SD	9	441	8	916	8	492	7	558
	Range	31	1212	27	3279	28	1555	22	1685
	High	1071	15829	1069	15650	1070	15683	1070	15740
	Low	1040	14617	1042	12371	1042	14128	1048	14055
Swiss 1 1/2F 63.5 Grain No Compression	Ave	1116	19770	1126	19817	1118	19455	1141	19799
	SD	5	871	17	500	9	1202	18	932
	Range	17	2645	61	1384	29	4004	45	3052
	High	1126	20834	1173	20517	1131	20948	1166	20549
	Low	1109	18189	1112	19133	1102	16944	1121	17497
Swiss 2F 63.5 Grain No Compression	Ave	1128	19845	1148	19995	1160	20153	1130	19411
	SD	9	492	20	811	21	629	20	1306
	Range	27	1570	51	2303	44	1888	56	3679
	High	1142	20679	1178	21273	1176	21062	1166	20688
	Low	1115	19109	1127	18970	1132	19174	1110	17009
Elephant 2F 69.0 Grain .100" Compression	Ave	1090	16736	1088	16816	1082	16180	1076	15716
	SD	11	1295	10	794	8	605	7	718
	Range	37	4753	32	2580	27	1945	20	2385
	High	1115	19093	1106	17758	1094	17001	1088	16920
	Low	1078	14340	1074	15178	1067	15056	1068	14535

CCI 250		CCI 300		Win WLR		Win WLRM		Rem 9-1/2 LR		Rem 9-1/2 LRM	
Vfps	Ppsi	Vfps	Ppsi	Vfps	Ppsi	Vfps	Ppsi	Vfps	Ppsi	Vfps	Ppsi
1050	15157	1050	14900	1059	15273	1054	15338	1048	14671	1054	14612
10	689	10	1242	12	876	8	620	10	1081	8	1565
31	1904	32	4582	40	3182	21	1831	30	3922	26	4769
1069	16309	1061	16407	1083	17502	1064	16513	1063	15902	1066	16749
1038	14405	1039	11825	1043	14320	1043	14682	1033	11980	1040	11980
1147	19647	1149	19965	Not Tested		Not Tested		Not Tested		Not Tested	
7	1554	9	1195								
19	4554	27	3646								
1156	21477	1165	21994								
1137	16924	1138	18348								
1046	14574	1049	14498	1063	14976	1064	14722	1063	14574	1065	15105
6	573	13	590	11	755	11	450	10	752	18	1031
19	1563	47	2051	31	2027	34	1620	32	2483	69	3858
1057	16293	1074	15439	1079	16098	1077	15333	1086	15675	1107	17270
1038	12855	1027	13388	1048	14071	1043	13713	1054	13192	1038	13412
1117	18814	1116	19156	1126	18830	1134	18420	1132	19123	1132	18898
6	699	9	661	10	687	8	943	5	647	7	723
22	2400	25	2214	27	2343	22	2751	17	2059	26	2539
1131	19613	1133	20037	1143	19556	1146	19418	1141	20126	1141	19670
1109	17213	1108	17283	1116	17213	1124	16667	1124	18067	1115	17131
1138	19537	1152	20331	1136	19828	1141	19586	1133	19319	1136	19332
15	835	20	349	9	616	8	498	10	476	8	557
52	2872	44	863	30	2116	22	1685	24	1343	21	1554
1176	20256	1176	20696	1155	20696	1152	20102	1145	20061	1151	19971
1124	17384	1132	19833	1125	18580	1130	18417	1121	18718	1130	18417
1084	16691	1080	16028	1076	15271	1068	14806	1068	14906	1073	15120
8	830	8	424	8	536	10	1342	9	1229	9	420
21	2360	25	1132	26	1733	35	4167	35	4476	30	1188
1096	18043	1094	16619	1093	16228	1086	16448	1087	16838	1089	15593
1075	15683	1069	15487	1067	14495	1051	12281	1052	12362	1059	14405

Introduction to the Rifle Data

The following section presents reloading data for Speer® bullets in popular rifle cartridges. We've added many new cartridges since printing the previous edition and retested others. If you have used older *Speer Reloading Manuals*, you will notice some differences in the format.

First of all, you will notice that the data table layout is different for *#14*. The new format was first adopted when we started publishing supplemental data on the revamped Speer Bullets website in 2004 and allows direct export of our internal data files to a publication format, greatly reducing the opportunities for transcription errors. We believe you'll find it easier to read and use. Loads are ranked by maximum charge velocity with the highest at the top.

Starting charges used to be set automatically as a fixed increment below the maximum based on case volume and were the same for every propellant used in a cartridge. Now the start charge increment is based on the pressure of the start charge, chosen to avoid low-pressure regions where ballistic uniformity suffers. Some propellants listed for the same bullet weight may have a two-grain reduction and others a four-grain spread. Read data tables carefully.

Beginning with *Manual #12*, we included the cartridge overall length (COAL) that we used in our testing. This was a much-requested feature and it is shown in the small table below the bullet illustrations. However, understand that this figure is a guideline, not gospel. Your rifle may require a longer or shorter length than we used. Case length also affects COAL of ammunition requiring a crimp. If your cases are a slightly different length from the lots we used in testing, you will need to make minor changes in COAL to apply a proper crimp.

It is your responsibility—and yours alone—to determine the proper and safe COAL for your rifle. Please refer to chapter 7 for more information on bullet seating techniques for rifle cartridges.

We show the letter "C" behind the charge weight where compression of the propellant was necessary to assemble the load. However, your propellant charging technique may not be the same as ours and your results may vary. Using a powder funnel with a long drop tube—we like the RCBS® Quick Change Powder funnel—will make charging easier and reduce the amount of compression you apply. However, difference in case construction and even propellant lot variation can mean that your loads may compress when ours did not.

Using the Tables

There is a very basic rule for using the tables:

Always start with the minimum load!

All gun authorities recognize there are differences among individual firearms. The maximum loads shown were safe in the test equipment—both pressure barrels and production rifles—that we used during load development. However, your rifle may have some dimensional differences that could result in higher or lower operating pressures. Because you cannot know whether a pressure change will be up or down, using the starting load will give you the margin of safety required due to individual rifle variations. Start charges are generally 4 to 8 percent below maximum, depending on the size of the case.

Maximum loads mean exactly that—MAXIMUM! Under no circumstances should you exceed these loads. They are presented to indicate the maximum performance potential for the cartridge based on industry standards; however, variations in individual rifles may not permit safely using them in every situation.

Here is the bottom line—read it twice:

You must always start with the minimum load and carefully work up toward the maximum in small steps, watching for pressure signs as you shoot each successive increment.

Changing Components

Any change in components—primers, bullets or cases—from those listed requires that you return to the starting load and work up, just as with a new load. We also recommend that you note the propellant lot you are using in your reloading records. If you change lots when assembling maximum loads, we suggest you drop the charge one to two grains and fire several test rounds to make sure the load is still safe for your rifle. Once this is established, you can carefully work up toward the old load level. Modern propellant manufacturing techniques give remarkable lot-to-lot consistency but some minor variations may still occur. We have no control over the manufacturing practices of other component companies. This is another reason why we provide starting loads and emphasize beginning with them.

• • • • •

SAFETY INFORMATION

- ◆ All reloading data contained herein is intended for use only by persons familiar with handloading practices, their own firearms and reloading equipment.

- ◆ Before using this data to assemble any ammunition, you must read and understand the reloading safety guidelines in chapters 6 and 10 and all safety-related cautions in the individual cartridge sections.

- ◆ We strongly urge new reloaders to read and understand the text of this manual. It has been written to give clear instruction in the principles and processes of reloading.

- ◆ Use the most current data. Components and cartridge standards change over time and these changes will affect load recommendations in the *Speer Manual*. It is fruitless to compare modern data to that published decades ago. Using old data with current components can create unsafe ammunition.

- ◆ If you are uncertain of the operation of your reloading equipment or the properties of any components, contact the manufacturer for additional assistance. Never be afraid to ask for help.

DISCLAIMER

These loads are for Speer bullets. Bullets of other makes will not produce the same pressures and velocities and can create an unsafe condition if used with loads shown here.

Because ATK has no control over individual loading practices or the quality of the firearms in which the resulting ammunition may be used, we assume no liability—either expressed or implied—for the use of this load data information and instructional materials.

The data contained herein replaces, supersedes and obsoletes all data previously published by Speer, Omark Industries and Blount International, Inc.

22 Hornet

Certain old cartridges never loose their charm and the tiny 22 Hornet is one of those. It evolved from an old black powder cartridge, the 22 WCF. Experimenters at the U.S. Springfield Armory, including Colonel Townsend Whelen and Captain G. L. Wotkyns, developed the cartridge with smokeless propellants, using M1922 Springfield rifles converted from rimfire. In its final form, the Hornet case was given a bit more shoulder so it could not chamber in older rifles intended for the low-pressure 22 WCF cartridge.

The cartridge was quickly picked up as a commercial item. Winchester produced the first 22 Hornet factory rifles and ammunition in the early 1930's. Traditional factory ammunition is loaded with 45 or 46-grain bullets at about 2650 ft/sec; in the last decade, Hornet loads with lighter bullets (33-35 grains) at higher velocities became available.

Myth: *An old 22 Hornet myth needs to be debunked. Decades ago, warnings went out to avoid hollow point bullets when hunting with a Hornet. If the bullet missed the varmint and struck the ground, it could produce a nasty ricochet, bouncing away nearly intact.*

Fact: *Old hollow point bullets were very primitive; with thick, hard jackets; they probably didn't expand even if they squarely hit the varmint at ranges beyond 50 yards at Hornet velocities. Today's hollow points are highly evolved, and much more likely to disrupt in a ground strike than modern soft points.*

The Hornet enjoyed immediate popularity as a medium-range varmint cartridge in North America and Europe; its mild report made it especially suitable for use in settled areas. A number of quality rifles have been chambered for the Hornet since its introduction. Currently, Ruger and Remington list Hornet rifles in their catalogs.

The Hornet is still an excellent choice for varmints out to 200 yards. Because of its small case, rifles can be built on light and compact actions. The popularity of the Hornet in Europe remains quite high and a number of high-grade Hornet rifles are still produced there, including expensive rifle/shotgun combination guns.

Because of its moderate velocities and the relatively slow 1-in-16 inch rifling twist found in some production rifles, the Hornet shoots best with 40 and 45-grain bullets. Bullets heavier than 52 grains will not stabilize in Hornet rifles unless they have twist rates faster than 1-in-16 inch.

In 2003, Speer added a special TNT® varmint bullet expressly designed for the Hornet. At 33 grains, it posted 3200 ft/sec from our Krico test rifle and shot 0.8 inch at 100 yards (average of five 5-shot groups).

The Hornet's case walls are quite thin and cases generally do not last as long as larger centerfire cases. Inspect often for incipient head separations after each firing and destroy any cases that are in questionable condition. If you are loading for only one rifle, consider neck sizing after the first firing for improved case life and accuracy.

A relatively new propellant, Hodgdon Lil' Gun, proved very effective; it produced significant velocity gains with all bullet weights except the 33-grain TNT.

The industry maximum average pressure of the Hornet is 43,000 CUP, and these loads are within those guidelines.

Important Note: *For this manual, we used CCI small pistol primers instead of rifle primers. This change allowed higher velocities at safe pressures, and greatly reduced the extreme variation of pressure that limited the number of propellants we showed in previous books. Do not use these loads with small rifle primers, as excessive pressure will result. We tested for primer flowback, a potential problem for thin-cupped pistol primers at rifle pressures. These loads did not produce flowback in any of the falling block, swinging block, or break-open actions we used. If you experience flowback in your rifle, it probably means there is too much clearance between the firing pin and the breechface, or the firing pin spring is weak. This should be correct by a gunsmith.*

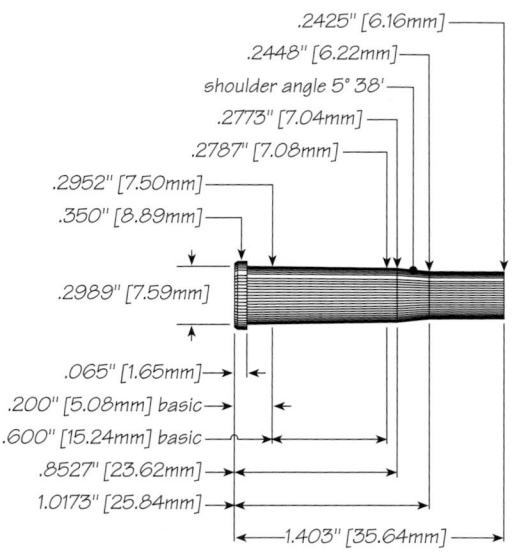

.2425" [6.16mm]
.2448" [6.22mm]
shoulder angle 5° 38'
.2773" [7.04mm]
.2787" [7.08mm]
.2952" [7.50mm]
.350" [8.89mm]
.2989" [7.59mm]
.065" [1.65mm]
.200" [5.08mm] basic
.600" [15.24mm] basic
.8527" [23.62mm]
1.0173" [25.84mm]
1.403" [35.64mm]

Max. Case Length:	1.403"	**Cart. Case:**	Winchester
Trim-to Length:	1.393"	**Primer:**	CCI 500
Max Cart. OAL:	1.723"	**Test Firearm:**	Krico Target
RCBS Shell Holder:	#12	**Barrel Length:**	24"

Lab Notes:

The standard Hornet chamber specification has no freebore between the end of the chamber and the start of the rifled section; that means the rifling origin is virtually at the case mouth. Some recent rifles have a bit of freebore and often do not shoot as well as those with standard chambers. Accuracy in these rifles can be improved by using a slightly longer cartridge overall length (COAL). However, cartridges with a COAL longer than the SAAMI maximum of 1.723 inch will probably not fit box magazines in repeating rifles. You will have to single-load.

0.224"	22 TNT HP
Weight, grains	33
Ballistic Coefficient	0.080
Sectional Density	0.094
COAL Tested:	1.680"
Speer Part No.	1014

| Propellant | START CHARGE | | MAXIMUM CHARGE | |
	Weight, grs	Muzzle Velocity, ft/sec	Weight, grs	Muzzle Velocity, ft/sec
H110	12.4	3198	12.8	3229
296	12.4	3054	12.8	3217
AA No. 9	10.2	2944	10.8	3106
H. Lil' Gun	13.5C	3068	14.0C	3093
2400	11.0	2953	11.5C	2985
Viht. N110	10.0	2879	10.6C	2947

0.224"	22 Spire SP
Weight, grains	40
Ballistic Coefficient	0.144
Sectional Density	0.114
COAL Tested:	1.723"
Speer Part No.	1017

| Propellant | START CHARGE | | MAXIMUM CHARGE | |
	Weight, grs	Muzzle Velocity, ft/sec	Weight, grs	Muzzle Velocity, ft/sec
H. Lil' Gun	12.0	2936	13.0C	3020
296	9.2	2639	10.2	2782
AA 1680	12.4	2574	13.4C	2757
H110	9.2	2589	10.2	2730
IMR 4227	10.5	2436	11.3C	2619
Viht. N110	8.1	2407	9.1	2587
2400	8.1	2278	9.1	2557

*Maximum Loads should be used with CAUTION • C = Compressed Load • *Magnum Primer used with this powder.*

0.224"	22 Spire SP
Weight, grains	45
Ballistic Coefficient	0.143
Sectional Density	0.128
COAL Tested:	1.723"
Speer Part No.	1023

Propellant	START CHARGE		MAXIMUM CHARGE	
	Weight, grs	Muzzle Velocity, ft/sec	Weight, grs	Muzzle Velocity, ft/sec
H. Lil' Gun	12.0	2750	13.0C	2913
296	9.0	2441	10.0	2619
H110	9.0	2458	10.0	2599
AA 1680	12.0	2442	13.0C	2565
IMR 4227	10.1	2300	11.1	2511
2400	8.0	2220	9.0	2506
Viht. N110	8.2	2349	9.0	2450

0.224"	22 Spire SP
Weight, grains	50
Ballistic Coefficient	0.207
Sectional Density	0.142
COAL Tested:	1.723"
Speer Part No.	1029

Propellant	START CHARGE		MAXIMUM CHARGE	
	Weight, grs	Muzzle Velocity, ft/sec	Weight, grs	Muzzle Velocity, ft/sec
H. Lil' Gun	11.0C	2655	12.0C	2712
296	9.0	2358	9.7	2503
H110	9.0	2382	9.7	2499
AA 1680	10.9	2243	11.8	2381
Viht. N110	7.9	2201	8.6	2306
AA 2015	11.5C	2035	12.0C	2071

0.224"	22 HP
Weight, grains	52
Ballistic Coefficient	0.168
Sectional Density	0.148
COAL Tested:	1.723"
Speer Part No.	1035

Propellant	START CHARGE		MAXIMUM CHARGE	
	Weight, grs	Muzzle Velocity, ft/sec	Weight, grs	Muzzle Velocity, ft/sec
H. Lil' Gun	9.0	2401	9.7	2515
H110	7.9	2123	8.9	2315
296	7.9	2118	8.9	2311
IMR 4227	8.6	1863	9.6	2261
AA 1680	10.1	2054	10.8	2257
IMR 4198	9.7	2069	10.5C	2216
Viht. N110	7.4	2071	8.0	2101
2400	6.7	1853	7.7	2128

Ben Amonette,
Customer Service
Manager, Alliant Powder.

Maximum Loads should be used with CAUTION • C = Compressed Load • *Magnum Primer used with this powder.

218 Bee

This cartridge appeared in 1938 as a small game and varmint cartridge in the Model 65 Winchester lever-action rifle. The Bee was conceived as an improvement over the popular 22 Hornet. Based on the 25/20 Winchester case, the Bee has more capacity than the Hornet. Factory ammo is cataloged at 2760 ft/sec with a 46-grain bullet (24-inch SAAMI pressure barrel). However, recent lots of ammunition often clock only between 2500 and 2600 ft/sec in production rifles.

The 218 Bee never achieved the popularity of other contemporary varmint cartridges, probably due to some less-than-accurate lever-action rifles in which it was originally chambered. In quality single-shot or bolt-action rifles, the Bee can give outstanding groups.

In 1989, Marlin and Browning reintroduced the 218 Bee in lever-action rifles and both rifles sold well. These were the first production rifles for the 218 Bee since Kimber made a few bolt-action sporters several years before. Because the new rifles have tubular magazines, Speer's 46-grain flat point bullet for the Bee is mandatory for safety. Do not use pointed bullets in rifles with tubular magazines. Ruger announced the Bee in two rifles in 1993, and still catalog the Bee in one model of their #1 single-shot rifle. The following data can be used with the Speer 45-grain spitzer soft point bullet in single-shot and bolt-action rifles only.

Much of the older published data was not developed in pressure guns. We found that several powders such as 4227 and 2400, traditionally considered good choices for Bee-class cartridges, fail to generate adequate velocities when normal working pressures are reached; their performance is not better than a 22 Hornet. Although a compressed load, 14.2 grains of IMR 4198 gave the best velocities, matching nominal factory ballistics in the Browning test rifle. Several groups shot under two minutes of angle using iron sights.

We screened the new 33-grain TNT 22 Hornet bullet in the Bee, but it did not give significant velocity increases over the Hornet. Apparently, the light bullet does not offer enough resistance to pressure in the larger Bee case.

These loads do not exceed the SAAMI maximum average pressure of 40,000 CUP. Winchester still catalogs ammo and component cases. Like other small-capacity cartridges, the Bee is very sensitive to component substitutions. We strongly recommend that the listed loads be used exactly as shown.

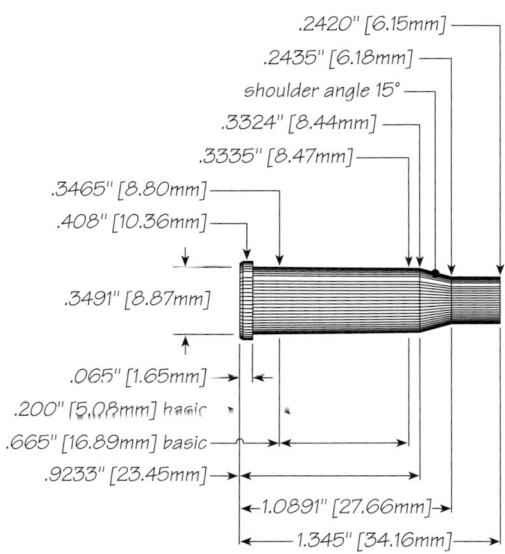

.2420" [6.15mm]
.2435" [6.18mm]
shoulder angle 15°
.3324" [8.44mm]
.3335" [8.47mm]
.3465" [8.80mm]
.408" [10.36mm]
.3491" [8.87mm]
.065" [1.65mm]
.200" [5.08mm] basic
.665" [16.89mm] basic
.9233" [23.45mm]
1.0891" [27.66mm]
1.345" [34.16mm]

Max. Case Length:	1.345"	Cart. Case:	Winchester
Trim-to Length:	1.335"	Primer:	CCI 400
Max Cart. OAL:	1.680"	Test Firearm:	Browning M92
RCBS Shell Holder:	#1	Barrel Length:	24"

0.224"	22 FNSP /cann
Weight, grains	45
Ballistic Coefficient	0.087
Sectional Density	0.131
COAL Tested:	1.655"
Speer Part No.	1024

Propellant	START CHARGE		MAXIMUM CHARGE	
	Weight, grs	Muzzle Velocity, ft/sec	Weight, grs	Muzzle Velocity, ft/sec
IMR 4198	12.8	2466	14.2C	2738
H. Lil' Gun	9.5	2441	10.5	2662
AA 2460	15.3	2365	17.0C	2551
AA 1680	10.8	2329	12.0	2517
Viht. N110	8.3	2224	9.2	2379
Ramshot Enforcer	8.7	2234	9.4	2376
296	8.1	2161	9.0	2325
AA No. 9	7.8	2082	8.7	2290
H110	8.1	1959	9.0	2215
2400	7.5	1997	8.3	2151
IMR 4227	8.9	1914	9.8	2127

*Maximum Loads should be used with CAUTION • C = Compressed Load • *Magnum Primer used with this powder.*

222 Remington

In 1950, Remington made history by introducing America's first true rimless, 22-caliber centerfire cartridge (the older 220 Swift is technically semi-rimmed). Originally chambered in Remington's Model 722 bolt-action rifle, the "Triple-Deuce" used a totally new design not based on any previous cartridge. The cartridge's superb accuracy—not impressive velocity— made the 222 Remington famous.

Firing a 50-grain bullet at 3140 ft/sec, the new cartridge was a natural for varmints. Fine accuracy, even from untuned factory rifles, attracted the attention of the benchrest fraternity. Competitors found that, in custom rifles, tiny one-hole groups were possible. This well-mannered cartridge dominated benchrest competition for years. The PPC family of benchrest cartridges eventually usurped its position, but 222's are occasionally found on the line today. Nearly every major rifle maker has chambered guns for the 222 Remington at one time or another. The wildly popular 223 Remington was derived from the 222 Remington case.

Today, the real appeal of the 222 is as a varmint cartridge. Its inherent accuracy gives it a useful range of around 250 yards—and somewhat more on still days. Best accuracy is usually obtained with bullets between 50 and 55 grains. Speer's 52-grain hollow point and 50-grain TNT® give excellent accuracy and terminal performance. In fact, our TNT was designed with the 222 Remington in mind. Its thin, fluted jacket gives explosive expansion usually seen only in higher velocity cartridges. The 55-grain full metal jacket bullet can be loaded to around 2000 ft/sec for a turkey or pelt load. The modest velocity of the reduced load helps reduce damage to hides and edible meat.

The 222 Remington is a reloader's dream. The long neck provides excellent bullet alignment and the small case means a pound of powder will last a long time.

Ammo and components are still listed by most major ammo makers. The listed loads fall within the industry standard operating pressure of 46,000 CUP.

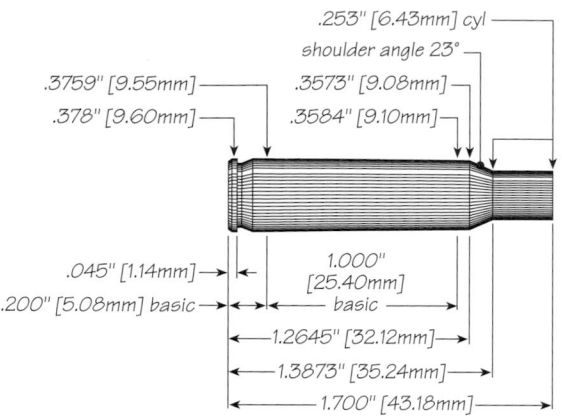

.253" [6.43mm] cyl
shoulder angle 23°
.3759" [9.55mm]
.378" [9.60mm]
.3573" [9.08mm]
.3584" [9.10mm]
.045" [1.14mm]
.200" [5.08mm] basic
1.000" [25.40mm] basic
1.2645" [32.12mm]
1.3873" [35.24mm]
1.700" [43.18mm]

Max. Case Length:	1.700"	Cart. Case:	Remington
Trim-to Length:	1.690"	Primer:	CCI 400, 450*
Max Cart. OAL:	2.130"	Test Firearm:	Remington 40-X
RCBS Shell Holder:	#10	Barrel Length:	24"

Bernie Ness, ATK Government Sales Manager, with a fine fallow deer.

0.224"	22 Spire SP
Weight, grains	40
Ballistic Coefficient	0.144
Sectional Density	0.114
COAL Tested:	2.040"
Speer Part No.	1017

	START CHARGE		MAXIMUM CHARGE	
Propellant	Weight, grs	Muzzle Velocity, ft/sec	Weight, grs	Muzzle Velocity, ft/sec
Reloder 7	20.0	3382	22.0	3617
AA 2015	22.0	3301	24.0	3608
AA 2460*	23.5	3212	25.5C	3581
H322	22.5	3273	24.5	3538
BL-C(2)*	24.5	3236	26.5C	3502
H4198	19.5	3306	21.5	3498
AA 2230*	22.5	3143	24.5	3465
AA 2520	24.0	3299	26.0C	3447
IMR 4198	19.0	3237	21.0	3444
IMR 4895	23.0	3157	25.0C	3432
748*	23.0	3079	25.0	3402
Viht. N120	18.0	3049	20.0	3395
H335*	23.0	3078	25.0	3382
H4895	22.0	3000	24.0C	3333
IMR 3031	22.0	3080	24.0C	3312

*Maximum Loads should be used with CAUTION • C = Compressed Load • *Magnum Primer used with this powder.*

0.224"	22 Spitz SP
Weight, grains	45
Ballistic Coefficient	0.143
Sectional Density	0.128
COAL Tested:	2.130"
Speer Part No.	1023

Propellant	START CHARGE		MAXIMUM CHARGE	
	Weight, grs	Muzzle Velocity, ft/sec	Weight, grs	Muzzle Velocity, ft/sec
BL-C(2)*	24.5	3148	26.5C	3498
AA 2460*	23.0	3071	25.0C	3431
Reloder 7	19.5	3150	21.5	3424
AA 2015	21.0	3160	23.0	3398
H322	21.5	3154	23.5	3338
AA 2520*	24.0	3037	26.0C	3301
IMR 4198	18.5	3032	20.5	3278
H4198	18.5	3038	20.5	3267
IMR 4895	22.5	3064	24.5C	3260
748*	23.0	3008	25.0	3234
Viht. N120	17.5	2910	19.5	3216
H4895	22.0	2942	24.0C	3215
H335*	22.5	3002	24.5	3211
AA 2230*	21.0	2891	23.0	3177

0.224"	22 Spitz SP	22 TNT HP
Weight, grains	50	50
Ballistic Coefficient	0.207	0.228
Sectional Density	0.142	0.142
COAL Tested:	2.110"	2.130"
Speer Part No.	1029	1030

Propellant	START CHARGE Weight, grs	START CHARGE Muzzle Velocity, ft/sec	MAXIMUM CHARGE Weight, grs	MAXIMUM CHARGE Muzzle Velocity, ft/sec
AA 2015	21.0	3161	23.0	3345
AA 2520*	24.0	3130	26.0C	3270
BL-C(2)*	24.0	2992	26.0	3238
Reloder 7	19.0	3010	21.0	3237
H322	21.0	2967	23.0	3225
AA 2460*	22.0	2892	24.0	3224
IMR 3031	21.0	2959	23.0C	3199
AA 2230*	21.5	2890	23.5	3178
IMR 4895	22.0	2874	24.0C	3158
H4895	22.0	2825	24.0C	3156
IMR 4198	18.0	2931	20.0	3135
IMR 4320	24.0	2945	26.0C	3134
Viht. N120	17.0	2808	19.0	3126
H4198	18.0	2922	20.0	3109
H335*	22.0	2800	24.0	3094

*Maximum Loads should be used with CAUTION • C = Compressed Load • *Magnum Primer used with this powder.*

0.224"	22 HP	22 MATCH BTHP
Weight, grains	52	52
Ballistic Coefficient	0.168	0.230
Sectional Density	0.148	0.148
COAL Tested:	2.130"	2.130"
Speer Part No.	1035	1036

Propellant	START CHARGE Weight, grs	START CHARGE Muzzle Velocity, ft/sec	MAXIMUM CHARGE Weight, grs	MAXIMUM CHARGE Muzzle Velocity, ft/sec
AA 2520*	24.0	3003	26.0C	3337
Viht. N133	20.5	3077	22.5C	3326
IMR 4895	22.5	3049	24.5C	3279
H4895	22.0	3048	24.0	3277
H322	20.5	2979	22.5	3256
IMR 3031	21.5	3035	23.5C	3246
BL-C(2)*	23.5	2926	25.5	3233
AA 2460*	21.5	2930	23.5	3185
Reloder 7	18.0	2835	20.0	3115
AA 2230*	21.0	2922	23.0	3109
748*	22.5	2904	24.5	3106
H4198	17.5	2917	19.5	3087
H335*	21.5	2880	23.5	3064
IMR 4198	17.5	2821	19.5	3050

0.224"	22 FMJ BT	22 Spitz SP	22 Spitz SP/cann
Weight, grains	55	55	55
Ballistic Coefficient	0.269	0.212	0.212
Sectional Density	0.157	0.157	0.157
COAL Tested:	2.130"	2.130"	2.130"
Speer Part No.	1044	1047	1049

Propellant	START CHARGE		MAXIMUM CHARGE	
	Weight, grs	Muzzle Velocity, ft/sec	Weight, grs	Muzzle Velocity, ft/sec
AA 2520*	24.0	2912	26.0C	3235
H4895	22.0	2906	24.0C	3159
H322	20.5	2909	22.5	3145
IMR 4895	22.0	2969	24.0C	3142
Viht. N133	20.0	2866	22.0	3132
AA 2460*	21.5	2826	23.5	3106
IMR 3031	21.0	2836	23.0C	3083
BL-C(2)*	23.0	2780	25.0	3072
Reloder 7	18.0	2832	20.0	3045
748*	22.5	2838	24.5	3035
IMR 4064	21.5	2775	23.5C	3033
IMR 4320	23.0	2794	25.0C	3020
IMR 4198	17.5	2804	19.5	2999
Reloder 15	22.0	2781	24.0C	2990
H4198	17.5	2794	19.5	2974
SR 4759 (reduced load)	9.0	1866	10.0	2070

*Maximum Loads should be used with CAUTION • C = Compressed Load • *Magnum Primer used with this powder.*

223 Remington

The 223 Remington resulted from military development of a new service rifle cartridge. Adopted by the U.S. Military in February 1964 as the 5.56mm Ball Cartridge M193, the 223 Remington was announced as a commercial cartridge a month earlier.

Based on the 222 Remington case head dimensions, the 223 case is only .060" longer than its parent. However, it has greater powder capacity because the case body was lengthened at the expense of the neck. It also has a higher maximum pressure assignment. With equivalent bullet weights in factory ammo, the 223 Remington enjoys a 100 to 300 ft/sec velocity advantage over its predecessor.

Original military and commercial rifles had a 1-in-14 inch rifling twist, later changed to 1-in-12 inches for better long-range stability with the 55-grain service bullet. However, when the military adopted a heavier 62-grain service round, military rifles were fitted with 1-in-7 inch twist barrels to handle the new bullet. Several commercial makers of semi-automatic rifles followed suit and changed to the faster twist.

Although the fast twist works well with military ammo, handloaders have a problem. Most conventional jacketed bullets are of light construction for varmint hunting. When fired at 3200 ft/sec in a 1-in-7 inch twist barrel, the bullet is rotating at nearly 330,000 rpm when it leaves the muzzle. This rotational speed is more than most varmint bullets can withstand so they are literally ripped apart as they leave the barrel. This phenomenon will not damage the firearm, but few bullets will reach the target intact. Most bolt-action and single-shot rifles have the slower twist recommended for varmint bullets, but at least one maker of bolt-action rifles has sold 223 Remington rifles with the 1-in-7 inch twist. Research before you buy; if you want to use conventional varmint bullets to their full potential, avoid the fast-twist models.

If you have a rifle with the faster 1-in-7 inch twist, you should limit the muzzle velocity of varmint bullets to around 2800 ft/sec. Speer sells a 62-grain FMJ-BT bullet that is a duplicate of the bullet in the new M855 service cartridge. The Speer 70-grain semi-spitzer is also a good bullet in the fast-twist rifles; however, be sure to watch overall length, as the long bullet can stick in the throat if seated too long. The tough 55-grain Trophy Bonded Bear Claw will survive fast twist barrels, and gives deeper penetration than most 22-caliber bullets. The TBBC retained 93 percent of its weight when fired into test media at 3000 ft/sec.

Some rifle makers recommend that bullets be crimped if used in their semi-automatic rifles. Three Speer 22-caliber bullets feature a cannelure for easy crimping. The 62-grain FMJ-BT is not properly stabilized by 12-inch twist barrels, and should be restricted to rifles with 10-inch or faster rifling twists.

The commercial IMI cases used for our tests are built to the same specification as military cases, so load reduction is not required when using surplus military brass with these loads. Remember that military cases have crimped primers. The crimp must be removed before repriming.

We have added reduced loads for bullets through 55 grains using Accurate Arms XMP-5744. This propellant gave exceptional consistency at the modest pressures these loads generate. With the 40-grain bullet, 11.0 grains of this powder drove the bullet at just over 22 Magnum RF velocities.

The 223 Remington's maximum average pressure is 52,000 CUP. These loads do not exceed that limit.

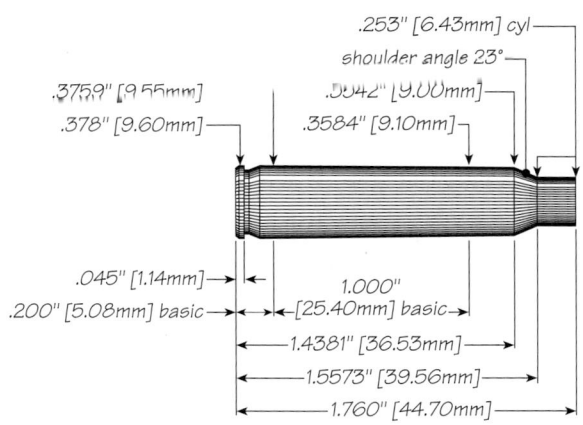

Max. Case Length:	1.760"	Cart. Case:	IMI
Trim-to Length:	1.750"	Primer:	CCI 400, 450*
Max Cart. OAL:	2.260"	Test Firearm:	Ruger M77 MkII
RCBS Shell Holder:	#10	Barrel Length:	22"

NOTE: *CCI No. 41 primers may be substituted for CCI 450.*

0.224"	22 Spire SP
Weight, grains	40
Ballistic Coefficient	0.144
Sectional Density	0.114
COAL Tested:	2.060"
Speer Part No.	1017

| Propellant | START CHARGE | | MAXIMUM CHARGE | |
	Weight, grs	Muzzle Velocity, ft/sec	Weight, grs	Muzzle Velocity, ft/sec
748*	28.0	3339	30.0C	3557
Viht. N133	23.0	3139	25.0C	3486
Reloder 10X	22.5	3198	24.5	3481
AA 2015	23.5	3068	25.5	3461
Varget	26.0	3148	28.0C	3461
AA 2460*	24.5	3086	26.5	3445
IMR 3031	25.0	3032	27.0C	3410
H322	24.0	3027	26.0	3388
AA 2230	24.0	3062	26.0	3361
H4198	20.5	2981	22.5	3342
BL-C(2)*	26.0	3064	28.0	3315
H4895	23.5	2954	25.5C	3297
H335*	26.5	2903	28.5	3133
Reloder 7	18.5	2694	20.5	3011
AA 5744 (reduced load)	11.0	1990	12.0	2134

0.224"	22 Spitz SP
Weight, grains	45
Ballistic Coefficient	0.143
Sectional Density	0.128
COAL Tested:	2.155"
Speer Part No.	1023

Propellant	START CHARGE		MAXIMUM CHARGE	
	Weight, grs	Muzzle Velocity, ft/sec	Weight, grs	Muzzle Velocity, ft/sec
IMR 4895	25.0	3098	27.0C	3404
748*	27.0	2988	29.0C	3396
Varget	26.0	3109	28.0C	3387
IMR 4198	21.0	3006	23.0	3377
H322	24.0	2959	26.0	3362
IMR 3031	25.0	3070	27.0C	3337
Reloder 10X	22.0	3039	24.0	3292
AA 2460*	24.0	2948	26.0	3275
Viht. N133	22.5	2969	24.5C	3263
AA 2015	23.0	2901	25.0	3260
BL-C(2)*	26.0	2897	28.0C	3219
AA 2230	23.5	2777	25.5	3156
Reloder 7	18.0	2814	20.0	3059
H335*	25.0	2688	27.0C	3020
AA 5744 (reduced load)	11.0	1949	12.0	2091

*Maximum Loads should be used with CAUTION • C = Compressed Load • *Magnum Primer used with this powder.*

0.224"	22 Spitz SP	22 TNT HP
Weight, grains	50	50
Ballistic Coefficient	0.207	0.228
Sectional Density	0.142	0.142
COAL Tested:	2.185"	2.235"
Speer Part No.	1029	1030

	START CHARGE		MAXIMUM CHARGE	
Propellant	Weight, grs	Muzzle Velocity, ft/sec	Weight, grs	Muzzle Velocity, ft/sec
748*	26.5	3083	28.5C	3398
AA 2520*	26.0	3178	28.0C	3328
Varget	25.5	3034	27.5C	3316
IMR 4895	25.0	3028	27.0C	3313
H322	24.0	3001	26.0	3300
IMR 3031	24.0	2969	26.0C	3284
Reloder 10X	21.5	2997	23.5	3267
AA 2015	22.5	2951	24.5	3266
H335*	25.0	2975	27.0	3262
Viht. N133	22.0	2899	24.0	3237
H4895	23.5	2871	25.5C	3203
BL-C(2)*	25.5	2961	27.5	3200
H4198	20.0	2850	22.0	3178
AA 2230	23.0	2847	25.0	3138
AA 5744 (reduced load)	11.0	1905	12.0	2047

0.224"	22 HP	22 Match BTHP
Weight, grains	52	52
Ballistic Coefficient	0.168	0.230
Sectional Density	0.148	0.148
COAL Tested:	2.200"	2.200"
Speer Part No.	1035	1036

Propellant	START CHARGE		MAXIMUM CHARGE	
	Weight, grs	Muzzle Velocity, ft/sec	Weight, grs	Muzzle Velocity, ft/sec
748*	26.0	3138	28.0C	3448
Varget	25.0	2995	27.0	3276
IMR 4895	24.5	2850	26.5C	3202
IMR 3031	24.0	2876	26.0C	3195
Reloder 10X	20.5	2914	22.5	3179
Viht. N133	22.0	2826	24.0	3175
Reloder 15	25.0	2790	27.0C	3170
H4895	23.5	2863	25.5C	3146
H335*	24.5	2879	26.5	3129
H322	22.5	2822	24.5	3101
IMR 4064	24.0	2840	26.0C	3087
BL-C(2)*	25.0	2695	27.0	3062
AA 2460*	23.0	2750	25.0	3056
Reloder 7	18.5	2609	20.5	2931
AA 5744 (reduced load)	11.0	1899	12.0	2036

*Maximum Loads should be used with CAUTION • C = Compressed Load • *Magnum Primer used with this powder.*

0.224"	22 TNT HP	22 FMJ BT	22 Spitz SP	22 SP/cann
Weight, grains	55	55	55	55
Ballistic Coefficient	0.233	0.269	0.212	0.212
Sectional Density	0.157	0.157	0.157	0.157
COAL Tested:	2.235"	2.215"	2.175"	2.215"
Speer Part No.	1032	1044	1047	1049

Propellant	START CHARGE Weight, grs	START CHARGE Muzzle Velocity, ft/sec	MAXIMUM CHARGE Weight, grs	MAXIMUM CHARGE Muzzle Velocity, ft/sec
748*	26.0	2965	28.0C	3313
AA 2230	24.0	3017	26.0	3233
IMR 3031	24.0	2976	26.0C	3223
Varget	25.0	2969	27.0	3216
H4895	23.5	2908	25.5C	3194
AA 2520*	25.0	3021	27.0C	3187
Reloder 10X	21.0	2934	23.0	3159
H322	22.5	2823	24.5	3158
IMR 4064	24.5	2843	26.5	3143
BL-C(2)*	25.0	2868	27.0	3138
H335*	24.0	2805	26.0	3092
Viht. N133	21.5	2775	23.5	3091
AA 2015	21.5	2753	23.5	3026
H4198	19.0	2693	21.0	2978
AA 5744 (reduced load)	11.0	1885	12.0	2022

0.224"	22 TBBC SP
Weight, grains	55
Ballistic Coefficient	0.201
Sectional Density	0.157
COAL Tested:	2.220"
Speer Part No.	1725

	START CHARGE		MAXIMUM CHARGE	
Propellant	Weight, grs	Muzzle Velocity, ft/sec	Weight, grs	Muzzle Velocity, ft/sec
AA 2230	23.0	2950	24.0	3077
Varget	25.0	2910	26.0C	3046
IMR 4064	24.5	2927	25.5C	3024
Win 748*	25.0	2888	26.0C	3009
H322	22.0	2888	23.0	3003
AA 2015	22.0	2822	23.0	2950
Viht. N133	21.0	2809	22.0	2947

NOTE: *Trophy Bonded Bear Claw and Trophy Bonded Sledgehammer Solid bullets have unique ballistic behavior compared to conventional bullets. Loads for TBBC and TBSS bullets may not "track" with data for conventional bullets. Use TBBC and TBSS data ONLY for TBBC and TBSS bullets.*

Bob Zastrow, Engineering Manager, ATK Onalaska Operations, with son Danny; 308 Winchester, 165-grain Grand Slam®; Wisconsin whitetail.

*Maximum Loads should be used with CAUTION • C = Compressed Load • *Magnum Primer used with this powder.*

0.224"	22 FMJ BT
Weight, grains	62
Ballistic Coefficient	0.307
Sectional Density	0.177
COAL Tested:	2.255"
Speer Part No.	1050

Propellant	START CHARGE		MAXIMUM CHARGE	
	Weight, grs	Muzzle Velocity, ft/sec	Weight, grs	Muzzle Velocity, ft/sec
AA 2520*	24.5	2875	26.5C	3024
AA 2460*	22.5	2636	24.5	2962
Viht. N133	21.0	2646	23.0	2939
AA 2230	22.0	2642	24.0	2919
IMR 4895	22.5	2548	24.5C	2896
IMR 4064	23.5	2661	25.5C	2892
748*	23.5	2556	25.5	2888
H335*	23.0	2625	25.0	2885
Viht. N135	22.0	2590	24.0	2878
AA 2015	20.5	2509	22.5	2851
Reloder 15	23.0	2549	25.0C	2832
IMR 4320	23.5	2568	25.5C	2822
BL-C(2)*	23.0	2476	25.0	2782
IMR 3031	21.5	2466	23.5C	2778

NOTE: *Recommended only for rifles with 1-in-10 inch or faster twist rates.*

0.224"	22 Semi Spitz SP
Weight, grains	70
Ballistic Coefficient	0.219
Sectional Density	0.199
COAL Tested:	2.140"
Speer Part No.	1053

Propellant	START CHARGE		MAXIMUM CHARGE	
	Weight, grs	Muzzle Velocity, ft/sec	Weight, grs	Muzzle Velocity, ft/sec
748*	25.0	2824	27.0	3068
H414*	26.0	2658	28.0	2883
IMR 4895	22.5	2628	24.5C	2826
H335*	22.5	2592	24.5	2812
AA 2460*	21.5	2500	23.5	2778
AA 2230	21.0	2464	23.0	2715
H380*	26.0	2533	28.0	2700
Viht. N135	20.5	2425	22.5	2661
IMR 4320	22.5	2450	24.5	2644
BL-C(2)*	21.5	2450	23.5	2618
AA 2015	18.0	2328	20.0	2555

*Maximum Loads should be used with CAUTION • C = Compressed Load • *Magnum Primer used with this powder.*

222 Remington Magnum

The 222 Remington Magnum, like the 223 Remington, started life as an experimental cartridge for military consideration. Although the 222 Magnum was rejected by the U.S. military, Remington introduced it as a commercial cartridge. Like the 223, the 222 Magnum was based on the excellent 222 Remington case. The magnum case is longer than the 223 (mostly in the neck). Case capacity is 20 percent greater than the 222 Remington, and about 5 percent greater than the 223. The magnum version is loaded to slightly lower pressure than the 223, so the real performance of the two cartridges is virtually the same.

Varmint hunters looking for more range than the 222 Remington offered readily accepted a magnum version. When the 222 Magnum was commercialized in 1958, a number of firms chambered rifles for it. However, most of these companies dropped the 222 Magnum chambering when the 223 Remington was announced in 1964. This was a logical move, as every U.S. service cartridge has proved popular as commercial versions.

The 222 Remington Magnum was and still is an excellent varmint cartridge. However, it will be hard to find a new rifle in this caliber unless it is special-ordered or built as a custom project. Although the 222 Remington Magnum stayed popular in Europe (as the 5.6x47mm) longer than in North America, it seems to have faded away there, too, losing the race to the 223 and the more powerful 5.6X50 Magnum. Until recently, there was no performance reason to trade a good 222 Magnum rifle for a 223. Unfortunately, 222 Magnum ammunition or unprimed cases are no longer cataloged on the Remington website for 2006, and cases cannot be easily formed from another case. Although Midway USA still lists 222 Magnum cases in bulk at press time, the cartridge is close to fading away.

Industry operating pressures for the 222 Remington Magnum are 50,000 CUP. As usual, approach all maximum loads with caution.

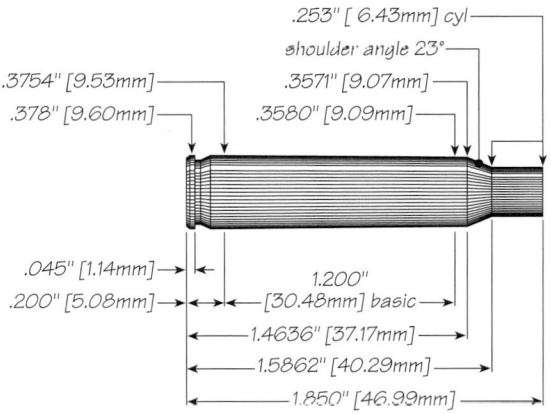

Max. Case Length:	1.850"	Cart. Case:	Remington
Trim-to Length:	1.840"	Primer:	CCI 400, 450*
Max Cart. OAL:	2.280"	Test Firearm:	Sako
RCBS Shell Holder:	#10	Barrel Length:	23.75"

0.224"	22 Spire SP
Weight, grains	40
Ballistic Coefficient	0.144
Sectional Density	0.114
COAL Tested:	2.200"
Speer Part No.	1017

Propellant	START CHARGE Weight, grs	START CHARGE Muzzle Velocity, ft/sec	MAXIMUM CHARGE Weight, grs	MAXIMUM CHARGE Muzzle Velocity, ft/sec
H335*	27.0	3429	29.0	3730
IMR 4320	27.0	3450	29.0	3692
748*	29.0	3404	31.0	3660
IMR 3031	25.0	3370	27.0	3622
BL-C(2)*	26.0	3309	28.0	3587
IMR 4198	21.5	3251	23.5	3540
IMR 4064	26.0	3255	28.0	3489
SR 4759 (reduced load)	8.0	1541	10.0	1912

*Maximum Loads should be used with CAUTION • C = Compressed Load • *Magnum Primer used with this powder.*

0.224"	22 Spire SP
Weight, grains	45
Ballistic Coefficient	0.143
Sectional Density	0.128
COAL Tested:	2.220"
Speer Part No.	1023

Propellant	START CHARGE Weight, grs	START CHARGE Muzzle Velocity, ft/sec	MAXIMUM CHARGE Weight, grs	MAXIMUM CHARGE Muzzle Velocity, ft/sec
H335*	27.0	3390	29.0	3661
748*	28.0	3389	30.0	3653
IMR 4320	27.0	3332	29.0	3561
IMR 3031	25.0	3269	27.0	3524
IMR 4198	21.5	3197	23.5	3488
IMR 4895	25.0	3161	27.0	3396
Reloder 7	21.5	3077	23.5	3348
SR 4759 (reduced load)	8.5	1607	10.5	1986

0.224"	22 Spitz SP	22 TNT HP
Weight, grains	50	50
Ballistic Coefficient	0.207	0.228
Sectional Density	0.142	0.142
COAL Tested:	2.250"	2.250"
Speer Part No.	1029	1030

Propellant	START CHARGE Weight, grs	START CHARGE Muzzle Velocity, ft/sec	MAXIMUM CHARGE Weight, grs	MAXIMUM CHARGE Muzzle Velocity, ft/sec
H335*	26.5	3243	28.5	3514
IMR 4320	27.0	3255	29.0	3482
IMR 4198	21.0	3132	23.0	3415
IMR 4064	26.0	3190	28.0	3414
BL-C(2)*	25.0	3190	27.0	3398
IMR 3031	24.5	3149	26.5	3396
H414*	29.0	3133	31.0	3381
SR 4759 (reduced load)	9.0	1690	11.0	2075

0.224"	22 HP	22 Match BTHP
Weight, grains	52	52
Ballistic Coefficient	0.168	0.230
Sectional Density	0.147	0.147
COAL Tested:	2.250"	2.250"
Speer Part No.	1035	1036

| Propellant | START CHARGE | | MAXIMUM CHARGE | |
	Weight, grs	Muzzle Velocity, ft/sec	Weight, grs	Muzzle Velocity, ft/sec
H335*	26.0	3225	28.0	3480
BL-C(2)*	24.5	3181	26.5	3458
IMR 4320	27.0	3222	29.0	3446
IMR 3031	24.5	3171	26.5	3421
IMR 4064	26.0	3189	28.0	3415
IMR 4895	25.0	3098	27.0	3330
H414*	29.0	3060	31.0	3294
Reloder 7	20.0	2930	22.0	3220

0.224"	22 TNT HP	22 FMJ BT	22 Spitz SP
Weight, grains	55	55	55
Ballistic Coefficient	0.233	0.269	0.212
Sectional Density	0.157	0.157	0.157
COAL Tested:	2.250"	2.250"	2.250"
Speer Part No.	1032	1044	1047

| Propellant | START CHARGE | | MAXIMUM CHARGE | |
	Weight, grs	Muzzle Velocity, ft/sec	Weight, grs	Muzzle Velocity, ft/sec
H335*	25.5	3084	27.5	3343
IMR 4320	26.0	3085	28.0	3311
BL-C(2)*	24.5	3038	26.5	3295
IMR 4064	25.5	3077	27.5	3294
IMR 3031	24.0	3053	26.0	3290
IMR 4895	24.5	3040	26.5	3275
H414*	29.0	2983	31.0	3223
SR 4759 (reduced load)	9.0	1694	11.0	2066

*Maximum Loads should be used with CAUTION • C = Compressed Load • *Magnum Primer used with this powder.*

0.224"	22 Semi Spitz SP
Weight, grains	70
Ballistic Coefficient	0.219
Sectional Density	0.199
COAL Tested:	2.260"
Speer Part No.	1053

Propellant	START CHARGE		MAXIMUM CHARGE	
	Weight, grs	Muzzle Velocity, ft/sec	Weight, grs	Muzzle Velocity, ft/sec
IMR 4064	24.5	2820	26.5	3043
IMR 4320	24.5	2777	26.5	2983
IMR 4895	23.0	2723	25.0	2938
H335*	23.0	2681	25.0	2938
IMR 3031	22.0	2655	24.0	2880
H414*	26.0	2651	28.0	2873
H380*	27.0	2617	29.0	2850
SR 4759 (reduced load)	10.0	1615	12.0	1925

Brandon Graves, ATK Law Enforcement/ OEM Sales Manager; fallow deer.

Maximum Loads should be used with CAUTION • C = Compressed Load • *Magnum Primer used with this powder.

22 PPC

The 22 PPC is a wildcat cartridge for benchrest competition developed by Dr. Lou Palmisano and gunsmith Ferris Pindell in 1975. They began with an obscure target cartridge called the 220 Russian that was based on the 7.62x39mm Eastern Bloc service cartridge.

Palmisano and Pindell modified the Russian cartridge by reducing case taper to 10° and increasing the shoulder angle to 30°. The new design also incorporated a small primer pocket with a smaller flash hole (.066") than is normally used in centerfire cases. The short, stubby case was perfectly suited to the ignition power provided by a small rifle primer.

In its first year, the 22 PPC racked up an impressive series of benchrest titles and its incredible accuracy dethroned that old benchrest favorite, the 222 Remington. Its efficient design also makes the 22 PPC a very potent varmint cartridge, falling somewhere between the 223 and the 22-250.

At one time, the 22 PPC was available in factory rifles, but the latest search of web sites and catalogs indicates that anyone wishing one today will be shopping for a custom or semi-custom rifle. Even component cases have dried up. RCBS makes die sets to reform 7.62x39mm cases to 22 PPC.

This cartridge is still classed as a wildcat and no American pressure standards exist. The late Dan Pawlak did pressure research on this cartridge using electronic transducer equipment. According to his research, the loads listed here should not exceed 55,000 psi. However, because of variations in individual rifles, use great care in working up maximum loads.

Custom benchrest rifles in this caliber are often built with very tight throats and necks. Turning case necks is mandatory in these rifles and failing to perform this operation can result in excessive pressures. Contact the maker of a custom rifle and follow his recommendations for preparing cases.

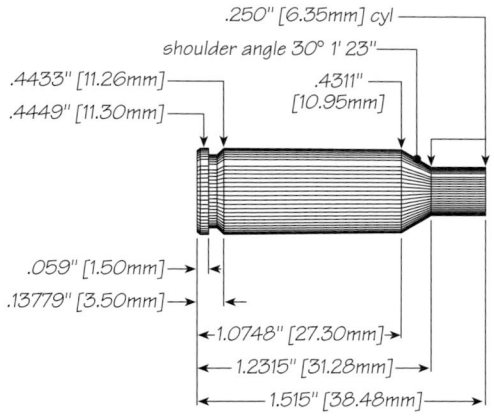

.250" [6.35mm] cyl
shoulder angle 30° 1' 23"
.4433" [11.26mm]
.4449" [11.30mm]
.4311" [10.95mm]
.059" [1.50mm]
.13779" [3.50mm]
1.0748" [27.30mm]
1.2315" [31.28mm]
1.515" [38.48mm]

Max. Case Length:	1.515"	Cart. Case:	Sako
Trim-to Length:	1.505"	Primer:	CCI BR4
Max Cart. OAL:	2.193"	Test Firearm:	Pindell-Wichita
RCBS Shell Holder:	#32	Barrel Length:	24"

0.224"	22 HP	22 Match BTHP
Weight, grains	52	52
Ballistic Coefficient	0.168	0.230
Sectional Density	0.148	0.148
COAL Tested:	2.040"	2.050"
Speer Part No.	1035	1036

	START CHARGE		MAXIMUM CHARGE	
Propellant	Weight, grs	Muzzle Velocity, ft/sec	Weight, grs	Muzzle Velocity, ft/sec
BL-C(2)	26.5	3277	28.5C	3550
H335	26.0	3230	28.0C	3491
H322	25.0	3155	27.0C	3393
Reloder 7	22.0	3064	24.0	3327
IMR 4198	21.5	3053	23.5	3323
748	28.0	3082	30.0C	3321
IMR 4895	25.0	3010	27.0C	3237
IMR 3031	24.0	2993	26.0C	3221

0.224"	22 TNT HP	22 Spitz SP
Weight, grains	55	55
Ballistic Coefficient	0.233	0.212
Sectional Density	0.157	0.157
COAL Tested:	2.080"	2.050"
Speer Part No.	1032	1047

	START CHARGE		MAXIMUM CHARGE	
Propellant	Weight, grs	Muzzle Velocity, ft/sec	Weight, grs	Muzzle Velocity, ft/sec
BL-C(2)	26.0	3150	28.0C	3392
H335	26.0	3101	28.0C	3339
H322	25.0	3093	27.0C	3322
Reloder 7	22.0	3019	24.0	3277
748	27.5	2990	29.5C	3228
IMR 4320	26.0	2994	28.0C	3203
IMR 4895	25.0	2966	27.0C	3186
IMR 4198	21.0	2914	23.0	3174

*Maximum Loads should be used with CAUTION • C = Compressed Load • *Magnum Primer used with this powder.*

225 Winchester

In 1964, Winchester announced the somewhat odd-looking 225 Winchester cartridge to replace the aging 220 Swift. They chambered the revamped Model 70 bolt action in both sporter and varmint models for the new cartridge. Current specs show a 55-grain bullet at 3570 ft/sec.

The 225 is officially designated as a semi-rimmed case as is the Swift; however, the 225 semi-rim is quite large for its type. Most people would call it rimmed. There was a good reason for this rim—it is exactly the same as the 30-06 rim diameter yet feeds just like a rimless cartridge from box magazines. Even though existing actions with standard bolt faces could easily be chambered for the new cartridge, it was the pressure of competition, not technical problems, which kept the 225 from becoming popular.

Just a year after the 225 was introduced, Remington announced that it was going to commercialize the 22-250, one of the most popular wildcat cartridges ever. The 22-250 was a more conventional case design with an established reputation for long-range varmint performance and accuracy, and beat the 225 Winchester factory loads by 100 ft/sec. Other gun makers opted to chamber for the 22-250 instead. With the exception of the Savage Model 340, no other major commercial manufacturer ever chambered rifles for it. In one of the great ironies of the shooting industry, the 225 Winchester is facing obsolescence while the cartridge it was supposed to replace, the 220 Swift, has made a strong comeback.

Winchester still lists 225 ammo and cases on their 2006 website. J.D. Jones at SSK Industries used the 225 case as the basis for a remarkable series of handgun cartridges for custom-made T/C Contender pistols. However, more irony would strike the 225 Winchester; in spite of the continued availability of cases, Jones has shifted his parent case to the more common 220 Swift for his newer developments.

Loading the 225 is no different than other rifle cartridges. Any .224" bullet can be used, and it generates enough velocity to stabilize the long 70-grain Speer semi-spitzer. Best accuracy is obtained with 50, 52 and 55-grain bullets. We previously did not recommend the 50-grain TNT hollow point in this cartridge, but continued testing has shown that this bullet is usable in most rifles with a 1-in-14 inch twist (standard for the 225 Winchester) at 3600 ft/sec.

The industry maximum pressure for the 225 Winchester is 50,000 CUP; these loads do not exceed that level.

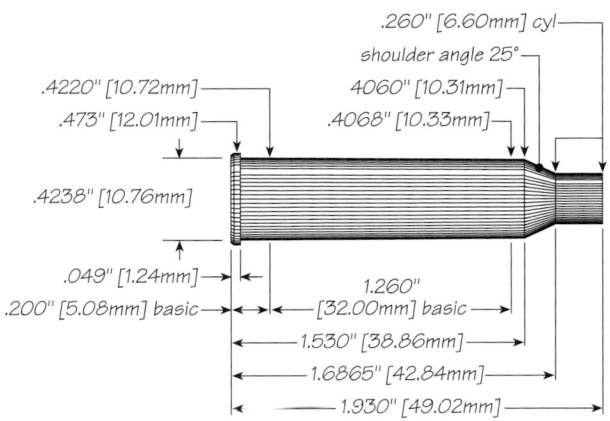

Max. Case Length:	1.930"	Cart. Case:	Winchester
Trim-to Length:	1.920"	Primer:	CCI 200, 250*
Max Cart. OAL:	2.500"	Test Firearm:	Winchester Model 70
RCBS Shell Holder:	#11	Barrel Length:	24"

0.224"	22 Spire SP
Weight, grains	40
Ballistic Coefficient	0.144
Sectional Density	0.114
COAL Tested:	2.370"
Speer Part No.	1017

	START CHARGE		MAXIMUM CHARGE	
Propellant	Weight, grs	Muzzle Velocity, ft/sec	Weight, grs	Muzzle Velocity, ft/sec
IMR 3031	28.5	3391	32.5	3815
IMR 4064	30.5	3344	34.5	3791
H380*	34.0	3351	38.0C	3717
748*	31.0	3310	35.0	3711
H322	27.5	3214	31.5	3683
760*	34.0	3331	38.0C	3682
IMR 4350	33.0	3273	37.0C	3614
H335*	27.5	3078	31.5	3496
SR 4759 (reduced load)	8.0	1560	10.0	1967

*Maximum Loads should be used with CAUTION • C = Compressed Load • *Magnum Primer used with this powder.*

225 Winchester

0.224"	22 Spitz SP
Weight, grains	45
Ballistic Coefficient	0.143
Sectional Density	0.128
COAL Tested:	2.240"
Speer Part No.	1023

Propellant	START CHARGE		MAXIMUM CHARGE	
	Weight, grs	Muzzle Velocity, ft/sec	Weight, grs	Muzzle Velocity, ft/sec
IMR 4064	30.0	3284	34.0	3737
748*	31.0	3237	35.0	3666
IMR 3031	28.0	3176	32.0	3650
760*	34.0	3244	38.0C	3639
H322	27.0	3163	31.0	3609
H380*	34.0	3181	38.0C	3588
IMR 4350	33.0	3164	37.0C	3535
H335*	27.0	3011	31.0	3452
SR 4759 (reduced load)	9.0	1659	11.0	2039

0.224"	22 Spitz SP	22 TNT HP
Weight, grains	50	50
Ballistic Coefficient	0.207	0.228
Sectional Density	0.142	0.142
COAL Tested:	2.460"	2.480"
Speer Part No.	1029	1030

Propellant	START CHARGE		MAXIMUM CHARGE	
	Weight, grs	Muzzle Velocity, ft/sec	Weight, grs	Muzzle Velocity, ft/sec
IMR 4064	29.5	3202	33.5	3641
748*	30.5	3224	34.5	3615
760*	33.0	3183	37.0	3557
H414*	33.0	3159	37.0	3545
IMR 4350	32.5	3150	36.5C	3526
H322	26.5	3138	30.5	3507
IMR 3031	27.5	3030	31.5	3446
H380*	32.0	3093	36.0	3440
SR 4759 (reduced load)	9.5	1679	11.5	2027

*Maximum Loads should be used with CAUTION • C = Compressed Load • *Magnum Primer used with this powder.*

0.224"	22 HP	22 Match BTHP
Weight, grains	52	52
Ballistic Coefficient	0.168	0.230
Sectional Density	0.147	0.147
COAL Tested:	2.500"	2.500"
Speer Part No.	1035	1036

	START CHARGE		MAXIMUM CHARGE	
Propellant	Weight, grs	Muzzle Velocity, ft/sec	Weight, grs	Muzzle Velocity, ft/sec
760*	33.0	3170	37.0C	3571
IMR 4064	29.0	3134	33.0	3551
748*	30.0	3075	34.0	3533
IMR 3031	27.0	3059	31.0	3524
IMR 4350	32.5	3122	36.5C	3519
H380*	31.5	3096	35.5	3502
H322	26.5	3018	30.5	3445
H414*	32.0	3047	36.0	3410
IMR 4895	27.0	2915	31.0	3362

0.224"	22 TNT HP	22 FMJ BT	22 Spitz SP
Weight, grains	55	55	55
Ballistic Coefficient	0.233	0.269	0.212
Sectional Density	0.157	0.157	0.157
COAL Tested:	2.500"	2.500"	2.500"
Speer Part No.	1032	1044	1047

	START CHARGE		MAXIMUM CHARGE	
Propellant	Weight, grs	Muzzle Velocity, ft/sec	Weight, grs	Muzzle Velocity, ft/sec
IMR 4064	28.5	3095	32.5	3503
748*	29.5	3036	33.5	3424
H380*	31.0	3023	35.0	3414
IMR 4350	32.0	3027	36.0C	3397
760*	32.0	3003	36.0	3359
H322	26.0	2888	30.0	3318
IMR 4895	26.5	2833	30.5	3251
H414*	31.0	2926	35.0	3279
SR 4759 (reduced load)	10.0	1679	12.0	2009

0.224"	22 Semi Spitz SP
Weight, grains	70
Ballistic Coefficient	0.219
Sectional Density	0.199
COAL Tested:	2.310"
Speer Part No.	1053

	START CHARGE		MAXIMUM CHARGE	
Propellant	Weight, grs	Muzzle Velocity, ft/sec	Weight, grs	Muzzle Velocity, ft/sec
760*	32.0	2740	36.0	3162
IMR 4831	32.0	2772	36.0C	3094
H414*	30.0	2740	34.0	3092
IMR 4350	30.5	2743	34.5	3064
IMR 4895	24.5	2543	28.5	2988
H380*	28.0	2590	32.0	2983
IMR 4064	26.0	2585	30.0	2980
IMR 3031	24.0	2596	28.0	2938
SR 4759 (reduced load)	12.0	1719	14.0	1988

Ken Alexander, retired CCI/Speer Engineer; 223 Remington, Speer 52-grain HP; black-tailed jackrabbit near Jackpot, Nevada.

*Maximum Loads should be used with CAUTION • C = Compressed Load • *Magnum Primer used with this powder.*

22-250 Remington

This classic, long-range varmint cartridge started life as a wildcat. Although there is some question about who actually invented the cartridge and when it occurred, varmint shooters all agree that the result is no less than spectacular.

In the 1930's a number of experimenters worked to develop a 22-caliber centerfire cartridge based on the efficient 250 Savage case. Although each version was slightly different, the ballistic performance of these early variants was similar. J.E. Gebby trademarked the name "22 Varminter" for his version; other "wildcatters" simply tacked on the name of the parent cartridge and called the cartridge the 22-250.

In 1965, Remington announced that it would introduce the 22-250 as a factory cartridge, although some time earlier Browning offered bolt-action rifles chambered for the wildcat version.

Factory ammunition has a nominal velocity of 3650 ft/sec with a 55-grain bullet, although Federal Premium® lists a 40-grain load at over 4100 ft/sec. The 22-250 is effective on varmints to ranges beyond 300 yards. Most rifles give exceptional accuracy and the 22-250 is every bit as effective as the famed 220 Swift cartridge in terminal performance. Many reloaders claim the 22-250 offers longer case and barrel life than the Swift and cases and factory ammunition are easier to find.

The 52-grain Speer hollow point is a very popular varmint bullet in the 22-250. The 22-250 is also powerful enough to stabilize Speer's long 70-grain semi-spitzer. We get reports of this combination being used on deer but don't consider this an adequate deer cartridge unless the animals are quite small. Although the 50-grain Speer TNT® hollow point is not generally recommended at maximum 22-250 velocities, we know of a number of reloaders who can get 3600-3700 ft/sec from the TNT without problems. Bore smoothness varies from gun to gun, and this seems to be the key factor in using the TNT in a 22-250. The newer 55-grain TNT was designed for the 22-250 and the 220 Swift, and will stand up to any appropriate and safe load for either cartridge.

Although factory brass is readily available, some 22-250 shooters still form their own from 308, 30-06 or 250. Reformed cases have less capacity than factory 22-250 cases and loads should be reduced 5 percent and tested. Custom rifles made before the cartridge was standardized will have dimensional variations in the chambers. Work loads up carefully in these rifles.

These loads do not exceed the industry working pressure of 53,000 CUP.

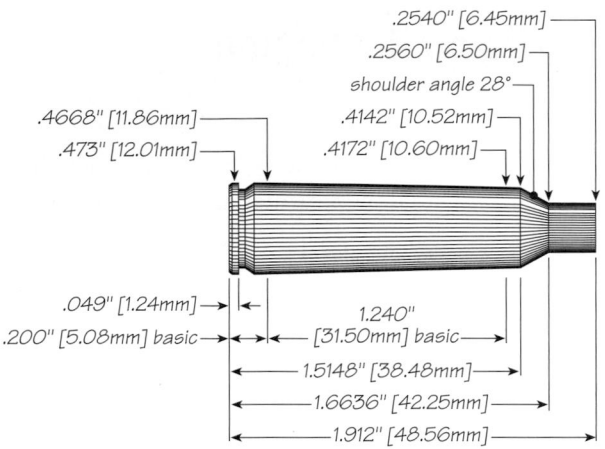

.2540" [6.45mm]
.2560" [6.50mm]
shoulder angle 28°
.4668" [11.86mm]
.473" [12.01mm]
.4142" [10.52mm]
.4172" [10.60mm]
.049" [1.24mm]
.200" [5.08mm] basic
1.240"
[31.50mm] basic
1.5148" [38.48mm]
1.6636" [42.25mm]
1.912" [48.56mm]

Max. Case Length:	1.912"	**Cart. Case:**	Remington
Trim-to Length:	1.902"	**Primer:**	CCI 200, 250*
Max Cart. OAL:	2.350"	**Test Firearm:**	Remington Model 700
RCBS Shell Holder:	#3	**Barrel Length:**	24"

0.224"	22 Spire SP
Weight, grains	40
Ballistic Coefficient	0.144
Sectional Density	0.114
COAL Tested:	2.235"
Speer Part No.	1017

Propellant	START CHARGE		MAXIMUM CHARGE	
	Weight, grs	Muzzle Velocity, ft/sec	Weight, grs	Muzzle Velocity, ft/sec
Reloder 10X	31.5	3780	35.5	4164
Varget	35.0	3582	39.0	4090
AA 2460*	34.0	3468	38.0	4033
Reloder 15	36.0	3443	40.0	4027
H4895	34.0	3542	38.0	4025
Viht. N135	33.0	3463	37.0	3958
IMR 4320	36.0	3360	40.0	3930
AA 2520*	33.0	3382	37.0	3910
748*	35.5	3403	39.5	3867
760*	38.0	3342	42.0	3841
IMR 4064	34.0	3390	38.0	3830
H380*	39.0	3284	43.0C	3796
H335*	33.0	3280	37.0	3748
IMR 3031	32.0	3315	36.0	3746
SR 4759 (reduced load)	9.0	1641	11.0	1979

*Maximum Loads should be used with CAUTION • C = Compressed Load • *Magnum Primer used with this powder.*

0.224"	22 Spitzer SP
Weight, grains	45
Ballistic Coefficient	0.143
Sectional Density	0.128
COAL Tested:	2.235"
Speer Part No.	1023

	START CHARGE		MAXIMUM CHARGE	
Propellant	Weight, grs	Muzzle Velocity, ft/sec	Weight, grs	Muzzle Velocity, ft/sec
Reloder 10X	30.5	3569	34.5	3974
AA 2460*	33.5	3333	37.5	3898
Reloder 15	35.0	3351	39.0	3897
Varget	33.5	3345	37.5	3881
IMR 4320	35.5	3364	39.5	3867
Viht. N135	32.5	3372	36.5	3832
H380*	38.5	3317	42.5C	3748
748*	34.5	3170	38.5	3708
760*	37.5	3194	41.5C	3693
IMR 4064	33.5	3207	37.5	3665
H414*	37.5	3183	41.5C	3659
IMR 4895	32.0	3209	36.0	3647
BL-C(2)*	33.5	3179	37.5	3633
IMR 3031	31.5	3211	35.5	3628
SR 4759 (reduced load)	9.5	1656	11.5	1984

0.224"	22 Spitzer SP
Weight, grains	50
Ballistic Coefficient	0.207
Sectional Density	0.142
COAL Tested:	2.350"
Speer Part No.	1029

| Propellant | START CHARGE | | MAXIMUM CHARGE | |
	Weight, grs	Muzzle Velocity, ft/sec	Weight, grs	Muzzle Velocity, ft/sec
Reloder 10X	30.0	3491	34.0	3837
AA 2460*	33.0	3355	37.0	3804
Varget	32.5	3283	36.5	3796
Reloder 15	34.0	3209	38.0	3736
Viht. N135	32.0	3231	36.0	3693
H380*	38.0	3229	42.0C	3693
AA 2230*	31.0	3188	35.0	3685
760*	37.0	3218	41.0	3636
IMR 4064	33.0	3136	37.0	3625
H414*	37.0	3081	41.0	3604
IMR 4320	34.0	3117	38.0	3603
748*	34.0	3079	38.0	3601
IMR 4895	31.5	3116	35.5	3561
BL-C(2)*	33.0	3149	37.0	3558
SR 4759 (reduced load)	10.0	1650	12.0	1982

*Maximum Loads should be used with CAUTION • C = Compressed Load • *Magnum Primer used with this powder.*

0.224"	22 HP	22 Match BTHP
Weight, grains	52	52
Ballistic Coefficient	0.168	0.230
Sectional Density	0.148	0.148
COAL Tested:	2.350"	2.350"
Speer Part No.	1035	1036

Propellant	START CHARGE		MAXIMUM CHARGE	
	Weight, grs	Muzzle Velocity, ft/sec	Weight, grs	Muzzle Velocity, ft/sec
Reloder 10X	29.0	3406	33.0	3744
IMR 3031	32.0	3251	36.0	3715
748*	34.0	3231	38.0	3714
H4895	32.5	3230	36.5	3713
AA 2460*	32.5	3173	36.5	3711
Varget	32.0	3338	36.0	3706
H380*	38.0	3164	42.0C	3700
Viht. N140	33.5	3233	37.5	3674
Reloder 15	33.5	3204	37.5	3662
Viht. N135	31.5	3177	35.5	3610
760*	36.5	3120	40.5	3607
H414*	36.5	3093	40.5	3597
IMR 4064	32.5	3064	36.5	3563
IMR 4320	33.5	3150	37.5	3559
IMR 4895	31.0	3121	35.0	3526

0.224"	22 Spitzer SP	22 TNT HP
Weight, grains	55	55
Ballistic Coefficient	0.212	0.233
Sectional Density	0.157	0.157
COAL Tested:	2.350"	2.350"
Speer Part No.	1047	1032

Propellant	START CHARGE		MAXIMUM CHARGE	
	Weight, grs	Muzzle Velocity, ft/sec	Weight, grs	Muzzle Velocity, ft/sec
IMR 3031	32.0	3132	36.0	3663
AA 2460*	32.0	3168	36.0	3662
748*	34.0	3237	38.0	3658
Varget	32.0	3260	36.0	3655
H380*	38.0	3143	42.0C	3633
H4895	32.0	3104	36.0	3630
Viht. N140	33.0	3134	37.0	3582
H335*	32.0	3091	36.0	3532
AA 2520*	30.0	2972	34.0	3476
IMR 4064	32.0	2999	36.0	3467
760*	35.5	2949	39.5	3449
IMR 4895	31.0	2993	35.0	3421
IMR 4350	36.0	3012	40.0C	3403
SR 4759 (reduced load)	11.0	1688	13.0	2002

*Maximum Loads should be used with CAUTION • C = Compressed Load • *Magnum Primer used with this powder.*

0.224"	22 TBBC SP
Weight, grains	55
Ballistic Coefficient	0.201
Sectional Density	0.157
COAL Tested:	2.235"
Speer Part No.	1725

	START CHARGE		MAXIMUM CHARGE	
Propellant	Weight, grs	Muzzle Velocity, ft/sec	Weight, grs	Muzzle Velocity, ft/sec
IMR 4895	35.0	3543	37.0	3705
IMR 3031	33.0	3461	35.0	3673
H4895	34.0	3532	36.0	3667
Varget	35.0	3509	37.0	3653
AA 4064	35.0	3439	37.0	3634
748*	34.5	3460	36.5	3624
Reloder 15	35.0	3506	37.0	3621
Viht. N140	34.0	3427	36.0	3596
H. BenchMark	32.0	3431	34.0	3591

NOTE: *Trophy Bonded Bear Claw and Trophy Bonded Sledgehammer Solid bullets have unique ballistic behavior compared to conventional bullets. Loads for TBBC and TBSS bullets may not "track" with data for conventional bullets. Use TBBC and TBSS data ONLY for TBBC and TBSS bullets.*

0.224"	22 Semi Spitz SP
Weight, grains	70
Ballistic Coefficient	0.219
Sectional Density	0.199
COAL Tested:	2.330"
Speer Part No.	1053

Propellant	START CHARGE		MAXIMUM CHARGE	
	Weight, grs	Muzzle Velocity, ft/sec	Weight, grs	Muzzle Velocity, ft/sec
H414*	35.0	2888	39.0	3300
IMR 4320	31.0	2701	35.0	3158
IMR 4831	35.0	2727	39.0	3135
IMR 4350	34.0	2751	38.0C	3126
H380*	33.0	2651	37.0	3083
IMR 4064	29.5	2725	33.5	3079
Viht. N140	29.0	2666	33.0	3064
IMR 4895	28.0	2671	32.0	3052
IMR 3031	28.0	2611	32.0	3018
748*	29.5	2665	33.5	3011
AA 2460*	27.0	2623	31.0	2964
H335*	27.0	2486	31.0	2908
AA 2520*	26.0	2441	30.0	2838
Reloder 7	21.0	2381	25.0	2753
SR 4759 (reduced load)	13.0	1711	15.0	1939

*Maximum Loads should be used with CAUTION • C = Compressed Load • *Magnum Primer used with this powder.*

220 Swift

The 220 Swift was the first factory-loaded "ultra-velocity" centerfire rifle cartridge. Introduced by Winchester in 1935, it pushed a 46-grain bullet at speeds over 4000 ft/sec. In the strong Winchester Model 54 rifle (and later the popular Model 70), the Swift was widely acclaimed as the deadliest varmint cartridge.

Unfortunately, the Swift also received some bad press. The speedy, light factory bullet was very sensitive to crosswinds and the operating pressure, higher than most people were accustomed to in 1935, was rough on cases. With the powders then available, throat erosion was a problem and some experts stated that the useful life of a Swift barrel would be less than 1000 rounds. Today, modern propellants combined with heavier bullets fired in the 3700 to 3900 ft/sec range give case and barrel life comparable to any other high-intensity 22-caliber centerfire cartridge.

Poor judgment on the part of some shooters didn't help the Swift either. Some early writers, letting enthusiasm get in the way of reason, touted the ability of such high-velocity bullets to produce spectacular kills on deer. Even though it should have been obvious that the light, varmint-type bullets couldn't give adequate penetration on big game, some hunters paid more attention to the press than common sense. As a result, the Swift accounted for more than its share of wounded deer.

With modern components and reasonable expectations, the Swift is still among the best long-range varmint cartridges. Modern shooters have rediscovered its attributes and pulled it from the brink of obscurity to a strong position in the varmint hunting market. Remington and Ruger have produced new Swift rifles in recent years.

We recommend bullets between 50 and 55 grains for most varmint shooting. The 55-grain TNT was designed with the Swift in mind. For large varmints up to the size of coyotes, the 70-grain Speer semi-spitzer can be used if your rifle has a 1-in-14 inch twist rate. If you choose the 70-grain bullet, remember to watch seating length so the long bullet doesn't contact the rifling. Speer doesn't consider the Swift to be a deer cartridge, even when handloaded with the 70-grain bullet.

The maximum industry pressure for the Swift is 54,000 CUP. These loads do not exceed this level.

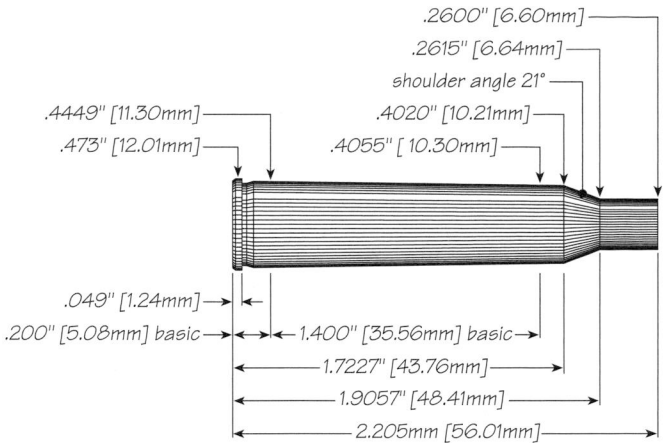

.2600" [6.60mm]
.2615" [6.64mm]
shoulder angle 21°
.4449" [11.30mm]
.473" [12.01mm]
.4020" [10.21mm]
.4055" [10.30mm]
.049" [1.24mm]
.200" [5.08mm] basic
1.400" [35.56mm] basic
1.7227" [43.76mm]
1.9057" [48.41mm]
2.205mm [56.01mm]

Max. Case Length:	2.205"	Cart. Case:	Winchester
Trim-to Length:	2.195"	Primer:	CCI 200, 250*
Max Cart. OAL:	2.680"	Test Firearm:	Ruger M77V
RCBS Shell Holder:	#11	Barrel Length:	26"

0.224"	22 Spire SP
Weight, grains	40
Ballistic Coefficient	0.144
Sectional Density	0.114
COAL Tested:	2.625"
Speer Part No.	1017

Propellant	START CHARGE		MAXIMUM CHARGE	
	Weight, grs	Muzzle Velocity, ft/sec	Weight, grs	Muzzle Velocity, ft/sec
H380*	41.0	3659	45.0C	4008
Reloder 15	37.0	3580	41.0	3996
Viht. N140	36.0	3537	40.0	3943
Viht. N160	42.0	3504	46.0C	3924
760*	39.0	3497	43.0	3903
IMR 4350	41.0	3424	45.0C	3883
IMR 3031	34.5	3509	38.5	3878
AA 4350	41.0	3322	45.0C	3767
Reloder 19	42.0	3345	46.0C	3746
IMR 4064	35.0	3380	39.0	3715
SR 4759 (reduced load)	10.5	1662	12.5	1973

NOTE: COAL is under minimum. May required single-loading in some rifles..

*Maximum Loads should be used with CAUTION • C = Compressed Load • * Magnum Primer used with this powder.*

0.224"	22 Spitz SP
Weight, grains	45
Ballistic Coefficient	0.143
Sectional Density	0.128
COAL Tested:	2.650"
Speer Part No.	1023

Propellant	START CHARGE		MAXIMUM CHARGE	
	Weight, grs	Muzzle Velocity, ft/sec	Weight, grs	Muzzle Velocity, ft/sec
Reloder 15	37.5	3537	41.5	4010
Viht. N160	42.0	3484	46.0C	3901
H380*	40.5	3548	44.5C	3887
Viht. N140	35.5	3421	39.5	3818
760*	38.5	3301	42.5	3788
AA 4350	41.0	3330	45.0C	3776
Reloder 19	42.0	3338	46.0C	3732
IMR 3031	33.5	3332	37.5	3723
IMR 4064	33.5	3284	37.5	3653
IMR 4350	40.5	3066	44.5C	3476
SR 4759 (reduced load)	10.5	1631	12.5	1938

0.224"	22 Spitz SP
Weight, grains	50
Ballistic Coefficient	0.207
Sectional Density	0.142
COAL Tested:	2.650"
Speer Part No.	1029

Propellant	START CHARGE		MAXIMUM CHARGE	
	Weight, grs	Muzzle Velocity, ft/sec	Weight, grs	Muzzle Velocity, ft/sec
Viht. N160	42.0	3453	46.0C	3868
H380*	40.0	3515	44.0	3851
Reloder 15	36.0	3388	40.0	3782
H414*	38.5	3431	42.5	3770
AA 4350	41.0	3346	45.0C	3760
760*	38.5	3369	42.5	3743
Viht. N140	35.0	3402	39.0	3739
Reloder 19	42.0	3274	46.0C	3721
IMR 4350	40.0	3265	44.0C	3703
IMR 3031	33.0	3282	37.0	3607
IMR 4831	40.0	3112	44.0C	3599
IMR 4064	34.0	3208	38.0	3564
AA 2700*	36.0	3168	40.0	3520
SR 4759 (reduced load)	11.0	1669	13.0	1977

*Maximum Loads should be used with CAUTION • C = Compressed Load • *Magnum Primer used with this powder.*

0.224"	22 HP	22 Match BTHP
Weight, grains	52	52
Ballistic Coefficient	0.168	0.230
Sectional Density	0.148	0.148
COAL Tested:	2.680"	2.680"
Speer Part No.	1035	1036

	START CHARGE		MAXIMUM CHARGE	
Propellant	Weight, grs	Muzzle Velocity, ft/sec	Weight, grs	Muzzle Velocity, ft/sec
Viht. N160	42.0	3433	46.0C	3844
Reloder 15	35.5	3353	39.5	3742
AA 4350	41.0	3296	45.0C	3737
Reloder 19	42.0	3324	46.0C	3715
Viht. N140	35.0	3325	39.0	3712
I1380*	39.5	3387	43.5	3710
IMR 4350	39.0	3253	43.0	3688
760*	37.5	3267	41.5	3647
IMR 4831	40.0	3075	44.0C	3576
IMR 3031	32.5	3254	36.5	3576
H4831	41.0	3135	45.0C	3559
SR 4759 (reduced load)	11.0	1680	13.0	2001

0.224"	22 TNT HP	22 Spitz SP
Weight, grains	55	55
Ballistic Coefficient	0.233	0.212
Sectional Density	0.157	0.157
COAL Tested:	2.680"	2.650"
Speer Part No.	1032	1047

| Propellant | START CHARGE | | MAXIMUM CHARGE | |
	Weight, grs	Muzzle Velocity, ft/sec	Weight, grs	Muzzle Velocity, ft/sec
Viht. N160	42.0	3400	46.0C	3807
AA 4350	41.0	3337	45.0C	3784
Reloder 19	42.0	3227	46.0C	3710
Viht. N140	35.0	3312	39.0	3696
H380*	39.0	3362	43.0	3682
Reloder 15	35.0	3276	39.0	3656
IMR 4320	35.0	3280	39.0	3605
IMR 4350	39.0	3167	43.0	3591
H4831SC	41.0	3101	45.0C	3584
AA 2700*	37.0	3257	41.0	3567
760*	36.5	3166	40.5	3534
IMR 3031	32.0	3201	36.0	3506
SR 4759 (reduced load)	11.5	1709	13.5	2000

*Maximum Loads should be used with CAUTION • C = Compressed Load • *Magnum Primer used with this powder.*

0.224"	22 Semi Spitz SP
Weight, grains	70
Ballistic Coefficient	0.219
Sectional Density	0.199
COAL Tested:	2.570"
Speer Part No.	1053

Propellant	START CHARGE		MAXIMUM CHARGE	
	Weight, grs	Muzzle Velocity, ft/sec	Weight, grs	Muzzle Velocity, ft/sec
Viht. N160	38.0	2944	42.0C	3364
AA 3100	39.0	2886	43.0C	3269
Reloder 15	32.0	2895	36.0	3231
Reloder 19	38.0	2875	42.0C	3219
IMR 4320	32.0	2818	36.0	3156
H380*	34.0	2873	38.0	3147
AA 2700*	34.0	2852	38.0	3117
760*	33.0	2813	37.0	3085
IMR 4831	36.0	2635	40.0	3046
H414*	33.0	2742	37.0	3017
IMR 4350	34.0	2639	38.0	2992
SR 4759 (reduced load)	12.0	1642	14.0	1906

*Maximum Loads should be used with CAUTION • C = Compressed Load • *Magnum Primer used with this powder.*

223 Winchester Super Short Magnum

After its success with its Short Magnum series, Winchester looked to the smaller bores for new cartridge opportunities using the basic short magnum case. It became apparent that simply necking down the case was going to make it too spacious for most propellants in the smaller bore diameters. The solution was to further shorten the parent case from 2.100 inch to 1.670 inch. Winchester built 22, 24, and 25-caliber cartridges on the "shortened Short Mag" case and called the series Winchester Super Short Magnums.

The 223 Winchester Super Short Magnum (WSSM) proves to be a very useful cartridge, carving its niche at the top of the 22-caliber performance scale. The 223 WSSM handloads we developed exceeded the velocities of any other commercial 22-caliber cartridges we have tested. We could drive the 50-grain spitzer at 4000 ft/sec, beating the top 220 Swift load by almost 150 ft/sec. The heavy 70-grain Speer semi-spitzer broke 3500 ft/sec with Reloder 22.

All this performance does not come free. The case requires as much or more propellant than the 220 Swift. The standard rifling twist of 1 turn in 10 inches is much faster than most 22-250 and 220 Swift rifles. Speer's 40 and 45-grain bullets, designed with the 22 Hornet and 222 Remington in mind, are stable at high velocities in slower 1-in-12 and 1-in-14 inch twist barrels. However, they can come apart in flight at extreme velocity in a 10-inch twist. The 50 and 55-grain spitzers worked well in the 223 WSSM, but the 50-grain TNT is too lightly built for the WSSM. The 55-grain TNT is the preferred Speer varmint bullet for this cartridge. Its jacket is built to handle these velocities.

Most propellants in the medium- to slow-burning range gave good results in this cartridge. Typical of small, high-pressure cartridges, propellant granule size is the key to top performance. Propellants with smaller granules make best use of the compact WSSM case.

With reasonable care in bullet and propellant selection, the 223 WSSM is staged to usurp the 22-250 and the 220 Swift as the "top dog" among 22-caliber varmint cartridges. The loads presented here remain within the 65,000 psi pressure limit established for this cartridge.

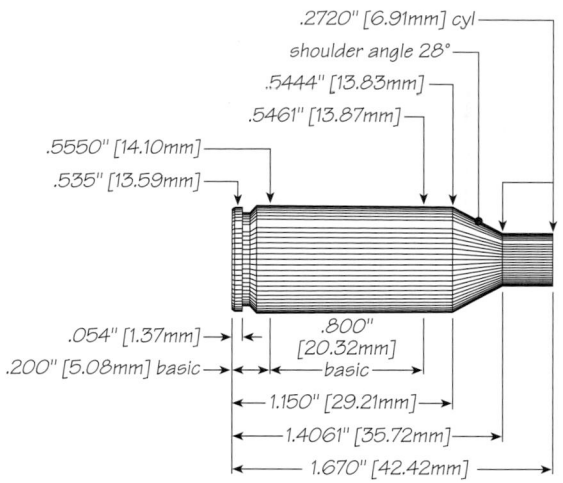

.2720" [6.91mm] cyl
shoulder angle 28°
.5444" [13.83mm]
.5461" [13.87mm]
.5550" [14.10mm]
.535" [13.59mm]
.054" [1.37mm]
.200" [5.08mm] basic
.800" [20.32mm] basic
1.150" [29.21mm]
1.4061" [35.72mm]
1.670" [42.42mm]

Max. Case Length:	1.670"	Cart. Case:	Winchester
Trim-to Length:	1.660"	Primer:	Federal 210, 215*
Max Cart. OAL:	2.360"	Test Firearm:	Universal Receiver
RCBS Shell Holder:	#43	Barrel Length:	Wiseman 24"

0.224"	22 Spitz SP
Weight, grains	50
Ballistic Coefficient	0.207
Sectional Density	0.142
COAL Tested:	2.100"
Speer Part No.	1029

	START CHARGE		MAXIMUM CHARGE	
Propellant	Weight, grs	Muzzle Velocity, ft/sec	Weight, grs	Muzzle Velocity, ft/sec
Reloder 15	42.5	3846	44.5	4036
Varget	43.0	3890	45.0	4033
H414*	47.0	3866	49.0	4027
760*	47.5	3834	49.5	4009
Viht. N540	43.5	3816	45.5	3995
IMR 4895	42.0	3820	44.0	3993
IMR 4064	41.5	3807	43.5	3988
Ramshot Big Game*	45.5	3780	47.5	3971
AA 4064	42.0	3765	44.0	3952
Reloder 10X	36.5	3795	38.5	3929

0.224"	22 TNT HP	22 Spitz SP
Weight, grains	55	55
Ballistic Coefficient	0.233	0.212
Sectional Density	0.157	0.157
COAL Tested:	2.210"	2.210"
Speer Part No.	1032	1047

Propellant	START CHARGE		MAXIMUM CHARGE	
	Weight, grs	Muzzle Velocity, ft/sec	Weight, grs	Muzzle Velocity, ft/sec
H414*	45.5	3724	47.5	3900
760*	46.0	3727	48.0	3894
IMR 4895	41.0	3706	43.0	3873
Reloder 15	40.5	3703	42.5	3867
Varget	41.5	3712	43.5	3867
Ramshot Big Game*	45.0	3722	47.0	3860
IMR 4350	46.0	3671	48.0C	3837
Reloder 19	47.5	3500	49.5C	3746
AA 4350	46.0	3567	48.0C	3733
Viht. N560	49.0	3558	51.0C	3717

Drew Goodlin, Director of Product Development, ATK Civil Ammunition, hunts the Idaho back country.

Maximum Loads should be used with CAUTION • C = Compressed Load • *Magnum Primer used with this powder.

0.224"	22 Semi Spitz SP
Weight, grains	70
Ballistic Coefficient	0.219
Sectional Density	0.199
COAL Tested:	2.080"
Speer Part No.	1053

Propellant	START CHARGE		MAXIMUM CHARGE	
	Weight, grs	Muzzle Velocity, ft/sec	Weight, grs	Muzzle Velocity, ft/sec
Reloder 22	45.5	3407	47.5	3523
Viht. N560	45.0	3358	47.0	3495
Magpro*	48.0	3329	50.0	3489
Reloder 19	43.5	3361	45.5	3478
H414*	40.0	3308	42.0	3432
760*	40.5	3307	42.5	3424
IMR 4350	40.0	3282	42.0	3412
H4350	39.0	3282	41.0	3397
Ramshot Big Game*	39.0	3252	41.0	3383
AA 4350	40.5	3260	42.5	3382

*Maximum Loads should be used with CAUTION • C = Compressed Load • *Magnum Primer used with this powder.*

6mm PPC

A companion to the 22 PPC (Pindell-Palmisano Cartridge), the 6mm PPC is another cartridge developed from the 220 Russian case. The 6mm has an advantage over the 22 PPC in 200-yard benchrest events, where the heavier 24-caliber bullets are less sensitive to crosswinds.

Although bullets from 55 to 70 grains are common for competition, the 6mm PPC is also a great little varmint cartridge with bullets up to 85 grains. Its superb accuracy will surely endear it to varmint shooters and it has sufficient power to take the smaller deer species when loaded with Speer's 90-grain spitzer. Shooters loading the newer 70-grain TNT hollow point should use the loads for the 75-grain hollow point.

Benchrest rifles commonly have rifling twists of 1-in-14 inch because light bullets are normally used. The Speer test rifle has 1-in-12 inch twist and also performed well with the heavier bullets. However, bullets weighing more than 90 grains will not be properly stabilized.

Wichita Engineering built custom benchrest and varmint rifles in 6mm PPC caliber. Sako imported factory rifles in this caliber, along with ammunition. In 1993, Ruger announced that it would produce both 22 and 6mm PPC rifles in the No. 1 single-shot and the M77 Mk II Target rifle. However, neither PPC cartridge is currently offered by any major gunmaker. Cases remained available from Sako as we went to press.

Custom benchrest rifles often have tight chambers that require that case necks be turned and/or reamed for a snug fit in the chamber. Failure to perform this step will raise pressures in a rifle with such a minimum chamber. If you have a custom rifle, ask the builder if special neck preparation is required and follow his recommendations.

Like other wildcat cartridges, no industry pressure standards exist. There are no U.S. dimensional standards for the PPC cartridges. The European standards agency, Commission Internationale Permanente (CIP), lists two versions of the 6mm PPC with slightly different dimensions. The cartridge drawing here is the version submitted to CIP by Sako.

6mm PPC

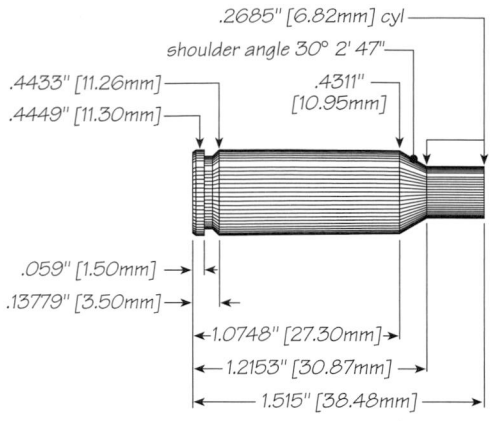

.2685" [6.82mm] cyl
shoulder angle 30° 2' 47"
.4433" [11.26mm]
.4449" [11.30mm]
.4311" [10.95mm]
.059" [1.50mm]
.13779" [3.50mm]
1.0748" [27.30mm]
1.2153" [30.87mm]
1.515" [38.48mm]

Max. Case Length:	1.515"	Cart. Case:	Sako
Trim-to Length:	1.505"	Primer:	CCI BR4
Max Cart. OAL:	2.193"	Test Firearm:	Pindell-Wichita
RCBS Shell Holder:	#32	Barrel Length:	24"

0.243"	6mm HP
Weight, grains	75
Ballistic Coefficient	0.192
Sectional Density	0.181
COAL Tested:	2.115"
Speer Part No.	1205

	START CHARGE		MAXIMUM CHARGE	
Propellant	Weight, grs	Muzzle Velocity, ft/sec	Weight, grs	Muzzle Velocity, ft/sec
H335	26.0	2790	30.0C	3257
BL-C(2)	27.0	2931	29.0C	3169
H322	26.5	2910	28.5C	3127
Reloder 7	23.0	2791	25.0	3011
IMR 4198	24.0	2620	26.0	2910
748	27.0	2634	29.0C	2904
IMR 4895	24.0	2508	26.0C	2705

0.243"	6mm Spitz SP
Weight, grains	80
Ballistic Coefficient	0.325
Sectional Density	0.194
COAL Tested:	2.115"
Speer Part No.	1211

Propellant	START CHARGE		MAXIMUM CHARGE	
	Weight, grs	Muzzle Velocity, ft/sec	Weight, grs	Muzzle Velocity, ft/sec
H335	26.0	2764	30.0C	3201
BL-C(2)	27.0	2929	29.0C	3148
H322	26.5	2887	28.5	3095
Reloder 7	22.5	2664	24.5	2897
748	27.0	2642	29.0C	2839
IMR 4198	24.0	2562	26.0	2766
IMR 4895	24.0	2468	26.0C	2670

0.243"	6mm Spitz BTSP
Weight, grains	85
Ballistic Coefficient	0.380
Sectional Density	0.206
COAL Tested:	2.115"
Speer Part No.	1213

Propellant	START CHARGE		MAXIMUM CHARGE	
	Weight, grs	Muzzle Velocity, ft/sec	Weight, grs	Muzzle Velocity, ft/sec
H335	25.5	2703	29.5C	3156
BL-C(2)	26.5	2858	28.5C	3098
H322	26.0	2878	28.0C	3083
IMR 4198	23.5	2838	25.5C	3068
Reloder 7	22.0	2633	24.0	2863
748	27.0	2625	29.0C	2838
IMR 4320	25.0	2623	27.0C	2815

*Maximum Loads should be used with CAUTION • C = Compressed Load • *Magnum Primer used with this powder.*

6mm PPC

0.243"	6mm Spitz SP
Weight, grains	90
Ballistic Coefficient	0.365
Sectional Density	0.218
COAL Tested:	2.115"
Speer Part No.	1217

	START CHARGE		MAXIMUM CHARGE	
Propellant	Weight, grs	Muzzle Velocity, ft/sec	Weight, grs	Muzzle Velocity, ft/sec
H335	25.0	2601	29.0C	3031
H322	25.5	2718	27.5C	2958
BL-C(2)	26.0	2714	28.0C	2945
IMR 4198	23.0	2699	25.0C	2916
748	26.5	2505	28.5C	2712
IMR 4320	24.5	2463	26.5C	2678
IMR 4895	23.5	2412	25.5C	2603
IMR 4064	23.5	2308	25.5C	2510

Eric Pedersen, ATK Southwest Regional Law Enforcement Specialist; 50-caliber muzzle-loader; blackbuck taken in Texas.

*Maximum Loads should be used with CAUTION • C = Compressed Load • *Magnum Primer used with this powder.*

243 Winchester

Although metric cartridge designations sound European, the 6mm bore was primarily an American development. Winchester introduced a military cartridge, the 6mm Lee Navy, that delivered a 112-grain bullet at 2550 ft/sec. In 1899, the 6mm Lee Navy was the highest velocity cartridge in the Winchester catalog. Winchester sold both military and sporting versions of the rifles. However, straight-pull rifles proved less reliable than turn-bolt actions, and the cartridge failed to gain lasting popularity.

Industry development with this caliber brought forth no new commercial cartridges for decades, but wildcat cartridges using 0.243" diameter bullets begin to show up between 1930 and 1950. Experimenters like Warren Page and RCBS's Fred Huntington designed 6mm wildcats using the 308 Winchester and 257 Roberts cases, respectively. These cartridges performed well on both varmints and deer-sized game and pointed the way for commercial development of similar dual-purpose cartridges.

In 1955, Winchester developed the 243 by simply necking down the 308 Winchester case to accept 24-caliber bullets. The case was a natural for light, short-action sporters. The 243 is excellent for varmints and smaller varieties of deer, so many one-gun hunters choose it for its versatility. Factory loads offer an 80-grain bullet for varmints, and a 100-grain bullet for deer; the handloader has many more options.

The 243 became very popular and most major rifle makers now offer it as a standard cartridge. Because of its light recoil, the 243 is often picked as the first rifle for new shooters. Although it is appropriate for game animals up to and including deer and antelope, it is definitely underpowered for elk, moose and caribou.

For animals at the upper end of the cartridge's capabilities, Speer's 100-grain Grand Slam and 105-grain Hot-Cor spitzer offers the bullet integrity for deep penetration. For varmints, the 70-grain TNT and 75-grain hollow point are excellent choices.

Even though the case is relatively small, slower-burning propellants gave the best velocities. We found that IMR 4350, Reloder 19 and similar propellants performed best with most bullets weights.

The Speer 100-grain boat tail bullet featured in past manuals had a long bearing surface that caused it to produce higher pressures than the 100-grain Grand Slam and the 105-grain Hor-Cor. Older manuals had a separate data chart for the boat tail as a result. We have redesigned that bullet with a longer nose and a shorter bearing surface. Newer 100-grain boat tail bullets can use the Grand Slam and Hot-Cor data. You have bullets of the older style if the last character in the lot number is "F" or lower (silver, black, and red-banded label), or if in the older-style, largely yellow labels. If you have the older style 100-grain BT bullet, do not exceed the start loads in the 100-105 grain section.

The data presented here are the results of a complete retest of this cartridge using the latest components and piezo-electric methods. Velocities shown are from a 24-inch pressure test barrel; our 22-inch Ruger Model 77 Mk II posted velocities that were consistently 98 percent of velocities from the longer test barrel.

We found the 243 Winchester to be very sensitive to case make; we used Winchester cases. Do not substitute cases of other makes with these loads or excessive pressure can result. These loads do not exceed the industry maximum pressure of 60,000 psi.

WARNING: *Do not substitute other brands of cartridge case. Excessive pressure may result.*

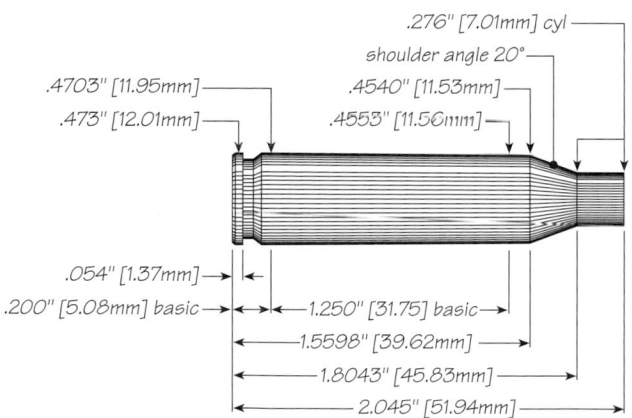

Max. Case Length:	2.045"	Cart. Case:	Winchester
Trim-to Length:	2.035"	Primer:	Federal 210; 215*
Max Cart. OAL:	2.710"	Test Firearm:	Universal Receiver
RCBS Shell Holder:	#3	Barrel Length:	Wilson 24"

0.243"	6mm TNT HP
Weight, grains	70
Ballistic Coefficient	0.279
Sectional Density	0.169
COAL Tested:	2.625"
Speer Part No.	1206

Propellant	START CHARGE		MAXIMUM CHARGE	
	Weight, grs	Muzzle Velocity, ft/sec	Weight, grs	Muzzle Velocity, ft/sec
Viht. N540	41.0	3237	45.0	3552
IMR 4895	39.0	3303	43.0	3540
H414*	45.0	3332	47.0	3520
Varget	39.0	3236	43.0	3515
760*	44.0	3195	48.0	3514
Ramshot Big Game*	42.0	3303	46.0	3508
Reloder 15	39.5	3189	43.5	3506
IMR 4350	44.6	3135	48.5	3461
Reloder 10X	32.5	3189	36.5	3421
AA 4064	39.0	3089	43.0	3419

WARNING: *Do not substitute other brands of cartridge case. Excessive pressure may result.*

*Maximum Loads should be used with CAUTION • C = Compressed Load • *Magnum Primer used with this powder.*

0.243"	6mm HP
Weight, grains	75
Ballistic Coefficient	0.192
Sectional Density	0.181
COAL Tested:	2.590"
Speer Part No.	1205

Propellant	START CHARGE		MAXIMUM CHARGE	
	Weight, grs	Muzzle Velocity, ft/sec	Weight, grs	Muzzle Velocity, ft/sec
Viht. N540	40.5	3099	44.5	3447
IMR 4895	38.5	3183	42.5	3407
Reloder 15	39.0	3077	43.0	3400
Ramshot Big Game*	41.0	3185	45.0	3390
Varget	38.0	3186	42.0	3388
760*	43.5	3114	47.5	3387
IMR 4350	44.0	3043	48.0C	3384
H414*	42.0	3087	46.0	3376
AA 4064	38.5	2930	42.5	3301
Reloder 10X	32.0	3023	36.0	3240
AA 4350	44.0	2916	48.0C	3238

WARNING: *Do not substitute other brands of cartridge case. Excessive pressure may result.*

Kay Curran, Materials Technician, CCI/Speer Operations; 243 Winchester, 100-grain Grand Slam®; pronghorn taken northwest of Baggs, Wyoming.

0.243"	6mm Spitz SP
Weight, grains	80
Ballistic Coefficient	0.325
Sectional Density	0.194
COAL Tested:	2.615"
Speer Part No.	1211

Propellant	START CHARGE		MAXIMUM CHARGE	
	Weight, grs	Muzzle Velocity, ft/sec	Weight, grs	Muzzle Velocity, ft/sec
760*	42.0	3057	46.0	3355
IMR 4350	43.0	3023	47.0	3340
IMR 4895	38.0	3049	42.0	3330
H414*	41.5	3051	45.5	3329
Varget	38.0	3094	42.0	3321
Reloder 15	37.5	2993	41.5	3310
Ramshot Big Game*	40.5	3096	44.5	3309
AA 4350	43.0	2931	47.0	3246
Reloder 19	46.0	3063	48.0C	3206
Reloder 10X	31.0	2912	35.0	3162
AA 5744 (reduced load)	20.0	2075	22.0	2265

WARNING: *Do not substitute other brands of cartridge case. Excessive pressure may result.*

*Maximum Loads should be used with CAUTION • C = Compressed Load • *Magnum Primer used with this powder.*

0.243"	6mm Spitz BTSP
Weight, grains	85
Ballistic Coefficient	0.380
Sectional Density	0.206
COAL Tested:	2.625"
Speer Part No.	1213

| Propellant | START CHARGE | | MAXIMUM CHARGE | |
	Weight, grs	Muzzle Velocity, ft/sec	Weight, grs	Muzzle Velocity, ft/sec
Varget	37.5	3023	41.5	3268
760*	41.0	2991	45.0	3265
IMR 4895	37.5	2910	41.5	3249
Ramshot Big Game*	39.5	2999	43.5	3240
H414*	40.5	2904	44.5	3236
IMR 4350	42.0	2873	46.0	3231
Reloder 15	37.0	2902	41.0	3218
Viht. N560	46.0	2890	50.0C	3216
Reloder 19	46.0	3016	48.0C	3182
AA 4350	43.0	2858	47.0C	3172
Reloder 10X	31.0	2910	35.0	3122

WARNING: *Do not substitute other brands of cartridge case. Excessive pressure may result.*

Justin Moss, PC/Network Technician, CCI/Speer Operations; 54-caliber muzzleloader with CCI caps; whitetail buck from Asotin Co, WA.

0.243"	6mm Spitz SP
Weight, grains	90
Ballistic Coefficient	0.365
Sectional Density	0.218
COAL Tested:	2.625"
Speer Part No.	1217

Propellant	START CHARGE		MAXIMUM CHARGE	
	Weight, grs	Muzzle Velocity, ft/sec	Weight, grs	Muzzle Velocity, ft/sec
Viht. N560	45.0	2880	49.0C	3175
IMR 4350	41.0	2877	45.0	3149
H4350	40.0	2853	44.0	3132
H414*	39.5	2830	43.5	3126
Ramshot Big Game*	37.5	2856	41.5	3084
AA 4350	41.5	2805	45.5C	3080
Reloder 19	43.0	2879	47.0C	3079
IMR 4895	36.0	2020	39.0	3071
760*	39.0	2749	43.0	3056
Reloder 22	44.0	2837	48.0C	3053
Reloder 15	34.0	2767	38.0	3020
AA 5744 (reduced load)	21.0	2105	23.0	2273

WARNING: *Do not substitute other brands of cartridge case. Excessive pressure may result.*

*Maximum Loads should be used with CAUTION • C = Compressed Load • *Magnum Primer used with this powder.*

0.243"	6mm Spitz BTSP	6mm GS SP	6mm Spitz SP
Weight, grains	100	100	105
Ballistic Coefficient	0.446	0.327	0.424
Sectional Density	0.242	0.242	0.254
COAL Tested:	2.625"	2.580"	2.625"
Speer Part No.	1220	1222	1229

	START CHARGE		MAXIMUM CHARGE	
Propellant	Weight, grs	Muzzle Velocity, ft/sec	Weight, grs	Muzzle Velocity, ft/sec
Viht. N560	41.5	2736	45.5	2966
Reloder 22	42.0	2773	46.0	2960
IMR 4831	38.0	2659	42.0	2913
Reloder 19	39.5	2731	43.5	2903
IMR 4350	37.5	2643	41.5	2880
H4831SC	40.0	2639	44.0	2874
Ramshot Magnum*	45.0	2673	49.0C	2868
H414*	36.5	2602	40.5	2862
760*	36.5	2558	40.5	2828
AA 4350	37.0	2581	41.0	2802
Reloder 15	30.0	2443	34.0	2691

WARNING: *Do not substitute other brands of cartridge case. Excessive pressure may result.*

*Maximum Loads should be used with CAUTION • C = Compressed Load • *Magnum Primer used with this powder.*

6mm Remington *(and 244 Remington)*

The 6mm Remington evolved from an older Remington cartridge that suffered a pummeling in the sales arena. The product that evolved proved to be a very impressive solution, and one of this writer's favorites.

There is a definite "twist" to the 6mm Remington story. Remington introduced the 244 Remington in 1955, the same year that Winchester announced its 243. The 244 was very close to Fred Huntington's wildcat, the 243 Rock Chucker. Both were based on the 257 Roberts case, but the commercial version has a 26° shoulder instead of the wildcat's more abrupt 32° shoulder.

Remington intended the 244 to be a "super" varmint cartridge and accordingly cut their barrels with a 1-in-12 inch twist. Factory ammo was loaded with 75 and 90-grain bullets; the heavier factory bullet was closer to a varmint bullet than a deer bullet. Handloading heavier deer bullets (up to 105) grains that were suitable for the 243 Winchester was not a viable solution; they seldom stabilized in the slow twist rate of factory 244 Remington rifles.

On the other hand, the 243 Winchester was conceived and delivered as a dual-purpose cartridge, handling varmints and deer with equal aplomb with barrels having a 1-in-10 inch twist. This versatility allowed the 243 to grow in popularity while the 244 Remington stumbled.

In 1963, Remington reintroduced the cartridge as the 6mm Remington loaded with 80, 90, and 100-grain bullets. The case remained unchanged, but the barrels were fitted with a 1-in-9 inch twist. This simple change made the 6mm Remington the dual-purpose cartridge that the 244 should have been. It has been said that the change was "too little, too late" to overcome the long-standing market advantage of the 243 Winchester, but the result was and is still an impressive entry.

Although the 6mm occupies the same ballistic niche with the 243, handloaders appreciate its longer neck. The slightly larger case also permits a little more velocity, especially with 100 to 105-grain bullets. In the lab, we found the 6mm Remington to be much more flexible than the 243 during load development; however, the average handloader using published data will not notice this.

Although probably the better cartridge, the 6mm Remington still struggles with the entrenched popularity of the 243 Winchester. Nevertheless, it appears here to stay and is still an excellent choice for the reloader who wants one rifle for both varmints and whitetail deer.

Owners of original 244 Remington rifles may also use these loads, but should limit the maximum bullet weight to the Speer 90-grain Hot-Cor spitzer. This tough bullet was designed for deer in original 244 rifles with 1-in-12 inch twists, something that old factory ammo could not claim. 6mm Remington rifles with their faster rifling twist will handle any Speer .243" bullet quite well.

The Speer 100-grain boat tail bullet featured in past manuals had a long bearing surface that caused it to produce higher pressures than the 100-grain Grand Slam and the 105-grain Hor-Cor. Older manuals had a separate data chart for the boat tail as a result. Several years ago, we changed the profile of the bullet to give a longer ogive and shorter bearing surface. This change means current 100-grain boat tail bullets can use the Grand Slam and Hot-Cor data. You have bullets of the older style if the last character in the lot number is "F" or lower (silver, black and red banded labels), or if in the older style largely yellow labels. If you have the older style, do not exceed the 105-grain start loads.

These loads do not exceed the 52,000 CUP industry pressure limit for this cartridge.

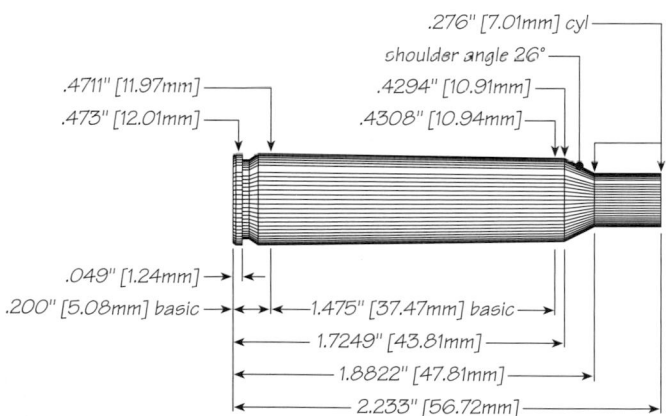

Max. Case Length:	2.233"	Cart. Case:	Remington
Trim-to Length:	2.223"	Primer:	CCI 200; 250*
Max Cart. OAL:	2.825"	Test Firearm:	Remington 700
RCBS Shell Holder:	#3	Barrel Length:	24"

0.243"	6mm TNT HP
Weight, grains	70
Ballistic Coefficient	0.279
Sectional Density	0.169
COAL Tested:	2.775"
Speer Part No.	1206

Propellant	START CHARGE		MAXIMUM CHARGE	
	Weight, grs	Muzzle Velocity, ft/sec	Weight, grs	Muzzle Velocity, ft/sec
H4350	47.0	3198	51.0C	3593
AA 4350	48.0	3106	52.0C	3531
Reloder 19	49.0	3262	53.0C	3507
Reloder 22	50.0	3287	54.0C	3497
IMR 4831	48.0	3171	52.0C	3485
H380*	42.0	3132	47.0	3442
IMR 4064	40.0	3119	44.0	3427
760*	44.0	3078	48.0	3420
IMR 4350	45.0	3040	49.0	3416
IMR 4895	38.0	3111	42.0	3381
H414*	44.0	3100	48.0	3370
Viht. N140	39.0	3023	43.0	3322
H4831*	48.0	3104	52.0C	3302

*Maximum Loads should be used with CAUTION • C = Compressed Load • *Magnum Primer used with this powder.*

0.243"	6mm HP
Weight, grains	75
Ballistic Coefficient	0.192
Sectional Density	0.181
COAL Tested:	2.775"
Speer Part No.	1205

Propellant	START CHARGE		MAXIMUM CHARGE	
	Weight, grs	Muzzle Velocity, ft/sec	Weight, grs	Muzzle Velocity, ft/sec
H4350	46.0	3157	50.0C	3515
AA 4350	47.0	3083	51.0C	3495
Reloder 22	49.0	3262	53.0C	3474
AA 2700*	43.0	3147	47.0	3458
Reloder 19	48.0	3165	52.0C	3440
IMR 4350	44.0	3064	48.0C	3367
760*	43.0	3018	47.0	3318
H4831*	47.0	3045	51.0C	3310
H380*	42.0	3012	46.0	3310
IMR 4831	45.0	3001	49.0C	3298
Viht. N140	39.0	2999	43.0	3293
IMR 4064	38.5	3010	42.5	3272
IMR 4895	37.0	2969	41.0	3248
H414*	42.0	2959	46.0	3216

John Nelson, son of Jim Nelson, Maintenance Supervisor, ATK Onalaska Operations; 243 Winchester, 100-grain Grand Slam®; Wisconsin whitetail buck.

0.243"	6mm Spitz SP
Weight, grains	80
Ballistic Coefficient	0.325
Sectional Density	0.194
COAL Tested:	2.775"
Speer Part No.	1211

Propellant	START CHARGE		MAXIMUM CHARGE	
	Weight, grs	Muzzle Velocity, ft/sec	Weight, grs	Muzzle Velocity, ft/sec
AA 4350	46.0	2989	50.0C	3388
Reloder 19	47.0	3132	51.0C	3368
H4350	45.0	3014	49.0C	3355
Reloder 22	49.0	3141	53.0C	3344
AA 2700*	42.0	2938	46.0	3278
H4831*	47.0	3074	51.0C	3271
IMR 4350	43.0	2939	47.0	3266
H380*	41.0	2931	45.0	3228
IMR 4831	44.0	2968	48.0	3192
IMR 4895	36.0	2870	40.0	3139
760*	42.0	2874	46.0	3124
IMR 4064	37.0	2873	41.0	3123
H414*	41.0	2859	45.0	3108
IMR 4198 (reduced load)	16.0	1801	18.0	2037

*Maximum Loads should be used with CAUTION • C = Compressed Load • *Magnum Primer used with this powder.*

0.243"	6mm Spitz BTSP
Weight, grains	85
Ballistic Coefficient	0.380
Sectional Density	0.206
COAL Tested:	2.775"
Speer Part No.	1213

Propellant	START CHARGE		MAXIMUM CHARGE	
	Weight, grs	Muzzle Velocity, ft/sec	Weight, grs	Muzzle Velocity, ft/sec
Reloder 22	48.0	3048	52.0C	3285
Reloder 19	46.5	3007	50.5C	3269
AA 4350	45.0	2878	49.0	3264
H4831*	47.0	2968	51.0C	3226
760*	41.0	2859	46.0	3152
IMR 4350	41.0	2881	46.0	3138
AA 2700*	40.5	2846	44.5	3128
IMR 4831	43.0	2838	47.0	3085
AA 2520*	36.0	2786	40.0	3061
H380*	39.0	2777	43.0	3052
IMR 4895	35.0	2742	39.0	3000
IMR 4064	36.0	2704	40.0	2965
Viht. N140	35.5	2723	39.5	2960
H414*	40.0	2685	44.0	2921

0.243"	6mm Spitz SP
Weight, grains	90
Ballistic Coefficient	0.365
Sectional Density	0.218
COAL Tested:	2.775"
Speer Part No.	1217

| Propellant | START CHARGE | | MAXIMUM CHARGE | |
	Weight, grs	Muzzle Velocity, ft/sec	Weight, grs	Muzzle Velocity, ft/sec
Reloder 22	47.0	3063	51.0C	3258
Reloder 19	46.0	2976	50.0	3256
AA 4350	44.0	2852	48.0C	3205
H4350	43.0	2821	47.0	3170
AA 3100	45.0	2870	49.0C	3154
IMR 4350	42.0	2858	46.0	3107
7G0*	41.0	2011	45.0	3055
IMR 4831	43.0	2755	47.0	3026
H414*	40.0	2759	44.0	2999
IMR 4064	35.0	2685	39.0	2982
AA 2700*	39.0	2706	43.0	2974
IMR 4895	34.0	2711	38.0	2967
Viht. N140	35.0	2675	39.0	2908
IMR 4198 (reduced load)	17.0	1770	19.0	1987

*Maximum Loads should be used with CAUTION • C = Compressed Load • *Magnum Primer used with this powder.*

6mm Remington

0.243"	6mm Spitz BTSP	6mm GS SP	6mm Spitz SP
Weight, grains	100	100	105
Ballistic Coefficient	0.446	0.327	0.424
Sectional Density	0.242	0.242	0.254
COAL Tested:	2.800"	2.775"	2.800"
Speer Part No.	1220	1222	1229

	START CHARGE		MAXIMUM CHARGE	
Propellant	Weight, grs	Muzzle Velocity, ft/sec	Weight, grs	Muzzle Velocity, ft/sec
IMR 4831	41.0	2831	45.0	3145
IMR 7828*	46.0	2814	50.0	3059
AA 4350	41.5	2622	45.5	2979
Reloder 22	43.0	2763	47.0	2971
AA 3100	43.0	2716	47.0	2952
H4350	40.0	2570	44.0	2888
IMR 4350	39.0	2533	43.0	2846
Reloder 19	41.0	2608	45.0	2835
760*	37.0	2506	41.0	2754
AA 2700*	36.0	2466	40.0	2710
IMR 4064	33.0	2478	37.0	2694
H380*	35.0	2381	39.0	2616
H414*	36.0	2353	40.0	2614
IMR 4198 (reduced load)	18.0	1725	20.0	1924

*Maximum Loads should be used with CAUTION • C = Compressed Load • *Magnum Primer used with this powder.*

243 Winchester Super Short Magnum

The 243 Winchester Super Short Magnum is another in a series of Winchester cartridges that use a "shortened short magnum" case. Had the 243 WSSM and its siblings, the 223 WSSM and 25 WSSM been built on the standard WSM case, they would be badly overbore in capacity. The 1.670-inch case shared by the three WSSM cartridges seems well balanced for those bore diameters.

The 243 WSSM has a small capacity increase over both the 243 Winchester and the 6mm Remington. Unlike the 223 WSSM, which showed an noticeable velocity advantage over other popular 22-caliber cartridges, the 243 WSSM is much closer in performance to the two older 24-caliber cartridges. The new cartridge beats the velocities of the 243 Winchester by about 75-150 ft/sec. Medium- to slow-burning propellants with a small granule size work best in this compact case, even with the lightest bullets.

Like the other 24-caliber cartridges, the 243 WSSM is a dual-purpose cartridge capable of handling both varmints and game animals up to the size of medium deer. For varmints, the 75-grain hollow point is probably a better choice than the 70-grain TNT. The velocity potential of the 243 WSSM is at the upper limit of that which the TNT will tolerate without in-flight jacket ruptures. If you are loading it the 3400 ft/sec range, the TNT should be fine. However, at maximum velocities or if fired in a rifle with a rough or fouled bore, the TNT may be too fragile.

The premier medium deer bullets for this cartridge are the 100-grain Grand Slam and the 105-grain Hot-Cor spitzer. Either at over 3000 ft/sec will deliver the penetration you need for game at the upper end of the cartridge's capabilities.

The loads presented here remain within the industry pressure limit for this cartridge—65,000 psi.

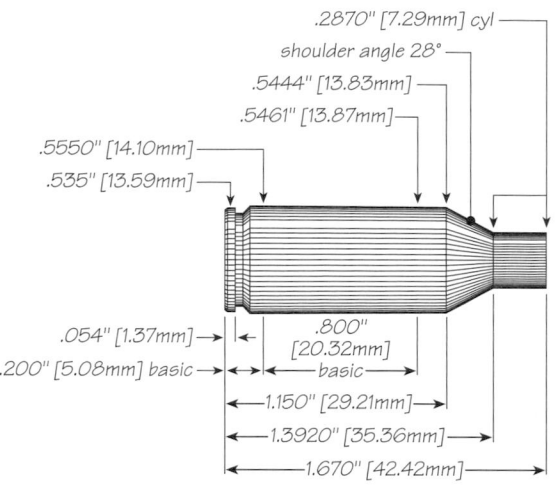

Max. Case Length:	1.670"	**Cart. Case:**	Winchester
Trim-to Length:	1.660"	**Primer:**	Federal 210; 215*
Max Cart. OAL:	2.360"	**Test Firearm:**	Universal Receiver
RCBS Shell Holder:	#43	**Barrel Length:**	Wiseman 24"

Kent Snyder, ATK LE Specialist; 7mm Remington Magnum; whitetail buck taken in Idaho's Clearwater National Forest.

0.243"	6mm TNT HP	6mm HP
Weight, grains	70	75
Ballistic Coefficient	0.279	0.192
Sectional Density	0.169	0.181
COAL Tested:	2.250"	2.185"
Speer Part No.	1206	1205

| Propellant | START CHARGE | | MAXIMUM CHARGE | |
	Weight, grs	Muzzle Velocity, ft/sec	Weight, grs	Muzzle Velocity, ft/sec
H414*	45.0	3417	47.0	3547
760*	45.5	3409	47.5	3531
Viht. N540	40.0	3367	42.0	3484
IMR 4350	44.5	3358	46.5	3483
Reloder 15	39.0	3350	41.0	3478
Reloder 19	47.5	3337	49.5C	3464
IMR 4895	38.5	3333	40.5	3461
Varget	39.0	3347	41.0	3456
Ramshot Big Game*	43.0	3339	45.0	3454
AA 4350	45.0	3262	47.0C	3404
AA 4064	37.5	3214	39.5	3341

*Maximum Loads should be used with CAUTION • C = Compressed Load • *Magnum Primer used with this powder.*

0.243"	6mm Spitz SP
Weight, grains	80
Ballistic Coefficient	0.325
Sectional Density	0.194
COAL Tested:	2.255"
Speer Part No.	1211

Propellant	START CHARGE		MAXIMUM CHARGE	
	Weight, grs	Muzzle Velocity, ft/sec	Weight, grs	Muzzle Velocity, ft/sec
Reloder 19	46.5	3284	48.5C	3432
H414*	42.5	3303	44.5	3412
760*	43.0	3293	45.0	3407
Reloder 15	38.5	3267	40.5	3386
IMR 4350	42.5	3272	44.5	3382
Ramshot Big Game*	41.5	3253	43.5	3368
Varget	37.5	3212	39.5	3357
Viht. N540	38.0	3224	40.0	3346
IMR 4895	37.0	3217	39.0	3342
AA 4350	42.5	3199	44.5	3320

Larry Teague, Production Coordinator, RCBS Operations; 300 Win Mag, 180-grain Grand Slam®; bull elk taken near Paonia CO.

0.243"	6mm Spitz BTSP
Weight, grains	85
Ballistic Coefficient	0.380
Sectional Density	0.206
COAL Tested:	2.255"
Speer Part No.	1213

Propellant	START CHARGE		MAXIMUM CHARGE	
	Weight, grs	Muzzle Velocity, ft/sec	Weight, grs	Muzzle Velocity, ft/sec
H414*	41.5	3169	43.5	3274
Reloder 19	45.0	3131	47.0C	3272
760*	41.5	3162	43.5	3271
Reloder 15	37.0	3146	39.0	3260
IMR 4350	41.0	3145	43.0	3252
Ramshot Big Game*	39.5	3113	41.5	3222
AA 4350	41.5	3086	43.5	3201
Viht. N540	36.0	3076	38.0	3191
IMR 4895	35.0	3066	37.5	3184

*Maximum Loads should be used with CAUTION • C = Compressed Load • *Magnum Primer used with this powder.*

0.243"	6mm Spitz SP
Weight, grains	90
Ballistic Coefficient	0.365
Sectional Density	0.218
COAL Tested:	2.360"
Speer Part No.	1217

Propellant	START CHARGE		MAXIMUM CHARGE	
	Weight, grs	Muzzle Velocity, ft/sec	Weight, grs	Muzzle Velocity, ft/sec
Reloder 22	44.5	3149	46.5	3250
Reloder 19	43.0	3114	45.0	3218
IMR 4350	40.5	3088	42.5	3208
H414*	41.0	3095	43.0	3205
760*	40.5	3080	42.5	3182
AA 4350	41.0	3023	43.0	3140
Ramshot Magnum*	50.0	3007	52.0C	3122
Ramshot Big Game*	38.0	3010	40.0	3113
IMR 4895	34.5	2960	36.5	3079

0.243"	6mm Spitz BTSP	6mm GS SP	6mm Spitz SP
Weight, grains	100	100	105
Ballistic Coefficient	0.446	0.327	0.424
Sectional Density	0.242	0.242	0.254
COAL Tested:	2.360"	2.310"	2.360"
Speer Part No.	1220	1222	1229

	START CHARGE		MAXIMUM CHARGE	
Propellant	Weight, grs	Muzzle Velocity, ft/sec	Weight, grs	Muzzle Velocity, ft/sec
Ramshot Magnum*	50.5	2993	52.5C	3116
Reloder 22	41.5	2920	43.5	3004
Viht. N560	40.0	2860	42.0	2948
Reloder 19	38.5	2829	40.5	2915
AA 4350	38.5	2785	40.5	2904
IMR 4350	36.5	2792	38.5	2894
H4350	35.5	2780	37.5	2881
H414*	36.0	2745	38.0	2856
760*	35.5	2733	37.5	2835

Lana Ulmer with Brandon Graves, ATK Law Enforcement/OEM Sales Manager; Corsican ram.

Maximum Loads should be used with CAUTION • C = Compressed Load • *Magnum Primer used with this powder.

240 Weatherby Magnum

The 240 Weatherby is the only modern 6mm belted magnum. Two older belted cartridges—the 240 Belted Rimless Nitro Express and the 244 H&H Magnum—predate the Weatherby development by decades, but were nearly unknown in the United States. Introduced in 1968 in Weatherby's famous Mark V bolt-action rifle, the 240 Weatherby was a totally new case design.

The case has the same rim diameter as the 30-06 so rifles can be built on standard actions. As with most cartridges of this class, the belt is strictly cosmetic. Best accuracy and case life is obtained when the case headspaces on the generous shoulder.

The 240 Weatherby is capable of firing a 100-grain bullet in excess of 3200 ft/sec and the lighter varmint bullets can reach 3700 ft/sec from a 24-inch barrel. Although a fine cartridge, the 240 has seen only limited acceptance largely because cases are hard to find, expensive and cannot be formed from any other case. However, 240 rifles and ammo were still listed on Weatherby's website in 2006.

For the reloader who has an ample supply of cases, the 240 Weatherby is the premier 6mm cartridge. Its use on game heavier than deer is limited by bullet selection. Most 6mm diameter bullets were designed for lighter game, and often aren't tough enough to handle the Weatherby's velocity potential. One exception is the Speer 100-grain Grand Slam. Its thick, tough jacket allows deeper penetration than bullets of weaker construction. Even with the Grand Slam, we cannot recommend the 240 as an elk cartridge, although it should be able to handle the larger deer species.

Most Weatherby cartridges were standardized by the industry in 1994. The 240 Weatherby has a pressure assignment of 53,500 CUP.

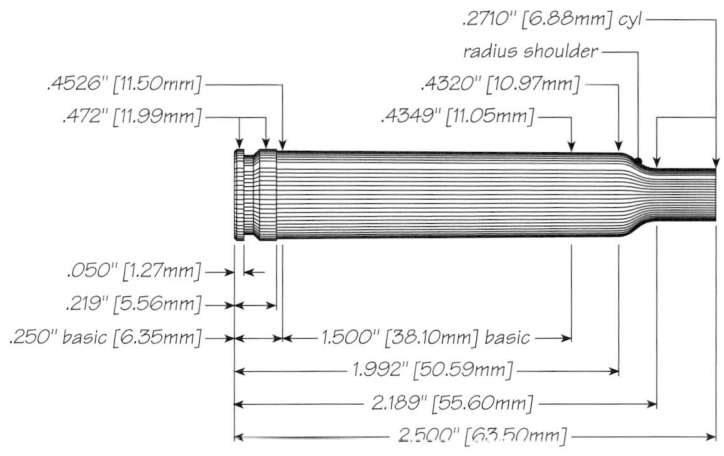

.2710" [6.88mm] cyl
radius shoulder
.4320" [10.97mm]
.4349" [11.05mm]
.4526" [11.50mm]
.472" [11.99mm]

.050" [1.27mm]
.219" [5.56mm]
.250" basic [6.35mm]
1.500" [38.10mm] basic
1.992" [50.59mm]
2.189" [55.60mm]
2.500" [63.50mm]

Max. Case Length:	2.500"	Cart. Case:	Weatherby
Trim-to Length:	2.490"	Primer:	CCI 250*
Max Cart. OAL:	3.100"	Test Firearm:	Weatherby Mk V
RCBS Shell Holder:	#3	Barrel Length:	24"

0.243"	6mm HP
Weight, grains	75
Ballistic Coefficient	0.192
Sectional Density	0.181
COAL Tested:	3.060"
Speer Part No.	1205

Propellant	START CHARGE		MAXIMUM CHARGE	
	Weight, grs	Muzzle Velocity, ft/sec	Weight, grs	Muzzle Velocity, ft/sec
H414*	52.0	3447	56.0	3734
IMR 4831*	51.0	3322	55.0C	3620
760*	47.5	3281	51.5	3602
IMR 4350*	49.0	3334	53.0	3583
IMR 4064	42.0	3126	46.0	3481
H380*	45.0	3094	49.0	3429

NOTE: *6mm TNT not recommended for this cartridge.*

*Maximum Loads should be used with CAUTION • C = Compressed Load • *Magnum Primer used with this powder.*

0.243"	6mm Spitz SP
Weight, grains	80
Ballistic Coefficient	0.325
Sectional Density	0.194
COAL Tested:	3.060"
Speer Part No.	1211

	START CHARGE		MAXIMUM CHARGE	
Propellant	Weight, grs	Muzzle Velocity, ft/sec	Weight, grs	Muzzle Velocity, ft/sec
IMR 4831*	50.0	3327	54.0C	3583
H414*	49.0	3237	53.0	3546
IMR 4350*	48.5	3256	52.5	3509
760*	47.0	3141	51.0	3451
IMR 4064*	41.0	3132	45.0	3408
H380*	44.0	3029	48.0	3357

0.243"	6mm Spitz BTSP
Weight, grains	85
Ballistic Coefficient	0.380
Sectional Density	0.206
COAL Tested:	3.060"
Speer Part No.	1213

	START CHARGE		MAXIMUM CHARGE	
Propellant	Weight, grs	Muzzle Velocity, ft/sec	Weight, grs	Muzzle Velocity, ft/sec
IMR 4831*	49.0	3304	53.0C	3473
H414*	48.0	3161	52.0	3430
IMR 4350*	47.5	3162	51.5	3417
760*	46.0	3071	50.0	3349
IMR 4064*	40.0	2976	44.0	3242
H380*	43.0	2949	47.0	3236

0.243"	6mm Spitz SP
Weight, grains	90
Ballistic Coefficient	0.365
Sectional Density	0.218
COAL Tested:	3.060"
Speer Part No.	1217

Propellant	START CHARGE		MAXIMUM CHARGE	
	Weight, grs	Muzzle Velocity, ft/sec	Weight, grs	Muzzle Velocity, ft/sec
IMR 4831*	48.0	3176	52.0C	3420
H414*	48.0	3057	52.0	3367
IMR 4350*	46.5	3059	50.5	3304
760*	46.0	2992	50.0	3302
H380	43.0	2813	47.0	3107
IMR 4064*	40.0	2854	44.0	3098

0.243"	6mm Spitz BTSP	6mm GS SP	6mm Spitz SP
Weight, grains	100	100	105
Ballistic Coefficient	0.446	0.327	0.424
Sectional Density	0.242	0.242	0.254
COAL Tested:	3.060"	3.060"	3.060"
Speer Part No.	1220	1222	1229

Propellant	START CHARGE		MAXIMUM CHARGE	
	Weight, grs	Muzzle Velocity, ft/sec	Weight, grs	Muzzle Velocity, ft/sec
760*	45.0	2922	49.0	3209
H414*	46.0	2897	50.0	3167
IMR 4831*	45.5	2915	49.5C	3154
IMR 4350*	43.5	2768	47.5	3007
IMR 4064*	38.0	2714	42.0	2977
H380*	41.0	2601	45.0	2901

*Maximum Loads should be used with CAUTION • C = Compressed Load • * Magnum Primer used with this powder.*

25-20 Winchester *(25 W.C.F)*

The 25-20 Winchester was first introduced in the 1890's for the popular Winchester Model 92 lever-action rifle. The action required a short case, so the 25-20 was based on the older 32-20 WCF case that is about 1.3 inches long.

In the days before the 218 Bee and the 22 Hornet, the 25-20 was popular as a small game and varmint cartridge. Some advertising even suggested using the 25-20 for deer. However, it probably wounded as much game as it killed. It is not enough cartridge for deer-sized game by any measure beyond emergency survival.

In the last half of the 20th century, the 25-20 was almost a fond memory. Marlin brought new life and interest back to the old cartridge by reintroducing it in their excellent Model 1894CL lever action rifle in 1989. It remained in the line for several years, but is not shown in the 2006 Marlin catalog.

Speer introduced a new bullet in 1990 to support the introduction of the Marlin rifle. Input from shooters indicated that 60-grain bullets were too light and the factory 86-grain bullets couldn't be driven fast enough. Therefore, Speer built a 75-grain Hot-Cor bullet that features a crimping cannelure and a flat point so that it can be safely used in tubular magazines. Our scope-sighted Marlin rifle has fired 100-yard groups measuring just over an inch.

We obtained excellent results from IMR 4198, AA 1680 and AA 2015BR. In fact, these propellants posted much better performance than powders like 2400 and 4227, which are traditional in such small cases. The walls of the case neck are quite thin so you may find that crimping is better done as a separate operation after bullet seating.

The 25-20 should not be used on animals larger than coyotes. It will never be a deer cartridge, regardless of loading technique or bullet choice. However, it is one of the nicest centerfire turkey cartridges around because its modest velocity destroys less edible meat.

The industry pressure standard for the 25-20 Winchester is 28,000 CUP, and these loads do not exceed that limit. Do not attempt to use pointed bullets in rifles with tubular magazines. Doing so may cause cartridges to explode in the magazine, damaging the firearm and possibly injuring the shooter.

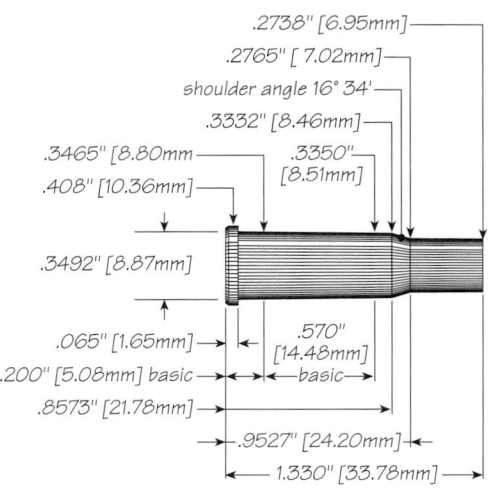

Max. Case Length:	1.330"	Cart. Case:	Winchester
Trim-to Length:	1.320"	Primer:	CCI 400; 450*
Max Cart. OAL:	1.592"	Test Firearm:	Marlin
RCBS Shell Holder:	#1	Barrel Length:	22"

0.257"	25 FN SP/cann
Weight, grains	75
Ballistic Coefficient	0.135
Sectional Density	0.162
COAL Tested:	1.545"
Speer Part No.	1237

	START CHARGE		MAXIMUM CHARGE	
Propellant	Weight, grs	Muzzle Velocity, ft/sec	Weight, grs	Muzzle Velocity, ft/sec
AA 1680*	11.5	1778	12.5	2008
IMR 4198	11.6	1744	12.6C	1901
AA 2015	13.5	1768	14.5C	1890
Viht. N110	7.8	1658	8.8	1838
296*	7.6	1643	8.6	1790
H110*	7.4	1550	8.4	1743
IMR 4227	9.0	1550	10.0	1701
AA No. 9	6.8	1492	7.8	1692
2400	7.0	1550	8.0	1685

*Maximum Loads should be used with CAUTION • C = Compressed Load • *Magnum Primer used with this powder.*

250 Savage

The 250 Savage was one of the first high-velocity rifle cartridges introduced to the American market that didn't start life as a military cartridge. Designed for Savage by Charles Newton of Newton Rifle Company fame, the cartridge was first offered in the venerable Savage 99 lever-action rifle in 1915. Newton wanted to use a 100-grain bullet to make the cartridge suitable for deer-size game, but Savage insisted on delivering 3000 ft/sec at the muzzle, probably for advertising and marketing purposes. Today, this velocity doesn't seem too impressive but, in 1915, no other commercial cartridge had ever reached that speed.

Newton determined that an 87-grain bullet was the heaviest which would achieve 3000 ft/sec at safe pressures. Savage used the name "250-3000" to emphasize the velocity achievement. It made a excellent varmint cartridge, but its penetration was too limited to make it effective on game other than the smallest deer. Western Cartridge Company corrected this by introducing a 100-grain load at about 2800 ft/sec in 1921. Soon, the 250 became popular as a dual-purpose cartridge and the name changed to the 250 Savage. Because of its mild recoil, many youngsters started their shooting careers with a 250 Savage rifle.

The 250 Savage forever changed the role of the lever action rifle. The first Savage 99s were chambered for the same modest-power cartridges as the Winchester 94. The introduction of the 250 cartridge and, later, the 300 Savage, moved lever gun technology to modern, high-pressure cartridges, giving ballistic performance on par with contemporary bolt-action rifles and shedding their bulk and weight in the process.

The introduction of the 243 Winchester and 244 Remington in 1955 caused a decline in the popularity of the 250. In spite of this, the old cartridge retains its fan base among those who value a cartridge's good manners and accuracy above raw power. Savage reintroduced the 250 for a time in the Model 99 in 1971, and Ruger, Remington and Weatherby have produced limited runs of modern bolt-action rifles in this caliber. Most of these rifles prove the accuracy potential of this fine cartridge; this writer's Remington 700 Classic from 1984 consistently delivers sub-MOA groups. Unfortunately, as of press time, no major U.S. manufacturers are chambering it.

With 120-grain bullets, the 250 Savage suffers a significant velocity loss compared to 100-grain bullets. The long bullets seated to industry specification take up a lot of room in the small case. However, velocities between 2400 and 2500 ft/sec are possible with the right propellants. The long bullets at this modest velocity give good penetration and are useful in heavy cover.

If your rifle has a 1-in-10 inch twist like the Remington 700 Classic, it will stabilize the 120-grain bullets to longer ranges. For larger deer, the 120-grain Speer Grand Slam or the 120-grain Hot-Cor spitzer are the best choices. Older rifles may have a 1-in-12 inch or 1-in-14 inch twist; if you have one of the slower twist barrels, stick with the 100-grain Hot-Cor or boat tail spitzers for deer. Varmint hunters find that the 87-grain TNT hollow point gives spectacular results regardless of twist rate. Owners of bolt-action rifles may find that seating the bullets slightly longer than the length required for the short Savage 99 magazine can significantly improve accuracy. Make sure that the bullet jacket does not engage the rifling.

Unprimed cases we purchased in the mid-1990's have slightly less capacity than older ones—typically about one grain of most rifle propellants. If you have a pet load worked up in old cases, reduce charge weights in new cases at least one grain to compensate for the case differences. Winchester still catalogs 250 Savage unprimed cases at press time.

The industry maximum pressure for the 250 Savage is set at a reasonable 45,000 CUP in deference to lever-action rifles; these loads fall within those limits.

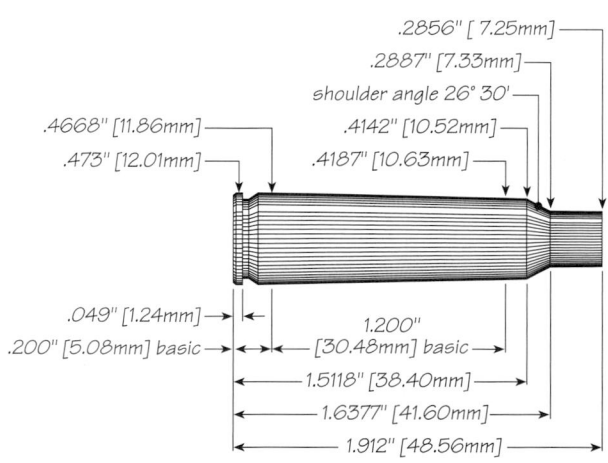

Max. Case Length:	1.912"	Cart. Case:	Winchester
Trim-to Length:	1.902"	Primer:	CCI 200; 250*
Max Cart. OAL:	2.515"	Test Firearm:	Remington 700 Classic
RCBS Shell Holder:	#3	Barrel Length:	24"

0.257"	25 FNSP
Weight, grains	75
Ballistic Coefficient	0.135
Sectional Density	0.162
COAL Tested:	2.175"
Speer Part No.	1237

Propellant	START CHARGE		MAXIMUM CHARGE	
	Weight, grs	Muzzle Velocity, ft/sec	Weight, grs	Muzzle Velocity, ft/sec
AA 2520*	31.5	2821	35.5	3121
H380*	38.0	2832	42.0C	3109
Viht. N133	28.0	2772	32.0	3074
Reloder 15	33.0	2645	37.0	3027
760*	37.0	2711	41.0C	3020
H414*	37.0	2709	41.0C	2994
IMR 4350	37.0	2714	41.0C	2966
IMR 4064	32.0	2580	36.0	2929
AA 2015	27.0	2485	31.0	2860
H4895	29.0	2437	33.0	2783
IMR 4198 (reduced load)	16.0	1802	18.0	1991

Larry Mitchell of Salt Lake Wholesale, an ATK Law Enforcement distributor; 338 Federal; 6x6 bull elk taken near St. Anthony ID.

0.257"	25 Spitz SP	25 TNT HP
Weight, grains	87	87
Ballistic Coefficient	0.300	0.337
Sectional Density	0.188	0.188
COAL Tested:	2.450"	2.500"
Speer Part No.	1241	1246

| Propellant | START CHARGE | | MAXIMUM CHARGE | |
	Weight, grs	Muzzle Velocity, ft/sec	Weight, grs	Muzzle Velocity, ft/sec
H380*	38.0	2821	42.0C	3097
H414*	37.0	2749	41.0C	3005
760*	37.0	2733	41.0C	2994
Reloder 15	33.0	2642	37.0	2982
IMR 4350	37.0	2589	41.0C	2963
AA 2700*	37.0	2646	41.0	2901
IMR 4831	38.0	2507	42.0C	2866
IMR 4064	31.0	2578	35.0	2849
748*	31.0	2486	35.0	2793
AA 3100	37.0	2451	41.0C	2788
BL-C(2)*	31.0	2476	35.0	2767
SR 4759 (reduced load)	12.5	1622	14.5	1928

*Maximum Loads should be used with CAUTION • C = Compressed Load • *Magnum Primer used with this powder.*

0.257"	25 Spitz SP	25 HP	25 Spitz BTSP
Weight, grains	100	100	100
Ballistic Coefficient	0.334	0.263	0.393
Sectional Density	0.216	0.216	0.216
COAL Tested:	2.450"	2.400"	2.450"
Speer Part No.	1405	1407	1408

Propellant	START CHARGE Weight, grs	START CHARGE Muzzle Velocity, ft/sec	MAXIMUM CHARGE Weight, grs	MAXIMUM CHARGE Muzzle Velocity, ft/sec
AA 2520*	29.0	2392	33.0	2763
H414*	34.0	2504	38.0C	2743
760*	34.0	2480	38.0C	2716
H4350	34.0	2340	38.0C	2674
AA 3100	36.0	2340	40.0C	2670
748*	30.0	2294	34.0	2649
IMR 4350	33.5	2313	37.5C	2647
IMR 4831	35.0	2301	39.0C	2633
IMR 4064	29.0	2346	33.0	2622
H380*	31.0	2256	35.0	2604
Reloder 15	28.0	2244	32.0	2532
BL-C(2)*	28.0	2223	32.0	2509

0.257"	25 Spitz BTSP	25 Spitz SP	25 GS SP
Weight, grains	120	120	120
Ballistic Coefficient	0.480	0.405	0.356
Sectional Density	0.260	0.260	0.260
COAL Tested:	2.450"	2.450"	2.515"
Speer Part No.	1410	1411	1415

Propellant	START CHARGE		MAXIMUM CHARGE	
	Weight, grs	Muzzle Velocity, ft/sec	Weight, grs	Muzzle Velocity, ft/sec
H414*	32.0	2290	36.0	2511
760*	32.0	2289	36.0	2507
Reloder 19	34.0	2200	38.0	2497
IMR 4831	33.0	2116	37.0	2421
AA 3100	33.0	2163	37.0C	2411
Reloder 15	27.0	2123	31.0	2397
IMR 4320	27.0	2084	31.0	2371
H380*	29.0	2159	33.0	2370
H4350	31.0	2059	35.0C	2354
IMR 4350	30.0	2062	34.0	2344
IMR 4198 (reduced load)	18.0	1644	20.0	1858

*Maximum Loads should be used with CAUTION • C = Compressed Load • *Magnum Primer used with this powder.*

257 Roberts +P

This fine cartridge started as a wildcat based on the 7mm Mauser case. N. H. (Ned) Roberts necked down the parent case to hold .257" diameter bullets and modified the shoulder angle from 20° to 15°. The cartridge, which he called the 25 Roberts, quickly became popular with custom rifle makers such as Niedner and Griffin & Howe.

Remington decided to make the wildcat a commercial cartridge, changing only the shoulder to the original 20° angle of the parent cartridge. To avoid confusion with the wildcat version and the older 25 Remington cartridge, it was named the 257 Roberts. In 1934, Remington offered their Model 30-S bolt-action in 257. Soon, nearly every rifle maker was producing the 257 Roberts as a standard chambering.

Until the mid-50's, the Roberts was one of the most popular sporting cartridges under 30 caliber. Its ample case gave it a significant performance advantage over the 250 Savage and, with proper bullet selection, the Roberts is suitable for game from big varmints to mule deer.

The introduction of the 243 Winchester and the 6mm Remington (as the 244 Remington) cartridges in 1955 dramatically cut into the popularity of both the Roberts and the 250 Savage. As sales dropped, most rifle manufacturers abandoned the 257 in favor of the newcomers. This was unfortunate because the Roberts' ability to drive 115 to 120-grain bullets at 2800 ft/sec gives it an advantage over either 24-caliber for big deer. Today, a deer hunter with a 257 Roberts is still well equipped for North American hunting.

In 1972, Ruger built a short run of its Model 77 bolt-action rifle in 257 Roberts. Later it was added as a standard caliber in several variations of the M77 and the No. 1 single-shot rifle. In the 1980's both Remington and Winchester reintroduced the Roberts in their bolt-actions. Today only Ruger still catalogs 257 Roberts rifles.

The 87-grain Speer TNT is a great varmint bullet for spring varminting. Look to the 115-grain Trophy Bonded Bear Claw or the 120-grain Grand Slam for game at the top end of the cartridge's capability.

Winchester introduced a +P (additional pressure) 257 Roberts loading for bolt-action rifles, using a case with thicker walls. The industry pressure limit for the standard 257 is 45,000 CUP; the 257 +P limit is 50,000 CUP. These loads were worked to the higher limit in +P cases for use in modern bolt-action rifles only. If you are loading for a pre-World War II rifle, a slide-action rifle, or one built on the Mauser 93/95 action, reduce maximum loads by two grains.

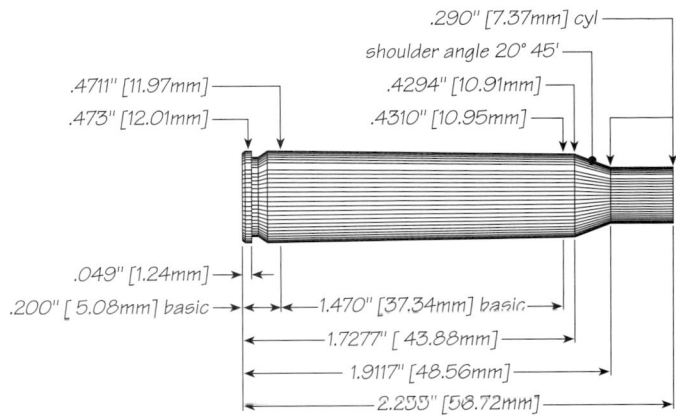

Max. Case Length:	2.233"	Cart. Case:	Winchester
Trim-to Length:	2.223"	Primer:	CCI 200; 250*
Max Cart. OAL:	2.780"	Test Firearm:	Ruger Model 77
RCBS Shell Holder:	#3	Barrel Length:	24"

Mike Miller, Chemistry Department, CCI/Speer Operations; 300 Winchester Magnum, Speer 180-grain boat tail; 46-3/4" moose.

0.257"	25 FNSP
Weight, grains	75
Ballistic Coefficient	0.135
Sectional Density	0.162
COAL Tested:	2.500"
Speer Part No.	1237

Propellant	START CHARGE		MAXIMUM CHARGE	
	Weight, grs	Muzzle Velocity, ft/sec	Weight, grs	Muzzle Velocity, ft/sec
AA 2700*	44.0	3078	48.0	3413
760*	45.0	3004	49.0	3375
AA 4350	47.0	2937	51.0C	3319
IMR 4350	45.0	2895	49.0C	3265
AA 3100	48.0	2973	52.0C	3250
Reloder 15	39.0	2852	43.0	3223
H414*	44.0	2920	48.0	3205
IMR 4895	37.0	2772	41.0	3157
IMR 4064	38.0	2795	42.0	3126
Viht. N133	33.0	2705	37.0	3092

NOTE: *Overall length less than 257 Roberts minimum. May require single-feeding in some rifles.*

0.257"	25 Spitz SP	25 TNT HP
Weight, grains	87	87
Ballistic Coefficient	0.300	0.337
Sectional Density	0.188	0.188
COAL Tested:	2.760"	2.780"
Speer Part No.	1241	1246

Propellant	START CHARGE		MAXIMUM CHARGE	
	Weight, grs	Muzzle Velocity, ft/sec	Weight, grs	Muzzle Velocity, ft/sec
H4350	47.0	3161	51.0C	3381
IMR 4831	47.0	2993	51.0	3226
Reloder 19	47.0	2947	51.0C	3187
IMR 7828	50.0	2955	54.0	3184
H380*	42.0	2884	46.0	3170
760*	43.0	2868	47.0	3163
AA 3100	48.0	2925	52.0C	3153
Reloder 15	39.0	2804	43.0	3129
IMR 4350	43.0	2876	47.0	3069
748*	39.0	2735	43.0	3056
H414*	42.0	2726	46.0	3009
SR 4759 (reduced load)	15.0	1762	17.0	2008

*Maximum Loads should be used with CAUTION • C = Compressed Load • *Magnum Primer used with this powder.*

0.257"	25 Spitz SP	25 HP	25 Spitz BTSP
Weight, grains	100	100	100
Ballistic Coefficient	0.334	0.263	0.393
Sectional Density	0.126	0.126	0.126
COAL Tested:	2.770"	2.760"	2.770"
Speer Part No.	1405	1407	1408

Propellant	START CHARGE		MAXIMUM CHARGE	
	Weight, grs	Muzzle Velocity, ft/sec	Weight, grs	Muzzle Velocity, ft/sec
760*	41.0	2804	45.0	3113
Reloder 19	45.0	2843	49.0	3094
H4350	43.0	2795	47.0C	3055
IMR 4831	44.0	2805	48.0	3053
H4831	46.0	2774	50.0C	3030
IMR 7828	47.0	2711	51.0C	3023
IMR 4350	41.0	2694	45.0	2944
H414*	40.0	2657	44.0	2878
IMR 4064	35.0	2584	39.0	2871
H380*	38.0	2566	42.0	2842
AA 2700*	37.0	2529	41.0	2807
Reloder 15	33.0	2509	37.0	2785
IMR 4320	35.0	2505	39.0	2768
SR 4759 (reduced load)	15.0	1728	17.0	1945

0.257"	25 TBBC SP
Weight, grains	115
Ballistic Coefficient	0.372
Sectional Density	0.249
COAL Tested:	2.780"
Speer Part No.	1730

Propellant	START CHARGE		MAXIMUM CHARGE	
	Weight, grs	Muzzle Velocity, ft/sec	Weight, grs	Muzzle Velocity, ft/sec
IMR 4831	41.0	2658	45.0C	2873
Reloder 22	42.0	2648	46.0C	2862
IMR 4350	40.0	2614	44.0	2846
H414*	38.0	2571	42.0	2837
Reloder 15	35.0	2584	39.0	2822
760*	38.0	2570	42.0	2819
Reloder 19	41.0	2500	45.0C	2786
IMR 4064	34.0	2498	38.0	2759

NOTE: *Trophy Bonded Bear Claw and Trophy Bonded Sledgehammer Solid bullets have unique ballistic behavior compared to conventional bullets. Loads for TBBC and TBSS bullets may not "track" with data for conventional bullets. Use TBBC and TBSS data ONLY for TBBC and TBSS bullets.*

*Maximum Loads should be used with CAUTION • C = Compressed Load • *Magnum Primer used with this powder.*

0.257"	25 Spitz BTSP	25 Spitz SP	25 GS SP
Weight, grains	120	120	120
Ballistic Coefficient	0.480	0.405	0.356
Sectional Density	0.260	0.260	0.260
COAL Tested:	2.770"	2.770"	2.780"
Speer Part No.	1410	1411	1415

Propellant	START CHARGE		MAXIMUM CHARGE	
	Weight, grs	Muzzle Velocity, ft/sec	Weight, grs	Muzzle Velocity, ft/sec
IMR 4831	41.0	2552	45.0	2793
760*	39.0	2496	43.0	2770
H414*	39.0	2507	43.0	2767
IMR 4350	39.0	2512	43.0	2758
Reloder 19	39.0	2476	43.0	2709
IMR 4064	34.0	2423	38.0	2705
Reloder 22	39.0	2399	43.0	2635
IMR 7828	40.0	2304	44.0	2583
IMR 4320	32.0	2316	36.0	2545
Reloder 15	30.0	2322	34.0	2541
IMR 4895	30.0	2249	34.0	2527
XMR 3100	38.0	2301	42.0	2507
H380*	33.0	2275	37.0	2482
SR 4759 (reduced load)	17.0	1776	19.0	2003

*Maximum Loads should be used with CAUTION • C = Compressed Load • *Magnum Primer used with this powder.*

25-06 Remington

The 25-06 is yet another fine wildcat that Remington has made into a successful commercial cartridge. Early references date from around 1920 when the A. O. Niedner Rifle Company offered custom rifles for a cartridge called the 25 Niedner. It was simply the 30-06 necked down to accept .257" bullets. As a custom wildcat, there were minor dimensional variations between the various versions but overall performance was similar.

In its early days, the 25 Niedner and its variants were not viewed as outstanding performers. The large case failed to offer much advantage over the 257 Roberts because very slow-burning propellants were not yet available. The introduction of powders such as H4831 after World War II caused shooters to look again at the large-case 25-caliber wildcat; such propellants gave the cartridge the boost it needed.

In 1969, Remington commercialized the wildcat as the 25-06 Remington and it has since become a standard chambering with many rifle makers. The cartridge is at its best for long-range shooting of animals up to the size of mule deer. With slow-burning propellants such as Reloder® 22 and 25, IMR 7828, H1000 and others available, the 25-06 can now live up to the expectations of its inventors.

Flat trajectory and high retained energy make the 25-06 an excellent choice for the Western rifleman. The 100-grain boat tail is excellent for shots up to 300 yards on antelope and smaller deer. The 120-grain Speer Grand Slam is perfect for large deer in the 25-06. The bullet's heavy construction is ideal for the velocities possible with this cartridge.

With the right bullet, the 25-06 in skilled hands can take elk, moose and caribou. The "right bullet" is the 115-grain Trophy Bonded Bear Claw soft point. Its combination of shock and penetration can let the cartridge move up a level in the game it can take.

The 25-06 also sees some use as a varmint cartridge, although recoil and propellant usage make it less desirable for this sport than more compact cartridges. The 87-grain TNT hollow point will handle velocities up to 3700 ft/sec making it the best Speer varmint bullet for the 25-06.

The industry maximum average pressure for the 25-06 is 53,000 CUP. These loads are within those limits.

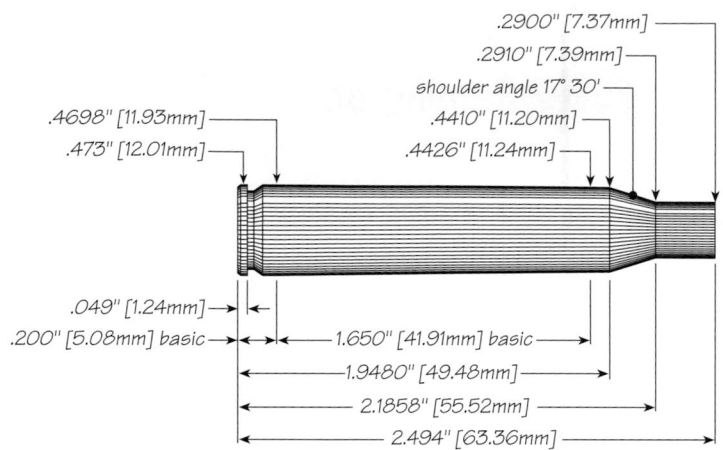

.2900" [7.37mm]
.2910" [7.39mm]
shoulder angle 17° 30'
.4410" [11.20mm]
.4426" [11.24mm]
.4698" [11.93mm]
.473" [12.01mm]
.049" [1.24mm]
.200" [5.08mm] basic
1.650" [41.91mm] basic
1.9480" [49.48mm]
2.1858" [55.52mm]
2.494" [63.36mm]

Max. Case Length:	2.494"	Cart. Case:	Winchester
Trim-to Length:	2.484"	Primer:	CCI 200; 250*
Max Cart. OAL:	3.250"	Test Firearm:	Remington 700
RCBS Shell Holder:	#3	Barrel Length:	24"

0.257"	25 Spitz SP	25 TNT HP
Weight, grains	87	87
Ballistic Coefficient	0.300	0.337
Sectional Density	0.188	0.188
COAL Tested:	3.115"	3.115"
Speer Part No.	1241	1246

Propellant	START CHARGE		MAXIMUM CHARGE	
	Weight, grs	Muzzle Velocity, ft/sec	Weight, grs	Muzzle Velocity, ft/sec
Viht. N560	53.0	3353	57.0	3552
Reloder 19	56.0	3089	60.0C	3452
H4350	54.0	3157	58.0	3431
IMR 4831	55.0	3102	59.0	3428
IMR 7828	59.0	3076	63.0C	3419
H4831SC	55.5	3298	57.5	3410
IMR 4350	52.0	3075	56.0	3380
H414*	47.0	3077	51.0	3359
AA 3100	57.0	3021	61.0C	3357
IMR 4064	45.0	3083	49.0	3352
H380*	48.0	2940	52.0	3268
Reloder 15	43.0	2983	47.0	3268
SR 4759 (reduced load)	13.0	1502	17.0	1933

*Maximum Loads should be used with CAUTION • C = Compressed Load • *Magnum Primer used with this powder.*

0.257"	25 Spitz SP	25 HP	25 Spitz BTSP
Weight, grains	100	100	100
Ballistic Coefficient	0.334	0.263	0.393
Sectional Density	0.216	0.216	0.216
COAL Tested:	3.095"	3.095"	3.095"
Speer Part No.	1405	1407	1408

Propellant	START CHARGE		MAXIMUM CHARGE	
	Weight, grs	Muzzle Velocity, ft/sec	Weight, grs	Muzzle Velocity, ft/sec
IMR 4350	49.0	3067	53.0	3298
IMR 4831	52.0	2997	56.0	3287
Reloder 22	54.0	2945	58.0	3248
Reloder 19	53.0	2903	57.0	3226
Reloder 25	57.0	3123	59.0C	3224
IMR 7828	56.0	2892	60.0C	3222
H4831SC	51.0	2999	55.0	3215
H1000	57.0	2933	61.0C	3151
Viht. N160	49.0	2828	53.0	3129
AA 3100	52.0	2845	56.0	3120
H414*	46.0	2783	50.0	3111
H870*	61.0	2887	65.0C	3106
SR 4759 (reduced load)	15.0	1524	19.0	1892

0.257"	25 TBBC SP
Weight, grains	115
Ballistic Coefficient	0.372
Sectional Density	0.249
COAL Tested:	3.200"
Speer Part No.	1730

Propellant	START CHARGE		MAXIMUM CHARGE	
	Weight, grs	Muzzle Velocity, ft/sec	Weight, grs	Muzzle Velocity, ft/sec
Reloder 25	52.0	2949	56.0	3155
IMR 7828	50.0	2904	54.0	3106
H1000	53.0	2889	57.0	3060
Reloder 22	48.0	2852	52.0	3054
H4831SC	47.0	2821	51.0	3025
IMR 4831	47.0	2908	49.0	3021
IMR 1350	46.0	2899	48.0	3013

NOTE: *Trophy Bonded Bear Claw and Trophy Bonded Sledgehammer Solid bullets have unique ballistic behavior compared to conventional bullets. Loads for TBBC and TBSS bullets may not "track" with data for conventional bullets. Use TBBC and TBSS data ONLY for TBBC and TBSS bullets.*

Allan Jernigan, RCBS General Manager; 300 WSM 180-grain Trophy Bonded® Bear Claw®; 6x6 bull elk from New Mexico.

Maximum Loads should be used with CAUTION • C = Compressed Load • *Magnum Primer used with this powder.

0.257"	25 Spitz BTSP	25 Spitz SP	25 GS SP
Weight, grains	120	120	120
Ballistic Coefficient	0.480	0.405	0.356
Sectional Density	0.260	0.260	0.260
COAL Tested:	3.200"	3.155"	3.090"
Speer Part No.	1410	1411	1415

	START CHARGE		MAXIMUM CHARGE	
Propellant	Weight, grs	Muzzle Velocity, ft/sec	Weight, grs	Muzzle Velocity, ft/sec
Reloder 25	56.0	2971	58.0C	3071
H870*	60.0	2791	64.0C	3006
IMR 4350	44.5	2773	48.5	2990
IMR 4831	46.0	2769	50.0	2980
H4831SC	48.0	2769	52.0	2958
Reloder 22	48.0	2699	52.0	2931
H1000	51.0	2644	55.0	2922
IMR 7828	51.0	2644	55.0	2885
AA 4350	45.0	2655	49.0	2843
AA 3100	47.0	2567	51.0	2818
H4350	44.0	2577	48.0	2792
SR 4759 (reduced load)	17.0	1501	21.0	1861

*Maximum Loads should be used with CAUTION • C = Compressed Load • *Magnum Primer used with this powder.*

25 Winchester Super Short Magnum

The 25 Winchester Super Short Magnum (25 WSSM) followed the 223 and 243 WSSM as Winchester extended its Short Magnum series to include bore diameters less than 270-caliber. The 25 WSSM shares the same head dimensions as the 300 Winchester Short Magnum but shortens the parent case from 2.100 inches to 1.670 inches.

The stubby case has similar propellant capacity to the 257 Roberts +P but, by virtue of its higher pressure limit, challenges—and sometimes equals—the velocities of the 25-06 Remington. This means the 25 WSSM can be used on the same classes of game as the 25-06.

We found that propellants in the burning rate range of IMR 4350 did best with the 100 and 120-grain bullets. The medium rate propellants like Reloder 15 get the nod for the 87-grain bullet but the slower powders still gave reasonable velocity.

Industry standard chamber dimensions require the Speer 25-caliber Hot-Cor bullets be seated to 2.270 inches to clear the rifling. This is almost exactly in the middle of the allowable COAL range for this cartridge. However, that length puts the base of the 120-grain bullets into the case body. This factor puts the 25 WSSM only slightly behind the 25-06 when loading heavy bullets. However, we suspect no game animal will notice.

The only handloading issue we found with this cartridge is that the case necks are thicker that other popular 25-caliber cartridges. You may need to lightly polish your expander ball when starting with new cases. The extra force required for neck expansion roughed up the neck interiors to the point that some cases exhibited bullet seating forces high enough to deform the case or bullet. We installed a 25-caliber bronze bore brush in an electric drill and polished the necks before charging and bullet seating. This reduced seating force to normal levels. Fired cases had normal neck expansion and bullet seating and do not require this extra attention.

Like the other short magnum cartridge from Winchester and Remington, the 25 WSSM produced very consistent ballistic performance in lab tests. Anyone seeking 25-06 performance in a short-action rifle would be well advised to consider the 25 WSSM. The loads presented do not exceed the 65,000 psi pressure limit assigned this cartridge.

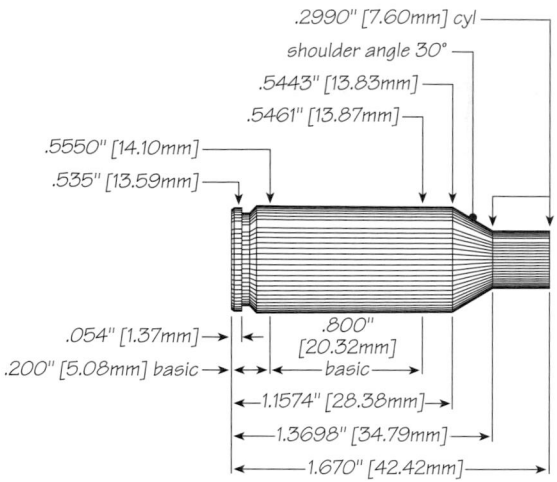

.2990" [7.60mm] cyl
shoulder angle 30°
.5443" [13.83mm]
.5461" [13.87mm]
.5550" [14.10mm]
.535" [13.59mm]
.054" [1.37mm]
.200" [5.08mm] basic
.800" [20.32mm] basic
1.1574" [28.38mm]
1.3698" [34.79mm]
1.670" [42.42mm]

Max. Case Length:	1.670"	**Cart. Case:**	Winchester
Trim-to Length:	1.660"	**Primer:**	CCI 200; 250*
Max Cart. OAL:	2.360"	**Test Firearm:**	Universal Receiver
RCBS Shell Holder:	#43	**Barrel Length:**	Krieger 24"

0.257"	25 Spitz SP	25 TNT HP
Weight, grains	87	87
Ballistic Coefficient	0.300	0.337
Sectional Density	0.188	0.188
COAL Tested:	2.270"	2.350"
Speer Part No.	1241	1246

	START CHARGE		MAXIMUM CHARGE	
Propellant	Weight, grs	Muzzle Velocity, ft/sec	Weight, grs	Muzzle Velocity, ft/sec
Ramshot Big Game*	46.0	3159	50.0	3445
Reloder 15	41.5	3176	45.5	3428
H414*	47.0	3183	51.0C	3428
H380*	46.0	3177	50.0C	3417
IMR 4895	40.0	3153	44.0	3411
760*	49.0	3258	51.0C	3392
Varget	39.0	3095	43.0	3358
IMR 4350	46.0	3073	50.0C	3354
Reloder 19	48.0	3066	52.0C	3333
Reloder 10X	35.0	3056	39.0	3313
AA 4350	48.0	3170	50.0C	3294
Viht. N560	48.0	3041	52.0C	3271
AA 5744 (reduced load)	19.0	1989	21.0	2141

*Maximum Loads should be used with CAUTION • C = Compressed Load • *Magnum Primer used with this powder.*

0.257"	25 Spitz SP	25 HP	25 Spitz BTSP
Weight, grains	100	100	100
Ballistic Coefficient	0.334	0.263	0.393
Sectional Density	0.216	0.216	0.216
COAL Tested:	2.270"	2.280"	2.270"
Speer Part No.	1405	1407	1408

	START CHARGE		MAXIMUM CHARGE	
Propellant	Weight, grs	Muzzle Velocity, ft/sec	Weight, grs	Muzzle Velocity, ft/sec
760*	45.5	2995	49.5	3254
H414*	44.5	2991	48.5	3222
AA 4350	44.0	2954	48.0C	3200
Reloder 19	45.5	2927	49.5C	3180
Viht. N560	46.0	2891	50.0C	3154
Ramshot Big Game*	42.0	2924	46.0	3141
IMR 4350	43.0	2909	47.0C	3137
H380*	41.5	2890	45.5	3135
Reloder 15	37.5	2890	41.5	3110
Varget	36.0	2886	40.0	3099
IMR 4895	36.0	2845	40.0	3084
Reloder 10X	31.0	2751	35.0	2984
AA 5744 (reduced load)	20.0	1996	22.0	2136

0.257"	25 Spitz BTSP	25 Spitz SP	25 GS SP
Weight, grains	120	120	120
Ballistic Coefficient	0.480	0.405	0.356
Sectional Density	0.260	0.260	0.260
COAL Tested:	2.270"	2.270"	2.325"
Speer Part No.	1410	1411	1415

Propellant	START CHARGE		MAXIMUM CHARGE	
	Weight, grs	Muzzle Velocity, ft/sec	Weight, grs	Muzzle Velocity, ft/sec
H414*	41.0	2709	45.0	2929
760*	41.0	2713	45.0	2921
Reloder 19	42.0	2685	46.0C	2914
Viht. N560	42.0	2662	46.0	2901
IMR 4350	39.0	2624	43.0	2881
AA 4350	39.0	2649	43.0	2861
H380*	38.5	2624	42.5	2846
Ramshot Big Game*	38.0	2622	42.0	2840
Reloder 15	34.0	2551	38.0	2792
IMR 4895	33.0	2528	37.0	2776
Varget	32.5	2522	36.5	2744
Reloder 10X	27.5	2368	31.5	2607

*Maximum Loads should be used with CAUTION • C = Compressed Load • *Magnum Primer used with this powder.*

257 Weatherby Magnum

Roy Weatherby built a successful career around the design of high-velocity cartridges and the rifles to handle them. The 257 Weatherby Magnum is based on the belted 300 H&H Magnum case necked down and shortened to operate through standard (30-06) length actions. All Weatherby cartridges also feature a minimum body taper to maximize case capacity.

The 257 Weatherby has established a strong reputation as an accurate long-range cartridge for medium game and, with lighter bullets, can be a varmint cartridge when you forget your 223. It has also been successfully used on African plains animals. Weatherby's case design uses a radiused shoulder instead of the angled one found on most bottleneck cartridges. This design is said to improve the gas flow out of the case resulting in a more efficient cartridge. Handloaders are very fond of the 257 Weatherby. Among the Weatherby cartridges, it is second in popularity to the 300 Weatherby in reloading die sales.

The 120-grain Grand Slam can be used on large mule deer and, in the hands of a good rifleman, passes as an elk cartridge. For long shots on smaller deer and antelope, the 100 and 120-grain boat tail bullets can cleanly take game beyond 300 yards. The 87-grain spitzer and the 100-grain hollow point should be used only on varmints in this cartridge. At velocities over 3600 ft/sec, these bullets are too explosive for larger game.

The 257 Weatherby has a 100 to 200 ft/sec advantage over the 25-06 but at the expense of larger powder charges and increased recoil. Like most other Weatherby cartridges, the 257 was not standardized by the industry until 1994.

The loads presented here represent a full retest of the cartridge on standard industry equipment and with modern components. Its pressure limit is 53,500 CUP.

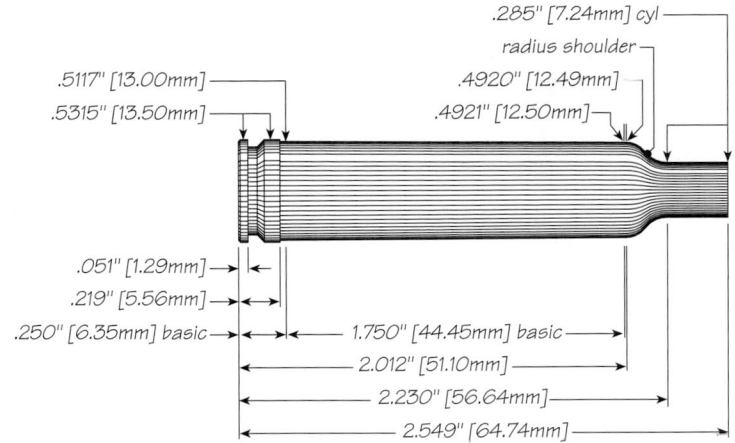

.285" [7.24mm] cyl
radius shoulder
.5117" [13.00mm]
.5315" [13.50mm]
.4920" [12.49mm]
.4921" [12.50mm]

.051" [1.29mm]
.219" [5.56mm]
.250" [6.35mm] basic
1.750" [44.45mm] basic
2.012" [51.10mm]
2.230" [56.64mm]
2.549" [64.74mm]

Max. Case Length:	2.549"	**Cart. Case:**	Federal
Trim-to Length:	2.539"	**Primer:**	CCI 250*
Max Cart. OAL:	3.170"	**Test Firearm:**	Universal Receiver
RCBS Shell Holder:	#4	**Barrel Length:**	Krieger 24"

0.257"	25 Spitz SP	25 TNT HP
Weight, grains	87	87
Ballistic Coefficient	0.300	0.337
Sectional Density	0.188	0.188
COAL Tested:	3.150"	3.170"
Speer Part No.	1241	1246

	START CHARGE		MAXIMUM CHARGE	
Propellant	Weight, grs	Muzzle Velocity, ft/sec	Weight, grs	Muzzle Velocity, ft/sec
Ramshot Magnum*	74.0	3570	78.0	3731
Retumbo*	74.0	3462	78.0C	3672
Reloder 25*	69.0	3427	73.0C	3670
Reloder 22*	67.0	3429	71.0	3661
Viht. N560*	68.0	3507	70.0	3651
Reloder 19*	64.0	3372	68.0	3637
IMR 7828*	67.0	3334	71.0	3604
IMR 4831*	63.0	3433	65.0	3564
Magpro*	68.0	3400	70.0	3504

0.257"	25 Spitz SP	25 HP	25 Spitz BTSP
Weight, grains	100	100	100
Ballistic Coefficient	0.334	0.263	0.393
Sectional Density	0.216	0.216	0.216
COAL Tested:	3.150"	3.140"	3.150"
Speer Part No.	1405	1407	1408

Propellant	START CHARGE		MAXIMUM CHARGE	
	Weight, grs	Muzzle Velocity, ft/sec	Weight, grs	Muzzle Velocity, ft/sec
Reloder 25*	69.0	3395	73.0	3545
Ramshot Magnum*	70.0	3339	74.0	3494
Reloder 22*	64.0	3225	68.0	3450
IMR 7828*	67.0	3306	69.0	3447
Viht. N560*	65.0	3290	67.0	3413
Retumbo*	71.0	3283	73.0	3411
H1000*	69.0	3302	71.0	3405
Reloder 19*	61.0	3188	65.0	3405
Magpro*	65.0	3197	67.0	3292

*Maximum Loads should be used with CAUTION • C = Compressed Load • *Magnum Primer used with this powder.*

0.257"	25 Spitz BTSP	25 Spitz SP	25 GS SP
Weight, grains	120	120	120
Ballistic Coefficient	0.480	0.405	0.356
Sectional Density	0.260	0.260	0.260
COAL Tested:	3.170"	3.150"	3.170"
Speer Part No.	1410	1411	1415

Propellant	START CHARGE		MAXIMUM CHARGE	
	Weight, grs	Muzzle Velocity, ft/sec	Weight, grs	Muzzle Velocity, ft/sec
Reloder 25*	63.0	3024	67.0	3236
Ramshot Magnum*	66.0	3046	70.0	3211
Viht. N560*	60.0	2963	64.0	3181
Retumbo*	65.0	2948	69.0	3159
Reloder 22*	59.0	2904	63.0	3120
H1000*	64.5	3006	66.5	3108
IMR 7828*	62.0	2988	64.0	3106
H4831SC*	61.0	3000	63.0	3103
Magpro*	62.0	2927	64.0	3027

*Maximum Loads should be used with CAUTION • C = Compressed Load • *Magnum Primer used with this powder.*

260 Remington *(also 6.5-08 A-Square)*

Although the 6.5mm cartridges have never been as popular in the U.S. as in other countries, they have held their own because of solid reputations as game getters. Much of their success is due to the superb penetration demonstrated by 26-caliber bullets at modest velocities. It's been said that these cartridges make up in penetration what they lack in energy.

Over the years, various 6.5mm wildcats based on the 308 Winchester case showed promise; one has now become a commercial cartridge. In January 1997, Remington announced the 260 Remington cartridge. Based on the 308 Winchester case necked to hold 26-caliber bullets, the 260 was conceived by writer Jim Carmichael as a target cartridge, but is also a fine medium game cartridge. Industry velocity specifications call for 2725 ft/sec with a 140-grain bullet from a test barrel.

Lighter bullet weights can be used on varmints out to 250 yards. Speer's 90-grain TNT allows velocities in excess of 3100 ft/sec for explosive expansion. Pick the Speer 120-grain Hot-Cor for heavy varmints and lighter deer, and the 140-grain Hot-Cor for heavier deer.

The 260's mild recoil will find favor with new shooters. It is a natural for short, light rifles like the Remington Model 7 as well as in heavier target rifles for metallic silhouette competition.

Like the 6.5x55 Swedish Mauser cartridge, reloaders will find best velocities with the medium- to slow-burning rifle powders. Many loads giving the best velocities require some powder compression during bullet seating. Pressures drop rather fast in this small case as you reduce the charge weight. Therefore, we set the start loads two grains under the maximum, and recommend that the slower powders not be loaded below these levels.

Expect less velocity from the shorter barrel of the Remington Model Seven. Spot-checking some of these loads in the Model Seven revealed that you will see reductions in the 80-140 ft/sec range. Factory ammunition posted a velocity of 2731 ft/sec in our Model 700 and 2597 ft/sec from the stainless Model 7 (20-inch barrel). Another brand posted velocities of 2484 ft/sec and 2386 ft/sec from the same rifles, respectively. Both types were loaded with 140-grain bullets.

260 Remington

The industry maximum average pressure for the 260 Remington is 60,000 psi. These loads were developed in a standard industry pressure barrel and do not exceed this level. They can also be used in the 6.5-08 A-Square cartridge.

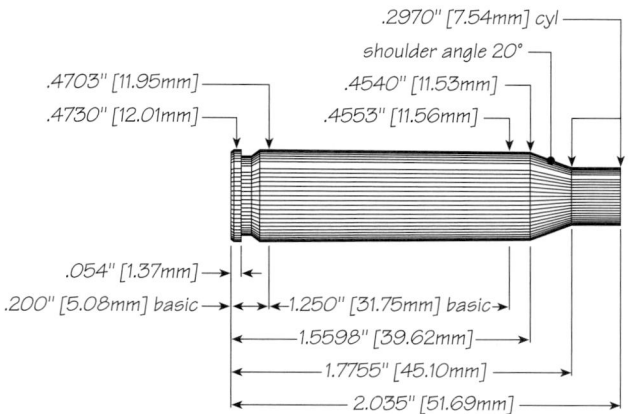

Max. Case Length:	2.035"	**Cart. Case:**	Remington
Trim-to Length:	2.025"	**Primer:**	CCI 200; 250*
Max Cart. OAL:	2.800"	**Test Firearm:**	Remington Model 700 BDL
RCBS Shell Holder:	#3	**Barrel Length:**	24"

0.264"	6.5mm TNT HP
Weight, grains	90
Ballistic Coefficient	0.281
Sectional Density	0.184
COAL Tested:	2.650"
Speer Part No.	1445

Propellant	START CHARGE		MAXIMUM CHARGE	
	Weight, grs	Muzzle Velocity, ft/sec	Weight, grs	Muzzle Velocity, ft/sec
H380*	45.0	3125	49.0	3367
H414*	46.0	3046	50.0	3348
Viht. N160	47.0	3008	51.0C	3315
Reloder 15	41.5	2970	45.5	3311
IMR 4064	40.0	2910	44.0	3297
IMR 4350	46.0	2947	50.0C	3268
Varget	40.5	2959	44.5	3261
760*	46.5	3096	48.5	3253
748*	40.0	2904	44.0	3250
AA 2700*	46.0	3071	48.0	3247
IMR 4895	39.0	2841	43.0	3205
AA 4350	46.0	2852	48.0C	3000
Reloder 19	48.0	2855	50.0C	2985
AA 5744 (reduced load)	20.0	1981	24.0	2294

*Maximum Loads should be used with CAUTION • C = Compressed Load • *Magnum Primer used with this powder.*

0.264"	6.5mm Spitz SP
Weight, grains	120
Ballistic Coefficient	0.392
Sectional Density	0.246
COAL Tested:	2.720"
Speer Part No.	1435

Propellant	START CHARGE		MAXIMUM CHARGE	
	Weight, grs	Muzzle Velocity, ft/sec	Weight, grs	Muzzle Velocity, ft/sec
Reloder 19	46.0	2815	48.0C	2950
IMR 4831	45.0	2794	47.0C	2919
H414*	43.5	2792	44.5	2895
IMR 4350	44.0	2759	46.0C	2888
Viht. N160	43.0	2760	45.0C	2870
760*	42.0	2771	44.0	2862
H380*	41.5	2739	43.5	2829
IMR 4064	37.0	2691	39.0	2822
Reloder 15	37.0	2698	39.0	2819
AA 3100	44.0	2615	46.0C	2789
Varget	37.0	2684	39.0	2774
IMR 4895	36.0	2658	38.0	2771
H4831SC	45.0	2621	47.0C	2762
AA 5744 (reduced load)	22.0	2016	24.0	2156

0.264"	6.5mm Spitz SP
Weight, grains	140
Ballistic Coefficient	0.498
Sectional Density	0.287
COAL Tested:	2.745"
Speer Part No.	1441

Propellant	START CHARGE		MAXIMUM CHARGE	
	Weight, grs	Muzzle Velocity, ft/sec	Weight, grs	Muzzle Velocity, ft/sec
Reloder 19	43.5	2603	45.5C	2731
IMR 4831	42.0	2587	44.0C	2722
Reloder 22	44.0	2554	46.0C	2701
AA 4350	41.0	2540	43.0C	2695
Viht. N165	45.0	2568	47.0C	2687
IMR 4350	41.0	2522	43.0C	2687
H4831SC	43.5	2531	45.5C	2635
760*	39.5	2528	41.5	2623
AA 3100	43.0	2542	45.0C	2614
H414*	39.5	2519	41.5	2596
IMR 4064	35.0	2460	37.0	2572
AA 5744 (reduced load)	22.0	1894	24.0	2021

*Maximum Loads should be used with CAUTION • C = Compressed Load • *Magnum Primer used with this powder.*

6.5 x 55mm Swedish Mauser *(Military Actions)*

Loads for rifles based on original military actions (Mauser 94 and 96; Krag-Jorgensen)

The 6.5x55mm cartridge was adopted in 1894 as the service cartridge by both Sweden and Norway. It was chambered in the various Swedish Mauser models and also the Norwegian Krag-Jorgensen rifle. Although it is one of the oldest smokeless powder loadings, it is still widely used in Europe as a sporting and target cartridge.

Accuracy in a quality bolt-action rifle is excellent, and its ability to handle long bullets up to 160 grains makes it an excellent game cartridge on species up to and including large deer and black bear. The cartridge uses standard .263" and .264" diameter bullets.

The 6.5x55mm was little known in the United States until the 1950's when large numbers of surplus Swedish rifles and carbines turned up. Norma of Sweden imported the first sporting ammunition and components and the cartridge has become popular with American shooters. Die sales at RCBS for this cartridge have been strong for years.

Surprising to some "armchair ballisticians," its success in the field is far better than anyone would imagine from looking at ballistics tables. In spite of this, we consider the 6.5mm Swede to be somewhat light for elk and moose in the hands of a novice hunter. However, plenty of these big animals have fallen to the cartridge—helped by a skilled rifleman and the deep penetration of heavy bullets at modest velocity.

We found that the medium- to slow-burning powders work best. Speer's 90-grain TNT hollow point is a great bullet to take afield for the spring varmint season. This is an excellent way to reinforce familiarity with your rifle more than once a year. The 120-grain Speer Hot-Cor® bullet is a good choice for smaller deer species and antelope. For game up to the size of mule deer, the 140-grain Hot-Cor spitzer provides the deep penetration that has endeared the "Swede" to so many hunters.

Reloaders should recall that most 6.5x55mm rifles have long chamber throats to accommodate the 160-grain military bullets used in the cartridge's early years. With this throating, you may seat the bullet to take advantage of the maximum cartridge length of 3.150-inch. However, make sure jacketed bullets do not touch the rifling at the seating length you choose.

Most U.S. and foreign ammo makers produce loaded ammunition and unprimed cases are now readily available. This is fortunate for handloaders because the Swede's case head diameter is unique, making modification of more common cases difficult.

At standard industry pressures, the 90 and 120-grain bullets are the best choice. Velocities with the 140-grain soft point were quite modest at these pressure levels. Note that our start loads are only two grains under the maximum loads. This cartridge has a steep pressure curve; reducing starting loads more than shown can result in inconsistent performance.

We have two sections for the 6.5x55mm cartridge. In the United States, the industry operating pressure for this cartridge is a modest 51,000 psi in deference to the original military actions lacking the "safety lug" of later Mausers. The loads in this section are for surplus military rifles or custom rifles using military actions and comply with current industry specifications. If in doubt about your rifle's capability and action type, check with a gunsmith familiar with military Mauser actions and their characteristics.

During the last two decades, Remington, Winchester, Ruger, and others have made 6.5x55 rifles. These are all strong bolt actions designed for cartridges rated at much higher pressure than the "Swede" produces. We created a second 6.5x55 section of handload data developed to pressures more in line with European sporting ammunition. They are to be used only in modern commercial rifles or custom rifles based on the strong M98 Mauser design.

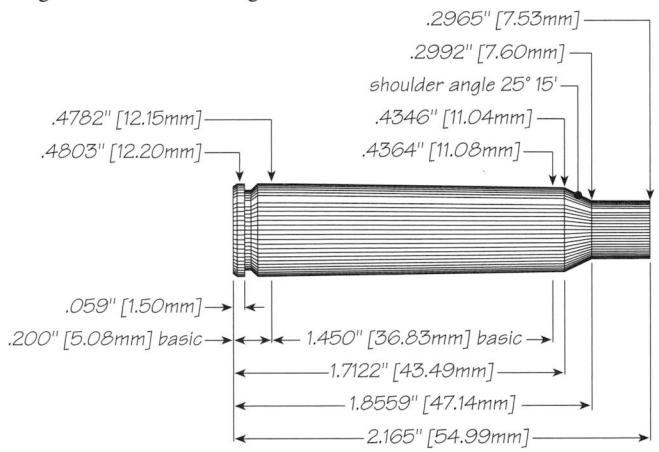

Max. Case Length:	2.165"	**Cart. Case:**	Remington
Trim-to Length:	2.155"	**Primer:**	CCI 200; 250*
Max Cart. OAL:	3.150"	**Test Firearm:**	Universal Receiver
RCBS Shell Holder:	#2	**Barrel Length:**	Krieger 24"

0.264"	6.5mm TNT HP
Weight, grains	90
Ballistic Coefficient	0.281
Sectional Density	0.184
COAL Tested:	2.850"
Speer Part No.	1445

	START CHARGE		MAXIMUM CHARGE	
Propellant	Weight, grs	Muzzle Velocity, ft/sec	Weight, grs	Muzzle Velocity, ft/sec
H414*	48.0	3155	50.0	3278
AA 2700*	47.0	3121	49.0	3244
IMR 4064	42.0	3105	44.0	3238
H4350	48.0	3098	50.0	3223
Varget	41.0	3084	43.0	3193
IMR 4895	41.0	3051	43.0	3185
IMR 4350	48.0	3048	50.0	3178
IMR 3031	39.5	3038	41.5	3169
AA 4350	49.0	3029	51.0C	3149
AA 5744 (reduced load)	19.0	1841	21.0	2018

0.264"	6.5mm Spitz SP
Weight, grains	120
Ballistic Coefficient	0.392
Sectional Density	0.246
COAL Tested:	3.000"
Speer Part No.	1435

Propellant	START CHARGE		MAXIMUM CHARGE	
	Weight, grs	Muzzle Velocity, ft/sec	Weight, grs	Muzzle Velocity, ft/sec
IMR 4350	40.0	2602	42.0	2705
H4350	39.0	2591	41.0	2700
IMR 4831	40.0	2567	42.0	2697
H4831SC	43.0	2581	45.0	2688
Reloder 22	40.0	2594	42.0	2670
Reloder 19	39.0	2509	41.0	2666
H414*	36.0	2536	38.0	2619
IMR 4064	34.0	2502	36.0	2608
Varget	34.0	2497	36.0	2603
AA 5744 (reduced load)	22.0	1918	24.0	2068

*Maximum Loads should be used with CAUTION • C = Compressed Load • *Magnum Primer used with this powder.*

0.264"	6.5mm Spitz SP
Weight, grains	140
Ballistic Coefficient	0.498
Sectional Density	0.287
COAL Tested:	3.000"
Speer Part No.	1441

Propellant	START CHARGE		MAXIMUM CHARGE	
	Weight, grs	Muzzle Velocity, ft/sec	Weight, grs	Muzzle Velocity, ft/sec
Reloder 22	38.0	2382	40.0	2461
Reloder 19	38.0	2312	40.0	2399
H4831SC	37.0	2288	39.0	2379
H4350	34.0	2257	36.0	2350
IMR 4831	34.0	2254	36.0	2339
IMR 4350	34.0	2254	36.0	2337
IMR 4064	31.0	3193	33.0	2300
Varget	31.0	2165	33.0	2276

*Maximum Loads should be used with CAUTION • C = Compressed Load • *Magnum Primer used with this powder.*

6.5 x 55mm Swedish Mauser *(Strong Commercial Actions)*

Loads for strong, modern commercial actions ONLY

The renewed interest in this old cartridge led several U.S. rifle makers to create 6.5x55mm rifles based on their very strong and modern actions. For handloaders, this means they can carefully assemble handloads that exceed the performance of most factory ammo yet stay comfortably within their rifle's design criteria. As of our printing date, only Ruger still lists 6.5x55 rifles in their product catalog.

Although the 6.5x55 is now one of our "Century" cartridges, its well-proportioned case with ample propellant capacity allows it to continue competing with more modern cartridges. Loaded to a more robust pressure limit, this cartridge can safely push most bullets 120 to 150 ft/sec faster than ammo loaded to U.S. industry pressure limits.

The handloads in this section approach pressures of 58,000 psi and are in the same class as the 257 Roberts +P and 6.5x55mm ammunition loaded in Europe. They are intended for modern commercial rifle actions that are routinely chambered for other cartridges having maximum pressure limits of up to 65,000 psi. The higher pressure level permits much better velocities from the 140-grain bullet.

Some fine custom 6.5x55 rifles have been crafted using both military and commercial Mauser Model 98 actions. Even then, you must verify your rifle's chamber dimensions and headspace are correct. These loads are not to be used in any rifle having a military surplus action other than a properly identified M98 Mauser. Users of the more common M94 and M96 Swedish Mauser actions must use the loading data provided in the previous section.

6.5 x 55mm Swedish Mauser *(Strong Commercial Actions)*

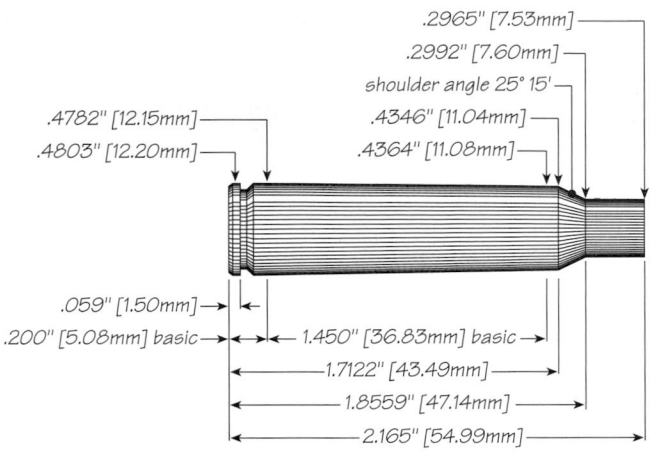

.2965" [7.53mm]
.2992" [7.60mm]
shoulder angle 25° 15'
.4346" [11.04mm]
.4364" [11.08mm]
.4782" [12.15mm]
.4803" [12.20mm]
.059" [1.50mm]
.200" [5.08mm] basic
1.450" [36.83mm] basic
1.7122" [43.49mm]
1.8559" [47.14mm]
2.165" [54.99mm]

Max. Case Length:	2.165"	Cart. Case:	Remington
Trim-to Length:	2.155"	Primer:	CCI 200; 250*
Max Cart. OAL:	3.150"	Test Firearm:	Universal Receiver
RCBS Shell Holder:	#2	Barrel Length:	Krieger 24"

0.264"	6.5mm TNT HP
Weight, grains	90
Ballistic Coefficient	0.281
Sectional Density	0.184
COAL Tested:	2.850"
Speer Part No.	1445

	START CHARGE		MAXIMUM CHARGE	
Propellant	Weight, grs	Muzzle Velocity, ft/sec	Weight, grs	Muzzle Velocity, ft/sec
Varget	45.0	3193	47.0	3410
H414*	50.0	3278	52.0	3401
AA 2700*	49.0	3244	51.0	3385
IMR 4350	51.0	3243	53.0C	3373
IMR 4064	44.0	3238	46.0	3371
H4350	50.0	3223	52.0C	3348
IMR 4895	43.0	3185	45.0	3320
IMR 3031	41.5	3169	43.5	3301

0.264"	6.5mm Spitz SP
Weight, grains	120
Ballistic Coefficient	0.392
Sectional Density	0.246
COAL Tested:	3.000"
Speer Part No.	1435

| Propellant | START CHARGE | | MAXIMUM CHARGE | |
	Weight, grs	Muzzle Velocity, ft/sec	Weight, grs	Muzzle Velocity, ft/sec
IMR 4350	43.0	2765	45.0	2851
IMR 4831	43.0	2737	45.0	2841
Reloder 22	44.0	2743	46.0	2830
Reloder 19	44.0	2754	46.0	2820
H4350	41.0	2700	43.0	2808
H4831SC	45.0	2600	47.0	2706
H414*	40.0	2705	42.0	2781
IMR 4064	37.0	2659	39.0	2764
Varget	37.0	2656	39.0	2762

*Maximum Loads should be used with CAUTION • C = Compressed Load • *Magnum Primer used with this powder.*

0.264"	6.5mm Spitz SP
Weight, grains	140
Ballistic Coefficient	0.498
Sectional Density	0.287
COAL Tested:	3.000"
Speer Part No.	1441

Propellant	START CHARGE		MAXIMUM CHARGE	
	Weight, grs	Muzzle Velocity, ft/sec	Weight, grs	Muzzle Velocity, ft/sec
Reloder 22	43.0	2579	**45.0**	2655
Reloder 19	43.0	2529	**45.0**	2616
H4831SC	41.0	2464	**43.0**	2558
IMR 4831	39.0	2467	**41.0**	2551
IMR 4350	39.0	2462	**41.0**	2545
H4350	38.0	2444	**40.0**	2531
Varget	35.0	2390	**37.0**	2498
IMR 4064	34.0	2351	**36.0**	2462

*Maximum Loads should be used with CAUTION • C = Compressed Load • *Magnum Primer used with this powder.*

6.5mm Remington Magnum

In the mid-1960's, Remington introduced a pair of short magnum cartridges chambered in the Model 600 and 660 carbines. The 6.5mm and the 350 Remington Magnum were among the first "short magnums," long before that name became a buzzword. They were well suited to the compact actions used in the new rifles. However, the 6.5mm didn't prove as popular as the 350 Magnum. Neither the ammunition nor rifles chambered for it were shown in Remington's 1994 catalog, but the resurgence of interest in older cartridges helped; 6.5mm rifles and ammo appear on the company's 2006 website.

With the exception of the 6.5x55mm, it seems that 6.5mm (.263-264" diameter) rifles have not generated much interest in the U.S. The most successful U.S. development was the powerful 264 Winchester Magnum, introduced several years before Remington's 6.5mm. Through an effective marketing campaign, the 264 Winchester took much of the 26-caliber interest before Remington's development appeared.

The short-action rifles for which the 6.5 Remington was originally designed require that the cartridge overall length be held under 2.800 inches. Long bullets like the 140-grain Speer Hot-Cor spitzer restrict powder capacity and thus velocity. In a more modern rifle with a longer action, you may be able to seat longer provided the cartridge fits and feeds from the magazine and the bullet does not touch the rifling origin. The new 260 Remington gives equal performance with less powder with both the 120 and 140-grain bullets.

Factory ammo was originally loaded with 100 and 120-grain bullets; today only the 120-grain version is cataloged. The 140-grain Speer bullet gives the reloader more flexibility for larger deer. Even on a good day, the 6.5 Remington is marginal for elk and moose. The Speer test rifle has a 24-inch barrel; expect to see a velocity loss of up to 150 ft/sec when these loads are fired in a carbine.

In spite of some limitations, it would seem that the 6.5 Remington still has some useful life left. The maximum average pressure for this cartridge is 53,000 CUP, and these loads do not exceed that limit.

6.5mm Remington Magnum

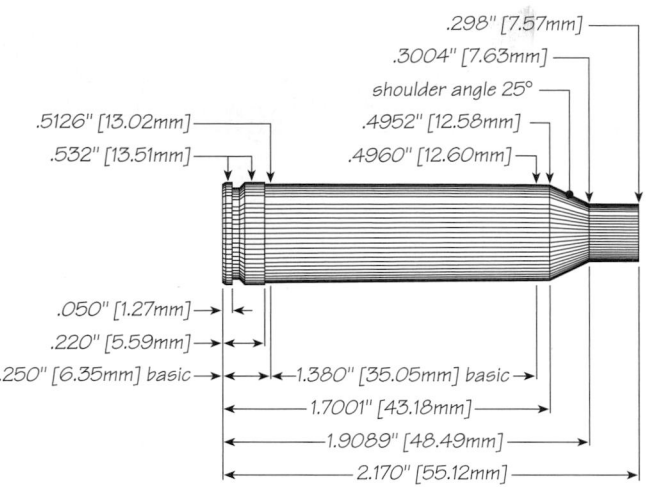

.298" [7.57mm]
.3004" [7.63mm]
shoulder angle 25°
.4952" [12.58mm]
.4960" [12.60mm]
.5126" [13.02mm]
.532" [13.51mm]
.050" [1.27mm]
.220" [5.59mm]
.250" [6.35mm] basic
1.380" [35.05mm] basic
1.7001" [43.18mm]
1.9089" [48.49mm]
2.170" [55.12mm]

Max. Case Length:	2.170"	Cart. Case:	Remington
Trim-to Length:	2.160"	Primer:	CCI 250*
Max Cart. OAL:	2.800"	Test Firearm:	Remington Model 700
RCBS Shell Holder:	#4	Barrel Length:	24"

0.264"	6.5mm Spitz SP
Weight, grains	120
Ballistic Coefficient	0.392
Sectional Density	0.246
COAL Tested:	2.790"
Speer Part No.	1435

	START CHARGE		MAXIMUM CHARGE	
Propellant	Weight, grs	Muzzle Velocity, ft/sec	Weight, grs	Muzzle Velocity, ft/sec
AA 3100*	53.0	2787	57.0C	2984
IMR 4831*	51.0	2724	55.0C	2970
IMR 4350*	49.0	2713	53.0C	2963
IMR 4895*	43.0	2753	47.0	2962
H414*	46.0	2665	50.0	2930
H380*	45.0	2625	49.0	2900
IMR 4320*	42.0	2605	46.0	2875
SR 4759* (reduced load)	20.0	1763	22.0	1958

0.264"	6.5mm Spitz SP
Weight, grains	140
Ballistic Coefficient	0.498
Sectional Density	0.287
COAL Tested:	2.790"
Speer Part No.	1441

Propellant	START CHARGE		MAXIMUM CHARGE	
	Weight, grs	Muzzle Velocity, ft/sec	Weight, grs	Muzzle Velocity, ft/sec
AA 3100*	48.0	2587	52.0C	2765
IMR 4831*	48.0	2547	52.0C	2755
IMR 4350*	46.0	2543	50.0C	2750
H380*	42.0	2396	46.0	2634
H414*	43.0	2373	47.0	2628
IMR 4320*	39.0	2324	43.0	2500
IMR 4895*	41.0	2321	45.0	2562
IMR 4198* (reduced load)	20.5	1617	22.5	1792

*Maximum Loads should be used with CAUTION • C = Compressed Load • *Magnum Primer used with this powder.*

264 Winchester Magnum

The 264 Winchester Magnum is one in a series of four belted magnum cartridges having the case length of a 30-06. The series was introduced by Winchester beginning in the mid 1950's. The 264 was the smallest of the group and was conceived as a flat-shooting, open country cartridge. The Winchester Model 70 rifle chambered for the new cartridge was appropriately named the "Westerner;" the flat trajectory and high retained energy of the 264 was well suited to the demands of western hunting. The 264 has also been used successfully on African plains game.

Factory ammunition comes with a 100-grain bullet for varmints and a 140-grain bullet for larger game. Handloaders can choose the Speer 120-grain spitzer for lighter species such as antelope and whitetail deer. The 140-grain spitzer is adequate for larger deer. For the deep penetration needed for elk and moose, choose the 140-grain Trophy Bonded Bear Claw.

We elected not to develop data for the 6.5mm TNT® hollow point. First, this cartridge is seldom used for varminting. Secondly, the velocity potential of the 264 Winchester is at the upper limit of what the thin-jacketed TNT will tolerate in a fast-twist barrel.

The small bore and the large case capacity of the 264 mean that very slow-burning powders will give best performance. Best handload accuracy is obtained when cases are sized to headspace on the shoulder, not the belt.

The 264 would likely have been more successful had the 7mm Remington Magnum not appeared in 1962. The 7mm Magnum delivers more energy and it could be loaded with bullets up to 175 grains. Handloaders also had access to a broader selection of bullets for the 7mm, thus increasing its flexibility. Still, the 264 Winchester is still popular with handloaders as evidenced by consistently high ranking in reloading die sales.

The data presented here is completely new, tested with modern cases and propellants to current pressure standards. The maximum average pressure for the 264 Magnum is 53,000 CUP. These loads do not exceed that limit.

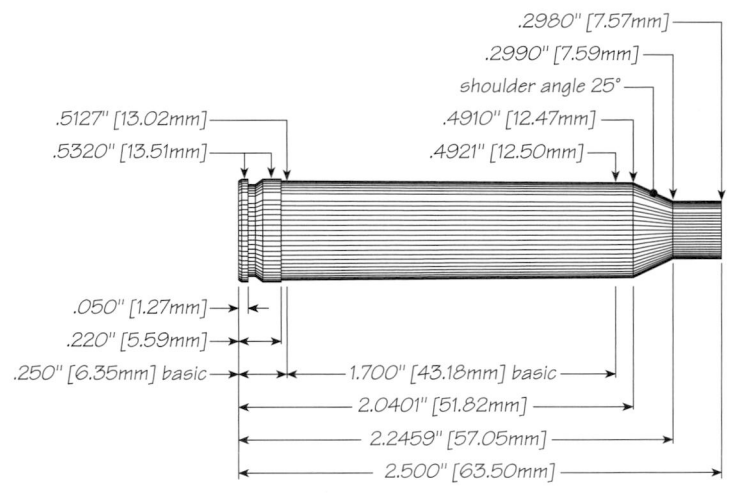

.2980" [7.57mm]
.2990" [7.59mm]
shoulder angle 25°
.4910" [12.47mm]
.4921" [12.50mm]

.5127" [13.02mm]
.5320" [13.51mm]

.050" [1.27mm]
.220" [5.59mm]
.250" [6.35mm] basic
1.700" [43.18mm] basic
2.0401" [51.82mm]
2.2459" [57.05mm]
2.500" [63.50mm]

Max. Case Length:	2.500"	**Cart. Case:**	Winchester
Trim-to Length:	2.490"	**Primer:**	CCI 250*
Max Cart. OAL:	3.340"	**Test Firearm:**	Universal Receiver
RCBS Shell Holder:	#4	**Barrel Length:**	Krieger 24"

Drawn bullet jackets headed for final assembly; Speer Bullet Facility, Lewiston.

0.264"	6.5mm Spitz SP
Weight, grains	120
Ballistic Coefficient	0.392
Sectional Density	0.246
COAL Tested:	3.300"
Speer Part No.	1435

Propellant	START CHARGE		MAXIMUM CHARGE	
	Weight, grs	Muzzle Velocity, ft/sec	Weight, grs	Muzzle Velocity, ft/sec
Retumbo*	64.0	3142	68.0	3236
Reloder 25*	59.0	3095	63.0	3219
Ramshot Magnum*	65.0	3092	69.0	3202
Viht. N560*	58.0	3078	62.0	3198
IMR 7828*	58.0	3042	62.0	3167
Reloder 22*	54.0	3041	58.0	3140
Reloder 19*	55.0	3006	59.0	3118
IMR 4350*	51.0	2964	55.0	3085

0.264"	6.5mm Spitz SP
Weight, grains	140
Ballistic Coefficient	0.498
Sectional Density	0.287
COAL Tested:	3.320"
Speer Part No.	1441

Propellant	START CHARGE		MAXIMUM CHARGE	
	Weight, grs	Muzzle Velocity, ft/sec	Weight, grs	Muzzle Velocity, ft/sec
US869*	72.0	2895	76.0	3042
Reloder 25*	56.0	2862	60.0	3005
Ramshot Magnum*	60.0	2825	64.0	2957
Retumbo*	57.0	2798	61.0	2946
Viht. N560*	51.0	2724	55.0	2877
IMR 7020*	52.0	2681	56.0	2862
Reloder 22*	49.0	2734	53.0	2857
AA 3100*	51.0	2704	55.0	2854
Reloder 19*	48.0	2686	52.0	2822

*Maximum Loads should be used with CAUTION • C = Compressed Load • *Magnum Primer used with this powder.*

0.264"	6.5mm TBBC
Weight, grains	140
Ballistic Coefficient	0.405
Sectional Density	0.287
COAL Tested:	3.340"
Speer Part No.	1735

Propellant	START CHARGE		MAXIMUM CHARGE	
	Weight, grs	Muzzle Velocity, ft/sec	Weight, grs	Muzzle Velocity, ft/sec
Reloder 25*	61.0	2940	65.0	3095
IMR 7828*	61.0	2929	63.0	3034
IMR 4831*	56.0	2834	58.0	2943
AA 3100*	56.0	2788	60.0	2939
Reloder 22*	55.0	2767	59.0	2938
H4831SC*	53.0	2715	57.0	2878

NOTE: *Trophy Bonded Bear Claw and Trophy Bonded Sledgehammer Solid bullets have unique ballistic behavior compared to conventional bullets. Loads for TBBC and TBSS bullets may not "track" with data for conventional bullets. Use TBBC and TBSS data ONLY for TBBC and TBSS bullets.*

*Maximum Loads should be used with CAUTION • C = Compressed Load • *Magnum Primer used with this powder.*

6.8mm Remington SPC

This diminutive cartridge is the sporting version of an experimental military cartridge that Remington is developing with the cooperation of U.S. Special Operations and the Army Marksmanship Unit. After two deployments into hostile desert terrain, Special Ops sought a better battle cartridge than the 5.56mm NATO, one with better long-range performance and improved lethality. Although the first weapon considered for the 6.8mm was the M4 carbine, any new cartridge for that platform could be easily adapted to the full range of M16 variants. If adopted, the military designation of the cartridge will be the 6.8x43mm.

Instead of starting with the 5.56mm case, Remington looked to a very old cartridge for the parent case of the 6.8mm Remington. The 30 Remington, now obsolete, is essentially a rimless 30-30 Winchester that is .045" larger in head diameter than the 5.56mm, just enough to allow the case to be used in the existing M16 upper unit with minor breechface alterations.

6.8mm sounds like an odd metric diameter but the cartridge uses standard .277" bullets. The 30 Remington case was necked to hold 270-caliber bullets and blown out to maximize powder capacity. Maximum cartridge length is 2.260", the same as the 5.56mm NATO so the 6.8mm will fit and feed from standard M16 magazines. Factory ammunition drives a 115-grain bullet at a nominal velocity of 2625 ft/sec.

As a sporting cartridge, the 6.8mm Remington is a natural for light, fast-handling rifles. It is more than adequate for the smaller deer species common to the Southeastern United States. For such hunting out to about 150 yards, the Speer 130-grain Hot-Cor® spitzer at 2400-2500 ft/sec is excellent. It should give excellent expansion and complete shoot-throughs on smaller deer. For varminting, either the 90-grain TNT HP or the 100-grain HP are excellent choices. However, our nod goes to the TNT; its higher velocity and ballistic coefficient give it a strong edge over the older 100-grain design.

Note that the propellants that work best in the 6.8mm Remington are also those commonly used in the 223 Remington. Winchester 748 gave the best velocity with the 130-grain bullet. We found that magnum primers were not required with the propellants we selected. Working pressure is 55,000 psi.

Time will tell if the shooting public will embrace the 6.8mm if it does not become a military service cartridge. Its mild recoil makes it an excellent choice for new shooters or those not fond of getting kicked.

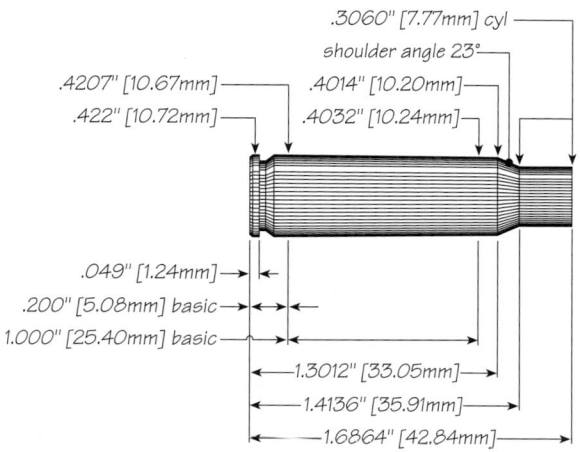

Max. Case Length:	1.686"	**Cart. Case:**	Remington
Trim-to Length:	1.676"	**Primer:**	CCI 200
Max Cart. OAL:	2.260"	**Test Firearm:**	Universal Receiver
RCBS Shell Holder:	#19	**Barrel Length:**	Krieger 24"

0.277"	270 TNT HP
Weight, grains	90
Ballistic Coefficient	0.303
Sectional Density	0.168
COAL Tested:	2.250"
Speer Part No.	1446

Propellant	START CHARGE		MAXIMUM CHARGE	
	Weight, grs	Muzzle Velocity, ft/sec	Weight, grs	Muzzle Velocity, ft/sec
AA 2230	31.5	2942	33.5C	3067
H322	29.0	2824	31.0C	2995
H335	33.0	2852	35.0C	2995
Reloder 10X	27.5	2822	29.5	2991
Reloder 7	25.5	2782	27.5	2983
Ramshot X-Terminator	31.5	2833	33.5C	2968
AA 2015	28.5	2746	30.5C	2924
IMR 4198	23.5	2733	25.5	2915
AA 1680	25.0	2740	27.0	2906
Viht. N120	23.5	2717	25.5	2905
AA 5744	21.5	2597	23.5	2787
IMR 4227	20.0	2579	22.0	2749

*Maximum Loads should be used with CAUTION • C = Compressed Load • *Magnum Primer used with this powder.*

6.8mm Remington SPC

0.277"	270 HP
Weight, grains	100
Ballistic Coefficient	0.201
Sectional Density	0.186
COAL Tested:	2.250"
Speer Part No.	1447

Propellant	START CHARGE		MAXIMUM CHARGE	
	Weight, grs	Muzzle Velocity, ft/sec	Weight, grs	Muzzle Velocity, ft/sec
Ramshot X-Terminator	31.0	2653	33.0	2815
Reloder 10X	26.5	2607	28.5C	2791
H322	27.5	2592	29.5C	2778
H335	31.0	2590	33.0C	2739
BL-C(2)	32.0	2614	34.0C	2727
IMR 4198	23.0	2566	25.0	2718
Reloder 7	24.0	2524	26.0	2715
AA 1680	24.0	2517	26.0	2702
Viht. N120	22.5	2504	24.5	2680
AA 2015	27.0	2504	29.0C	2677
AA 5744	21.0	2408	23.0	2582

0.277"	270 Spitz BTSP	270 Spitz SP
Weight, grains	130	130
Ballistic Coefficient	0.412	0.383
Sectional Density	0.242	0.242
COAL Tested:	2.250"	2.250"
Speer Part No.	1458	1459

Propellant	START CHARGE Weight, grs	START CHARGE Muzzle Velocity, ft/sec	MAXIMUM CHARGE Weight, grs	MAXIMUM CHARGE Muzzle Velocity, ft/sec
748	29.0	2408	31.0C	2547
Ramshot X-Terminator	27.0	2307	29.0C	2450
H335	27.5	2261	29.5C	2446
Reloder 10X	23.5	2276	25.5C	2431
BL-C(2)	28.0	2245	30.0C	2415
Ramshot TAC	26.5	2271	28.5	2399
Benchmark	25.0	2217	27.0C	2391
H322	24.5	2223	26.5	2385
AA 2015	24.0	2165	26.0	2360
Viht. N130	22.5	2185	24.5	2345
IMR 4198	20.0	2159	22.0	2317
AA 1680	20.5	2124	22.5	2262

*Maximum Loads should be used with CAUTION • C = Compressed Load • *Magnum Primer used with this powder.*

270 Winchester Short Magnum

Winchester introduced the 270 Winchester Short Magnum shortly after the 300 WSM, along with a 7mm version. Its strongest competition comes from another of Winchester's most successful cartridges—the 270 Winchester. The short and broad case allows the 270 WSM a small capacity advantage over the original Winchester 270 cartridge. Across the range of common 27-caliber bullet weights, 270 WSM velocities are on par with the big 270 Weatherby Magnum. In short, this is a potent hunting package.

If you already own a good 270 Winchester rifle, there is little if anything to gain in trading it for a 270 WSM. However, if you are buying your first 270-caliber rifle, consider the WSM. The only downside is in finding factory ammo in remote areas; although the WSM is now well established, it's still easier to find 270 Winchester ammo when you're miles from home. Obviously, as a reloader, you are not tied to factory ammunition.

Except for the 100-grain bullets, we found that slow-burning propellants gave the best velocities. None of the propellants we tested required compressed charges.

Speer's 130-grain Grand Slam® and Hot-Cor® spitzer are the best choices for medium deer. For large deer, elk, and moose, the 140-grain Trophy Bonded Bear Claw or the 150-grain Grand Slam will give the deep penetration required for these animals.

To keep in practice during the spring varmint season, try the 100-grain Speer hollow point. Although the 270 WSM is not a varmint cartridge, it drives that bullet at over 3600 ft/sec for impressive effects on varmints. You get the benefit of extra practice that will be useful in the fall.

The compact nature of the cartridge means you can safely assemble efficient reduced-recoil loads for teaching a youngster to shoot. The mild loads for the 100 and 130-grain bullets with Accurate Arms 5744 propellant exit the muzzle at less than 2100 ft/sec and produce mild recoil.

The loads here do not exceed the maximum average pressure of 65,000 psi established for this cartridge.

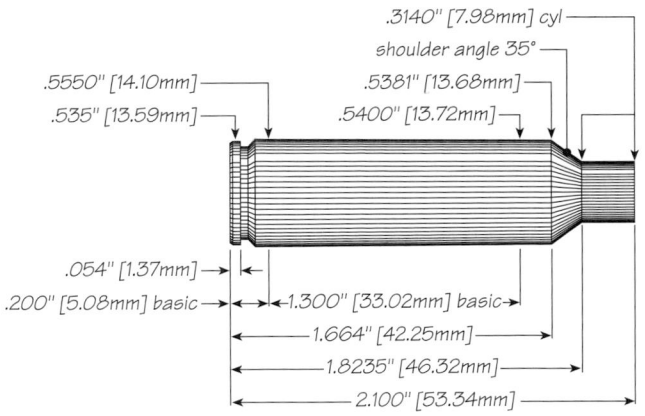

.3140" [7.98mm] cyl
shoulder angle 35°
.5550" [14.10mm]
.535" [13.59mm]
.5381" [13.68mm]
.5400" [13.72mm]
.054" [1.37mm]
.200" [5.08mm] basic
1.300" [33.02mm] basic
1.664" [42.25mm]
1.8235" [46.32mm]
2.100" [53.34mm]

Max. Case Length:	2.100"	Cart. Case:	Winchester
Trim-to Length:	2.090"	Primer:	CCI 200; 250*
Max Cart. OAL:	2.860"	Test Firearm:	Universal Receiver
RCBS Shell Holder:	#43	Barrel Length:	Krieger 24"

0.277"	270 HP
Weight, grains	100
Ballistic Coefficient	0.201
Sectional Density	0.186
COAL Tested:	2.730"
Speer Part No.	1447

| Propellant | START CHARGE | | MAXIMUM CHARGE | |
	Weight, grs	Muzzle Velocity, ft/sec	Weight, grs	Muzzle Velocity, ft/sec
IMR 4064	58.0	3451	62.0	3645
IMR 4350	66.0	3426	70.0	3637
Varget	57.0	3433	61.0	3613
IMR 4320	58.0	3381	62.0	3611
IMR 4895	57.0	3387	61.0	3600
Reloder 15	58.0	3373	62.0	3564
AA 5744 (reduced load)	25.0	2010	26.0	2075

*Maximum Loads should be used with CAUTION • C = Compressed Load • *Magnum Primer used with this powder.*

0.277"	270 Spitz BTSP	270 Spitz SP	270 GS SP
Weight, grains	130	130	130
Ballistic Coefficient	0.412	0.383	0.332
Sectional Density	0.242	0.242	0.242
COAL Tested:	2.700"	2.700"	2.670"
Speer Part No.	1458	1459	1465

| Propellant | START CHARGE | | MAXIMUM CHARGE | |
	Weight, grs	Muzzle Velocity, ft/sec	Weight, grs	Muzzle Velocity, ft/sec
IMR 7828	62.0	3105	66.0	3250
Reloder 19	62.0	3097	66.0	3241
Reloder 22	62.0	3096	66.0	3228
IMR 4831	58.0	3067	62.0	3226
AA 3100	62.0	3039	66.0	3213
IMR 4350	56.0	3026	60.0	3183
H4831SC	59.0	3035	63.0	3173
H4350	54.0	3013	58.0	3163
AA 5744 (reduced load)	25.0	1940	27.0	2048

0.277"	270 TBBC SP
Weight, grains	140
Ballistic Coefficient	0.392
Sectional Density	0.261
COAL Tested:	2.710"
Speer Part No.	1740

| Propellant | START CHARGE | | MAXIMUM CHARGE | |
	Weight, grs	Muzzle Velocity, ft/sec	Weight, grs	Muzzle Velocity, ft/sec
Reloder 25	65.0	3004	69.0	3179
Reloder 22	61.0	2938	65.0	3122
IMR 7828	62.0	2937	66.0	3105
Reloder 19	60.0	2895	64.0	3088
H4831SC	58.0	2847	62.0	3019

NOTE: *Trophy Bonded Bear Claw and Trophy Bonded Sledgehammer Solid bullets have unique ballistic behavior compared to conventional bullets. Loads for TBBC and TBSS bullets may not "track" with data for conventional bullets. Use TBBC and TBSS data ONLY for TBBC and TBSS bullets.*

Maximum Loads should be used with CAUTION • C = Compressed Load • *Magnum Primer used with this powder.

0.277"	270 Spitz BTSP	270 Spitz SP	270 GS SP
Weight, grains	150	150	150
Ballistic Coefficient	0.489	0.455	0.378
Sectional Density	0.279	0.279	0.279
COAL Tested:	2.700"	2.670"	2.700"
Speer Part No.	1604	1605	1608

Propellant	START CHARGE Weight, grs	START CHARGE Muzzle Velocity, ft/sec	MAXIMUM CHARGE Weight, grs	MAXIMUM CHARGE Muzzle Velocity, ft/sec
Reloder 25	60.0	2882	64.0	3058
IMR 7828	58.0	2796	62.0	3011
Reloder 22	57.0	2839	61.0	3009
Reloder 19	56.0	2831	60.0	2990
IMR 4831	54.0	2774	58.0	2959
H4831SC	56.0	2776	60.0	2959
IMR 4350	51.0	2757	55.0	2930
AA 3100	56.0	2796	60.0	2848

*Maximum Loads should be used with CAUTION • C = Compressed Load • *Magnum Primer used with this powder.*

270 Winchester

There are a number of really "good" cartridges available, but only a handful can be classed as "great." The 270 Winchester is surely one of the great ones. When the topic of conversation in the hunting camp turns to "the best all-around rifle," the 270 Winchester always gets lots of votes.

Introduced in 1925 in the Winchester Model 54 bolt-action rifle, the 270 was one of the first truly effective, long-range rifle cartridges produced. Necking the 30-06 case down to hold .277" bullets formed the new case. The original load, a 130-grain soft point traveling at over 3000 ft/sec, was flat-shooting and very effective on deer-sized game. Later a 100-grain hollow point was introduced. Although the 270 was not conceived as a varmint cartridge, the 100-grain loads were accurate and explosive on varmints out to 300 yards. In response to the demand for a heavier bullet for larger North American game, a 150-grain load soon appeared.

No other person had as much impact on the popularity of the 270 Winchester than outdoorsman and writer Jack O'Connor. He used the 270 for 40 years, taking game with it literally around the world. Jack's written praise of the 270 led many a shooter to choose this cartridge. Almost every make of rifle has been chambered for it.

Loaded with the tough 140-grain Trophy Bonded Bear Claw or the 150-grain Grand Slam, the 270 can readily handle all North American game with the exception of the grizzly and brown bear. If you spend most of your hunting time seeking whitetail and mule deer, any of Speer's 130-grain bullets are a great choice. The 90-grain TNT hollow point and the 100-grain hollow point give exceptional performance on varmints beyond 300 yards. Most North American hunters owning a good 270 have little reason to shop for a new rifle unless a hunt for dangerous Alaskan bear is part of their plans.

Most factory ammunition and handloads won't quite live up to published factory ballistics when fired in a 22" sporter barrel. The factory specs are measured in a longer pressure/velocity test barrel. Don't try over-loading to meet published factory velocities in the 270. Top velocities are obtained with the slower burning powders.

If the rifleman wants to improve on the long-range performance of the 270, he has to move up to a magnum case and then the improvement in ballistics is often only marginal. Even the new 270 Winchester Short Magnum does not add enough performance to make the original 270 a candidate for trade-in.

The listed loads do not exceed the 52,000 CUP maximum average pressure established by SAAMI.

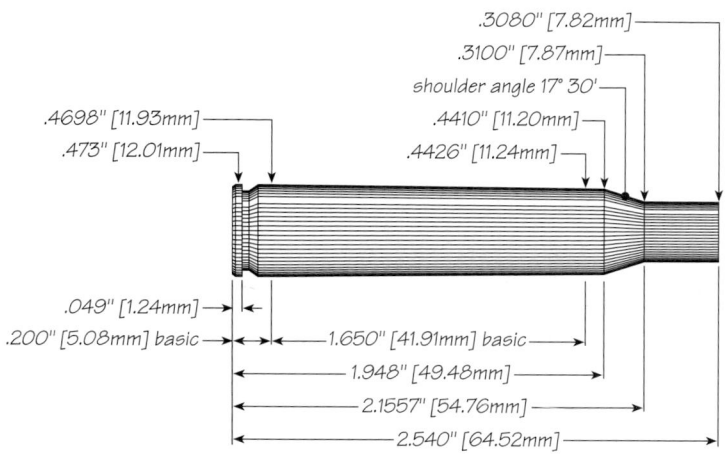

Max. Case Length:	2.540"	Cart. Case:	Winchester
Trim-to Length:	2.530"	Primer:	CCI 200; 250*
Max Cart. OAL:	3.340"	Test Firearm:	Ruger M77 MkII
RCBS Shell Holder:	#3	Barrel Length:	22"

0.277"	270 TNT HP
Weight, grains	90
Ballistic Coefficient	0.303
Sectional Density	0.168
COAL Tested:	3.170"
Speer Part No.	1446

Propellant	START CHARGE		MAXIMUM CHARGE	
	Weight, grs	Muzzle Velocity, ft/sec	Weight, grs	Muzzle Velocity, ft/sec
760*	53.0	3300	59.0	3514
Varget	51.5	3248	55.5	3511
Reloder 15	51.0	3179	55.0	3501
H380*	55.0	3224	59.0	3450
IMR 4064	51.0	3107	55.0	3433
Viht. N140	50.0	3095	54.0	3391
Reloder 19	60.0	3044	64.0C	3341
IMR 4831*	58.0	3101	62.0C	3274
AA 3100*	58.0	2995	62.0C	3212

*Maximum Loads should be used with CAUTION • C = Compressed Load • *Magnum Primer used with this powder.*

0.277"	270 HP
Weight, grains	100
Ballistic Coefficient	0.201
Sectional Density	0.186
COAL Tested:	3.100"
Speer Part No.	1447

Propellant	START CHARGE		MAXIMUM CHARGE	
	Weight, grs	Muzzle Velocity, ft/sec	Weight, grs	Muzzle Velocity, ft/sec
Varget	51.0	3186	55.0	3436
AA 4350	57.0	3215	61.0C	3414
IMR 4350	57.0	3133	61.0C	3356
H414*	55.0	3153	59.0	3346
760*	54.0	3114	58.0	3290
IMR 4320	49.0	3023	53.0	3288
Reloder 19	58.0	2990	62.0C	3220
Viht. N140	47.0	2951	51.0	3219
IMR 4064	48.0	2952	52.0	3210
H380*	51.0	2956	55.0	3197
IMR 4895	46.0	3079	50.0	3169
AA 3100*	58.0	2937	62.0C	3164
SR 4759 (reduced load)	16.0	1548	20.0	1915

0.277"	270 Spitz BTSP	270 Spitz SP	270 GS SP
Weight, grains	130	130	130
Ballistic Coefficient	0.412	0.383	0.332
Sectional Density	0.242	0.242	0.242
COAL Tested:	3.240"	3.240"	3.240"
Speer Part No.	1458	1459	1465

Propellant	START CHARGE		MAXIMUM CHARGE	
	Weight, grs	Muzzle Velocity, ft/sec	Weight, grs	Muzzle Velocity, ft/sec
H1000*	60.0	2789	64.0	3117
IMR 7828*	58.0	2821	62.0	3066
760*	50.0	2801	54.0	3008
IMR 4831	54.0	2698	58.0	2971
H4350	52.0	2733	56.0	2949
Rcloder 22	54.0	2689	60.0	2947
Viht. N160	51.5	2716	55.5	2930
H414*	50.0	2719	54.0	2920
IMR 4350	51.0	2873	55.0	2907
Reloder 19	53.0	2699	57.0	2904
AA 3100*	52.0	2549	56.0	2823
IMR 4064	43.0	2627	47.0	2801
Reloder 15	41.0	2548	45.0	2742
SR 4759 (reduced load)	20.0	1651	24.0	1998

*Maximum Loads should be used with CAUTION • C = Compressed Load • *Magnum Primer used with this powder.*

0.277"	270 TBBC SP
Weight, grains	140
Ballistic Coefficient	0.392
Sectional Density	0.261
COAL Tested:	3.260"
Speer Part No.	1740

Propellant	START CHARGE		MAXIMUM CHARGE	
	Weight, grs	Muzzle Velocity, ft/sec	Weight, grs	Muzzle Velocity, ft/sec
Reloder 22	52.5	2751	56.5	2949
IMR 7828*	52.0	2777	56.0	2941
Reloder 19	52.0	2750	56.0	2923
IMR 4831	49.5	2685	53.5	2900
AA 3100	52.0	2672	56.0	2897
IMR 4350	49.0	2695	53.0	2894
H4831SC	52.0	2672	56.0	2872

NOTE: *Trophy Bonded Bear Claw and Trophy Bonded Sledgehammer Solid bullets have unique ballistic behavior compared to conventional bullets. Loads for TBBC and TBSS bullets may not "track" with data for conventional bullets. Use TBBC and TBSS data ONLY for TBBC and TBSS bullets.*

Terry Roberts, Engineer, CCI/Speer Operations; 270 Winchester, Fusion® ammo; 6-point bull elk taken near Waha, Idaho.

0.277"	270 Spitz BTSP	270 Spitz SP	270 GS SP
Weight, grains	150	150	150
Ballistic Coefficient	0.489	0.455	0.378
Sectional Density	0.279	0.279	0.279
COAL Tested:	3.270"	3.270"	3.250"
Speer Part No.	1604	1605	1608

Propellant	START CHARGE		MAXIMUM CHARGE	
	Weight, grs	Muzzle Velocity, ft/sec	Weight, grs	Muzzle Velocity, ft/sec
IMR 7828*	54.0	2694	58.0C	2907
760*	49.0	2634	53.0	2874
AA 3100	53.0	2644	57.0	2867
IMR 4831	51.0	2606	55.0	2832
H4831SC	53.5	2638	57.5	2823
Reloder 22	50.0	2562	54.0	2769
Reloder 19	49.0	2565	53.0	2745
IMR 4350	48.0	2533	52.0	2727
H414*	46.0	2487	50.0	2680
Viht. N160	47.0	2465	51.0	2670
H4350	47.0	2456	51.0	2644
IMR 4064	41.0	2453	45.0	2635
SR 4759 (reduced load)	22.0	1655	26.0	1957

*Maximum Loads should be used with CAUTION • C = Compressed Load • *Magnum Primer used with this powder.*

270 Weatherby Magnum

The 270 Weatherby was among the first in Roy Weatherby's line of ultra-velocity magnum rifle cartridges, dating to 1943. Like several other Weatherby Magnums, it is based on the belted 300 H&H case shortened, blown out, and necked down to hold .277" bullets. The cartridge is short enough to function in standard-length (30-06) actions.

Obviously, the decision to upgrade 27-caliber bullet performance was based on the success of the older 270 Winchester. Yet it is the superb performance of the Winchester cartridge that was and is the 270 Weatherby's greatest challenge. The Weatherby cartridge requires a steep increase in propellant to gain a modest velocity gain over the 270 Winchester. With the 270 Winchester Short Magnum now in the mix, the 270 Weatherby has a more robust challenger; the Short Magnum virtually duplicates the performance of the venerable Weatherby cartridge in some bullet weights.

Still, the 270 is a fine cartridge for shooters who prefer Weatherby rifles. Flat-shooting and accurate, the 270 Weatherby with the right bullet will handle any North American game at long range with the exception of the great bears. Of course, bullets must be matched to the game. The tough construction of the 130 and 150-grain Speer Grand Slam® is needed at these velocity levels. Using 150-grain bullets will reduce velocity damage for meat hunters.

Large capacity, small-bore cartridges have the reputation for being rough on barrel throats, although there is emerging evidence that the Weatherby's radiused shoulder slows throat erosion to some extent. Nevertheless, careful loading and avoiding prolonged rapid-fire shooting can help preserve barrel throats in these high-intensity cartridges.

Most Weatherby cartridges were standardized in 1994; prior to then they were proprietary cartridges. The loads we present here are the results of a complete retest on this cartridge on piezo-electric equipment using the latest components and propellant lots. The 270 Weatherby's maximum average pressure assignment is 62,500 psi.

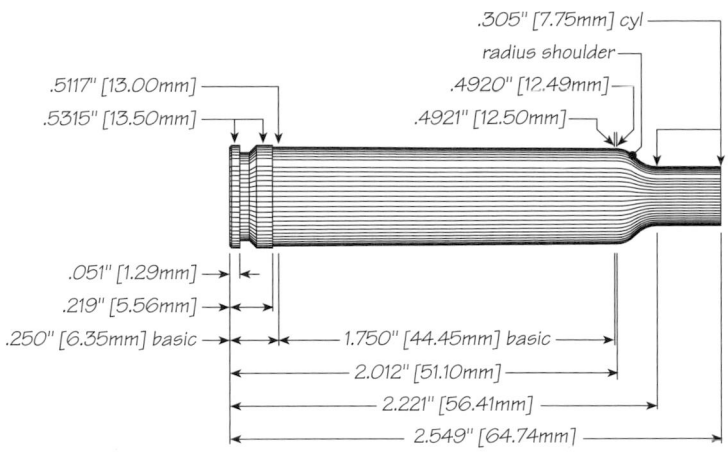

.305" [7.75mm] cyl
radius shoulder
.4920" [12.49mm]
.5117" [13.00mm]
.4921" [12.50mm]
.5315" [13.50mm]

.051" [1.29mm]
.219" [5.56mm]
.250" [6.35mm] basic
1.750" [44.45mm] basic
2.012" [51.10mm]
2.221" [56.41mm]
2.549" [64.74mm]

Max. Case Length:	2.549"	Cart. Case:	Federal
Trim-to Length:	2.539"	Primer:	Federal 215*
Max Cart. OAL:	3.295"	Test Firearm:	Universal Receiver
RCBS Shell Holder:	#4	Barrel Length:	HS Precision 24"

Mark Allen, husband of Brenda Allen, Rimfire Production, CCI/Speer Operations; 300 Win Mag, 180-grain Grand Slam®; bull moose.

*Maximum Loads should be used with CAUTION • C = Compressed Load • *Magnum Primer used with this powder.*

0.277"	270 HP
Weight, grains	100
Ballistic Coefficient	0.201
Sectional Density	0.186
COAL Tested:	3.250"
Speer Part No.	1447

Propellant	START CHARGE		MAXIMUM CHARGE	
	Weight, grs	Muzzle Velocity, ft/sec	Weight, grs	Muzzle Velocity, ft/sec
Reloder 22*	72.0	3423	76.0C	3627
Magpro*	76.0	3451	80.0C	3618
IMR 4831*	67.0	3360	71.0	3575
Reloder 19*	69.0	3359	73.0	3570
Ramshot Magnum*	77.0	3386	81.0C	3557
H4831SC*	71.0	3371	75.0	3534
IMR 7828*	72.0	3338	76.0	3531
Reloder 25*	73.0	3270	77.0C	3478
Retumbo*	75.0	3226	77.0C	3329
Viht. N560*	72.0	3062	76.0	3294

0.277"	270 Spitz BTSP	270 Spitz SP	270 GS SP
Weight, grains	130	130	130
Ballistic Coefficient	0.412	0.383	0.332
Sectional Density	0.242	0.242	0.242
COAL Tested:	3.250"	3.250"	3.250"
Speer Part No.	1458	1459	1465

Propellant	START CHARGE		MAXIMUM CHARGE	
	Weight, grs	Muzzle Velocity, ft/sec	Weight, grs	Muzzle Velocity, ft/sec
Reloder 25*	68.0	3080	72.0	3267
Ramshot Magnum*	71.0	3079	75.0	3254
Viht. N560*	65.0	3030	69.0	3222
IMR 7828*	65.0	3054	69.0	3217
Reloder 22*	64.0	3048	68.0	3214
Retumbo*	69.0	3026	73.0	3209
Magpro*	68.0	3014	72.0	3189
IMR 4831*	60.0	3019	64.0	3181
Reloder 19*	61.0	3040	65.0	3176
H4831SC*	62.0	2980	66.0	3120

*Maximum Loads should be used with CAUTION • C = Compressed Load • *Magnum Primer used with this powder.*

0.277"	270 Spitz BTSP	270 Spitz SP	270 GS SP
Weight, grains	150	150	150
Ballistic Coefficient	0.489	0.455	0.378
Sectional Density	0.279	0.279	0.279
COAL Tested:	3.250"	3.250"	3.260"
Speer Part No.	1604	1605	1608

	START CHARGE		MAXIMUM CHARGE	
Propellant	Weight, grs	Muzzle Velocity, ft/sec	Weight, grs	Muzzle Velocity, ft/sec
Ramshot Magnum*	68.0	2865	72.0	3028
US869*	77.0	2862	81.0C	2987
Retumbo*	64.0	2862	68.0	2980
Reloder 25*	62.0	2839	66.0	2966
AA 8700*	77.0	2832	81.0C	2957
IMR 7828*	60.0	2803	64.0	2950
Reloder 22*	59.0	2800	63.0	2942
IMR 4831*	56.0	2759	60.0	2914
Reloder 19*	56.0	2790	60.0	2903
H4831SC*	58.0	2771	62.0	2903
Viht. N560*	58.0	2771	62.0	2902

Conner Beckvold, son of Brenda Allen, Rimfire Production, CCI/Speer Operations; 25-06 Rem, 120-grain Grand Slam®; buffalo.

*Maximum Loads should be used with CAUTION • C = Compressed Load • *Magnum Primer used with this powder.*

7-30 Waters

Well-known experimenter and writer Ken Waters conceived this cartridge as a flatter-shooting, lever-action rifle cartridge that could be used in the Model 94 Winchester. Development work began in 1976, and U.S. Repeating Arms announced production rifles eight years later. Federal Premium makes the ammunition.

The Waters cartridge uses a 30-30 case necked to hold 7mm (.284") bullets. The new cartridge offers modern ballistic performance in a traditional lever-rifle design. Thompson/Center also has chambered the 7-30 Waters in its Contender carbine.

Factory ammunition fires a 120-grain flat-point bullet at 2700 ft/sec. This load has a flatter trajectory than a 30-30, making hits easier between 150 to 225 yards. Its light recoil will appeal to shooters who are recoil-sensitive. For best ballistic performance, the rifle with a 24-inch barrel should be chosen over the carbine version.

Because the cartridge is intended for use in a tubular magazine, factory ammunition is loaded with a flat point bullet. Speer has an excellent 130-grain Hot-Cor flat point bullet developed expressly for the 7-30 cartridge. The added weight means more energy at longer ranges, and excellent penetration on deer-sized game. Pointed bullets shown in the data must either be singly loaded, or loaded with one cartridge in the chamber and only one in the magazine, if used in a tubular magazine rifle. Never load more than one cartridge with a pointed bullet in a tubular magazine. To do so will expose the shooter and bystanders to the danger of a cartridge exploding in the magazine under recoil. Because the Contender carbine is a single-shot action, any bullet shape may be used as long as it clears the rifling.

The 7-30 Waters has proven accurate and well suited to game animals up to medium deer. The cartridge has also found a niche with handgun hunters in the Thompson/Center Contender pistol, where it compares favorably with a potent wildcat cartridge, the 6.5 JDJ. See the Handgun Data section for more information on this cartridge.

With the demise of U.S. Repeating Arms in 2005, the future of this cartridge in rifles is not clear. We believe it has enough handgun fans to keep it popular with the Contender crowd.

The industry maximum pressure of the 7-30 is 40,000 CUP. These loads do not exceed that limit.

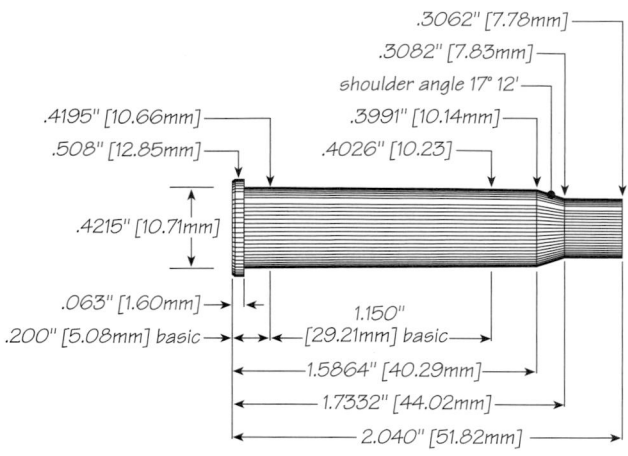

.3062" [7.78mm]
.3082" [7.83mm]
shoulder angle 17° 12'
.4195" [10.66mm]
.508" [12.85mm]
.3991" [10.14mm]
.4026" [10.23]
.4215" [10.71mm]
.063" [1.60mm]
.200" [5.08mm] basic
1.150"
[29.21mm] basic
1.5864" [40.29mm]
1.7332" [44.02mm]
2.040" [51.82mm]

Max. Case Length:	2.040"	Cart. Case:	Federal
Trim-to Length:	2.030"	Primer:	Federal 200; 250*
Max Cart. OAL:	2.550"	Test Firearm:	Winchester Model 94AE
RCBS Shell Holder:	#2	Barrel Length:	24"

Rocky Allen, son of Brenda Allen, Rimfire Production, CCI/Speer Operations; 300 Win Mag, 180-grain Fusion® ammo; mule deer.

0.284"	7mm TNT HP
Weight, grains	110
Ballistic Coefficient	0.384
Sectional Density	0.195
COAL Tested:	2.550"
Speer Part No.	1616

Propellant	START CHARGE		MAXIMUM CHARGE	
	Weight, grs	Muzzle Velocity, ft/sec	Weight, grs	Muzzle Velocity, ft/sec
748*	35.0	2503	39.0C	2834
AA 2015	29.0	2533	33.0	2767
Reloder 15	33.0	2354	37.0	2757
H4895	32.0	2425	36.0	2739
Viht. N135	31.0	2354	35.0	2735
H335*	32.0	2498	36.0	2716
BL-C(2)*	31.0	2432	35.0	2665
IMR 4895	30.5	2325	34.5	2655
AA 2230*	27.5	2226	31.5	2642
IMR 3031	30.0	2228	34.0	2615

NOTE: Do not use pointed bullets in tubular magazines.

*Maximum Loads should be used with CAUTION • C = Compressed Load • *Magnum Primer used with this powder.*

0.284"	7mm HP
Weight, grains	115
Ballistic Coefficient	0.250
Sectional Density	0.204
COAL Tested:	2.550"
Speer Part No.	1617

Propellant	START CHARGE Weight, grs	Muzzle Velocity, ft/sec	MAXIMUM CHARGE Weight, grs	Muzzle Velocity, ft/sec
Reloder 15	31.0	2228	35.0	2480
IMR 4895	30.0	2130	34.0	2449
748*	30.0	2088	34.0	2435
H4895	29.0	2103	33.0	2400
BL-C(2)*	31.0	2164	35.0	2395
AA 2015	26.0	2086	30.0	2381
Viht. N135	29.0	2130	33.0	2378
H335*	28.0	2052	32.0	2360
IMR 3031	27.0	1979	31.0	2311
AA 2230*	24.0	1793	28.0	2201

NOTE: *Do not use this bullet in tubular magazines.*

0.284"	7mm Spitz SP	7mm Spitz BTSP	7-30 FN SP/cann
Weight, grains	130	130	130
Ballistic Coefficient	0.368	0.424	0.257
Sectional Density	0.230	0.230	0.230
COAL Tested:	2.550"	2.550"	2.525"
Speer Part No.	1623	1624	1625

	START CHARGE		MAXIMUM CHARGE	
Propellant	Weight, grs	Muzzle Velocity, ft/sec	Weight, grs	Muzzle Velocity, ft/sec
Reloder 15	31.5	2253	35.5	2609
H335*	29.0	2030	33.0	2583
Viht. N135	28.5	2148	32.5	2532
H4895	30.0	2241	34.0	2514
BL-C(2)*	32.0	2320	36.0	2510
IMR 3031	29.0	2320	33.0	2509
740*	31.0	2096	35.0	2487
AA 2015	26.0	2206	30.0	2480
AA 2230*	26.0	2039	30.0	2396

NOTE: Do not use pointed bullets in tubular magazines.

*Maximum Loads should be used with CAUTION • C = Compressed Load • * Magnum Primer used with this powder.*

0.284"	7mm Spitz SP
Weight, grains	145
Ballistic Coefficient	0.416
Sectional Density	0.257
COAL Tested:	2.550"
Speer Part No.	1629

| Propellant | START CHARGE | | MAXIMUM CHARGE | |
	Weight, grs	Muzzle Velocity, ft/sec	Weight, grs	Muzzle Velocity, ft/sec
Reloder 15	31.0	2228	35.0	2480
IMR 4895	30.0	2130	34.0	2449
748*	30.0	2088	34.0	2435
H4895	29.0	2103	33.0	2400
BL-C(2)*	31.0	2164	35.0	2395
AA 2015	26.0	2086	30.0	2381
Viht. N135	29.0	2130	33.0	2378
H335*	28.0	2052	32.0	2360
IMR 3031	27.0	1979	31.0	2311
AA 2230*	24.0	1793	28.0	2201

NOTE: *Do not use pointed bullets in tubular magazines.*

*Maximum Loads should be used with CAUTION • C = Compressed Load • *Magnum Primer used with this powder.*

7mm-08 Remington

The 7mm-08 evolved from the wildcat 7mm-308, a 308 Winchester case necked down to hold .284" bullets. Remington announced the 7mm-08 as a commercial cartridge in 1980 and offered it in the very successful Model 700 rifle and the less expensive Model 788. Factory ammunition was loaded with a 140-grain bullet at 2845 ft/sec, and a 120-grain bullet at 3000 ft/sec (24" test barrel velocities).

Metallic silhouette rifle shooters found that the 7mm-08 combined accuracy and power with moderate recoil and immediately accepted the cartridge. It soon became obvious that this cartridge's compact size in no way reflected on its performance. Velocities from the 24-inch Model 700V rifle compare favorably (considering the difference in how much powder used) with those of the 270 Winchester and the 280 Remington in some sporter-length barrels. In addition, we found that the 7mm-08 showed exceptional accuracy with all Speer bullets, from the 110-grain TNT to the 175-grain Mag-Tip and Grand Slam.

With this level of performance, the 7mm-08 is suitable for use on just about any North American game (with the exception of large bear) as long as the proper bullet is used.

Many early rifles in this caliber were intended for target shooting and have 24-inch barrels. In more recent years, the cartridge has found greater acceptance as a hunting cartridge and has been chambered in shorter rifles such as the Remington Model Seven. In the 18.5-inch barrel of the model Seven, expect to see velocities between 80 and 140 ft/sec lower than the ones we show for the Model 700V. Even with this reduction, the 7mm-08 is still a potent hunting cartridge and is very appealing in compact, lightweight rifles.

Some 7mm-08 rifles have short throats. When seating bullets, make sure they do not contact the rifling. The industry operating pressure for the 7mm-08 Remington is 52,000 CUP. These loads do not exceed that limit.

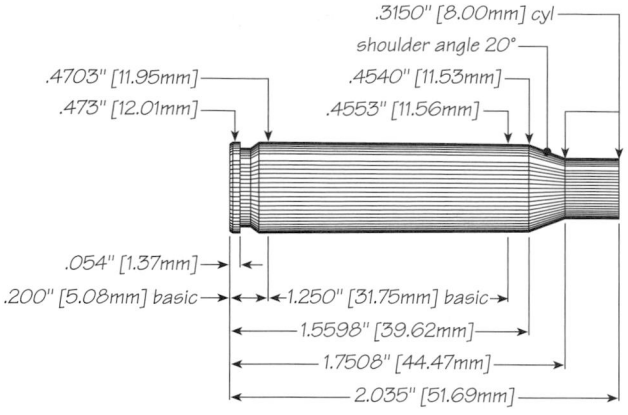

.3150" [8.00mm] cyl
shoulder angle 20°
.4703" [11.95mm]
.4540" [11.53mm]
.473" [12.01mm]
.4553" [11.56mm]
.054" [1.37mm]
.200" [5.08mm] basic
1.250" [31.75mm] basic
1.5598" [39.62mm]
1.7508" [44.47mm]
2.035" [51.69mm]

Max. Case Length:	2.035"	Cart. Case:	Remington
Trim-to Length:	2.025"	Primer:	CCI 200; 250*
Max Cart. OAL:	2.800"	Test Firearm:	Remington M700V
RCBS Shell Holder:	#3	Barrel Length:	24"

Tony Imthurn,
son of Dave Imthurn, Sr.
Engineering Technician,
CCI/Speer Operations;
7mm-08 Rem, Fusion®
ammo; 4-point whitetail
buck near Kamiah, Idaho.

0.284"	7mm TNT HP
Weight, grains	110
Ballistic Coefficient	0.384
Sectional Density	0.195
COAL Tested:	2.760"
Speer Part No.	1616

Propellant	START CHARGE		MAXIMUM CHARGE	
	Weight, grs	Muzzle Velocity, ft/sec	Weight, grs	Muzzle Velocity, ft/sec
IMR 3031	42.0	3023	46.0C	3250
Reloder 15	44.0	2930	48.0	3238
760*	47.0	2917	51.0C	3206
Varget	43.0	2891	47.0	3194
H414*	48.0	2858	52.0C	3176
H380*	49.0	2857	53.0C	3174
IMR 4064	42.0	2890	46.0	3141
Viht. N140	42.0	2855	46.0	3137
IMR 4895	40.0	2851	44.0	3066
H4350	47.0	2779	51.0C	3044
IMR 4350	47.0	2777	51.0C	3035
IMR 4320	41.0	2735	45.0	2973
AA 2460*	39.0	2690	43.0	2908
H335*	39.0	2659	43.0	2906

*Maximum Loads should be used with CAUTION • C = Compressed Load • *Magnum Primer used with this powder.*

0.284"	7mm HP
Weight, grains	115
Ballistic Coefficient	0.250
Sectional Density	0.204
COAL Tested:	2.655"
Speer Part No.	1617

	START CHARGE		MAXIMUM CHARGE	
Propellant	Weight, grs	Muzzle Velocity, ft/sec	Weight, grs	Muzzle Velocity, ft/sec
IMR 3031	41.0	2971	45.0	3195
760*	46.0	2851	50.0	3116
Varget	42.0	2835	46.0	3115
H380*	48.0	2818	52.0C	3114
Reloder 15	42.0	2795	46.0	3106
H414*	46.0	2797	50.0C	3057
IMR 4064	41.0	2812	45.0	3040
IMR 4350	46.0	2758	50.0	3031
Viht. N140	41.0	2775	45.0	3027
H4350	46.0	2709	50.0C	2993
IMR 4895	39.0	2719	43.0	2955
AA 2460*	38.0	2721	42.0	2942

Chad Smith, Machine Shop, CCI/Speer Operations; 7mm WSM 150-grain Fusion® ammo; bull elk.

0.284"	7mm Spitz SP	7mm Spitz BTSP
Weight, grains	130	130
Ballistic Coefficient	0.368	0.424
Sectional Density	0.230	0.230
COAL Tested:	2.730"	2.730"
Speer Part No.	1623	1624

Propellant	START CHARGE		MAXIMUM CHARGE	
	Weight, grs	Muzzle Velocity, ft/sec	Weight, grs	Muzzle Velocity, ft/sec
IMR 4064	41.0	2835	45.0	3065
IMR 4350	46.0	2766	50.0	3006
H4350	46.0	2715	50.0C	2984
760*	45.0	2727	49.0	2980
H414*	45.0	2673	49.0	2954
H380*	44.0	2652	48.0	2898
Varget	39.0	2641	43.0	2888
IMR 3031	38.0	2684	42.0	2886
IMR 4831	46.0	2678	50.0C	2880
Viht. N140	38.0	2531	42.0	2812
H335*	37.0	2607	41.0	2788
Reloder 15	38.0	2577	42.0	2786
AA 2520*	34.0	2409	38.0	2662

*Maximum Loads should be used with CAUTION • C = Compressed Load • *Magnum Primer used with this powder.*

0.284"	7mm Spitz BTSP	7mm Spitz SP	7mm Match BTHP	7mm GS SP
Weight, grains	145	145	145	145
Ballistic Coefficient	0.472	0.416	0.468	0.353
Sectional Density	0.257	0.257	0.257	0.257
COAL Tested:	2.730"	2.730"	2.800"	2.775"
Speer Part No.	1628	1629	1631	1632

Propellant	START CHARGE Weight, grs	START CHARGE Muzzle Velocity, ft/sec	MAXIMUM CHARGE Weight, grs	MAXIMUM CHARGE Muzzle Velocity, ft/sec
Reloder 19	47.0	2692	51.0C	2933
760*	45.0	2628	49.0	2920
H4350	44.0	2707	48.0C	2911
AA 4350	44.0	2644	48.0C	2843
IMR 4350	44.0	2644	48.0	2841
H414*	43.0	2560	47.0	2814
Viht. N165	47.0	2553	51.0C	2781
AA 2520*	38.0	2519	42.0	2772
H380*	42.0	2520	46.0	2739
AA 3100	45.0	2480	49.0C	2725
IMR 4895	37.0	2507	41.0	2724
Varget	37.0	2473	41.0	2707
Reloder 15	37.0	2458	41.0	2705

0.284"	7mm Spitz BTSP	7mm Spitz SP	7mm MT SP	7mm GS SP
Weight, grains	160	160	160	160
Ballistic Coefficient	0.519	0.504	0.340	0.389
Sectional Density	0.283	0.283	0.283	0.283
COAL Tested:	2.800"	2.800"	2.645"	2.760"
Speer Part No.	1634	1635	1637	1638

Propellant	START CHARGE Weight, grs	START CHARGE Muzzle Velocity, ft/sec	MAXIMUM CHARGE Weight, grs	MAXIMUM CHARGE Muzzle Velocity, ft/sec
760*	41.0	2475	45.0C	2735
Reloder 19	43.0	2456	47.0C	2710
H414*	41.0	2474	45.0C	2704
AA 4350	42.0	2484	46.0C	2671
IMR 4350	41.0	2463	45.0C	2666
AA 2520*	36.0	2425	40.0	2659
Viht. N165	45.0	2415	49.0C	2654
IMR 4831	42.0	2406	46.0C	2615
H4350	41.0	2423	45.0C	2611
H4831SC	46.0	2512	48.0C	2598
Reloder 15	34.0	2343	38.0	2506
748*	35.0	2315	39.0	2503
H380*	38.0	2281	42.0	2502

*Maximum Loads should be used with CAUTION • C = Compressed Load • *Magnum Primer used with this powder.*

0.284"	7mm MT SP	7mm GS SP
Weight, grains	175	175
Ballistic Coefficient	0.382	0.436
Sectional Density	0.310	0.310
COAL Tested:	2.745"	2.745"
Speer Part No.	1641	1643

Propellant	START CHARGE		MAXIMUM CHARGE	
	Weight, grs	Muzzle Velocity, ft/sec	Weight, grs	Muzzle Velocity, ft/sec
Reloder 19	43.0	2396	47.0C	2628
Viht. N165	43.0	2330	47.0C	2575
IMR 4350	40.0	2365	44.0	2542
AA 3100	43.0	2336	47.0C	2536
H4350	40.0	2326	44.0C	2507
AA 2520*	35.0	2314	39.0	2502
IMR 4831	41.0	2240	45.0	2465
H4831SC	43.5	2355	45.5C	2461
760*	41.0	2264	45.0	2461
H414*	38.0	2208	42.0	2419
H380*	38.0	2203	42.0	2408
Reloder 15	32.0	2153	36.0	2312

*Maximum Loads should be used with CAUTION • C = Compressed Load • *Magnum Primer used with this powder.*

7mm Mauser *(7x57mm)*

The 7mm Mauser (7x57mm) is one of the oldest sporting cartridges still in active use. Developed for military service around 1892 by Mauser, it was adopted as the Spanish military cartridge in the Model 1893 Mauser rifle. Mexico and several South American countries adopted the 7mm as their service cartridge. In spite of its age, its popularity with knowledgeable hunters has remained constant.

Between the wars, Remington and Winchester chambered rifles for the 7x57 but most were dropped before World War II. American shooters who wanted a 7x57 hunting rifle had to buy a foreign model or have a surplus military rifle sporterized. In spite of the poor availability of commercial rifles, the cartridge maintained its popularity.

Outdoor writers have always viewed the 7mm Mauser cartridge in a favorable light and thus kept interest in this fine cartridge alive. Carriage-trade rifle shops like Griffin & Howe made beautiful custom rifles in 7x57. Not everyone could afford a Griffin & Howe rifle, but almost anyone could experience the cartridge thanks to large numbers of quality military surplus Mausers that could be bought for a reasonable price.

Sturm-Ruger built some No. 1 single-shot rifles in this caliber in the early 1970's, and made a short, uncataloged run of M77 bolt rifles with the round top receiver profile in 1972. Later, the cartridge was listed as a standard chambering in both models and is still in their current catalog. Remington and Winchester have also chambered bolt-action rifles in 7x57 in the past decade, and many European manufacturers include it in their cartridge listings.

The 7mm Mauser's reputation is built on solid performance in the hunting fields. It is suitable for game up to large deer and, with heavy bullets, has been successfully used on moose and elk. For years, the only factory ammunition was loaded with a 175-grain soft-point bullet at 2400 ft/sec that duplicated early military loads. Although a good load for large deer at close range, the heavy bullet did not develop the full potential of the cartridge. With a wide choice of component bullets available, it was handloaders who fully realized what the 7mm Mauser could do. The major ammo makers eventually followed and now offer several 140-grain loadings velocities approaching 2700 ft/sec.

The 7mm has rather mild recoil and is often picked for lightweight sporters or as a first rifle for young shooters. New shooters can start with the 110-grain TNT hollow point or the 115-grain hollow point and move to heavier bullets as their tolerance to recoil increases. The 130 and 145-grain bullets are perfect for smaller deer and antelope, and the 160 and 175-grain bullets provide deep penetration for larger game. For maximum shock and penetration, look to the Trophy Bonded Bear Claw soft points. The 140-grain version will out-penetrate most conventional 150 and 160 soft points.

The U.S. industry maximum pressure for the 7mm Mauser is 46,000 CUP in deference to the weaker Model 93 and 95 Mausers still in use; European ammo tends to be loaded to somewhat higher pressure The new commercial sporters and original model 98 Mausers have stronger actions and can handle heavier loads. The following loads were developed to match European pressures with a maximum pressure of 50,000 CUP—the same as the 30-06—and should only be fired in modern commercial rifles and Model 98 Mausers known to be in good condition. Owners of Model 93 and 95 Mausers should not exceed the starting loads. Do not use these loads in any Remington rolling block rifle. If you plan to shoot a sporterized military rifle and are unsure of the action model, have a gunsmith identify and inspect it before reloading.

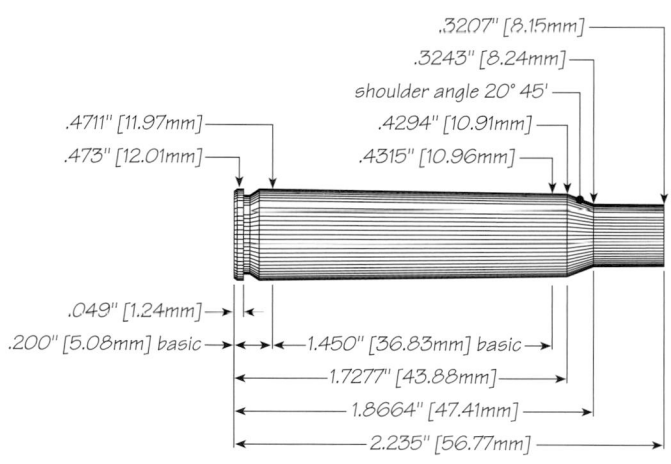

Max. Case Length:	2.235"	Cart. Case:	Remington
Trim-to Length:	2.225"	Primer:	CCI 200; 250*
Max Cart. OAL:	3.065"	Test Firearm:	Ruger M77
RCBS Shell Holder:	#3/#11	Barrel Length:	22"

0.284"	7mm TNT HP
Weight, grains	110
Ballistic Coefficient	0.384
Sectional Density	0.195
COAL Tested:	2.985"
Speer Part No.	1616

	START CHARGE		MAXIMUM CHARGE	
Propellant	Weight, grs	Muzzle Velocity, ft/sec	Weight, grs	Muzzle Velocity, ft/sec
760*	50.0	2941	54.0C	3250
H414*	50.0	2843	54.0C	3141
IMR 4064	44.0	2757	48.0	3098
Reloder 15	44.0	2784	48.0	3093
IMR 3031	42.0	2760	46.0	3084
Viht. N140	43.5	2723	47.5	3042
AA 2700*	47.0	2721	51.0C	3023
H380*	46.0	2654	50.0C	2949
IMR 4320	43.0	2603	47.0	2941
BL-C(2)*	41.0	2601	45.0	2923
H4895	40.5	2660	44.5	2907
IMR 4895	40.0	2585	44.0	2905

*Maximum Loads should be used with CAUTION • C = Compressed Load • *Magnum Primer used with this powder.*

7mm Mauser (7x57mm)

0.284"	7mm HP
Weight, grains	115
Ballistic Coefficient	0.250
Sectional Density	0.204
COAL Tested:	2.890"
Speer Part No.	1617

	START CHARGE		MAXIMUM CHARGE	
Propellant	Weight, grs	Muzzle Velocity, ft/sec	Weight, grs	Muzzle Velocity, ft/sec
760*	49.0	2770	53.0C	3095
H414*	49.0	2732	53.0C	3053
IMR 4064	43.0	2691	47.0	3041
Reloder 15	43.0	2722	47.0	3024
IMR 3031	41.0	2666	45.0	2996
Viht. N140	42.0	2692	46.0	2975
AA 2700*	47.0	2651	51.0C	2946
H380*	46.0	2653	50.0C	2931
IMR 4350	47.0	2630	51.0C	2913
IMR 4320	42.0	2568	46.0	2902
Reloder 19	50.0	2591	54.0C	2879
H4350	47.0	2560	51.0C	2844
IMR 4895	39.0	2593	43.0	2828

Stan Eccles, Technical Coordinator, Centerfire Ammo Production, CCI/Speer Operations; 30-06, 180-grain Mag-Tip®, Idaho Public Lands 7x7 bull elk.

0.284"	7mm Spitz SP	7mm Spitz BTSP
Weight, grains	130	130
Ballistic Coefficient	0.368	0.424
Sectional Density	0.230	0.230
COAL Tested:	2.800"	2.800"
Speer Part No.	1623	1624

Propellant	START CHARGE		MAXIMUM CHARGE	
	Weight, grs	Muzzle Velocity, ft/sec	Weight, grs	Muzzle Velocity, ft/sec
H414*	46.0	2649	50.0C	2960
760*	46.0	2627	50.0C	2952
Reloder 15	41.0	2624	45.0	2913
AA 4350	47.0	2595	51.0C	2899
H4350	46.0	2630	50.0C	2890
IMR 4064	42.0	2555	46.0	2871
Reloder 22	49.0	2603	53.0C	2860
IMR 4350	46.0	2605	50.0C	2856
Reloder 19	48.0	2612	52.0C	2855
IMR 4320	41.0	2565	45.0	2850
IMR 3031	39.0	2495	43.0	2788
IMR 4895	38.0	2481	42.0	2772
Viht. N140	38.0	2489	42.0	2750
SR 4759 (reduced load)	18.0	1658	22.0	2004

*Maximum Loads should be used with CAUTION • C = Compressed Load • *Magnum Primer used with this powder.*

0.284"	140 TBBC SP
Weight, grains	140
Ballistic Coefficient	0.360
Sectional Density	0.248
COAL Tested:	2.800"
Speer Part No.	1745

Propellant	START CHARGE		MAXIMUM CHARGE	
	Weight, grs	Muzzle Velocity, ft/sec	Weight, grs	Muzzle Velocity, ft/sec
AA 4350	46.0	2586	50.0C	2861
H4350	45.0	2595	49.0C	2843
760*	44.0	2523	48.0	2785
H414*	43.0	2522	47.0	2760
IMR 4831	45.0	2454	49.0C	2731
IMR 4350	43.0	2449	47.0C	2719
Reloder 19	45.0	2407	49.0C	2653

NOTE: *Trophy Bonded Bear Claw and Trophy Bonded Sledgehammer Solid bullets have unique ballistic behavior compared to conventional bullets. Loads for TBBC and TBSS bullets may not "track" with data for conventional bullets. Use TBBC and TBSS data ONLY for TBBC and TBSS bullets.*

Christine's first elk. She's the daughter of Darrell Lundgren, Machinist, CCI/Speer Operations; 7x57 Mauser, 175-grain Mag-Tip®; near Deary, Idaho.

0.284"	7mm Spitz BTSP	7mm Spitz SP	7mm Match BTHP	7mm GS SP
Weight, grains	145	145	145	145
Ballistic Coefficient	0.472	0.416	0.468	0.353
Sectional Density	0.257	0.257	0.257	0.257
COAL Tested:	2.800"	2.800"	3.000"	2.970"
Speer Part No.	1628	1629	1631	1632

Propellant	START CHARGE Weight, grs	START CHARGE Muzzle Velocity, ft/sec	MAXIMUM CHARGE Weight, grs	MAXIMUM CHARGE Muzzle Velocity, ft/sec
Reloder 19	48.0	2543	52.0C	2795
H4350	46.0	2520	50.0C	2784
AA 4350	47.0	2481	51.0C	2757
H414*	44.0	2501	48.0C	2748
IMR 4831	47.0	2512	51.0C	2745
760*	44.0	2482	48.0C	2710
IMR 4350	45.0	2469	49.0C	2727
Reloder 22	47.0	2442	51.0C	2684
IMR 4064	39.0	2398	43.0	2679
Viht. N160	44.0	2425	48.0C	2665
Reloder 15	38.0	2325	42.0	2598
IMR 4895	36.0	2336	40.0	2565
SR 4759 (reduced load)	18.0	1517	22.0	1842

*Maximum Loads should be used with CAUTION • C = Compressed Load • *Magnum Primer used with this powder.*

0.284"	7mm Spitz BTSP	7mm Spitz SP	7mm MT SP	7mm GS SP
Weight, grains	160	160	160	160
Ballistic Coefficient	0.519	0.504	0.340	0.389
Sectional Density	0.284	0.284	0.284	0.284
COAL Tested:	3.000"	3.000"	2.960"	2.960"
Speer Part No.	1634	1635	1637	1638

Propellant	START CHARGE Weight, grs	START CHARGE Muzzle Velocity, ft/sec	MAXIMUM CHARGE Weight, grs	MAXIMUM CHARGE Muzzle Velocity, ft/sec
760*	42.0	2371	46.0	2605
H414*	42.0	2363	46.0	2582
IMR 4064	38.0	2263	42.0	2573
Reloder 19	45.0	2311	49.0C	2570
IMR 4831	44.0	2281	48.0C	2548
AA 4350	43.0	2255	47.0C	2520
IMR 4350	42.0	2262	46.0C	2515
Reloder 22	45.0	2237	49.0C	2514
H4350	42.0	2252	46.0C	2502
IMR 4895	35.0	2196	39.0	2467
IMR 4320	36.0	2142	40.0	2420
AA 3100	42.0	2145	47.0C	2397
IMR 4198 (reduced load)	21.0	1651	25.0	1942

Paul Westlund, Chief Reloading Manual Ballistician, Federal Premium®; 7x57 Mauser, Federal Premium ammo; mule deer, Wyoming. Paul loaded and tested half the ammunition fired in creating Speer Manual 14.

0.284"	7mm TBBC SP
Weight, grains	160
Ballistic Coefficient	0.380
Sectional Density	0.283
COAL Tested:	2.970"
Speer Part No.	1750

	START CHARGE		MAXIMUM CHARGE	
Propellant	Weight, grs	Muzzle Velocity, ft/sec	Weight, grs	Muzzle Velocity, ft/sec
AA 4350	42.0	2310	46.0C	2623
760*	41.0	2344	45.0	2593
H414*	40.0	2342	44.0	2585
IMR 4831	43.0	2315	47.0C	2584
H4350	41.0	2354	45.0C	2580
IMR 4350	41.0	2200	46.0C	2570
Reloder 22	46.0C	2405	48.0C	2538
IMR 4064	36.0	2281	40.0	2527
Reloder 19	43.0	2245	47.0C	2518

NOTE: *Trophy Bonded Bear Claw and Trophy Bonded Sledgehammer Solid bullets have unique ballistic behavior compared to conventional bullets. Loads for TBBC and TBSS bullets may not "track" with data for conventional bullets. Use TBBC and TBSS data ONLY for TBBC and TBSS bullets.*

*Maximum Loads should be used with CAUTION • C = Compressed Load • *Magnum Primer used with this powder.*

7mm Mauser (7x57mm)

0.284"	7mm MT SP	7mm GS SP
Weight, grains	175	175
Ballistic Coefficient	0.382	0.436
Sectional Density	0.310	0.310
COAL Tested:	3.015"	2.995"
Speer Part No.	1641	1643

Propellant	START CHARGE		MAXIMUM CHARGE	
	Weight, grs	Muzzle Velocity, ft/sec	Weight, grs	Muzzle Velocity, ft/sec
Reloder 22	47.0	2362	51.0C	2596
IMR 7828*	46.0	2266	50.0C	2518
Reloder 19	44.0	2265	48.0C	2503
IMR 4831	43.0	2211	47.0	2443
760*	40.0	2234	44.0	2442
IMR 4350	41.0	2214	45.0	2433
H4350	41.0	2188	45.0	2418
H414*	40.0	2163	44.0	2403
AA 3100	44.0	2195	48.0C	2399
IMR 4064	36.0	2128	40.0	2378
AA 4350	41.0	2138	45.0C	2339
Reloder 15	34.0	2042	38.0	2282
IMR 4198 (reduced load)	22.0	1633	26.0	1915

*Maximum Loads should be used with CAUTION • C = Compressed Load • *Magnum Primer used with this powder.*

280 Remington *(7mm Remington Express)*

The 280 Remington was introduced in 1957 in the model 740 semi-automatic rifle. It was nearly identical to the European 7x64mm and the wildcat 7mm/06, both excellent cartridges. The 280 Remington delivered all the performance of the 270 Winchester with added flexibility in handling a wider range of bullet weights.

A short time later, Remington added the 280 to its Model 721 and 725 bolt-action rifles and the slide-action Model 760. In spite of the excellent performance of this cartridge, it wasn't an immediate success. Apparently, the 270 had too much head start. Remington ultimately discontinued the 280 in its bolt guns, leaving the autoloader model 742 as the only rifle chambered for the 280.

In 1979, Remington reintroduced the 280 in the Model 700 bolt action, renaming it the 7mm Remington Express. Some confusion arose between the new name and the 7mm Remington Magnum so the designation reverted back to the 280 Remington. The 280 is still available in the Remington Model 700. Ruger and Browning also catalog rifles chambered for this cartridge.

The 280 is one of the finest hunting cartridges around, capable of taking any North American game with the exception of the great bears. For the handloader, it comes closer to qualifying as the "all-around cartridge" than the 270 Winchester because of excellent bullet selection. The popularity of the 7mm Remington Magnum has surely taken away interest from the 280 because shooters traditionally have been attracted to the "magnum" concept. However, the performance of the 280 isn't all that far from the 7mm Magnum and it uses significantly less powder. If you own a good 280, there's little practical advantage in trading up to any of the 7mm Magnums.

To prevent 280 ammunition from being accidentally chambered in 270 Winchester rifles, the 280 case shoulder is positioned about .050" forward. This is the major difference between the 280 and the wildcat 7mm/06 or the 7x64mm cartridges.

The 280 case is large enough to use the full range of 28-caliber Trophy Bonded Bear Claw bullets. These are the best choice for large game when deep penetration must accompany full expansion. With Speer's 110-grain TNT or 115-grain hollow points, the 280 is an excellent, long-range varmint cartridge. The three weights of Grand Slam bullets allow the 280 to take almost any species of thin-skinned game.

When loading for semi-automatic and slide-action rifles, use the starting loads shown here. These actions lack the camming power of a manually operated bolt action, and may experience extraction problems with maximum loads which function fine in bolt-action rifles.

The industry maximum average pressure for the 280 Remington is 60,000 psi; these loads remain safely within that maximum.

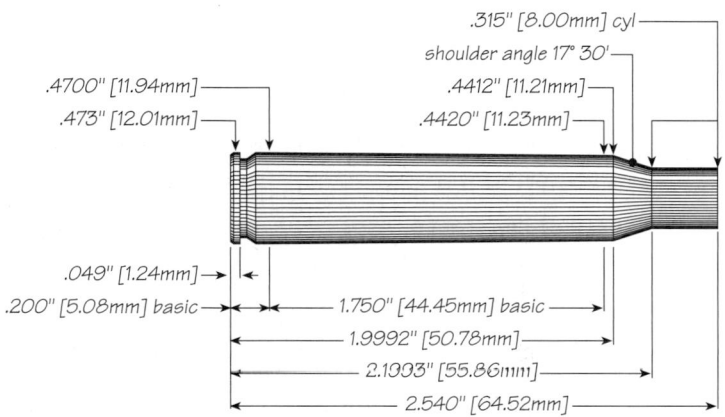

Max. Case Length:	2.540"	Cart. Case:	Remington
Trim-to Length:	2.530"	Primer:	CCI 200; 250*
Max Cart. OAL:	3.330"	Test Firearm:	Ruger M77 MkII
RCBS Shell Holder:	#3	Barrel Length:	24"

0.284"	7mm TNT HP	7mm HP
Weight, grains	110	115
Ballistic Coefficient	0.384	0.250
Sectional Density	0.195	0.204
COAL Tested:	3.300"	3.200"
Speer Part No.	1616	1617

	START CHARGE		MAXIMUM CHARGE	
Propellant	Weight, grs	Muzzle Velocity, ft/sec	Weight, grs	Muzzle Velocity, ft/sec
Reloder 19	59.0	2991	63.0C	3286
H4350	55.0	2963	59.0	3261
IMR 4831	60.0	3117	62.0C	3237
IMR 4350	55.0	2912	59.0	3215
IMR 4064	47.0	2950	51.0	3196
760*	53.0	2971	57.0	3190
AA 4350	56.0	2872	60.0	3187
AA 3100	60.0	3043	62.0C	3143
IMR 4895	45.0	2883	49.0	3133
Varget	45.0	2773	49.0	3026
IMR 3031	44.0	2814	48.0	3061

*Maximum Loads should be used with CAUTION • C = Compressed Load • *Magnum Primer used with this powder.*

0.284"	7mm Spitz SP	7mm Spitz BTSP
Weight, grains	130	130
Ballistic Coefficient	0.368	0.424
Sectional Density	0.230	0.230
COAL Tested:	3.205"	3.205"
Speer Part No.	1623	1624

Propellant	START CHARGE		MAXIMUM CHARGE	
	Weight, grs	Muzzle Velocity, ft/sec	Weight, grs	Muzzle Velocity, ft/sec
Reloder 19	55.0	2835	59.0	3134
IMR 4831	53.0	2828	57.0	3108
IMR 4350	53.0	2773	57.0	3106
H4350	50.0	2827	54.0	3073
AA 4350	53.0	2791	57.0	3066
H414*	48.5	2844	52.5	2993
H4831SC	53.5	2783	57.5	2993
Viht. N160	50.0	2794	54.0	2977
760*	48.5	2801	52.5	2975
AA 3100	54.0	2721	58.0	2972
IMR 4895	42.0	2790	46.0	2969
Reloder 15	43.0	2774	47.0	2967
IMR 4064	43.0	2729	47.0	2958
IMR 4320	43.0	2743	47.0	2946
SR 4759 (reduced load)	20.0	1680	24.0	2024

0.284"	140 TBBC SP
Weight, grains	140
Ballistic Coefficient	0.360
Sectional Density	0.248
COAL Tested:	3.200"
Speer Part No.	1745

| Propellant | START CHARGE | | MAXIMUM CHARGE | |
	Weight, grs	Muzzle Velocity, ft/sec	Weight, grs	Muzzle Velocity, ft/sec
H4530	53.5	2880	55.5	2976
Reloder 19	57.0	2852	59.0C	2962
IMR 4831	55.0	2838	57.0C	2954
Viht. N160	55.0	2827	57.0C	2917
AA 3100	56.0	2753	58.0C	2875

NOTE: *Trophy Bonded Bear Claw and Trophy Bonded Sledgehammer Solid bullets have unique ballistic behavior compared to conventional bullets. Loads for TBBC and TBSS bullets may not "track" with data for conventional bullets. Use TBBC and TBSS data ONLY for TBBC and TBSS bullets.*

David Nau, General Manager, ATK Onalaska Operations; 280 Remington, Federal Premium ammo; pronghorn, New Mexico.

*Maximum Loads should be used with CAUTION • C = Compressed Load • *Magnum Primer used with this powder.*

0.284"	7mm Spitz BTSP	7mm Spitz SP	7mm Match BTHP	7mm GS SP
Weight, grains	145	145	145	145
Ballistic Coefficient	0.472	0.416	0.468	0.353
Sectional Density	0.257	0.257	0.257	0.257
COAL Tested:	3.180"	3.160"	3.280"	3.275"
Speer Part No.	1628	1629	1631	1632

	START CHARGE		MAXIMUM CHARGE	
Propellant	Weight, grs	Muzzle Velocity, ft/sec	Weight, grs	Muzzle Velocity, ft/sec
IMR 4831	54.0	2815	56.0	2975
Reloder 19	55.0	2752	57.0	2973
H4350	50.5	2779	52.5	2950
IMR 4350	51.0	2697	55.0	2949
Reloder 22	54.0	2621	58.0C	2880
AA 4350	50.0	2650	54.0	2879
H4831SC	54.0	2798	56.0	2861
IMR 4064	42.0	2609	46.0	2818
AA 3100	54.0	2726	56.0	2806
H414*	48.0	2681	50.0	2789
Viht. N160	48.0	2573	52.0	2777
760*	47.5	2692	49.5	2776
IMR 7828	56.0	2621	58.0C	2767
Varget	42.0	2517	46.0	2734
SR 4759 (reduced load)	21.0	1689	25.0	2012

0.284"	7mm Spitz BTSP	7mm Spitz SP	7mm MT SP	7mm GS SP
Weight, grains	160	160	160	160
Ballistic Coefficient	0.519	0.504	0.340	0.389
Sectional Density	0.283	0.283	0.283	0.283
COAL Tested:	3.200"	3.200"	3.265"	3.265"
Speer Part No.	1634	1635	1637	1638

Propellant	START CHARGE		MAXIMUM CHARGE	
	Weight, grs	Muzzle Velocity, ft/sec	Weight, grs	Muzzle Velocity, ft/sec
AA 4350	50.0	2691	52.0	2854
H4350	47.0	2571	51.0	2828
Reloder 19	53.0	2658	55.0	2813
IMR 4831	52.0	2686	54.0	2808
Reloder 22	54.0	2707	56.0	2807
IMR 4350	49.0	2522	53.0	2701
H4831SC	53.0	2697	55.0	2773
IMR 7828	55.0	2654	57.0	2743
AA 3100	53.0	2637	55.0C	2725
IMR 4064	41.0	2492	45.0	2677
H414*	44.0	2468	48.0	2631
IMR 4895	39.0	2412	43.0	2624
SR 4759 (reduced load)	22.0	1711	26.0	2008

*Maximum Loads should be used with CAUTION • C = Compressed Load • *Magnum Primer used with this powder.*

0.284"	7mm TBBC SP
Weight, grains	160
Ballistic Coefficient	0.380
Sectional Density	0.283
COAL Tested:	3.260"
Speer Part No.	1750

Propellant	START CHARGE		MAXIMUM CHARGE	
	Weight, grs	Muzzle Velocity, ft/sec	Weight, grs	Muzzle Velocity, ft/sec
IMR 7828	56.0	2720	58.0C	2819
IMR 4831	53.0	2703	55.0C	2809
Reloder 22	55.0	2712	57.0C	2808
Reloder 19	54.0	2688	56.0C	2789
AA 4350	51.0	2680	53.0	2782
H4831SC	55.0	2672	57.0C	2758
H4350	50.0	2662	52.0	2757
IMR 4350	50.0	2631	52.0	2753

NOTE: *Trophy Bonded Bear Claw and Trophy Bonded Sledgehammer Solid bullets have unique ballistic behavior compared to conventional bullets. Loads for TBBC and TBSS bullets may not "track" with data for conventional bullets. Use TBBC and TBSS data ONLY for TBBC and TBSS bullets.*

Cody Lundgren, son of Darrell Lundgren, Machinist, CCI/Speer Operations; 30-06, 180-grain Mag-Tip® bullet; whitetail deer taken near Deary, Idaho.

0.284"	7mm MT SP	7mm GS SP
Weight, grains	175	175
Ballistic Coefficient	0.382	0.436
Sectional Density	0.310	0.310
COAL Tested:	3.320"	3.330"
Speer Part No.	1641	1643

	START CHARGE		MAXIMUM CHARGE	
Propellant	Weight, grs	Muzzle Velocity, ft/sec	Weight, grs	Muzzle Velocity, ft/sec
Viht. N560	50.0	2567	52.0	2644
Reloder 22	51.0	2520	53.0	2616
H1000	53.0	2434	57.0C	2615
Reloder 19	48.0	2420	52.0	2597
IMR 4350	45.0	2338	49.0	2578
IMR 4831	48.0	2479	50.0	2570
IMR 7828	51.0	2465	53.0	2568
H4831C	50.0	2454	52.0	2558
H4350	43.0	2388	47.0	2555
AA 3100	49.0	2416	51.0	2520
H414*	44.0	2401	46.0	2461
760*	44.0	2370	46.0	2452
SR 4759 (reduced load)	21.0	1490	25.0	1753

*Maximum Loads should be used with CAUTION • C = Compressed Load • *Magnum Primer used with this powder.*

0.284"	7mm TBBC SP
Weight, grains	175
Ballistic Coefficient	0.400
Sectional Density	0.310
COAL Tested:	3.320"
Speer Part No.	1755

Propellant	START CHARGE		MAXIMUM CHARGE	
	Weight, grs	Muzzle Velocity, ft/sec	Weight, grs	Muzzle Velocity, ft/sec
IMR 7828	53.0	2533	55.0C	2640
Reloder 19	51.0	2521	53.0C	2621
IMR 4831	50.0	2520	52.0	2620
H4831SC	52.0	2511	54.0C	2602
Reloder 22	51.0	2504	53.0C	2600
H4350	47.0	2475	49.0	2575
IMR 4350	48.0	2480	50.0	2573
AA 4350	47.0	2460	49.0	2555

NOTE: *Trophy Bonded Bear Claw and Trophy Bonded Sledgehammer Solid bullets have unique ballistic behavior compared to conventional bullets. Loads for TBBC and TBSS bullets may not "track" with data for conventional bullets. Use TBBC and TBSS data ONLY for TBBC and TBSS bullets.*

*Maximum Loads should be used with CAUTION • C = Compressed Load • *Magnum Primer used with this powder.*

284 Winchester

Introduced in 1963, the 284 Winchester was long considered an "unusual cartridge" because of its rebated rim case. Today it would be a "short magnum." It was conceived as a compact cartridge that would give the performance of a 270 Winchester or 280 Remington but be better suited for lever-action and semi-automatic rifles. The cartridge was chambered in Winchester's Model 88 lever rifle and Model 100 autoloader. The Savage Model 99 lever-action was also made in 284 for a time.

The case is classed as rebated rimless. The rim diameter is the same as the 30-06 but the short body is .030" larger to preserve powder capacity. This is precisely the evolutionary path of the current popular "short magnums" that appeared starting in 2001. Although the case capacity of the 284 is similar to that of the 270 and 280, the short cartridge overall length requires that proper seating of heavy bullets can reduce effective capacity. Still the 284 manages to challenge the velocities of the longer 280 Remington with most bullet weights. Custom bolt-actions rifles with the proper throating could take better advantage of the cartridge's powder capacity.

Winchester never chambered any bolt-action rifles in this caliber. Ruger once offered their M77 bolt guns in 284 but, at press time, no major U.S. gun makers catalog the cartridge. The Winchester and Remington 7mm Short Magnums better fill the 284's old niche. With big game bullets over 130 grains, even the 7mm-08 Remington approaches the 284's performance with a standard case and less powder. Therefore, it appears that the 284 Winchester is headed for the retirement home. To its credit, the 284 case has spawned a number of excellent wildcat cartridges like the 6.5/284.

When loading for semi-auto and lever-action rifles, reduce maximum loads by at least two grains to avoid extraction problems. The following loads do not exceed the industry maximum average pressure of 54,000 CUP, an unusually high assignment for a cartridge conceived for rifles other than bolt-actions.

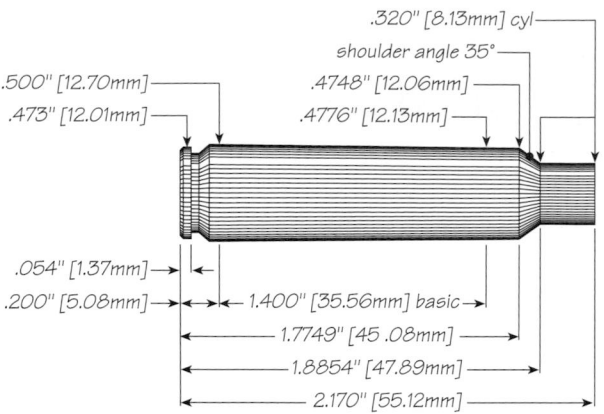

.320" [8.13mm] cyl
shoulder angle 35°
.500" [12.70mm]
.473" [12.01mm]
.4748" [12.06mm]
.4776" [12.13mm]
.054" [1.37mm]
.200" [5.08mm]
1.400" [35.56mm] basic
1.7749" [45.08mm]
1.8854" [47.89mm]
2.170" [55.12mm]

Max. Case Length:	2.170"	Cart. Case:	Winchester
Trim-to Length:	2.160"	Primer:	CCI 200; 250*
Max Cart. OAL:	2.800"	Test Firearm:	Ruger Model 77
RCBS Shell Holder:	#3	Barrel Length:	22"

*Eric Pedersen
ATK Southwest Regional
Law Enforcement
Specialist; 338 Federal;
elk taken in Idaho.*

0.284"	7mm TNT HP
Weight, grains	110
Ballistic Coefficient	0.384
Sectional Density	0.195
COAL Tested:	2.780"
Speer Part No.	1616

| Propellant | START CHARGE | | MAXIMUM CHARGE | |
	Weight, grs	Muzzle Velocity, ft/sec	Weight, grs	Muzzle Velocity, ft/sec
760*	58.0	3207	62.0C	3438
Reloder 15	53.0	3136	57.0	3384
AA 2460*	48.0	3075	52.0	3354
748*	53.0	3087	57.0	3352
BL-C(2)*	52.0	3074	56.0	3345
H414*	57.0	3107	61.0C	3341
Viht. N135	48.0	3003	52.0	3282
IMR 4350	56.0	3001	60.0C	3220
IMR 4831	58.0	2973	62.0C	3200
Reloder 19	58.0	2934	62.0C	3159
H4350	55.0	2879	59.0C	3090
AA 4350	55.0	2860	59.0C	3069

*Maximum Loads should be used with CAUTION • C = Compressed Load • *Magnum Primer used with this powder.*

0.284"	7mm HP
Weight, grains	115
Ballistic Coefficient	0.250
Sectional Density	0.204
COAL Tested:	2.770"
Speer Part No.	1617

Propellant	START CHARGE		MAXIMUM CHARGE	
	Weight, grs	Muzzle Velocity, ft/sec	Weight, grs	Muzzle Velocity, ft/sec
IMR 4350	55.0	2952	59.0	3167
IMR 4831	56.0	2919	60.0	3143
760*	53.0	2914	57.0	3122
IMR 4064	46.0	2751	50.0	2992
748*	47.0	2716	51.0	2950
IMR 4320	46.0	2697	50.0	2910

0.284"	7mm Spitz SP	7mm Spitz BTSP
Weight, grains	130	130
Ballistic Coefficient	0.368	0.424
Sectional Density	0.230	0.230
COAL Tested:	2.800"	2.800"
Speer Part No.	1623	1624

Propellant	START CHARGE		MAXIMUM CHARGE	
	Weight, grs	Muzzle Velocity, ft/sec	Weight, grs	Muzzle Velocity, ft/sec
IMR 4350	54.0	2893	58.0	3100
IMR 4831	55.0	2846	59.0	3039
760*	52.0	2779	56.0	3003
748*	46.0	2661	50.0	2895
IMR 4064	45.0	2606	49.0	2841
SR 4759 (reduced load)	20.0	1694	24.0	2029

0.284"	7mm Spitz BTSP	7mm Spitz SP	7mm GS SP
Weight, grains	145	145	145
Ballistic Coefficient	0.472	0.416	0.353
Sectional Density	0.257	0.257	0.257
COAL Tested:	2.800"	2.800"	2.800"
Speer Part No.	1628	1629	1632

	START CHARGE		MAXIMUM CHARGE	
Propellant	Weight, grs	Muzzle Velocity, ft/sec	Weight, grs	Muzzle Velocity, ft/sec
IMR 4350	52.0	2744	56.0	2940
IMR 4831	53.0	2720	57.0	2907
IMR 4895	44.0	2601	48.0	2862
760*	50.0	2629	54.0	2846
IMR 4064	43.0	2488	47.0	2712
SR 4759 (reduced load)	21.0	1666	25.0	1000

*Maximum Loads should be used with CAUTION • C = Compressed Load • *Magnum Primer used with this powder.*

0.284"	7mm Spitz BTSP	7mm Spitz SP	7mm MT SP	7mm GS SP
Weight, grains	160	160	160	160
Ballistic Coefficient	0.519	0.504	0.340	0.389
Sectional Density	0.283	0.283	0.283	0.283
COAL Tested:	2.800"	2.800"	2.800"	2.800"
Speer Part No.	1634	1635	1637	1638

Propellant	START CHARGE		MAXIMUM CHARGE	
	Weight, grs	Muzzle Velocity, ft/sec	Weight, grs	Muzzle Velocity, ft/sec
IMR 4350	50.0	2587	54.0C	2808
IMR 4831	51.0	2580	55.0C	2765
760*	48.0	2479	52.0	2703
IMR 4064	41.0	2372	45.0	2610
748*	42.0	2388	46.0	2610
IMR 4198 (reduced load)	23.0	1674	27.0	1968

Ernest Durham, CCI/Speer Ammunition Engineer and wife Roxanna enjoying quality time at the range.

0.284"	7mm MT SP	7mm GS SP
Weight, grains	175	175
Ballistic Coefficient	0.382	0.436
Sectional Density	0.310	0.310
COAL Tested:	2.800"	2.800"
Speer Part No.	1641	1643

| Propellant | START CHARGE | | MAXIMUM CHARGE | |
	Weight, grs	Muzzle Velocity, ft/sec	Weight, grs	Muzzle Velocity, ft/sec
IMR 4831	49.0	2451	53.0C	2638
IMR 4350	48.0	2427	52.0C	2618
760*	45.0	2274	49.0	2493
IMR 4064	38.5	2169	42.5	2392
IMR 4320	38.0	2093	42.0	2314
IMR 4198 (reduced load)	24.0	1000	20.0	1040

*Maximum Loads should be used with CAUTION • C = Compressed Load • *Magnum Primer used with this powder.*

7mm Remington Short Action Ultra Magnum

Remington answered the 7mm Winchester Short Magnum with the 7mm Remington Short Action Ultra Magnum in 2002. As with the 30-caliber short magnums from each manufacturer, the Remington version has slightly less case capacity than the Winchester due to a shorter body and a less abrupt shoulder angle.

However, that's strictly theory. We see the Remington version as equal to the 7mm Winchester in every bullet weight. There is simply no significant ballistic difference between the two in our test barrels. The choice comes down to "intangibles," those matters of customer preference that keep Ford and Chevy competing and make Marketing departments necessary. Intangibles include choice of rifle brand, propellant consumption, and ease of reloading.

What does this mean? One rifle may have features that you can't find in another. The fact that one is a WSM and the other is a RSAUM makes no practical difference in field ballistics. The Remington version uses less powder (typically 2 to 5 grains) to accomplish the same velocities. This could add up for a high-volume shooter. The Remington has a longer neck than the WSM version; to many reloaders, that is an advantage.

The 140-grain Trophy Bonded˚ Bear Claw˚ SP bullet is an excellent all-around bullet for premium performance in this cartridge. It should be adequate for any North American game with the exception of the dangerous bear species. Do not attempt to compare data for the TBBC to other bullet types. The unique construction on the TBBC means that it may use the same powder charge as a lighter bullet of conventional design.

The 115-grain Speer hollow point is a varmint bullet that is useful for extending your time afield with your big game rifle. The hollow point can achieve nearly 3500 ft/sec in this cartridge. The 130-grain Hot-Cor and boat tail bullets are of light construction and, in this cartridge, should be limited to long shots on large varmints or the smaller deer species. The 145-grain bullets—the Grand Slam, Hot-Cor, and boat tail—are excellent for medium deer species.

These loads remain within the 65,000 psi pressure limit established for this cartridge.

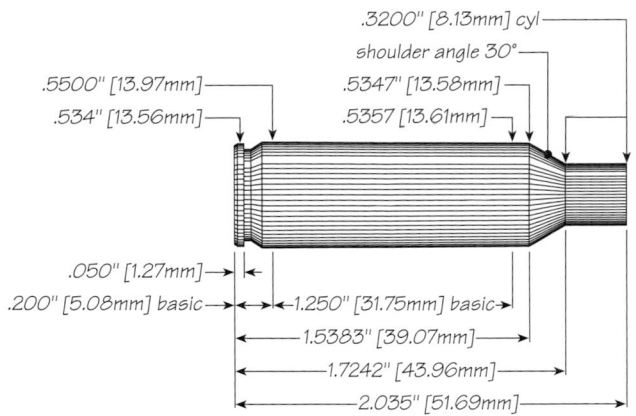

Max. Case Length:	2.035"	Cart. Case:	Remington
Trim-to Length:	2.025"	Primer:	CCI 200; 250*
Max Cart. OAL:	2.825"	Test Firearm:	Universal Receiver
RCBS Shell Holder:	#38	Barrel Length:	Krieger 24"

0.284"	7mm TNT HP	7mm HP
Weight, grains	110	115
Ballistic Coefficient	0.384	0.250
Sectional Density	0.195	0.204
COAL Tested:	2.710"	2.680"
Speer Part No.	1616	1617

	START CHARGE		MAXIMUM CHARGE	
Propellant	Weight, grs	Muzzle Velocity, ft/sec	Weight, grs	Muzzle Velocity, ft/sec
AA 4350	64.0	3283	68.0C	3487
760*	62.0	3265	66.0	3458
IMR 4350	62.0	3223	66.0	3451
Reloder 19	66.0	3224	70.0C	3419
H414*	61.0	3188	65.0	3416
Big Game*	59.0	3230	63.0	3401
Reloder 15	55.0	3194	59.0	3387
Varget	54.0	3182	58.0	3384
IMR 4895	53.0	3153	57.0	3374

*Maximum Loads should be used with CAUTION • C = Compressed Load • *Magnum Primer used with this powder.*

0.284"	7mm Spitz SP	7mm Spitz BTSP
Weight, grains	130	130
Ballistic Coefficient	0.368	0.424
Sectional Density	0.230	0.230
COAL Tested:	2.785"	2.785"
Speer Part No.	1623	1624

Propellant	START CHARGE		MAXIMUM CHARGE	
	Weight, grs	Muzzle Velocity, ft/sec	Weight, grs	Muzzle Velocity, ft/sec
IMR 4831	58.0	3042	62.0	3231
Reloder 19	61.0	3051	65.0	3229
Viht. N165	62.0	3106	66.0C	3229
Reloder 22	61.0	3051	65.0	3214
760*	56.0	3032	60.0	3186
IMR 4350	55.0	3003	59.0	3173
H4831SC	59.0	2952	63.0	3112
Reloder 15	48.0	2924	52.0	3085

Hal Price, ATK LE Sales Specialist; 375 H&H; blackbuck.

0.284"	7mm TBBC SP
Weight, grains	140
Ballistic Coefficient	0.360
Sectional Density	0.248
COAL Tested:	2.840"
Speer Part No.	1745

Propellant	START CHARGE		MAXIMUM CHARGE	
	Weight, grs	Muzzle Velocity, ft/sec	Weight, grs	Muzzle Velocity, ft/sec
IMR 4831	58.0	2959	62.0	3138
Reloder 22	60.0	2941	64.0	3117
AA 3100	60.0	2919	64.0	3096
Reloder 19	59.0	2928	63.0	3094
H4350	53.0	2849	57.0	3054
IMR 4350	54.0	2860	58.0	3062
H4831SC	58.0	2854	62.0	3050

NOTE: *Trophy Bonded Bear Claw and Trophy Bonded Sledgehammer Solid bullets have unique ballistic behavior compared to conventional bullets. Loads for TBBC and TBSS bullets may not "track" with data for conventional bullets. Use TBBC and TBSS data ONLY for TBBC and TBSS bullets.*

*Maximum Loads should be used with CAUTION • C = Compressed Load • *Magnum Primer used with this powder.*

0.284"	7mm Spitz BTSP	7mm Spitz SP	7mm Match BTHP	7mm GS SP
Weight, grains	145	145	145	145
Ballistic Coefficient	0.472	0.257	0.468	0.353
Sectional Density	0.257	0.257	0.257	0.257
COAL Tested:	2.785"	2.785"	2.800"	2.750"
Speer Part No.	1628	1629	1631	1632

Propellant	START CHARGE		MAXIMUM CHARGE	
	Weight, grs	Muzzle Velocity, ft/sec	Weight, grs	Muzzle Velocity, ft/sec
Viht. N560	59.0	2876	63.0	3085
Reloder 22	59.0	2901	63.0	3061
IMR 4831	56.0	2872	60.0	3051
Reloder 19	58.0	2869	62.0	3040
IMR 4350	53.0	2816	57.0	3006
760*	54.0	2831	58.0	3004
H4831SC	57.0	2830	61.0	2984
H4350	52.0	2806	56.0	2981
AA 5744 (reduced load)	26.0	1914	28.0	2045

0.284"	7mm Spitz BTSP	7mm Spitz SP	7mm MT SP	7mm GS SP
Weight, grains	160	160	160	160
Ballistic Coefficient	0.519	0.504	0.340	0.389
Sectional Density	0.283	0.283	0.283	0.283
COAL Tested:	2.800"	2.800"	2.765"	2.785"
Speer Part No.	1634	1635	1637	1638

Propellant	START CHARGE		MAXIMUM CHARGE	
	Weight, grs	Muzzle Velocity, ft/sec	Weight, grs	Muzzle Velocity, ft/sec
Reloder 25	62.0	2836	66.0C	3024
IMR 7828	59.0	2794	63.0	2990
Reloder 22	57.0	2783	61.0	2930
IMR 4350	53.0	2731	57.0	2922
IMR 4831	54.0	2706	58.0	2913
Reloder 19	56.0	2774	60.0	2913
AA 3100	57.0	2730	61.0	2908
H4831SC	57.0	2717	61.0	2900

*Maximum Loads should be used with CAUTION • C = Compressed Load • *Magnum Primer used with this powder.*

7mm Winchester Short Magnum

The 7mm Winchester Short Magnum is another in Winchester's successful series of short magnums, announced just after the 300 WSM in 2002. With the excellent selection of .284-inch bullets available, this was a logical step in Winchester's short magnum strategy.

The case is simply the 300 WSM case necked down with the shoulder origin moved forward at the expense of the neck. The fat case body gives the WSM a small capacity advantage over the 280 Remington. Performance of the 7mm WSM falls in the narrow velocity gap between the 280 Remington and the 7mm Remington Magnum. It also makes Winchester a strong player in the 7mm market that Remington has dominated for years. The niche for the 7mm WSM is the short-action bolt rifle. The older Remington cartridges require a standard length action. When building a light rifle, the option of the short action can save ¼ to ½ pounds depending on options.

The 7mm WSM can handle any game that the larger Remington cartridges can. For game at the top of the rifle's capabilities, there is no better bullet than the 140-grain Trophy Bonded Bear Claw soft point. Its penetration rivals that of heavier bullets, yet it can be loaded to significant velocities to keep the trajectory flat. Among standard bullets, the 160-grain Hot-Cor® is an excellent all-around choice, allowing muzzle velocities over 2900 ft/sec. Choose the 145-grain Hot-Cor for whitetail and game of similar size. The 130-grain bullets are of lighter construction and should be reserved for large varmints and pronghorn.

The 115-grain hollow point is included here to give you a varmint option. Although the 7mm WSM is not a varmint cartridge, it can be used on them with this bullet. It's a good idea to try a little varminting with your deer rifle to keep familiar. We also show low-recoil loads for the lighter bullets to allow user-friendly training of new shooters.

The 160 and 175-grain Bear Claws and the 175-grain Grand Slam and Mag-Tip bullets are very long and encroach on the 7mm WSM's propellant space. Therefore, we elected not to show loads for these heavy bullets. The velocity potential of the short magnums diminishes with the heaviest bullets.

Note that maximum loads for the 140-grain TBBC are often higher than for the 130 SP. This is not an error; it is because of the TBBC's rigid rear shank. We find most TBBC bullets do not follow the "usual load tracking" of bullets by weight due to their unique construction. Rigid solid-shank construction means Bear Claw upsets less at ignition than bullets with a full lead core when the initial pressure wave strikes, producing lower pressures. This characteristic often more than offsets the usual penalty of the additional bullet length.

These loads remain within the 65,000 psi pressure limit established for the 7mm WSM.

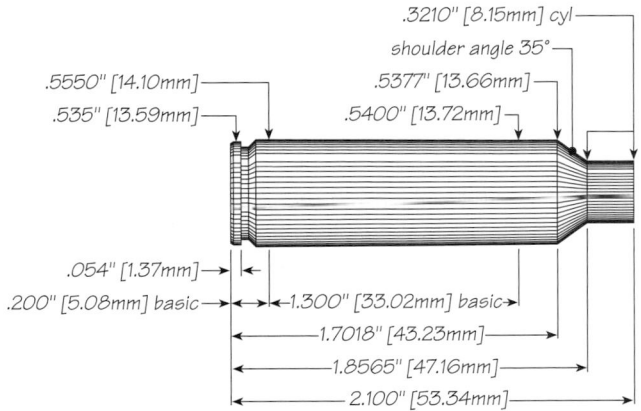

Max. Case Length:	2.100"	Cart. Case:	Winchester
Trim-to Length:	2.090"	Primer:	CCI 200; 250*
Max Cart. OAL:	2.860"	Test Firearm:	Universal Receiver
RCBS Shell Holder:	#43	Barrel Length:	Krieger 24"

0.284"	7mm TNT HP	7mm HP
Weight, grains	110	115
Ballistic Coefficient	0.384	0.250
Sectional Density	0.195	0.204
COAL Tested:	2.800"	2.770"
Speer Part No.	1616	1617

Propellant	START CHARGE		MAXIMUM CHARGE	
	Weight, grs	Muzzle Velocity, ft/sec	Weight, grs	Muzzle Velocity, ft/sec
760*	65.0	3260	69.0	3425
Reloder 19	68.0	3192	72.0	3392
IMR 4350	64.0	3185	68.0	3391
IMR 4064	56.0	3207	60.0	3385
H4831SC	70.0	3201	74.0	3376
H4350	63.0	3200	67.0	3363
Viht. N540	57.0	3167	61.0	3357
Reloder 15	55.0	3144	59.0	3312
AA 5744 (reduced load)	25.0	1975	27.0	2098

Valerie Snyder, wife of Kent Snyder, ATK LE Sales Specialist, with her first deer; 7mm Remington Magnum; whitetail buck taken in Idaho's Clearwater National Forest.

0.284"	7mm Spitz SP	7mm Spitz BTSP
Weight, grains	130	130
Ballistic Coefficient	0.368	0.424
Sectional Density	0.230	0.230
COAL Tested:	2.775"	2.775"
Speer Part No.	1623	1624

	START CHARGE		MAXIMUM CHARGE	
Propellant	Weight, grs	Muzzle Velocity, ft/sec	Weight, grs	Muzzle Velocity, ft/sec
Reloder 19	63.0	3077	67.0	3230
Reloder 22	63.0	3064	67.0	3228
IMR 4831	60.0	3062	64.0	3228
AA 3100	64.0	3044	68.0	3216
IMR 4350	58.0	3035	62.0	3204
H4350	56.0	3011	60.0	3172
H4831SC	61.0	3024	65.0	3151
Viht. N160	57.0	2995	61.0	3112
AA 5744 (reduced load)	26.0	1990	28.0	2084

*Maximum Loads should be used with CAUTION • C = Compressed Load • *Magnum Primer used with this powder.*

0.284"	7mm TBBC SP
Weight, grains	140
Ballistic Coefficient	0.360
Sectional Density	0.248
COAL Tested:	2.800"
Speer Part No.	1745

Propellant	START CHARGE		MAXIMUM CHARGE	
	Weight, grs	Muzzle Velocity, ft/sec	Weight, grs	Muzzle Velocity, ft/sec
Reloder 19	64.0	2984	68.0	3134
Reloder 22	64.0	3002	68.0	3132
IMR 4831	61.0	2970	65.0	3120
IMR 4350	59.0	2981	63.0	3092
AA 3100	64.0	2903	68.0	3073
H4831SC	62.0	2949	66.0	3045
H4350	56.0	2860	60.0	3036

NOTE: *Trophy Bonded Bear Claw and Trophy Bonded Sledgehammer Solid bullets have unique ballistic behavior compared to conventional bullets. Loads for TBBC and TBSS bullets may not "track" with data for conventional bullets. Use TBBC and TBSS data ONLY for TBBC and TBSS bullets.*

0.284"	7mm Spitz BTSP	7mm Spitz SP	7mm Match BTHP	7mm GS SP
Weight, grains	145	145	145	145
Ballistic Coefficient	0.472	0.416	0.468	0.353
Sectional Density	0.257	0.257	0.257	0.257
COAL Tested:	2.780"	2.780"	2.800"	2.745"
Speer Part No.	1628	1629	1631	1632

Propellant	START CHARGE		MAXIMUM CHARGE	
	Weight, grs	Muzzle Velocity, ft/sec	Weight, grs	Muzzle Velocity, ft/sec
Reloder 22	62.0	2927	66.0	3079
Reloder 19	61.0	2893	65.0	3063
AA 3100	62.0	2898	66.0	3052
IMR 4831	58.0	2878	62.0	3047
IMR 4350	56.0	2851	60.0	3027
H4350	54.0	2818	58.0	2990
H4831SC	59.0	2839	63.0	2986
Viht. N160	55.0	2814	59.0	2933
AA 5744 (reduced load)	28.0	1959	30.0	2084

*Maximum Loads should be used with CAUTION • C = Compressed Load • *Magnum Primer used with this powder.*

7mm Winchester Short Magnum

0.284"	7mm Spitz BTSP	7mm Spitz SP	7mm MT SP	7mm GS SP
Weight, grains	160	160	160	160
Ballistic Coefficient	0.519	0.504	0.340	0.389
Sectional Density	0.283	0.283	0.283	0.283
COAL Tested:	2.820"	2.820"	2.790"	2.800"
Speer Part No.	1634	1635	1637	1638

Propellant	START CHARGE		MAXIMUM CHARGE	
	Weight, grs	Muzzle Velocity, ft/sec	Weight, grs	Muzzle Velocity, ft/sec
Reloder 25	66.0	2963	70.0	3090
IMR 7828	61.0	2881	65.0	2958
Reloder 19	59.0	2797	63.0	2956
Reloder 22	59.0	2780	63.0	2936
IMR 4831	55.0	2677	59.0	2926
AA 3100	60.0	2763	64.0	2893
H4831SC	57.0	2692	61.0	2890
IMR 4350	53.0	2630	57.0	2866

*Maximum Loads should be used with CAUTION • C = Compressed Load • *Magnum Primer used with this powder.*

7mm Remington Magnum

This is one of the most successful magnum rifle cartridges ever developed. Prior to its introduction in 1962, there were a number of excellent 7mm proprietary, wildcat and foreign cartridges based on the 300 H&H Magnum belted case shortened enough to function in a 30-06 length action. Some notable and successful of these were the 7mm Weatherby Magnum, the 7mm Mashburn Magnum and the 7x61mm Sharpe & Hart.

The problem with these cartridges was that they were available only in expensive imported or custom rifles and often required that the owner be a handloader willing to form cases. Only the 7mm Weatherby was available in U.S. factory rifles.

Remington took the best features of the other 7mm cartridges and introduced their 7mm Remington Magnum in their popularly priced Model 700 bolt-action rifle. Shooters' acceptance was almost immediate. The excellent sectional density of 7mm bullets and the velocity potential of the cartridge combine to make a hard-hitting, flat-shooting cartridge that is deadly on most species of North American game. The 7mm Magnum has also proved effective on many African plains animals.

Many experienced hunters rightly feel any 7mm bore is too light for the great bears regardless of how much velocity can be generated. However, some people use the 7mm Magnum on the big bruins anyway, but we strongly suggest you look to a much heavier caliber for these animals.

The 7mm Remington Magnum is at its best when taking long shots on deer, sheep and elk. With 160 and 175-grain bullets, retained energy is high and accuracy is sufficient to insure hits at longer ranges. Speer recommends that the 145-grain and lighter bullets (with the exception of the 145-grain Grand Slam) be limited to game the size of antelope or smaller. The high velocity of the 7mm Magnum can cause light bullets to break up on tissue resulting in shallow penetration on larger deer. When shooting any high-velocity rifle cartridge, sacrificing a little velocity in favor of bullet weight means less destruction of useful meat.

The Trophy Bonded Bear Claw adds some top-end capability to the 7mm Remington Magnum, but does not quite put it into the dangerous game class. The high retained weight and large mushroom afforded by the TBBC design deliver a combination of shock and penetration that is not available in conventional bullets. Unique construction means that its internal ballistic behavior differs from other Speer bullets. Do not use data for other bullets when loading TBBC, or use TBBC data for loading other bullets. These unique characteristics also mean that the TBBC data will not "track" when comparing charge weights to other bullets across a range of weights.

There is quite a variation in published loading data for this caliber. Differences in cases, primers, and bullets all have an effect. This emphasizes our constant caution to always reduce loads whenever changing components from those used to develop the data.

Seldom will either handloads or factory ammunition match nominal factory ballistics in a sporting rifle and there is a great deal of velocity variation among sporters in this caliber. Rifles in the Speer lab's collection posted velocities varying from 400 ft/sec under to 300 ft/sec over those posted by the SAAMI pressure barrel with the same ammo. Because of this, we have departed from our usual policy of showing velocities from a sporter. The velocities for the 7mm Remington Magnum are from a 24-inch pressure barrel.

These loads stay within the industry pressure limit of 52,000 CUP.

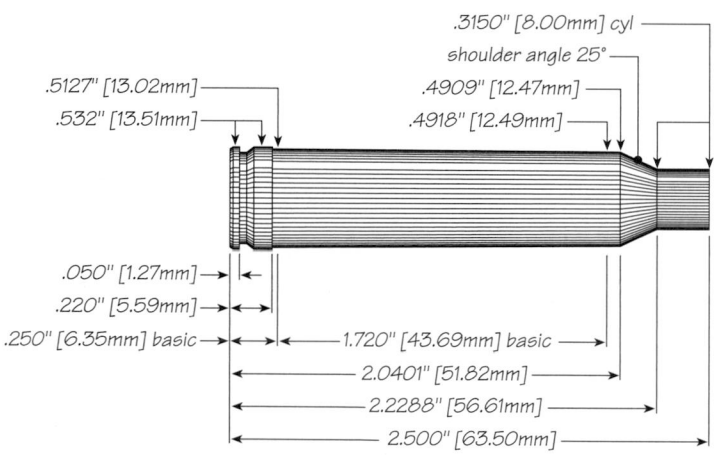

Max. Case Length:	2.500"	Cart. Case:	Remington
Trim-to Length:	2.490"	Primer:	CCI 250*
Max Cart. OAL:	3.290"	Test Firearm:	Universal Receiver
RCBS Shell Holder:	#4	Barrel Length:	Krieger 24"

0.284"	7mm TNT HP	7mm HP
Weight, grains	110	115
Ballistic Coefficient	0.384	0.250
Sectional Density	0.195	0.204
COAL Tested:	3.250"	3.200"
Speer Part No.	1616	1617

Propellant	START CHARGE Weight, grs	START CHARGE Muzzle Velocity, ft/sec	MAXIMUM CHARGE Weight, grs	MAXIMUM CHARGE Muzzle Velocity, ft/sec
Reloder 22*	71.0	3265	75.0C	3503
Reloder 19*	70.0	3237	74.0C	3489
Viht. N165*	73.0	3275	77.0C	3481
H4350*	67.0	3227	71.0C	3451
AA 4350*	67.0	3255	71.0	3427
IMR 4831*	67.0	3208	71.0	3412
IMR 4350*	62.0	3211	66.0	3379
AA 3100*	68.0	3160	73.0C	3368
H4831SC*	68.0	3174	72.0	3348
760*	61.0	3117	65.0	3323
Reloder 15*	54.0	3034	58.0	3256

Mark Matusevich, General Manager, CCI/Speer Operations; 7mm Rem Mag, 150-grain Fusion® ammo; bull elk taken in Colorado.

*Maximum Loads should be used with CAUTION • C = Compressed Load • *Magnum Primer used with this powder.*

0.284"	7mm Spitz SP	7mm Spitz BTSP
Weight, grains	130	130
Ballistic Coefficient	0.368	0.424
Sectional Density	0.230	0.230
COAL Tested:	3.285"	3.285"
Speer Part No.	1623	1624

Propellant	START CHARGE Weight, grs	START CHARGE Muzzle Velocity, ft/sec	MAXIMUM CHARGE Weight, grs	MAXIMUM CHARGE Muzzle Velocity, ft/sec
Reloder 22*	66.0	3118	70.0	3314
Reloder 19*	65.0	3057	69.0	3270
IMR 4831*	61.0	3044	65.0	3243
IMR 4350*	59.0	3040	63.0	3234
Viht. N165*	68.0	3017	72.0	3231
AA 4350*	60.0	3027	64.0	3227
760*	58.0	2989	62.0	3211
H4350*	60.0	3004	64.0	3189
H414*	58.0	2960	62.0	3164
H4831SC*	62.0	3001	66.0	3141
H380*	55.0	2841	59.0	3052
Reloder 15*	51.0	2814	55.0	3049
IMR 4895*	46.0	2737	50.0	2964
SR 4759* (reduced load)	22.0	1768	26.0	2084

0.284"	7mm TBBC SP
Weight, grains	140
Ballistic Coefficient	0.360
Sectional Density	0.248
COAL Tested:	3.280"
Speer Part No.	1745

Propellant	START CHARGE Weight, grs	START CHARGE Muzzle Velocity, ft/sec	MAXIMUM CHARGE Weight, grs	MAXIMUM CHARGE Muzzle Velocity, ft/sec
Reloder 25*	67.5	3020	71.5	3173
IMR 7828*	64.5	2957	68.5	3121
AA 3100*	65.5	2998	67.5	3096
Reloder 19*	63.0	2977	67.0	3095
IMR 4831*	60.5	2910	64.5	3093
H1000*	69.0	2945	73.00	3070
Reloder 22*	62.0	2962	66.0	3074
H4350*	57.0	2891	61.0	3049
IMR 4350*	59.0	2930	61.0	3034
H4831SC*	62.0	2877	66.0	3024

NOTE: *Trophy Bonded Bear Claw and Trophy Bonded Sledgehammer Solid bullets have unique ballistic behavior compared to conventional bullets. Loads for TBBC and TBSS bullets may not "track" with data for conventional bullets. Use TBBC and TBSS data ONLY for TBBC and TBSS bullets.*

*Maximum Loads should be used with CAUTION • C = Compressed Load • *Magnum Primer used with this powder.*

7mm Remington Magnum

0.284"	7mm Spitz BTSP	7mm Spitz SP	7mm Match BTHP	7mm GS SP
Weight, grains	145	145	145	145
Ballistic Coefficient	0.472	0.416	0.468	0.353
Sectional Density	0.257	0.257	0.257	0.257
COAL Tested:	3.280"	3.280"	3.290"	3.235"
Speer Part No.	1628	1629	1631	1632

Propellant	START CHARGE Weight, grs	START CHARGE Muzzle Velocity, ft/sec	MAXIMUM CHARGE Weight, grs	MAXIMUM CHARGE Muzzle Velocity, ft/sec
Reloder 19*	63.0	2948	67.0	3153
Reloder 22*	64.0	2919	68.0	3136
IMR 7828*	65.0	2974	69.0	3103
H1000*	69.0	2910	73.0C	3090
IMR 4831*	59.0	2920	63.0	3081
IMR 4350*	56.0	2881	60.0	3070
H870*	76.0	2860	80.0	3037
Viht. N165*	64.0	2828	68.0	3019
AA 4350*	60.0	2837	64.0	3015
760*	54.0	2819	58.0	3012
AA 3100*	62.0	2826	66.0	3008
H4350*	59.0	2801	63.0	2987
H4831SC*	59.5	2835	63.5	2981
SR 4759* (reduced load)	24.0	1811	28.0	2112

0.284"	7mm Spitz BTSP	7mm Spitz SP	7mm MT SP	7mm GS SP
Weight, grains	160	160	160	160
Ballistic Coefficient	0.519	0.504	0.340	0.389
Sectional Density	0.283	0.283	0.283	0.283
COAL Tested:	3.280"	3.280"	3.225"	3.225"
Speer Part No.	1634	1635	1637	1638

Propellant	START CHARGE Weight, grs	START CHARGE Muzzle Velocity, ft/sec	MAXIMUM CHARGE Weight, grs	MAXIMUM CHARGE Muzzle Velocity, ft/sec
Reloder 25*	66.0	2875	70.0	3012
Reloder 22*	61.0	2773	65.0	2976
H870*	75.0	2819	79.0	2970
Reloder 19*	60.0	2729	64.0	2941
H1000*	65.0	2761	69.0	2936
IMR 4831*	57.0	2784	61.0	2915
H4350*	57.0	2735	61.0	2904
IMR 4350*	54.0	2725	58.0	2901
AA 8700*	75.0	2736	79.0	2870
AA 3100*	60.0	2691	64.0	2869
Viht. N165*	60.0	2692	64.0	2867
H4831SC*	58.0	2711	62.0	2853
AA 4350*	57.0	2680	61.0	2849
SR 4759* (reduced load)	26.0	1770	30.0	2067

*Maximum Loads should be used with CAUTION • C = Compressed Load • *Magnum Primer used with this powder.*

0.284"	7mm TBBC SP
Weight, grains	160
Ballistic Coefficient	0.380
Sectional Density	0.283
COAL Tested:	3.280"
Speer Part No.	1750

Propellant	START CHARGE		MAXIMUM CHARGE	
	Weight, grs	Muzzle Velocity, ft/sec	Weight, grs	Muzzle Velocity, ft/sec
Reloder 25*	65.0	2842	69.0	2998
IMR 7828*	61.0	2773	65.0	2914
AA 3100*	61.0	2740	65.0	2909
Reloder 19*	59.9	2758	63.5	2898
H1000*	65.0	2770	69.0	2894
IMR 4831*	57.0	2719	61.0	2877
Reloder 22*	58.5	2725	62.5	2865
H4831SC*	58.5	2689	62.5	2833
IMR 4350*	54.0	2620	58.0	2815
H4350*	53.0	2675	57.0	2813

NOTE: *Trophy Bonded Bear Claw and Trophy Bonded Sledgehammer Solid bullets have unique ballistic behavior compared to conventional bullets. Loads for TBBC and TBSS bullets may not "track" with data for conventional bullets. Use TBBC and TBSS data ONLY for TBBC and TBSS bullets.*

0.284"	7mm MT SP	7mm GS SP
Weight, grains	175	175
Ballistic Coefficient	0.382	0.436
Sectional Density	0.310	0.310
COAL Tested:	3.200"	3.260"
Speer Part No.	1641	1643

	START CHARGE		MAXIMUM CHARGE	
Propellant	Weight, grs	Muzzle Velocity, ft/sec	Weight, grs	Muzzle Velocity, ft/sec
H870*	74.0	2790	78.0	2954
Reloder 25*	65.0	2792	67.0	2888
Reloder 22*	57.0	2618	61.0	2830
IMR 4831*	55.0	2641	59.0	2827
Reloder 19*	58.0	2604	62.0	2812
IMR 4350*	52.0	2000	56.0	2780
H1000*	61.0	2620	65.0	2782
Viht. N165*	58.0	2565	62.0	2742
H4831SC*	56.0	2588	60.0	2733
AA 8700*	71.0	2639	75.0	2722
AA 4350*	55.0	2547	59.0	2713
H4350*	55.0	2546	59.0	2703
SR 4759* (reduced load)	28.0	1831	32.0	2085

*Maximum Loads should be used with CAUTION • C = Compressed Load • *Magnum Primer used with this powder.*

0.284"	7mm TBBC SP
Weight, grains	175
Ballistic Coefficient	0.400
Sectional Density	0.310
COAL Tested:	3.260"
Speer Part No.	1755

Propellant	START CHARGE		MAXIMUM CHARGE	
	Weight, grs	Muzzle Velocity, ft/sec	Weight, grs	Muzzle Velocity, ft/sec
Reloder 25*	61.0	2670	65.0	2788
H870*	77.0	2717	79.0C	2786
IMR 7828*	58.0	2585	62.0	2742
H1000*	62.0	2624	66.0	2741
Reloder 19*	56.0	2589	60.0	2720
Reloder 22*	55.0	2558	59.0	2703
H4831SC*	58.0	2598	60.0	2682
IMR 4831*	56.0	2582	58.0	2672
IMR 4350*	54.0	2551	56.0	2649
Viht. N165*	55.0	2496	59.0	2612

NOTE: Trophy Bonded Bear Claw and Trophy Bonded Sledgehammer Solid bullets have unique ballistic behavior compared to conventional bullets. Loads for TBBC and TBSS bullets may not "track" with data for conventional bullets. Use TBBC and TBSS data ONLY for TBBC and TBSS bullets.

*Maximum Loads should be used with CAUTION • C = Compressed Load • *Magnum Primer used with this powder.*

7mm Weatherby Magnum

Roy Weatherby developed this fine cartridge in the 1940's but it didn't get a lot of exposure until the next decade when Weatherby rifles became more common and 28-caliber cartridges received more press attention. It is a fine cartridge for the one-rifle sportsman who routinely hunts open country. For years, it was the premier 7mm Magnum and the only one available in American-made rifles until the 7mm Remington Magnum appeared in 1962.

In spite of a larger case, it is nearly identical in ballistics to the newer Remington Magnum. Reloaders who like cartridges with long necks will appreciate the Weatherby version. Beyond that factor, choosing between the two is more a matter of whose rifle you like best.

For years, reloading was necessary to get maximum flexibility from the 7mm Weatherby. Original factory ammunition was loaded with 139 and 154-grain bullets yet the cartridge easily handles the full range of 7mm bullets.

The 7mm Weatherby can handle the same classes of game as the Remington Magnum, but no 7mm is a dangerous game rifle. We recommend bullets of tough construction such as Grand Slam and Mag-Tip for big game. Lightweight bullets at high velocity in this cartridge and other 7mm Magnums can cause quite a bit of meat damage on medium deer. A way to reduce this is to stay with heavier (160 grains and up) bullets when hunting to fill the freezer.

Although the 7mm Weatherby isn't considered a varmint cartridge, accuracy with Speer's hollow points is excellent, allowing long-range hits on varmints. The 110-grain TNT may be used but test some for in-flight integrity in your rifle before loading a large quantity. With some propellants, the thin-jacketed TNT is on the edge of its useful velocity in this cartridge. Our pressure barrel is 24 inches long. The more common 26-inch length found in some Weatherby rifles will produce a little higher velocity with the lighter bullets but the tight tolerances of the pressure barrel makes that difference small enough to dismiss.

The 7mm Weatherby became a standard industry cartridge in 1994. The loads here represent a total retest of this cartridge with the latest components and standards. Its maximum average pressure is set at 65,000 psi.

Important Note: *We used Federal cases for data development. These have slightly less propellant capacity than Weatherby-branded cases. The listed loads are safe in either make but, if you have a pet load developed in Weatherby brass, you should drop the maximum charge weight one to two grains when switching to other brands of cases.*

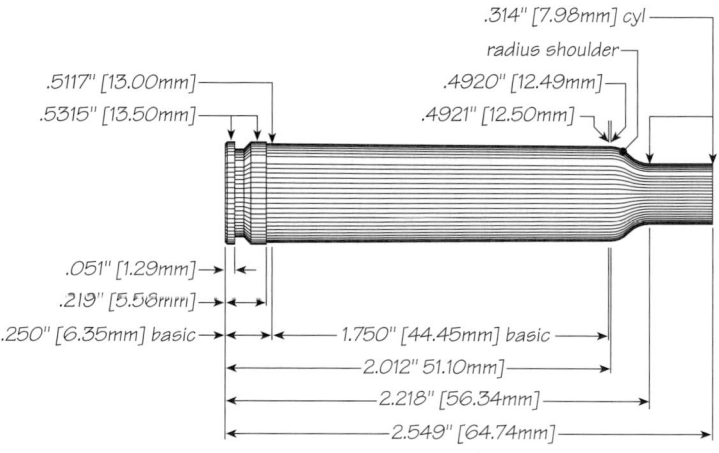

Max. Case Length:	2.549"	**Cart. Case:**	Federal
Trim-to Length:	2.539"	**Primer:**	Federal 215
Max Cart. OAL:	3.360"	**Test Firearm:**	Universal Receiver
RCBS Shell Holder:	#4	**Barrel Length:**	Wiseman 24"

0.284"	7mm TNT HP	7mm HP
Weight, grains	110	115
Ballistic Coefficient	0.384	0.250
Sectional Density	0.195	0.204
COAL Tested:	3.280"	3.260"
Speer Part No.	1616	1617

Propellant	START CHARGE Weight, grs	START CHARGE Muzzle Velocity, ft/sec	MAXIMUM CHARGE Weight, grs	MAXIMUM CHARGE Muzzle Velocity, ft/sec
Reloder 22*	72.0	3301	76.0	3507
Reloder 19*	70.0	3264	74.0	3485
IMR 4831*	68.0	3266	72.0	3481
Viht. N560*	72.0	3276	76.0	3476
Ramshot Magnum*	78.5	3242	82.5	3471
IMR 4350*	67.0	3272	71.0	3459
H4350*	66.0	3214	73.0	3455
H4831SC*	72.0	3247	76.0	3433
AA 3100*	69.0	3233	73.0	3425
760*	64.0	3227	68.0	3425
Reloder 15*	59.0	3217	63.0	3405

*Maximum Loads should be used with CAUTION • C = Compressed Load • *Magnum Primer used with this powder.*

0.284"	7mm Spitz SP	7mm Spitz BTSP
Weight, grains	130	130
Ballistic Coefficient	0.368	0.424
Sectional Density	0.230	0.230
COAL Tested:	3.330"	3.330"
Speer Part No.	1623	1624

Propellant	START CHARGE		MAXIMUM CHARGE	
	Weight, grs	Muzzle Velocity, ft/sec	Weight, grs	Muzzle Velocity, ft/sec
Ramshot Magnum*	78.0	3219	82.0	3374
Reloder 22*	70.0	3153	74.0	3345
Viht. N560*	70.0	3153	74.0	3338
AA 3100*	68.0	3133	72.0	3328
IMR 4831*	66.0	3121	70.0	3321
Reloder 19*	68.0	3087	72.0	3317
IMR 4350*	64.0	3066	68.0	3269
H4350*	63.0	3100	67.0	3261
H4831SC*	69.0	3063	73.0	3251
Reloder 15*	56.0	3053	60.0	3185

0.284"	7mm Spitz BTSP	7mm Spitz SP	7mm Match BTHP	7mm GS SP
Weight, grains	145	145	145	145
Ballistic Coefficient	0.472	0.416	0.468	0.353
Sectional Density	0.257	0.257	0.257	0.257
COAL Tested:	3.350"	3.350"	3.360"	3.290"
Speer Part No.	1628	1629	1631	1632

Propellant	START CHARGE		MAXIMUM CHARGE	
	Weight, grs	Muzzle Velocity, ft/sec	Weight, grs	Muzzle Velocity, ft/sec
Reloder 22*	67.0	2960	71.0	3177
Viht. N560*	67.5	2964	71.5	3167
Magnum*	73.0	2989	77.0	3139
IMR 4831*	63.0	2948	67.0	3134
Reloder 19*	65.0	2944	69.0	3133
IMR 4350*	62.0	2913	66.0	3117
AA 3100*	64.0	2927	68.0	3105
H4831SC*	66.5	2931	70.5	3096
Reloder 15*	52.0	2811	56.0	2940

*Maximum Loads should be used with CAUTION • C = Compressed Load • *Magnum Primer used with this powder.*

0.284"	7mm Spitz BTSP	7mm Spitz SP	7mm MT SP	7mm GS SP
Weight, grains	160	160	160	160
Ballistic Coefficient	0.519	0.504	0.340	0.389
Sectional Density	0.283	0.283	0.283	0.283
COAL Tested:	3.350"	3.350"	3.350"	3.350"
Speer Part No.	1634	1635	1637	1638

Propellant	START CHARGE		MAXIMUM CHARGE	
	Weight, grs	Muzzle Velocity, ft/sec	Weight, grs	Muzzle Velocity, ft/sec
Reloder 25*	71.0	2930	75.0C	3132
Viht. N560*	67.0	2891	71.0	3095
Ramshot Magnum*	72.0	2926	76.0	3079
Reloder 22*	66.0	2849	70.0	3065
IMR 7828*	67.0	2859	71.0C	3052
Reloder 19*	64.5	2837	68.5	3035
IMR 4350*	61.0	2829	65.0	3019
IMR 4831*	62.0	2856	66.0	3013
AA 3100*	63.5	2825	67.5	2992
H4831SC*	66.0	2818	70.0	2989
H4350*	60.0	2838	64.0	2988

0.284"	7mm MT SP	7mm GS SP
Weight, grains	175	175
Ballistic Coefficient	0.382	0.436
Sectional Density	0.310	0.310
COAL Tested:	3.250"	3.250"
Speer Part No.	1641	1643

Propellant	START CHARGE		MAXIMUM CHARGE	
	Weight, grs	Muzzle Velocity, ft/sec	Weight, grs	Muzzle Velocity, ft/sec
Reloder 25*	70.0	2791	74.0C	2982
Viht. N560*	65.0	2742	69.0	2942
IMR 7828*	66.0	2752	70.0	2935
Ramshot Magnum*	70.0	2761	74.0	2934
Reloder 22*	65.0	2731	69.0	2904
Reloder 19*	63.0	2724	67.0	2885
AA 3100*	63.0	2716	67.0	2882
IMR 4831*	60.0	2699	64.0	2864
IMR 4350*	59.0	2693	63.0	2862
H4350*	58.0	2711	62.0	2858
H4831SC*	64.0	2702	68.0	2854

*Maximum Loads should be used with CAUTION • C = Compressed Load • *Magnum Primer used with this powder.*

7mm Shooting Times Westerner

The 7mm STW is a creation of writer Layne Simpson at *Shooting Times* magazine. Around 1989, Simpson experimented with necking down the big 8mm Remington Magnum case to accept 7mm (0.284 inch) diameter bullets. He named the cartridge after his "home" magazine and added "Westerner" to indicate the geographic region where such a cartridge would be most useful. In 1998, the U.S. ammunition and firearms industry accepted the cartridge and it successfully made the transition from wildcat to commercial status.

In a market already well populated with excellent 7mm sporting cartridges, the STW has competed reasonably well. Although somewhat "reined in" by reasonable industry pressure limits, it still gives a modest velocity advantage over the 7mm Remington and Weatherby Magnums. Its full-length H&H case requires rifles with magazines capable of handling the cartridge's maximum loaded length of 3.600 inches, but there are plenty of bolt-action rifles that can do so.

With bullet weights between 145 and 175 grains, the STW enjoys a velocity advantage of about 100 ft/sec over its smaller cousins. The extra case volume imposes one handicap not found in the older 7mm Magnums—getting any acceptable level of ballistic uniformity with bullets lighter that 145 grains is difficult. To some extent, we encountered this with our 145-grain bullets; we tested many more propellants than we show. Only those consumer propellants we list for the 145-grain bullets gave acceptable uniformity. This is not a condemnation; most long magnum cartridges show the same behavior.

Factory ammunition carries 140, 150, and 160-grain bullets. Our experience tells us that the 160 and 175-grain bullets are better suited to this cartridge than the lighter ones. Heavier bullets at high velocities give better performance over very long shooting distances and will damage less edible meat when you are hunting to stock the freezer. If you currently own any modern 7mm Magnum, upgrading to the STW will gain you little. However, if you plan to upgrade from a non-magnum cartridge, the STW is as worthy of your consideration as any other.

The standard industry test barrel for this cartridge is 24 inches. We screened these loads for velocity in sporting rifles with 26-inch barrels and observed little if any velocity improvements over the test barrel with its tight tolerances. Therefore, the test barrel velocities here can be assumed to represent the majority of sporting rifles available.

The industry pressure limit for the 7mm STW is 53,000 CUP.

Important Note: *We strongly caution handloaders to carefully review data gathered before the cartridge was standardized in 1998. Some data published while the cartridge was still in "wildcat" status produce pressures as much as 20 percent over the current limit, enough to damage the case beyond further usefulness on the first firing.*

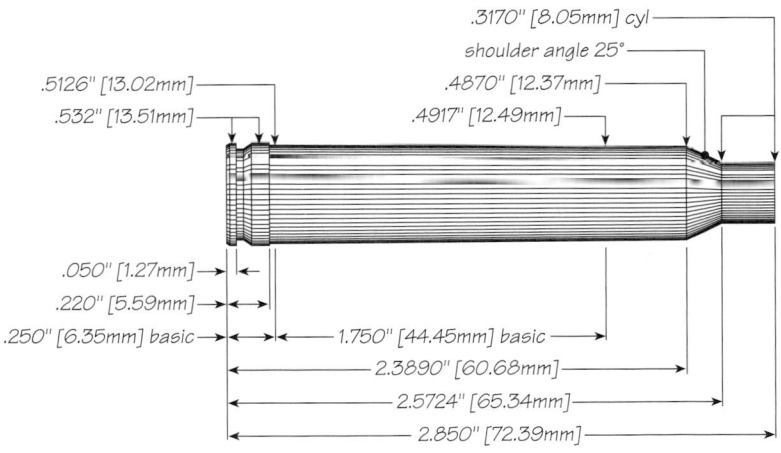

Max. Case Length:	2.850"	Cart. Case:	Remington
Trim-to Length:	2.840"	Primer:	CCI 250*
Max Cart. OAL:	3.600"	Test Firearm:	Universal Receiver
RCBS Shell Holder:	#4	Barrel Length:	Krieger 24"

0.284"	7mm Spitz BTSP	7mm Spitz SP	7mm GS SP
Weight, grains	145	145	145
Ballistic Coefficient	0.472	0.416	0.353
Sectional Density	0.257	0.257	0.257
COAL Tested:	3.600"	3.600"	3.600"
Speer Part No.	1628	1629	1631

	START CHARGE		MAXIMUM CHARGE	
Propellant	Weight, grs	Muzzle Velocity, ft/sec	Weight, grs	Muzzle Velocity, ft/sec
Reloder 22*	75.0	3184	77.0	3273
Reloder 25*	76.0	3122	80.0	3273
IMR 7828*	72.0	3079	76.0	3228
AA 3100*	76.0	3126	78.0	3201
H4350*	66.0	3016	70.0	3159
IMR 4350*	67.5	3073	69.5	3154
IMR 4831*	69.0	3082	71.0	3149
H414*	62.0	2940	66.0	3052

Lab Notes:

Some very experienced riflemen who know how to do statistically valid accuracy testing have reported an interesting phenomenon: some 7mm STW rifles shoot nearly the same size groups at 200 yards as they do at 100 yards. Magic? No, physics.

Every bullet fired from a rifled barrel experiences some degree of yaw, a slight wobbling of the bullet about its long axis, just as it exits the barrel. The wobble settles down and the bullet becomes fully stable under the influence of the spin imparted by the rifling. This transition usually occurs with the first 25 to 75 yards of flight but can happen at longer ranges. At high velocities, long bullets fired from fast-twist barrels may take longer to reach stable flight, or "go to sleep," an informal but understandable phrase for this event. The 7mm STW has all three factors—velocity, bullet length, and a 9.5" twist—needed for the bullet to pass the 100-yard mark before it sleeps.

0.284"	7mm Spitz BTSP	7mm Spitz SP	7mm MT SP	7mm GS SP
Weight, grains	160	160	160	160
Ballistic Coefficient	0.519	0.504	0.340	0.389
Sectional Density	0.283	0.283	0.283	0.283
COAL Tested:	3.580"	3.600"	3.530"	3.550"
Speer Part No.	1634	1635	1367	1638

Propellant	START CHARGE		MAXIMUM CHARGE	
	Weight, grs	Muzzle Velocity, ft/sec	Weight, grs	Muzzle Velocity, ft/sec
AA 8700*	87.0	3001	91.0C	3133
IMR 7828*	72.0	2954	76.0	3097
AA 3100*	74.0	3020	76.0	3093
Reloder 25*	71.0	2952	75.0	3076
Reloder 22*	69.0	2947	73.0	3074
IMR 4831*	69.0	2967	71.0	3040
IMR 4350*	05.5	2895	69.5	3033
H4831SC*	66.0	2884	70.0	3019
H1000*	75.0	2890	79.0	3010
Viht. N170*	72.0	2827	76.0	2955

0.284"	7mm MT SP	7mm GS SP
Weight, grains	175	175
Ballistic Coefficient	0.382	0.436
Sectional Density	0.310	0.310
COAL Tested:	3.580"	3.600"
Speer Part No.	1641	1643

	START CHARGE		MAXIMUM CHARGE	
Propellant	Weight, grs	Muzzle Velocity, ft/sec	Weight, grs	Muzzle Velocity, ft/sec
AA 8700*	85.0	2948	87.0	3009
AA 3100*	71.0	2868	73.0	2951
Reloder 25*	72.0	2881	74.0	2947
IMR 7828*	71.0	2874	73.0	2929
H1000*	73.0	2800	77.0	2909
IMR 4831*	67.0	2830	69.0	2906
Reloder 22*	66.0	2746	70.0	2879

*Maximum Loads should be used with CAUTION • C = Compressed Load • *Magnum Primer used with this powder.*

7mm Remington Ultra Magnum

In 2001, the 7mm Remington Ultra Magnum joined the 300, 338, and 375 Ultra Magnums in Remington's family of long-body, unbelted magnums inspired by the large-diameter 404 Jeffery cartridge case. The impressive case can hold over 100 grains of some propellants, giving it a velocity advantage of 100-150 ft/sec over its nearest competitor, the 7mm Shooting Times Westerner. This gain requires adding 10 to 15 grains of propellant compared to STW charge weights.

In spite of the modest difference in velocity, the 7mm RUM has one significant advantage for handloaders over the STW—an unbelted case. Without any special handling, the non-belted case usually offers both accuracy and case life benefits compared to belted cases.

Like the STW, meat hunters will find that the 160 and 175-grain bullets produce less meat damage than lighter bullets. They also offer better downrange performance for shots at long ranges. The 145-grain bullets should be limited to smaller deer and antelope.

In very large cases, less bullet weight means a greater variation in pressure and velocity. The 7mm Ultra Magnum is no exception; like the 7mm STW we found the 145-grain bullet was the lightest that could maintain some semblance of ballistic uniformity.

The only caution to reloaders is to respect the large case. It takes longer for a 90-grain charge of propellant to move from the powder measure into the case than a 50-grain charge. Be ready to modify the rhythm you normally use in metering propellant and be sure to hold the case in contact with the measure until all the charge has found its way into the case. Failing to do so will result in a grossly undercharged case and spilled propellant.

Do not load lighter charges than those shown here. This cartridge has a steep pressure fall-off as the charge weight decreases. All start loads produce at least 50,000 psi. We do not show reduced loads for this cartridge; this is not a cartridge for light practice loads.

The loads presented here remain within the 65,000 psi pressure limit established for this cartridge.

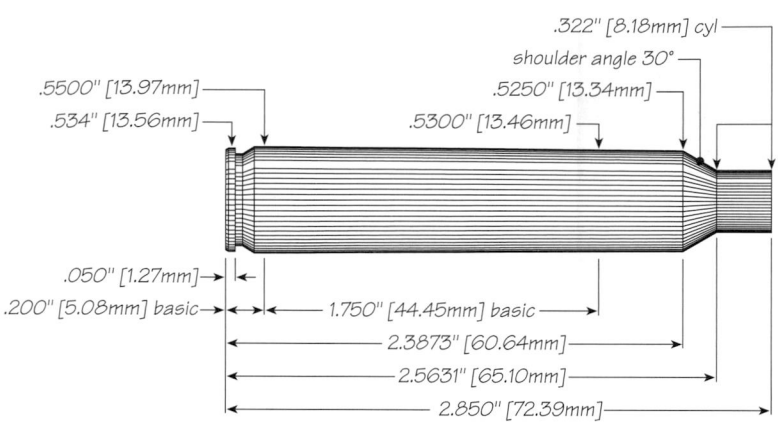

.322" [8.18mm] cyl
shoulder angle 30°
.5250" [13.34mm]
.5300" [13.46mm]
.5500" [13.97mm]
.534" [13.56mm]

.050" [1.27mm]
.200" [5.08mm] basic
1.750" [44.45mm] basic
2.3873" [60.64mm]
2.5631" [65.10mm]
2.850" [72.39mm]

Max. Case Length:	2.850"	Cart. Case:	Remington
Trim-to Length:	2.840"	Primer:	Federal 215*
Max Cart. OAL:	3.600"	Test Firearm:	Universal Receiver
RCBS Shell Holder:	#38	Barrel Length:	Remington 24"

0.284"	7mm Spitz BTSP	7mm Spitz SP	7mm Match BTHP	7mm GS SP
Weight, grains	145	145	145	145
Ballistic Coefficient	0.472	0.416	0.468	0.353
Sectional Density	0.257	0.257	0.257	0.257
COAL Tested:	3.600"	3.600"	3.600"	3.550"
Speer Part No.	1628	1629	1631	1632

	START CHARGE		MAXIMUM CHARGE	
Propellant	Weight, grs	Muzzle Velocity, ft/sec	Weight, grs	Muzzle Velocity, ft/sec
Viht. N560*	89.0	3280	93.0	3422
AA 8700*	102.0	3068	106.0	3305
US 869*	103.0	3165	107.0	3305
Retumbo*	92.0	3095	96.0	3261
IMR 7828*	85.0	3150	89.0	3259
Reloder 25*	88.0	3089	92.0	3251
Reloder 22*	84.0	3101	88.0	3250
Ramshot Magnum*	89.0	3107	93.0	3236
Reloder 19*	81.0	3058	85.0	3200

0.284"	7mm Spitz BTSP	7mm Spitz SP	7mm MT SP	7mm GS SP
Weight, grains	160	160	160	160
Ballistic Coefficient	0.519	0.504	0.340	0.389
Sectional Density	0.283	0.283	0.283	0.283
COAL Tested:	3.600"	3.600"	3.570"	3.580"
Speer Part No.	1634	1635	1637	1638

Propellant	START CHARGE		MAXIMUM CHARGE	
	Weight, grs	Muzzle Velocity, ft/sec	Weight, grs	Muzzle Velocity, ft/sec
Viht. N560*	87.0	3145	91.0	3311
US869*	101.0	3075	105.0	3237
Retumbo*	91.0	3031	95.0	3219
AA 8700*	99.0	3054	103.0	3198
Reloder 22*	83.0	3014	87.0	3177
Reloder 25*	87.0	3005	91.0	3174
Ramshot Magnum*	88.0	3016	92.0	3169
IMR 7828*	83.0	2984	87.0	3149
Reloder 19*	81.0	2928	85.0	3132

Steve Moore, Development Engineer, CCI/Speer Operations; heading back to camp after a successful hunt.

Maximum Loads should be used with CAUTION • C = Compressed Load • *Magnum Primer used with this powder.

0.284"	7mm MT SP	7mm GS SP
Weight, grains	175	175
Ballistic Coefficient	0.382	0.436
Sectional Density	0.310	0.310
COAL Tested:	3.550"	3.570"
Speer Part No.	1641	1643

	START CHARGE		MAXIMUM CHARGE	
Propellant	Weight, grs	Muzzle Velocity, ft/sec	Weight, grs	Muzzle Velocity, ft/sec
US869*	98.0	2936	102.0	3106
Retumbo*	89.0	2889	93.0	3081
AA 8700*	97.0	2908	101.0	3073
Reloder 25*	86.0	2896	90.0	3059
IMR 7828*	82.0	2873	86.0	3045
Viht. N560*	81.0	2855	85.0	3031
H1000*	86.0	2865	90.0	3017
Ramshot Magnum*	85.0	2868	89.0	3009
Reloder 22*	81.0	2871	85.0	2974

*Maximum Loads should be used with CAUTION • C = Compressed Load • *Magnum Primer used with this powder.*

30 M1 Carbine

Shortly before World War II, Army Ordnance determined that certain military units might be better off with a light carbine instead of the 45-caliber service pistol. The cartridge developed for this purpose was a small-capacity, rimless design that fired a 110-grain full metal jacket bullet at just less than 2000 ft/sec. Both praised and cursed, the cartridge and its rifle, the U.S. Model M1 Carbine, served in two wars in spite of relatively anemic performance.

Generally, surplus carbines are not known for impressive accuracy and the cartridge is much too underpowered for deer. However, the carbine has remained popular with civilians for its compactness, light recoil, and ease of handling. In short, it's just plain fun to shoot. It shouldn't be used on any animals larger than a coyote.

The full metal jacket military bullet does not expand and thus lacks the stopping power of commercial ammo or handloads with expanding bullets. The handloader can chose from four Speer bullets. The 110-grain TMJ® can be used to duplicate the military load or for small game loads where minimal meat damage is required. The 100-grain Plinker® is an inexpensive bullet for either practice or small game hunting. The large, exposed lead tip expands rapidly although penetration is usually quite limited. For deeper penetration, choose the 110-grain Hot-Cor® soft point. The 110-grain Varminter® provides rapid expansion.

The choice of bullet may be limited by the condition of your carbine. Some have rough feed ramps and show a strong preference for the TMJ and Hot-Cor bullets. Getting the Varminter and the Plinker to feed may require polishing the feed ramp, something you may not want to do if your carbine is of collection quality.

Hodgdon H110 and Winchester 296 closely approximate the original military propellants used in this cartridge. They give adequate gas volume to cycle the carbine's gas-operated action. The other propellants listed functioned our test carbine, but we recommend you load a small sample and test them in your carbine before loading several hundred rounds, regardless of the propellant you choose. This cartridge headspaces on the case mouth, so taper crimping is strongly recommended to remove any flare at the case mouth.

These loads do not exceed the SAAMI maximum average pressure of 40,000 CUP.

30 M1 Carbine

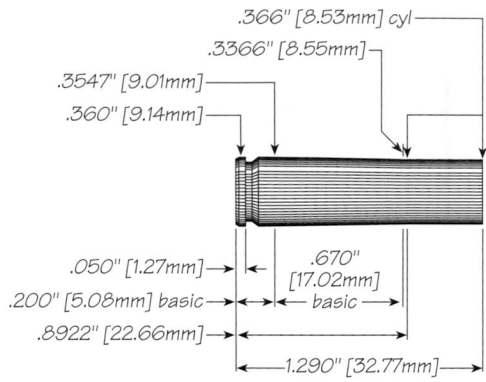

.366" [8.53mm] cyl
.3366" [8.55mm]
.3547" [9.01mm]
.360" [9.14mm]
.050" [1.27mm]
.200" [5.08mm] basic
.8922" [22.66mm]
.670" [17.02mm] basic
1.290" [32.77mm]

Max. Case Length:	1.290"	Cart. Case:	IMI
Trim-to Length:	1.285"	Primer:	CCI 400; CCI 450*
Max Cart. OAL:	1.680"	Test Firearm:	M1 Carbine
RCBS Shell Holder:	#17	Barrel Length:	18"

NOTE: *CCI No. 41 primer may be substituted for CCI 450.*

0.308"	30 RNSP Plinker®
Weight, grains	100
Ballistic Coefficient	0.144
Sectional Density	0.151
COAL Tested:	1.625"
Speer Part No.	1805

	START CHARGE		MAXIMUM CHARGE	
Propellant	Weight, grs	Muzzle Velocity, ft/sec	Weight, grs	Muzzle Velocity, ft/sec
AA No. 9	12.3	1908	14.3	2185
296*	13.5	1756	15.5	2010
H110*	12.5	1678	14.5	1951
IMR 4227	13.5	1693	15.5	1946
Viht. N110	11.0	1696	13.0C	1939
2400	10.5	1526	12.5	1817
IMR 4198	13.5	1459	15.5	1685
AA 1680	14.0	1465	16.0C	1677

0.308"	30 HP	30 RNSP	30 TMJ RN
Weight, grains	110	110	110
Ballistic Coefficient	0.128	0.136	0.179
Sectional Density	0.166	0.166	0.166
COAL Tested:	1.635"	1.675"	1.680"
Speer Part No.	1835	1845	1846

	START CHARGE		MAXIMUM CHARGE	
Propellant	Weight, grs	Muzzle Velocity, ft/sec	Weight, grs	Muzzle Velocity, ft/sec
296*	13.0	1796	15.0	1981
AA No. 9	11.4	1739	13.4	1950
H110*	12.0	1610	14.0	1885
IMR 4227	13.0	1627	15.0	1883
Viht. N110	10.5	1567	12.5C	1822
2400	10.0	1469	12.0	1745
SR 4759	10.0	1497	12.0	1678
AA 1680	14.0	1468	16.0C	1674
IMR 4100	13.0	1428	15.0	1631

*Maximum Loads should be used with CAUTION • C = Compressed Load • *Magnum Primer used with this powder.*

30-30 Winchester

If we judged cartridges by ballistics alone, the 30-30 Winchester would be only a fond memory. However, the combination of mild recoil and America's affection for lever-actions rifles keeps the 30-30 popular. Most American rifle makers have chambered the 30-30 at some time, usually in lever- or slide-action rifles.

The 30-30 has the distinction of being the first American small-bore sporting cartridge loaded with smokeless propellant. It was introduced in 1895 in the famous Winchester Model 1894 lever-action rifle and was an immediate success. Original loading specifications called for a 160-grain bullet at 1970 ft/sec. The new rifle was almost as light and handy as the earlier Model 1892 but could handle longer and more powerful cartridges. By 1895 standards, the Model 94 gave the hunter significant power in an easily carried package. Although 110 years of sporting cartridge development and advancement have faded the 30-30's former glory, it still remains in consideration as the first deer rifle for many new shooters.

For rifles having tubular magazines, the 30-30 must be loaded with flat point bullets. This prevents cartridge detonation in the magazine during recoil. Speer makes four flat point bullets suitable for the 30-30 in weights from 110 to 170 grains. These bullets are designed to give optimum expansion at modest velocities. They all have a cannelure to allow secure crimping of the bullet. Crimping is mandatory for cartridges going into tubular magazines so that bullets are not pressed into the case by recoil and the tension of the magazine spring. The 170-grain Hot-Cor is the best choice for game up to medium-size deer, which is the effective game limit of the cartridge. The 130 and 150-grain Hot-Cor flat points are fine for smaller deer.

When using the 100-grain Speer Plinker® we recommend that they be fed singly into the barrel. The short overall cartridge length may cause feeding problems in tubular magazines and the magazine spring can push bullets deeper into the case.

Some bolt-action and single-shot rifles have been chambered for this cartridge. Reloaders may use spitzer-type bullets in these rifles, but should keep the weight to 150 grains or less. Heavier spitzer bullets cannot be driven fast enough in the 30-30 to expand reliably at normal hunting ranges. We are occasionally asked if the 30-30 can be loaded to higher pressures in a modern bolt action like the Remington Model 788. The answer is no! Although the M788 action is strong, the 30-30 cartridge case has relatively thin walls by today's standards. Attempting to load "hotter" would risk a dangerous case failure.

The listed loads do not exceed the industry maximum average pressure of 38,000 CUP. The data for round nose and flat point bullets can also be used in the 30 Remington cartridge, a rimless version of the 30-30 designed for Remington semi-automatic and slide-action rifles. Spitzer bullets may be used in the Models 8 and 81 rifles chambered for 30 Remington; they have box magazines.

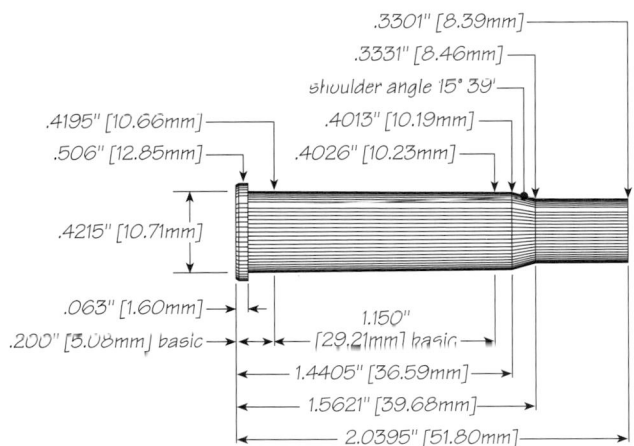

Max. Case Length:	2.0395"	Cart. Case:	Winchester	
Trim-to Length:	2.030"	Primer:	CCI 200; 250*	
Max Cart. OAL:	2.550"	Test Firearm:	Winchester Model 94	
RCBS Shell Holder:	#2	Barrel Length:	20"	

0.308"	30 RNSP
Weight, grains	100
Ballistic Coefficient	0.144
Sectional Density	0.151
COAL Tested:	2.345"
Speer Part No.	1805

Propellant	START CHARGE		MAXIMUM CHARGE	
	Weight, grs	Muzzle Velocity, ft/sec	Weight, grs	Muzzle Velocity, ft/sec
Reloder 7	31.0	2457	35.0	2792
H322	33.0	2375	37.0	2730
AA 2015	31.0	2366	35.0	2658
IMR 4064	33.5	2173	37.5C	2527
BL-C(2)*	34.0	2172	38.0	2497
748*	36.0	2111	40.0C	2483
Viht. N133	28.0	2140	32.0	2405
H4895	31.0	2054	35.0	2388
H380*	36.0	1971	40.0C	2319

NOTE: *See "Lab Notes" before loading this bullet.*

0.308"	30 HP
Weight, grains	110
Ballistic Coefficient	0.128
Sectional Density	0.166
COAL Tested:	2.415"
Speer Part No.	1835

Propellant	START CHARGE Weight, grs	START CHARGE Muzzle Velocity, ft/sec	MAXIMUM CHARGE Weight, grs	MAXIMUM CHARGE Muzzle Velocity, ft/sec
Reloder 7	30.0	2302	**34.0**	2708
H322	31.0	2230	**35.0**	2593
AA 2015	30.0	2254	**34.0**	2591
748*	36.0	2256	**40.0C**	2564
IMR 4064	33.0	2091	**37.0C**	2460
BL-C(2)*	33.0	2090	**37.0**	2430
IMR 4895	31.0	2101	**35.0**	2415
Viht. N133	27.0	1934	**31.0**	2362
H4895	30.0	1955	**34.0C**	2300
IMR 4350	36.0	1976	**40.0C**	2298
AA 2230	27.0	1998	**31.0**	2296
AA 2460*	28.0	1988	**32.0**	2259

Lab Notes:

In the last two decades, several makes of 30-30 rifles appeared with much shorter throats than previously seen. Although within industry specs, these short throats preclude loading the 110-grain Speer Varminter® HP to the cartridge length we tested. Before loading this bullet for your rifle, make a dummy round to test for throat interference. If you encounter interference with the rifling, seat bullets to the FRONT cannelure and load singly.

*Maximum Loads should be used with CAUTION • C = Compressed Load • *Magnum Primer used with this powder.*

0.308"	30 FNSP
Weight, grains	130
Ballistic Coefficient	0.312
Sectional Density	0.196
COAL Tested:	2.550"
Speer Part No.	2007

Propellant	START CHARGE Weight, grs	Muzzle Velocity, ft/sec	MAXIMUM CHARGE Weight, grs	Muzzle Velocity, ft/sec
AA 2520*	31.0	2068	35.0C	2433
AA 2460*	30.0	2086	34.0	2425
Reloder 7	27.0	2106	31.0	2393
H322	29.0	2036	33.0	2367
Varget	31.0	1987	35.0	2294
Reloder 10X	26.5	2039	30.5	2273
Reloder 15	32.0	1943	36.0C	2259
Viht. N140	31.0	1964	35.0C	2257
748*	31.2	1866	35.5	2221
IMR 4895	28.0	1857	32.0	2134
IMR 4064	29.0	1757	33.0	2067

0.308"	30 FNSP
Weight, grains	150
Ballistic Coefficient	0.255
Sectional Density	0.226
COAL Tested:	2.550"
Speer Part No.	2011

Propellant	START CHARGE Weight, grs	START CHARGE Muzzle Velocity, ft/sec	MAXIMUM CHARGE Weight, grs	MAXIMUM CHARGE Muzzle Velocity, ft/sec
748*	33.0	1925	37.0C	2238
H322	27.0	1886	31.0	2219
AA 2520*	28.0	1863	32.0	2192
Reloder 7	25.0	1882	29.0	2188
Reloder 15	30.0	1823	34.0C	2170
Viht. N140	30.0	1854	34.0	2156
Varget	29.0	1825	33.0	2139
Reloder 10X	24.0	1839	28.0	2117
H335*	28.0	1731	32.0	2111
H414*	34.0	1725	38.0C	2078
IMR 4320	29.0	1699	33.0	2047
H4895	27.0	1674	31.0	2041
IMR 4895	27.0	1698	31.0	2018
IMR 4350	32.0	1690	36.0C	2012

*Maximum Loads should be used with CAUTION • C = Compressed Load • *Magnum Primer used with this powder.*

0.308"	30 FNSP
Weight, grains	170
Ballistic Coefficient	0.298
Sectional Density	0.256
COAL Tested:	2.550"
Speer Part No.	2041

Propellant	START CHARGE		MAXIMUM CHARGE	
	Weight, grs	Muzzle Velocity, ft/sec	Weight, grs	Muzzle Velocity, ft/sec
748*	30.0	1833	34.0	2118
Varget	27.0	1626	31.0	2006
H322	25.0	1684	29.0	2005
H335*	27.0	1669	31.0	1988
Viht. N140	27.0	1643	31.0	1983
IMR 3031	25.5	1699	29.5	1975
Reloder 10X	22.5	1646	26.5	1972
IMR 4064	27.0	1654	31.0	1964
760*	31.0	1635	35.0	1946
H414*	31.0	1599	35.0	1926
IMR 4350	30.5	1570	34.5	1915
IMR 4895	25.0	1616	29.0	1879
AA 2460*	24.0	1590	28.0	1871

*Maximum Loads should be used with CAUTION • C = Compressed Load • *Magnum Primer used with this powder.*

300 Savage

This fine old cartridge dates to 1920 when Savage introduced it in its famous Model 99 lever-action rifle. Although a compact cartridge, the 300 Savage managed to deliver respectable velocities (for 1920) and was superior to the 30-30 Winchester in all respects.

Factory ammunition is loaded with 150 and 180-grain bullets. The handloader has much more flexibility because of the wide selection of 30-caliber component bullets. With Speer's 110-grain spire point or the 125-grain TNT® hollow point, the 300 Savage can be used on varmints out to 200 yards. Even the big Speer 200-grain spitzer can be used, although velocity is limited to around 2300 ft/sec, restricting shots to under 150 yards. For large deer and elk, the 180-grain Mag-Tip is an excellent choice because this bullet expands well at the modest velocities achieved by the 300 Savage.

Accuracy of the 300 Savage is usually on par with any other 30-caliber sporting cartridge. However, its velocities aren't as high as many newer cartridges, making long shots more difficult due to the arched trajectory. Even so, the 300 Savage is effective out to 200 yards on deer-sized game.

Reloading this cartridge is fairly simple as long as you remember a couple of points:

- Most 300 Savage rifles are either lever- or slide-action, so we recommend full length resizing after every shot. Some rifles may give better feeding and extraction if a small-base sizing die (available from RCBS) is used.
- The unusually sharp 30° shoulder can cause sizing problems in the form of shoulder dents if too much lubricant is applied to the case before resizing.

The case capacity of the 300 Savage is similar to the 308 Winchester. However, the Savage is loaded to lower pressures in deference to its use in lever guns, so it can't match the velocities of the newer cartridge. We found that two newer propellants, Reloder 15 and VihtaVuori N140, allowed up to 100 ft/sec velocity gains with heavier bullets compared to other powders.

These loads do not exceed the SAAMI maximum average pressure of 46,000 CUP.

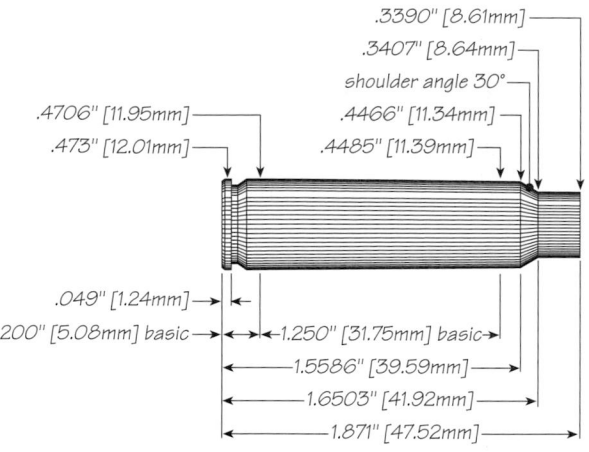

.3390" [8.61mm]
.3407" [8.64mm]
shoulder angle 30°
.4706" [11.95mm]
.473" [12.01mm]
.4466" [11.34mm]
.4485" [11.39mm]
.049" [1.24mm]
.200" [5.08mm] basic
1.250" [31.75mm] basic
1.5586" [39.59mm]
1.6503" [41.92mm]
1.871" [47.52mm]

Max. Case Length:	1.871"	Cart. Case:	Federal
Trim-to Length:	1.861"	Primer:	CCI 200; 250*
Max Cart. OAL:	2.600"	Test Firearm:	Savage 99E
RCBS Shell Holder:	#3	Barrel Length:	20"

0.308"	30 RNSP
Weight, grains	100
Ballistic Coefficient	0.144
Sectional Density	0.151
COAL Tested:	2.475"
Speer Part No.	1805

Propellant	START CHARGE		MAXIMUM CHARGE	
	Weight, grs	Muzzle Velocity, ft/sec	Weight, grs	Muzzle Velocity, ft/sec
748*	44.0	2826	48.0C	3096
Reloder 7	36.0	2727	40.0	3061
AA 2230*	41.0	2705	45.0	3007
IMR 4064	42.0	2723	46.0C	3003
IMR 3031	39.0	2711	43.0C	3003
IMR 4895	41.0	2710	45.0C	2967
Viht. N130	36.0	2948	40.0	2948
IMR 4320	41.0	2618	45.0C	2847
IMR 4350	42.0	2306	46.0C	2538
SR 4759 (reduced load)	16.0	1675	18.0	1897

NOTE: *Limit 110 HP velocities to 2900 fps maximum.*

0.308"	30 HP	30 RNSP	30 Spire SP
Weight, grains	110	110	110
Ballistic Coefficient	0.128	0.136	0.245
Sectional Density	0.166	0.166	0.166
COAL Tested:	2.255"	2.330"	2.475"
Speer Part No.	1835	1845	1855

	START CHARGE		MAXIMUM CHARGE	
Propellant	Weight, grs	Muzzle Velocity, ft/sec	Weight, grs	Muzzle Velocity, ft/sec
AA 2230*	41.0	2709	45.0	3007
H322	40.0	2824	44.0	2983
Viht. N130	36.0	2674	40.0	2948
748*	43.0	2684	47.0C	2941
IMR 3031	31.0	2611	47.0C	2874
IMR 4064	41.0	2586	45.0C	2849
IMR 4895	40.0	2583	44.0C	2833
IMR 4198	31.0	2500	35.0	2020
Reloder 7	34.0	2497	38.0	2811
H380*	44.0	2451	48.0C	2685
IMR 4350	42.0	2272	46.0C	2506
SR 4759 (reduced load)	15.0	1531	19.0	1923

Lab Notes:

Please do not confuse the 300 Savage with the older 303 Savage. The older (and obsolete) 303 Savage is a rimmed cartridge in the 30-30 Winchester performance class and was chambered in early Model 1899 Savage rifles. It cannot use data for the more powerful 300 Savage. Carefully observe the barrel cartridge markings and make certain you are loading for the correct cartridge.

*Maximum Loads should be used with CAUTION • C = Compressed Load • *Magnum Primer used with this powder.*

0.308"	30 TNT HP
Weight, grains	125
Ballistic Coefficient	0.341
Sectional Density	0.188
COAL Tested:	2.580"
Speer Part No.	1986

Propellant	START CHARGE		MAXIMUM CHARGE	
	Weight, grs	Muzzle Velocity, ft/sec	Weight, grs	Muzzle Velocity, ft/sec
AA 2460*	40.0	2586	44.0C	2906
Viht. N140	42.0	2567	46.0C	2868
IMR 4895	40.0	2546	44.0C	2813
BL-C(2)*	36.0	2529	40.0C	2810
748*	43.0	2493	47.0C	2786
IMR 4320	41.0	2442	45.0C	2759
IMR 3031	38.0	2496	42.0C	2728
IMR 4064	39.0	2407	43.0C	2645
H380*	44.0	2286	48.0C	2569
H414*	43.0	2237	47.0C	2486
IMR 4350	41.0	2170	45.0C	2398

Jon Miller, Machinist, CCI/Speer Operations; 300 Win Mag, 180-grain Fusion® ammo; 7 ft.-3 in. leopard from the Luangwa Valley, Zambia.

0.308"	30 HP	30 FNSP
Weight, grains	130	130
Ballistic Coefficient	0.244	0.213
Sectional Density	0.196	0.196
COAL Tested:	2.520"	2.375"
Speer Part No.	2005	2007

Propellant	START CHARGE		MAXIMUM CHARGE	
	Weight, grs	Muzzle Velocity, ft/sec	Weight, grs	Muzzle Velocity, ft/sec
Viht. N140	41.0	2552	45.0C	2795
AA 2460*	39.0	2525	43.0	2794
H322	38.0	2492	42.0	2768
IMR 4064	39.0	2458	43.0	2717
748*	40.0	2430	44.0	2688
IMR 4895	38.0	2416	42.0	2660
IMR 3031	36.0	2379	40.0	2632
H380*	43.0	2383	47.0C	2597
IMR 4320	00.0	2249	42.0	2506
IMR 4350	41.0	2226	45.0C	2433

*Maximum Loads should be used with CAUTION • C = Compressed Load • *Magnum Primer used with this powder.*

0.308"	30 FNSP	30 RNSP	30 Spitz BTSP	30 Spitz SP	30 MT SP	30 GS SP
Weight, grains	150	150	150	150	150	150
Ballistic Coefficient	0.255	0.235	0.417	0.377	0.278	0.295
Sectional Density	0.226	0.226	0.226	0.226	0.226	0.226
COAL Tested:	2.375"	2.495"	2.550"	2.550"	2.540"	2.535"
Speer Part No.	2011	2017	2022	2023	2025	2026

Propellant	START CHARGE		MAXIMUM CHARGE	
	Weight, grs	Muzzle Velocity, ft/sec	Weight, grs	Muzzle Velocity, ft/sec
Viht. N140	40.0	2405	44.0C	2663
AA 2460*	38.0	2415	42.0	2660
IMR 4064	37.5	2334	41.5	2590
H322	36.0	2308	40.0	2573
H380*	42.0	2289	46.0C	2513
IMR 4895	37.0	2250	41.0	2506
748*	38.0	2260	42.0	2488
IMR 3031	34.5	2228	38.5	2475
IMR 4320	37.5	2208	41.5	2445
SR 4759 (reduced load)	17.0	1523	21.0	1873

0.308"	30 Spitz BTSP	30 Spitz SP	30 GS SP
Weight, grains	165	165	165
Ballistic Coefficient	0.520	0.444	0.354
Sectional Density	0.248	0.248	0.248
COAL Tested:	2.550"	2.550"	2.540"
Speer Part No.	2034	2035	2038

Propellant	START CHARGE		MAXIMUM CHARGE	
	Weight, grs	Muzzle Velocity, ft/sec	Weight, grs	Muzzle Velocity, ft/sec
Reloder 15	40.0	2350	44.0C	2614
Viht. N140	39.0	2327	43.0C	2589
H322	35.0	2205	39.0	2469
IMR 4064	36.0	2197	40.0	2445
H380*	41.0	2220	45.0C	2427
748*	37.0	2192	41.0	2421
IMR 4805	35.0	2140	39.0	2398
AA 2700*	40.0	2176	44.0C	2389
IMR 4350	41.0	2151	45.0C	2381
IMR 4320	36.0	2094	40.0	2342
SR 4759 (reduced load)	19.0	1597	21.0	1776

*Maximum Loads should be used with CAUTION • C = Compressed Load • *Magnum Primer used with this powder.*

0.308"	30 RNSP	30 Spitz BTSP	30 Spitz SP	30 MT SP	30 GS SP
Weight, grains	180	180	180	180	180
Ballistic Coefficient	0.312	0.545	0.441	0.349	0.374
Sectional Density	0.271	0.271	0.271	0.271	0.271
COAL Tested:	2.480"	2.550"	2.550"	2.535"	2.535"
Speer Part No.	2047	2052	2053	2059	2063

Propellant	START CHARGE		MAXIMUM CHARGE	
	Weight, grs	Muzzle Velocity, ft/sec	Weight, grs	Muzzle Velocity, ft/sec
Reloder 15	39.0	2277	43.0C	2469
Viht. N140	38.0	2228	42.0C	2462
IMR 4350	41.0	2146	45.0C	2370
H414*	41.0	2136	45.0C	2369
760*	40.5	2124	44.5C	2353
H380*	40.0	2128	44.0C	2347
748*	36.0	2089	40.0	2331
IMR 4895	34.0	2078	38.0	2326
IMR 4064	35.0	2094	39.0	2315
AA 2700*	38.0	2034	42.0C	2243
IMR 4198 (reduced load)	20.0	1588	24.0	1742

0.308"	30 Spitz SP	30 GS SP
Weight, grains	200	200
Ballistic Coefficient	0.478	0.453
Sectional Density	0.301	0.301
COAL Tested:	2.550"	2.535"
Speer Part No.	2211	2212

Propellant	START CHARGE Weight, grs	START CHARGE Muzzle Velocity, ft/sec	MAXIMUM CHARGE Weight, grs	MAXIMUM CHARGE Muzzle Velocity, ft/sec
Reloder 15	38.0	2021	42.0C	2379
Viht. N140	36.0	1997	40.0C	2264
H414*	41.0	2027	45.0C	2249
IMR 4350	39.0	2010	43.0C	2212
IMR 4064	32.0	1899	36.0	2137
H380	37.0	1900	41.0C	2128
760*	37.0	1916	41.0C	2128
748*	33.0	1888	37.0	2123
AA 2700*	36.0	1914	40.0C	2104
IMR 4895	31.0	1862	35.0	2092
IMR 4198 (reduced load)	22.0	1588	24.0	1742

*Maximum Loads should be used with CAUTION • C = Compressed Load • *Magnum Primer used with this powder.*

307 Winchester

The popularity of the American lever-action rifle led to numerous efforts to upgrade its performance. The most popular lever rifle ever built is the Winchester Model 94, but its original design physically limited the power of the cartridges that could be used.

U.S. Repeating Arms Company (USRAC) developed a stronger version of the Model 94 that could handle cartridge pressures up to 52,000 CUP, 37 percent higher than the 30-30. The improved action featured thicker receiver walls and improved metallurgy. It also allowed top-mounting of scope sights by lowering the right sidewall and repositioning the extractor and ejector so cases ejected to the side, not up as in the original Model 94. This feature gave the new rifle its name—the Model 94 Angle Eject.

Two new cartridges were developed for the 94AE. The 307 and 356 Winchester have the same external dimensions as the 308 and 358 Winchester, respectively, with the exception of the rims. The new cartridges have the same rim diameter as the 30-30, technically making the cases semi-rimmed. Pressure levels for both newcomers were established at 52,000 CUP.

The walls of the 307 case are thicker than those of the 308 Winchester, reducing case capacity. When loading the 307 Winchester, you must not use 308 Winchester data. Follow published 307 loads to the letter.

Ballistically the 307 Winchester is only slightly behind the 308 Winchester and equal in all respects to the 300 Savage, even though Savage rifles usually have longer barrels. Our test rifle gave impressive velocities considering that it has a 20-inch barrel. The only restriction is that flat point bullets must be used in tubular magazines for safety. This limits bullet selection. The shooter reloading the 308 Winchester can use bullets of various shapes up to 200 grains; the heaviest flat points suitable for the 307 are 170 grains.

In addition to Winchester, Marlin also produced 307 rifles. However, a check of catalogs and web sites as we went to press shows that, with the demise of USRAC in 2005, no firms are still producing rifles for this cartridge.

Safety Reminder: *Use only flat point bullets when loading cartridges for use in tubular magazines. Pointed bullets could cause a cartridge to explode in the magazine with the risk of property damage and/or personal injury.*

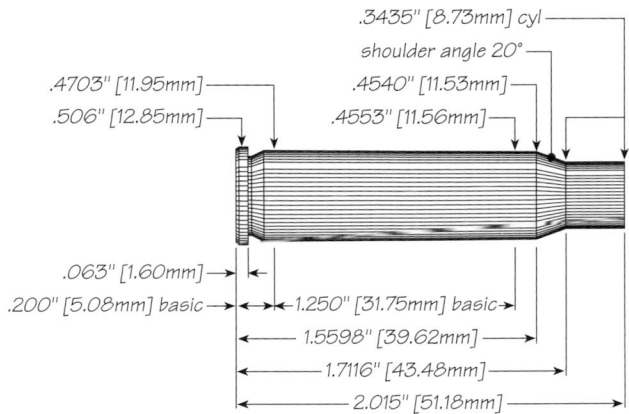

Max. Case Length:	2.015"	
Trim-to Length:	2.005"	
Max Cart. OAL:	2.560"	
RCBS Shell Holder:	#2	

Cart. Case:	Winchester
Primer:	CCI 200; 250*
Test Firearm:	Winchester 94AE
Barrel Length:	20"

0.308"	30 Spitz SP
Weight, grains	100
Ballistic Coefficient	0.144
Sectional Density	0.151
COAL Tested:	2.390"
Speer Part No.	1805

Propellant	START CHARGE		MAXIMUM CHARGE	
	Weight, grs	Muzzle Velocity, ft/sec	Weight, grs	Muzzle Velocity, ft/sec
Reloder 7	33.0	2474	37.0	2767
IMR 4320	38.0	2402	42.0	2630
IMR 4198	28.0	2380	32.0	3600
IMR 3031	36.0	2149	40.0	3530
2400	20.0	2180	24.0	2511
IMR 4895	36.0	2250	40.0	2474
748*	38.0	2261	42.0	2441
H322	31.0	2155	35.0	2419

NOTE: *COAL less than minimum. We recommend single loading into the chamber.*

0.308"	30 HP
Weight, grains	110
Ballistic Coefficient	0.128
Sectional Density	0.166
COAL Tested:	2.390"
Speer Part No.	1835

Propellant	START CHARGE		MAXIMUM CHARGE	
	Weight, grs	Muzzle Velocity, ft/sec	Weight, grs	Muzzle Velocity, ft/sec
Reloder 7	35.0	2489	39.0	2795
IMR 4198	33.0	2455	37.0	2788
H322	39.0	2461	41.0	2785
IMR 4895	40.0	2544	44.0C	2737
IMR 3031	39.0	2223	43.0	2701
IMR 4064	41.0	2341	45.0	2685
748*	42.0	2402	46.0	2683
2400	22.0	2244	26.0	2531

NOTE: *COAL less than minimum. We recommend single loading into the chamber.*

0.308"	30 FNSP
Weight, grains	130
Ballistic Coefficient	0.213
Sectional Density	0.196
COAL Tested:	2.520"
Speer Part No.	2007

Propellant	START CHARGE		MAXIMUM CHARGE	
	Weight, grs	Muzzle Velocity, ft/sec	Weight, grs	Muzzle Velocity, ft/sec
BL-C(2)*	46.0	2650	50.0C	2891
748*	45.0	2574	49.0C	2849
H335*	41.0	2562	45.0	2802
IMR 4895	41.0	2460	45.0	2785
IMR 3031	39.0	2301	43.0C	2672
IMR 4064	41.0	2296	45.0C	2666
H322	36.0	2210	40.0	2635
Reloder 7	33.0	2216	37.0	2566
IMR 4320	39.0	2204	43.0	2565

*Maximum Loads should be used with CAUTION • C = Compressed Load • *Magnum Primer used with this powder.*

0.308"	30 FNSP
Weight, grains	150
Ballistic Coefficient	0.255
Sectional Density	0.226
COAL Tested:	2.520"
Speer Part No.	2011

Propellant	START CHARGE		MAXIMUM CHARGE	
	Weight, grs	Muzzle Velocity, ft/sec	Weight, grs	Muzzle Velocity, ft/sec
748*	41.0	2452	45.0	2603
IMR 3031	37.0	2313	41.0	2598
IMR 4064	40.0	2276	44.0C	2566
H380*	45.0	2304	49.0C	2548
IMR 4895	38.0	2249	42.0	2547
H414*	44.0	2248	48.0	2542
H335*	37.0	2353	41.0	2537
760*	45.0	2241	49.0C	2502
H322	34.0	2146	38.0	2392

0.308"	30 FNSP
Weight, grains	170
Ballistic Coefficient	0.298
Sectional Density	0.256
COAL Tested:	2.520"
Speer Part No.	2041

Propellant	START CHARGE		MAXIMUM CHARGE	
	Weight, grs	Muzzle Velocity, ft/sec	Weight, grs	Muzzle Velocity, ft/sec
H414*	41.0	2136	45.0C	2455
748*	38.0	2189	42.0	2446
BL-C(2)*	39.0	2231	43.0	2444
H380*	45.0	2169	49.0C	2444
IMR 4064	38.0	2257	42.0C	2438
H335*	35.0	2114	39.0	2370
IMR 4320	37.0	2079	41.0C	2378
IMR 3031	36.0	2102	40.0	2370
IMR 4895	36.0	2041	44.0C	2357

*Maximum Loads should be used with CAUTION • C = Compressed Load • *Magnum Primer used with this powder.*

308 Winchester

Like several other successful sporting cartridges, the 308 Winchester began as a military development. The search for an effective and compact cartridge for machine guns and semi-auto service rifles began shortly after World War I and continued until the U.S. adopted the experimental T65 cartridge as the 7.62 NATO (7.62x51mm) service cartridge in 1954.

Winchester beat the military to the punch by introducing the T65 as the 308 Winchester in 1952. The case was almost a half-inch shorter than the 30-06 but, with special ball powders developed for the T65, the 308 could nearly match the ballistics of the older service cartridge. First offered in the Winchester Model 70 bolt action and the Model 88 lever action, the 308 was quickly picked up by other manufacturers. It was a natural for short-action rifles and quickly established a reputation for accuracy.

Winchester barrels for the 308 had a 1-in-12 inch twist rate. This limited the heaviest useful bullet weight to 200 grains instead of 220 grains found in the 30-06. Other rifle makers have built 308 rifles using 1-in-10 inch twist barrels. There seems to be little practical difference between the two twist rates with the most commonly-used hunting bullets.

In the hunting field, ballistic differences between the 308 and the 30-06 are negligible for bullets in the 165 to 180 grain range. The type of rifle action you prefer often drives the choice between the two cartridges. A short bolt-action or a semi-auto, lever- or slide-action favors the 308. In full-length actions, the 30-06 gets the nod. Both cartridges can be used on similar types of game. They are suitable for anything in North America with the exception of the great bears. We prefer a larger, heavier bullet for these animals.

In a target-grade rifle, the 308 can be used very effectively on steel and paper targets out to 1000 yards. Bullets such as Speer's 168-grain match boat tail hollow point are used for competition. In most rifles, the 308 is capable of top-notch accuracy.

For hunting, the 308 loaded with 150, 165, or 180-grain Trophy Bonded Bear Claw bullet will give excellent expansion and deep penetration on the heaviest non-dangerous game. The 200-grain TBBC is quite long and reduces powder capacity; we elected not to recommend it in the 308 Winchester. For lighter deer species, the best all-around bullet is the 165-grain Grand Slam or Hot-Cor. Our 125-grain TNT gives fine accuracy for practice or varmint shooting. We discovered that some shooters competing in 200-meter matches were using the TNT. It was more than accurate enough, and the shooters suffered less from recoil than when shooting more typical 168-grain match bullets.

The 100-grain Plinker® and the 110-grain Varminter® hollow point bullets have loaded lengths below the minimum for this cartridge. They may required single loading, especially in semi-automatic rifles.

Because the 308 Winchester is a military spin-off, surplus cases are readily available. Military cases are often thicker than commercial ones and have less case capacity. Reduce charges developed in commercial cases at least three percent when loading military brass. Also, try to match headstamps in one batch for more uniform results. Most 308 surplus cases have crimped primers; be sure to remove the crimp before attempting to insert new primers.

These loads do not exceed the industry maximum average pressure of 52,000 CUP. The commercial IMI cases we used for much of this testing have a mil-spec capacity and therefore require no reduction. The Trophy Bonded Bear Claw loads were tested in Federal Premium® cases.

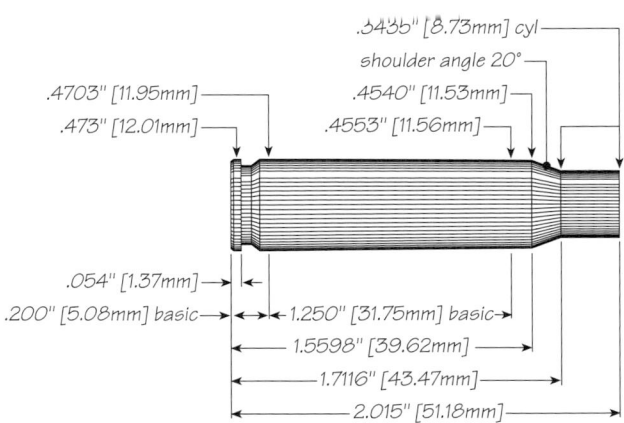

Max. Case Length:	2.015"	Cart. Case:	IMI Commercial
Trim-to Length:	2.005"	Primer:	CCI 200; 250*
Max Cart. OAL:	2.810"	Test Firearm:	Remington 700
RCBS Shell Holder:	#3	Barrel Length:	22"

NOTE: *CCI No. 34 primers may be substituted for CCI 250.*

0.308"	30 RNSP
Weight, grains	100
Ballistic Coefficient	0.144
Sectional Density	0.151
COAL Tested:	2.360"
Speer Part No.	1805

Propellant	START CHARGE Weight, grs	START CHARGE Muzzle Velocity, ft/sec	MAXIMUM CHARGE Weight, grs	MAXIMUM CHARGE Muzzle Velocity, ft/sec
AA 2460*	47.0	3044	51.0C	3345
H322	44.0	2968	48.0	3261
Viht. N120	35.0	2829	39.0	3143
H4895	44.0	2770	48.0C	3112
748*	48.0	2823	52.0C	3069
IMR 4064	45.0	2816	49.0C	3061
Reloder 7	37.0	2703	41.0	3003
SR 4759 (reduced load)	16.0	1571	20.0	1941

0.308"	30 HP
Weight, grains	110
Ballistic Coefficient	0.028
Sectional Density	0.166
COAL Tested:	2.405"
Speer Part No.	1835

Propellant	START CHARGE Weight, grs	START CHARGE Muzzle Velocity, ft/sec	MAXIMUM CHARGE Weight, grs	MAXIMUM CHARGE Muzzle Velocity, ft/sec
IMR 4895	39.0	2612	43.0	2869
IMR 4064	41.5	2614	45.5	2860
H380*	47.0	2639	51.0C	2855
IMR 3031	38.5	2590	42.5	2854
748*	42.0	2609	46.0	2849
IMR 4198	32.0	2534	36.0	2837
H322	37.0	2495	41.0	2794
Reloder 7	33.0	2456	37.0	2787
IMR 4227	25.0	2121	29.0	2469

NOTE: *These loads held to under 2900 fps due to bullet construction.*

0.308"	30 RNSP	30 TMJ RN	30 Spire SP
Weight, grains	110	110	110
Ballistic Coefficient	0.136	0.179	0.245
Sectional Density	0.166	0.166	0.166
COAL Tested:	2.490"	2.490"	2.550"
Speer Part No.	1845	1846	1855

Propellant	START CHARGE Weight, grs	START CHARGE Muzzle Velocity, ft/sec	MAXIMUM CHARGE Weight, grs	MAXIMUM CHARGE Muzzle Velocity, ft/sec
AA 2460*	46.0	2832	50.0C	3218
H322	42.0	2904	46.0	3156
Reloder 15	47.0	2830	51.0C	3144
AA 2520*	45.0	2860	49.0C	3143
IMR 3031	44.0	2848	48.0C	3130
IMR 4895	44.5	2811	48.5C	3123
IMR 4320	47.0	2823	51.0C	3068
Varget	46.0	2916	48.0C	3062
H4895	43.0	2657	47.0C	3019
748*	47.0	2651	51.0	3013
Viht. N120	34.0	2676	38.0	3007
IMR 4064	44.5	2676	48.5C	3007
IMR 4198 (reduced load)	26.0	1927	30.0	2268

*Maximum Loads should be used with CAUTION • C = Compressed Load • *Magnum Primer used with this powder.*

0.308"	30 TNT HP	30 HP
Weight, grains	125	130
Ballistic Coefficient	0.341	0.244
Sectional Density	0.188	0.196
COAL Tested:	2.635"	2.615"
Speer Part No.	1986	2005

Propellant	START CHARGE		MAXIMUM CHARGE	
	Weight, grs	Muzzle Velocity, ft/sec	Weight, grs	Muzzle Velocity, ft/sec
Reloder 10X	38.0	2808	42.0	3073
Reloder 15	46.0	2756	50.0C	3062
AA 2460*	44.0	2694	48.0C	3061
IMR 4320	46.0	2663	50.0C	2992
AA 2230*	42.0	2624	46.0C	2982
748*	46.0	2726	50.0C	2963
AA 2520*	44.0	2682	48.0C	2947
H322	40.0	2638	44.0	2931
Viht. N135	42.0	2630	46.0C	2922
IMR 4895	42.0	2654	46.0C	2916
Varget	45.0	2784	47.0C	2913
IMR 4064	44.0	2613	48.0C	2903
IMR 3031	41.0	2670	48.0C	2902
IMR 4198 (reduced load)	25.0	1969	29.0	2185

0.308"	30 RNSP	30 FMJ BT	30 Spitz BTSP	30 Spitz SP	30 MT SP	30 GS SP
Weight, grains	150	150	150	150	150	150
Ballistic Coefficient	0.235	0.425	0.417	0.377	0.278	0.295
Sectional Density	0.266	0.266	0.266	0.266	0.266	0.266
COAL Tested:	2.490"	2.800"	2.700"	2.700"	2.685"	2.680"
Speer Part No.	2017	2018	2022	2023	2025	2026

Propellant	START CHARGE		MAXIMUM CHARGE	
	Weight, grs	Muzzle Velocity, ft/sec	Weight, grs	Muzzle Velocity, ft/sec
Reloder 15	45.0	2683	49.0C	2919
AA 2520*	44.0	2565	48.0C	2915
H335*	43.0	2562	47.0	2879
748*	46.0	2653	50.0C	2868
Varget	43.0	2632	47.0C	2856
Viht. N135	42.0	2605	46.0C	2822
IMR 4064	43.0	2533	47.0C	2814
IMR 4320	44.0	2488	48.0C	2795
IMR 4895	41.0	2554	45.0	2776
IMR 3031	40.0	2434	44.0	2762
Reloder 10X	35.5	2500	39.5	2755
H414*	47.0	2325	51.0C	2642
BL-C(2)*	40.0	2372	44.0	2607
SR 4759 (reduced load)	21.0	1632	25.0	1925

*Maximum Loads should be used with CAUTION • C = Compressed Load • *Magnum Primer used with this powder.*

0.308"	30 TBBC SP
Weight, grains	150
Ballistic Coefficient	0.335
Sectional Density	0.226
COAL Tested:	2.800"
Speer Part No.	1759

Propellant	START CHARGE		MAXIMUM CHARGE	
	Weight, grs	Muzzle Velocity, ft/sec	Weight, grs	Muzzle Velocity, ft/sec
Reloder 15	45.0	2720	47.0C	2850
Viht. N540	45.0	2716	47.0C	2850
IMR 4064	43.0	2719	45.0C	2842
Varget	45.0	2733	47.0C	2840
H4895	43.0	2709	45.0C	2838
748*	45.0	2698*	47.0	2818
IMR 3031	41.0	2680	43.0	2798

NOTE: *Trophy Bonded Bear Claw and Trophy Bonded Sledgehammer Solid bullets have unique ballistic behavior compared to conventional bullets. Loads for TBBC and TBSS bullets may not "track" with data for conventional bullets. Use TBBC and TBSS data ONLY for TBBC and TBSS bullets.*

0.308"	30 Spitz BTSP	30 Spitz SP	30 GS SP
Weight, grains	165	165	165
Ballistic Coefficient	0.520	0.444	0.354
Sectional Density	0.248	0.248	0.248
COAL Tested:	2.800"	2.800"	2.685"
Speer Part No.	2034	2035	2038

Propellant	START CHARGE Weight, grs	START CHARGE Muzzle Velocity, ft/sec	MAXIMUM CHARGE Weight, grs	MAXIMUM CHARGE Muzzle Velocity, ft/sec
Reloder 15	43.0	2587	47.0C	2812
AA 2520*	41.0	2501	45.0	2748
Viht. N140	42.0	2524	46.0C	2744
AA 2460*	40.0	2464	44.0	2738
IMR 4064	41.0	2482	45.0	2727
IMR 3031	39.0	2482	43.0	2725
748*	42.0	2469	46.0	2713
IMR 4320	42.0	2433	46.0C	2703
H414*	47.0	2402	51.0C	2699
760*	47.0	2358	51.0C	2679
IMR 4895	39.0	2352	43.0	2673
Reloder 10X	34.0	2344	38.0	2596
IMR 4350	45.0	2314	49.0C	2571
SR 4759 (reduced load)	22.0	1639	24.0	1805

*Maximum Loads should be used with CAUTION • C = Compressed Load • *Magnum Primer used with this powder.*

0.308"	30 TBBC SP
Weight, grains	165
Ballistic Coefficient	0.342
Sectional Density	0.248
COAL Tested:	2.800"
Speer Part No.	1760

| Propellant | START CHARGE | | MAXIMUM CHARGE | |
	Weight, grs	Muzzle Velocity, ft/sec	Weight, grs	Muzzle Velocity, ft/sec
IMR 4064	43.0C	2651	45.0C	2770
748*	45.0	2644	47.0C	2753
Reloder 15	44.0	2626	46.0C	2747
Varget	43.0	2604	45.0C	2716
AA 2520*	42.5	2566	44.5	2678
Viht. N140	42.0	2561	44.0C	2671
IMR 3031	40.0	2524	42.0C	2660

NOTE: *Trophy Bonded Bear Claw and Trophy Bonded Sledgehammer Solid bullets have unique ballistic behavior compared to conventional bullets. Loads for TBBC and TBSS bullets may not "track" with data for conventional bullets. Use TBBC and TBSS data ONLY for TBBC and TBSS bullets.*

0.308"	30 Match BTHP
Weight, grains	168
Ballistic Coefficient	0.534
Sectional Density	0.253
COAL Tested:	2.800"
Speer Part No.	2040

	START CHARGE		MAXIMUM CHARGE	
Propellant	Weight, grs	Muzzle Velocity, ft/sec	Weight, grs	Muzzle Velocity, ft/sec
†Varget	42.0	2539	46.0	2746
Viht. N150	43.0	2410	47.0C	2739
†IMR 4064	42.0	2479	46.0	2724
†748*	42.0	2448	46.0	2720
†Reloder 15	41.0	2412	45.0	2710
†IMR 4320	42.0	2457	46.0	2700
†AA 2460*	40.0	2369	44.0	2692
†AA 2520*	40.0	2447	44.0	2660
†IMR 4895	40.0	2390	44.0	2656
†IMR 3031	39.0	2442	43.0	2654
H414*	45.0	2318	49.0	2634
760*	45.0	2418	49.0	2629
†BL-C(2)*	41.0	2336	45.0	2625
H380*	45.0	2275	49.0C	2556

†—denotes propellant suitable for gas-operated semi-auto match rifles.

*Maximum Loads should be used with CAUTION • C = Compressed Load • * Magnum Primer used with this powder.*

0.308"	30 RNSP	30 Spitz BTSP	30 Spitz SP	30 MT SP	30 GS SP
Weight, grains	180	180	180	180	180
Ballistic Coefficient	0.312	0.545	0.411	0.349	0.374
Sectional Density	0.271	0.271	0.271	0.271	0.271
COAL Tested:	2.580"	2.800"	2.800"	2.680"	3.680"
Speer Part No.	2047	2052	2053	2059	2063

Propellant	START CHARGE Weight, grs	START CHARGE Muzzle Velocity, ft/sec	MAXIMUM CHARGE Weight, grs	MAXIMUM CHARGE Muzzle Velocity, ft/sec
Reloder 15	41.0	2299	45.0C	2613
AA 2460*	39.0	2317	43.0	2603
Varget	40.0	2402	44.0	2591
Viht. N150	41.0	2316	45.0C	2573
748^	41.0	2298	45.0	2553
IMR 4064	39.0	2294	43.0C	2521
760*	44.0	2301	48.0C	2501
H414*	44.0	2186	48.0C	2484
IMR 4320	40.0	2256	44.0	2479
H335*	38.0	2277	42.0	2475
AA 2520*	37.0	2255	41.0	2451
H380*	44.0	2147	48.0C	2440
IMR 4895	37.0	2176	41.0	2418
IMR 4350	44.0	2148	48.0C	2414
IMR 4198 (reduced load)	24.0	1591	28.0	1854

0.308"	30 TBBC SP
Weight, grains	180
Ballistic Coefficient	0.357
Sectional Density	0.271
COAL Tested:	2.800"
Speer Part No.	1765

Propellant	START CHARGE		MAXIMUM CHARGE	
	Weight, grs	Muzzle Velocity, ft/sec	Weight, grs	Muzzle Velocity, ft/sec
Viht. N540	43.0	2521	45.0C	2655
Reloder 15	42.0	2498	44.0C	2619
748*	42.0	2488	44.0C	2614
IMR 4064	41.0	2491	43.0C	2601
Varget	41.0	2464	43.0C	2574
AA 2460*	38.0	2360	40.0	2470

NOTE: *Trophy Bonded Bear Claw and Trophy Bonded Sledgehammer Solid bullets have unique ballistic behavior compared to conventional bullets. Loads for TBBC and TBSS bullets may not "track" with data for conventional bullets. Use TBBC and TBSS data ONLY for TBBC and TBSS bullets.*

*Maximum Loads should be used with CAUTION • C = Compressed Load • *Magnum Primer used with this powder.*

0.308"	30 Spitz SP	30 GS SP
Weight, grains	200	200
Ballistic Coefficient	0.478	0.453
Sectional Density	0.301	0.301
COAL Tested:	2.800"	2.680"
Speer Part No.	2211	2212

	START CHARGE		MAXIMUM CHARGE	
Propellant	Weight, grs	Muzzle Velocity, ft/sec	Weight, grs	Muzzle Velocity, ft/sec
Reloder 15	38.0	2126	42.0	2416
748*	39.0	2223	43.0	2416
AA 2460	36.5	2199	40.5	2415
H414*	42.0	2124	46.0C	2414
760*	44.0	2199	48.0C	2390
IMR 4350	43.0	2113	47.0C	2374
IMR 4320	38.0	2156	42.0	2369
IMR 4895	36.0	2082	40.0	2366
H380*	43.0	2127	47.0C	2363
IMR 4831	43.0	2125	47.0C	2361
Viht. N140	37.0	2093	41.0	2352
AA 2520*	36.0	2156	40.0	2344
IMR 4064	36.5	2048	40.5	2327
IMR 4198 (reduced load)	24.0	1514	28.0	1757

*Maximum Loads should be used with CAUTION • C = Compressed Load • *Magnum Primer used with this powder.*

30-40 Krag

The 30-40 Krag was the smokeless powder cartridge developed for the U.S. Army's first small-bore service rifle. Adopted in 1892 to replace the 45-70, the new cartridge propelled a 220-grain FMJ round nose bullet at a velocity of around 2100 ft/sec. The new service rifle was built on a bolt-action designed by Captain Ole H.J. Krag of Norway. Even though the new rifle was officially denoted as the U.S. Magazine Rifle Model in 1892, most people simply called it the Krag.

This somewhat odd-looking rifle proved to be reliable and has a reputation even today as one of the smoothest bolt actions around. The "odd-looking" part was a large, machined "door" on the right-hand side that opened to load the magazine. The magazine held five rounds, laying flat under the receiver, and curving up on the left side to feed from an 8-o'clock position (viewed from the rear).

The Krag action has been criticized for its metallurgy. Some receivers were rather brittle and could shatter in the event of a severe case head failure. The bolt has also suffered some derision because it has only a single locking lug. In fairness, the root of the bolt handle functions as a safety lug should the main lug fail. Using modern cases and staying within the modest pressure limit of 40,000 CUP largely eliminates these concerns.

The 30-40 Krag served its country well and, when the rifles were declared surplus, many fine Krags found civilian homes. The Director of Civilian Marksmanship (DCM) sold many Krag rifles and carbines along with low-cost reloading components. When the more robust U.S. Model 1903 Springfield rifle evolved to replace the Krag as a service rifle, its original military loadings were only slightly more powerful than the 30-40 and the 220-grain bullet was retained for a time.

The Krag proved quite successful as a hunting cartridge. Commercial ammunition was loaded with 220 or 225-grain soft point bullets that afforded deep penetration on large game. With heavy bullets, the Krag can take elk and moose although it is underpowered for the large bears. Loaded with a modern 180-grain soft point bullet (such as the Speer Hot-Cor), the Krag is an excellent deer cartridge out to 250 yards.

Most military Krag chambers have a generous throat to accommodate the long service bullet. Because of this, many Krag shooters have found that bullets lighter than 180 grains may not be as accurate as heavier ones. Also, many Krag rifles have trouble feeding spitzer bullets. However, most function fine with round nose designs.

Although the nominal groove diameter of the military Krag barrel is 0.308", manufacturing technology in the 1890's wasn't up to today's standards. Thus it is all too common to encounter Krags with odd groove diameters. This writer found one near-mint Krag rifle with a groove diameter of 0.314". Our best advice is to determine the groove diameter by slugging. If the bore is oversized (say .311" or .312") using .311" bullets intended for the 303 British should improve accuracy (you'll need a 0.310" expander button). If the bore measures over .312", the rifle probably won't shoot anything well with the exception of certain cast bullets. However, a Krag with a 0.308" barrel in nice shape can produce excellent groups today—over a hundred years after its birth.

Although the Krag cartridge is best known in the rifle of the same name, it was also chambered in Winchester's Model 1895 lever rifle and Model 1885 single-shot. Remington also chambered rifles for the 30-40. In the 1970's Ruger produced a short run of its #3 single-shot carbines for this cartridge. At press time, Winchester still catalogs ammunition and unprimed cases.

We show loads for the lighter Speer bullets (100-130 grains) whose loaded length are below the 2.965" minimum cartridge length for the 30-34 Krag cartridge. As a result, these may require single feeding.

The industry maximum average pressure for the 30-40 Krag cartridge is 40,000 CUP. These loads do not exceed that limit.

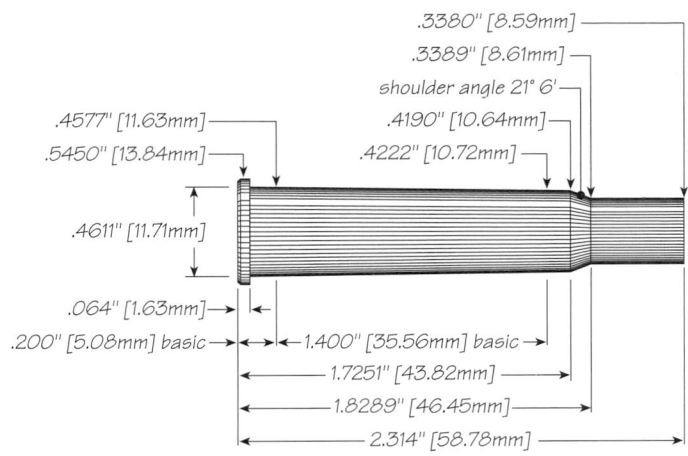

.3380" [8.59mm]
.3389" [8.61mm]
shoulder angle 21° 6'
.4190" [10.64mm]
.4222" [10.72mm]
.4577" [11.63mm]
.5450" [13.84mm]
.4611" [11.71mm]
.064" [1.63mm]
.200" [5.08mm] basic
1.400" [35.56mm] basic
1.7251" [43.82mm]
1.8289" [46.45mm]
2.314" [58.78mm]

Max. Case Length:	2.314"	Cart. Case:	Winchester
Trim-to Length:	2.304"	Primer:	CCI 200; 250*
Max Cart. OAL:	3.089"	Test Firearm:	US Krag 1892
RCBS Shell Holder:	#7	Barrel Length:	21"

0.308"	30 RN SP
Weight, grains	100
Ballistic Coefficient	0.144
Sectional Density	0.151
COAL Tested:	2.610"
Speer Part No.	1805

Propellant	START CHARGE		MAXIMUM CHARGE	
	Weight, grs	Muzzle Velocity, ft/sec	Weight, grs	Muzzle Velocity, ft/sec
H322	41.0	2743	45.0	3070
IMR 4320	44.0	2715	48.0	2952
IMR 3031	40.0	2562	44.0	2829
H380*	47.0	2608	51.0	2820
IMR 4064	42.0	2551	46.0	2811
IMR 4895	40.0	2473	44.0	2732
IMR 4350	49.0	2429	53.0	2634
SR 4759 (reduced load)	16.0	1571	20.0	1941

*Maximum Loads should be used with CAUTION • C = Compressed Load • *Magnum Primer used with this powder.*

0.308"	30 HP
Weight, grains	110
Ballistic Coefficient	0.128
Sectional Density	0.166
COAL Tested:	2.760"
Speer Part No.	1835

Propellant	START CHARGE		MAXIMUM CHARGE	
	Weight, grs	Muzzle Velocity, ft/sec	Weight, grs	Muzzle Velocity, ft/sec
IMR 4320	43.0	2569	47.0	2817
IMR 3031	39.0	2471	43.0	2732
H380*	46.0	2505	50.0	2710
IMR 4064	41.0	2413	45.0	2667
IMR 4895	39.0	2378	43.0	2625
H322	38.0	2315	42.0	2611
IMR 4350	48.0	2329	52.0	2538
IMR 4198 (reduced load)	26.0	1965	30.0	2268

NOTE: *This bullet not intended for velocities in excess of 2900 fps.*

0.308"	30 RNSP	30 Spire SP
Weight, grains	110	110
Ballistic Coefficient	0.136	0.245
Sectional Density	0.166	0.166
COAL Tested:	2.760"	2.760"
Speer Part No.	1845	1855

| Propellant | START CHARGE | | MAXIMUM CHARGE | |
	Weight, grs	Muzzle Velocity, ft/sec	Weight, grs	Muzzle Velocity, ft/sec
IMR 4320	44.0	2735	48.0	2971
IMR 3031	40.0	2607	44.0	2860
H380*	47.0	2638	51.0	2846
IMR 4064	42.0	2599	46.0	2843
IMR 4895	40.0	2509	44.0	2754
IMR 4350	49.0	2463	53.0	2655
H322	38.0	2336	42.0	2611
IMR 4198 (reduced load)	26.0	1927	30.0	2268

*Maximum Loads should be used with CAUTION • C = Compressed Load • *Magnum Primer used with this powder.*

0.308"	30 HP	30 FNSP
Weight, grains	130	130
Ballistic Coefficient	0.244	0.213
Sectional Density	0.196	0.196
COAL Tested:	2.865"	2.865"
Speer Part No.	2005	2007

Propellant	START CHARGE Weight, grs	START CHARGE Muzzle Velocity, ft/sec	MAXIMUM CHARGE Weight, grs	MAXIMUM CHARGE Muzzle Velocity, ft/sec
IMR 4064	42.0	2404	46.0	2647
IMR 4320	42.0	2353	46.0	2588
H380*	44.0	2373	48.0	2579
IMR 3031	39.0	2303	43.0	2568
H414*	47.0	2298	51.0	2541
IMR 4350	48.0	2329	52.0	2530
H322	33.0	1988	37.0	2227
IMR 4198 (reduced load)	25.0	1969	29.0	2185

0.308"	30 RNSP	30 Spitz BTSP	30 Spitz SP	30 MT SP	30 GS SP
Weight, grains	150	150	150	150	150
Ballistic Coefficient	0.235	0.417	0.377	0.278	0.295
Sectional Density	0.226	0.226	0.226	0.226	0.226
COAL Tested:	3.060"	3.089"	3.089"	3.089"	3.089"
Speer Part No.	2017	2022	2023	2025	2026

	START CHARGE		MAXIMUM CHARGE	
Propellant	Weight, grs	Muzzle Velocity, ft/sec	Weight, grs	Muzzle Velocity, ft/sec
IMR 4350	46.0	2211	50.0	2457
IMR 3031	37.0	2210	41.0	2454
IMR 4064	38.0	2204	42.0	2452
H380*	43.0	2196	47.0	2444
H414*	45.0	2147	49.0	2383
IMR 4895	35.0	2046	39.0	2326
H322	31.0	1876	35.0	2151
SR 4759 (reduced load)	21.0	1632	25.0	1925

*Maximum Loads should be used with CAUTION • C = Compressed Load • *Magnum Primer used with this powder.*

0.308"	30 Spitz BTSP	30 Spitz SP	30 GS SP
Weight, grains	165	165	165
Ballistic Coefficient	0.520	0.444	0.354
Sectional Density	0.266	0.266	0.266
COAL Tested:	3.089"	3.089"	3.089"
Speer Part No.	2034	2035	2038

Propellant	START CHARGE		MAXIMUM CHARGE	
	Weight, grs	Muzzle Velocity, ft/sec	Weight, grs	Muzzle Velocity, ft/sec
IMR 4064	37.0	2079	41.0	2309
IMR 4831	44.0	2096	48.0	2283
H380*	40.0	2016	44.0	2252
H414*	43.0	2028	47.0	2252
IMR 4350	44.0	2040	48.0	2232
IMR 4895	34.0	1934	38.0	2218
H322	30.0	1811	34.0	2080
SR 4759 (reduced load)	22.0	1639	24.0	1805

0.308"	30 RNSP	30 Spitz BTSP	30 Spitz SP	30 MT SP	30 GS SP
Weight, grains	180	180	180	180	180
Ballistic Coefficient	0.312	0.545	0.441	0.349	0.374
Sectional Density	0.271	0.271	0.271	0.271	0.271
COAL Tested:	3.089"	3.089"	3.089"	3.089"	3.089"
Speer Part No.	2047	2052	2053	2059	2063

Propellant	START CHARGE		MAXIMUM CHARGE	
	Weight, grs	Muzzle Velocity, ft/sec	Weight, grs	Muzzle Velocity, ft/sec
IMR 4831	43.0	1983	47.0	2162
IMR 4350	42.0	1947	46.0	2125
IMR 4895	33.0	1833	37.0	2125
760*	41.0	1903	45.0	2122
IMR 3031	33.0	1867	37.0	2118
IMR 4064	34.0	1863	38.0	2112
H414*	39.0	1847	43.0	2034
IMR 4198 (reduced load)	24.0	1591	28.0	1854

*Maximum Loads should be used with CAUTION • C = Compressed Load • *Magnum Primer used with this powder.*

0.308"	30 Spitz SP	30 GS SP
Weight, grains	200	200
Ballistic Coefficient	0.478	0.453
Sectional Density	0.301	0.301
COAL Tested:	3.089"	3.089"
Speer Part No.	2211	2212

	START CHARGE		MAXIMUM CHARGE	
Propellant	Weight, grs	Muzzle Velocity, ft/sec	Weight, grs	Muzzle Velocity, ft/sec
IMR 4350	42.0	1915	44.0	2018
IMR 4831	43.0	1898	45.0	2002
IMR 4895	34.0	1849	36.0	1963
IMR 3031	31.0	1712	35.0	1961
IMR 4064	35.0	1829	37.0	1941
760*	38.0	1711	42.0	1930
H414*	38.0	1738	40.0	1841
IMR 4198 (reduced load)	24.0	1514	28.0	1757

*Maximum Loads should be used with CAUTION • C = Compressed Load • *Magnum Primer used with this powder.*

30-06 Springfield

It is safe to say that the 30-06 Springfield is the most successful centerfire cartridge ever developed. Born for battle, it is one of the world's most respected sporting cartridges.

The U.S. military adopted its first rimless 30-caliber service cartridge in 1903 in the famous Model 1903 Springfield service rifle. However, this wasn't the 30-06 we know today. The transitional cartridge is sometimes called the "30-03" to clearly separate it from the final version adopted. Ballistically, the 30-03 was similar to the 30-40 Krag, using the same 220-grain bullet at only slightly higher velocity. In 1906, the cartridge was changed to incorporate a lighter spitzer bullet at higher velocity. Case dimensions were also changed enough to designate the improved version as a different cartridge. Pre-1906 service rifles were modified to shoot the new version. The new cartridge was designated "Ball Cartridge, Caliber 30, Model of 1906." Fortunately, this rather lengthy name was shortened to "30-06" for commercial use.

Almost every U.S. military service cartridge has been a commercial success, and the 30-06 is no exception. Hunters found that its power—quite impressive for 1906—made the 30-06 a versatile game cartridge. It has been used on every species of North American game and has also proved effective on many African plains animals.

Factory ammunition is loaded with a wide range of bullet weights from 125-grain soft points for varmints to the long, 220-grain bullets for large game. The most popular weights for big game fall between 150 and 180 grains. Although somewhat underpowered for the great bears, the 30-06 has been used on them anyway (with varying degrees of success). Normally, bullets capable of deep penetration, such as the 200-grain Trophy Bonded® Bear Claw®, would be chosen for bear. However, we strongly encourage using larger bores and heavier bullets for big and dangerous bruins.

The 30-06 with the Speer 165-grain flat base or boat tail bullet is a flat-shooting cartridge for most western deer hunting. The cartridge can handle the full range of 30-caliber Trophy Bonded Bear Claws for tougher game. The same cartridge loaded with a 180-grain round nose is quite at home in dense eastern woods. Load the 125-grain TNT® and you're ready for long shots on varmints. For formal target shooting, the Speer 168-grain match hollow point will print tight groups at long ranges. Are you teaching a youngster how to shoot a centerfire rifle? Load the 100-grain Speer Plinker at 2000 ft/sec and you have a low-recoil training round. Larger cases make loading accurate reduced loads difficult. The 30-06 case seems to be about the largest 30-caliber case that still allows loading efficient reduced loads.

For the North American hunter who wants one rifle to use on a wide variety of game, the 30-06 is still hard to beat. Velocities are only 200 to 400 ft/sec behind the big 30-caliber magnums and the 30-06 uses much less powder and kicks less.

From a handloader's standpoint, the 30-06 is the #1 cartridge in reloading die sales. Thus, one hundred years after its introduction, the 30-06 remains one of the most effective and flexible cartridges on the shooting scene.

The following data do not exceed the industry maximum average pressure of 50,000 CUP.

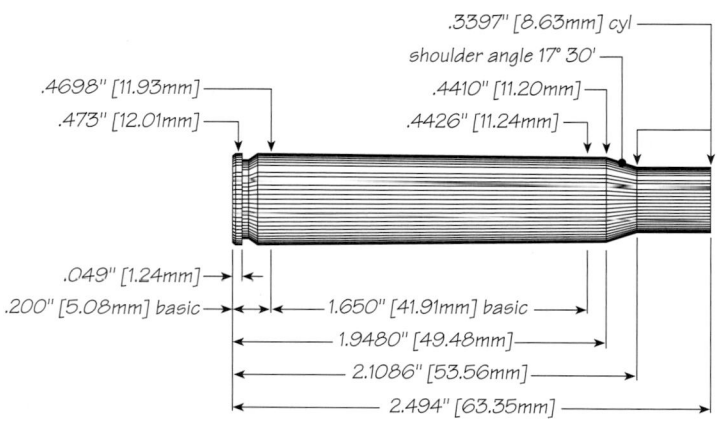

Max. Case Length:	2.494"	Cart. Case:	Winchester
Trim-to Length:	2.484"	Primer:	CCI 200; 250*
Max Cart. OAL:	3.340"	Test Firearm:	Remington 700
RCBS Shell Holder:	#3	Barrel Length:	22"

NOTE: *CCI No. 34 primers may be substituted for CCI 250.*

0.308"	30 RNSP
Weight, grains	100
Ballistic Coefficient	0.144
Sectional Density	0.151
COAL Tested:	2.935"
Speer Part No.	1805

Propellant	START CHARGE		MAXIMUM CHARGE	
	Weight, grs	Muzzle Velocity, ft/sec	Weight, grs	Muzzle Velocity, ft/sec
IMR 3031	53.0	3199	57.0	3448
IMR 4064	55.0	3152	59.0	3390
H335*	54.0	3099	58.0	3326
748*	56.0	3117	60.0	3313
IMR 4895	51.0	3028	55.0	3268
IMR 4320	54.0	3000	58.0	3236
H322	48.0	2943	52.0	3216
Reloder 7	43.0	2837	47.0	3188
SR 4759 (reduced load)	16.0	1548	20.0	1960

*Maximum Loads should be used with CAUTION • C = Compressed Load • *Magnum Primer used with this powder.*

0.308"	30 HP
Weight, grains	110
Ballistic Coefficient	0.128
Sectional Density	0.166
COAL Tested:	2.870"
Speer Part No.	1835

Propellant	START CHARGE		MAXIMUM CHARGE	
	Weight, grs	Muzzle Velocity, ft/sec	Weight, grs	Muzzle Velocity, ft/sec
760*	52.0	2651	56.0	2865
748*	44.5	2601	48.5	2850
IMR 4350	54.0	2621	58.0	2835
IMR 3031	42.5	2572	46.5	2833
IMR 4895	44.0	2560	48.0	2810
Reloder 7	38.0	2514	42.0	2799
H322	41.0	2504	45.0	2735
BL-C(2)*	48.0	2511	52.0	2732
IMR 4227 (reduced load)	29.0	2297	31.0	2475

NOTE: *This bullet not intended for velocities in excess of 2900 fps.*

0.308"	30 RNSP	30 TMJ RN	30 Spire SP
Weight, grains	110	110	110
Ballistic Coefficient	0.136	0.179	0.245
Sectional Density	0.166	0.166	0.166
COAL Tested:	2.915"	2.915"	3.000"
Speer Part No.	1845	1846	1855

Propellant	START CHARGE Weight, grs	START CHARGE Muzzle Velocity, ft/sec	MAXIMUM CHARGE Weight, grs	MAXIMUM CHARGE Muzzle Velocity, ft/sec
748*	58.0	3151	62.0C	3356
Reloder 15	56.0	3077	60.0C	3307
AA 2460*	51.0	3082	55.0	3293
AA 2520*	52.0	3096	56.0	3288
Varget	55.0	3018	59.0C	3258
IMR 4064	54.0	2924	58.0	3212
Viht. N135	51.0	3003	55.0	3206
AA 2495	51.0	2909	55.0	3167
IMR 4320	53.0	2891	57.0	3088
IMR 4895	50.5	2869	54.5	3080
H4895	49.0	2818	53.0	3076
BL-C(2)*	51.0	2779	55.0	3050
H322	46.0	2754	50.0	2901
AA 5744 (reduced load)	26.0	1956	27.0	2033

*Maximum Loads should be used with CAUTION • C = Compressed Load • *Magnum Primer used with this powder.*

0.308"	30 TNT HP
Weight, grains	125
Ballistic Coefficient	0.341
Sectional Density	0.188
COAL Tested:	3.100"
Speer Part No.	1986

| Propellant | START CHARGE | | MAXIMUM CHARGE | |
	Weight, grs	Muzzle Velocity, ft/sec	Weight, grs	Muzzle Velocity, ft/sec
AA 2460*	49.0	2932	53.0	3129
IMR 3031	50.0	2824	54.0	3118
Viht. N135	49.0	2807	53.0	3069
AA 2015	46.0	2866	50.0	3064
BL-C(2)*	51.0	2836	55.0	3060
AA 2495	50.0	2838	54.0	3059
AA 2230	47.0	2849	51.0	3057
H335*	51.0	2834	55.0	3047
AA 2520*	48.0	2829	52.0	3039
Varget	51.5	2729	55.5	2993
H4895	47.0	2708	51.0	2982
IMR 4320	51.0	2728	55.0	2968
IMR 4895	48.0	2742	52.0	2959
H322	44.0	2687	48.0	2877

0.308"	30 HP	30 FNSP
Weight, grains	130	130
Ballistic Coefficient	0.244	0.212
Sectional Density	0.196	0.196
COAL Tested:	3.060"	3.045"
Speer Part No.	2005	2007

	START CHARGE		MAXIMUM CHARGE	
Propellant	Weight, grs	Muzzle Velocity, ft/sec	Weight, grs	Muzzle Velocity, ft/sec
AA 2460*	47.5	2769	51.0	2987
IMR 4064	51.0	2767	55.0	2979
H414*	56.0	2752	60.0	2969
Varget	51.0	2737	55.0	2963
AA 2015	45.0	2768	49.0	2961
IMR 3031	48.5	2647	52.5	2960
H335*	50.0	2724	54.0	2937
IMR 4895	47.5	2695	51.5	2897
748*	51.0	2695	55.0	2871
BL-C(2)*	49.0	2667	53.0	2855
Viht. N140	48.0	2640	52.0	2830
H4895	45.0	2624	49.0	2730
H322	43.0	2519	47.0	2723
AA 5744 (reduced load)	25.0	1814	27.0	1941

*Maximum Loads should be used with CAUTION • C = Compressed Load • *Magnum Primer used with this powder.*

0.308"	30 RNSP	30 FMJ BT	30 Spitz BTSP	30 Spitz SP	30 MT SP	30 GS SP
Weight, grains	150	150	150	150	150	150
Ballistic Coefficient	0.235	0.425	0.417	0.377	0.278	0.295
Sectional Density	0.226	0.226	0.226	0.226	0.226	0.226
COAL Tested:	3.130"	3.295"	3.250"	3.250"	3.165"	3.160"
Speer Part No.	2017	2018	2022	2023	2025	2026

Propellant	START CHARGE		MAXIMUM CHARGE	
	Weight, grs	Muzzle Velocity, ft/sec	Weight, grs	Muzzle Velocity, ft/sec
H380*	54.0	2658	58.0	2847
IMR 4350	55.0	2591	59.0	2834
Viht. N540	45.0	2633	49.0	2829
H414*	54.0	2603	58.0	2803
Varget	49.0	2559	53.0	2781
760*	53.0	2531	57.0	2778
H4350	55.0	2514	59.0C	2765
IMR 4064	48.0	2520	52.0	2738
Reloder 15	48.0	2523	52.0	2728
IMR 4895	45.5	2516	49.5	2722
Reloder 19	58.0	2521	62.0C	2722
AA 2460*	44.0	2557	48.0	2716
H4895	42.0	2427	46.0	2572
AA 5744 (reduced load)	26.0	1933	28.0	2052

Lab Notes:

Look at the H4895 data above. The start load of 42.0 grains is only slightly faster than the same bullet weight in the 30-30 Winchester with the same bullet weight. This is an excellent hunting load for new shooters or those who are recoil-sensitive.

0.308"	30 TBBC SP
Weight, grains	150
Ballistic Coefficient	0.335
Sectional Density	0.226
COAL Tested:	3.250"
Speer Part No.	1759

Propellant	START CHARGE		MAXIMUM CHARGE	
	Weight, grs	Muzzle Velocity, ft/sec	Weight, grs	Muzzle Velocity, ft/sec
760*	55.0	2807	59.0	2985
IMR 4350	56.0	2768	60.0C	2971
H4350	54.0	2783	58.0	2954
Viht. N540	48.0	2737	52.0	2918
Reloder 19	58.0	2715	62.0C	2911
Varget	47.0	2673	51.0	2875
Reloder 15	47.0	2663	51.0	2867

NOTE: *Trophy Bonded Bear Claw and Trophy Bonded Sledgehammer Solid bullets have unique ballistic behavior compared to conventional bullets. Loads for TBBC and TBSS bullets may not "track" with data for conventional bullets. Use TBBC and TBSS data ONLY for TBBC and TBSS bullets.*

Dave Pupo, Machine Shop, CCI/Speer Operations; 300 WSM 180-grain Fusion® ammo; Alaskan caribou.

*Maximum Loads should be used with CAUTION • C = Compressed Load • *Magnum Primer used with this powder.*

0.308"	30 Spitz BTSP	30 Spitz SP	30 GS SP
Weight, grains	165	165	165
Ballistic Coefficient	0.520	0.444	0.354
Sectional Density	0.248	0.248	0.248
COAL Tested:	3.250"	3.250"	3.165"
Speer Part No.	2034	2035	2038

Propellant	START CHARGE		MAXIMUM CHARGE	
	Weight, grs	Muzzle Velocity, ft/sec	Weight, grs	Muzzle Velocity, ft/sec
760*	53.0	2601	57.0	2803
H4831SC	60.0	2508	62.0C	2772
IMR 4350	54.0	2476	58.0	2747
Viht. N540	43.0	2570	47.0	2740
Reloder 22	58.0	2504	62.0C	2725
H4350	54.0	2464	58.0C	2724
H414*	52.0	2494	56.0	2723
H380*	51.0	2517	55.0	2707
Varget	46.0	2438	50.0	2671
IMR 4831	55.0	2419	59.0	2670
Viht. N140	46.0	2465	50.0	2663
IMR 4064	46.5	2410	50.5	2640
Reloder 19	55.0	2351	59.0C	2614
AA 2520*	42.0	2333	46.0	2595
SR 4759 (reduced load)	21.0	1616	25.0	1941

0.308"	30 TBBC SP
Weight, grains	165
Ballistic Coefficient	0.342
Sectional Density	0.248
COAL Tested:	3.290"
Speer Part No.	1760

Propellant	START CHARGE		MAXIMUM CHARGE	
	Weight, grs	Muzzle Velocity, ft/sec	Weight, grs	Muzzle Velocity, ft/sec
760*	53.0	2601	57.0	2803
H4831SC	60.0	2508	62.0C	2772
IMR 4350	54.0	2476	58.0	2747
Viht. N540	43.0	2570	47.0	2740
Reloder 22	58.0	2504	62.0C	2725
H4350	54.0	2404	50.0C	2724

NOTE: *Trophy Bonded Bear Claw and Trophy Bonded Sledgehammer Solid bullets have unique ballistic behavior compared to conventional bullets. Loads for TBBC and TBSS bullets may not "track" with data for conventional bullets. Use TBBC and TBSS data ONLY for TBBC and TBSS bullets.*

*Maximum Loads should be used with CAUTION • C = Compressed Load • *Magnum Primer used with this powder.*

0.308"	30 Match BTHP
Weight, grains	168
Ballistic Coefficient	0.534
Sectional Density	0.253
COAL Tested:	3.295"
Speer Part No.	2040

Propellant	START CHARGE		MAXIMUM CHARGE	
	Weight, grs	Muzzle Velocity, ft/sec	Weight, grs	Muzzle Velocity, ft/sec
Viht. N160	57.0	2581	61.0	2825
H4350	56.0	2563	60.0C	2795
IMR 4350	55.0	2558	59.0	2782
†H380*	51.0	2454	55.0	2736
IMR 7828*	58.0	2547	62.0	2706
Reloder 19	57.0	2464	61.0C	2697
H4831*	57.0	2426	61.0C	2661
IMR 4831*	56.0	2376	60.0	2633
H414*	50.0	2429	54.0	2633
760*	50.0	2389	54.0	2628
†IMR 4895	44.0	2437	48.0	2605
†IMR 4064	45.0	2367	49.0	2549

†—denotes propellant suitable for gas-operated semi-auto match rifles.

0.308"	30 RNSP	30 Spitz BTSP	30 Spitz SP	30 MT SP	30 GS SP
Weight, grains	180	180	180	180	180
Ballistic Coefficient	0.312	0.545	0.411	0.349	0.374
Sectional Density	0.271	0.271	0.271	0.271	0.271
COAL Tested:	3.130"	3.250"	3.160"	3.160"	3.160"
Speer Part No.	2047	2052	2053	2059	2063

Propellant	START CHARGE		MAXIMUM CHARGE	
	Weight, grs	Muzzle Velocity, ft/sec	Weight, grs	Muzzle Velocity, ft/sec
H4350	54.0	2640	58.0C	2756
IMR 4064	46.0	2583	50.0	2756
Reloder 22	58.0	2618	62.0C	2721
H4831SC	60.0	2581	62.0C	2719
IMR 4831	55.0	2544	59.0C	2684
760*	51.0	2540	55.0	2677
H414*	51.0	2545	55.0	2673
Reloder 19	55.0	2458	59.0C	2640
IMR 4350	52.0	2497	56.0C	2639
AA 4350	53.0	2445	57.0C	2615
Viht. N160	52.0	2331	56.0	2556
Reloder 15	45.0	2411	49.0	2551
IMR 4895	43.0	2365	47.0	2537
IMR 4198 (reduced load)	26.0	1723	30.0	2000

*Maximum Loads should be used with CAUTION • C = Compressed Load • *Magnum Primer used with this powder.*

0.308"	30 TBBC SP
Weight, grains	180
Ballistic Coefficient	0.357
Sectional Density	0.271
COAL Tested:	3.320"
Speer Part No.	1765

Propellant	START CHARGE		MAXIMUM CHARGE	
	Weight, grs	Muzzle Velocity, ft/sec	Weight, grs	Muzzle Velocity, ft/sec
IMR 7828	58.0C	2627	60.0C	2729
H4350	52.0	2630	54.0	2707
Reloder 22	56.0	2616	58.0C	2699
H4831SC	57.0	2606	59.0C	2689
IMR 4350	52.0	2568	54.0	2666
760*	51.0	2574	53.0	2658
Viht. N540	46.0	2518	48.0	2615

NOTE: *Trophy Bonded Bear Claw and Trophy Bonded Sledgehammer Solid bullets have unique ballistic behavior compared to conventional bullets. Loads for TBBC and TBSS bullets may not "track" with data for conventional bullets. Use TBBC and TBSS data ONLY for TBBC and TBSS bullets.*

0.308"	30 Spitz SP	30 GS SP
Weight, grains	200	200
Ballistic Coefficient	0.478	0.453
Sectional Density	0.301	0.301
COAL Tested:	3.295"	3.160"
Speer Part No.	2211	2212

Propellant	START CHARGE		MAXIMUM CHARGE	
	Weight, grs	Muzzle Velocity, ft/sec	Weight, grs	Muzzle Velocity, ft/sec
H4350	53.0	2337	57.0C	2554
Reloder 22	54.0	2263	58.0C	2499
Reloder 25	58.0	2357	60.0C	2481
H414*	49.0	2319	53.0	2453
IMR 4350	50.0	2247	54.0	2449
H4831SC	53.0	2219	57.0C	2447
IMR 4831	52.0	2283	56.0C	2429
Viht. N160	50.0	2198	54.0	2386
Reloder 15	43.0	2203	47.0	2371
H1000	57.0	2152	61.0C	2371
H380*	46.0	2162	50.0	2361
760*	47.0	2240	51.0	2348
Reloder 19	51.0	2158	55.0	2335
IMR 4064	42.0	2146	46.0	2312
IMR 4198 (reduced load)	27.0	1721	31.0	1988

*Maximum Loads should be used with CAUTION • C = Compressed Load • *Magnum Primer used with this powder.*

0.308"	30 TBBC SP
Weight, grains	200
Ballistic Coefficient	0.392
Sectional Density	0.301
COAL Tested:	3.330"
Speer Part No.	1770

Propellant	START CHARGE		MAXIMUM CHARGE	
	Weight, grs	Muzzle Velocity, ft/sec	Weight, grs	Muzzle Velocity, ft/sec
Reloder 25	56.0	2481	58.0C	2571
Reloder 22	53.0	2433	55.0	2515
IMR 7828	53.0	2416	55.0	2502
H4350	48.0	2386	50.0	2462
H4831SC	52.0	2367	54.0	2447
IMR 4350	48.0	2357	50.0	2447
AA 3100	52.0	2353	54.0	2443

NOTE: *Trophy Bonded Bear Claw and Trophy Bonded Sledgehammer Solid bullets have unique ballistic behavior compared to conventional bullets. Loads for TBBC and TBSS bullets may not "track" with data for conventional bullets. Use TBBC and TBSS data ONLY for TBBC and TBSS bullets.*

*Maximum Loads should be used with CAUTION • C = Compressed Load • *Magnum Primer used with this powder.*

300 Remington Short Action Ultra Magnum

Shortly after Winchester announced its 300 Winchester Short Magnum cartridge, Remington answered with its own entry, the 300 Remington Short Action Ultra Magnum. Remington already had a large-diameter, unbelted case inspired by the 404 Jeffery—the 300 Remington Ultra Magnum—so finding a parent case for the Short Action Ultra Magnum was easy.

The Remington case head is only 0.005-inch smaller than the Winchester Short Magnum, and the slightly rebated rim is within 0.001-inch of Winchester's. Still, these are two different cartridges and are not interchangeable.

The Remington SAUM case is slightly shorter than the Winchester SM case, and the shoulder angle is 30° compared to Winchester's 35° angle. This puts the Remington's propellant capacity a few grains behind the WSM. Even so, SAUM handloads produced velocities very close to the larger WSM. Typical velocity differences were 50 ft/sec or less than the WSM with the same propellants and bullets. We doubt that a trophy buck would notice such a small difference.

How do you choose between the Remington SAUM and the Winchester SM? Their performance is so close that the choice comes down to rifle brand and features rather than raw cartridge performance.

Like the other short magnums, the 300 Remington SAUM is suitable for all but the heaviest 30-caliber bullets. Bullets weighing over 180 grains extend into the powder space significantly, reducing velocities almost to 30-06 levels. The 180-grain Trophy Bonded Bear Claw is as long as most 200-grain conventional bullets; we elected not to show data for it for the same reason. However, the 150 and 165-grain Bear Claws are superb bullets in this cartridge.

Compressed charges are common in this compact cartridge. You will need a long drop tube for your powder funnel or powder measure to better settle the charge. This reduces the amount of compression during bullet seating.

The loads presented here remain just under the established maximum average pressure of 65,000 psi.

300 Remington Short Action Ultra Magnum

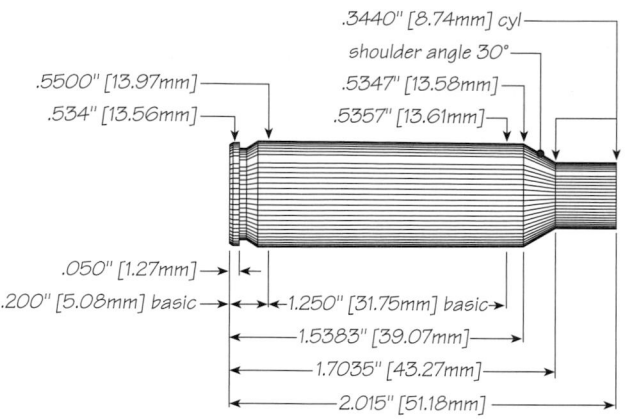

- .3440" [8.74mm] cyl
- shoulder angle 30°
- .5500" [13.97mm]
- .534" [13.56mm]
- .5347" [13.58mm]
- .5357" [13.61mm]
- .050" [1.27mm]
- .200" [5.08mm] basic
- 1.250" [31.75mm] basic
- 1.5383" [39.07mm]
- 1.7035" [43.27mm]
- 2.015" [51.18mm]

Max. Case Length:	2.015"	Cart. Case:	Remington
Trim-to Length:	2.005"	Primer:	CCI 200; 250*
Max Cart. OAL:	2.825"	Test Firearm:	Universal Receiver
RCBS Shell Holder:	#38	Barrel Length:	Krieger 24"

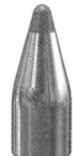

0.308"	30 Spire SP
Weight, grains	110
Ballistic Coefficient	0.245
Sectional Density	0.166
COAL Tested:	2.650"
Speer Part No.	1855

	START CHARGE		MAXIMUM CHARGE	
Propellant	Weight, grs	Muzzle Velocity, ft/sec	Weight, grs	Muzzle Velocity, ft/sec
Ramshot Big Game	67.0	3416	71.0	3591
H380*	67.0	3427	71.0	3585
Reloder 15	61.0	3350	65.0	3575
H414*	68.0	3385	72.0	3564
760*	69.0	3405	73.0	3562
IMR 4064	60.0	3336	64.0	3561
Varget	59.0	3331	63.0	3550
AA 5744 (reduced load)	27.0	2058	29.0	2183

0.308"	30 HP
Weight, grains	130
Ballistic Coefficient	0.244
Sectional Density	0.196
COAL Tested:	2.625"
Speer Part No.	2005

Propellant	START CHARGE		MAXIMUM CHARGE	
	Weight, grs	Muzzle Velocity, ft/sec	Weight, grs	Muzzle Velocity, ft/sec
760*	66.0	3189	70.0C	3381
IMR 4064	57.0	3127	61.0	3370
Viht. N540	58.0	3089	62.0	3366
H414*	65.0	3170	69.0C	3366
Reloder 15	58.0	3063	62.0	33½
H380*	62.0	3110	66.0	3313
Ramshot Big Game*	62.0	3125	66.0	3306
IMR 4350	65.0C	3128	69.0C	3293
Varget	56.0	3064	60.0	3277
AA 5744 (reduced load)	27.0	1977	29.0	2104

NOTE: *125-gr TNT HP not recommended for this cartridge.*

Mark VonLindern, Manager of Manufacturing Engineering, CCI/Speer Operations, on a mounted hunt in the Idaho back country.

*Maximum Loads should be used with CAUTION • C = Compressed Load • *Magnum Primer used with this powder.*

0.308"	30 RNSP	30 Spitz BTSP	30 Spitz SP	30 MT SP	30 GS SP
Weight, grains	150	150	150	150	150
Ballistic Coefficient	0.235	0.417	0.377	0.278	0.295
Sectional Density	0.226	0.226	0.226	0.226	0.226
COAL Tested:	2.670"	2.800"	2.800"	2.685"	2.680"
Speer Part No.	2017	2022	2023	2025	2026

Propellant	START CHARGE Weight, grs	START CHARGE Muzzle Velocity, ft/sec	MAXIMUM CHARGE Weight, grs	MAXIMUM CHARGE Muzzle Velocity, ft/sec
Viht. N560	69.0	3030	73.0C	3210
760*	64.0	3041	68.0	3194
AA 4350	64.0	2974	68.0C	3173
IMR 4831	65.0	2963	69.0C	3158
H414*	62.0	3004	66.0	3158
H4350	62.0	2969	66.0	3152
IMR 4350	63.0	2981	67.0	3150
Reloder 19	67.0	2969	71.0C	3150
AA 2700*	60.0	2963	64.0	3106
Varget	54.0	2913	58.0	3088
H4831SC	67.0	2910	71.0C	3072
AA 5744 (reduced load)	28.0	1922	30.0	2039

0.308"	30 TBBC SP
Weight, grains	150
Ballistic Coefficient	0.335
Sectional Density	0.226
COAL Tested:	2.800"
Speer Part No.	1759

Propellant	START CHARGE		MAXIMUM CHARGE	
	Weight, grs	Muzzle Velocity, ft/sec	Weight, grs	Muzzle Velocity, ft/sec
760*	63.0	2959	67.0	3151
Viht. N560	67.0	2906	71.0	3120
Reloder 19	66.0	2901	70.0	3104
H414*	61.0	2898	65.0	3104
Ramshot Big Game*	59.0	2923	63.0	3086
IMR 4350	61.0	2837	65.0	3075
H4831SC	67.0	2908	71.0	3051
Varget	53.0	2869	57.0	3011

NOTE: *Trophy Bonded Bear Claw and Trophy Bonded Sledgehammer Solid bullets have unique ballistic behavior compared to conventional bullets. Loads for TBBC and TBSS bullets may not "track" with data for conventional bullets. Use TBBC and TBSS data ONLY for TBBC and TBSS bullets.*

*Maximum Loads should be used with CAUTION • C = Compressed Load • *Magnum Primer used with this powder.*

0.308"	30 Spitz BTSP	30 Spitz SP	30 GS SP
Weight, grains	165	165	165
Ballistic Coefficient	0.520	0.444	0.354
Sectional Density	0.248	0.248	0.248
COAL Tested:	2.800"	2.800"	2.685"
Speer Part No.	2034	2035	2038

Propellant	START CHARGE		MAXIMUM CHARGE	
	Weight, grs	Muzzle Velocity, ft/sec	Weight, grs	Muzzle Velocity, ft/sec
Viht. N560	67.0	2886	71.0C	3063
760*	62.0	2860	66.0	3035
IMR 4831	63.0	2808	67.0C	3011
Reloder 22	66.0	2839	70.0C	3006
Reloder 19	65.0	2807	69.0C	2999
H4350	60.0	2809	64.0	2983
IMR 4350	60.5	2784	64.5	2978
IMR 7828	67.0	2834	69.0C	2928

0.308"	30 TBBC SP
Weight, grains	165
Ballistic Coefficient	0.342
Sectional Density	0.248
COAL Tested:	2.800"
Speer Part No.	1760

Propellant	START CHARGE		MAXIMUM CHARGE	
	Weight, grs	Muzzle Velocity, ft/sec	Weight, grs	Muzzle Velocity, ft/sec
IMR 4831	63.0	2828	67.0C	3032
Reloder 19	65.0	2854	69.0C	3029
H4350	60.0	2841	64.0	3021
IMR 4350	60.0	2804	64.0	3013
760*	61.0	2846	65.0	3004
Viht. N560	67.0	2900	69.0C	2988
Reloder 22	66.0	2868	68.0C	2952
H4831SC	64.0	2764	68.0C	2934
IMR 7828	65.0	2725	67.0C	2830

NOTE: *Trophy Bonded Bear Claw and Trophy Bonded Sledgehammer Solid bullets have unique ballistic behavior compared to conventional bullets. Loads for TBBC and TBSS bullets may not "track" with data for conventional bullets. Use TBBC and TBSS data ONLY for TBBC and TBSS bullets.*

*Maximum Loads should be used with CAUTION • C = Compressed Load • *Magnum Primer used with this powder.*

0.308"	30 RNSP	30 Spitz BTSP	30 Spitz SP	30 MT SP	30 GS SP
Weight, grains	180	180	180	180	180
Ballistic Coefficient	0.312	0.545	0.441	0.349	0.374
Sectional Density	0.271	0.271	0.271	0.271	0.271
COAL Tested:	2.580"	2.800"	2.800"	2.680"	2.680"
Speer Part No.	2047	2052	2053	2059	2063

Propellant	START CHARGE		MAXIMUM CHARGE	
	Weight, grs	Muzzle Velocity, ft/sec	Weight, grs	Muzzle Velocity, ft/sec
IMR 4831	61.0	2731	65.0C	2921
Reloder 19	63.0	2727	67.0C	2896
Reloder 22	63.0	2736	67.0C	2896
IMR 7828	64.0	2722	68.0C	2892
IMR 4350	58.0	2703	62.0	2880
H414*	57.0	2726	61.0	2877
760*	57.0	2700	61.0	2854
H4350	57.0	2700	61.0	2853

*Maximum Loads should be used with CAUTION • C = Compressed Load • *Magnum Primer used with this powder.*

300 Winchester Short Magnum

Introduced in 2001, the 300 Winchester Short Magnum cartridge soon evolved into other diameters and even shorter versions. All use the theory of a short case body of larger than "normal" diameter.

Although the Winchester Short Magnum series and similar cartridges from Remington stirred up a lot of press coverage as the "latest and greatest," they are in reality an evolutionary product of a much older cartridge concept, the 284 Winchester (1963). The 284 used a short, rebated-rim case to roughly equal the velocity potential of the longer 280 Remington case with lighter hunting bullets. The rebated rim allowed the cartridge to fit standard 0.473-inch bolt faces yet has a larger body diameter to boost propellant capacity. The 284 was the ideal length for compact actions suitable for cartridges such as the 243 and 308 Winchester.

It is the last feature that makes today's short magnums so appealing. In the continuing trend toward ever-lighter hunting rifles, ounces count. A rifle built on a 308-length action can be four to twelve ounces lighter than a similar rifle built on a 30-06 length action. For this reason alone, the 300 WSM is worthy of existence. The short-action ultralight rifle, once restricted to cartridges of modest performance, enters the magnum arena. With bullets up to 180 grains, the 300 WSM virtually equals the venerable 300 H&H Magnum.

The Winchester Short Magnum series uses a non-belted case, an excellent design decision. The maximum body diameter seems inspired by an old British cartridge, the 404 Jeffery. The Jeffery's rebated rim is so subtle that most casual observers would not notice. The WSM series' rebated rim is likewise a mere 0.020-inch smaller than the body.

In developing reloading data for the 300 WSM, we were impressed by the consistency of performance over a broad range of bullet weights and propellant types. Unlike its large-capacity forebears, a compact cartridge does not become "ragged" in velocity and pressure when light bullets and/or faster-burning propellants are loaded. Some shooters must see some magic in the short case design as they expect miraculous velocities from it. Yes, the short case is efficient; no, it cannot perform miracles. It delivers excellent performance in spite of its size. The loads presented here can take any North American game with the exception of dangerous bear species.

The only limitation to the 300 WSM and its look-a-likes is that long bullets (200 grains and up) protrude into the case and take up powder space. Velocities with heavy bullets do not track with those of lighter bullets, and we elected to not show data for our 200-grain bullets. We screened some 200-grain loads and there was little gain over the 30-06. Best performance comes with 180-grain bullets and lighter. Most 30-caliber hunting bullets fired each season are between 150 and 180 grains, so this should not present a problem. The 180-grain Trophy Bonded Bear Claw is as long as most conventional 200-grain bullets; we elected not to show data for it for the same reason. The 165-grain Bear Claw will out-penetrate virtually all 180-grain bullets of conventional construction.

At the other end of the bullet weight spectrum, the 300 WSM shows remarkably uniform performance with varmint bullets as light as 110 grains, something large-case 30-caliber magnums do not. Velocities over 3700 ft/sec were common. This is not a varmint cartridge, but clearly has varmint capability should you wisely choose to spend some quality time with your rifle in the spring. Being familiar with your rifle is a key to being an outstanding rifle shot; spring varmint hunts maintain that familiarity.

In handloading the 300 WSM, we encountered nothing out of the ordinary. As with many compact cases, a number of loads were compressed. Be prepared to use a funnel or powder measure with a long drop tube, such as included the RCBS Quick Change series of powder dispensing products.

The industry maximum average pressure assigned the 300 WSM is 65,000 psi.

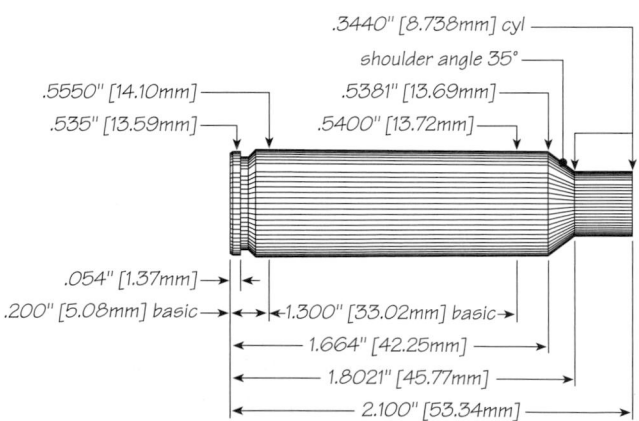

Max. Case Length:	2.100"	Cart. Case:	Winchester
Trim-to Length:	2.090"	Primer:	CCI 200; 250*
Max Cart. OAL:	2.860"	Test Firearm:	Universal Receiver
RCBS Shell Holder:	#43	Barrel Length:	Krieger 24"

0.308"	30 Spire SP
Weight, grains	110
Ballistic Coefficient	0.245
Sectional Density	0.166
COAL Tested:	2.750"
Speer Part No.	1855

Propellant	START CHARGE		MAXIMUM CHARGE	
	Weight, grs	Muzzle Velocity, ft/sec	Weight, grs	Muzzle Velocity, ft/sec
H414*	75.0	3637	79.0	3799
760*	76.0	3603	80.0	3764
IMR 4064	64.0	3510	68.0	3727
H380	72.0	3554	76.0	3720
Reloder 15	65.0	3506	69.0	3692
Varget	66.0	3481	70.0	3666
IMR 4350	73.0	3436	75.0	3514
AA 5744 (reduced load)	28.0	2054	30.0	2190

Lab Notes:

The term "short magnum," although indisputably descriptive, probably should not have been applied to the 300 WSM and its kin. Why? The term has already been used.

The first sporting "magnums" for American shooters were based on the long 375 Holland & Holland case. This 3.6-inch cartridge required special long actions when it first appeared. Wildcats based on this case without a reduction in case length also required similarly generous actions that were not always readily available. Suitable actions were sold as "magnum length" actions.

Eventually, experimenters shortened the H&H case to 30-06 length (ex., 300 Winchester Magnum; 7mm Remington Magnum) to fit the 1903 Springfield and other similar actions. These were classed as "short magnums" and were intended to fit lengthwise in any action that could handle the 30-06 cartridge. This action class became known as "standard length." Actions whose maximum length capacity is limited to the 308 Winchester are "short actions."

In a way, calling the recent developments "short magnums" high-jacks a useful and previously defined term. Remington's moniker, "short action ultra magnum," is probably the better term in light of our sport's heritage.

*Maximum Loads should be used with CAUTION • C = Compressed Load • *Magnum Primer used with this powder.*

0.308"	30 HP
Weight, grains	130
Ballistic Coefficient	0.244
Sectional Density	0.196
COAL Tested:	2.800"
Speer Part No.	2005

Propellant	START CHARGE		MAXIMUM CHARGE	
	Weight, grs	Muzzle Velocity, ft/sec	Weight, grs	Muzzle Velocity, ft/sec
760*	72.0	3353	76.0	3533
H414*	70.0	3345	74.0	3523
IMR 4064	63.0	3325	67.0	3505
Viht. N540	64.0	3314	68.0	3498
IMR 4350	71.0	3277	75.0C	3476
Varget	64.0	3269	68.0	3468
Reloder 15	63.0	3285	67.0	3459
H380	68.0	3272	72.0	3437
AA 5744 (reduced load)	29.0	2113	31.0	2227

Mike VonLindern, brother of Mark VonLindern, CCI/Speer Manufacturing Engineering Manager, took this trophy bighorn in Idaho's Frank Church Wilderness near Big Creek with a 270 Winchester and a prototype 150-grain Fusion bullet.

0.308"	30 RNSP	30 Spitz BTSP	30 Spitz SP	30 MT SP	30 GS SP
Weight, grains	150	150	150	150	150
Ballistic Coefficient	0.235	0.417	0.377	0.278	0.295
Sectional Density	0.226	0.226	0.226	0.226	0.226
COAL Tested:	2.700"	2.810"	2.810"	2.760"	2.780"
Speer Part No.	2017	2022	2023	2025	2026

Propellant	START CHARGE Weight, grs	START CHARGE Muzzle Velocity, ft/sec	MAXIMUM CHARGE Weight, grs	MAXIMUM CHARGE Muzzle Velocity, ft/sec
AA 4350	67.0	3115	71.0C	3269
Viht. N560	71.5	3098	75.5C	3265
IMR 4831	67.0	3101	71.0	3256
H4350	64.0	3086	68.0	3256
H414*	64.0	3109	68.0	3255
IMR 4350	65.0	3043	69.0	3245
Reloder 19	69.5	3049	73.5	3244
760*	64.5	3085	68.5	3238
AA 2700*	61.0	3069	65.0	3197
H4831SC	69.0	3040	73.0	3177
Varget	55.0	2972	59.0	3154
H380*	61.0	2994	65.0	3150
748*	55.0	2966	59.0	3112
Viht. N140	52.0	2880	56.0	3024
AA 5744 (reduced load)	29.0	2035	33.0	2259

*Maximum Loads should be used with CAUTION • C = Compressed Load • *Magnum Primer used with this powder.*

0.308"	30 TBBC SP
Weight, grains	150
Ballistic Coefficient	0.335
Sectional Density	0.226
COAL Tested:	2.855"
Speer Part No.	1759

Propellant	START CHARGE		MAXIMUM CHARGE	
	Weight, grs	Muzzle Velocity, ft/sec	Weight, grs	Muzzle Velocity, ft/sec
H414*	70.0	3246	72.0	3334
760*	70.5	3194	72.5	3283
IMR 4350	67.0	3080	71.0C	3270
Viht. N560	72.5	3086	76.5C	3260
Reloder 19	71.0	3072	75.0C	3250
Varget	60.0	3050	64.0	3202
H4831SC	73.0	3064	77.0C	3199

NOTE: *Trophy Bonded Bear Claw and Trophy Bonded Sledgehammer Solid bullets have unique ballistic behavior compared to conventional bullets. Loads for TBBC and TBSS bullets may not "track" with data for conventional bullets. Use TBBC and TBSS data ONLY for TBBC and TBSS bullets.*

0.308"	30 Spitz BTSP	30 Spitz SP	30 GS SP
Weight, grains	165	165	165
Ballistic Coefficient	0.520	0.444	0.354
Sectional Density	0.248	0.248	0.248
COAL Tested:	2.810"	2.810"	2.780"
Speer Part No.	2034	2035	2038

Propellant	START CHARGE		MAXIMUM CHARGE	
	Weight, grs	Muzzle Velocity, ft/sec	Weight, grs	Muzzle Velocity, ft/sec
IMR 7828	71.0C	3019	75.0C	3167
Viht. N560	70.0	3012	74.0C	3151
AA 4350	66.0	2968	70.0C	3138
Reloder 19	69.0	2983	73.0C	3135
IMR 4831	66.5	2984	70.5C	3131
Reloder 22	69.0	2978	73.0C	3126
IMR 4350	64.5	2932	68.5	3103
H414*	63.5	2961	67.5C	3099
760*	64.0	2968	68.0	3097
AA 3100	71.0	2979	73.0C	3075
H4350	61.0	2944	65.0	3073
H4831SC	68.5	2925	72.5C	3062

*Maximum Loads should be used with CAUTION • C = Compressed Load • *Magnum Primer used with this powder.*

0.308"	30 TBBC SP
Weight, grains	165
Ballistic Coefficient	0.342
Sectional Density	0.248
COAL Tested:	2.810"
Speer Part No.	1760

Propellant	START CHARGE		MAXIMUM CHARGE	
	Weight, grs	Muzzle Velocity, ft/sec	Weight, grs	Muzzle Velocity, ft/sec
IMR 4831	65.0	2948	69.0	3115
Viht. N560	66.0	2932	70.0	3091
Reloder 22	67.0	2946	71.0	3086
Reloder 19	66.0	2919	70.0	3086
760*	62.0	2963	66.0	3083
IMR 4350	62.0	2919	66.0	3079
H4350	61.0	2905	65.0	3074
H4831SC	67.0	2915	71.0	3065

NOTE: *Trophy Bonded Bear Claw and Trophy Bonded Sledgehammer Solid bullets have unique ballistic behavior compared to conventional bullets. Loads for TBBC and TBSS bullets may not "track" with data for conventional bullets. Use TBBC and TBSS data ONLY for TBBC and TBSS bullets.*

0.308"	30 RNSP	30 Spitz BTSP	30 Spitz SP	30 MT SP	30 GS SP
Weight, grains	180	180	180	180	180
Ballistic Coefficient	0.312	0.545	0.441	0.349	0.374
Sectional Density	0.271	0.271	0.271	0.271	0.271
COAL Tested:	2.700"	2.800"	2.780"	2.740"	2.760"
Speer Part No.	2047	2052	2053	2059	2063

Propellant	START CHARGE		MAXIMUM CHARGE	
	Weight, grs	Muzzle Velocity, ft/sec	Weight, grs	Muzzle Velocity, ft/sec
Reloder 19	64.5	2819	68.5C	2978
IMR 4831	63.0	2820	67.0C	2970
Reloder 22	64.5	2797	68.5C	2958
IMR 7828	66.0	2805	70.0C	2947
IMR 4350	61.0	2782	65.0	2946
760*	61.0	2786	65.0	2941
H414*	60.0	2786	64.0	2939
H4350	59.5	2745	63.5	2920
H4831SC	65.0	2780	69.0C	2906
AA 2700*	58.0	2750	62.0	2896
Viht. N160	61.0	2732	65.0	2867
H380*	58.0	2705	62.0	2843

*Maximum Loads should be used with CAUTION • C = Compressed Load • *Magnum Primer used with this powder.*

300 H&H Magnum

The famous British firm of Holland & Holland pioneered the belted rifle case in 1905. The 400/375 Belted Nitro Express case featured a raised belt of metal just ahead of the extraction cannelure to give reliable headspace control to a case that lacked an adequate shoulder. This eliminated the need for a traditional rim and allowed the cartridge to feed reliably in magazine-fed bolt-action rifles. In 1912, the longer 375 H&H Magnum appeared wearing a belt, followed around 1920 by "Holland's Super 30" based on the long 375 case. The 30-caliber version later became known to the U.S. industry as the 300 Holland & Holland Magnum.

Because the loaded H&H cartridge was 0.30-inch longer than the 30-06, there were no commercial U.S. bolt-action rifles long enough to handle the 300 H&H in 1920. 300 H&H rifles were either expensive English imports or custom models built on the costly Magnum Mauser action. Domestic ammunition was offered by Western Cartridge Company as early as 1925 but over a decade passed before the first American-built rifles appeared, encouraged by a major match victory.

In 1935, Ben Comfort won the prestigious 1000-yard Wimbledon Cup at the National Matches using a custom 300 H&H built by Griffin & Howe. His victory helped Winchester elect to chamber its Model 70 for the 300 H&H in 1937. For the first time, there was an American production rifle for the powerful 300 Magnum. It was the "super-gun" of its day.

Until the introduction of the 300 Winchester Magnum in 1963, the H&H version was THE 300 Magnum (the 300 Weatherby Magnum was not a standardized cartridge until 1994). It quickly established a reputation for accurate, flat-shooting power and has been used on almost every game species around the world. Because the case diameter is larger than the 30-06, the case holds more powder for a significant ballistic advantage. This advantage led to it becoming the parent to a staggering variety of both wildcat and commercial magnum cartridges.

The belted case has become synonymous with the word "magnum," although the 300 H&H and its big brother, the 375 H&H are among a tiny number of bottleneck cartridges today that rely on the belt for headspace control. Newer belted magnum rifle cartridges have adequate shoulders for headspacing. For years, it seemed the shooting public wanted a belt on anything called a "magnum." Fortunately, the recent development of "short magnums" has convinced the shooting public of the redundancy of a case belt when a generous case shoulder is provided.

The 300 H&H can be loaded with the full range of Speer 30-caliber bullets. In spite of its tapered case and long, sloping shoulder, it remains today as one of the most efficient 30-caliber magnums and delivers very respectable velocities with less propellant than some newer magnums. It is a tribute to the case design that it survived over 80 years before a smaller case, the 300 Winchester Short Magnum, equaled its overall performance. Still the 300 H&H holds an advantage over the WSM and its kin for the heavy-bullet hunter: the long H&H allows plenty of velocity with 200 and 220-grain bullets. The newer short magnums give up a lot of powder space when long bullets are used.

The 300 H&H is probably more cartridge than needed for smaller deer. However, it is a potent cartridge for any other North American game with the exception of the largest bears. For long shots on mule deer, mountain sheep or goats, elk and moose, the 300 H&H is hard to beat.

The loads listed here do not exceed the SAAMI maximum average of 54,000 CUP.

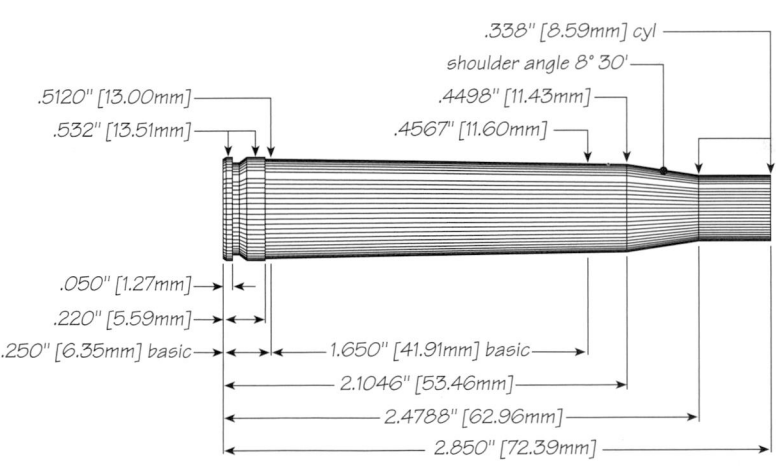

Max. Case Length:	2.850"	Cart. Case:	Winchester
Trim-to Length:	2.840"	Primer:	CCI 200; 250*
Max Cart. OAL:	3.600"	Test Firearm:	Winchester Model 70
RCBS Shell Holder:	#4	Barrel Length:	26"

0.308"	30 RNSP
Weight, grains	100
Ballistic Coefficient	0.144
Sectional Density	0.151
COAL Tested:	3.260"
Speer Part No.	1805

| Propellant | START CHARGE | | MAXIMUM CHARGE | |
	Weight, grs	Muzzle Velocity, ft/sec	Weight, grs	Muzzle Velocity, ft/sec
IMR 4895	54.0	3148	58.0	3367
IMR 4064	52.0	2973	56.0	3195
IMR 4320	52.0	2751	56.0	3040
H380*	54.0	2813	58.0	3030
IMR 3031	47.0	2758	51.0	2976
IMR 4198	39.0	2591	43.0	2907
748*	51.0	2655	55.0	2901
IMR 4350	54.0	2604	58.0	2809
SR 4759 (reduced load)	21.0	1671	23.0	1844

Coy Getman, Technical Services Coordinator, CCI/Speer Operations; 375 H&H, 285-grain Grand Slam®; cape buffalo taken in Zimbabwe.

0.308"	30 HP
Weight, grains	110
Ballistic Coefficient	0.128
Sectional Density	0.166
COAL Tested:	3.230"
Speer Part No.	1835

| Propellant | START CHARGE | | MAXIMUM CHARGE | |
	Weight, grs	Muzzle Velocity, ft/sec	Weight, grs	Muzzle Velocity, ft/sec
IMR 4198	39.0	2631	43.0	2890
748*	51.0	2611	55.0	2876
IMR 4064	48.0	2663	52.0	2874
IMR 3031	47.0	2588	51.0	2864
IMR 4895	46.0	2636	50.0	2850
IMR 4350	56.0	2651	60.0	2849
SR 4759†	35.0	2563	39.0	2842
IMR 4320	48.0	2597	52.0	2825
IMR 4227	33.0	2402	37.0	2688

NOTE: *Do not exceed 2900 fps with this bullet. †—do not confuse with SR 4756 or excessive pressures will result.*

*Maximum Loads should be used with CAUTION • C = Compressed Load • *Magnum Primer used with this powder.*

0.308"	30 RNSP	30 Spire SP
Weight, grains	110	110
Ballistic Coefficient	0.136	0.245
Sectional Density	0.166	0.166
COAL Tested:	3.300"	3.430"
Speer Part No.	1845	1855

Propellant	START CHARGE		MAXIMUM CHARGE	
	Weight, grs	Muzzle Velocity, ft/sec	Weight, grs	Muzzle Velocity, ft/sec
IMR 4350	71.0	3429	75.0	3662
IMR 4831	72.0	3384	76.0C	3621
H380*	67.0	3303	71.0	3570
Reloder 19*	75.0	3257	79.0	3538
IMR 4064	61.0	3345	65.0	3515
AA 4350*	73.0	3285	77.0C	3508
IMR 4895	58.0	3265	62.0	3486
Viht. N160*	70.0	3259	74.0	3480
760*	67.0	3195	71.0	3462
AA 3100*	75.0	3074	79.0C	3290
IMR 4320	54.0	3003	58.0	3275
SR 4759 (reduced load)	19.0	1632	23.0	1908

0.308"	30 HP
Weight, grains	130
Ballistic Coefficient	0.244
Sectional Density	0.196
COAL Tested:	3.440"
Speer Part No.	2005

Propellant	START CHARGE		MAXIMUM CHARGE	
	Weight, grs	Muzzle Velocity, ft/sec	Weight, grs	Muzzle Velocity, ft/sec
IMR 4831	70.0	3197	74.0C	3390
IMR 4350	68.0	3129	72.0C	3375
IMR 3031	55.0	3094	59.0	3311
AA 4350*	70.0	3060	74.0	3301
Reloder 19*	71.0	3098	75.0	3300
AA 3100*	74.0	3103	78.0C	3291
IMR 4064	58.0	3011	62.0	3259
Viht. N160*	66.0	2984	70.0	3227
760*	65.0	2952	69.0	3195
IMR 4895	55.0	2982	59.0	3167
H380*	58.0	2765	62.0	3021
SR 4759 (reduced load)	22.0	1737	24.0	1901

*Maximum Loads should be used with CAUTION • C = Compressed Load • *Magnum Primer used with this powder.*

0.308"	30 RNSP	30 FMJ BT	30 Spitz BTSP	30 Spitz SP	30 MT SP	30 GS SP
Weight, grains	150	150	150	150	150	150
Ballistic Coefficient	0.235	0.425	0.417	0.377	0.278	0.295
Sectional Density	0.226	0.226	0.226	0.226	0.226	0.226
COAL Tested:	3.385"	3.600"	3.500"	3.500"	3.520"	3.515"
Speer Part No.	2017	2018	2022	2023	2025	2026

Propellant	START CHARGE		MAXIMUM CHARGE	
	Weight, grs	Muzzle Velocity, ft/sec	Weight, grs	Muzzle Velocity, ft/sec
IMR 4831	69.0	3133	73.0	3322
IMR 4350	66.0	3099	70.0	3295
Reloder 19*	68.0	3004	72.0	3223
Viht. N165*	69.0	2984	73.0	3178
IMR 4064	57.0	2944	61.0	3159
AA 3100*	68.0	2963	72.0	3142
AA 4350*	64.0	2927	68.0	3113
IMR 3031	52.0	2969	56.0	3102
IMR 4895	53.0	2737	57.0	2993
IMR 4320	52.0	2674	56.0	2918
H380*	57.0	2651	61.0	2914
SR 4759 (reduced load)	25.0	1795	27.0	1942

0.308"	30 Spitz BTSP	30 Spitz SP	30 GS SP
Weight, grains	165	165	165
Ballistic Coefficient	0.520	0.444	0.354
Sectional Density	0.248	0.248	0.248
COAL Tested:	3.500"	3.500"	3.355"
Speer Part No.	2034	2035	2038

Propellant	START CHARGE		MAXIMUM CHARGE	
	Weight, grs	Muzzle Velocity, ft/sec	Weight, grs	Muzzle Velocity, ft/sec
IMR 4831	67.0	2996	71.0	3185
IMR 4350	65.0	2991	69.0	3185
Reloder 19	63.0	2874	67.0	3048
IMR 4064	56.0	2837	60.0	3035
760*	63.0	2777	67.0	3024
AA 4350*	61.0	2766	65.0	2940
Viht. N165	63.0	2749	67.0	2922
AA 3100*	64.0	2728	68.0	2910
IMR 4895	52.0	2619	56.0	2881
IMR 3031	52.0	2629	56.0	2872
AA 2700*	54.0	2660	58.0	2815
IMR 4320	51.0	2546	55.0	2795
SR 4759 (reduced load)	24.0	1642	28.0	1908

*Maximum Loads should be used with CAUTION • C = Compressed Load • *Magnum Primer used with this powder.*

0.308"	30 RNSP	30 Spitz BTSP	30 Spitz SP	30 MT SP	30 GS SP
Weight, grains	180	180	180	180	180
Ballistic Coefficient	0.312	0.545	0.441	0.349	0.374
Sectional Density	0.271	0.271	0.271	0.271	0.271
COAL Tested:	3.430"	3.500"	3.500"	3.520"	3.515"
Speer Part No.	2047	2052	2053	2059	2063

	START CHARGE		MAXIMUM CHARGE	
Propellant	Weight, grs	Muzzle Velocity, ft/sec	Weight, grs	Muzzle Velocity, ft/sec
IMR 4350	64.0	2897	68.0	3086
IMR 4831	66.0	2853	70.0	3039
Reloder 22*	66.0	2812	70.0	2996
760*	61.0	2688	65.0	2921
H414*	59.0	2652	63.0	2892
Viht. N165*	63.5	2732	67.5	2891
IMR 4064	54.0	2619	58.0	2868
AA 3100*	65.0	2682	69.0	2850
AA 4350*	60.0	2676	64.0	2832
IMR 4198 (reduced load)	31.0	1841	35.0	2088

0.308"	30 Spitz SP	30 GS SP
Weight, grains	200	200
Ballistic Coefficient	0.478	0.453
Sectional Density	0.301	0.301
COAL Tested:	3.500"	3.515"
Speer Part No.	2211	2212

Propellant	START CHARGE		MAXIMUM CHARGE	
	Weight, grs	Muzzle Velocity, ft/sec	Weight, grs	Muzzle Velocity, ft/sec
IMR 4350	62.0	2658	66.0	2879
IMR 4831	63.0	2660	67.0	2844
Reloder 22*	61.0	2605	65.0	2774
H414*	58.0	2539	62.0	2767
AA 4350*	57.0	2514	61.0	2705
Viht. N165*	59.0	2469	63.0	2687
AA 3100*	59.0	2484	63.0	2629
IMR 4198 (reduced load)	32.0	1818	36.0	2032

Susan Getman, wife of Coy Getman, Technical Services Coordinator, CCI/Speer Operations; 300 Win Mag, 180-grain Grand Slam®; her first impala, taken in Zimbabwe.

Maximum Loads should be used with CAUTION • C = Compressed Load • *Magnum Primer used with this powder.

308 Norma Magnum

The 308 Norma Magnum was developed around 1960 as a belted magnum cartridge suitable for use in converted 30-06 length actions. At that time, no commercial 30-caliber magnum used the shorter case and Norma saw the opportunity to enter the magnum market in a big way. They chose a unique method for introducing American shooters to their new cartridge.

In 1961, Norma made unprimed brass and loading data available in the U.S. and courted gunsmiths to start rechambering 30-06 rifles. To this end, they supplied chambering reamers on a "loaner" basis. This encouraged gunsmiths to build rifles and resulted in very uniform chambers. A good 30-06 sporter could be easily converted to the new magnum by opening the bolt face to accept the larger H&H case head diameter and rechambering.

About a year later, Norma imported loaded ammunition for those who chose not to handload. Some factory European rifles were also chambered for the 308 Norma. The cartridge and the converted rifles were quite successful for a time, but the introduction of the 300 Winchester Magnum in 1963 and the availability of standard-price U.S. factory rifles and ammo diminished interest in the Norma cartridge.

There is little real difference in performance between the Norma and Winchester Magnums. They can be used on the same type of game, so the one-gun hunter can be quite satisfied with the 308 Norma.

Although chamber uniformity is usually good with this cartridge, some gunsmiths used different barrel throat lengths. Before reloading, establish the proper cartridge overall length that keeps the bullet from engaging the rifling before it is fired.

There are no U.S. pressure standards for this cartridge. Norma reports a maximum pressure of 55,100 psi. These loads were completely safe in the test rifle but, as with any cartridge, always begin with the published starting loads and work up carefully in your rifle.

If 308 Norma cases can't be found in your area, they can be readily formed from 338 Winchester cases by necking down in the sizer die and trimming if required.

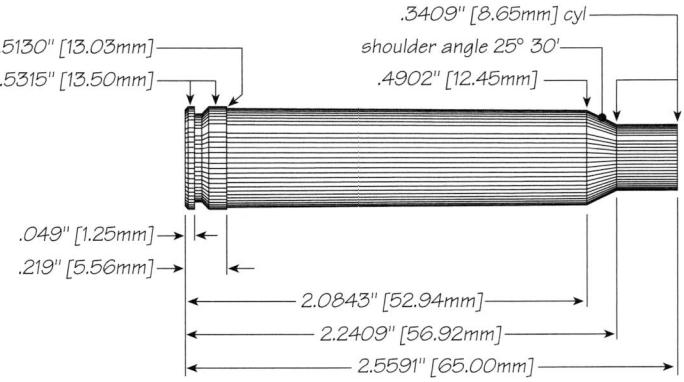

Max. Case Length:	2.559"	Cart. Case:	Norma
Trim-to Length:	2.549"	Primer:	CCI 250*
Max Cart. OAL:	3.346"	Test Firearm:	Sako
RCBS Shell Holder:	#4	Barrel Length:	24.5"

0.308"	30 RNSP
Weight, grains	100
Ballistic Coefficient	0.144
Sectional Density	0.151
COAL Tested:	2.870"
Speer Part No.	1805

	START CHARGE		MAXIMUM CHARGE	
Propellant	Weight, grs	Muzzle Velocity, ft/sec	Weight, grs	Muzzle Velocity, ft/sec
H414*	73.0	3411	**77.0**	3663
H380*	66.0	3289	**70.0**	3497
IMR 3031*	57.0	3231	**61.0**	3448
IMR 4895*	59.0	3209	**63.0**	3422
IMR 4064*	62.0	3179	**66.0**	3388
IMR 4320*	62.0	3159	**66.0**	3367
IMR 4198*	46.0	2977	**50.0**	3220
SR 4759* (reduced load)	20.0	1739	**22.0**	1908

*Maximum Loads should be used with CAUTION • C = Compressed Load • *Magnum Primer used with this powder.*

308 Norma Magnum

0.308"	30 HP
Weight, grains	110
Ballistic Coefficient	0.128
Sectional Density	0.166
COAL Tested:	2.960"
Speer Part No.	1835

	START CHARGE		MAXIMUM CHARGE	
Propellant	Weight, grs	Muzzle Velocity, ft/sec	Weight, grs	Muzzle Velocity, ft/sec
H414*	56.0	2692	60.0	2909
IMR 4064*	50.0	2679	54.0	2882
IMR 4895*	48.0	2669	52.0	2882
IMR 3031*	48.0	2662	52.0	2880
H322*	46.0	2631	50.0	2879
H380*	53.0	2676	57.0	2873
SR 4759*	37.0	2562	41.0	2846
IMR 4198*	41.0	2576	45.0	2844
IMR 4350	58.0	2648	62.0	2843

NOTE: *Limit velocities to 2900 fps with this bullet.*

0.308"	30 RNSP	30 Spire SP
Weight, grains	110	110
Ballistic Coefficient	0.136	0.245
Sectional Density	0.166	0.166
COAL Tested:	3.185"	3.185"
Speer Part No.	1845	1855

	START CHARGE		MAXIMUM CHARGE	
Propellant	Weight, grs	Muzzle Velocity, ft/sec	Weight, grs	Muzzle Velocity, ft/sec
H414*	72.0	3362	76.0	3586
IMR 4831*	74.0	3281	78.0	3521
H380*	66.0	3252	70.0	3511
IMR 4350*	73.0	3239	77.0	3496
IMR 3031*	58.0	3202	62.0	3482
IMR 4064*	61.0	3212	65.0	3482
IMR 4895*	59.0	3123	63.0	3399
IMR 4320*	61.0	3137	65.0	3397
H322*	52.0	3154	56.0	3296

0.308"	30 HP	30 FNSP
Weight, grains	130	130
Ballistic Coefficient	0.244	0.213
Sectional Density	0.196	0.196
COAL Tested:	3.185"	3.090"
Speer Part No.	2005	2007

Propellant	START CHARGE		MAXIMUM CHARGE	
	Weight, grs	Muzzle Velocity, ft/sec	Weight, grs	Muzzle Velocity, ft/sec
IMR 4350*	71.0	3149	75.0	3382
H380*	66.0	3127	70.0	3377
IMR 4831*	72.0	3109	76.0	3350
IMR 4064*	60.0	3062	64.0	3318
760*	70.0	3049	74.0	3295
IMR 4320*	60.0	3003	64.0	3271
H414*	68.0	3017	72.0	3270
IMR 4895*	58.0	2888	62.0	3134

NOTE: *125-gr TNT HP not recommended at these velocities.*

*Maximum Loads should be used with CAUTION • C = Compressed Load • *Magnum Primer used with this powder.*

0.308"	30 RNSP	30 Spitz BTSP	30 Spitz SP	30 MT SP	30 GS SP
Weight, grains	150	150	150	150	150
Ballistic Coefficient	0.235	0.417	0.377	0.278	0.295
Sectional Density	0.226	0.226	0.226	0.226	0.226
COAL Tested:	3.220"	3.300"	3.300"	3.230"	3.220"
Speer Part No.	2017	2022	2023	2025	2026

Propellant	START CHARGE		MAXIMUM CHARGE	
	Weight, grs	Muzzle Velocity, ft/sec	Weight, grs	Muzzle Velocity, ft/sec
IMR 4350*	70.0	2986	74.0	3226
H380*	64.0	2977	68.0	3222
H4831SC*	71.0	2961	75.0	3188
IMR 4895*	58.0	2892	62.0	3137
IMR 4064*	58.0	2920	62.0	3145
IMR 4320*	59.0	2869	63.0	3111
H414*	62.0	2751	66.0	2995
760*	63.0	2762	67.0	2986

0.308"	30 Spitz BTSP	30 Spitz SP	30 GS SP
Weight, grains	165	165	165
Ballistic Coefficient	0.520	0.444	0.354
Sectional Density	0.248	0.248	0.248
COAL Tested:	3.400"	3.400"	3.230"
Speer Part No.	2034	2035	2038

	START CHARGE		MAXIMUM CHARGE	
Propellant	Weight, grs	Muzzle Velocity, ft/sec	Weight, grs	Muzzle Velocity, ft/sec
IMR 4831*	70.0	2962	74.0	3205
IMR 4350*	69.0	2941	73.0	3182
H380*	63.0	2862	67.0	3107
IMR 4064*	57.0	2764	61.0	3027
IMR 4895*	55.5	2716	59.5	2978
AA 3100*	67.0	2814	71.0	2973
IMR 4320*	57.0	2728	61.0	2973
760*	61.0	2582	65.0	2808

308 Norma Magnum

0.308"	30 Match BTHP
Weight, grains	168
Ballistic Coefficient	0.534
Sectional Density	0.253
COAL Tested:	3.345"
Speer Part No.	2040

	START CHARGE		MAXIMUM CHARGE	
Propellant	Weight, grs	Muzzle Velocity, ft/sec	Weight, grs	Muzzle Velocity, ft/sec
AA 3100*	67.0	2917	71.0	3102
IMR 4831*	68.0	2871	72.0	3048
IMR 4350*	65.0	2712	69.0	3046
IMR 7828*	74.0	2843	78.0	3014
IMR 4320*	55.0	2709	59.0	2933
760*	61.0	2718	65.0	2909
IMR 4064*	56.0	2702	60.0	2903
AA 8700*	80.0	2666	84.0	2813

0.308"	30 RNSP	30 Spitz BTSP	30 Spitz SP	30 MT SP	30 GS SP
Weight, grains	180	180	180	180	180
Ballistic Coefficient	0.312	0.545	0.441	0.348	0.374
Sectional Density	0.271	0.271	0.271	0.271	0.271
COAL Tested:	3.220"	3.345"	3.345"	3.225"	3.225"
Speer Part No.	2047	2052	2053	2059	2063

Propellant	START CHARGE		MAXIMUM CHARGE	
	Weight, grs	Muzzle Velocity, ft/sec	Weight, grs	Muzzle Velocity, ft/sec
IMR 4831*	67.0	2772	71.0	3011
H380*	59.0	2652	63.0	2898
AA 3100*	63.0	2653	67.0	2857
IMR 7828*	68.0	2674	72.0	2840
IMR 4064*	54.0	2567	58.0	2814
IMR 4320*	55.0	2569	59.0	2806
760*	59.0	2519	63.0	2737
IMR 4198* (reduced load)	29.0	1799	31.0	1918

*Maximum Loads should be used with CAUTION • C = Compressed Load • *Magnum Primer used with this powder.*

0.308"	30 Spitz SP	30 GS SP
Weight, grains	200	200
Ballistic Coefficient	0.478	0.453
Sectional Density	0.301	0.301
COAL Tested:	3.345"	3.225"
Speer Part No.	2211	2212

Propellant	START CHARGE		MAXIMUM CHARGE	
	Weight, grs	Muzzle Velocity, ft/sec	Weight, grs	Muzzle Velocity, ft/sec
IMR 4831*	66.0	2780	70.0	2941
IMR 4350*	65.0	2733	69.0	2916
H380*	56.5	2497	60.5	2717
AA 3100*	63.0	2552	67.0	2712
IMR 4064*	52.0	2414	56.0	2643
760*	57.0	2401	61.0	2617
H870*	75.0	2392	79.0	2569
IMR 4198* (reduced load)	30.0	1768	32.0	1882

*Maximum Loads should be used with CAUTION • C = Compressed Load • *Magnum Primer used with this powder.*

300 Winchester Magnum

The 300 Winchester Magnum was the fourth in a line of commercial short magnum cartridges developed by Winchester starting in 1956 with the 458 Winchester Magnum. Okay, today a "short magnum" means something else; before 2001, it meant the H&H belted case having a case length roughly the same as a 30-06.

Introduced in 1963, the 300 Winchester was designed as a long-range, big game cartridge that could be chambered in standard (30-06) length actions. To accomplish this, Winchester engineers started with the 300 H&H case and shortened it to 2.62 inches. The Winchester case has a short neck and minimum body taper to maximize powder capacity. The cartridge has been an unqualified success by any standard.

The popularity of the 300 Winchester has caused most rifle makers to drop the 300 H&H. Ballistically, the 300 Winchester is nearly equal to the longer 300 Weatherby Magnum. There is now a wide variety of rifle models available to the hunter shopping for a 300 Winchester Magnum and factory ammunition is available in almost any part of the world. The cartridge has proved very accurate and is commonly found in 1000-yard competition shooting.

Handloading for the 300 Winchester is straightforward. Like other belted cartridges, the shoulder—not the belt—should be used for headspace control. Note that we used the CCI 250 Magnum primer for all the load data. Our Ruger test rifle produced remarkably uniform velocities with most powders with bullet weights of 150 grains and heavier.

For large game where maximum penetration is important, the Trophy Bonded Bear Claw 180 and 200-grain soft points are excellent bullets. Tough construction is required for the high-velocity, 30-caliber magnums to avoid bullet break-up. The Speer Grand Slam will also hold up to maximum velocities. The 300 Winchester can be loaded with varmint weight bullets (except for the 125-grain TNT) and is quite accurate. However, the report, powder consumption and recoil may be more than the varmint shooter may enjoy in extended shooting sessions. Bullets lighter than 165 grains may lose excessive weight at close range when used on big game.

As you have seen from the other cartridge descriptions in this section, we feel that none of the various 30 calibers are adequate for the great bears. This cartridge with a tough bullet will likely drop a large bear that's not agitated, but we prefer a heavier caliber when the bear is in a bad mood.

The industry maximum average pressure for the 300 Winchester Magnum is 54,000 CUP. These loads do not exceed that limit.

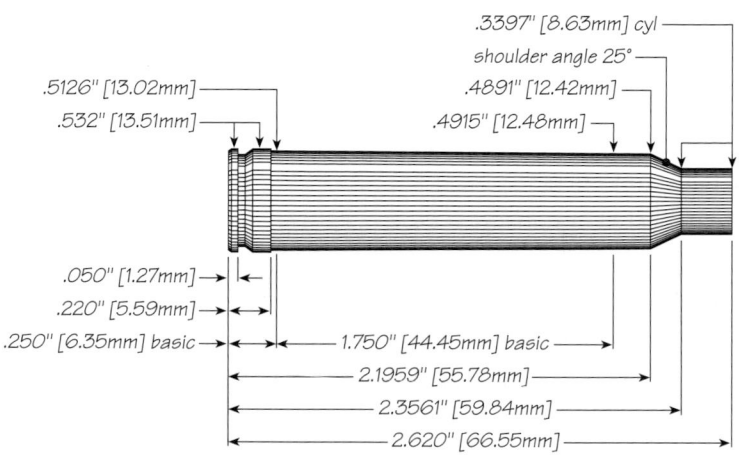

Max. Case Length:	2.620"	Cart. Case:	Winchester
Trim-to Length:	2.610"	Primer:	CCI 250*
Max Cart. OAL:	3.340"	Test Firearm:	Ruger M77 MkII
RCBS Shell Holder:	#4	Barrel Length:	24"

0.308"	30 RNSP
Weight, grains	100
Ballistic Coefficient	0.144
Sectional Density	0.151
COAL Tested:	2.960"
Speer Part No.	1805

	START CHARGE		MAXIMUM CHARGE	
Propellant	Weight, grs	Muzzle Velocity, ft/sec	Weight, grs	Muzzle Velocity, ft/sec
Reloder 15*	68.0	3352	**72.0**	3604
H322*	61.0	3339	**65.0**	3552
Viht. N135*	65.0	3330	**69.0**	3543
AA 2520*	64.0	3253	**68.0**	3479
IMR 4064*	65.0	3233	**69.0**	3421
H380*	70.0	3095	**74.0**	3396
IMR 4895*	62.0	3161	**66.0**	3381
IMR 4320*	64.0	3005	**68.0**	3258
SR 4759* (reduced load)	21.0	1801	**23.0**	1975

Paulina Pereyra Pose and brother Pablo Pereyra Pose, owners of Stahl Hunter, the ATK distributor in Argentina; on New Zealand's South Island with a wapiti; 300 Win Mag, 180-grain Trophy Bonded® Bear Claw® bullet. Paulina reports the bullet gave a "text book performance."

*Maximum Loads should be used with CAUTION • C = Compressed Load • *Magnum Primer used with this powder.*

0.308"	30 HP
Weight, grains	110
Ballistic Coefficient	0.128
Sectional Density	0.166
COAL Tested:	2.990"
Speer Part No.	1835

Propellant	START CHARGE		MAXIMUM CHARGE	
	Weight, grs	Muzzle Velocity, ft/sec	Weight, grs	Muzzle Velocity, ft/sec
IMR 4350*	60.0	2666	64.0	2857
IMR 4198*	42.0	2600	46.0	2857
IMR 3031*	48.0	2642	52.0	2853
IMR 4064*	50.0	2630	54.0	2849
H380*	53.0	2611	57.0	2846
IMR 4895*	50.0	2619	54.0	2841
SR 4759*	38.0	2548	42.0	2830
IMR 4227*	33.0	2316	37.0	2571
748*	46.0	2254	50.0	2497

NOTE: *Limit velocities to 2900 fps.*

0.308"	30 Spire SP
Weight, grains	110
Ballistic Coefficient	0.245
Sectional Density	0.166
COAL Tested:	3.215"
Speer Part No.	1855

Propellant	START CHARGE		MAXIMUM CHARGE	
	Weight, grs	Muzzle Velocity, ft/sec	Weight, grs	Muzzle Velocity, ft/sec
IMR 4831*	79.0	3401	83.0	3599
IMR 4350*	76.0	3400	80.0	3579
Reloder 19*	80.0	3360	84.0	3574
VN135*	64.0	3392	68.0	3571
AA 4350*	78.0	3334	82.0	3566
Reloder 15*	67.0	3294	71.0	3542
H414*	73.0	3305	77.0	3535
AA 2520*	63.0	3334	67.0	3528
760*	74.0	3275	78.0	3521
IMR 4064*	66.0	3286	70.0	3496
AA 3100*	79.0	3285	83.0C	3495
H4831*	80.0	3176	84.0C	3397
IMR 4895*	60.0	3210	64.0	3379
IMR 3031*	61.0	3137	65.0	3320
SR 4759* (reduced load)	23.0	1871	25.0	2024

*Maximum Loads should be used with CAUTION • C = Compressed Load • *Magnum Primer used with this powder.*

0.308"	30 HP
Weight, grains	130
Ballistic Coefficient	0.244
Sectional Density	0.196
COAL Tested:	3.260"
Speer Part No.	2005

Propellant	START CHARGE		MAXIMUM CHARGE	
	Weight, grs	Muzzle Velocity, ft/sec	Weight, grs	Muzzle Velocity, ft/sec
Viht. N160*	76.0	3222	80.0	3465
H4350*	74.0	3165	78.0C	3385
IMR 4831*	76.0	3193	80.0	3379
AA 3100*	78.0	3161	82.0C	3363
IMR 4350*	73.0	3175	77.0	3342
H4831SC*	78.0	3110	82.0C	3291
Reloder 15*	63.0	3016	67.0	3243
H380*	68.0	3052	72.0	3213
IMR 4064*	62.0	2984	66.0	3174
IMR 3031*	57.0	2882	61.0	3050
IMR 4320*	53.0	2574	57.0	2738

NOTE: *125-gr TNT HP not recommended for velocities over 3100 fps.*

0.308"	30 RNSP	30 FMJ BT	30 Spitz BTSP	30 Spitz SP	30 MT SP	30 GS SP
Weight, grains	150	150	150	150	150	150
Ballistic Coefficient	0.235	0.425	0.417	0.377	0.278	0.295
Sectional Density	0.226	0.226	0.226	0.226	0.226	0.226
COAL Tested:	3.150"	3.330"	3.330"	3.330"	3.290"	3.285"
Speer Part No.	2017	2018	2022	2023	2025	2026

Propellant	START CHARGE Weight, grs	START CHARGE Muzzle Velocity, ft/sec	MAXIMUM CHARGE Weight, grs	MAXIMUM CHARGE Muzzle Velocity, ft/sec
Reloder 19*	74.0	3086	78.0C	3301
Reloder 22*	76.0	3001	80.0C	3227
AA 3100*	76.0	3064	80.0C	3225
H4350*	72.0	3026	76.0C	3219
Viht. N160*	72.0	2975	76.0	3199
H4831SC*	76.0	2902	80.0C	3156
IMR 4831*	72.0	2915	76.0	3118
IMR 4350*	69.0	2918	73.0	3091
760*	64.0	2932	68.0	3086
H414*	65.0	2902	69.0	3071
H380*	65.0	2855	69.0	3070
AA 2700*	65.0	2881	69.0	3065
H1000*	80.0	2910	84.0C	3063
Reloder 15*	60.0	3058	64.0	3058
SR 4759* (reduced load)	26.0	1884	28.0	2028

*Maximum Loads should be used with CAUTION • C = Compressed Load • *Magnum Primer used with this powder.*

0.308"	30 TBBC SP
Weight, grains	150
Ballistic Coefficient	0.335
Sectional Density	0.226
COAL Tested:	3.330"
Speer Part No.	1759

Propellant	START CHARGE		MAXIMUM CHARGE	
	Weight, grs	Muzzle Velocity, ft/sec	Weight, grs	Muzzle Velocity, ft/sec
Reloder 22*	77.0	3150	81.0	3313
Viht. N560*	76.0	3143	80.0	3270
Reloder 19*	74.0	3075	78.0	3263
IMR 4831*	70.0	3042	74.0	3239
IMR 4350*	68.0	3027	72.0	3211
H4350*	67.5	3040	71.5	3206
AA 3100*	72.0	3005	76.0	3201
H4831SC*	74.0	3007	78.0	3176

NOTE: *Trophy Bonded Bear Claw and Trophy Bonded Sledgehammer Solid bullets have unique ballistic behavior compared to conventional bullets. Loads for TBBC and TBSS bullets may not "track" with data for conventional bullets. Use TBBC and TBSS data ONLY for TBBC and TBSS bullets.*

0.308"	30 Spitz BTSP	30 Spitz SP	30 GS SP
Weight, grains	165	165	165
Ballistic Coefficient	0.520	0.444	0.354
Sectional Density	0.248	0.248	0.248
COAL Tested:	3.340"	3.340"	3.290"
Speer Part No.	2034	2035	2038

Propellant	START CHARGE		MAXIMUM CHARGE	
	Weight, grs	Muzzle Velocity, ft/sec	Weight, grs	Muzzle Velocity, ft/sec
IMR 7828*	79.0	3116	83.0	3280
Reloder 22*	73.0	2886	77.0	3103
H4831SC*	73.0	2868	77.0	3087
IMR 4350*	70.0	2865	74.0	3064
AA 3100*	72.0	2882	76.0	3050
Reloder 19*	71.0	2802	75.0	2997
AA 4350*	69.0	2844	73.0	2994
Viht. N160*	68.0	2785	72.0	2979
IMR 4831*	69.0	2742	73.0	2948
H414*	63.0	2726	67.0	2900
IMR 4064*	58.0	2735	62.0	2894
H1000*	78.0	2710	81.0	2883
760*	60.0	2701	64.0	2873
Reloder 15*	56.0	2655	60.0	2809
SR 4759* (reduced load)	25.0	1763	29.0	2000

*Maximum Loads should be used with CAUTION • C = Compressed Load • *Magnum Primer used with this powder.*

300 Winchester Magnum

0.308"	30 TBBC SP
Weight, grains	165
Ballistic Coefficient	0.342
Sectional Density	0.248
COAL Tested:	3.330"
Speer Part No.	1760

Propellant	START CHARGE		MAXIMUM CHARGE	
	Weight, grs	Muzzle Velocity, ft/sec	Weight, grs	Muzzle Velocity, ft/sec
IMR 4831*	71.0	2968	75.0C	3149
Reloder 19*	73.5	2964	77.5C	3146
IMR 4350*	67.5	2910	71.5	3102
760*	69.0	2987	71.0	3096
H4831SC*	73.5	2922	77.5C	3083
AA 3100*	72.0	2897	76.0C	3080
H4350*	67.0	2889	71.0	3053
Viht. N540*	61.0	2854	65.0	3038

NOTE: *Trophy Bonded Bear Claw and Trophy Bonded Sledgehammer Solid bullets have unique ballistic behavior compared to conventional bullets. Loads for TBBC and TBSS bullets may not "track" with data for conventional bullets. Use TBBC and TBSS data ONLY for TBBC and TBSS bullets.*

0.308"	30 Match BTHP
Weight, grains	168
Ballistic Coefficient	0.534
Sectional Density	0.253
COAL Tested:	3.340"
Speer Part No.	2040

Propellant	START CHARGE		MAXIMUM CHARGE	
	Weight, grs	Muzzle Velocity, ft/sec	Weight, grs	Muzzle Velocity, ft/sec
Reloder 22*	75.0	2983	79.0C	3190
H4350*	71.0	2984	75.0	3174
IMR 4831*	72.0	2951	76.0C	3139
Reloder 19*	73.0	2919	77.0	3138
Viht. N160*	71.0	2965	75.0	3138
IMR 7028*	76.0	2927	80.0C	3131
AA 3100*	73.0	2926	77.0C	3080
IMR 4350*	70.0	2895	74.0	3063
H4831SC*	73.0	2795	77.0C	3005
H380*	63.0	2750	67.0	2926
Reloder 15*	59.0	2722	63.0	2911
H870*	83.0	2724	87.0C	2867
H1000*	77.0	2699	81.0C	2856

*Maximum Loads should be used with CAUTION • C = Compressed Load • *Magnum Primer used with this powder.*

0.308"	30 RNSP	30 Spitz BTSP	30 Spitz SP	30 MT SP	30 GS SP
Weight, grains	180	180	180	180	180
Ballistic Coefficient	0.312	0.545	0.441	0.349	0.374
Sectional Density	0.271	0.271	0.271	0.271	0.271
COAL Tested:	3.250"	3.340"	3.340"	3.285"	3.285"
Speer Part No.	2047	2052	2053	2059	2063

Propellant	START CHARGE Weight, grs	START CHARGE Muzzle Velocity, ft/sec	MAXIMUM CHARGE Weight, grs	MAXIMUM CHARGE Muzzle Velocity, ft/sec
Reloder 19*	72.0	2845	76.0	3059
Reloder 22*	73.0	2844	77.0C	3055
Reloder 25*	75.5	2893	79.5C	3050
IMR 7828*	74.0	2818	78.0C	2990
IMR 4350*	68.0	2802	72.0	2988
IMR 4831*	69.0	2789	73.0C	2951
H4831SC*	71.0	2816	75.0	2950
H1000*	77.0	2781	81.0C	2943
H4350*	67.0	2762	71.0	2938
AA 3100*	71.0	2762	75.0C	2937
Viht. N160*	68.0	2754	72.0	2925
760*	61.0	2670	65.0	2811
H414*	60.0	2647	64.0	2786
AA 8700*	82.0	2526	86.0C	2716
IMR 4198 (reduced load)	31.0	1879	33.0	1998

0.308"	30 TBBC SP
Weight, grains	180
Ballistic Coefficient	0.357
Sectional Density	0.271
COAL Tested:	3.330"
Speer Part No.	1765

Propellant	START CHARGE Weight, grs	START CHARGE Muzzle Velocity, ft/sec	MAXIMUM CHARGE Weight, grs	MAXIMUM CHARGE Muzzle Velocity, ft/sec
Reloder 22*	73.0	2866	77.0C	3044
IMR 4831*	70.0	2852	74.0	3028
AA 3100*	71.5	2826	75.5C	3015
Reloder 25*	77.0	2906	79.0C	2999
H4831SC*	72.0	2820	76.0	2996
IMR 7828*	74.0	2900	76.0C	2984
Viht. N560*	75.0	2908	79.0C	2980
H1000*	77.0	2820	79.0C	2898

NOTE: *Trophy Bonded Bear Claw and Trophy Bonded Sledgehammer Solid bullets have unique ballistic behavior compared to conventional bullets. Loads for TBBC and TBSS bullets may not "track" with data for conventional bullets. Use TBBC and TBSS data ONLY for TBBC and TBSS bullets.*

0.308"	30 Spitz SP	30 GS SP
Weight, grains	200	200
Ballistic Coefficient	0.478	0.453
Sectional Density	0.301	0.301
COAL Tested:	3.340"	3.285"
Speer Part No.	2211	2212

Propellant	START CHARGE		MAXIMUM CHARGE	
	Weight, grs	Muzzle Velocity, ft/sec	Weight, grs	Muzzle Velocity, ft/sec
Reloder 25*	71.0	2735	75.0C	2857
IMR 7828*	71.0	2656	75.0C	2856
Reloder 22*	69.0	2652	73.0C	2852
IMR 4350*	65.0	2672	69.0	2843
H1000*	73.0	2629	77.0C	2797
H4350*	65.0	2637	69.0	2776
H4831SC*	67.0	2653	71.0	2770
Viht. N165*	68.0	2601	72.0	2767
Reloder 19^	67.0	2582	71.0	2761
H870*	81.0	2579	85.0C	2758
760*	60.0	2605	64.0	2742
H414*	60.0	2597	64.0	2741
AA 4350*	63.0	2544	67.0	2735
AA 3100*	69.0	2496	73.0C	2641
IMR 4198* (reduced load)	31.0	1812	35.0	2036

0.308"	30 TBBC SP
Weight, grains	200
Ballistic Coefficient	0.392
Sectional Density	0.301
COAL Tested:	3.330"
Speer Part No.	1770

Propellant	START CHARGE		MAXIMUM CHARGE	
	Weight, grs	Muzzle Velocity, ft/sec	Weight, grs	Muzzle Velocity, ft/sec
Reloder 25*	72.0	2695	76.0C	2829
Reloder 22*	69.0	2669	73.0C	2796
IMR 7828*	69.0	2648	73.0C	2785
IMR 4031*	66.0	2618	70.0C	2770
Viht. N560*	69.0	2640	73.0C	2761
H1000*	75.0	2686	77.0C	2761
AA 3100*	68.0	2600	72.0	2753
H4831SC*	67.0	2606	71.0	2724

NOTE: *Trophy Bonded Bear Claw and Trophy Bonded Sledgehammer Solid bullets have unique ballistic behavior compared to conventional bullets. Loads for TBBC and TBSS bullets may not "track" with data for conventional bullets. Use TBBC and TBSS data ONLY for TBBC and TBSS bullets.*

*Maximum Loads should be used with CAUTION • C = Compressed Load • *Magnum Primer used with this powder.*

300 Weatherby Magnum

The 300 Weatherby Magnum was the first successful commercial improvement on the 300 H&H case. Roy Weatherby developed this cartridge during World War II by blowing out the full-length H&H case to give minimum body taper and adding the double-radius shoulder characteristic of his designs. Commercial ammunition has been available from Weatherby since 1948. In recent years, Remington, Winchester and Ruger have produced rifles for this cartridge, and most major ammunition manufacturers now supply factory loads.

The 300 Weatherby is an impressive cartridge. It can launch 180-grain bullets at velocities in excess of 3100 ft/sec. Hunters have killed game up to the size of elephant with the 300 Weatherby, although we can't recommend this practice. The 300 Weatherby is very accurate, permitting long-range kills on most species of North American game. It has also been very successful on the African plains where shots are often long and the animals are tough.

Although too powerful for most deer, the big Weatherby cartridge is used on them anyway with spectacular results. Meat hunters will find that the 180-grain Hot-Cor or Mag-Tip bullets kill deer just as dead as 150-grain bullets but without so much meat damage. For elk and moose, the 180 or 200-grain Grand Slam is hard to beat. We feel heavier calibers are better suited for large North American bears; however, the 300 Weatherby will take them down in a pinch. But, like the other 300 magnums, it may not have the bone-breaking power to anchor a charging bruin.

Recoil of the 300 Weatherby is impressive and it is not the rifle for a beginner. It takes practice to master. It is, however, an easy cartridge to handload. Handloading also allows the shooter to slightly reduce the power of the cartridge for off-season practice. Bullets weighing less than 150 grains produced large velocity variations with most powders, so we have shown only those propellants that minimize such variations. The 125-grain Speer TNT hollow point has a velocity limit of 3100 ft/sec and is not recommended for the 300 Weatherby.

Weatherby factory rifles are free-bored; that is, the rifling in the barrel throat is relieved for a greater distance than found in most mass-produced rifles. Owners of custom rifles that lack the free-bore feature will need to reduce loads and make sure that the bullet ogive doesn't contact the rifling. Custom rifles may have other dimensional variations from factory rifles with a standard chamber. Use care when working up loads in any custom rifle.

The 300 Weatherby was adopted as a standard industry cartridge in 1994. The loads shown here represent a complete retest of the cartridge using a piezoelectric pressure system. Thus you may find loads that are different from previously published data. The industry pressure limit for the 300 Weatherby is 65,000 psi.

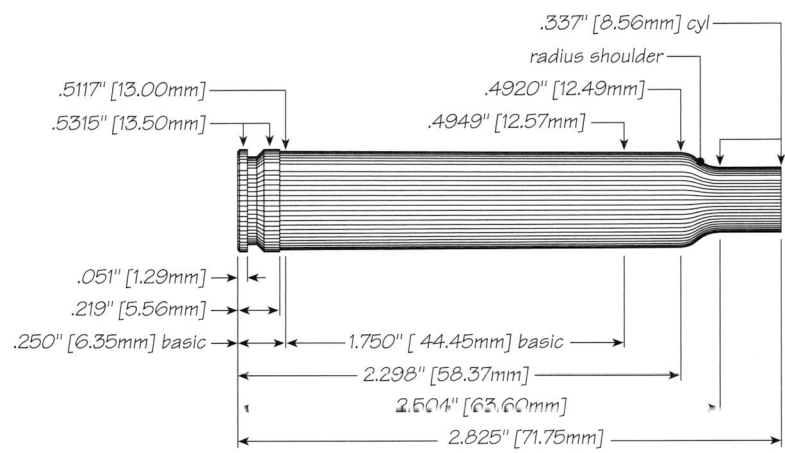

Max. Case Length:	2.825"	**Cart. Case:**	Remington
Trim-to Length:	2.815"	**Primer:**	CCI 250*
Max Cart. OAL:	3.560"	**Test Firearm:**	Weatherby Mark V
RCBS Shell Holder:	#4	**Barrel Length:**	26"

300 Weatherby Magnum

0.308"	30 Spire SP
Weight, grains	110
Ballistic Coefficient	0.245
Sectional Density	0.166
COAL Tested:	3.335"
Speer Part No.	1855

Propellant	START CHARGE		MAXIMUM CHARGE	
	Weight, grs	Muzzle Velocity, ft/sec	Weight, grs	Muzzle Velocity, ft/sec
IMR 4350*	83.0	3629	87.0	3804
IMR 4895*	71.0	3576	75.0	3777
AA 4350*	84.0	3578	88.0	3748
Reloder 19*	86.0	3557	90.0C	3722
IMR 4831*	84.5	3534	88.5	3701
H4350*	81.0	3515	85.0	3689
AA 3100*	85.0	3445	89.0C	3607

0.308"	30 HP
Weight, grains	130
Ballistic Coefficient	0.244
Sectional Density	0.196
COAL Tested:	3.530"
Speer Part No.	2005

Propellant	START CHARGE		MAXIMUM CHARGE	
	Weight, grs	Muzzle Velocity, ft/sec	Weight, grs	Muzzle Velocity, ft/sec
Reloder 19*	82.0	3244	86.0	3496
H4350*	77.5	3200	81.5	3467
AA 3100*	81.0	3222	85.0C	3429
IMR 7828*	84.0	3221	88.0C	3422
IMR 4831*	79.0	3138	83.0	3404
H4831SC*	82.0	3203	86.0C	3386
IMR 4350*	77.0	3109	81.0	3349
AA 4350*	75.0	3098	79.0	3347
H4895*	66.0	3129	70.0	3304

NOTE: *125-gr TNT HP not recommended at these velocities.*

0.308"	30 RNSP	30 Spitz BTSP	30 Spitz SP	30 MT SP	30 GS SP
Weight, grains	150	150	150	150	150
Ballistic Coefficient	0.235	0.417	0.377	0.278	0.295
Sectional Density	0.226	0.226	0.226	0.226	0.226
COAL Tested:	3.400"	3.560"	3.560"	3.495"	3.490"
Speer Part No.	2017	2022	2023	2025	2026

	START CHARGE		MAXIMUM CHARGE	
Propellant	Weight, grs	Muzzle Velocity, ft/sec	Weight, grs	Muzzle Velocity, ft/sec
H1000*	87.0	3205	91.0C	3380
Reloder 22*	82.0	3191	86.0	3363
Viht. N165*	85.0	3138	89.0C	3357
H414*	73.0	3087	77.0	3319
IMR 7828*	81.0	3096	85.0	3299
Reloder 19*	79.0	3063	83.0	3282
AA 3100*	78.0	3059	82.0	3266
Viht. N160*	76.0	3086	80.0	3250
H4831SC*	79.5	3030	83.5	3246
H4350*	74.0	2970	78.0	3245
IMR 4831*	76.0	3013	80.0	3222
AA 4350*	72.5	2981	76.5	3222
760*	73.0	3030	77.0	3115
IMR 4350*	73.0	2953	77.0	3100

*Maximum Loads should be used with CAUTION • C = Compressed Load • *Magnum Primer used with this powder.*

0.308"	30 Spitz BTSP	30 Spitz SP	30 GS SP	30 Match BTHP
Weight, grains	165	165	165	168
Ballistic Coefficient	0.520	0.444	0.354	0.534
Sectional Density	0.248	0.248	0.248	0.253
COAL Tested:	3.560"	3.560"	3.495"	3.560"
Speer Part No.	2034	2035	2038	2040

Propellant	START CHARGE Weight, grs	START CHARGE Muzzle Velocity, ft/sec	MAXIMUM CHARGE Weight, grs	MAXIMUM CHARGE Muzzle Velocity, ft/sec
Reloder 25*	85.0	3102	89.0C	3258
H1000*	84.0	3053	88.0	3237
Viht. N165*	82.0	2964	86.0	3212
Reloder 22*	79.0	3008	83.0	3170
AA 3100*	76.0	2966	80.0	3162
H4831SC*	78.0	2982	82.0	3160
Reloder 19*	76.0	2940	80.0	3155
IMR 4831*	74.0	2956	78.0	3142
IMR 7828*	78.0	2884	82.0	3098
H414*	70.0	2947	74.0	3090
H4350*	71.0	2837	75.0	3057
AA 4350*	70.0	2804	74.0	3027
760*	70.0	2858	74.0	2990
IMR 4350*	70.0	2761	74.0	2984

0.308"	30 RNSP	30 Spitz BTSP	30 Spitz SP	30 MT SP	30 GS SP
Weight, grains	180	180	180	180	180
Ballistic Coefficient	0.312	0.545	0.441	0.349	0.374
Sectional Density	0.271	0.271	0.271	0.271	0.271
COAL Tested:	3.450"	3.560"	3.560"	3.450"	3.450"
Speer Part No.	2047	2052	2053	2059	2063

	START CHARGE		MAXIMUM CHARGE	
Propellant	Weight, grs	Muzzle Velocity, ft/sec	Weight, grs	Muzzle Velocity, ft/sec
Reloder 25*	83.0	2917	87.0	3109
Viht. N165*	80.0	2866	84.0	3102
Viht. N560*	76.0	2900	80.0	3101
H1000*	81.5	2943	85.5	3084
Rolodor 22*	78.0	2884	82.0	3077
H4831SC*	77.0	2860	81.0	3050
AA 3100*	75.0	2800	79.0	3012
IMR 7828*	76.0	2796	80.0	3001
Reloder 19*	74.0	2806	78.0	2990
760*	69.0	2698	73.0	2984
IMR 4831*	72.0	2789	76.0	2953
H414*	68.5	2686	72.5	2949
AA 4350*	68.0	2667	72.0	2867
IMR 4350*	68.0	2627	72.0	2822

*Maximum Loads should be used with CAUTION • C = Compressed Load • *Magnum Primer used with this powder.*

0.308"	30 Spitz SP	30 GS SP
Weight, grains	200	200
Ballistic Coefficient	0.478	0.453
Sectional Density	0.301	0.301
COAL Tested:	3.560"	3.450"
Speer Part No.	2211	2212

	START CHARGE		MAXIMUM CHARGE	
Propellant	Weight, grs	Muzzle Velocity, ft/sec	Weight, grs	Muzzle Velocity, ft/sec
H870*	90.0	2887	94.0C	3043
Reloder 25*	81.0	2839	85.0C	3022
H1000*	78.0	2747	82.0	2908
Reloder 22*	74.5	2718	78.5	2881
Reloder 19*	73.0	2735	77.0	2878
AA 8700*	92.0	2822	94.0C	2858
IMR 7828*	73.0	2621	77.0	2841
H4831SC*	72.5	2655	76.5	2839
AA 3100*	71.0	2633	75.0	2824
IMR 4831*	69.0	2629	73.0	2779
AA 4350*	66.0	2470	70.0	2723
IMR 4350*	65.0	2465	69.0	2680
H414*	64.0	2510	68.0	2661
H4350*	65.0	2479	69.0	2649

*Maximum Loads should be used with CAUTION • C = Compressed Load • *Magnum Primer used with this powder.*

300 Remington Ultra Magnum

The 300 Remington Ultra Magnum was introduced in 1999 as another "mega-magnum," in the same class as the 30-378 Weatherby. Although some say the 300 Ultra Magnum case uses a modified 404 Jeffery case, it is better described as being "inspired by the Jeffery pattern," because critical dimensions are not an exact match. Common factors are a major case diameter larger than that of H&H Magnum cases, a slightly rebated rim, and an unbelted case. The resulting case can hold over 100 grains of many propellants, and industry specifications list a 180-grain bullet at 3225 ft/sec.

We were not quite able to achieve that velocity in a 24-inch test barrel with propellants available to reloaders. However, we closely matched specifications for the two other bullet weights called out in industry documents: 150-grain (3440 ft/sec) and 200-grain (3025 ft/sec). Comparing the Ultra Magnum to older 300 magnums shows it is using much more propellant to gain little if any velocity. Like the 25-06 in the 1920's, this and the other mega-magnums may need to wait for new generations of propellants before realizing their full potential.

Does this make the cartridge useless? Absolutely not. The unbelted case is a boon to reloaders, typically improving accuracy and case life compared to equivalent belted cases. The capacious case favors the heaviest bullets, especially specialty match bullets that may weigh more than most hunting bullets—up to 250 grains in some cases. This should appeal to long-range target shooters.

With 200-grain bullets, the new Hodgdon powder US 869 gave the highest velocity with excellent consistency. Alliant's Reloder 25 and 22 get our nod for 180-grain bullets. Hunters should remember this fact when using cartridges capable of high velocity: heavier bullets will damage less meat. A 150-grain bullet at over 3400 ft/sec will reduce the amount of meat you put in the freezer.

Ballistic consistency with bullets lighter than 150 grains is never good in a cartridge of this capacity. For that reason, we did not test lighter, varmint-weight bullets. This is no varmint cartridge.

We used Federal 215 Magnum primers for load development. However, the CCI 250 can be safely substituted without a charge adjustment. We emphatically recommend that you never load this cartridge with charges lighter than the start charges shown. We carefully selected start charge weights to keep their pressures in a range that maintains consistent performance, important when developing loads for such a large case. Like a highly tuned race car, this cartridge is best driven at maximum safe velocities.

The loads presented here remain within the cartridge's industry pressure limit of 65,000 psi.

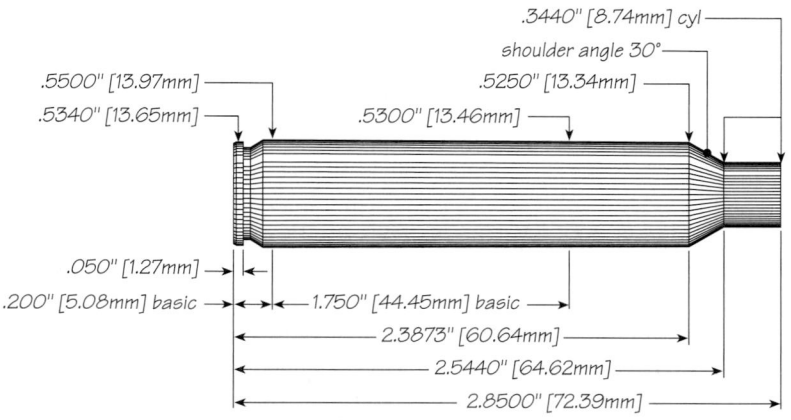

Max. Case Length:	2.850"	Cart. Case:	Federal
Trim-to Length:	2.840"	Primer:	Federal 215*
Max Cart. OAL:	3.600"	Test Firearm:	Universal Receiver
RCBS Shell Holder:	#38	Barrel Length:	HS Precision 24"

0.308"	30 Spitz BTSP	30 Spitz SP	30 GS SP
Weight, grains	150	150	150
Ballistic Coefficient	0.417	0.377	0.295
Sectional Density	0.226	0.226	0.226
COAL Tested:	3.495"	3.495"	3.460"
Speer Part No.	2022	2023	2026

	START CHARGE		MAXIMUM CHARGE	
Propellant	Weight, grs	Muzzle Velocity, ft/sec	Weight, grs	Muzzle Velocity, ft/sec
Viht. N560*	93.0	3308	97.0	3442
Reloder 22*	93.0	3283	97.0	3437
Ramshot Magnum*	100.0	3293	104.0	3425
IMR 7828*	93.0	3246	97.0	3419
Reloder 19*	90.0	3261	94.0	3401
AA 3100*	90.0	3257	94.0	3388
IMR 4031*	87.0	3217	91.0	3372
H4831SC*	92.0	3205	96.0	3335

Roger Braunstein of Ultramax Ammunition (Rapid City, SD), a longtime ATK customer and distributor, with a fine bull elk.

*Maximum Loads should be used with CAUTION • C = Compressed Load • *Magnum Primer used with this powder.*

0.308"	30 Spitz BTSP	30 Spitz SP	30 GS SP	30 Match BTHP
Weight, grains	165	165	165	168
Ballistic Coefficient	0.520	0.444	0.354	0.534
Sectional Density	0.226	0.226	0.226	0.253
COAL Tested:	3.600"	3.600	3.460"	3.600"
Speer Part No.	2034	2035	2038	2040

	START CHARGE		MAXIMUM CHARGE	
Propellant	Weight, grs	Muzzle Velocity, ft/sec	Weight, grs	Muzzle Velocity, ft/sec
Retumbo*	97.0	3146	101.0	3281
Reloder 25*	93.0	3140	97.0	3279
Ramshot Magnum*	97.0	3148	101.0	3270
Reloder 22*	89.0	3128	93.0	3268
Reloder 19*	87.0	3140	91.0	3263
AA 3100*	87.0	3154	91.0	3261
Viht. N560*	88.0	3137	92.0	3245
IMR 7828*	89.0	3103	93.0	3244
Magpro*	92.0	3103	96.0	3219
H4831SC*	88.0	3080	92.0	3203

0.308"	30 Spitz BTSP	30 Spitz SP	30 GS SP
Weight, grains	180	180	180
Ballistic Coefficient	0.545	0.411	0.374
Sectional Density	0.271	0.271	0.271
COAL Tested:	3.600"	3.600"	3.460"
Speer Part No.	2052	2053	2063

Propellant	START CHARGE		MAXIMUM CHARGE	
	Weight, grs	Muzzle Velocity, ft/sec	Weight, grs	Muzzle Velocity, ft/sec
Reloder 25*	90.0	3021	94.0	3146
Ramshot Magnum*	93.0	3001	97.0	3119
Reloder 22*	86.0	2997	90.0	3118
Retumbo*	90.0	2981	94.0	3099
IMR 7828*	85.0	2961	89.0	3095
Viht. N560*	82.0	2961	86.0	3077
AA 3100*	81.0	2931	85.0	3047
H1000*	90.0	2937	94.0	3043
Magpro*	84.0	2896	88.0	2996

*Maximum Loads should be used with CAUTION • C = Compressed Load • *Magnum Primer used with this powder.*

0.308"	30 Spitz SP	30 GS SP
Weight, grains	200	200
Ballistic Coefficient	0.478	0.453
Sectional Density	0.301	0.301
COAL Tested:	3.600"	3.460"
Speer Part No.	2211	2212

Propellant	START CHARGE		MAXIMUM CHARGE	
	Weight, grs	Muzzle Velocity, ft/sec	Weight, grs	Muzzle Velocity, ft/sec
US 869*	100.0	2889	104.0	3000
AA 8700*	100.0	2896	104.0C	2962
Retumbo*	86.0	2842	90.0	2949
Reloder 25*	84.0	2837	88.0	2942
Reloder 22*	82.0	2829	86.0	2936
Ramshot Magnum*	88.0	2825	92.0	2933
IMR 7828*	81.0	2781	85.0	2915
Viht. N560*	78.0	2789	82.0	2903
Magpro*	79.0	2714	83.0	2821

*Maximum Loads should be used with CAUTION • C = Compressed Load • *Magnum Primer used with this powder.*

30-378 Weatherby

The 30-378 Weatherby began as a wildcat cartridge intended for 1000-yard matches, where shooters like to keep the bullets supersonic (over approximately 1120 ft/sec) all the way to the target. The cartridge was easily made by necking down a 378 Weatherby to accept 30-caliber bullets; it retains the double-radius shoulder characteristic of all Weatherby cartridges. Weatherby eventually built sporting rifles for this cartridge and sold factory ammo. In 1998, the U.S. shooting industry standardized the cartridge.

The cartridge has much merit for target shooting, where low-drag match bullets weighing over 220 grains and longer barrels (28-30 inches) are more common. However, with bullet weights and barrel lengths appropriate to hunting, the 30-378 adds little to what the excellent 300 Weatherby can produce. Velocity gains are often less than 100 ft/sec in spite of burning 20-25 percent more propellant.

The 30-378 case has a huge capacity, capable of holding up to 120 grains of some propellants. This ability to handle large charges produces a handicap with lighter hunting bullets. We attempted no load development for bullets less than 150 grains, and the 150 and 165-grain data we have are the result of testing and rejecting many propellants. The most consistent loads we developed used 180 and 200-grain bullets.

A lab limitation we encountered is the lack of 30-378 reference ammunition for calibrating pressure barrels. We therefore loaded to match the pressures of Weatherby factory ammunition. The lot of 200-grain factory ammo we used produced 3081 ft/sec and an average pressure of 52,700 CUP.

Weatherby rifles for this cartridge have 26-inch barrels; the standard industry pressure barrel is 24 inches. We did velocity screening to compare the pressure barrel velocities to a Weatherby sporting rifle and found that differences in velocity were negligible between the two barrels. Some bullet/powder combinations even shot slightly slower from the sporting rifle than from the pressure barrel with its tight tolerances. Only with a few 150-grain loads did the difference approach 100 ft/sec. Therefore, the velocities shown here are representative of those from longer 26-inch barrels.

Do not attempt to reduce loads more than the starting loads we show. We selected them to keep the start charge pressures to at least 47,000 CUP. Most start loads are four grains under the maximum loads; a few have only a two-grain reduction.

We cannot recommend that a new reloader start with such a cartridge. The 30-378 Weatherby is highly specialized and does best in the niche for which it was conceived. Remember, a thoroughbred horse can win a four-minute race but can't pull a plow all day. The big Weatherby cartridge is a thoroughbred in its own right, with the same performance promises and limitations as a Kentucky Derby competitor.

The industry maximum average pressure for the 30-378 is 55,100 CUP. We developed these loads to match the average pressure of Weatherby factory ammunition at 52,700 CUP which, at 96 percent of maximum, is a safe and logical stopping point for any data development.

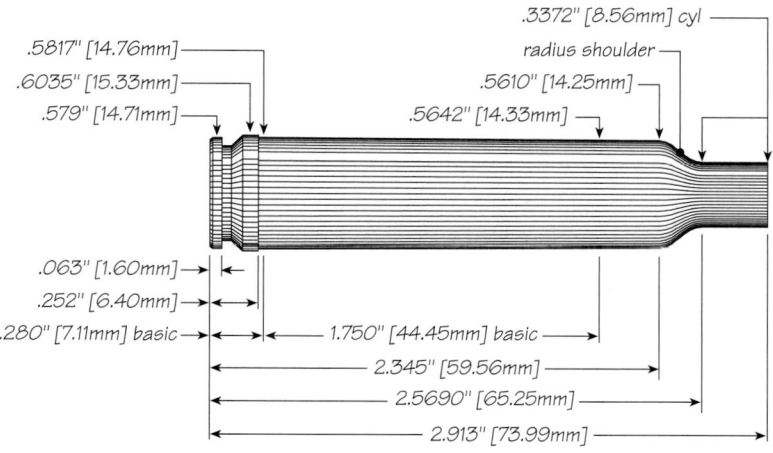

Max. Case Length:	2.913"	Cart. Case:	Weatherby
Trim-to Length:	2.903"	Primer:	CCI 250*
Max Cart. OAL:	3.648"	Test Firearm:	Universal Receiver
RCBS Shell Holder:	#14	Barrel Length:	Krieger 24"

0.308"	30 Spitz BTSP	30 Spitz SP	30 GS SP
Weight, grains	150	150	150
Ballistic Coefficient	0.417	0.377	0.295
Sectional Density	0.226	0.226	0.226
COAL Tested:	3.600"	3.600"	3.600"
Speer Part No.	2022	2023	2026

Propellant	START CHARGE		MAXIMUM CHARGE	
	Weight, grs	Muzzle Velocity, ft/sec	Weight, grs	Muzzle Velocity, ft/sec
AA 3100*	100.0	3269	104.0	3414
IMR 4831*	96.0	3279	100.0	3406
AA 4350*	97.0	3272	101.0	3405
Reloder 19*	101.0	3308	105.0	3404
IMR 4350*	93.0	3240	97.0	3385
H1000*	108.0	3236	112.0	3364
H4350*	90.0	3187	94.0	3317
H4831SC*	97.0	3185	101.0	3305

*Maximum Loads should be used with CAUTION • C = Compressed Load • *Magnum Primer used with this powder.*

0.308"	30 Spitz BTSP	30 Spitz SP	30 GS SP	30 Match BTSP
Weight, grains	165	165	165	168
Ballistic Coefficient	0.520	0.444	0.354	0.534
Sectional Density	0.248	0.248	0.248	0.253
COAL Tested:	3.645"	3.645"	3.645"	3.645"
Speer Part No.	2034	2035	2038	2040

Propellant	START CHARGE		MAXIMUM CHARGE	
	Weight, grs	Muzzle Velocity, ft/sec	Weight, grs	Muzzle Velocity, ft/sec
Reloder 19*	99.0	3185	103.0	3285
IMR 4831*	94.0	3162	98.0	3284
AA 3100*	97.0	3129	101.0	3268
IMR 7828*	104.0	3200	106.0	3267
H1000*	103.0	3125	109.0	3249
IMR 4350*	92.0	3093	96.0	3223
H4831SC*	95.0	3071	99.0	3187

Russell Ellis, Director Law Enforcement, Government, and OEM Sales, ATK; 300 Winchester Magnum; bull elk scoring 392, Southern Idaho.

0.308"	30 Spitz BTSP	30 Spitz SP	30 GS SP
Weight, grains	180	180	180
Ballistic Coefficient	0.545	0.441	0.374
Sectional Density	0.271	0.271	0.271
COAL Tested:	3.645"	3.645"	3.645"
Speer Part No.	2052	2053	2063

	START CHARGE		MAXIMUM CHARGE	
Propellant	Weight, grs	Muzzle Velocity, ft/sec	Weight, grs	Muzzle Velocity, ft/sec
H870*	119.0	3147	123.0C	3249
AA 8700*	115.0	3080	119.0	3206
IMR 7828*	96.0	3062	100.0	3189
IMR 4831*	91.0	3041	95.0	3161
H50BMG*	114.0	3019	118.0C	3137
H1000*	102.0	3029	106.0	3134
AA 3100*	94.0	2996	98.0	3121
H4831SC*	92.0	2945	96.0	3069
Viht. N170*	93.0	2957	97.0	3057

*Maximum Loads should be used with CAUTION • C = Compressed Load • * Magnum Primer used with this powder.*

0.308"	30 Spitz SP	30 GS SP
Weight, grains	200	200
Ballistic Coefficient	0.478	0.453
Sectional Density	0.301	0.301
COAL Tested:	3.645"	3.645"
Speer Part No.	2211	2212

	START CHARGE		MAXIMUM CHARGE	
Propellant	Weight, grs	Muzzle Velocity, ft/sec	Weight, grs	Muzzle Velocity, ft/sec
H870*	114.0	2973	118.0C	3088
AA 8700*	112.0	2952	116.0C	3074
H50BMG*	112.0	2930	116.0C	3036
AA 3100*	92.0	2889	96.0	3012
IMR 7828*	93.0	2941	95.0	3002
H1000*	99.0	2884	103.0	2994

*Maximum Loads should be used with CAUTION • C = Compressed Load • *Magnum Primer used with this powder.*

32-20 Winchester *(Std. Pressure)*

The 32-20 Winchester cartridge (also known as the 32 WCF) dates to 1882 when it was introduced in the famous Winchester Model 1873 lever action rifle, and was later offered in the Winchester Model 1885 single shot and the Model 1892 lever action rifle. It became very popular for varmint shooting and pest control, and was even touted as a deer cartridge. This last claim was grossly exaggerated because the 32-20 is by no means adequate for deer.

Other firms soon made 32-20 rifles. It was also available in revolvers so the shooter could use the same ammo in both his rifle and sidearm. The low cost of ammunition made it a popular working rifle for ranchers, farmers and trappers who were more interested in practical performance than theoretical ballistics.

In spite of its name the 32-20 is, like several "32-caliber" handgun cartridges, really a 31-caliber, requiring bullet diameters from .311 to .313 inch. Most 32-20 rifles seem to prefer .312" jacketed bullets and .313-.314" lead bullets. Using the correct bullet diameter is the key to accuracy with this cartridge.

In a rifle with a nice bore, the 32-20 can be quite accurate. Its modest velocity and flat point bullets (required for tubular magazines) restrict the effective hitting range to less than 150 yards, although it will kill (or wound) at longer ranges. With non-expanding cast lead bullets, the 32-20 is a nice 100-yard turkey cartridge in areas where rifles are permitted for the big birds.

In its prime, 32-20 ammunition was sold in a variety of bullet weights, styles and velocities. In addition to lead bullets, early factory ammo offered soft point, full-jacket and hollow point bullets. There were two pressure levels, the higher intended for strong rifles only. The high-velocity rifle loads fired an 80-grain hollow point at 2100 ft/sec. Standard pressure loads originally used a 115-grain bullet that was later reduced to 100 grains. The high-pressure rifle loads are no longer made because of industry concern that they would be dangerous if fired in poor-quality imported revolvers. The only factory ammo now made fires 100-grain lead or jacketed soft point bullets at a very leisurely 1200 ft/sec.

Case necks are quite thin, so we recommend seating and crimping in separate operations to avoid neck bulges and short case life. You can also extend case life by avoiding excessive flaring of case mouths. Ammunition to be used in lever-action rifles must be crimped to prevent bullet setback in tubular magazines.

The 32-20 is seeing renewed interest for Cowboy Action competition. Match rules limit competition rifle loads to plain-base lead bullets at a velocity no greater than 1400 ft/sec. Speer does not make a lead bullet suitable for these rules, but RCBS sells a bullet mould that casts a dandy 98-grain flat point bullet perfect for the 32-20. These loads use that bullet, and are held to the industry pressure of 16,000 CUP.

These same loads are shown in the Handgun section; refer to that section for revolver velocities. High-velocity rifle loads with a jacketed bullet are shown in the following section.

Do not attempt to use pointed bullets in rifles with tubular magazines. To do so can cause cartridges to explode in the magazine, injuring the shooter and damaging the firearm.

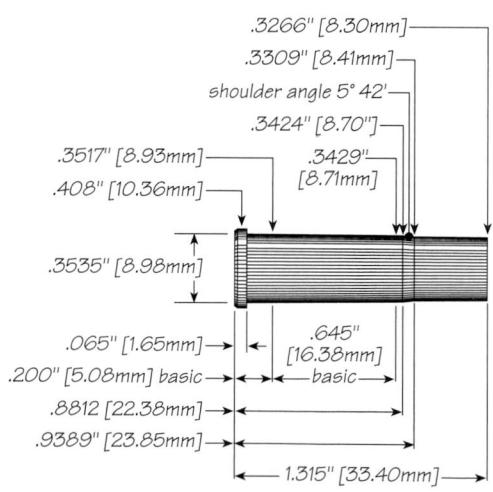

Max. Case Length:	1.315"	**Cart. Case:**	Starline
Trim-to Length:	1.305"	**Primer:**	CCI 400
Max Cart. OAL:	1.592"	**Test Firearm:**	Marlin 1894CL
RCBS Shell Holder:	#1	**Barrel Length:**	22"

0.314"	32 98-SWC
Weight, grains	98
Lead Alloy	hard
Ballistic Coefficient	0.134
Sectional Density	0.142
COAL Tested:	1.533"
RCBS Mould No.	82061

Cowboy

	START CHARGE		MAXIMUM CHARGE	
Propellant	Weight, grs	Muzzle Velocity, ft/sec	Weight, grs	Muzzle Velocity, ft/sec
Power Pistol	3.9	1199	4.4	1292
AA No. 5	4.5	1176	5.1	1284
AA No. 7	5.4	1186	6.1	1265
H. Universal	3.4	1068	3.8	1196
TiteGroup	2.6	1076	3.0	1184
700-X	2.7	1076	3.1	1182
Unique	3.0	1038	3.5	1168
Viht. 3N37	3.8	1058	4.3	1156
Bullseye	2.4	1005	2.9	1131
231	2.9	1022	3.3	1108

NOTE: *We sell bullet moulds, not cast bullets. These bullets were cast in RCBS moulds. Contact your dealer for more information on the RCBS line of premium bullet casting equipment, or visit on the internet at www.rcbs.com.*

Lab Notes:

The start loads for our 32-20 Cowboy loads were carefully adjusted to fall between 12,000 and 13,000 CUP for reliable performance. Do not attempt to load lighter than shown.

*Maximum Loads should be used with CAUTION • C = Compressed Load • *Magnum Primer used with this powder.*

32-20 Winchester *(Strong Actions)*

In the previous cartridge introduction for the 32-20 cartridge, we said that ammunition was once available in a higher pressure version, and today's factory ammunition is loaded to relatively low pressures and velocities.

The handloader can improve this performance significantly if he plans to use a strong, modern rifle such as the Marlin Model 1894 CL or the Browning Model 92. Original 1892 Winchesters in good condition can also handle somewhat higher loads than factory offerings. Many of these rifles have seen hard use, so have a gunsmith check out any original Model 92 Winchester before using the following loads. Check fired cases for signs of stretching after each firing.

The Speer 100-grain JHP—designed for the 32-20—has a crimping cannelure; any ammunition to be loaded in tubular magazines must be crimped to prevent bullet setback. These loads may also be used with hard-cast lead bullets weighing 100-110 grains. The industry pressure limit for the 32-20 is 16,000 CUP. The loads shown here generate pressures approaching 28,000 CUP, the same as the 25-20 Winchester. They are only for the Marlin Model 1894 CL, the Browning Model 92, and original Winchester Model 1892 rifles known to be in good condition. These loads must not be used in the Winchester 1873 rifle (or any replica thereof) or in any revolver except the Ruger Blackhawk (some years ago, Buckeye Sports commissioned a run of 32-20 Blackhawks).

Do not attempt to use pointed bullets in rifles with tubular magazines. To do so can cause cartridges to explode in the magazine, injuring the shooter and damaging the firearm.

Lab Notes:

We found that 32-20 cases from Winchester and Starline are up to .025" shorter than Remington cases. If the Speer 100-grain JHP is seated to the cannelure in a Remington case, it may engage the rifling prematurely. This can make chambering difficult and increase pressures. We recommend trimming Remington 32-20 cases to 1.280" before loading this bullet.

*Maximum Loads should be used with CAUTION • C = Compressed Load • *Magnum Primer used with this powder.*

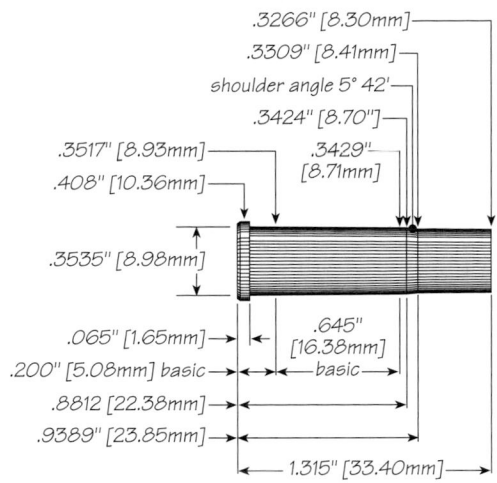

Max. Case Length:	1.315"	Cart. Case:	Winchester
Trim-to Length:	1.305"	Primer:	CCI 400
Max Cart. OAL:	1.592"	Test Firearm:	Marlin 1894CL
RCBS Shell Holder:	#1	Barrel Length:	22"

0.312"	32 HP
Weight, grains	100
Ballistic Coefficient	0.167
Sectional Density	0.147
COAL Tested:	1.560"
Speer Part No.	3981

Propellant	START CHARGE Weight, grs	START CHARGE Muzzle Velocity, ft/sec	MAXIMUM CHARGE Weight, grs	MAXIMUM CHARGE Muzzle Velocity, ft/sec
296	11.0	1635	13.0	1881
H110	11.0	1624	13.0	1858
SR 4759	10.0	1509	12.0	1735
H4198	13.0	1477	15.0C	1679
IMR 4198	13.0	1458	15.0C	1678
Viht. N110	8.5	1483	10.5	1667
AA 1680	12.5	1414	14.5	1636
Reloder 7	14.0	1466	16.0	1634
2400	7.0	1377	9.0	1583
Viht. N120	11.0	1420	13.0	1583
AA 2015	14.5	1311	16.5C	1462
IMR 4227	9.0	1259	11.0	1447

7.62 x 39mm

This compact cartridge was developed by the Soviet military to answer the effectiveness of the German 8x33mm light assault rifle cartridge during the bloody conflict on World War II's Eastern Front. Although the 8x33 was ballistically inferior to the standard 8x57mm German service rifle cartridge, it was significantly more effective than pistol cartridges fired in submachine guns. The assault rifle concept greatly impressed the Russians, who quickly copied it.

The Russian's new rifle cartridge (the Model 43) was initially chambered in the semi-automatic SKS rifle and later in the Automat Kalashnikov Model 47—the AK-47. This cartridge became the primary service cartridge for most Eastern Bloc countries. It fires a 123-grain FMJ bullet at a nominal 2350 ft/sec. The 7.62x39 cartridge was little known in the United States until our troops faced it in Viet Nam. During the last decade, a large number of rifles have been imported into this country.

Boxer-primed cases suitable for reloading are now available from several sources. The military FMJ bullet is .3095-inch, but military rifles typically have barrel diameters around .310" to .312". Mil-spec FMJ bullets make up for this apparent misfit by having a hollow base that can swell under pressure to seal the bore. We used a Ruger bolt-action rifle in our tests; muzzle velocities in semi-automatic carbines will average about 100 ft/sec slower.

Speer builds a .310-inch 123-grain Hot-Cor spitzer soft point that is expressly designed for the 7.62x39, featuring a profile to closely match military bullets and a cannelure to permit crimping. Its jacket configuration is also matched to allow normal expansion when fired at the modest velocities this cartridge generates.

In hunting performance, the 7.62x39 is one of those "in between" cartridges. At the muzzle, its performance is only slightly behind the 30-30 Winchester with a 150-grain factory load; pointed bullets can give the "Russian" a slight edge downrange. We feel that it is best limited to animals no larger than small deer. Bullets heavier than 123 grains produce relatively low velocities in this cartridge.

Another important factor for the hunter to remember is accuracy. If you plan to hunt with a surplus rifle, the responsible thing to do is determine if the rifle is accurate enough for longer shots, for example, beyond 100 yards. The 7.62x39 will never be a long-range hunting cartridge, and should be restricted to around a 200-yard maximum when fired from an accurate rifle. One that shoots larger groups will reduce that range.

The only challenge in reloading this one is case sorting. Some makes of reloadable cases require small rifle primers; check your cases before loading and sort them accordingly so mixed primer sizes will not complicate the loading process.

Millions of rounds of surplus, steel-case 7.63x39 ammunition have been imported in recent years. They are not suitable for reloading. Some have a brass or copper wash over the steel for corrosion resistance; this makes visual inspection less reliable. Before reloading, sort cases carefully to remove all steel cases. A large magnet makes fast work of this task. Remember to sort out Berdan-primed brass cases, too. The prudent 7.62x39 reloader will lay in a supply of new cases and not worry about range pick-ups.

The industry maximum average pressure of this cartridge is established at 50,000 CUP. These loads remain within this limit.

> **NOTE:** *Many variants of the SKS rifle lack a firing pin retractor spring. These may inadvertently slam-fire (the cartridge fires as the bolt closes but before the bolt fully locks). This is seldom a problem with military ammunition; military primers have traditionally been designed to be less sensitive than commercial primers since the development of semi and fully-automatic military small arms.*

However, ammunition reloaded with commercial primers can slam-fire when a series of conditions stack up. Improperly seated primers, misfit firing pins, incorrect headspace and dirty chambers can contribute to this phenomenon. Seat all primers .003" to .005" below flush and keep the chamber clean. If your rifle slam-fires, discontinue its use immediately until you can have the rifle checked by a gunsmith familiar with these rifles.

The best solution is to use primers made for such firearms and, wouldn't you know, CCI has the answer for you. We strongly recommend that you use the CCI M34 Arsenal primers. It has mil-spec sensitivity and can reduce the chance of a slam-fire when other factors get out of control. Reduce loads one grain if using M34 Arsenal primers with these loads.

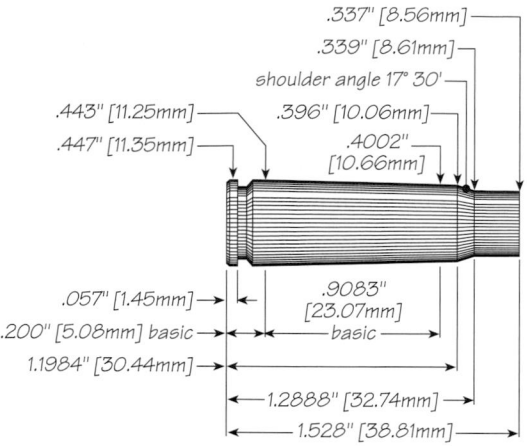

.337" [8.56mm]
.339" [8.61mm]
shoulder angle 17° 30'
.443" [11.25mm]
.447" [11.35mm]
.396" [10.06mm]
.4002" [10.66mm]
.057" [1.45mm]
.200" [5.08mm] basic
1.1984" [30.44mm]
.9083" [23.07mm]
basic
1.2888" [32.74mm]
1.528" [38.81mm]

Max. Case Length:	1.528"	Cart. Case:	IMI Commercial
Trim-to Length:	1.518"	Primer:	CCI 200
Max Cart. OAL:	2.200"	Test Firearm:	Ruger M77 MkII
RCBS Shell Holder:	#32	Barrel Length:	22"

Cole Allen Roberts, 10 year-old grandson of Sandy Forkner, Rimfire Priming, CCI/Speer Operations; 410 Federal Premium shotshells; forest grouse from Feather Creek near Boville, Idaho.

0.310"	303 Spitz SP
Weight, grains	123
Ballistic Coefficient	0.283
Sectional Density	0.183
COAL Tested:	2.150"
Speer Part No.	2213

Propellant	START CHARGE		MAXIMUM CHARGE	
	Weight, grs	Muzzle Velocity, ft/sec	Weight, grs	Muzzle Velocity, ft/sec
AA 1680	26.0	2422	28.0	2544
Reloder 7	25.0	2280	27.0	2429
AA 2015	26.5	2246	28.5	2410
IMR 4198	24.0	2246	26.0	2402
Viht. N120	22.0	2206	24.0	2350
H322	27.0	2195	29.0	2343
H335	29.5	2174	31.5	2325
AA 2230	28.0	2198	30.0	2308
BL-C(2)	29.5	2115	31.5	2250
IMR 4227	19.0	1976	21.0	2214
IMR 4895	27.0	2088	29.0	2198

*Maximum Loads should be used with CAUTION • C = Compressed Load • *Magnum Primer used with this powder.*

303 British

Although reasonably popular in the United States, this old British service cartridge has seen extensive use in the rest of the world, and particularly in those countries that were once part of the vast British Commonwealth. The 303 was adopted as a service cartridge in 1888 in the Lee-Medford Mk I rifle and carbine. Original military ammo featured a 215-grain full-jacketed bullet over a charge of black powder. Later, smokeless powder loads using Cordite propellant were introduced. During the First World War, a 174-grain spitzer bullet at 2400 ft/sec was adopted as the Mk VII round. The military 303 cartridge used this basic configuration until it was replaced by the 7.62mm NATO round in 1957.

Most soft point hunting ammunition for the 303 has been loaded with both 215 and 170-grain bullets, although other weights will be encountered. The famous Short Magazine Lee-Enfield rifle—the SMLE—has been widely distributed as a surplus item. One of the nicest variations is the light and handy No. 5 Mark I, the "Jungle Carbine." It can be used as a hunting rifle without any modification other than the fitting of a five-shot magazine where required by hunting regulations.

The 303 British is ballistically equivalent to the 30-40 Krag, and can be used on the same types of game with proper bullet selection. The reloader should use .310" to .312" bullets. True 30-caliber bullets are .308" in diameter and will seldom give good accuracy. Speer makes three Hot-Cor bullets suitable for the 303. The 150 and 180-grain bullets are the best choices for deer. The 123-grain Hot-Cor bullet, although designed for the 7.62x39mm cartridge, shot surprisingly well in our test rifle. This bullet can be used on varmints up to the size of coyotes. With its muzzle velocities approaching 3000 ft/sec, the 123-grain bullet should not be used on big game.

Lee-Enfield rifles were made in a dizzying number of variations but all share one common feature. The bolt locks at the rear causing the action to be somewhat springy. This limits the 303 to rather modest pressures and case life is usually short. Cases can be used for full-power loads for two firings but then must be relegated for use with lighter practice loads. Check often for signs of incipient case head separations. Winchester still sells unprimed 303 British cases; trying to extend case life by firing them too many times will prove to be false economy if you experience gun damage or personal injury from a failed case that should have been retired long ago.

Surplus rifles show a wide variation in condition, and some may have excessive head-space (see the Lab Notes in this section). Have your rifle thoroughly checked by a competent gunsmith before attempting to fire it with any ammunition. This is especially important with the Lee-Enfield, whose bolt locking lugs are toward the rear of the case. With use, the bolt body can compress enough to create a headspace problem. Another 303 service rifle, the Enfield Pattern 14, uses front locking lugs and is considered among the stronger military actions. It is much more robust than any Lee-Enfield, but is not as common on the surplus market. The P14 Enfield action design gives much longer case life than Lee-Enfields.

The loads presented here are from a complete retest of this cartridge on piezo-electric pressure equipment and modern components in 2006. They remain within the 49,000 psi maximum average pressure assigned to this cartridge.

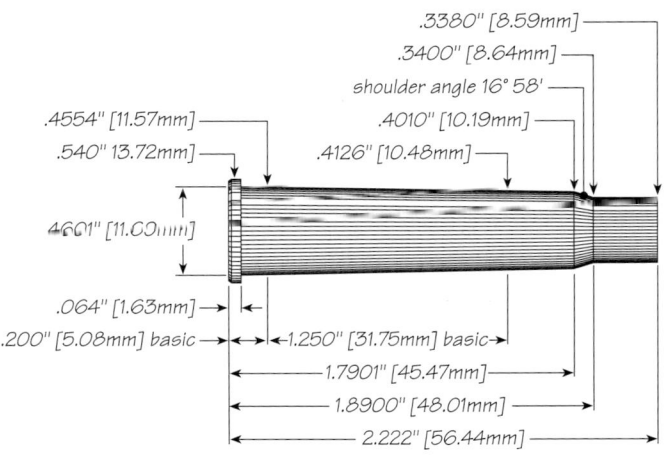

Max. Case Length:	2.222"	**Cart. Case:** Federal
Trim-to Length:	2.212"	**Primer:** Federal 210; 215*
Max Cart. OAL:	3.075"	**Test Firearm:** Universal Receiver
RCBS Shell Holder:	#7	**Barrel Length:** HS Precision 24"

0.310"	303 Spitz SP
Weight, grains	123
Ballistic Coefficient	0.283
Sectional Density	0.183
COAL Tested:	2.910"
Speer Part No.	2213

	START CHARGE		MAXIMUM CHARGE	
Propellant	Weight, grs	Muzzle Velocity, ft/sec	Weight, grs	Muzzle Velocity, ft/sec
Viht. N133	41.0	2754	45.0	2965
Reloder 10X	38.5	2724	42.5	2964
IMR 4895	44.0	2704	48.0C	2936
Ramshot TAC*	40.0	2733	44.0	2933
Varget	45.0	2706	49.0C	2930
H322	38.0	2756	42.0	2925
Reloder 15	44.0	2660	48.0C	2897
IMR 4198	34.5	2638	38.5	2891
AA 2015	39.5	2622	43.5	2888
748*	46.0	2670	50.0C	2854

Lab Notes:

Here's a handy tidbit of information: Most Lee-Enfield rifles have replaceable bolt heads that come in three lengths, marked 1, 2, and 3. The larger the number, the longer the bolt head. This clever design allowed field armorers to quickly adjust headspace as rifles wore, something that would cause other rifles to be sent in for arsenal repair.

The armorer dropped a headspace gauge in the action. If the bolt closed on the gauge indicating too much headspace, the armorer looked at the number on the bolt head. If the head was marked "1" he unscrewed it and installed one marked "2." The whole operation took only minutes and kept rifles in the field where they were needed. Only when a bolt with a "3" head closed on the headspace gauge did the rifle need arsenal refurbishing.

Replacement Lee-Enfield bolt heads are still found on those "parts tables" at many gun shows. Look for ones marked "2" and "3."

0.311"	303 Spitz SP
Weight, grains	150
Ballistic Coefficient	0.351
Sectional Density	0.222
COAL Tested:	3.040"
Speer Part No.	2217

Propellant	START CHARGE		MAXIMUM CHARGE	
	Weight, grs	Muzzle Velocity, ft/sec	Weight, grs	Muzzle Velocity, ft/sec
Ramshot Big Game*	46.0	2637	50.0	2781
760*	47.0	2595	51.0	2763
Reloder 15	41.0	2511	45.0	2746
Varget	41.0	2501	45.0	2724
Viht. N540	41.5	2459	45.5	2701
IMR 4895	40.0	2473	44.0	2695
AA 4064	38.5	2402	42.5	2611
Reloder 10X	33.5	2416	37.5	2606
H322	33.5	2341	37.5	2580
IMR 4350	44.0	2344	48.0C	2516
AA 5744 (reduced load)	25.0	1966	27.0	2078

Allan Jernigan, General Manager, RCBS Operations; 300 WSM 180-grain Trophy Bonded® Bear Claw® bullet; bull elk taken in a Colorado snowstorm.

Maximum Loads should be used with CAUTION • C = Compressed Load • *Magnum Primer used with this powder.

0.311"	303 RNSP
Weight, grains	180
Ballistic Coefficient	0.299
Sectional Density	0.266
COAL Tested:	3.075"
Speer Part No.	2223

Propellant	START CHARGE		MAXIMUM CHARGE	
	Weight, grs	Muzzle Velocity, ft/sec	Weight, grs	Muzzle Velocity, ft/sec
760*	44.0	2351	48.0	2514
Viht. N540	40.0	2303	44.0	2497
Reloder 15	38.0	2274	42.0	2479
Ramshot Big Game*	41.0	2316	45.0	2471
IMR 4895	37.0	2212	41.0	2420
Varget	37.0	2238	41.0	2408
IMR 4350	43.0	2181	47.0C	2389
XMR 4064	35.0	2128	39.0	2339
Reloder 10X	30.5	2125	34.5	2324
H322	31.5	2122	35.5	2320
XMP 5744 (reduced load)	27.0	1956	29.0	2076

*Maximum Loads should be used with CAUTION • C = Compressed Load • *Magnum Primer used with this powder.*

32 Winchester Special

The background of the 32 Winchester Special cartridge is so clogged with myth and gratuitous assertions that we did additional research to sort out the "why" of this cartridge. We extend our thanks to M.L. "Mic" McPherson and John Kort for their invaluable help in sorting facts from flotsam.

Many have assumed that the cartridge appeared at the same time as the 30-30 Winchester cartridge—1895. The 32 WS did not appear in Winchester catalogs until January, 1902. Perhaps the 1902 Winchester catalog offers the best explanation of the 32 WS's existence in light of its current similarity to the 30-30:

> *"The .32 Winchester Special Cartridge, which we have just perfected, is offered to meet the demand of many sportsmen, for a smokeless powder cartridge of larger caliber than the .30 Winchester (ed., 30-30) and not yet so powerful as the .30 U.S. Army (ed., 30-40 Krag), which could be reloaded with black powder and give satisfactory results. The .32 Winchester Special Cartridge meets all of these requirements. Loaded with Smokeless powder and a 165-gr. bullet, it has a muzzle velocity of 2,057 foot seconds. With a charge of 40 grs. of black powder, the .32 Winchester Special develops a velocity of 1,385 foot seconds, which makes it a powerful black powder cartridge."*

It is clear from this description that, when introduced, the 32 WS was truly intermediate in power between the two older cartridges. By 1902, 30-30 velocities (160-grain bullet) had dropped to 1885 ft/sec. The original 32 WS offered 22 percent greater muzzle energy than contemporary 30-30 loads. That's a similar energy difference to that between the 300 Winchester Magnum and the 30-06 today with 180-grain bullets. Starting around 1904, differences in bullet weight and velocity between the two started to fade and today's industry nominal energy figures give the 32 WS only a 5 percent energy advantage.

The 32 Special's standard rifling twist is 1 turn in 16 inches; the standard 30-30 twist is 1 turn in 12 inches. Some say this reflects the recommended use of black powder reloads in the 32 WS. There is a simpler explanation—Winchester had already proved the mating of 32-caliber bullets to a 1-in-16 inch twist rate with the very accurate 32-40 cartridge.

The twist rate raises the most repeated "MythConception" about the 32 Special:

"30-30's with worn bores still shoot pretty well but worn 32's can't hit a barn. The 32 Special's slower twist loses accuracy faster as the barrel wears."

McPherson has, in my opinion, struck upon the origin of the "loss of accuracy" rumor and it has nothing to do with twist rate. Mic bought an old Marlin lever gun in 32 WS with a typical bore—well-used. His handloads with .321" bullets shot as well as most old lever guns can, about three inches at 100 yards with iron sights. Mic found an ancient box of 32 WS factory ammo with the cardboard deteriorating. He fired a few rounds that "hung fire" and never touched the target. He pulled apart the remaining old ammo and found the bullet diameters measured only .318".

That alone explains the ancient myth that "worn 32 Special bores won't shoot." The undersized bullets could likely get some grip on new rifling, enough to shoot acceptably. Once the lands' sharp edges started to round off, the "skinny" bullets lost their grip. Modern ammunition and Speer bullets for the 32 Winchester are .321" for proper fit and accuracy.

With modern ammunition and components, there is no reason to pass up a good used 32 Winchester Special rifle when you're shopping for a 30-30 class rifle. The 32 WS is suitable for the same classes of game animals as the 30-30 and reloading is no different. With the right bullet, it should shoot as well as any 30-30 in similar condition.

As the vast majority of these rifles have tubular magazines, it is imperative to use flat point bullets. At press time, Winchester still catalogs ammunition and unprimed cases on their website. The industry maximum average pressure for the 32 Special is 38,000 CUP.

Editor's Note: *McPherson's full report on his 32 WS Marlin can be found on his website, www.levergun.com/articles/special.*

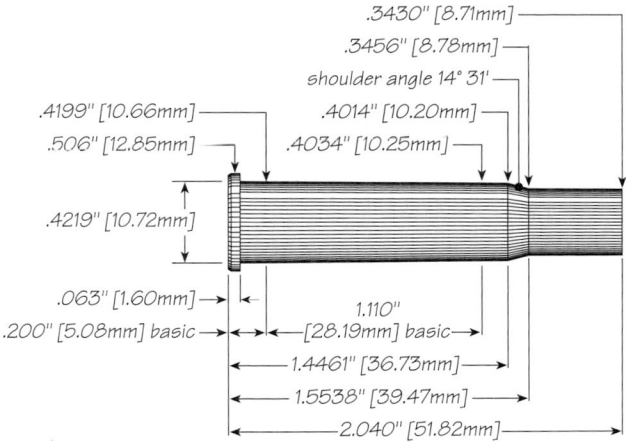

.3430" [8.71mm]
.3456" [8.78mm]
shoulder angle 14° 31'
.4199" [10.66mm]
.4014" [10.20mm]
.506" [12.85mm]
.4034" [10.25mm]
.4219" [10.72mm]
.063" [1.60mm]
1.110"
.200" [5.08mm] basic
[28.19mm] basic
1.4461" [36.73mm]
1.5538" [39.47mm]
2.040" [51.82mm]

Max. Case Length:	2.040"	Cart. Case:	Winchester
Trim-to Length:	2.030"	Primer:	CCI 200; 250*
Max Cart. OAL:	2.565"	Test Firearm:	Winchester Model 94
RCBS Shell Holder:	#2	Barrel Length:	20"

0.321"	32 FNSP
Weight, grains	170
Ballistic Coefficient	0.283
Sectional Density	0.236
COAL Tested:	2.560"
Speer Part No.	2259

Propellant	START CHARGE		MAXIMUM CHARGE	
	Weight, grs	Muzzle Velocity, ft/sec	Weight, grs	Muzzle Velocity, ft/sec
IMR 4895	33.0	2067	35.0	2205
IMR 3031	32.0	2058	34.0	2201
748*	34.0	2062	36.0	2197
IMR 4064	34.0	2038	36.0	2172
BL-C(2)*	31.0	2019	33.0	2166
IMR 4320	33.5	1941	35.5	2070
IMR 4198	23.5	1906	25.5	2062
IMR 4350	35.0	1829	37.0	1944
SR 4759 (reduced load)	16.0	1529	18.0	1710

*Maximum Loads should be used with CAUTION • C = Compressed Load • *Magnum Primer used with this powder.*

8mm Mauser *(8x57mm)*

The 8mm Mauser was adopted as the German service rifle cartridge in 1888. It became as popular in Europe as the 30-06 is here, both for military and sporting use. The 8x57 was the first smokeless powder cartridge adopted by any major military organization. Original loads featured a 227-grain round nose bullet that was .318" in diameter. In 1905, a high-velocity version, often known as the JS, was adopted. The JS cartridge used 150-grain spitzer bullets of .323" diameter for improved long-range performance. Rifles for the new high-velocity loads had a larger bore diameter and much stronger actions than the original Model 1888.

The 8mm Mauser was chambered in only a handful of common U.S. sporting rifles, including the Model 54 Winchester. However, the influx of surplus military rifles in this caliber have kept it alive and RCBS die sales tell us there continues to be a lot of interest in handloading this cartridge.

Part of the interest in handloading the 8mm Mauser can be traced to the low power of U.S. factory ammunition. Because of industry concerns over shooters using JS-type ammunition in the weaker (and tight-bored) Model 1888 action, the industry pressure limit is set very low—37,000 CUP. As a result, the performance of American 8mm Mauser factory ammo is rather disappointing—not much better than a 30-30. European ammunition is loaded to higher limits allowing the true nature of the cartridge to be experienced. Speer pressure-tested some surplus 8x57mm Turkish military ammunition and it was loaded to 50,000 CUP. Handloaded to higher pressures, the 8mm Mauser is close to the 308 Winchester in power and is suitable for most North American game except the great bears.

In a quality Model 98 Mauser in good condition, the handloader can have a very versatile hunting rifle. However, military Mausers have been built at arsenals around the world and quality varies considerably. You should also be aware that many surplus rifles had the bolts removed and mixed during shipping or storage. Even a surplus Mauser from the best factory may not have its original bolt. It is very important that any surplus rifles be inspected for headspace and overall quality before attempting to fire them with any ammunition.

Speer makes three Hot-Cor bullets suitable for the 8mm Mauser. The 150-grain spitzer is a fine, all-around bullet and the 170-grain semi-spitzer is an excellent woods bullet.

The 200-grain spitzer was designed for 8mm Remington Magnum velocities; however, it can be used for close shots on elk and moose in the 8mm Mauser at maximum permissible velocities.

We developed the following loads along European guidelines, so these exceed the SAAMI pressure limit; pressures approach 50,000 CUP. Do not use these loads in any 8mm rifles other than Model 98 Mausers that have been inspected by a gunsmith familiar with these actions. Do not use these loads in any rifle that has the smaller .318" bore.

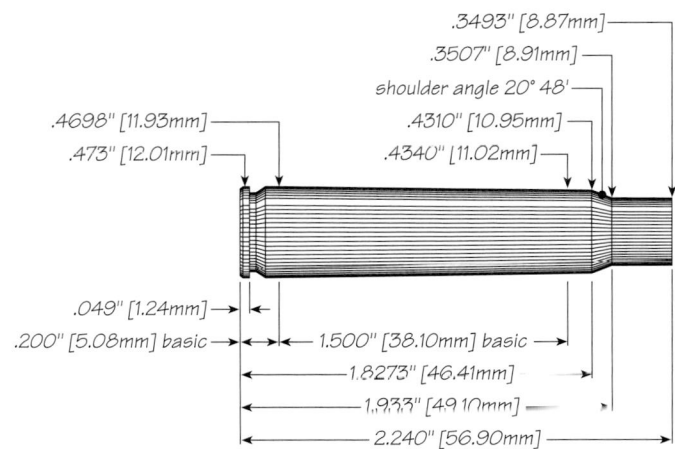

Max. Case Length:	2.240"	Cart. Case:	Remington
Trim-to Length:	2.230"	Primer:	CCI 200; 250*
Max Cart. OAL:	3.250"	Test Firearm:	Mauser M98 VZ24
RCBS Shell Holder:	#3	Barrel Length:	24"

0.323"	8mm Spitz SP
Weight, grains	150
Ballistic Coefficient	0.343
Sectional Density	0.205
COAL Tested:	2.890"
Speer Part No.	2277

Propellant	START CHARGE		MAXIMUM CHARGE	
	Weight, grs	Muzzle Velocity, ft/sec	Weight, grs	Muzzle Velocity, ft/sec
IMR 4064	47.0	2695	51.0	2915
H335*	46.0	2513	50.0	2771
IMR 3031	45.0	2488	49.0	2757
Reloder 15	47.0	2439	51.0	2726
H322	44.0	2433	48.0	2699
Viht. N140	46.0	2436	50.0	2695
IMR 4895	44.0	2428	48.0	2675
IMR 4350	51.0	2458	55.0	2660
AA 2700*	46.0	2358	50.0	2580
BL-C(2)*	40.0	2324	44.0	2544
AA 4350	52.0	2317	56.0C	2507
H414*	51.0	2281	55.0	2506
IMR 4198(R)	24.0	1809	26.0	1955

0.323"	8mm Semi Spitz SP
Weight, grains	170
Ballistic Coefficient	0.311
Sectional Density	0.233
COAL Tested:	.2890"
Speer Part No.	2283

Propellant	START CHARGE Weight, grs	Muzzle Velocity, ft/sec	MAXIMUM CHARGE Weight, grs	Muzzle Velocity, ft/sec
IMR 4064	45.0	2509	**49.0**	2723
748*	50.0	2451	**54.0**	2716
IMR 4895	42.0	2401	**46.0**	2640
Reloder 15	45.0	2425	**49.0**	2632
IMR 4350	54.0	2429	**55.0C**	2632
IMR 3031	40.0	2356	**44.0**	2600
H380*	50.0	2359	**54.0**	2588
Viht. N140	44.0	2378	**48.0**	2574
H335*	42.0	2262	**46.0**	2525
AA 2700*	45.0	2266	**49.0**	2486
AA 4350	49.0	2185	**53.0C**	2368
H322	38.0	2049	**42.0**	2324
IMR 4198 (reduced load)	25.0	1778	**27.0**	1914

*Maximum Loads should be used with CAUTION • C = Compressed Load • *Magnum Primer used with this powder.*

0.323"	8mm Spitz SP
Weight, grains	200
Ballistic Coefficient	0.440
Sectional Density	0.274
COAL Tested:	3.200"
Speer Part No.	2285

Propellant	START CHARGE		MAXIMUM CHARGE	
	Weight, grs	Muzzle Velocity, ft/sec	Weight, grs	Muzzle Velocity, ft/sec
H380*	48.0	2242	52.0	2469
IMR 4064	42.0	2196	46.0	2434
IMR 4350	49.0	2208	53.0C	2432
IMR 4831	50.0	2213	54.0	2395
760*	48.0	2171	52.0	2392
AA 2700*	44.0	2110	48.0C	2324
H335*	38.0	2066	42.0	2322
Reloder 15	40.0	2051	44.0	2267
Viht. N140	39.0	2040	43.0	2242
AA 4350	46.0	2022	50.0C	2149

*Maximum Loads should be used with CAUTION • C = Compressed Load • *Magnum Primer used with this powder.*

8mm-06

Wildcat cartridges come and go and some have proved their worth better than others. The 8mm-06 is one of the worthy ones, arising from a very practical need.

Owners of surplus 8mm Model 98 Mauser rifles wanted a way to improve the power of their rifles at minimum expense. The solution was to simply rechamber the rifle to handle a 30-06 case necked up to hold 0.323" bullets. The result is a happy combination. Cheap 30-06 brass is plentiful and the handloader has a reasonable selection of good bullets. The only limitation of the 8mm-06 is that no true varmint-type bullets are available in this diameter.

Readers will note the 8mm-06 cartridge overall length is the same as the max length for the 8mm Mauser cartridge—3.250 inches, slightly shorter than the 30-06 max cartridge length of 3.340 inches. This is an accommodation for the M98 Mauser action.

As a hunting cartridge, the 8mm-06 is equal to the 30-06 in all respects and can be used on the same types of game. Case forming can usually be accomplished in the sizer die alone. Bullet recommendations are the same as in the text for the 8mm Mauser cartridge.

When considering the conversion to 8mm-06, you must make certain that the rifle has the later .323" diameter barrel and not the older .318" barrel. Rifles having the smaller bore diameter also have weaker actions making them unsuitable for conversion to any modern, high-pressure cartridge. Have the rifle thoroughly checked before committing to such a conversion.

The 8mm-06 is a wildcat cartridge so no pressure or dimensional standards exist for it. The cartridge drawing we show matches the chamber in our test rifle. These loads are estimated to produce pressures similar to the 30-06—up to 50,000 CUP. 8mm-06 reloading dies are available from RCBS.

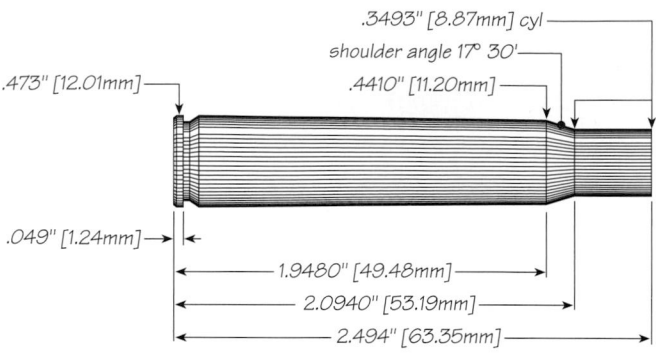

.3493" [8.87mm] cyl
shoulder angle 17° 30'
.4410" [11.20mm]
.473" [12.01mm]
.049" [1.24mm]
1.9480" [49.48mm]
2.0940" [53.19mm]
2.494" [63.35mm]

Max. Case Length:	2.494"	Cart. Case:	Winchester (reformed 30-06)
Trim-to Length:	2.484"	Primer:	CCI 200; 250*
Max Cart. OAL:	3.250"	Test Firearm:	Mauser M98 (rechambered)
RCBS Shell Holder:	#3	Barrel Length:	24"

0.323"	8mm Spitz SP
Weight, grains	150
Ballistic Coefficient	0.343
Sectional Density	0.205
COAL Tested:	3.250"
Speer Part No.	2277

Propellant	START CHARGE Weight, grs	START CHARGE Muzzle Velocity, ft/sec	MAXIMUM CHARGE Weight, grs	MAXIMUM CHARGE Muzzle Velocity, ft/sec
BL-C(2)*	49.0	2509	53.0	2981
IMR 4064	51.0	2585	55.0C	2881
IMR 4320	50.0	2614	54.0	2849
H380*	55.0	2662	59.0C	2844
760*	58.0	2581	62.0	2826
IMR 3031	48.0	2482	52.0C	2806
748*	51.0	2552	55.0	2795
IMR 4895	48.0	2523	52.0	2786
IMR 4350	55.0	2463	59.0C	2677
IMR 4831	56.0	2455	60.0C	2573

0.323"	8mm Semi Spitz SP
Weight, grains	170
Ballistic Coefficient	0.311
Sectional Density	0.233
COAL Tested:	3.250"
Speer Part No.	2283

| Propellant | START CHARGE | | MAXIMUM CHARGE | |
	Weight, grs	Muzzle Velocity, ft/sec	Weight, grs	Muzzle Velocity, ft/sec
BL-C(2)*	47.0	2513	51.0	2762
IMR 4064	50.0	2437	54.0C	2675
H380*	55.0	2551	59.0C	2653
760*	58.0	2418	62.0C	2643
IMR 4320	49.0	2406	53.0	2640
748*	50.0	2369	54.0	2619
IMR 4350	54.0	2355	58.0C	2580
IMR 4831	50.0	2352	00.0C	2570
IMR 4895	46.0	2303	50.0	2543
IMR 3031	46.0	2287	50.0C	2522

*Maximum Loads should be used with CAUTION • C = Compressed Load • *Magnum Primer used with this powder.*

0.323"	8mm Spitz SP
Weight, grains	200
Ballistic Coefficient	0.440
Sectional Density	0.274
COAL Tested:	3.250"
Speer Part No.	2285

Propellant	START CHARGE		MAXIMUM CHARGE	
	Weight, grs	Muzzle Velocity, ft/sec	Weight, grs	Muzzle Velocity, ft/sec
IMR 4064	49.0	2411	53.0C	2647
760*	58.0	2411	62.0C	2615
IMR 4320	48.0	2354	52.0	2612
BL-C(2)*	45.0	2353	49.0	2599
H380*	53.0	2367	57.0C	2595
748*	49.0	2341	53.0	2583
IMR 4350	54.0	2347	58.0C	2580
IMR 4831	56.0	2337	60.0C	2546
IMR 3031	44.0	2194	48.0	2429
IMR 4895	44.0	2174	48.0	2420

*Maximum Loads should be used with CAUTION • C = Compressed Load • *Magnum Primer used with this powder.*

325 Winchester Short Magnum

The 325 Winchester Short Magnum joined the 7mm, 270, and 300 WSM in 2005 to provide the option of a larger diameter bullet in Winchester's Short Magnum line. The developers settled on 0.323-inch bullets, making the 325 the only purely American 8mm factory cartridge since the 8mm Remington Magnum in 1977. Its performance is roughly equal to the longer Remington cartridge, with the advantages of a non-belted case and working through a short-action rifle. The Remington cartridge requires a magnum-length action.

Factory loads include a 180-grain bullet at 3060 ft/sec, a 200-grain bullet at 2950 ft/sec, and a 220-grain bullet at 2840 ft/sec, posting muzzle energies between 3750 and 3950 ft/lbs. The cartridge is suitable for any North American game as well as the largest African plains animals. Bullet choice becomes important when the 325 is turned on dangerous bear species. Two of the factory loads use polymer-tipped bullets. As a group, tipped bullets do not penetrate as deeply as conventional soft points of the same weight. All three Speer 8mm bullets are conventional soft points featuring Hot-Cor® construction, making them excellent choices for the range of game this potent cartridge can handle.

Of the three Speer bullets, the 200-grain spitzer is the toughest. It was designed with the 8mm Remington Magnum in mind, and has a heavier jacket for magnum velocities. Vernon Speer designed the 150 and 170-grain bullets years ago for 8mm Mauser velocities. They are still effective deer bullets in the 8mm magnums, but should not be used for dangerous game.

Although "magnum" often calls to mind the slow-burning rate propellants, the combination of case capacity and bore diameter in the 325 WSM means that the medium rate powers give excellent performance.

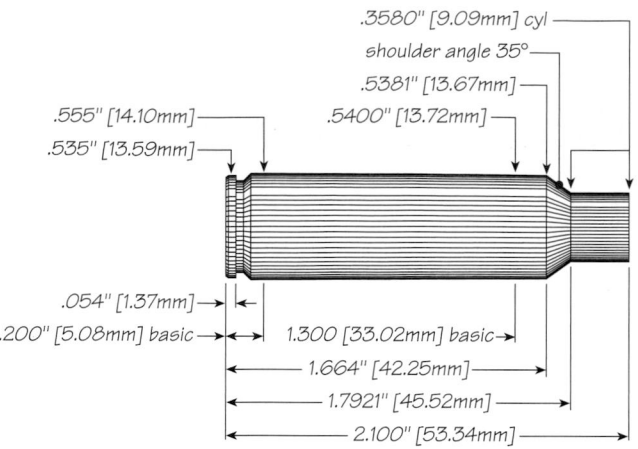

Max. Case Length:	2.100"	**Cart. Case:**	Winchester
Trim-to Length:	2.090"	**Primer:**	Federal 210/215*
Max Cart. OAL:	2.860"	**Test Firearm:**	Universal Receiver
RCBS Shell Holder:	#43	**Barrel Length:**	Wiseman 24"

0.323"	8mm Spitz SP
Weight, grains	150
Ballistic Coefficient	0.343
Sectional Density	0.205
COAL Tested:	2.850"
Speer Part No.	2277

	START CHARGE		MAXIMUM CHARGE	
Propellant	Weight, grs	Muzzle Velocity, ft/sec	Weight, grs	Muzzle Velocity, ft/sec
760*	70.0	3134	**74.0**	3303
H414*	67.0	3103	**71.0**	3263
Ramshot Big Game*	68.0	3121	**72.0**	3260
Viht. N540	63.0	3060	**67.0**	3257
Reloder 15	61.0	3090	**65.0**	3245
IMR 4895	61.0	3047	**65.0**	3232
Varget	61.0	3076	**65.0**	3222
IMR 3031	57.0	3022	**61.0**	3207
AA 4064	60.0	2986	**64.0**	3147
AA 5744 (reduced load)	30.0	1985	**32.0**	2097

0.323"	8mm Semi Spitz SP
Weight, grains	170
Ballistic Coefficient	0.311
Sectional Density	0.233
COAL Tested:	2.790"
Speer Part No.	2283

Propellant	START CHARGE		MAXIMUM CHARGE	
	Weight, grs	Muzzle Velocity, ft/sec	Weight, grs	Muzzle Velocity, ft/sec
760*	66.0	2910	70.0	3074
Reloder 19	70.0	2874	74.0C	3064
Viht. N540	60.0	2879	64.0	3063
H414*	64.0	2878	68.0	3045
Ramshot Big Game*	64.0	2905	68.0	3044
Reloder 15	58.0	2878	62.0	3038
IMR 4350	65.0	2839	69.0	3027
Varget	50.0	2805	62.0	3023
IMR 4895	58.0	2852	62.0	3018
AA 4064	56.0	2746	60.0	2906

*Maximum Loads should be used with CAUTION • C = Compressed Load • *Magnum Primer used with this powder.*

0.323"	8mm Spitz SP
Weight, grains	200
Ballistic Coefficient	0.440
Sectional Density	0.274
COAL Tested:	2.840"
Speer Part No.	2285

Propellant	START CHARGE		MAXIMUM CHARGE	
	Weight, grs	Muzzle Velocity, ft/sec	Weight, grs	Muzzle Velocity, ft/sec
Reloder 19	65.0	2671	69.0	2837
IMR 4350	61.0	2638	65.0	2802
H414*	60.0	2650	64.0	2791
Ramshot Big Game*	60.0	2654	64.0	2789
760*	60.0	2614	64.0	2775
AA 4350	62.0	2602	66.0	2766
Reloder 15	53.0	2592	57.0	2742
Viht. N540	54.0	2559	58.0	2729

*Maximum Loads should be used with CAUTION • C = Compressed Load • *Magnum Primer used with this powder.*

8mm Remington Magnum

Certain metric rifle calibers have not been as successful in the U.S. as in the rest of the world. With the exception of the various 7mm cartridges, they have been slow sellers compared to more "traditional" cartridges. Thus, it was a bit of a surprise when Remington announced the 8mm Remington Magnum in 1977. At a time when belted magnums of 30-06 case length were the rage, Remington designed its new magnum on the full-length 300 H&H case. The result was a case with a large powder capacity—not much less than the powerful 340 Weatherby Magnum. Remington initially made factory ammunition in two bullet weights: 185 and 220 grains.

Remington's position in marketing the 8mm Magnum was to provide "...optimum characteristics of flat shooting and high energy without developing excessively uncomfortable recoil." Most riflemen familiar with the big cartridge will readily agree with the first part of the statement but will probably challenge the last claim. In spite of its heavy recoil, the 8mm Remington lives up to the promise of hard-hitting power at long ranges.

This cartridge is probably too much for most North American game (other than the large bears) but would do well for long shots on elk. It has been used with very good results on the African plains, where long shots on tough animals like kudu are common. Before choosing the 8mm Magnum for African hunting, check the game regulations in the area you plan to hunt. Some countries have bore size restrictions.

The Speer 200-grain Hot-Cor spitzer was designed specifically for the 8mm Magnum. Its tough construction and relatively high ballistic coefficient are a perfect match for the cartridge's performance characteristics. The lighter 150 and 170-grain Speer bullets can be used for reduced-recoil practice but, as they were designed for lower velocity cartridges, we don't recommend them for heavy game.

Competition from the excellent 338 Winchester and the lack of consumer comfort with the 8mm bore meant the big Remington cartridge was never a big seller. The newer 338 Remington Ultra Magnum fills its niche in the Remington cartridge lineup and the 325 Winchester Short Magnum, a new 8mm cartridge, comes very close to matching 8mm Remington velocities. Remington no longer catalogs rifles in this caliber. Their ammunition is still available, but only in a single load with a 200-grain bullet. Remington catalogs unprimed cases on its 2006 website.

The SAAMI maximum average pressure for the 8mm Remington Magnum is 54,000 CUP. These loads do not exceed that limit.

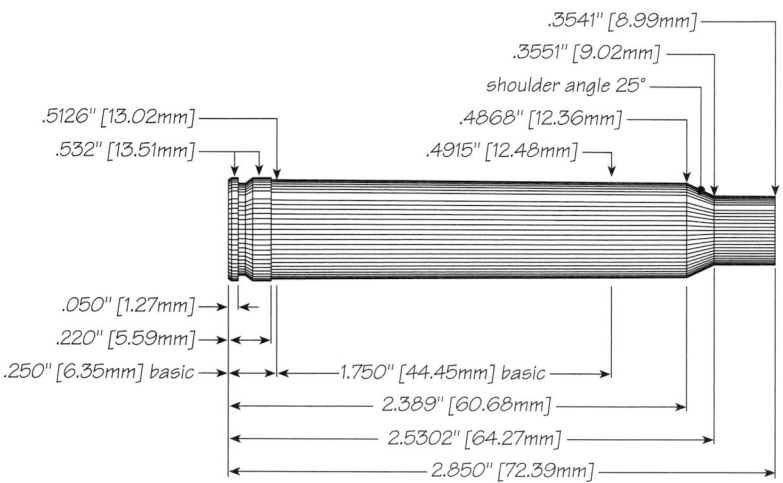

Max. Case Length:	2.850"	Cart. Case:	Remington
Trim-to Length:	2.840"	Primer:	CCI 250*
Max Cart. OAL:	3.600"	Test Firearm:	Remington Model 700
RCBS Shell Holder:	#4	Barrel Length:	24"

0.323"	8mm Spitz SP
Weight, grains	150
Ballistic Coefficient	0.343
Sectional Density	0.205
COAL Tested:	3.575"
Speer Part No.	2277

	START CHARGE		MAXIMUM CHARGE	
Propellant	Weight, grs	Muzzle Velocity, ft/sec	Weight, grs	Muzzle Velocity, ft/sec
IMR 4841*	80.0	3194	86.0C	3436
IMR 4350*	77.0	3158	81.0	3322
760*	76.0	3076	80.0	3225
H380*	72.0	3038	76.0	3214
H414*	74.0	3025	78.0	3191
IMR 3031*	63.0	2969	67.0	3149
IMR 4895*	62.0	2955	66.0	3134

CCI/Speer Engineer Steve Moore caring for the pack mules on an Idaho back county hunt.

*Maximum Loads should be used with CAUTION • C = Compressed Load • *Magnum Primer used with this powder.*

0.323"	8mm Semi Spitz SP
Weight, grains	170
Ballistic Coefficient	0.311
Sectional Density	0.233
COAL Tested:	3.575"
Speer Part No.	2283

	START CHARGE		MAXIMUM CHARGE	
Propellant	Weight, grs	Muzzle Velocity, ft/sec	Weight, grs	Muzzle Velocity, ft/sec
IMR 4831*	74.0	2865	80.0	3114
IMR 4350*	73.0	2902	77.0	3078
H380*	67.0	2828	71.0	3000
H414*	69.0	2817	73.0	2970
760*	70.0	2795	74.0	2965
IMR 4064*	62.0	2761	66.0	2940
IMR 4895*	59.0	2740	63.0	2919

Travis Saleen and dad, Tom Saleen, Director of International Sales, ATK CCI/Speer Operations; 270 Win 150-grain Grand Slam®; axis deer, Texas.

0.323"	8mm Spitz SP
Weight, grains	200
Ballistic Coefficient	0.440
Sectional Density	0.274
COAL Tested:	3.575"
Speer Part No.	2285

	START CHARGE		MAXIMUM CHARGE	
Propellant	Weight, grs	Muzzle Velocity, ft/sec	Weight, grs	Muzzle Velocity, ft/sec
IMR 4831*	72.0	2763	78.0	2996
IMR 7828*	79.0	2712	83.0C	2938
IMR 4350*	70.0	2770	74.0	2936
IMR 4064*	60.0	2638	64.0	2803
IMR 4895*	57.0	2564	61.0	2736
IMR 3031*	57.0	2561	61.0	2732
IMR 4320*	58.0	2544	62.0	2717

*Maximum Loads should be used with CAUTION • C = Compressed Load • *Magnum Primer used with this powder.*

338 Federal

The 338 Federal was introduced in 2006 to provide a modern medium-caliber, compact cartridge for light rifles. Its inspiration was the wildcat 338-08, a 308 Winchester necked up to hold .338" bullets. To be a commercial success, the 338-08 needed some minor refinements that the 338 Federal provides.

The 338 Federal's niche is one once occupied by such woods cartridges as the 348 Winchester, the 35 Remington, and the 358 Winchester. Although these are fine cartridges, their modest velocities and short bullets limit their useful range for most shooters. By selecting a 338-caliber bullet, engineers at Federal Cartridge succeeded in creating a new cartridge that does everything its predecessors did in the deep woods, but has the range to make it effective for longer shots. A 338-caliber bullet has a higher sectional density and therefore a better ballistic coefficient than a 35-caliber bullet of the same weight and shape.

Having the experience of 338-08 owners such as Lane Pearce, reloading editor for *Shooting Times Magazine,* made the development process easier for Federal engineer Kris Ostman, who was assigned the project. The final case design is somewhat different from most variants of the wildcat. As you know, wildcat cartridges do not have standardized dimensions; chambers can vary from one gunsmith to another. There is enough difference that Federal's Larry Head cautions against using 338 Federal ammunition or cases in a custom 338-08 rifle.

Factory ballistics specify a 180-grain bullet at a muzzle velocity of 2830 ft/sec or a 210-grain bullet at 2630 ft/sec. Both loads deliver over 3200 ft/lbs of muzzle energy, and rise just over 2 inches between muzzle and target when sighted for 200 yards. That means a lot of power and flexibility in a small package.

Propellants useful in reloading the 338 Federal are often those that do well in the 223 Remington. For most hunting, the 200-grain Speer Hot-Cor is the best choice. When you know your shots will be close, consider the 225-grain Speer boat tail. The added weight gives plenty of penetration on larger game.

The 338 has already taken all species of North American deer, plus black bear and elk. In spite of its superb game performance, the felt recoil is about the same as 30-06. Ruger, Kimber, Sako, Steyr, and Thompson-Center are chambering rifles for the 338 Federal at press time, and we feel sure that more firms will join them.

The industry pressure limit for the 338 Federal is 62,000 psi.

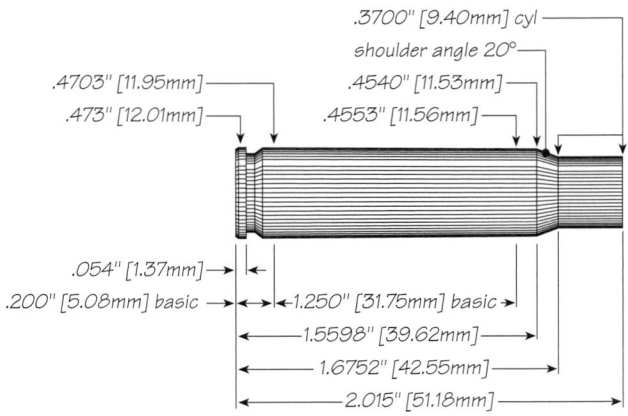

.3700" [9.40mm] cyl
shoulder angle 20°
.4703" [11.95mm]
.473" [12.01mm]
.4540" [11.53mm]
.4553" [11.56mm]
.054" [1.37mm]
.200" [5.08mm] basic
1.250" [31.75mm] basic
1.5598" [39.62mm]
1.6752" [42.55mm]
2.015" [51.18mm]

Max. Case Length:	2.015"	Cart. Case:	Federal
Trim-to Length:	2.005"	Primer:	Federal 210
Max Cart. OAL:	2.820"	Test Firearm:	Universal Receiver
RCBS Shell Holder:	#3	Barrel Length:	HS Precision 24"

0.338"	338 Spitz SP
Weight, grains	200
Ballistic Coefficient	0.426
Sectional Density	0.250
COAL Tested:	2.820"
Speer Part No.	2405

	START CHARGE		MAXIMUM CHARGE	
Propellant	Weight, grs	Muzzle Velocity, ft/sec	Weight, grs	Muzzle Velocity, ft/sec
Reloder 15	44.0	2508	46.0C	2598
Varget	45.0	2485	47.0C	2571
748	45.5	2504	47.5	2570
Ramshot TAC	42.0	2421	44.0	2504
H322	38.0	2303	40.0	2451
Reloder 10X	36.5	2345	38.5	2444
AA 2015	38.0	2303	40.0	2404
Reloder 7	34.5	2306	36.5	2403
IMR 4198	33.5	2268	35.5	2368

*Maximum Loads should be used with CAUTION • C = Compressed Load • *Magnum Primer used with this powder.*

0.338"	338 Spitz BTSP
Weight, grains	225
Ballistic Coefficient	0.497
Sectional Density	0.281
COAL Tested:	2.820"
Speer Part No.	2406

	START CHARGE		MAXIMUM CHARGE	
Propellant	Weight, grs	Muzzle Velocity, ft/sec	Weight, grs	Muzzle Velocity, ft/sec
Reloder 15	42.0	2350	**44.0C**	2440
Varget	42.5	2326	**44.5**	2408
748	42.5	2309	**44.5**	2392
Ramshot TAC	40.0	2277	**42.0**	2368
IMR 3031	37.0	2204	**39.0**	2323
Reloder 10X	35.0	2207	**37.0**	2299
H322	35.5	2174	**37.5**	2276
Reloder 7	33.0	2161	**35.0**	2256
AA 2015	35.5	2139	**37.5**	2237

Larry Head, Product Development Manager, Federal Premium® Operations; 338 Federal; bull elk from central Idaho.

Maximum Loads should be used with CAUTION • C = Compressed Load • *Magnum Primer used with this powder.

338-06 A-Square

Interest in necking up the 30-06 case to hold larger diameter bullets goes back to the 1920's when the 35 Whelen was developed. Around 1945, Charles O'Neil, Elmer Keith and Don Hopkins collaborated to design an improvement to the Whelen.

When very heavy component bullets suitable for the Whelen disappeared, Elmer Keith wanted another cartridge for which 275 to 300 grain bullets were available. The cartridge the team developed was the 333 OKH using the 30-06 case necked up to hold bullets designed for the 333 Jeffery, a proprietary English cartridge. Jeffery bullets weighed up to 300 grains—just what Keith wanted. The wildcat OKH cartridge proved successful on all types of North American game. Heavy bullets at moderate velocity gave tremendous penetration for reliable kills. The only disadvantage was that .333" bullets were usually in short supply and had to be ordered from England.

When the 338 Winchester Magnum was introduced in 1958, American bullet makers like Speer introduced a wide variety of .338" bullets for handloading. Shooters who wanted a 333 OKH but were put off by the bullet problem quickly found an alternative in the 338-06. Although 338-caliber bullets weighing over 250 grains are rare today, modern jacketed projectiles will probably out-penetrate most of the heavier bullets Keith loved.

The 338-06 is a very flexible cartridge. With lighter bullets, it is an excellent deer cartridge that kills cleanly and damages much less meat than any of the 300 magnums. Loaded with the 250-grain Speer Grand Slam, the cartridge is ready for elk and moose. Although at the "light" end for the great bears, a 338-06 with the 250-grain Grand Slam would probably trump a 300 Magnum if a grizzly were sniffing around your camp.

Ballistically, the 338-06 has a slight edge over the 35 Whelen. In the Whelen, 250-grain bullets failed to reach 2400 ft/sec. In the 338-06, the same weight bullets approached 2500 ft/sec and exceeded this mark with one propellant. Velocities with the 200-grain spitzer were nearly 2800 ft/sec, less 200 ft/sec behind the same bullet in the 338 Winchester Magnum.

The fact that .338" bullets have higher ballistic coefficients than .358" bullets of the same weight, and that heavier and tougher bullets are available for the 338 combine to make the 338-06 superior to the Whelen for the reloader who commonly hunts large game like moose, elk and bear.

The 338-06 is one of the nicest medium-caliber rifle cartridges on the scene, and is better suited for most North American hunting than the 8mm Remington Magnum or the 338 Winchester Magnum. In recognition of its merits, it was adopted as a standard industry cartridge in 1998. The maximum average is established at 53,000 CUP.

Editor's Note: *Our special thanks to Steve Comus, magazine editor at Safari Club International, for the kind loan of his fine custom A-Square™ rifle built by Art Alphin.*

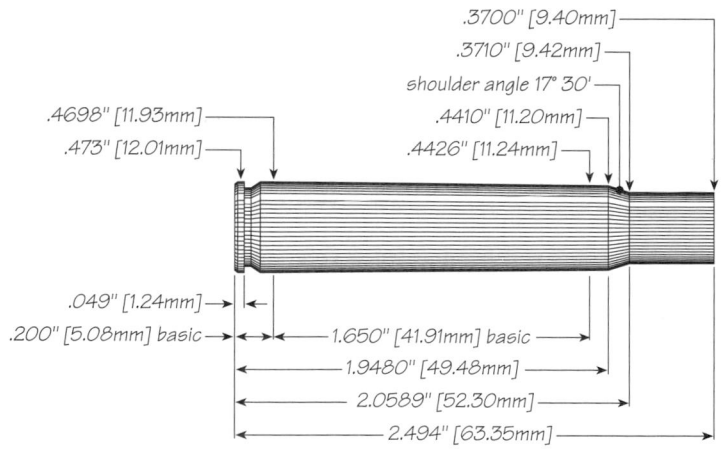

Max. Case Length:	2.494"	Cart. Case:	Reformed Rem 35 Whelen
Trim-to Length:	2.484"	Primer:	CCI 200
Max Cart. OAL:	3.340"	Test Firearm:	A-Square Hamilcar
RCBS Shell Holder:	#3	Barrel Length:	23"

0.338"	338 Spitz SP
Weight, grains	200
Ballistic Coefficient	0.426
Sectional Density	0.250
COAL Tested:	3.340"
Speer Part No.	2405

	START CHARGE		MAXIMUM CHARGE	
Propellant	Weight, grs	Muzzle Velocity, ft/sec	Weight, grs	Muzzle Velocity, ft/sec
H4350	59.0	2602	63.0C	2773
IMR 4064	52.0	2568	56.0	2766
IMR 4320	52.5	2564	56.5	2759
Reloder 15	51.0	2552	55.0	2752
Vlht. N150	52.5	2558	56.5	2752
H380	58.0	2573	62.0C	2750
760	58.5	2563	62.5C	2740
IMR 4350	58.0	2560	62.0C	2736
AA 4350	60.5	2564	64.5C	2733
H414	58.5	2550	62.5	2724

*Maximum Loads should be used with CAUTION • C = Compressed Load • *Magnum Primer used with this powder.*

0.338"	338 Spitz BTSP	338 GS SP
Weight, grains	225	225
Ballistic Coefficient	0.497	0.382
Sectional Density	0.281	0.281
COAL Tested:	3.340"	3.340"
Speer Part No.	2406	2407

	START CHARGE		MAXIMUM CHARGE	
Propellant	Weight, grs	Muzzle Velocity, ft/sec	Weight, grs	Muzzle Velocity, ft/sec
Reloder 19	60.5	2512	64.5C	2678
Viht. N160	59.5	2507	63.5C	2675
H4350	58.0	2499	62.0C	2671
Reloder 15	50.5	2462	54.5	2656
IMR 4350	57.0	2482	61.0C	2655
760	57.0	2476	61.0	2650
IMR 4320	50.5	2418	54.5	2610
IMR 4064	49.0	2395	53.0	2591
Viht. N150	50.0	2396	54.0	2588
AA 4350	56.0	2309	60.0C	2566
IMR 4831	57.0	2389	61.0C	2557
AA 3100	59.0	2385	63.0C	2547

0.338"	338 GS SP
Weight, grains	250
Ballistic Coefficient	0.436
Sectional Density	0.313
COAL Tested:	3.340"
Speer Part No.	2408

Propellant	START CHARGE		MAXIMUM CHARGE	
	Weight, grs	Muzzle Velocity, ft/sec	Weight, grs	Muzzle Velocity, ft/sec
Reloder 19	57.0	2366	61.0C	2531
H4831	57.5	2330	61.5C	2492
IMR 4350	53.5	2318	57.5	2491
H4350	54.0	2317	58.0C	2489
IMR 4831	55.5	2311	59.5C	2470
Viht. N160	54.0	2256	58.0	2473
760	52.5	2294	56.5	2468
H414	53.0	2293	57.0	2467
IMR 4064	46.5	2220	50.5	2411
Reloder 15	46.0	2216	50.0	2409
AA 3100	56.0	2247	60.0C	2408
IMR 4320	47.0	2215	51.0	2403

*Maximum Loads should be used with CAUTION • C = Compressed Load • *Magnum Primer used with this powder.*

338 Winchester Magnum

Winchester announced two new short magnums in 1958 (then meaning the case is 30-06 length)—the 264 and the 338 Winchester Magnums. Of the two, the 338 has been the most successful because it filled a huge performance gap between the various 300 magnums and the 375 H&H Magnum. Intended for the largest North American game, the 338 has proved its effectiveness on grizzly and brown bear and gives excellent performance on the larger species of African plains game in regions permitting this bore diameter.

The 338 functions in standard length bolt actions so most rifle makers now chamber it. Factory ammunition has been loaded with 200, 250 and even 300-grain bullets. Almost any bullet can achieve 4000 ft/lbs of muzzle energy in the 338, really making it more gun than most North American game requires. However, it has become popular in the West as an elk rifle where its high retained energy gives it an advantage over the 300 magnums.

For large deer and elk, Speer's 200-grain Hot-Cor and 225-grain boat tail are both good choices. Slow either by a couple of hundred ft/sec and you have a whitetail rifle that won't tear up much edible meat. Their high ballistic coefficients give flat trajectories for long shots. For large bears, the 225-grain Trophy Bonded Bear Claw and the 225 and 250-grain Grand Slams are the best choices.

If the owner of a 270 or 30-06 rifle wants to move up to a more powerful cartridge to extend the number of species he can hunt, the 338 is a much better option than any of the various 300 magnums, which are borderline performers on the largest bear. The 270 and 30-06 are more than adequate for the lesser species. With the possible exceptions of the 325 Winchester Short Magnum and the 8mm Remington Magnum, we feel the .338" bore is the smallest that the serious bear hunter should consider. We are aware that many bear are killed with 30-caliber rifles—but many are wounded, too. The 338 bore allows the use of heavy, tough bullets on the big bruins.

Some reloaders of the 338 seem to encounter case stretching ahead of the belt. Like other belted magnums, we recommend setting your loading dies so that the case headspaces on the shoulder, not the belt. The RCBS Precision Mic is available in 338 Winchester Magnum for precisely adjusting your dies for a custom fit in your chamber.

This will improve case life and accuracy and reduce the chance of a case head separation. See chapter 8 for additional information on this subject.

The following loads do not exceed the 54,000 CUP pressure limit of the 338 Winchester.

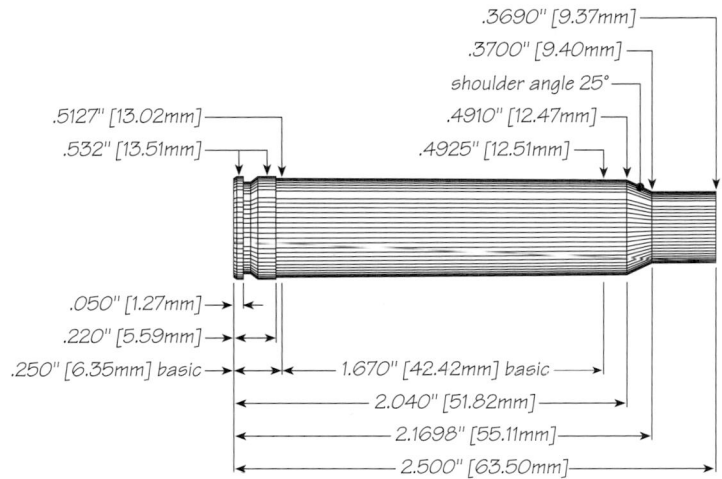

Max. Case Length:	2.500"	**Cart. Case:**	Winchester
Trim-to Length:	2.490"	**Primer:**	CCI 250*
Max Cart. OAL:	3.340"	**Test Firearm:**	Winchester Model 70
RCBS Shell Holder:	#4	**Barrel Length:**	24"

0.338"	338 Spitz SP
Weight, grains	200
Ballistic Coefficient	0.426
Sectional Density	0.250
COAL Tested:	3.300"
Speer Part No.	2405

Propellant	START CHARGE Weight, grs	Muzzle Velocity, ft/sec	MAXIMUM CHARGE Weight, grs	Muzzle Velocity, ft/sec
IMR 4350*	69.5	2791	73.5	2959
IMR 4831*	70.5	2782	74.5	2956
H4350*	71.0	2697	75.0C	2932
H414*	66.0	2793	70.0	2905
H4831SC*	74.0	2781	78.0C	2887
IMR 7828*	77.0	2682	81.0C	2882
Viht. N150*	61.0	2598	65.0	2824
AA 3100*	73.0	2654	77.0C	2823
760*	66.0	2604	70.0	2816
Reloder 19*	72.0	2596	76.0C	2806
AA 2700*	65.0	2550	69.0	2757
IMR 3031^	55.0	2469	59.0	2627
IMR 4064*	57.0	2440	61.0	2610

0.338"	338 Spitz BTSP	338 GS SP
Weight, grains	225	225
Ballistic Coefficient	0.497	0.382
Sectional Density	0.281	0.281
COAL Tested:	3.340"	3.300"
Speer Part No.	2406	2407

| Propellant | START CHARGE | | MAXIMUM CHARGE | |
	Weight, grs	Muzzle Velocity, ft/sec	Weight, grs	Muzzle Velocity, ft/sec
Reloder 19*	74.0	2791	78.0C	2944
H4350*	71.0	2739	75.0C	2898
AA 2700*	68.0	2700	72.0	2855
IMR 4350*	65.0	2644	69.0	2819
IMR 4831*	66.0	2655	70.0	2811
AA 3100*	73.0	2653	77.0C	2807
H4831SC*	69.0	2611	73.0	2761
IMR 4064*	56.0	2585	60.0	2721
Viht. N165*	70.0	2496	74.0C	2670

*Maximum Loads should be used with CAUTION • C = Compressed Load • *Magnum Primer used with this powder.*

0.338"	338 TBBC SP
Weight, grains	225
Ballistic Coefficient	0.376
Sectional Density	0.281
COAL Tested:	3.300"
Speer Part No.	1775

Propellant	START CHARGE		MAXIMUM CHARGE	
	Weight, grs	Muzzle Velocity, ft/sec	Weight, grs	Muzzle Velocity, ft/sec
Reloder 19*	71.0	2681	75.0C	2843
Reloder 22*	71.0	2684	75.0C	2829
IMR 4831*	70.0C	2735	72.0C	2813
IMR 4350*	66.0	2652	70.0	2809
IMR 7828*	73.0C	2706	75.0C	2782
AA 2700*	62.0	2828	66.0	2772
H414*	63.0	2636	67.0	2766
H4831SC*	72.0C	2657	74.0C	2721
Reloder 15*	57.0	2552	61.0	2709

NOTE: *Trophy Bonded Bear Claw and Trophy Bonded Sledgehammer Solid bullets have unique ballistic behavior compared to conventional bullets. Loads for TBBC and TBSS bullets may not "track" with data for conventional bullets. Use TBBC and TBSS data ONLY for TBBC and TBSS bullets.*

0.338"	338 GS SP
Weight, grains	250
Ballistic Coefficient	0.436
Sectional Density	0.313
COAL Tested:	3.300"
Speer Part No.	2408

Propellant	START CHARGE		MAXIMUM CHARGE	
	Weight, grs	Muzzle Velocity, ft/sec	Weight, grs	Muzzle Velocity, ft/sec
Reloder 19*	68.0	2478	72.0C	2664
IMR 4350*	65.0	2509	69.0	2655
Reloder 22*	69.0	2441	73.0C	2653
IMR 7828*	71.0	2480	75.0	2652
Viht. N165*	70.0	2439	74.0C	2637
IMR 4831*	65.0	2451	69.0	2620
AA 3100*	69.0	2472	73.0C	2616
H4831SC*	67.0	2492	71.0C	2616
H4350*	64.0	2387	68.0C	2581
H414*	62.0	2357	66.0	2548
H1000*	73.0	2380	77.0C	2545
AA 2700*	61.0	2394	65.0	2526

*Maximum Loads should be used with CAUTION • C = Compressed Load • *Magnum Primer used with this powder.*

340 Weatherby Magnum

The 340 Weatherby was introduced in 1962 to fill the gap between the 300 Weatherby and the massive 378 Weatherby cartridge. Part of the drive to bring out this cartridge was the quick acceptance of the 338 Winchester Magnum by American shooters a few years earlier. Like the 300 Weatherby, the 340 is based on the full-length H&H case and requires that rifles have a long action capable of handling cartridge lengths approaching 3.7 inches.

In spite of the larger case, the 340 Weatherby has a velocity advantage of only about 100 to 150 ft/sec over the 338 Winchester. The choice between the two can be made on the shooter's preference of rifle manufacturer. The 340 can be used on the same classes of game as the 338 Winchester. Although unprimed cases may be hard to find in some areas, they can be easily made from unfired 300 Weatherby cases or, with a bit more work, from 300 or 375 H&H brass. The 375 H&H case would be our first choice, as it easily allows the reloader to fit the shoulder precisely to his rifle's chamber in the sizing operation. A good fit in this area insures good accuracy and longer case life.

For Alaskan or thinned-skinned African game, the 340 Weatherby is an excellent cartridge. Recoil seems to be more noticeable than with the 338 Winchester, largely due to the heavier charge weights required in the Weatherby.

The loads here are the result of a complete retest of the cartridge in 2006 using the latest components and standards. Like many other Weatherby cartridges, the 340 was adopted as a standard industry cartridge in 1994. The maximum average pressure is set at 62,500 psi.

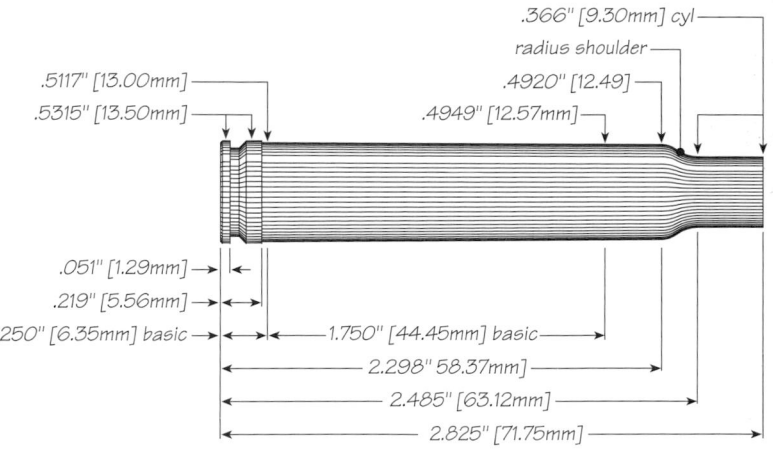

.366" [9.30mm] cyl
radius shoulder
.4920" [12.49]
.4949" [12.57mm]
.5117" [13.00mm]
.5315" [13.50mm]
.051" [1.29mm]
.219" [5.56mm]
.250" [6.35mm] basic
1.750" [44.45mm] basic
2.298" 58.37mm]
2.485" [63.12mm]
2.825" [71.75mm]

Max. Case Length:	2.825"	Cart. Case:	Federal
Trim-to Length:	2.815"	Primer:	Federal 215*
Max Cart. OAL:	3.675"	Test Firearm:	Universal Receiver
RCBS Shell Holder:	#4	Barrel Length:	HS Precision 24"

Brandon Graves, ATK Law Enforcement/OEM Sales Manager, with wife Shoni and a fine bull elk.

0.338"	338 Spitz SP
Weight, grains	200
Ballistic Coefficient	0.426
Sectional Density	0.250
COAL Tested:	3.560"
Speer Part No.	2405

| Propellant | START CHARGE | | MAXIMUM CHARGE | |
	Weight, grs	Muzzle Velocity, ft/sec	Weight, grs	Muzzle Velocity, ft/sec
IMR 4831*	81.0	2923	85.0C	3073
IMR 4350*	79.0	2907	83.0C	3058
Reloder 19*	83.0	2899	87.0C	3032
760*	76.0	2879	80.0	3012
Viht. N540*	71.0	2872	75.0	3006
H4350*	77.0	2854	81.0	3004
H4831SC*	85.0	2881	89.0C	2989
Reloder 15*	69.0	2796	73.0	2973
AA 4350*	80.0	2821	84.0C	2962
Ramshot Big Game*	71.0	2776	75.0	2945

0.338"	338 Spitz BTSP	338 GS SP
Weight, grains	225	225
Ballistic Coefficient	0.497	0.382
Sectional Density	0.281	0.281
COAL Tested:	3.670"	3.610"
Speer Part No.	2406	2407

Propellant	START CHARGE Weight, grs	START CHARGE Muzzle Velocity, ft/sec	MAXIMUM CHARGE Weight, grs	MAXIMUM CHARGE Muzzle Velocity, ft/sec
Reloder 19*	81.0	2776	85.0C	2924
IMR 4831*	78.0	2765	82.0	2911
Reloder 22*	83.0	2799	87.0C	2901
H4350*	75.0	2742	79.0	2892
IMR 4350*	76.0	2738	80.0	2886
H4831SC*	82.0	2755	86.0	2882
AA 4350*	77.0	2697	81.0	2864
760ᴬ	73.0	2728	77.0	2854
Viht. N540*	68.0	2686	72.0	2822
Reloder 15*	66.0	2653	70.0	2799
Ramshot Big Game*	67.0	2611	71.0	2751

*Maximum Loads should be used with CAUTION • C = Compressed Load • *Magnum Primer used with this powder.*

0.338"	338 GS SP
Weight, grains	250
Ballistic Coefficient	0.436
Sectional Density	0.313
COAL Tested:	3.610"
Speer Part No.	2408

Propellant	START CHARGE		MAXIMUM CHARGE	
	Weight, grs	Muzzle Velocity, ft/sec	Weight, grs	Muzzle Velocity, ft/sec
Viht. N560*	81.0	2668	85.0C	2802
Magpro*	84.0	2669	88.0C	2789
Reloder 19*	79.0	2644	83.0	2788
Reloder 22*	81.0	2634	85.0	2781
IMR 7828*	81.0	2613	85.0C	2747
IMR 4831*	75.0	2607	79.0	2746
H4350*	73.0	2608	77.0	2733
IMR 4350*	73.0	2596	77.0	2731
AA 4350*	75.0	2574	79.0C	2720
Ramshot Magnum*	86.0	2623	90.C	2711

*Maximum Loads should be used with CAUTION • C = Compressed Load • *Magnum Primer used with this powder.*

338 Remington Ultra Magnum

The 338 Remington Ultra Magnum was introduced in 1999 as another member of Remington's line of long-case unbelted magnum rifle cartridges. Unlike the first in the series, the 300 Ultra Magnum, which does not provide a significant advantage over older 30-caliber magnums, the 338 Ultra Magnum provides a real velocity boost over the very popular 338 Winchester Magnum. With most bullet weights, the advantage is a noticeable 200 to 300 ft/sec that adds nearly 1000 ft/lbs of energy with a 250-grain bullet.

Another advantage to the Remington version is case design. The belted 338 Winchester is not known for impressive case life; the unbelted Ultra Magnum case should provide longer service.

Remington catalogs only 250-grain bullets at 2850 ft/sec. Handloading this cartridge allows more flexibility with the choice of lighter weights and different styles.

With several propellants, the 338 Ultra Magnum can push the Speer 200-grain Hot Cor to over 3200 ft/sec. This bullet is a bit light in construction for use on the heaviest game, but can be used on large deer species over the effective range of the cartridge. For heavier game, consider the 225 and 250-grain Grand Slams. They have heavier jackets and are designed for tough game. Nearly all the 250-grain loads we show exceed the factory nominal velocities by modest margins, yet remain within industry pressure limits.

We used Federal 215 Magnum rifle primers for load development. You may safely substitute CCI 250 Magnum primers if you wish. The industry pressure limit for the 338 Remington Ultra Magnum is 65,000 psi.

338 Remington Ultra Magnum

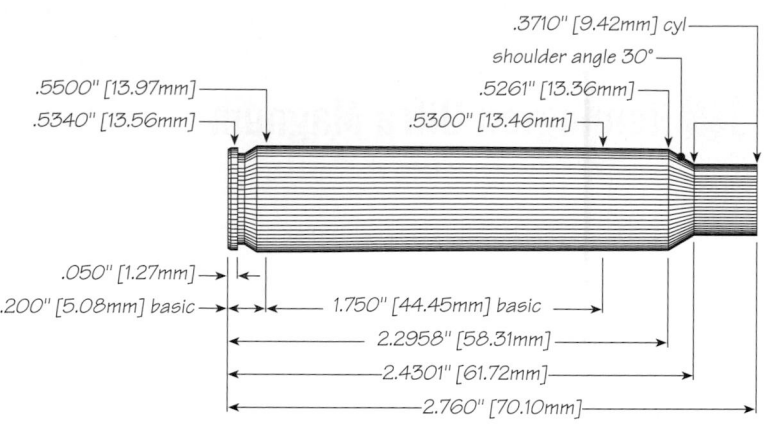

.3710" [9.42mm] cyl
shoulder angle 30°
.5500" [13.97mm]
.5340" [13.56mm]
.5261" [13.36mm]
.5300" [13.46mm]
.050" [1.27mm]
.200" [5.08mm] basic
1.750" [44.45mm] basic
2.2958" [58.31mm]
2.4301" [61.72mm]
2.760" [70.10mm]

Max. Case Length:	2.760"	Cart. Case:	Federal
Trim-to Length:	2.750"	Primer:	Federal 215*
Max Cart. OAL:	3.600"	Test Firearm:	Universal Receiver
RCBS Shell Holder:	#38	Barrel Length:	HS Precision 24"

0.338"	338 Spitz SP
Weight, grains	200
Ballistic Coefficient	0.426
Sectional Density	0.250
COAL Tested:	3.500"
Speer Part No.	2405

	START CHARGE		MAXIMUM CHARGE	
Propellant	Weight, grs	Muzzle Velocity, ft/sec	Weight, grs	Muzzle Velocity, ft/sec
Reloder 22*	94.0	3105	98.0	3255
Viht. N560*	93.0	3062	97.0	3223
Reloder 19*	91.0	3085	95.0	3216
Reloder 25*	97.0	3060	101.0C	3193
H4350*	85.0	3043	89.0	3180
IMR 7828*	92.0	3015	96.0	3179
Ramshot Magnum*	101.0	3078	105.0C	3168
Magpro*	96.0	2985	100.0	3167
IMR 4350*	84.0	2981	88.0	3151

0.338"	338 Spitz BTSP	338 GS SP
Weight, grains	225	225
Ballistic Coefficient	0.497	0.382
Sectional Density	0.281	0.281
COAL Tested:	3.600"	3.550"
Speer Part No.	2406	2407

	START CHARGE		MAXIMUM CHARGE	
Propellant	Weight, grs	Muzzle Velocity, ft/sec	Weight, grs	Muzzle Velocity, ft/sec
Reloder 25*	95.0	2965	99.0C	3103
Ramshot Magnum*	98.0	2953	102.0C	3062
Viht. N560*	89.0	2911	93.0	3045
Reloder 22*	89.0	2891	93.0	3029
Reloder 19*	87.0	2884	91.0	3028
Retumbo*	97.0	2913	101.0C	3015
Magpro*	92.0	2922	96.0	3007
IMR 7828*	88.0	2840	92.0	2998
IMR 4831*	83.0	2839	87.0	2997
H4831SC*	88.0	2833	92.0	2965

*Maximum Loads should be used with CAUTION • C = Compressed Load • *Magnum Primer used with this powder.*

0.338"	338 GS SP
Weight, grains	250
Ballistic Coefficient	0.436
Sectional Density	0.313
COAL Tested:	3.550"
Speer Part No.	2408

Propellant	START CHARGE		MAXIMUM CHARGE	
	Weight, grs	Muzzle Velocity, ft/sec	Weight, grs	Muzzle Velocity, ft/sec
Ramshot Magnum*	96.0	2839	100.0	2936
Reloder 25*	91.0	2803	95.0	2915
Retumbo*	94.0	2790	98.0	2907
Reloder 22*	87.0	2779	91.0	2895
Viht. N560*	85.0	2733	89.0	2877
IMR 7828*	87.0	2763	91.0	2871
Magpro*	89.0	2742	93.0	2862
Reloder 19*	83.0	2712	87.0	2849
H4831SC*	85.0	2687	89.0	2817

*Maximum Loads should be used with CAUTION • C = Compressed Load • *Magnum Primer used with this powder.*

357 Magnum

Although developed as a handgun cartridge, the 357 Magnum is seeing increased use as a rifle cartridge. It is simply a modern version of the old concept of packing a rifle and sidearm that fire the same cartridge. In the latter part of the 19th Century, Winchester and Colt sold quite a few rifles and revolvers to shooters who found this concept important.

Not long after the 357 was introduced, custom gunsmiths started converting Model 1892 Winchesters to fire the new cartridge. In 1979, Marlin reintroduced its classic 1894 carbine chambered for the 357 Magnum. Rossi and Browning have produced Winchester Model 92 replicas in this caliber and Ruger made a limited production run of 357 Magnum No. 1 single-shot rifles in the 1980's.

As a rifle cartridge, the 357 has worked reasonably well within its limits. Although trajectory isn't as flat as a high-speed 32-20 bullet, the heavier .357" bullets will deliver more energy and are nearly as powerful as the obsolete 351 Winchester Self-loader cartridge. With 125-grain hollow points, the 357 is effective on varmints out to 100 yards. The 357 carbine can also be used for small whitetail deer with heavier bullets if the range is under 100 yards.

For deer hunting, we recommend the 170-grain Gold Dot soft point or the 158-grain Uni-Cor jacketed soft point. Hollow point bullets, designed for optimum expansion in the 1000 to 1300 ft/sec velocity range, can cause shallow wounds on deer at rifle velocities.

Rifle loads for the 357 Magnum are held to the normal industry pressure of 35,000 psi.

• • • • •

Special Notes Regarding 357 Magnum Rifles:

- ⬥ Never attempt to use any pointed or full-jacketed bullets in lever-action rifles with tubular magazines.

- ⬥ All lever-action 357 Magnum rifles have bolts that lock at the rear. This allows the bolt to spring slightly during firing, stretching the case. Use only new or once-fired cases for maximum loads.

- ⬥ Do not use loads less than the minimum charges shown. Small charges of powder may not be sufficient to push a jacketed bullet down an 18-inch barrel; a dangerous bore obstruction may result.

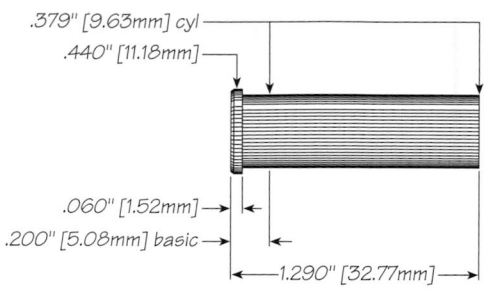

.379" [9.63mm] cyl
.440" [11.18mm]
.060" [1.52mm]
.200" [5.08mm] basic
1.290" [32.77mm]

Max. Case Length:	1.290"	Cart. Case:	Speer
Trim-to Length:	1.280"	Primer:	CCI 500; 550
Max Cart. OAL:	1.590"	Test Firearm:	Marlin M1894
RCBS Shell Holder:	#6	Barrel Length:	18"

0.357"	38 UCHP
Weight, grains	110
Ballistic Coefficient	0.113
Sectional Density	0.123
COAL Tested:	1.575"
Speer Part No.	4007

	START CHARGE		MAXIMUM CHARGE	
Propellant	Weight, grs	Muzzle Velocity, ft/sec	Weight, grs	Muzzle Velocity, ft/sec
Viht. N110	19.5	2331	21.5C	2467
H110*	21.0	2218	23.0C	2353
296*	21.0	2131	23.0C	2321
Blue Dot	14.0	2188	16.0	2317
2400	17.5	2068	19.5	2291
HS-7*	12.5	1703	14.4	1926

NOTE: *Do not use the 110-gr Gold Dot Short Barrel bullet (#4009). It is not intended for 357 Magnum pressures.*

0.357"	38 UCSP	38 GDHP	38 UCHP
Weight, grains	125	125	125
Ballistic Coefficient	0.129	0.140	0.129
Sectional Density	0.140	0.140	0.140
COAL Tested:	1.575"	1.580"	1.575"
Speer Part No.	4011	4012	4013

Propellant	START CHARGE		MAXIMUM CHARGE	
	Weight, grs	Muzzle Velocity, ft/sec	Weight, grs	Muzzle Velocity, ft/sec
H110*	18.0	1923	20.0C	2125
296*	18.3	1938	20.3C	2125
Viht. N110	16.8	1942	17.8	2042
2400	16.5	1851	17.5	2019
Blue Dot	11.5	1729	13.0	1916
AA No. 7	12.0	1588	13.5	1770

0.357"	38 UCHP
Weight, grains	140
Ballistic Coefficient	0.145
Sectional Density	0.157
COAL Tested:	1.590"
Speer Part No.	4203

Propellant	START CHARGE		MAXIMUM CHARGE	
	Weight, grs	Muzzle Velocity, ft/sec	Weight, grs	Muzzle Velocity, ft/sec
296*	17.0	1819	18.0	1934
IMR 4227	17.2	1672	19.2C	1882
H110*	16.2	1731	17.2	1873
Viht. N110	14.2	1695	15.2C	1795
2400	13.1	1683	15.1	1795
AA No. 9	13.0	1549	14.0	1677

*Maximum Loads should be used with CAUTION • C = Compressed Load • *Magnum Primer used with this powder.*

0.357"	38 UCHP	38 GDHP	38 UCSP
Weight, grains	158	158	158
Ballistic Coefficient	0.163	0.168	0.164
Sectional Density	0.177	0.177	0.177
COAL Tested:	1.570"	1.575"	1.570"
Speer Part No.	4211	4215	4217

	START CHARGE		MAXIMUM CHARGE	
Propellant	Weight, grs	Muzzle Velocity, ft/sec	Weight, grs	Muzzle Velocity, ft/sec
Viht. N110	13.5	1564	15.0	1738
H110*	13.9	1473	15.5	1648
2400	13.8	1527	14.8	1628
IMR 4227	15.0	1397	17.0C	1588
296*	13.2	1341	14.7	1564
AA No. 9	12.3	1353	13.7	1551
Blue Dot	9.0	1265	10.2	1426

0.357"	357 GDSP
Weight, grains	170
Ballistic Coefficient	0.185
Sectional Density	0.191
COAL Tested:	1.590"
Speer Part No.	4230

	START CHARGE		MAXIMUM CHARGE	
Propellant	Weight, grs	Muzzle Velocity, ft/sec	Weight, grs	Muzzle Velocity, ft/sec
H. Lil' Gun*	14.8	1636	15.4	1684
H110*	14.4	1549	15.2	1622
2400	13.9	1539	14.5	1616
Viht. N110	13.2	1492	13.8	1579
IMR 4227	16.1	1471	16.7	1540
AA No. 9*	11.0	1235	11.7	1345
Blue Dot	8.8	1220	9.4	1306

*Maximum Loads should be used with CAUTION • C = Compressed Load • *Magnum Primer used with this powder.*

35 Remington

At one time, Remington offered a series of rimless rifle cartridges designed for the various semi-auto and slide-action rifles that they manufactured. The 25, 30, 32 and 35 Remington cartridges were reasonably popular in the first half of this century and the three smaller ones virtually matched the performance of similar Winchester cartridges. Today all are obsolete except the 35-caliber version. The 35 Remington case is unusual in that it uses a non-standard .457" head size, smaller than the 30-06 yet larger than the three obsolete Remington cartridges.

The continued popularity of the 35 Remington is due to its excellent reputation as a short-range woods cartridge for deer and black bear. Usually chambered in light, handy carbines, the 35 Remington is a better hunting cartridge than the 30-30. Although "paper ballistics" show little difference, the 35 Remington handles heavier bullets for deeper penetration. Even today, the Eastern woods hunter who doesn't take shots beyond 150 yards would be well equipped with a 35 Remington.

Over the years, many different rifles were offered in 35 Remington. Today the only survivor is Marlin's Model 336C lever-action carbine. Factory ammunition is loaded with a 150-grain pointed soft point and a 200-grain round nose bullet. The 150-grain factory load gained a poor reputation for accuracy and game performance; heavier bullets are needed for best results.

Handloading greatly extends the usefulness of the cartridge. Pistol bullets can be used for varmints at moderate ranges. Speer's 180 and 220-grain Hot-Cor bullets were designed for the 35 Remington and offer better performance than either factory load. For most hunting, the 180-grain bullet allows you to keep muzzle velocities over 2000 ft/sec. Although the 35 Remington operates at modest pressures, the reloader should keep an eye out for incipient case head separations in lever guns.

We are often asked if the Speer 250-grain Hot-Cor spitzer and Grand Slam bullets can be loaded in the 35 Remington. We don't recommend them for two reasons:

- ◆ At 35 Remington velocities, these bullets are close to their lower limit of expansion, even at the muzzle.
- ◆ Flat point bullets must be used in rifles having tubular magazines. Pointed bullets must not be used; they can cause cartridges to explode in the magazine with the risk of gun damage and personal injury.

The 35 Remington is seeing renewed interest among handgun hunters. See the Handgun Data section for loading information for the Thompson/Center Contender pistol. The industry maximum average pressure for the 35 Remington is 35,000 CUP.

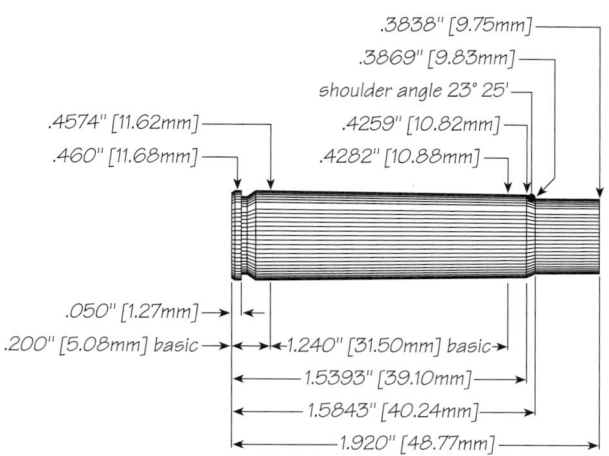

Max. Case Length:	1.920"	Cart. Case:	Winchester
Trim-to Length:	1.910"	Primer:	CCI 200; 250*
Max Cart. OAL:	2.525"	Test Firearm:	Marlin M336
RCBS Shell Holder:	#9	Barrel Length:	20"

0.357"	38 UCHP	38 UCSP
Weight, grains	158	158
Ballistic Coefficient	0.163	0.164
Sectional Density	0.177	0.177
COAL Tested:	2.220"	2.220"
Speer Part No.	4211	4217

	START CHARGE		MAXIMUM CHARGE	
Propellant	Weight, grs	Muzzle Velocity, ft/sec	Weight, grs	Muzzle Velocity, ft/sec
Reloder 7	33.0	2091	37.0	2357
IMR 4895	35.0	1932	39.0	2185
IMR 3031	33.0	1896	37.0	2141

NOTE: *Short COAL may require single-loading.*

0.358"	35 FNSP
Weight, grains	180
Ballistic Coefficient	0.236
Sectional Density	0.201
COAL Tested:	2.470"
Speer Part No.	2435

Propellant	START CHARGE Weight, grs	START CHARGE Muzzle Velocity, ft/sec	MAXIMUM CHARGE Weight, grs	MAXIMUM CHARGE Muzzle Velocity, ft/sec
H335*	34.0	1954	38.0	2224
AA 2015	32.0	1937	36.0	2138
BL-C(2)*	31.0	1831	35.0	2097
748*	38.0	1858	42.0	2072
IMR 4895	34.0	1811	38.0	2055
Viht. N133	31.0	1852	35.0	2054
H414*	43.0	1847	47.0	2041
H380*	40.0	1807	44.0	2023
IMR 4320	32.0	1729	36.0	1983
Reloder 7	26.0	1679	30.0	1967
SR 4759 (reduced load)	18.0	1499	20.0	1653

*Maximum Loads should be used with CAUTION • C = Compressed Load • *Magnum Primer used with this powder.*

0.358"	35 FNSP
Weight, grains	220
Ballistic Coefficient	0.286
Sectional Density	0.245
COAL Tested:	2.470"
Speer Part No.	2439

Propellant	START CHARGE		MAXIMUM CHARGE	
	Weight, grs	Muzzle Velocity, ft/sec	Weight, grs	Muzzle Velocity, ft/sec
AA 2015	29.0	1665	33.0	1901
IMR 4064	32.0	1641	36.0	1840
H414*	36.0	1656	40.0	1831
748*	31.0	1674	35.0	1830
Viht. N133	27.0	1594	31.0	1807
BL-C(2)*	31.0	1557	35.0	1794
IMR 4895	31.5	1640	35.5	1789
H335*	28.0	1476	32.0	1784
IMR 3031	29.5	1531	33.5	1781
IMR 4320	29.0	1502	33.0	1692
Reloder 7	20.5	1173	24.5	1536

*Maximum Loads should be used with CAUTION • C = Compressed Load • *Magnum Primer used with this powder.*

350 Remington Magnum

The 350 Remington Magnum is a companion cartridge to the 6.5mm Remington Magnum. Both were introduced in the mid-1960's in the Model 660 bolt-action carbine. The very short action of these rifles required a minimum cartridge length of 2.800-inch so the 350 Remington is about a half-inch shorter than the original "short magnums" such as the 300 Winchester and slightly less than the "new short magnums" like the 300 Remington Short Action Ultra Magnum.

Factory ammunition fires a 200-grain bullet at 2775 ft/sec (24-inch test barrel). The handloader can load the cartridge with greater flexibility because there are a number of component bullets available in other weights. When handloading, special attention to bullet seating depth is required to keep within the 2.800-inch maximum cartridge length if you shoot one of the original Model 660 or 600 actions. The heavier bullets must be seated with the base well below the neck of the cartridge, thus restricting powder capacity. Magazines in current actions used for this cartridge may allow longer seating, but the bullet must not touch the rifling. Fortunately, the standard chamber has about a quarter-inch of freebore.

The 350 Remington is similar in performance to the 35 Whelen cartridge. For deer, the 180-grain Speer Hot-Cor flat point is a very good performer. Some propellants were able to drive this bullet up to 2900 ft/sec. We recommend the 220-grain flat point for close-range use on elk and moose. The 350 Magnum can be used on large bear if the 250-grain Grand Slam or spitzer bullet is loaded. Some elk hunters prefer the 250-grain spitzer or Grand Slam because of its more aerodynamic shape. Velocities with the 250-grain bullets are roughly equal to the 35 Whelen. We have also listed loads for two Speer 158-grain Uni-Cor® revolver bullets. These can be used effectively on varmints or for low-cost plinking but, at rifle velocities, are too fragile for game animal.

When we wrote *Speer Manual #13*, there were no rifles, ammo, or unprimed cases cataloged by the major manufactures. Nostalgia is a good thing because both Ruger and Remington show 350 Remington rifles on their websites in 2006, and Remington again catalogs ammo and cases. The industry maximum pressure for this cartridge is 53,000 CUP. These loads are within those guidelines.

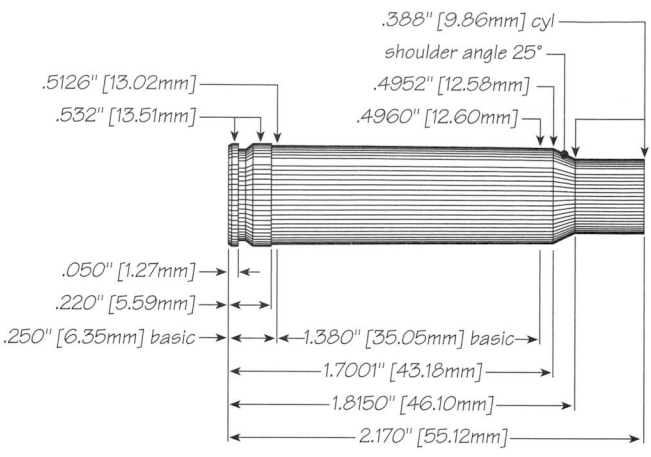

Max. Case Length:	2.170"	Cart. Case:	Remington
Trim-to Length:	2.160"	Primer:	CCI 200; 250*
Max Cart. OAL:	2.800"	Test Firearm:	Ruger M77
RCBS Shell Holder:	#4	Barrel Length:	22"

0.357"	38 UCHP	38 UCSP
Weight, grains	158	158
Ballistic Coefficient	0.163	0.164
Sectional Density	0.177	0.177
COAL Tested:	2.470"	2.470"
Speer Part No.	4211	4217

Propellant	START CHARGE		MAXIMUM CHARGE	
	Weight, grs	Muzzle Velocity, ft/sec	Weight, grs	Muzzle Velocity, ft/sec
Reloder 7	51.0	2656	55.0	2901
IMR 3031	54.0	2462	58.0	2865
IMR 4064	58.0	2454	62.0	2841

NOTE: *Short COAL may require single-loading.*

0.358"	35 FNSP
Weight, grains	180
Ballistic Coefficient	0.236
Sectional Density	0.201
COAL Tested:	2.800"
Speer Part No.	2435

| Propellant | START CHARGE | | MAXIMUM CHARGE | |
	Weight, grs	Muzzle Velocity, ft/sec	Weight, grs	Muzzle Velocity, ft/sec
BL-C(2)*	56.0	2696	60.0	2942
IMR 4064	58.0	2720	62.0C	2914
IMR 4895	56.0	2699	60.0	2900
IMR 4320	57.0	2600	61.0C	2786
748*	58.0	2461	62.0	2679
H380*	58.0	2461	62.0C	2635
Reloder 7	47.0	2329	51.0	2574
760*	61.0	2206	65.0C	2422
SR 4759 (reduced load)	26.0	1784	28.0	1926

Andy McConkey, Sr.
Programming Analyst,
CCI/Speer Operations;
338 Win Mag; moose.

*Maximum Loads should be used with CAUTION • C = Compressed Load • * Magnum Primer used with this powder.*

0.358"	35 FNSP
Weight, grains	220
Ballistic Coefficient	0.286
Sectional Density	0.245
COAL Tested:	2.740"
Speer Part No.	2439

	START CHARGE		MAXIMUM CHARGE	
Propellant	Weight, grs	Muzzle Velocity, ft/sec	Weight, grs	Muzzle Velocity, ft/sec
BL-C(2)*	56.0	2496	60.0	2676
748*	58.0	2489	62.0	2664
IMR 4895	56.0	2525	60.0	2655
IMR 3031	55.0	2451	59.0	2642
IMR 4320	56.0	2447	60.0C	2629
H322	51.0	2428	55.0C	2563
H380*	58.0	2407	62.0C	2496
760*	61.0	2301	65.0C	2471
Reloder 7	45.5	2240	49.5	2426

0.358"	35 Spitz SP	35 GS SP
Weight, grains	250	250
Ballistic Coefficient	0.422	0.353
Sectional Density	0.279	0.279
COAL Tested:	2.800"	2.800"
Speer Part No.	2453	2455

	START CHARGE		MAXIMUM CHARGE	
Propellant	Weight, grs	Muzzle Velocity, ft/sec	Weight, grs	Muzzle Velocity, ft/sec
748*	53.0	2266	57.0C	2484
IMR 3031	48.0	2188	52.0C	2382
IMR 4895	49.0	2159	53.0C	2353
IMR 4064	51.0	2170	55.0C	2348
760*	54.0	2116	58.0C	2294
BL-C(2)*	48.0	2073	52.0	2257
IMR 4320	50.0	2053	54.0C	2219
H380*	54.0	2018	58.0C	2170
SR 4759 (reduced load)	28.0	1680	30.0	1800

*Maximum Loads should be used with CAUTION • C = Compressed Load • *Magnum Primer used with this powder.*

356 Winchester

The 356 Winchester is basically a rimmed 358 Winchester for use in traditional lever-action rifles developed by U.S. Repeating Arms Company (USRAC). It is a companion cartridge to the 307 Winchester, and both were introduced in Winchester 94 rifles redesigned to handle higher pressures than those of the 30-30 cartridge. The 356 gives the lever rifle hunter a significant increase in performance over the 35 Remington, and can be used on game up to elk and moose if the range isn't too great.

Although it shares most external dimensions with the 358 Winchester, the 356 has heavier walls that reduce its case capacity. 358 Winchester reloading data must not be used for loading this cartridge.

As with other cartridges for tubular magazines, the 356 Winchester must be loaded with flat point bullets to prevent the hazards of cartridges exploding in the magazine. Although originally designed for the 35 Remington, Speer's 180 and 220-grain flat points both perform well in this cartridge. Shortly after the 356 was announced, Speer modified the cannelure position on these bullets to provide the correct cartridge over-all length for reliable feeding in 356 lever-action rifles.

Speer handgun bullets intended for the 357 Magnum cartridge can be used in the 356 for low-cost practice and short-range varmint shooting. However, do not use them on any animal larger than a coyote. These bullets have very limited penetration at rifle velocities.

Marlin once made 356 Winchester rifles but, with the demise of USRAC, no rifles are currently chambered for it. Ammunition and unprimed cases are still listed on the 2006 Winchester website.

Propellants in the middle of the burning rate range gave the best performance in the 356 Winchester. The industry working pressure for the 356 Winchester is 52,000 CUP. These loads do not exceed that limit.

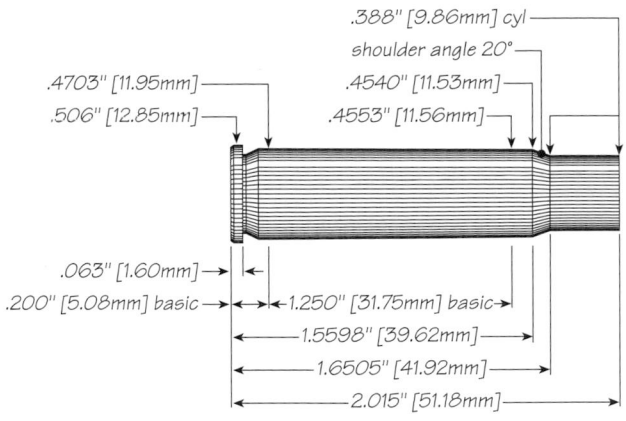

.388" [9.86mm] cyl
shoulder angle 20°
.4703" [11.95mm]
.506" [12.85mm]
.4540" [11.53mm]
.4553" [11.56mm]
.063" [1.60mm]
.200" [5.08mm] basic
1.250" [31.75mm] basic
1.5598" [39.62mm]
1.6505" [41.92mm]
2.015" [51.18mm]

Max. Case Length:	2.015"	Cart. Case:	Winchester
Trim-to Length:	2.005"	Primer:	CCI 200; 250*
Max Cart. OAL:	2.560"	Test Firearm:	Winchester Model 94 AE
RCBS Shell Holder:	#2	Barrel Length:	20"

0.357"	38 UCHP	38 UCSP
Weight, grains	158	158
Ballistic Coefficient	0.163	0.164
Sectional Density	0.177	0.177
COAL Tested:	2.315"	2.315"
Speer Part No.	4211	4217

	START CHARGE		MAXIMUM CHARGE	
Propellant	Weight, grs	Muzzle Velocity, ft/sec	Weight, grs	Muzzle Velocity, ft/sec
H322	45.0	2435	49.0	2574
IMR 3031	45.0	2174	49.0	2504
Reloder 7	36.0	2131	40.0	2329

NOTE: *Short COAL may require single-loading into chamber.*

*Maximum Loads should be used with CAUTION • C = Compressed Load • *Magnum Primer used with this powder.*

0.358"	35 FNSP
Weight, grains	180
Ballistic Coefficient	0.236
Sectional Density	0.201
COAL Tested:	2.550"
Speer Part No.	2435

	START CHARGE		MAXIMUM CHARGE	
Propellant	Weight, grs	Muzzle Velocity, ft/sec	Weight, grs	Muzzle Velocity, ft/sec
AA 2015	43.0	2321	47.0C	2654
Viht. N133	42.0	2354	46.0C	2577
H322	44.0	2310	48.0	2569
H335*	44.0	2284	48.0	2502
IMR 4064	46.0	2318	50.0	2470
BL-C(2)*	47.0	2267	51.0C	2466
IMR 4895	45.0	2169	49.0	2403
IMR 3031	42.0	2150	46.0	2395
Reloder 7	36.0	2095	40.0	2358
748*	47.0	2175	51.0	2351
IMR 4320	43.0	2180	47.0	2328

David Biery, son-in-law of Tom Saleen, Director of International Sales, ATK CCI/Speer Operations; 7mm Rem Mag, 175-grain Grand Slam®; mule deer, Idaho.

0.358"	35 FNSP
Weight, grains	220
Ballistic Coefficient	0.286
Sectional Density	0.245
COAL Tested:	2.550"
Speer Part No.	2439

	START CHARGE		MAXIMUM CHARGE	
Propellant	Weight, grs	Muzzle Velocity, ft/sec	Weight, grs	Muzzle Velocity, ft/sec
AA 2015	38.0	2114	42.0C	2344
748*	45.5	2143	49.5	2328
Viht. N135	41.0	2128	45.0C	2306
IMR 4064	42.0	2024	46.0	2301
H322	39.0	2117	43.0	2285
IMR 4320	42.0	2099	46.0	2273
H335*	39.0	2040	43.0	2258
IMR 4895	42.0	1987	46.0	2243
BL-C(2)*	42.0	2032	46.0C	2242
H380*	46.0	1973	50.0C	2116
Reloder 7	31.0	1865	35.0	2090

*Maximum Loads should be used with CAUTION • C = Compressed Load • *Magnum Primer used with this powder.*

358 Winchester

The 358 Winchester is a short- to medium-range cartridge suitable for almost any type of North American game within its range limitations. It is simply a 308 Winchester case necked up to handle .358" diameter bullets. It was introduced in 1955 in the Winchester Model 70 bolt-action rifle. Later, Winchester offered the 358 in the Model 88 rifle, a sleek lever-action that proved very accurate. The 358 is often described as an improved version of the old rimmed 348 Winchester cartridge, which had an excellent reputation in the woods but was not suitable to most bolt-action rifles.

The 358 is one of the nicest woods cartridges ever designed. It is much superior to the 35 Remington and gives up little to the 35 Whelen. It is surprising that the 358 has not been more popular. We can only assume that, like other fine cartridges, it fell victim to "magnum-mania." The deep-woods deer and elk hunter would be hard-pressed to find another cartridge that would show significant gains in field performance unless he needs something for longer shots—like the new 338 Federal.

Factory ammunition was originally loaded with 200 and 250-grain bullets. The handloader has more flexibility; he can use .357" diameter pistol bullets for varmints or inexpensive practice. The 180-grain Speer flat point is excellent for whitetail deer under almost any hunting conditions within the cartridge's range. For black bear, elk and moose at moderate ranges, the 220-grain flat point is a better choice. For longer ranges, the 250-grain spitzer and the 250-grain Grand Slam get the nod. Although the 358's velocity is a little low for large bears, it can certainly handle them in an emergency.

We show plinking loads using 158-grain 38-caliber revolver bullets. These bullets behave like varmint bullets at these speeds and they should not be used to shoot anything larger than a coyote. Their overall loaded length is less than the 358's minimum so single loading may be necessary in some rifles.

In addition to the Winchester rifles mentioned, both Savage and Browning have made 358 rifles. Ruger made a short run of their Model 77 bolt-action rifles in this caliber in the early 1970's and these rifles are in demand among Ruger collectors. In 2006, Ruger again offered the 358 Winchester in its compact M77 Mk II Frontier rifle.

Winchester shows a 200-grain factory load and unprimed cases on their 2006 website. They both returned to the lineup after being discontinued in 1998. The 358 Winchester's industry pressure limit is 52,000 CUP; these loads remain within that limit.

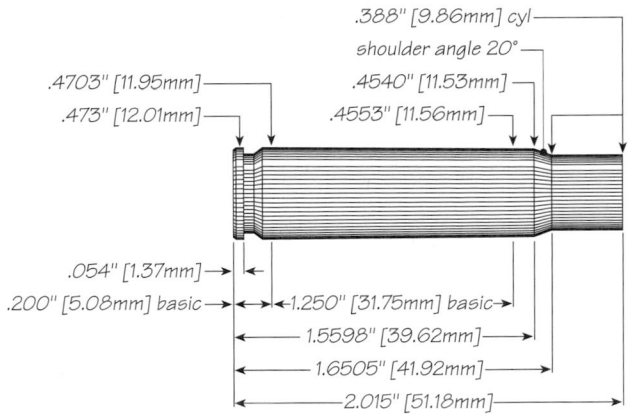

.388" [9.86mm] cyl
shoulder angle 20°
.4703" [11.95mm]
.473" [12.01mm]
.4540" [11.53mm]
.4553" [11.56mm]
.054" [1.37mm]
.200" [5.08mm] basic
1.250" [31.75mm] basic
1.5598" [39.62mm]
1.6505" [41.92mm]
2.015" [51.18mm]

Max. Case Length:	2.015"	Cart. Case:	Winchester
Trim-to Length:	2.005"	Primer:	CCI 200; 250*
Max Cart. OAL:	2.780"	Test Firearm:	Savage Model 99
RCBS Shell Holder:	#3	Barrel Length:	22"

0.357"	38 UCHP	38 UCSP
Weight, grains	158	158
Ballistic Coefficient	0.163	0.164
Sectional Density	0.177	0.177
COAL Tested:	2.315"	2.315"
Speer Part No.	4211	4217

	START CHARGE		MAXIMUM CHARGE	
Propellant	Weight, grs	Muzzle Velocity, ft/sec	Weight, grs	Muzzle Velocity, ft/sec
Reloder 7	44.0	2512	48.0	2850
H322	48.0	2535	52.0	2782
IMR 4064	48.0	2496	52.0	2730

*Maximum Loads should be used with CAUTION • C = Compressed Load • *Magnum Primer used with this powder.*

0.358"	35 FNSP
Weight, grains	180
Ballistic Coefficient	0.236
Sectional Density	0.201
COAL Tested:	2.680"
Speer Part No.	2435

Propellant	START CHARGE		MAXIMUM CHARGE	
	Weight, grs	Muzzle Velocity, ft/sec	Weight, grs	Muzzle Velocity, ft/sec
H335*	48.0	2511	52.0	2732
Reloder 7	41.0	2456	45.0	2728
IMR 3031	47.0	2481	51.0	2721
IMR 4895	47.0	2467	51.0	2701
H322	46.0	2467	50.0	2681
IMR 4198	38.0	2379	42.0	2674
Viht. N133	44.0	2469	48.0C	2668
AA 2015	43.0	2401	47.0C	2628
BL-C(2)*	49.0	2416	53.0C	2590
748*	49.0	2339	53.0	2565
IMR 4320	47.0	2420	51.0	2565

0.358"	35 FNSP
Weight, grains	220
Ballistic Coefficient	0.286
Sectional Density	0.245
COAL Tested:	2.680"
Speer Part No.	2439

	START CHARGE		MAXIMUM CHARGE	
Propellant	Weight, grs	Muzzle Velocity, ft/sec	Weight, grs	Muzzle Velocity, ft/sec
748*	48.0	2328	52.0	2481
Viht. N135	44.0	2290	48.0C	2452
IMR 3031	43.0	2215	47.0	2450
AA 2520*	44.0	2269	48.0C	2431
H322	41.0	2058	45.0	2411
H335*	43.5	2227	47.5	2405
IMR 4064	44.0	2262	48.0	2404
IMR 4320	43.5	2197	47.5	2371
AA 2015	39.0	2186	43.0	2368
BLC-(2)*	46.0	2191	50.0C	2366
H380*	46.0	1992	50.0C	2214
Reloder 7	34.0	2077	38.0	2193

*Maximum Loads should be used with CAUTION • C = Compressed Load • *Magnum Primer used with this powder.*

0.358"	35 Spitz SP	35 GS SP
Weight, grains	250	250
Ballistic Coefficient	0.422	0.353
Sectional Density	0.279	0.279
COAL Tested:	2.760"	2.760"
Speer Part No.	2453	2455

	START CHARGE		MAXIMUM CHARGE	
Propellant	Weight, grs	Muzzle Velocity, ft/sec	Weight, grs	Muzzle Velocity, ft/sec
H335*	41.0	2119	45.0	2333
AA 2015	39.0	2141	43.0	2314
Viht. N135	42.0	2127	46.0C	2302
H322	39.0	2053	43.0	2289
IMR 4064	40.0	2039	44.0	2264
BL-C(2)*	43.0	2069	47.0C	2261
748*	43.0	2031	47.0	2255
IMR 4320	40.0	2007	44.0	2241
IMR 3031	38.0	2011	42.0	2240
Reloder 7	33.0	1919	37.0	2169

*Maximum Loads should be used with CAUTION • C = Compressed Load • *Magnum Primer used with this powder.*

35 Whelen

The 35 Whelen began as one of the most successful wildcat cartridges of the 20th century. Its development is credited to renowned gun maker James Howe, who necked up 30-06 cases to accept 0.358" bullets. Named for the noted shooting authority Colonel Townsend Whelen, this cartridge became very popular in custom rifles.

The Whelen is the same length as the 30-06 and can be built on standard-length actions. It is an excellent cartridge for all North American game. We have to credit much of its early success to the limited cartridge selection at that time. The Whelen conveniently bridged the large performance gap between affordable 30-06 rifles and expensive ones chambered for the 375 H&H cartridge.

Remington has been a leader in converting excellent wildcats into commercial cartridges. In 1987, they announced that they would offer production rifles and factory ammunition in 35 Whelen. Factory loads include a 200-grain bullet at 2675 ft/sec and a 250-grain bullet at 2400 ft/sec (factory nominal velocities).

With the current selection of 35-caliber rifle bullets, the 35 Whelen is an excellent cartridge for the North American sportsman who routinely hunts large deer, elk, and moose. Heavy bullets at modest velocity will damage much less meat than most 30-caliber magnums.

Speer sells four Hot-Cor® 35-caliber rifle bullets: flat point designs in 180 and 220 grains, a 250-grain spitzer and a 250-grain Grand Slam. Both 250-grain bullets were designed for the Whelen. The two flat point bullets are fine for game up to medium deer, and the 250-grain bullets should handle any other North American game. The Grand Slam should be chosen for large bear where deep penetration and bullet integrity are vital.

The 225-grain Trophy Bonded Bear Claw soft point is the premier bullet in this diameter. Its tough bonded construction lets it out-penetrate heavier conventional bullets and, at over 2600 ft/sec, provides a respectably flat trajectory for a rifle of this class.

The Speer 158-grain Uni-Cor® handgun bullets (.357" diameter) are useful for inexpensive plinking or close-range varminting. Driven at rifle velocities, these disrupt quickly and should never be used on any animal larger than a coyote. We recommend you lightly crimp these bullets to improve shot-to-shot uniformity.

Look to propellants of moderate burning rates when reloading the Whelen. The case has a minimum amount of shoulder and the slow-burning propellants often give low velocity even with heavy bullets. Powders like Reloder 15, IMR 4064, H335, AA 2460, and Winchester 748 worked well in this case. We used commercial Remington cases for data development. If you plan to use reformed 30-06 cases, reduce the starting loads by three percent and work up slowly. Shoulder position is important for reliable ignition, case life and accuracy. Avoid pushing the shoulder back during resizing or case forming.

Factory 250-grain soft point ammo gave an average velocity of 2350 ft/sec in our test rifle. The industry maximum average pressure for the 35 Whelen is 52,000 CUP.

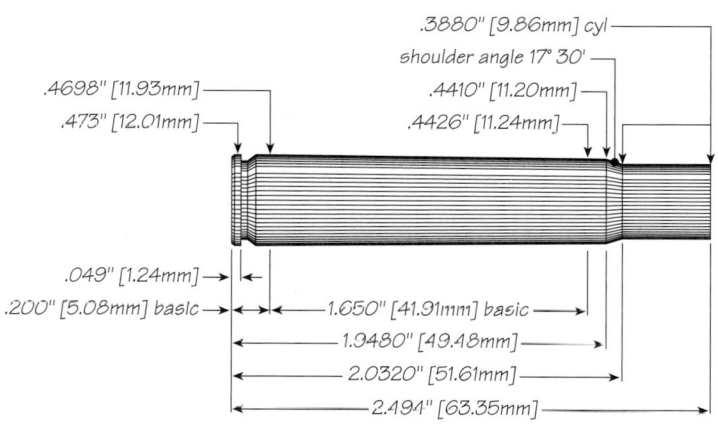

Max. Case Length:	2.494"	**Cart. Case:**	Remington
Trim-to Length:	2.484"	**Primer:**	CCI 200; 250*
Max Cart. OAL:	3.340"	**Test Firearm:**	Remington Model 700
RCBS Shell Holder:	#3	**Barrel Length:**	22"

0.357"	38 UCHP	38 UCSP
Weight, grains	158	158
Ballistic Coefficient	0.163	0.164
Sectional Density	0.177	0.177
COAL Tested:	2.800"	2.800"
Speer Part No.	4211	4217

	START CHARGE		MAXIMUM CHARGE	
Propellant	Weight, grs	Muzzle Velocity, ft/sec	Weight, grs	Muzzle Velocity, ft/sec
Reloder 7	DNR	—	42.0	2193
AA 2015	DNR	—	40.0	2125
IMR 4895	DNR	—	45.0	1979

NOTE: *COAL is less than minimum; may require single loading. DNR—Do not reduce.*

Bruce Young, Chief Reloading Manual Ballistician, Lewiston, at the pressure gun in the Speer test tunnel.

*Maximum Loads should be used with CAUTION • C = Compressed Load • *Magnum Primer used with this powder.*

0.358"	35 FNSP
Weight, grains	180
Ballistic Coefficient	0.236
Sectional Density	0.201
COAL Tested:	3.030"
Speer Part No.	2435

Propellant	START CHARGE		MAXIMUM CHARGE	
	Weight, grs	Muzzle Velocity, ft/sec	Weight, grs	Muzzle Velocity, ft/sec
H335*	61.0	2804	65.0C	2891
AA 2460*	56.0	2722	60.0C	2860
AA 2230	54.0	2671	58.0C	2852
BL-C(2)*	60.0	2686	64.0	2825
AA 2015	50.0	2563	54.0	2797
H322	54.0	2645	58.0C	2797
H4895	54.0	2594	58.0C	2782
Viht. N140	58.0	2636	62.0C	2771
IMR 4895	53.0	2512	57.0C	2762
IMR 3031	53.0	2472	57.0C	2741
IMR 4064	56.0	2510	60.0C	2731
Reloder 15	56.0	2485	60.0C	2678

0.358"	35 FNSP
Weight, grains	220
Ballistic Coefficient	0.286
Sectional Density	0.245
COAL Tested:	3.230"
Speer Part No.	2439

Propellant	START CHARGE Weight, grs	START CHARGE Muzzle Velocity, ft/sec	MAXIMUM CHARGE Weight, grs	MAXIMUM CHARGE Muzzle Velocity, ft/sec
Reloder 15	56.0	2422	60.0C	2599
748*	59.0	2415	63.0C	2560
H335*	52.0	2293	56.0	2558
AA 2460*	50.0	2368	54.0	2494
Viht. N140	54.0	2310	58.0C	2480
IMR 3031	51.0	2275	55.0C	2478
BL-C(2)*	53.0	2350	57.0	2456
IMR 4064	52.0	2242	56.0C	2444
H380*	57.0	2281	61.0C	2422
AA 2015	45.0	2235	49.0	2415
IMR 4895	49.0	2212	53.0	2378
H322	45.0	2219	49.0	2375
IMR 4320	50.0	2100	54.0	2279

*Maximum Loads should be used with CAUTION • C = Compressed Load • *Magnum Primer used with this powder.*

0.358"	35 TBBC SP
Weight, grains	225
Ballistic Coefficient	0.350
Sectional Density	0.281
COAL Tested:	3.270"
Speer Part No.	1777

| Propellant | START CHARGE | | MAXIMUM CHARGE | |
	Weight, grs	Muzzle Velocity, ft/sec	Weight, grs	Muzzle Velocity, ft/sec
IMR 4895	55.0	2532	59.0C	2669
Varget	57.0	2590	59.0C	2653
IMR 3031	51.0	2481	55.0C	2632
Benchmark	50.0	2481	54.0	2609
Reloder 10X	47.0	2425	51.0	2603
Reloder 15	55.0	2495	57.0C	2593
748*	58.0	2497	60.0C	2583
Viht. N133	49.0	2424	53.0	2583
AA 2015	49.0	2377	53.0	2545

NOTE: *Trophy Bonded Bear Claw and Trophy Bonded Sledgehammer Solid bullets have unique ballistic behavior compared to conventional bullets. Loads for TBBC and TBSS bullets may not "track" with data for conventional bullets. Use TBBC and TBSS data ONLY for TBBC and TBSS bullets.*

Toni Saleen, wife of Tom Saleen, Director of International Sales, ATK CCI/Speer Operations; 30-06, 180-grain Grand Slam®; wart hog, South Africa.

0.358"	35 Spitz SP	35 GS SP
Weight, grains	250	250
Ballistic Coefficient	0.422	0.353
Sectional Density	0.279	0.279
COAL Tested:	3.340"	3.265"
Speer Part No.	2453	2455

Propellant	START CHARGE Weight, grs	START CHARGE Muzzle Velocity, ft/sec	MAXIMUM CHARGE Weight, grs	MAXIMUM CHARGE Muzzle Velocity, ft/sec
H335*	49.0	2204	53.0	2386
748*	53.0	2277	57.0	2350
AA 2460*	48.0	2193	52.0	2334
BL-C(2)*	50.0	2163	54.0	2314
IMR 4064	49.0	2050	53.0	2311
Viht. N140	50.0	2130	54.0	2299
H380*	55.0	2143	59.0C	2287
Reloder 15	50.0	2134	54.0	2284
AA 2015	43.0	2159	47.0	2244
IMR 3031	47.0	2060	51.0	2244
H322	44.0	2120	48.0	2181
IMR 4895	45.0	2084	49.0	2142

*Maximum Loads should be used with CAUTION • C = Compressed Load • *Magnum Primer used with this powder.*

358 Norma Magnum

Norma of Sweden introduced the 358 Magnum to the U.S. market in 1959. As they did with its companion cartridge, the 308 Norma Magnum, Norma made unprimed brass available before importing loaded ammunition and loaned chambering reamers to custom gunsmiths. The 358 Norma has a significant velocity advantage over the 35 Whelen but isn't quite up to the level of the 375 H&H. It still fills a niche in the array of hunting cartridges. Because its maximum cartridge length is near that of the 30-06, it can be chambered in standard-length actions.

Factory rifles for this cartridge have never been produced in the U.S. However, several custom rifle makers have chambered for it. Swedish Husqvarna rifles and Schultz & Larsen rifles from Denmark have also been chambered for the 358 Magnum. It is likely that there are more custom rifles in 358 Norma Magnum than factory rifles.

The 358 Norma Magnum is over-powered for any deer species but would be a good choice for Alaskan hunting. The 180-grain Speer soft point should not be used on game larger than deer in the 358 Norma; it was designed for cartridges that produce much lower velocities. The Speer 250-grain Hot-Cor spitzer and Grand Slam are the best large-game bullets in this cartridge.

Norma ammunition and components are imported into the U.S. and their availability has improved in the last several years. If factory brass cannot be readily found in your area, cases can be made by necking up 338 Winchester cases and fire-forming.

There is no U.S. pressure standard for the 358 Norma. European standards call for a maximum pressure of 4400 bar, putting it in the same pressure class as the 338 Winchester Magnum. These loads were completely safe in several test rifles.

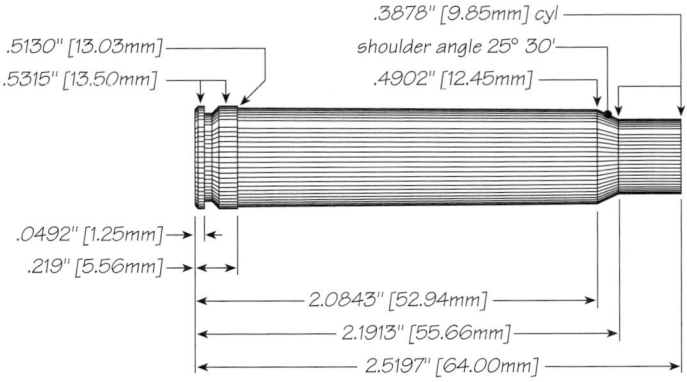

.3878" [9.85mm] cyl
shoulder angle 25° 30'
.5130" [13.03mm]
.5315" [13.50mm]
.4902" [12.45mm]

.0492" [1.25mm]
.219" [5.56mm]

2.0843" [52.94mm]
2.1913" [55.66mm]
2.5197" [64.00mm]

Max. Case Length:	2.520"	Cart. Case:	Norma
Trim-to Length:	2.510"	Primer:	CCI 250*
Max Cart. OAL:	3.346"	Test Firearm:	Custom Winchester M70
RCBS Shell Holder:	#4	Barrel Length:	24"

0.358"	35 FNSP
Weight, grains	180
Ballistic Coefficient	0.236
Sectional Density	0.201
COAL Tested:	3.340"
Speer Part No.	2435

Propellant	START CHARGE		MAXIMUM CHARGE	
	Weight, grs	Muzzle Velocity, ft/sec	Weight, grs	Muzzle Velocity, ft/sec
IMR 4895*	65.0	2943	69.0	3133
IMR 4320*	68.0	2945	72.0	3132
IMR 4064*	67.0	2933	71.0	3124
H380*	68.0	2910	72.0	3075
IMR 4350*	74.0	2778	78.0	2948
H414*	73.0	2652	77.0	2836
SR 4759* (reduced load)	30.0	1893	32.0	2013

*Maximum Loads should be used with CAUTION • C = Compressed Load • *Magnum Primer used with this powder.*

0.358"	35 Spitz SP	35 GS SP
Weight, grains	250	250
Ballistic Coefficient	0.422	0.353
Sectional Density	0.279	0.279
COAL Tested:	3.340"	3.340"
Speer Part No.	2453	2455

Propellant	START CHARGE		MAXIMUM CHARGE	
	Weight, grs	Muzzle Velocity, ft/sec	Weight, grs	Muzzle Velocity, ft/sec
IMR 4350*	72.0	2581	76.0	2732
IMR 4320*	63.0	2483	67.0	2644
IMR 4064*	61.0	2458	65.0	2638
IMR 4895*	59.0	2414	63.0	2584
H380*	63.0	2429	67.0	2579
SR 4759* (reduced load)	30.0	1705	32.0	1821

Dave Imthurn, Sr. Engineering Technician, CCI/Speer Operations; 35 Whelen, 250-grain Grand Slam®; bull elk harvested near Pierce, Idaho.

*Maximum Loads should be used with CAUTION • C = Compressed Load • *Magnum Primer used with this powder.*

9.3 x 62mm

Rifles with 9.3mm (.366") bores are seldom seen in the United States but have enjoyed reasonable popularity in the rest of the world. They remain quite common in African countries that are former Dutch or German colonies.

The 9.3x62mm has consistently been one of the more popular of the various 9.3mm cartridges. It can be chambered in affordable bolt-action rifles and has seen wider distribution than the 9.3x74 designed for expensive single-shot and double rifles or rifle/shotgun combinations. For African ranchers, it was often their working rifle.

European ammo usually has 286-grain bullets although Norma lists one load with a 232-grain bullet. Factory ballistics put the 9.3x62mm slightly ahead of the 35 Whelen and about equal to the 338-06 A-Square. Handloaded with Speer's 270-grain .366" Hot-Cor® semi-spitzer, the 9.3mm enjoys a modest advantage over the 338-06 for heavy game.

Case forming can be as simple as necking up 30-06 or 35 Whelen cases in the 9.3x62mm sizer die. RCBS dies for this cartridge have a special expander ball to perform this operation in one pass. However, the chamber shoulder location may vary in custom rifles and a modified case-forming technique will optimize accuracy and case life. Use a .375" tapered expander to neck up new 35 Whelen cases. Gradually size these cases in a 9.3x62mm sizer die, pushing the new shoulder back a little at a time until the rifle's action fully closes on the case with slight resistance. This will leave an auxiliary shoulder to support the case against the firing pin blow. Load with a published start charge and fire-form. The case shoulder will be precisely positioned for your rifle. Avoid moving the small shoulder during subsequent resizing; this can create excessive headspace.

The cartridge drawing shown with the data reflects current CIP* standards. Some custom rifle chambers may differ from these dimensions.

The 9.3x62mm can be used on any North American big game. Although seldom considered for deer, its modest velocities produce less meat damage than many popular 7mm and 30-caliber "magnum" cartridges.

The loads listed were tested by case head expansion because there are no U.S. pressure standards for the 9.3x62mm. All loads were safe in our test rifle.

*CIP: Commission Internationale Permanente; the European organization that sets firearms and ammunition standards.

9.3 x 62mm

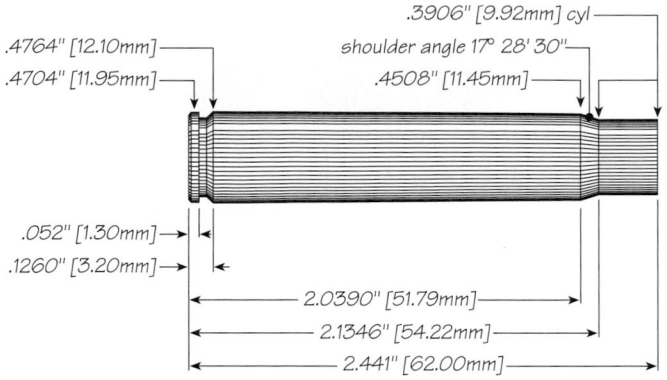

.3906" [9.92mm] cyl
shoulder angle 17° 28' 30"
.4508" [11.45mm]
.4764" [12.10mm]
.4704" [11.95mm]
.052" [1.30mm]
.1260" [3.20mm]
2.0390" [51.79mm]
2.1346" [54.22mm]
2.441" [62.00mm]

Max. Case Length:	2.441"	**Cart. Case:**	Formed from Winchester 30-06
Trim-to Length:	2.431"	**Primer:**	CCI 200; 250
Max Cart. OAL:	3.291"	**Test Firearm:**	Custom Remington 700
RCBS Shell Holder:	#3	**Barrel Length:**	26"

0.366"	9.3mm Semi Spitz SP
Weight, grains	270
Ballistic Coefficient	0.361
Sectional Density	0.288
COAL Tested:	3.280"
Speer Part No.	2459

	START CHARGE		MAXIMUM CHARGE	
Propellant	Weight, grs	Muzzle Velocity, ft/sec	Weight, grs	Muzzle Velocity, ft/sec
H414*	56.0	2388	60.0	2583
760*	56.0	2408	60.0	2552
IMR 4350	60.0	2486	64.0	2550
H380*	55.0	2310	59.0	2542
IMR 4064	54.0	2403	58.0	2530
IMR 4895	52.0	2340	56.0	2495
IMR 4831	60.0	2166	64.0	2493
748*	50.0	2253	54.0	2440

*Maximum Loads should be used with CAUTION • C = Compressed Load • *Magnum Primer used with this powder.*

9.3 x 74R

This metric cartridge dates to the turn of the last century. It evolved as a smokeless powder upgrade of an older black powder cartridge, the 9.3x72R. The 72mm version had a straight tapered case while the newer 74mm version has a slight shoulder and a longer case to prevent it from accidentally being fired in rifles chambered for the older cartridge.

An impressive cartridge length precludes using the 9.3x74R in repeating arms. It is most commonly encountered in single-shots, double rifles and combination guns. The cartridge was little known in North America other than by a few shooters who brought back war souvenirs from Europe. However, in the 1980's Valmet of America imported the excellent Model 412S over/under rifle in 9.3x74R. There are also a number of European gun makers who still chamber it in rifles and combination guns. Beretta, Bernardelli and Heym rifles are imported into this country. The Ruger website in 2006 showed their No. 1 single-shot rifle chambered for this cartridge. Cases are the only limitation because they cannot be made from any common case. However, both RWS and Norma now import them, and Hornady announced in 2006 that they will be supplying ammunition.

Speer makes one bullet in .366" diameter for the 9.3mm. It weighs 270 grains and is a Hot-Cor® design for tough game. The 9.3x74R is suitable for anything on the North American continent and on lighter African game in countries where game regulations allow this bore diameter (some countries specify a minimum caliber for big game).

No SAAMI pressure or dimensional standards exist for this cartridge. The cartridge drawing reflects European CIP maximum dimensions. These loads closely approximate the velocities of European factory ammunition with similar bullet weights, and were completely safe in the test rifle.

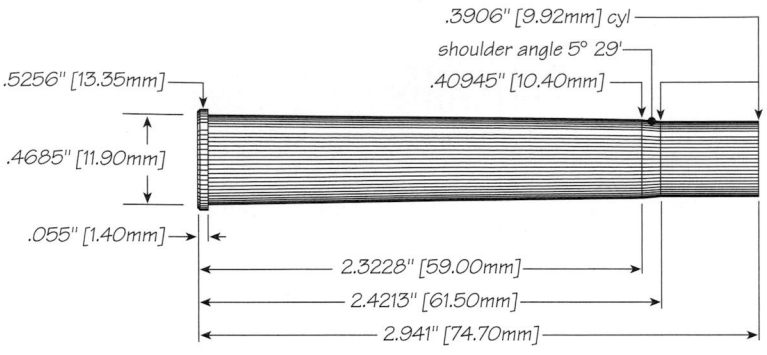

.3906" [9.92mm] cyl
shoulder angle 5° 29'
.40945" [10.40mm]
.5256" [13.35mm]
.4685" [11.90mm]
.055" [1.40mm]
2.3228" [59.00mm]
2.4213" [61.50mm]
2.941" [74.70mm]

Max. Case Length:	2.941"	Cart. Case:	RWS
Trim-to Length:	2.931"	Primer:	CCI 200
Max Cart. OAL:	3.720"	Test Firearm:	Valmet Model 412S
RCBS Shell Holder:	#4	Barrel Length:	24"

0.366"	9.3mm Semi Spitz SP
Weight, grains	270
Ballistic Coefficient	0.361
Sectional Density	0.288
COAL Tested:	3.665"
Speer Part No.	2459

	START CHARGE		MAXIMUM CHARGE	
Propellant	Weight, grs	Muzzle Velocity, ft/sec	Weight, grs	Muzzle Velocity, ft/sec
H380	57.0	2183	61.0	2329
IMR 4350	61.0	2113	65.0C	2306
IMR 4895	51.0	2097	55.0	2288
IMR 4064	54.0	2157	58.0	2279
IMR 4831	62.0	2156	66.0C	2264
748	56.0	2108	60.0	2235
AA 3100	60.0	1898	64.0C	2086

*Maximum Loads should be used with CAUTION • C = Compressed Load • *Magnum Primer used with this powder.*

375 Winchester

The 375 Winchester was announced in 1978 by Winchester as a new woods cartridge for the Model 94 Big Bore, a strengthened version of the popular Model 94 carbine. Actually, the 375 is a modernized, high-pressure version of the old 38-55 Winchester cartridge. The 38-55 has a well-earned reputation for accuracy and woods performance but operates at relatively low pressures (less than 30,000 CUP). The 375 uses a slightly shortened 38-55 case with much heavier walls to contain the higher operating pressures.

In addition to the Winchester Big Bore, Ruger's No. 3 single shot carbine and a few Marlin Model 336 carbines have been chambered for the 375 Winchester cartridge. However, a quick review of the literature at press time showed no current rifles chambered for this cartridge. Thompson/Center's Custom Shop, Fox Ridge Outfitters, offers 375 Winchester barrels for its Contender single-shot carbine. The 375 is an excellent choice for the handgun hunter who uses the Contender pistol. See the Handgun section for more information.

The 375 Winchester can be used on most North American game at modest ranges with the exception of the great bears. Its effective hunting range is well under 200 yards but it would be hard to beat the 375 in the eastern woods. Speer does not manufacture a .375" diameter bullet that is suitable for use in a tubular magazine. The 235-grain semi-spitzer bullet can be used in single-shot rifles, or loaded singly into the chamber of a lever rifle. Cartridges using this bullet must not be used in any tubular magazine unless you load only one in the magazine, giving you a two-shot rifle. With this cartridge, two should be plenty.

The industry maximum pressure for the 375 Winchester is 52,000 CUP. Never attempt to fire 375 Winchester ammunition in any rifle chambered for the 38-55 cartridge. Rifles chambered for the 38-55 cartridge were never designed to handle pressures in this range and property damage and/or personal injury can result.

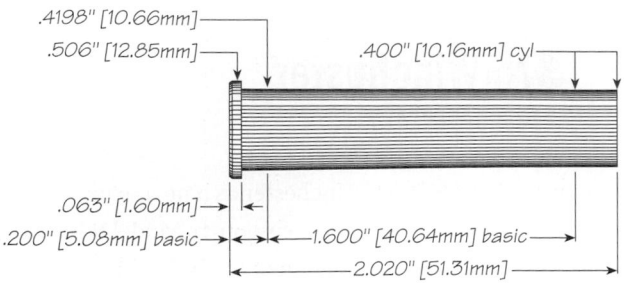

.4198" [10.66mm]
.506" [12.85mm]
.400" [10.16mm] cyl
.063" [1.60mm]
.200" [5.08mm] basic
1.600" [40.64mm] basic
2.020" [51.31mm]

Max. Case Length:	2.020"	Cart. Case:	Winchester
Trim-to Length:	2.010"	Primer:	CCI 200
Max Cart. OAL:	2.560"	Test Firearm:	Winchester M94 Big Bore
RCBS Shell Holder:	#2	Barrel Length:	20"

0.375"	375 Semi Spitz SP
Weight, grains	235
Ballistic Coefficient	0.301
Sectional Density	0.239
COAL Tested:	2.560"
Speer Part No.	2471

Propellant	START CHARGE		MAXIMUM CHARGE	
	Weight, grs	Muzzle Velocity, ft/sec	Weight, grs	Muzzle Velocity, ft/sec
Reloder 7	31.0	1810	35.0C	2067
IMR 4198	28.0	1727	32.0	1987
AA 2015	32.0	1742	36.0C	1975
Viht. N133	33.0	1740	37.0C	1963
IMR 4895	32.0	1580	36.0C	1933
AA 2230	33.5	1721	37.5C	1911
H322	31.0	1662	35.0	1851
IMR 3031	31.0	1536	35.0C	1779

*Maximum Loads should be used with CAUTION • C = Compressed Load • *Magnum Primer used with this powder.*

375 H&H Magnum

The 375 H&H dates to 1912 when it was introduced by the famous English gunmaking firm of Holland & Holland. It was among the first belted cases and quickly established itself as a premier heavy game cartridge. In some African countries, it is the minimum bore diameter that can be used. With proper bullet selection and reasonable hunting skill, the 375 can take any game known to man.

The Western Cartridge Company first offered factory ammunition in the U.S. in 1925; however, it wasn't until 1937 that an American-made rifle—the Winchester Model 70—was available. Since then, Remington, Browning, Ruger and others have chambered the 375. It is just as popular today as ever, putting it among the oldest chamberings surviving today. Quality American-made rifles in this caliber have been continually available since 1937 (except during World War II when sporting arms were unavailable in any caliber).

Although theoretically too powerful for North American game other than the largest bears, the 375 is quite popular on this continent. Its continued popularity is the 375's inherent accuracy and flat trajectory. Sighted for 300 yards, the 235-grain semi-spitzer at 2900 ft/sec rises only 5.5 inches at 200 yards. The 300-yard energy is still 2250 ft/lbs! This type of performance shows why the 375 is a popular long-range elk cartridge.

The 235-grain Speer Hot-Cor® semi-spitzer was designed to give reduced recoil for practice and hunting lighter game. Loaded down to 2600 ft/sec, it has been very successful on deer. At this velocity, damage to edible meat is usually less than caused by smaller, high-velocity bullets. The 270-grain boat tail is excellent for long shots in open country. An interesting observation is that many 375 H&H rifles seem to be able to place bullets of different weights very near the same point of impact.

The premier bullet for the toughest North American game is the 250-grain Trophy Bonded Bear Claw. Launched at over 2700 ft/sec, this bullet will out-penetrate most conventional bullets weighing 270-300 grains. Fired into expansion media at muzzle velocity, this bullet retained over 95 percent of its original weight. The 300-grain TBBC is also an excellent bullet for dangerous bruins.

The 375 is very versatile for African game. Although marginal for elephant with attitude problems, the cartridge has taken many of them through the years. It is quite adequate for Cape buffalo with the proper bullet and its flat shooting qualities make it an excellent choice for plains game at long ranges. We recommend both the 250 Trophy Bonded Bear Claw and the 285-grain Grand Slam soft point for plains animals. Use the 300-grain TBBC on larger thin-skinned game and the Trophy Bonded SledgeHammer solid for elephant. Before packing any 375 rifle to Africa, check with your professional hunter. Some countries place minimum caliber restrictions on dangerous game rifles.

After over 90 years on the shooting scene, the 375 H&H has proved its ability to age gracefully. More powerful cartridges like the 378 Winchester and the 375 Remington Ultra Magnum don't seem to threaten the 375 H&H's title as "King of the Medium Calibers."

The data presented here is a complete reshoot of this cartridge on the latest electronic transducer equipment. Because of the differences in sensing technology between the older crusher system and the new electronic gear, some loads changed positions but, overall, the performance was excellent with a wide variety of propellants. The industry maximum average pressure for the 375 H&H is 62,000 psi.

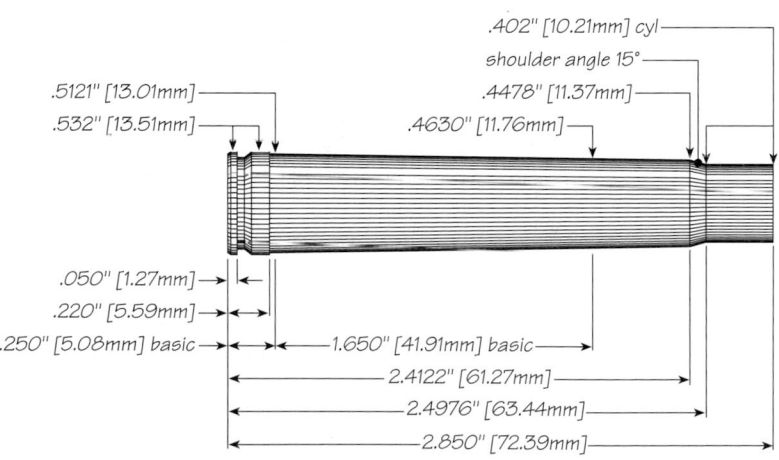

Max. Case Length:	2.850"	**Cart. Case:**	Winchester
Trim-to Length:	2.840"	**Primer:**	CCI 250*
Max Cart. OAL:	3.600"	**Test Firearm:**	Remington M700
RCBS Shell Holder:	#4	**Barrel Length:**	24"

0.375"	375 Semi Spitz SP
Weight, grains	235
Ballistic Coefficient	0.301
Sectional Density	0.239
COAL Tested:	3.600"
Speer Part No.	2471

Propellant	START CHARGE		MAXIMUM CHARGE	
	Weight, grs	Muzzle Velocity, ft/sec	Weight, grs	Muzzle Velocity, ft/sec
Viht. N540*	70.0	2835	74.0	2948
H380*	80.0	2826	84.0	2930
Reloder 15*	74.0	2828	78.0	2920
AA 4350*	81.0	2738	85.0C	2877
Viht. N140*	71.0	2766	75.0	2873
IMR 4064*	70.0	2707	74.0	2854
IMR 4350*	81.0	2672	85.0C	2840
H414*	84.0	2736	86.0C	2808
Varget*	70.0	2686	74.0	2803
H4350*	78.0	2715	82.0C	2799
AA 2700*	74.0	2647	78.0	2778
IMR 3031*	63.0	2478	67.0	2702
IMR 4895*	64.0	2420	68.0	2591
SR 4759* (reduced load)	28.0	1610	30.0	1701

*Maximum Loads should be used with CAUTION • C = Compressed Load • *Magnum Primer used with this powder.*

0.375"	375 TBBC SP
Weight, grains	250
Ballistic Coefficient	0.286
Sectional Density	0.254
COAL Tested:	3.580"
Speer Part No.	1778

	START CHARGE		MAXIMUM CHARGE	
Propellant	Weight, grs	Muzzle Velocity, ft/sec	Weight, grs	Muzzle Velocity, ft/sec
H380*	79.0	2800	83.0C	2869
Viht. N540*	73.0	2729	77.0	2866
Reloder 15*	72.0	2717	76.0	2847
IMR 4064*	69.0	2713	73.0	2835
IMR 4350*	79.0	2705	83.0C	2823
H4350*	77.0	2680	81.0C	2795
Varget*	66.0	2650	70.0	2770
XMR 4350*	81.0	2710	83.0C	2764

NOTE: *Trophy Bonded Bear Claw and Trophy Bonded Sledgehammer Solid bullets have unique ballistic behavior compared to conventional bullets. Loads for TBBC and TBSS bullets may not "track" with data for conventional bullets. Use TBBC and TBSS data ONLY for TBBC and TBSS bullets.*

Paul Snider, father of Jack Snider, Plating System Technician, CCI/Speer Operations; 375 H&H, Trophy Bonded Bear Claw bullet; 40" Cape buffalo. The Sniders (left to right) are: Paul Jr., Travis, Jack and Paul.

0.375"	375 Spitz BTSP
Weight, grains	270
Ballistic Coefficient	0.478
Sectional Density	0.274
COAL Tested:	3.600"
Speer Part No.	2472

	START CHARGE		MAXIMUM CHARGE	
Propellant	Weight, grs	Muzzle Velocity, ft/sec	Weight, grs	Muzzle Velocity, ft/sec
AA 4350*	79.0	2667	83.0C	2797
H4350*	76.0	2611	80.0C	2731
H414*	80.0	2655	82.0C	2708
Reloder 15*	67.0	2527	71.0	2675
Viht. N140*	66.0	2541	70.0	2665
IMR 4350*	76.0	2557	80.0C	2655
IMR 4831*	80.0	2579	82.0C	2643
Viht. N160*	78.0	2562	80.0C	2622
AA 2700*	70.0	2472	74.0	2621
Reloder 19*	81.0	2530	83.0C	2589
760*	80.0	2525	82.0C	2564
Varget*	63.0	2363	67.0	2549

Lab Notes:

The 270-grain boat tail bullet is slightly longer than the 285-grain Grand Slam. If a charge fills the case, the BT doesn't leave as much room and we did not apply as much compression with the BT as with the flat-base bullets. That's why some compressed charges for the boat tail are lighter than those for the heavier bullet. We've verified this on two independent pressure systems.

*Maximum Loads should be used with CAUTION • C = Compressed Load • *Magnum Primer used with this powder.*

0.375"	375 GS SP
Weight, grains	285
Ballistic Coefficient	0.354
Sectional Density	0.290
COAL Tested:	3.560"
Speer Part No.	2473

	START CHARGE		MAXIMUM CHARGE	
Propellant	Weight, grs	Muzzle Velocity, ft/sec	Weight, grs	Muzzle Velocity, ft/sec
H414*	82.0	2645	84.0C	2697
AA 4350*	77.0	2562	81.0C	2694
760*	83.0	2617	85.0C	2658
IMR 4831ᴬ	79.0	2504	83.0C	2649
H4350*	75.0	2519	79.0C	2615
IMR 4350*	75.0	2462	79.0C	2575
Viht. N160*	78.0	2531	80.0C	2570
H4831SC*	82.0	2465	86.0C	2561
IMR 4064*	64.0	2405	68.0	2552
Reloder 15*	65.0	2410	69.0	2533
AA 2700*	69.0	2392	73.0	2523
Varget*	64.0	2363	68.0	2510
Reloder 19*	78.0	2413	80.0C	2456
IMR 4895*	60.0	2231	64.0	2400

0.375"	375 TBBC SP	375 TBSS (Solid)
Weight, grains	300	300
Ballistic Coefficient	0.336	0.240
Sectional Density	0.305	0.305
COAL Tested:	3.600"	3.575"
Speer Part No.	1780	1781

	START CHARGE		MAXIMUM CHARGE	
Propellant	Weight, grs	Muzzle Velocity, ft/sec	Weight, grs	Muzzle Velocity, ft/sec
H414*	79.0	2512	81.0C	2575
760*	79.0	2495	81.0C	2549
Viht. N540*	69.0	2432	73.0	2547
IMR 4064*	65.0	2383	69.0	2506
AA 2700^	75.0	2456	77.0C	2495
Reloder 15*	66.0	2378	70.0	2485
IMR 4895*	64.0	2368	68.0	2472
IMR 4350*	73.0	2345	75.0C	2400

NOTE: *Trophy Bonded Bear Claw and Trophy Bonded Sledgehammer Solid bullets have unique ballistic behavior compared to conventional bullets. Loads for TBBC and TBSS bullets may not "track" with data for conventional bullets. Use TBBC and TBSS data ONLY for TBBC and TBSS bullets.*

*Maximum Loads should be used with CAUTION • C = Compressed Load • *Magnum Primer used with this powder.*

378 Weatherby Magnum

The 378 Weatherby was the first of Roy Weatherby's "mega-magnums," dating to 1953. The concept was to create a dangerous game cartridge that significantly exceeded the power of the renowned 375 H&H cartridge and Weatherby's 375 Magnum. Mr. Weatherby succeeded.

It features a belted case with a body diameter 13% larger than the famous Holland & Holland belted case that was the basis for Weatherby's original magnum cartridges. The larger case of the 378 Magnum gives a velocity increase of nearly 400 ft/sec with 300-grain bullets when compared to the 375 H&H. Its muzzle energy significantly exceeds that of the newer 458 Winchester Magnum.

Although the case was technically a new design, it was certainly influenced by the 416 Rigby. Major body diameters differ by only a few thousands of an inch, and the Weatherby case is just 0.013 inches longer than the Rigby. Weatherby added a belt; we can argue that, had the cartridge been designed in the last few years, the belt would not have been added. However, in 1953, any respectable "magnum" that was to gain commercial acceptance wore a belt.

People who have experienced both the Weatherby and 45-caliber African cartridges swear that the 378 takes the blue ribbon for abusive recoil. This is expected; adding a lot of velocity adds more recoil energy than adding a lot of bullet weight.

This level of recoil also means that bullet crimping is mandatory. All bullets we tested have crimping grooves—use them.

This is a very powerful cartridge capable of propelling a 250-grain bullet at 3200 ft/sec and yielding over 5600 ft/lbs of energy. For the largest North American and African plains game, the 250-grain Trophy Bonded® Bear Claw® and the 285-grain Grand Slam soft points are excellent choices. For dangerous game, look to the 300-grain Bear Claw soft point and the Sledgehammer® solid.

We elected not to show data for our 235-grain semi-spitzer, that bullet was designed as a whitetail deer option for the 375 H&H. From a 378 Weatherby, this bullet at an estimated 3400 ft/sec would behave like a varmint bullet.

Other than the need to weigh or meter a prodigious amount of propellant, this cartridge presents no particular reloading problems. Remember, when metering large charges in any cartridge, you must allow enough time for the entire charge to pass from the powder measure into the case. As with any massive cartridge, you will find that charges that nearly fill the case will give you the most consistent velocities. There is no practical way to make reduced loads that provide any hope of reasonable efficiency. For that reason, do not load lighter than the start loads we show.

The loads shown here do not exceed the pressure of factory-loaded Weatherby ammunition, and are within the 55,100 CUP pressure limit established for this cartridge.

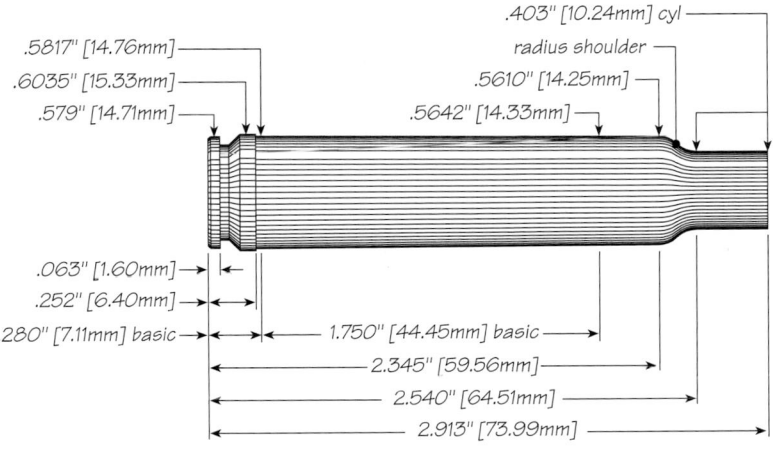

Max. Case Length:	2.913"	Cart. Case:	Weatherby
Trim-to Length:	2.903"	Primer:	CCI 250*
Max Cart. OAL:	3.655"	Test Firearm:	Universal Receiver
RCBS Shell Holder:	#14	Barrel Length:	Krieger 24"

0.375"	375 TBBC SP
Weight, grains	250
Ballistic Coefficient	0.286
Sectional Density	0.245
COAL Tested:	3.645"
Speer Part No.	1778

Propellant	START CHARGE		MAXIMUM CHARGE	
	Weight, grs	Muzzle Velocity, ft/sec	Weight, grs	Muzzle Velocity, ft/sec
Reloder 19*	111.0	3055	117.0	3227
Reloder 22*	113.0	3056	119.0	3223
IMR 4831*	107.0	3021	113.0	3202
IMR 4350*	105.0	3007	111.0	3196
H4350*	102.0	2930	108.0	3097
AA 4350*	104.0	2882	110.0	3085

NOTE: *Trophy Bonded Bear Claw and Trophy Bonded Sledgehammer Solid bullets have unique ballistic behavior compared to conventional bullets. Loads for TBBC and TBSS bullets may not "track" with data for conventional bullets. Use TBBC and TBSS data ONLY for TBBC and TBSS bullets.*

Jack Snider, Plating System Technician, CCI/Speer Operations; 270 Winchester, 150-grain; a very fine 8x8 whitetail buck.

0.375"	375 GS SP
Weight, grains	285
Ballistic Coefficient	0.354
Sectional Density	0.290
COAL Tested:	3.635"
Speer Part No.	2473

	START CHARGE		MAXIMUM CHARGE	
Propellant	Weight, grs	Muzzle Velocity, ft/sec	Weight, grs	Muzzle Velocity, ft/sec
IMR 7828*	109.0	2812	115.0	2996
IMR 4831*	103.0	2823	109.0	2989
Reloder 25*	113.0	2848	117.0C	2974
Reloder 22*	106.0	2788	112.0	2971
Reloder 19*	105.0	2796	111.0	2967
IMR 4350*	99.0	2862	105.0	2948
AA 4350*	100.0	2732	108.0	2918
H4350*	97.0	2746	103.0	2912

*Maximum Loads should be used with CAUTION • C = Compressed Load • *Magnum Primer used with this powder.*

0.375"	375 TBBC SP	375 TBSS (Solid)
Weight, grains	300	300
Ballistic Coefficient	0.336	0.240
Sectional Density	0.305	0.305
COAL Tested:	3.640"	3.630"
Speer Part No.	1780	1781

	START CHARGE		MAXIMUM CHARGE	
Propellant	Weight, grs	Muzzle Velocity, ft/sec	Weight, grs	Muzzle Velocity, ft/sec
Reloder 25*	110.0	2724	116.0C	2907
IMR 7828*	107.0	2644	113.0C	2856
IMR 4831*	100.0	2695	106.0	2836
Reloder 19*	103.0	2674	109.0	2829
Reloder 22*	104.0	2670	110.0	2827
IMR 4350*	97.0	2660	103.0	2823
AA 4350*	99.0	2668	103.0	2793

NOTE: *Trophy Bonded Bear Claw and Trophy Bonded Sledgehammer Solid bullets have unique ballistic behavior compared to conventional bullets. Loads for TBBC and TBSS bullets may not "track" with data for conventional bullets. Use TBBC and TBSS data ONLY for TBBC and TBSS bullets.*

Mark Vogel, son of Don Vogel, Rimfire Technical Coordinator, CCI/Speer Operations; 300 Win Mag, 180-grain Fusion® ammo; whitetail deer.

*Maximum Loads should be used with CAUTION • C = Compressed Load • * Magnum Primer used with this powder.*

38-40 Winchester *(38 W.C.F.)*

The 38-40 is among the oldest centerfire cartridges still in use. Winchester developed the 38-40 in 1874, just after introducing the 44-40 cartridge. Both were first offered in the Winchester Model 1873 lever-action rifle and were quickly adapted to revolvers such as the Colt Single Action. Remington and Colt also built slide-action rifles for the 38-40. Later, the much stronger Winchester Model 1892 and the Marlin Model 1894 were offered in 38-40.

The cartridge name is a misnomer; it should have been called the "40-40." The bullet diameter is 0.401 inches and many Colt barrels are as large as 0.403 inches. Factory ammunition is typically loaded with a 180-grain jacketed soft point bullet at 1160 ft/sec. Although once offered in a high-pressure version for strong actions, the surviving loads are held to a relatively low pressure—14,000 CUP—because of concern over worn or inherently weak older firearms.

The 38-40 and 44-40 were once touted as "all-around" cartridges, capable of bagging the Thanksgiving turkey or stopping a charging grizzly. It could never live up to those claims, even with high-speed loads. In reality, the 38-40 with current loadings is a borderline choice for whitetail deer even at close range.

Handloading the 38-40 presents some challenges. There is a significant difference between new cases and fired cases. Factory ammo and new component cases have a long neck (see photo) to allow the placement of a rolled cannelure below the bullet to resist bullet setback in tubular magazines. Most loading dies are designed to return the case to industry chamber spec, not the original case profile, leaving the neck quite short.

38-40 factory load, cast bullet load, and a fired case. Note the difference in profile between new cases, the chamber drawing and the fired case.

When loading the RCBS 40-180-FN bullet for a tubular magazine rifle, we recommend using new brass. The bullet lacks a crimp groove, so the extra neck length will provide additional resistance to the bullet being pushed deeper into the case. The newer RCBS 40-180-CAS bullet design features a generous crimp groove and is the best choice for rifle reloading.

Always separate the seating and crimping operations. The 38-40 case has a very thin neck and care must be exercised to avoid crumpled cases. Trimming cases to uniform length before loading makes the crimp operation much more effective.

Like many other old cartridges, the 38-40 is gaining renewed interest because of Cowboy Action Shooting. CAS rules require a lead bullet. Speer does not make a lead bullet suitable for the 38-40 but bullets from two RCBS moulds fill the need for bullets.

The maximum loads presented here are held to the industry pressure standard of 14,000 CUP. The starting loads were carefully selected to produce at least 10,000 CUP and you should never attempt to load lighter charges. Doing so will produce inconsistent loads and increase the risk of a bullet lodged in the bore.

There is a great deal of variation in 38-40 rifle bores and chambers making it difficult to find a representative sporting rifle for reporting velocities. We elected to show the velocities from the 24-inch pressure barrel. Because most of the propellants we used were relatively quick-burning, a 20-inch carbine barrel will not be much slower.

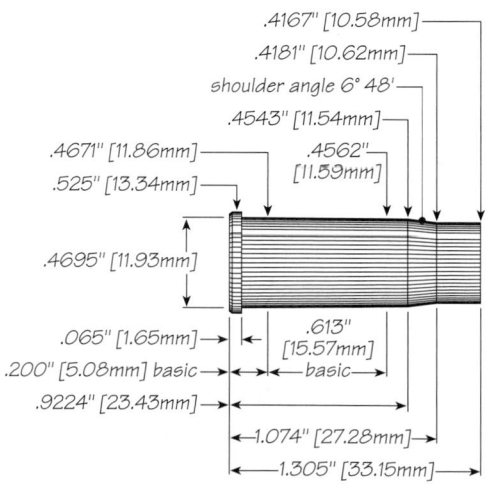

Max. Case Length:	1.305"	Cart. Case:	Winchester
Trim-to Length:	1.295"	Primer:	CCI 300
Max Cart. OAL:	1.592"	Test Firearm:	Universal Receiver
RCBS Shell Holder:	#35	Barrel Length:	HS Precision 24"

0.401"	40-180 FN	40-180 CM
Weight, grains	180	180
Lead Alloy	hard	hard
Ballistic Coefficient	0.143	0.135
Sectional Density	0.160	0.160
COAL Tested:	1.560"	1.585"
RCBS Mould No.	82066	82306

	START CHARGE		MAXIMUM CHARGE	
Propellant	Weight, grs	Muzzle Velocity, ft/sec	Weight, grs	Muzzle Velocity, ft/sec
Viht. N105	11.9	1398	12.5	1514
Viht. N350	7.8	1234	8.4	1314
AA 5744	14.0	1243	15.0	1309
H. Universal	6.5	1220	7.0	1286
Unique	6.4	1162	7.4	1275
TiteGroup	4.9	1128	5.5	1213
700-X	4.6	1085	5.1	1192
231	5.2	1080	6.0	1183
Bullseye	4.5	1064	5.3	1178
AA No. 2 Impr.	5.1	1097	5.7	1164
AA Nitro 100	4.3	1044	5.0	1145
Red Dot	4.3	996	5.2	1135
American Select	4.6	1032	5.2	1113
Trail Boss	4.9	996	5.4	1051

NOTE: *We sell bullet moulds, not cast bullets. These bullets were cast in RCBS moulds. Contact your dealer for more information on the RCBS line of premium bullet casting equipment, or visit on the internet at www.rcbs.com.*

*Maximum Loads should be used with CAUTION • C = Compressed Load • *Magnum Primer used with this powder.*

41 Remington Magnum

The popularity of their 357 and 44 Magnum carbines led Marlin to also chamber some of their Model 1894 lever guns in 41 Magnum. Although no longer listed in Marlin catalogs, quite a few of these were sold and their owners seem quite satisfied with accuracy and performance.

In earlier manuals, we did not show rifle data for the 41 Magnum because our only 41-caliber handgun bullets did not have the right kind of crimping surface for tubular magazines. That changed when Speer developed a 41 Magnum Gold Dot® hollow point in 2003.

The 41-caliber Gold Dot weighs 210 grains and was designed for hunting. Although handgun hunting was the driving force behind the new bullet, tough Uni-Cor® bonded construction means the bullet is still "in the zone" when driven 400 ft/sec faster in a rifle. The bullet has the wide crimping cannelure characteristic of all Gold Dot revolver bullets. This cannelure design is equally at home in a revolver's cylinder or a rifle's tubular magazine.

A heavy crimp is a must. In addition to improving ballistics uniformity with the propellants tested, the crimp helps the bullet resist being forced deeper into the case in a tubular carbine magazine.

When loading any handgun cartridge for a rifle, pay attention to load selection. If you load light charges of fast-burning propellants, a jacketed bullet may not make it down a 20-inch barrel. The loads here provided adequate pressure even at the starting loads in our test rifle. However, you must never load lighter than the start loads to avoid a bore obstruction.

Velocities are nearly the same as 240-grain 44 Magnum loads fired in a similar rifle. Although the energy is somewhat less, the 41 Magnum loaded with the 210-grain Gold Dot is a nice 100-yard deer rifle. Like the 44 Magnum, the 41's recoil—stout in a revolver—becomes rather tame when experienced in a rifle.

These loads remain within the 36,000 psi pressure limit assigned the 41 Magnum. Please see the Handgun Data section for additional information on this cartridge.

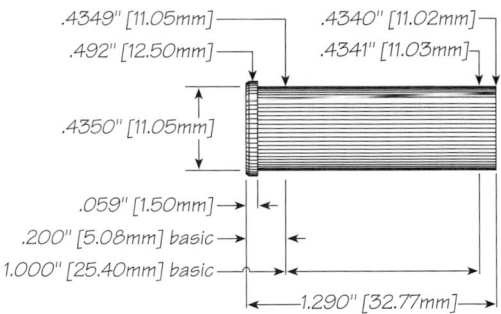

.4349" [11.05mm]
.492" [12.50mm]
.4340" [11.02mm]
.4341" [11.03mm]
.4350" [11.05mm]
.059" [1.50mm]
.200" [5.08mm] basic
1.000" [25.40mm] basic
1.290" [32.77mm]

Max. Case Length:	1.290"	Cart. Case:	Winchester
Trim-to Length:	1.280"	Primer:	CCI 300; 350*
Max Cart. OAL:	1.590"	Test Firearm:	Marlin 1894
RCBS Shell Holder:	#30	Barrel Length:	20"

0.410"	41 GDHP
Weight, grains	210
Ballistic Coefficient	0.183
Sectional Density	0.178
COAL Tested:	1.575"
Speer Part No.	4430

Propellant	START CHARGE		MAXIMUM CHARGE	
	Weight, grs	Muzzle Velocity, ft/sec	Weight, grs	Muzzle Velocity, ft/sec
H110*	20.5	1704	21.5	1776
296*	20.5	1685	21.5	1775
2400	18.0	1605	19.0	1699
Viht. N110	17.0	1580	18.0	1690
AA No. 9	17.0	1575	18.0	1656
IMR 4227	21.0	1480	22.0	1583
Blue Dot	12.0	1354	13.0	1489
Unique	8.7	1208	9.7	1331
Viht. N350	9.8	1255	10.5	1314

*Maximum Loads should be used with CAUTION • C = Compressed Load • *Magnum Primer used with this powder.*

416 Remington Magnum

The 416 Remington joined the shooters' arsenal in 1988 during a time of renewed interest in heavy-caliber rifles. Based on the 8mm Remington Magnum case, the 416 requires a long action rifle. Remington offered the 416 in their Model 700 Safari rifle.

The choice of a .416" diameter bullet seems odd without a look at past heavy rifles. The superb 416 Rigby has been around since 1911; however, its popularity was limited because of the difficulty in obtaining guns and ammunition in this country. Two popular wildcats from the 1970's, the 416 Taylor and 416 Hoffman, had already demonstrated the feasibility of using the full-length H&H case to create a modern version of the 416 Rigby.

Like the two wildcats, the 416 Remington affords the same performance level as the Rigby cartridge—a 400-grain bullet at 2400 ft/sec—but offered the advantage of rifles built on existing popular actions and ammunition based on a standard, belted case. The introduction of the 416 Remington as a commercial cartridge immediately resulted in a better selection of bullets for the handloader.

The 416 Remington fills a gap in performance between the 375 H&H and the 458 Winchester Magnum. It has the trajectory advantages of the 375, but with much greater energy. With the proper bullet the 416 should handle any game encountered. Primarily designed for African game, the cartridge is grossly over-powered for most North American hunting with the exception of the great bears. For dangerous game, Speer offers two Trophy Bonded® 400-grain bullets. The Bear Claw® soft point should handle most animals but, for the heaviest game, the SledgeHammer® Solid will give maximum penetration.

Speer also makes a popularly priced 350-grain Mag-Tip® that is better suited to most North American hunting than the two African bullets and produces less recoil if not loaded to maximum velocity. Economical, reduced-recoil practice should appeal to any 416 shooter; the calculated recoil of full-power 416 loads is greater than the 458 Magnum!

Ammunition used in magazine rifles should be assembled with a firm case mouth crimp to prevent bullets from moving during recoil. Because the 416 case neck is somewhat thin, it may be necessary to seat and crimp in separate operations. Propellants that perform well in the 375 H&H can be used in the 416. Very slow-burning propellants are not efficient in this nearly straight case.

Ironically, the better selection of 416-caliber bullets sparked by the introduction of the 416 Remington has revived interest in the venerable 416 Rigby. Today, more rifle models are cataloged for the 90-year old Rigby cartridge than Remington's newcomer.

The maximum average pressure for the 416 Remington is 54,000 CUP.

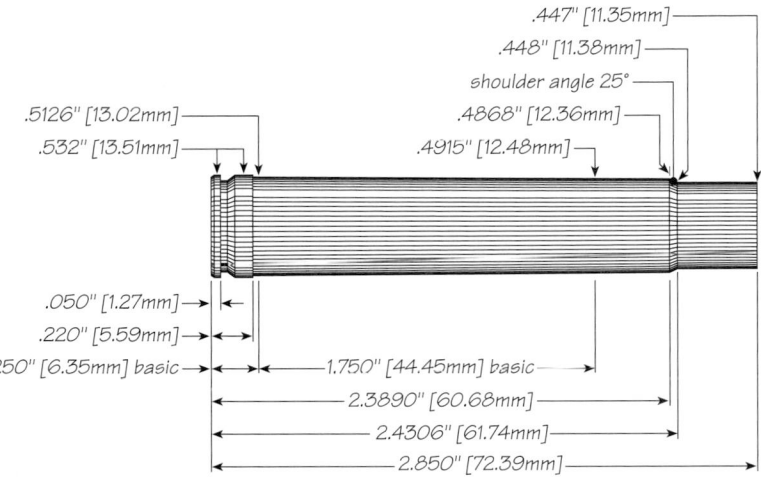

Max. Case Length:	2.850"	Cart. Case:	Remington
Trim-to Length:	2.840"	Primer:	CCI 250*
Max Cart. OAL:	3.600"	Test Firearm:	Remington M700
RCBS Shell Holder:	#4	Barrel Length:	24"

0.416"	416 MT SP
Weight, grains	350
Ballistic Coefficient	0.332
Sectional Density	0.289
COAL Tested:	3.580"
Speer Part No.	2477

	START CHARGE		MAXIMUM CHARGE	
Propellant	Weight, grs	Muzzle Velocity, ft/sec	Weight, grs	Muzzle Velocity, ft/sec
Viht. N540*	78.0	2553	82.0	2636
Reloder 15*	81.0	2541	85.0	2629
BL-C(2)*	83.0	2496	87.0	2586
IMR 4064*	77.0	2468	81.0	2565
Viht. N140*	76.0	2410	80.0	2512
AA 2520*	71.0	2364	75.0	2465
IMR 3031*	69.0	2375	73.0	2456
IMR 4895*	70.0	2326	74.0	2420

Don Vogel, Rimfire Technical Coordinator, CCI/Speer Operations, with wife Vicki; 300 Win Mag, 180-grain Grand Slam®; 6x6 bull elk.

0.416"	416 TBBC SP	416 TBSS (Solid)
Weight, grains	400	400
Ballistic Coefficient	0.374	0.273
Sectional Density	0.330	0.330
COAL Tested:	3.550"	3.350"
Speer Part No.	1790	1791

	START CHARGE		MAXIMUM CHARGE	
Propellant	Weight, grs	Muzzle Velocity, ft/sec	Weight, grs	Muzzle Velocity, ft/sec
Viht. N540*	77.0	2324	81.0C	2446
Reloder 15*	75.0	2267	79.0C	2380
H4895*	71.0	2242	75.0	2361
IMR 4064*	72.0	2241	76.0	2357
AA 4064*	76.0	2227	80.0C	2330
Varget*	70.5	2220	74.5	2317
IMR 3031*	68.0	2184	72.0C	2296

NOTE: *Trophy Bonded Bear Claw and Trophy Bonded Sledgehammer Solid bullets have unique ballistic behavior compared to conventional bullets. Loads for TBBC and TBSS bullets may not "track" with data for conventional bullets. Use TBBC and TBSS data ONLY for TBBC and TBSS bullets.*

*Maximum Loads should be used with CAUTION • C = Compressed Load • *Magnum Primer used with this powder.*

416 Rigby

Although quite modern in appearance, the 416 Rigby dates to 1911 when John Rigby developed it for use in bolt-action magazine rifles based on the Magnum Mauser action. The unusual 45° shoulder provides positive headspace control and eliminates the need for a belt. The rimless, beltless case means smooth and, more importantly, reliable feeding. A jammed rifle is the last thing you need when facing a Cape buffalo who's having a bad day!

The Rigby is a very powerful cartridge that has taken all the dangerous game species. Typical factory loads move a 400 or 410-grain bullet at 2370 ft/sec. Federal is the only major American ammo maker to offer 416 Rigby ammunition.

The Rigby offers some unique ballistic challenges to those of us who develop reloading manuals. The case is quite large but the operating pressure is not much greater than the 303 British. Powder charges must fill the case but not create excessive pressure.

Only a handful of slow-burning propellants meet this requirement. Faster-burning propellants exceed the operating pressure before velocity reaches factory levels. The very slow-burning propellants run out of case space before normal pressures are reached and, once again, velocity suffers. The propellants shown were the ones that worked best. We found that CCI® 250 Magnum primers were quite satisfactory but, should you use the Federal 215 primer, reduce the maximum charge weights by one grain to maintain normal pressure levels.

The 400-grain Trophy Bonded® Bear Claw® soft point is the choice for thin-skinned African game and the Sledgehammer® solid provides deep, straight-line penetration for tougher critters. The 350-grain Speer Mag-Tip® reduces recoil somewhat and provides a more cost-effective option for practice or for hunting large North American game or African plains animals.

The 416 Rigby proves that good design can serve for years. The maximum average pressure assignment is 52,000 psi.

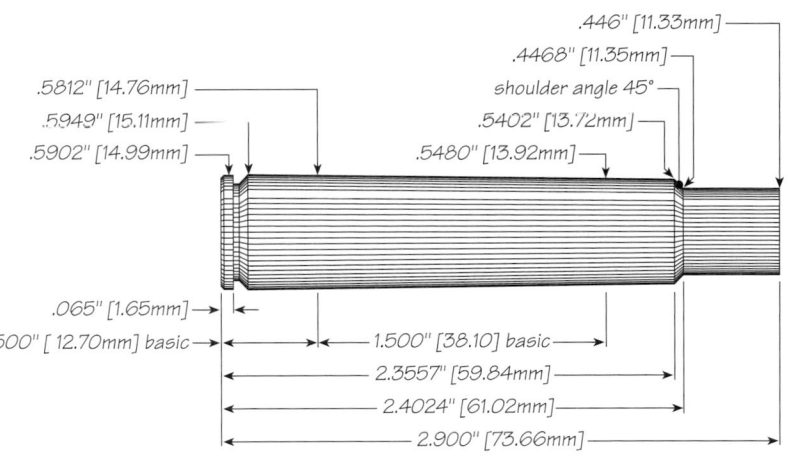

.446" [11.33mm]
.4468" [11.35mm]
.5812" [14.76mm]
.5949" [15.11mm]
.5902" [14.99mm]
shoulder angle 45°
.5402" [13.72mm]
.5480" [13.92mm]
.065" [1.65mm]
.500" [12.70mm] basic
1.500" [38.10] basic
2.3557" [59.84mm]
2.4024" [61.02mm]
2.900" [73.66mm]

Max. Case Length:	2.900"	Cart. Case:	Federal
Trim-to Length:	2.890"	Primer:	CCI 250*
Max Cart. OAL:	3.750"	Test Firearm:	Universal Receiver
RCBS Shell Holder:	#37	Barrel Length:	Krieger 24"

0.416"	416 MT SP
Weight, grains	350
Ballistic Coefficient	0.332
Sectional Density	0.289
COAL Tested:	3.360"
Speer Part No.	2477

	START CHARGE		MAXIMUM CHARGE	
Propellant	Weight, grs	Muzzle Velocity, ft/sec	Weight, grs	Muzzle Velocity, ft/sec
IMR 4831*	98.0	2441	102.0	2577
IMR 4350*	95.0	2424	99.0	2560
Reloder 19*	101.0	2438	105.0	2560
H4831SC*	103.0	2457	107.0	2555
AA 3100*	101.0	2395	105.0	2524
IMR 7828*	101.0	2379	105.0	2510

*Maximum Loads should be used with CAUTION • C = Compressed Load • *Magnum Primer used with this powder.*

0.416"	416 TBBC SP	416 TBSS (Solid)
Weight, grains	400	400
Ballistic Coefficient	0.374	0.273
Sectional Density	0.330	0.330
COAL Tested:	3.600"	3.585"
Speer Part No.	1785	1786

	START CHARGE		MAXIMUM CHARGE	
Propellant	Weight, grs	Muzzle Velocity, ft/sec	Weight, grs	Muzzle Velocity, ft/sec
H4831SC*	100.0	2304	104.0C	2372
Reloder 19*	99.0	2271	103.0	2365
IMR 4831*	95.0	2273	97.0C	2343
IMR 7828*	98.0	2261	100.0C	2319
Reloder 22*	99.0	2238	101.0C	2311
AA 3100*	96.0	2196	98.0C	2252

NOTE: *Trophy Bonded Bear Claw bullets have unique ballistic behavior compared to conventional bullets. Loads for TBBC bullets may not "track" with data for conventional bullets. Use TBBC data ONLY for TBBC bullets.*

Jon Miller, Machinist, CCI/Speer Operations with daughter Jeri and professional hunter Alister Norton; 416 Rigby, 400-grain Trophy Bonded® Bear Claw® bullet; Cape buffalo from Zambia's Luangwa Valley.

*Maximum Loads should be used with CAUTION • C = Compressed Load • *Magnum Primer used with this powder.*

44-40 Winchester *(44 W.C.F.)*

The 44-40 Winchester dates to 1873 when it and the fast-firing 1873 Winchester caught the attention of the shooting world. It was available in both rifles and handguns and was one of the most effective and popular cartridges on the American frontier. When you read of an Old West character armed with a "44," it was probably a 44-40.

Colt produced more 44-40 handguns than any other firm although just about every American gun maker chambered firearms for this cartridge. Its popularity remained strong until World War II when it began to fade from the gun makers' catalogs. However, ammunition and components remain available today, over 130 years after its debut.

At one time the selection of factory ammo was as great as many of today's popular cartridges. It made the transition from black powder to smokeless propellants and several high-velocity loadings were available for strong rifles like the 1892 Winchester. The ammo selection dwindled as the number of new guns built shrank. Eventually only one load remained, a 200-grain JSP at a modest 1190 ft/sec. Winchester and Remington both list the 44-40 in their online catalogs.

Then Cowboy Action Shooting happened. In their quest for authentic gear, CAS shooters have revived the interest in the 44-40. Today you can buy new rifles and revolvers and easily find reloading components.

The nominal bullet diameter for the 44-40 is 0.428", slightly smaller than the more common 44 Special and 44 Magnum bullets. Speer doesn't make a suitable jacketed bullet but RCBS makes bullet moulds that cast excellent projectiles for this old veteran.

The 44-40 has very thin case necks. The reloader must be careful not to deform or crumple them. We strongly recommend that bullets be seated and crimped in separate operations to

44-40 factory soft point and a cast bullet load for Cowboy Action Shooting.

prevent case damage. Keep loaded cartridge length under 1.592" for reliable function in lever guns.

There is a wide variation in chamber and bore dimensions in 44-40 rifles and we did not find a truly representative sporting rifle. We show the velocities from the 24-inch pressure barrel. Expect a drop of about 50-75 ft/sec in a carbine with most propellants.

The industry maximum pressure for the 44-40 is a conservative 13,000 CUP. These loads are within that limit. The start loads were selected to produce at least 10,000 CUP. Do not load lighter than the listed start loads to avoid lodging a bullet in the bore.

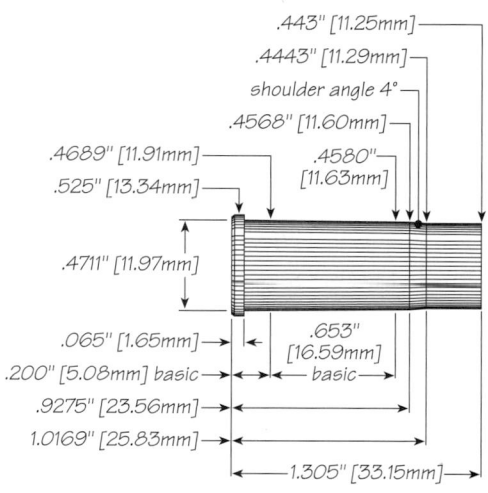

Max. Case Length:	1.305"	Cart. Case:	Remington
Trim-to Length:	1.295"	Primer:	CCI 300
Max Cart. OAL:	1.592"	Test Firearm:	Universal Receiver
RCBS Shell Holder:	#35	Barrel Length:	HS Precision 24"

0.428"	44-200 FN	44-200 CM
Weight, grains	200	200
Lead Alloy	hard	hard
Ballistic Coefficient	0.136	0.124
Sectional Density	0.156	0.156
COAL Tested:	1.590"	1.585"
RCBS Mould No.	82036	82307

Propellant	START CHARGE		MAXIMUM CHARGE	
	Weight, grs	Muzzle Velocity, ft/sec	Weight, grs	Muzzle Velocity, ft/sec
Viht. N350	9.0	1284	9.5	1347
H. Universal	6.5	1236	6.9	1346
AA 5744	16.0	1267	17.0	1335
Unique	7.8	1240	8.6	1326
TiteGroup	5.8	1178	6.3	1239
231	6.4	1156	7.1	1234
700-X	5.5	1148	6.1	1217
Bullseye	5.5	1137	6.1	1206
AA No. 2 Impr.	6.1	1145	6.6	1205
Nitro 100	5.3	1122	5.8	1188
Red Dot	5.4	1097	5.9	1157
American Select	5.5	1093	6.0	1148
Trail Boss	5.9	1041	6.4	1084

NOTE: *We sell bullet moulds, not cast bullets. These bullets were cast in RCBS moulds. Contact your dealer for more information on the RCBS line of premium bullet casting equipment, or visit on the internet at www.rcbs.com.*

---

*Maximum Loads should be used with CAUTION • C = Compressed Load • *Magnum Primer used with this powder.*

44 Remington Magnum

Soon after the 44 Remington Magnum cartridge was introduced in revolvers in 1956, custom gunsmiths saw the potential for the new cartridge in light carbines. They converted old Model 1892 Winchester carbines to 44 Magnum and found they had effective short-range woods rifles.

In 1961, Sturm-Ruger designed its first rifle in 44 Magnum. Derived from the gas-operated action of the military M1 Carbine, the rifle was a semi-automatic with a tubular magazine that held four cartridges. Later Marlin, Winchester and Browning introduced 44 lever action carbines and Remington built 44 Magnum Model 788 bolt-action rifles for a short time.

The various 44 Magnum carbines are excellent whitetail deer and black bear rifles for ranges to 100 yards. Beyond this distance, hitting the target becomes more difficult because of the arched trajectory. Although the 44 Magnum generates wicked recoil in a handgun, it is well behaved in the little carbines and can be easily handled by youngsters or other shooters of light build.

For coyotes and small deer, the Speer 200-grain hollow point works fine. The 210-grain Gold Dot hollow point penetrates deeper and can be used on somewhat larger deer. The best bullets for most deer and black bear are the 240-grain Gold Dot hollow point and soft point and the 270-grain Gold Dot soft point. We prefer the two soft points because they retain more weight after expansion when fired from carbine barrels.

The 300-grain Uni-Cor soft point has a trajectory that's even more arched than 240-grain bullets but it is capable of giving very deep penetration. It is a good choice for black bear or hogs at close range or for dangerous bears only in a life-threatening emergency. However, test for bullet stability before loading a bushel of cartridges. Older 44 Magnum rifles have 1-in-38 inch twist barrels; some of these seem to nicely handle the 300-grain bullet and others fail to stabilize it. Heavy-bullet stability can vary from gun to gun; only testing on paper at realistic hunting distances will answer the stability question for your rifle. Ruger tells us that their current 44 Magnum carbines have 1-in-20 inch twist rates. This should improve accuracy with bullets heavier than 240 grains compared to older slow-twist rifles.

Note that the 300-grain bullet has two cannelures for crimping. The rear cannelure is intended for revolvers only. For proper feeding, the bullet must be crimped in the front cannelure. The loads are already adjusted for the seating depth required.

Do not use the Speer 240-grain TMJ Silhouette Match bullet in any tubular magazine.

Ruger's gas-operated 44 Magnum carbines function best with 240 and 270-grain bullets. We also recommend sticking with the slow-burning handgun propellants for best functioning. A start charge of Unique that works fine in a lever gun may not operate a semi-auto.

The industry pressure limit for the 44 Magnum is 36,000 psi whether the ammo is intended for a rifle or a handgun. These loads are within that limit.

Lab Notes:

The 300-grain loads were tested on copper crusher equipment because the long bullet covers part of the sensing transducer in the newer electronic pressure barrels. Pressure assignments for the 44 Magnum are different between transducer and crusher systems, making the loads for the heavy bullet very close to those for the next lighter one. The 300-grain loads were chronographed in a Ruger Carbine with an 18.5-inch barrel. These loads were thoroughly tested in production firearms and were safe.

Primers

Use CCI® Magnum primers only where indicated. Changing from standard to magnum primers with Alliant 2400 or VihtaVuori N110 can raise pressures up to 5,000 psi without adding much velocity.

Lead Bullets

Do not use lead bullets in Ruger semi-automatic 44 Magnum carbines. Lead particles and lubricate can clog the gas system and cause malfunctions.

Lead bullets of appropriate shape may be used in lever-action 44 Magnum rifles. Cast semi-wadcutter revolver bullets have sharp shoulders and may not feed smoothly. Choose a bullet that loads close to 1.610 inches overall for better feeding.

Many 44 Magnum carbines have shallow rifling. Cast lead bullets should be made from linotype or other hard rifle bullet alloy. Bullets cast from typical wheelweight alloys may not shoot accurately in shallow rifling.

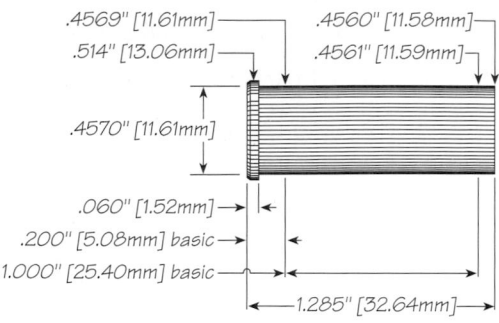

Max. Case Length:	1.285"	Cart. Case:	Winchester
Trim-to Length:	1.275"	Primer:	CCI 300; 350*
Max Cart. OAL:	1.610"	Test Firearm:	Marlin M1894
RCBS Shell Holder:	#18	Barrel Length:	20"

0.429"	44 JHP
Weight, grains	200
Ballistic Coefficient	0.122
Sectional Density	0.155
COAL Tested:	1.590"
Speer Part No.	4425

Propellant	START CHARGE Weight, grs	START CHARGE Muzzle Velocity, ft/sec	MAXIMUM CHARGE Weight, grs	MAXIMUM CHARGE Muzzle Velocity, ft/sec
H110*	26.5	1985	28.5	2116
296*	26.0	1888	28.0	2028
Viht. N110	22.0	1816	24.0	1984
IMR 4227*	26.0	1802	28.0	1914
2400	22.0	1748	24.0	1878
Power Pistol	13.5	1636	15.5	1810
AA No. 7	16.5	1503	18.5	1649
Unique	11.1	1384	12.4	1612

0.429"	44 GDHP
Weight, grains	210
Ballistic Coefficient	0.154
Sectional Density	0.163
COAL Tested:	1.600"
Speer Part No.	4428

Propellant	START CHARGE		MAXIMUM CHARGE	
	Weight, grs	Muzzle Velocity, ft/sec	Weight, grs	Muzzle Velocity, ft/sec
Lil' Gun*	26.5	2044	28.5	2102
H110*	25.5	1879	27.5	2015
296*	25.5	1893	27.5	2009
Ramshot Enforcer*	23.0	1846	25.0	1955
Viht. N110	21.0	1735	23.0	1912
2400	21.5	1734	23.5	1885
AA No. 9	21.0	1768	23.0	1878
Power Pistol	12.5	1522	14.5	1721
HS-7*	14.0	1377	16.0	1576
Unique	10.5	1318	12.5	1520
H. Universal	9.0	1179	11.0	1408

*Maximum Loads should be used with CAUTION • C = Compressed Load • *Magnum Primer used with this powder.*

0.429"	44 JHP	44 GDHP	44 GDSP	44 JSP
Weight, grains	240	240	240	240
Ballistic Coefficient	0.165	0.175	0.175	0.164
Sectional Density	0.186	0.186	0.186	0.186
COAL Tested:	1.575"	1.590"	1.595"	1.575"
Speer Part No.	4453	4455	4456	4457

Propellant	START CHARGE		MAXIMUM CHARGE	
	Weight, grs	Muzzle Velocity, ft/sec	Weight, grs	Muzzle Velocity, ft/sec
H110*	22.0	1674	24.0	1788
Lil' Gun*	21.0	1663	23.0	1780
296*	22.0	1625	24.0	1734
2400	19.0	1521	21.0	1698
Viht. N110	18.0	1545	20.0	1647
IMR 4227*	21.4	1503	23.4	1629
AA No. 9	18.0	1483	20.0	1624
Ramshot Enforcer*	18.5	1486	20.5	1616
AA No. 7	15.5	1369	17.5	1538
HS-7*	13.8	1239	15.8	1423
H. Universal	8.8	1118	9.6	1237

Maximum Loads should be used with CAUTION • C = Compressed Load • *Magnum Primer used with this powder.

0.429"	44 GDSP
Weight, grains	270
Ballistic Coefficient	0.193
Sectional Density	0.210
COAL Tested:	1.595"
Speer Part No.	4461

Propellant	START CHARGE		MAXIMUM CHARGE	
	Weight, grs	Muzzle Velocity, ft/sec	Weight, grs	Muzzle Velocity, ft/sec
H110*	19.0	1468	21.0	1573
Lil' Gun*	17.5	1455	19.5	1557
296*	18.5	1418	20.5	1551
Ramshot Enforcer*	17.0	1353	19.0	1519
Viht. N110	16.0	1363	18.0	1472
AA 1680*	22.5	1290	24.5C	1389
AA No. 9	14.0	1183	16.0	1373
2400	15.5	1232	17.5	1367
IMR 4227	18.5	1251	20.5	1365

0.429"	44 UCSP
Weight, grains	300
Ballistic Coefficient	0.213
Sectional Density	0.233
COAL Tested:	1.585"
Speer Part No.	4463

Propellant	START CHARGE		MAXIMUM CHARGE	
	Weight, grs	Muzzle Velocity, ft/sec	Weight, grs	Muzzle Velocity, ft/sec
H110*	18.5	1347	20.5	1503
296*	18.9	1337	21.0	1499
IMR 4227*	18.9	1194	21.0	1392
AA 1680*	20.7	1148	23.0C	1319

NOTE: *Seat to front cannelure for rifles. See "Lab Notes" for additional information.*

444 Marlin

America's traditional love affair with lever-action rifles took a big hit following World War II. Shooters found that new lever rifles were limited to 35-caliber and less; the powerful big-bore lever guns that had been around since the 1880's were casualties of the war effort.

Marlin remedied this situation in 1964 by reintroducing a large-frame lever-action that was not limited to 30-30 class cartridges. In cooperation with Remington, they developed the new 444 Marlin cartridge and chambered it in the Model 444.

The 444 Marlin is best described as a 44 Magnum case with an extra inch of length. Bore dimensions are the same as the 44 Magnum, so .429" bullets for the handgun cartridge can be used. Factory loads launch a 240-grain jacketed soft point at a nominal velocity of 2320 ft/sec. The handloader can safely achieve this performance level with several propellants, and load heavier bullets that more truly reflect the performance potential of the cartridge.

The 444 is a fine brush cartridge for large deer and black bear out to about 150 yards. The soft point should be chosen over the hollow point to maximize penetration; the hollow point may fragment on impact and cause shallow wounds. The 444 cannot be considered an effective cartridge for larger bear since the factory load bullets are of light construction and, with the exception of the 300-grain Uni-Cor soft point, may not penetrate well enough for reliable grizzly stopping.

The 444 Marlin had a perceived handicap that hurt its acceptance: original rifles had a slow 1-in-38 inch rifling twist with relatively shallow grooves. Armchair ballisticians pronounced that the 240-grain bullet was too light and the slow twist rate could not stabilize the heavier bullets that could put the 444 Marlin on par with 45-70 performance. Although this was probably true for cast lead bullets, the later development of heavy 44-caliber jacketed bullets proved the pundits were not entirely correct.

After Speer introduced its 300-grain Uni-Cor® soft point for 44 Magnum handguns in 1990, we tried it in an early, slow-twist 444 Marlin in our lab inventory. Our rifle fired 1.5-inch groups at 100 yards with this bullet—its best groups ever. Other 444 owners have also reported decent accuracy with the 300-grain bullet. We can't say that every slow-twist Marlin will shoot heavy bullets this well but it's worth a try.

Newer Marlin 444 rifles have a more conventional 1-in-20 inch twist rate; they should handle any of the heavier bullets quite well. With safe handloads, 300-grain bullets in the 444 Marlin can exceed the muzzle energy of 300-grain 45-70 factory ammunition by 700 ft/lbs.

The 300-grain bullet must be crimped in the front cannelure for proper feeding and chambering. The new 270-grain Gold Dot® soft point is probably the best all-around bullet for light to medium game. It is constructed somewhat lighter than the 300 and therefore will show better expansion on deer.

Our early-production Marlin has a 24-inch barrel that exactly matches velocities from the pressure test barrel. New Marlin rifles have 22-inch barrels; this difference should make less than 50 ft/sec difference in velocity with this cartridge.

The loads here represent a complete retest of the 444 Marlin using current components and equipment, and supersede all previously published Speer data. The industry pressure limit for the 444 Marlin is 44,000 CUP; these loads do not exceed that limit.

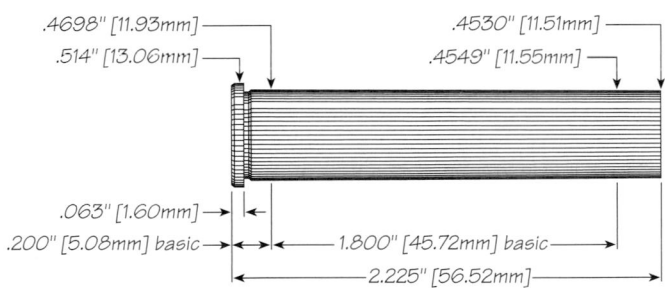

Max. Case Length:	2.225"	Cart. Case:	Remington
Trim-to Length:	2.215"	Primer:	CCI 200; 250*
Max Cart. OAL:	2.570"	Test Firearm:	Marlin M444
RCBS Shell Holder:	#28	Barrel Length:	24"

0.429"	44 JHP	44 GDHP	44 GDSP	44 JSP
Weight, grains	240	240	240	240
Ballistic Coefficient	0.165	0.175	0.175	0.164
Sectional Density	0.186	0.186	0.186	0.186
COAL Tested:	2.530"	2.540"	2.540"	2.530"
Speer Part No.	4453	4455	4456	4457

Propellant	START CHARGE		MAXIMUM CHARGE	
	Weight, grs	Muzzle Velocity, ft/sec	Weight, grs	Muzzle Velocity, ft/sec
Reloder 7	46.0	2184	50.0	2354
Reloder 10X	49.0	2152	53.0	2348
Viht. N133	54.0	2184	56.0C	2319
H322	50.0	2107	54.0C	2307
Benchmark	50.0	2065	54.0C	2267
IMR 4198	40.0	2079	44.0	2245
AA 2015	50.0	2048	54.0	2240
Ramshot X-Terminator*	49.0	2021	53.0	2165
AA 5744	33.0	1833	37.0	2032

Tom Saleen, Director of International Sales on a back country hunt with family and friends. Left to right: Gary Meisner, Tom Saleen, Travis Saleen, Kelly Saleen, Merrill Saleen; 270 Win. 150-grain, Grand Slam®; bull elk, Idaho.

0.429"	44 GDSP
Weight, grains	270
Ballistic Coefficient	0.193
Sectional Density	0.210
COAL Tested:	2.530"
Speer Part No.	4461

Propellant	START CHARGE		MAXIMUM CHARGE	
	Weight, grs	Muzzle Velocity, ft/sec	Weight, grs	Muzzle Velocity, ft/sec
Viht. N133	50.0	2089	54.0C	2256
Reloder 7	43.0	2034	47.0	2216
Reloder 10X	46.0	2042	50.0	2212
H322	46.0	1961	50.0	2148
Benchmark	47.0	1969	51.0	2134
AA 2015	47.0	1948	51.0	2114
IMR 4895	50.0	1904	54.0C	2062
IMR 4198	36.0	1882	40.0	2052
Ramshot X-Terminator*	46.0	1883	50.0	2028

Lab Notes:

"How can I tell if my 444 Marlin has the older slow-twist rifling or the new faster twist?"

It's quite easy. Open the action, verify that the rifle is unloaded and look in the muzzle. A small flashlight or light-colored card laid in the breech makes this easier. Notice the rifling grooves. Slow-twist 444 rifles had 12 grooves; newer rifles with the faster twist (1-in-20 inch) have six grooves.

*Maximum Loads should be used with CAUTION • C = Compressed Load • *Magnum Primer used with this powder.*

0.429"	44 UCSP
Weight, grains	300
Ballistic Coefficient	0.213
Sectional Density	0.233
COAL Tested:	2.515"
Speer Part No.	4463

	START CHARGE		MAXIMUM CHARGE	
Propellant	Weight, grs	Muzzle Velocity, ft/sec	Weight, grs	Muzzle Velocity, ft/sec
Viht. N133	50.0	2129	52.0C	2216
Reloder 7	42.0	2000	46.0	2161
Reloder 10X	43.5	1892	47.5	2086
H. BenchMark	45.0	1811	49.0	2013
H322	44.0	1802	48.0	2033
AA 2015	44.0	1794	48.0	1962
IMR 4198	35.0	1724	39.0	1881
IMR 3031	45.0	1731	49.0C	1995
Ramshot TAC*	44.0	1804	48.0	1930

NOTE: *Seat to front cannelure for rifles. See "Lab Notes" for additional information.*

---

*Maximum Loads should be used with CAUTION • C = Compressed Load • *Magnum Primer used with this powder.*

45 Colt

Although most widely known as a handgun cartridge, the 45 Colt is seeing increased use in rifles and carbines for Cowboy Action Shooting (CAS). The loads here are intended expressly for this sport. They use bullets from the RCBS 45-225-CAV mould or the 45-230-CM mould. Both bullets are profiled to work well in both rifles and handguns, and have proved quite accurate in both.

A CAS cartridge must provide reliable feeding in lever-action rifles. A significant factor in obtaining reliability is paying attention to loaded cartridge lengths. When using the CAV bullet, best results are obtained by trimming all cases to 1.275 inches before loading. If seated in cases that are at the top of the length spec, this bullet may be slightly over the 1.600-inch maximum cartridge length for this cartridge; this could cause feeding problems in some rifles. Trimming cases to uniform length should give reliable feeding with the bullet firmly crimped in the groove provided. The newer 230-grain CM bullet does not require any special attention. It should produce a cartridge of proper length in most cases.

Do not load lighter charges than the listed starting loads under any circumstance. Doing so can cause unacceptably high shot-to-shot variations in velocity and pressure, and increases the risk of a bullet lodging in the bore. Starting loads were carefully chosen to keep the minimum pressures above 12,000 psi, an important factor when loading rather small volumes of smokeless powder in this large case. We also used a substantial roll crimp to increase bullet pull and to prevent bullets from telescoping into the cases in a tubular magazine.

Maximum loads listed here do not exceed the industry limit of 14,000 psi. For additional information on this cartridge, see the Handgun Section.

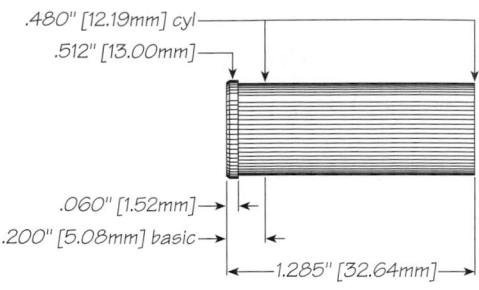

.480" [12.19mm] cyl
.512" [13.00mm]
.060" [1.52mm]
.200" [5.08mm] basic
1.285" [32.64mm]

Max. Case Length:	1.285"	Cart. Case:	Winchester
Trim-to Length:	1.275"	Primer:	CCI 300
Max Cart. OAL:	1.600"	Test Firearm:	Winchester Model 95 "Trapper"
RCBS Shell Holder:	#20	Barrel Length:	16"

NOTE: *We sell bullet moulds, not cast bullets. These bullets were cast in RCBS moulds. Contact your dealer for more information on the RCBS line of premium bullet casting equipment, or visit on the internet at www.rcbs.com.*

0.454"	45-225 CAV	45-230 CM
Weight, grains	225	230
Lead Alloy	hard	hard
Ballistic Coefficient	0.128	0.126
Sectional Density	0.158	0.162
COAL Tested:	1.600"	1.590"
RCBS Mould No.	82081	82308

Cowboy ACTION SHOOTING DATA

	START CHARGE		MAXIMUM CHARGE	
Propellant	Weight, grs	Muzzle Velocity, ft/sec	Weight, grs	Muzzle Velocity, ft/sec
H. Universal	7.8	991	8.5	1086
SR 4756	9.5	1019	10.3	1071
Viht. N350	8.8	962	9.7	1059
Unique	7.8	974	8.5	1043
231	6.5	942	7.2	1029
TiteGroup	5.6	954	6.2	1013
700-X	5.2	913	6.0	1004
Bullseye	5.0	873	6.0	990
Nitro 100	5.1	876	5.9	983
AA No. 2 Impr.	6.4	914	6.8	978
American Select	5.5	882	6.0	936
Trail Boss	5.8	864	6.5	932

*Maximum Loads should be used with CAUTION • C = Compressed Load • *Magnum Primer used with this powder.*

45-70 Government *(Trap-Door Actions)*

These loads are for use in original Trapdoor Springfields (see text), modern Trapdoor replicas, original Sharp's Model 1874, and all rolling block actions.

Of the many large-caliber, rimmed rifle cartridges developed during the last third of the 19th century, only the 45-70 has survived as a standardized cartridge. In fact, it is making a strong comeback after years of only lukewarm interest.

The 45-70 was first introduced in the Model 1873 Springfield rifle, also known as the "Trapdoor" for its unusual single-shot action. Adopted by the U.S. military as the standard service cartridge, most major gun makers in the U.S. had soon developed 45-70 sporters. Like so many other military rifles, surplus trapdoors were sold to civilians and they were quite popular because of their low price.

> **Myth:** *The breechblock hinge pin in the 1873 Springfield action is the sole load-bearing point at peak firing pressure.*
>
> **Fact:** *The hole in the breechblock is oblong so the pin does not bear any significant load during firing. The breechblock bears against the rear of the receiver when the action is closed, providing positive support directly in line with the axis of the cartridge.*

The first military ammo was loaded with a 405-grain lead bullet. Later a 500-grain version was developed to give better long-range accuracy in the rifle. The 405-grain bullet was retained with a reduced powder charge for the light cavalry carbines. Many years later, sporting ammunition was offered with a jacketed soft point bullet.

The Speer 300-grain Uni-Cor hollow point and the 400-grain soft point are the best jacketed bullets for the low velocities of Trapdoor loads. The 350-grain Mag-Tip soft point is a tougher bullet designed for expansion at velocities over 1900 ft/sec and may not expand at trapdoor velocities. Crimping is not necessary in single shots, although we developed these loads using a crimp for consistency. Accuracy with jacketed bullets in original trapdoors can vary from excellent to pathetic and owners should consider lead bullets. Some rifles have barrels that are oversized and many trapdoor barrels are in bad condition from years of neglect.

We show loads for two bullets cast from RCBS moulds. The 325-grain bullet meets the industry spec for cartridge length and will function in lever-action rifles. The 500-grain BPS bullet properly seated is too long for most repeaters, but is an excellent long-range bullet in single shot rifles. We crimped the BPS bullet in the top lube groove. We sized both bullets 0.459" for modern rifles. If you're loading cast bullets in an original Springfield, slug the bore to determine your bore diameter and size bullets accordingly. Some bores are as large as .462 inches; casting with a softer alloy will allow the bullet to "slug up" for a proper fit.

Modern shooters must remember that original rifles are now over 130 years old and that smokeless powder did not exist in 1873. The old rifles must be treated with respect. Current 45-70 factory ammunition is loaded well under the maximum average pressure of 28,000 CUP for safe use in trapdoor actions. The following loads were held to a pressure limit of 21,000 CUP, the same as the highest black powder loads we tested. Our test rifle has a 26-inch barrel instead of the usual 32½-inch barrel of the service rifles. Even so, the velocities with some of the slower-burning propellants were nearly equal to those of higher-pressure loads fired in the Marlin lever rifle (see next section) that has a shorter barrel.

Any original trapdoor Springfield, Sharps, or Remington Rolling Block rifle must be inspected by a gunsmith familiar with these actions before shooting with any ammunition.

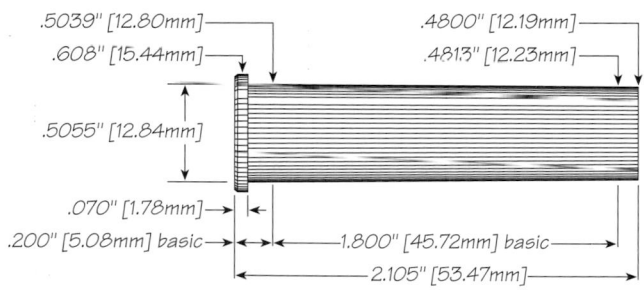

Max. Case Length:	2.105"	Cart. Case:	Winchester
Trim-to Length:	2.095"	Primer:	CCI 200; 250*
Max Cart. OAL:	2.550"	Test Firearm:	Custom single-shot
RCBS Shell Holder:	#14	Barrel Length:	26"

0.458"	45 UC FNHP
Weight, grains	300
Ballistic Coefficient	0.206
Sectional Density	0.204
COAL Tested:	2.530"
Speer Part No.	2482

Propellant	START CHARGE		MAXIMUM CHARGE	
	Weight, grs	Muzzle Velocity, ft/sec	Weight, grs	Muzzle Velocity, ft/sec
Reloder 7	38.0	1668	42.0	1775
Viht. N133	47.0	1622	49.0	1745
IMR 4198	36.0	1527	38.0	1733
H4895	52.0	1486	56.0	1713
AA 2015	45.0	1585	49.0	1686
Reloder 10X	40.0	1552	44.0	1679
IMR 3031	50.0	1465	54.0	1678
IMR 4064	53.0	1575	55.0	1669
Varget	51.0	1499	55.0	1662
IMR 4895	50.0	1458	54.0	1649
Benchmark	49.0	1573	51.0	1648
H322	49.0	1517	51.0	1569
IMR 4227	30.0	1451	32.0	1540
AA 5744	30.0	1360	34.0	1531
SR 4759	26.0	1353	28.0	1482

*Maximum Loads should be used with CAUTION • C = Compressed Load • *Magnum Primer used with this powder.*

0.458"	45 MT SP
Weight, grains	350
Ballistic Coefficient	0.218
Sectional Density	0.238
COAL Tested:	2.715"
Speer Part No.	2478

| Propellant | START CHARGE | | MAXIMUM CHARGE | |
	Weight, grs	Muzzle Velocity, ft/sec	Weight, grs	Muzzle Velocity, ft/sec
AA 2015	46.0	1516	50.0	1715
Viht. N133	44.0	1474	48.0	1700
IMR 4064	51.0	1512	55.0	1633
H4895	48.0	1459	52.0	1625
IMR 4198	32.0	1421	36.0	1608
IMR 3031	48.0	1390	52.0	1585
Reloder 10X	32.0	1347	36.0	1481
SR 4759	26.0	1374	30.0	1463
Reloder 7	31.0	1294	35.0	1458

Shooting Times *magazine reloading editor Lane Pearce has helped Allan Jones with the text review on the last three* Speer Manuals. *Here he shows a fine whitetail from the Stasney-Cook Ranch near Albany, Texas. Lane used a 270 WSM rifle and Federal Vital-Shok® ammo. Photo by Bryce Towsley.*

0.458"	45 FN SP
Weight, grains	400
Ballistic Coefficient	0.259
Sectional Density	0.272
COAL Tested:	2.540"
Speer Part No.	2479

Propellant	START CHARGE		MAXIMUM CHARGE	
	Weight, grs	Muzzle Velocity, ft/sec	Weight, grs	Muzzle Velocity, ft/sec
748*	55.0	1668	59.0C	1799
Viht. N133	43.0	1518	47.0	1750
H4895	49.0	1536	53.0C	1711
AA 2015	42.0	1432	46.0	1620
IMR 3031	45.0	1389	49.0	1584
IMR 4064	47.0	1391	51.0	1502
Reloder 10X	35.0	1309	39.0	1464
IMR 4198	30.0	1195	34.0	1352
H322	37.0	1086	41.0	1285

*Maximum Loads should be used with CAUTION • C = Compressed Load • *Magnum Primer used with this powder.*

0.459"	45-325 FN-U
Weight, grains	325
Lead Alloy	hard
Ballistic Coefficient	0.204
Sectional Density	0.220
COAL Tested:	2.465"
RCBS Mould No.	82045

Cowboy ACTION SHOOTING DATA

	START CHARGE		MAXIMUM CHARGE	
Propellant	Weight, grs	Muzzle Velocity, ft/sec	Weight, grs	Muzzle Velocity, ft/sec
AA 2015	48.0	1799	52.0	2009
H322	48.0	1743	52.0	1931
Reloder 7	46.0	1737	50.0	1915
Varget	52.0	1681	56.0	1867
Viht. N133	45.0	1649	49.0	1839
IMR 3031	47.0	1573	51.0	1804
IMR 4198	35.0	1562	39.0	1729
AA 5744	28.0	1443	32.0	1611
SR 4759	26.0	1314	30.0	1522

NOTE: *We sell bullet moulds, not cast bullets. These bullets were cast in RCBS moulds. Contact your dealer for more information on the RCBS line of premium bullet casting equipment, or visit on the internet at www.rcbs.com.*

0.459"	45-500 BPS
Weight, grains	500
Lead Alloy	hard
Ballistic Coefficient	0.350
Sectional Density	0.341
COAL Tested:	2.765"
RCBS Mould No.	82085

Cowboy

Propellant	START CHARGE		MAXIMUM CHARGE	
	Weight, grs	Muzzle Velocity, ft/sec	Weight, grs	Muzzle Velocity, ft/sec
AA 2015	36.0	1366	40.0	1503
Varget	41.0	1337	45.0	1466
Viht. N133	35.0	1304	39.0	1450
IMR 3031	38.0	1280	42.0	1446
H322	36.0	1309	40.0	1415
IMR 4198	28.0	1244	32.0	1382
SR 4759	22.0	1102	26.0	1325
AA 5744	23.0	1166	27.0	1321
Reloder 7	28.0	1169	32.0	1259

NOTE: *We sell bullet moulds, not cast bullets. These bullets were cast in RCBS moulds. Contact your dealer for more information on the RCBS line of premium bullet casting equipment, or visit on the internet at www.rcbs.com.*

*Maximum Loads should be used with CAUTION • C = Compressed Load • *Magnum Primer used with this powder.*

45-70 Government *(Lever Actions)*

These loads are for use in Marlin Model 1895 rifles; Browning Model 1886 rifles; replica—not original—Sharp's Model 1874 single-shots; and original Winchester Model 1886 lever actions and Model 1885 single-shot actions known to be in good condition.

45-70 ammunition is loaded rather "soft" in deference to trapdoor actions and does not give a true picture of the cartridge's capabilities. Handloading close to the industry pressure limit of 28,000 CUP safely yields significant improvement if you have a modern rifle.

We show loads in this section for the Speer 300-grain Uni-Cor® hollow point and the 400-grain flat soft point. The 350-grain Speer Hot-Cor® is designed for the 458 Winchester Magnum and will not feed properly through most lever-action rifles.

Excellent velocities are possible. The 300-grain bullet posted 2000 ft/sec in the Marlin's 22-inch barrel. That's much better than the fastest 300-grain factory loads in a 24-inch test barrel.

Crimp bullets going into lever guns firmly to hold the bullet securely in tubular magazines. Use the front cannelure if loading the 400-grain bullet. Some lots of 45-70 cases have thin case mouths and you may find that separating the seating and crimping operations will improve the quality of the crimp. Ammo for single shot rifles need not be crimped although it helps ballistic uniformity.

With these loads the 45-70 is powerful enough for any North American game except the dangerous bears provided the shots are less than 200 yards. The construction of the 400-grain bullet is not tough enough to penetrate properly on large bears.

Many original 1885 and 1886 Winchester rifles have seen considerable use (and abuse) since they left the factory. Some have been altered or repaired by persons of questionable competence. Have any original rifle thoroughly checked by a gunsmith familiar with these actions before attempting to fire it with any ammunition.

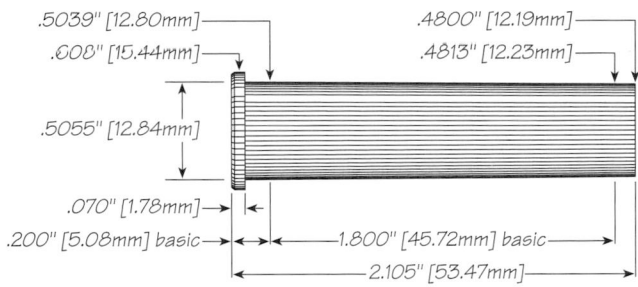

.5039" [12.80mm]
.608" [15.44mm]
.5055" [12.84mm]
.4800" [12.19mm]
.4813" [12.23mm]
.070" [1.78mm]
.200" [5.08mm] basic
1.800" [45.72mm] basic
2.105" [53.47mm]

Max. Case Length:	2.105"	**Cart. Case:**	Winchester
Trim-to Length:	2.095"	**Primer:**	CCI 200; 250*
Max Cart. OAL:	2.550"	**Test Firearm:**	Marlin Model 1895
RCBS Shell Holder:	#14	**Barrel Length:**	22"

WARNING! *Do not use these loads in any rifle action listed in the preceding section, "45-70 Government (Trapdoor)." Never use pointed bullets in any rifle having a tubular magazine.*

Tom Saleen, Director of International Sales, ATK CCI/Speer Operations, with brother Merrill from Kuna, ID; 270 Win 150-grain Grand Slam®; elk, Idaho.

0.458"	300 UC FNHP
Weight, grains	300
Ballistic Coefficient	0.206
Sectional Density	0.204
COAL Tested:	2.530"
Speer Part No.	2482

	START CHARGE		MAXIMUM CHARGE	
Propellant	Weight, grs	Muzzle Velocity, ft/sec	Weight, grs	Muzzle Velocity, ft/sec
Reloder 7	43.0	1846	47.0	2001
H4895	58.0	1737	62.0	1978
Varget	57.0	1790	61.0	1967
Reloder 10X	48.0	1832	52.0	1964
H322	52.0	1674	56.0	1943
IMR 4895	57.0	1721	61.0	1916
IMR 3031	55.0	1689	59.0	1911
Viht. N133	50.0	1691	54.0	1908
IMR 4064	57.0	1731	61.0	1901
XMR 2015	51.0	1704	55.0	1872
Benchmark	52.0	1613	56.0	1864
IMR 4320	55.0	1583	59.0	1822
IMR 4198	39.0	1610	43.0	1762
XMP 5744	36.0	1561	40.0	1742
SR 4759	29.0	1485	31.0	1604

0.458"	45 FNSP
Weight, grains	400
Ballistic Coefficient	0.259
Sectional Density	0.272
COAL Tested:	2.540"
Speer Part No.	2479

Propellant	START CHARGE		MAXIMUM CHARGE	
	Weight, grs	Muzzle Velocity, ft/sec	Weight, grs	Muzzle Velocity, ft/sec
H335*	54.0	1722	58.0	1870
AA 2015	48.0	1684	52.0	1865
Viht. N133	47.0	1671	51.0	1842
748*	58.0	1678	62.0C	1834
H4895	52.0	1668	56.0C	1824
IMR 4064	51.0	1553	55.0	1718
IMR 3031	49.0	1541	53.0	1704
H322	45.0	1437	49.0	1652
Reloder 10X	40.0	1487	44.0	1641
IMR 4320	49.0	1447	53.0	1616
IMR 4198	36.0	1368	40.0	1596
SR 4759 (reduced load)	26.0	1184	30.0	1351

*Maximum Loads should be used with CAUTION • C = Compressed Load • *Magnum Primer used with this powder.*

45-70 Government *(Strong Actions)*

These loads are only for Ruger No. 1 and No. 3 single-shots; modern production Browning Model 1885 single-shots; and M98 Mausers properly converted to fire 45-70 ammunition.

The fact that we have three sections devoted to the 45-70 is testimony to its flexibility and popularity. This section lists loads that approach average pressures of 35,000 CUP for use in only the strongest actions. The top loads with the 350-grain bullet produce over 3500 ft/lbs of muzzle energy.

The continued popularity of the 45-70 resulted in its introduction in the strong Ruger and Browning single-shot rifles some years ago. Custom bolt-action rifles have been built on the Siamese Model 98 Mauser action. These rifles were originally designed to fire a large, rimmed 8mm cartridge with head dimensions similar to the 45-70. The Siamese Mauser has a deep magazine suitable for rimmed cartridges.

For deer hunting, the Uni-Cor 300-grain hollow point will give excellent results. It allows plenty of velocity, and its bonded-core construction means high retained weights not typical of hollow points.

For large bear, the 350-grain Mag-Tip soft point bullet loaded to maximum safe velocity is the best choice. Its tough construction provides sufficient penetration to handle such large game. Because the velocity loss with flat point bullets is rapid, shots should be limited to 200 yards or less. The 400-grain bullet can be used for most non-dangerous game.

The 400-grain bullet has two cannelures; it must be seated to the front cannelure for a loaded cartridge length of 2.54 inches. The 350-grain bullet should be seated to the rear cannelure making it longer than standard cartridge maximums. This is not a problem in single-shot rifles. Because of the heavy recoil, ammunition for bolt-action rifles must be heavily crimped to prevent bullet movement in the magazine. Ammunition for single-shots need not be crimped but doing so improves ballistic uniformity in this cartridge.

These are powerful loads to be used only in the firearms listed at the top of this page. Do not use them in any other 45-70 firearm.

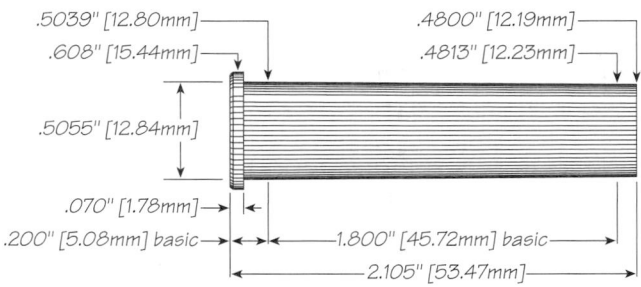

.5039" [12.80mm]	.4800" [12.19mm]
.608" [15.44mm]	.4813" [12.23mm]
.5055" [12.84mm]	
.070" [1.78mm]	
.200" [5.08mm] basic	1.800" [45.72mm] basic
	2.105" [53.47mm]

Max. Case Length:	2.105"	**Cart. Case:**	Winchester
Trim-to Length:	2.095"	**Primer:**	CCI 200; 250*
Max Cart. OAL:	2.550"	**Test Firearm:**	Ruger #1
RCBS Shell Holder:	#14	**Barrel Length:**	22"

WARNING! *Do not use these loads in any rifle action listed in the preceding two sections, "45-70 Government (Trapdoor)" and "45-70 Government (Lever Action)."*

Curtis DeYoung, age 13, son of Mark DeYoung, ATK Senior Vice President; President, ATK Ammunition Systems Group; 30-06; whitetail deer, Albany, Texas.

0.458"	45 UC FNHP
Weight, grains	300
Ballistic Coefficient	0.206
Sectional Density	0.204
COAL Tested:	2.530"
Speer Part No.	2482

Propellant	START CHARGE Weight, grs	START CHARGE Muzzle Velocity, ft/sec	MAXIMUM CHARGE Weight, grs	MAXIMUM CHARGE Muzzle Velocity, ft/sec
Viht. N133	56.0	1973	60.0	2186
Reloder 10X	53.0	2005	57.0	2152
H322	57.0	1921	61.0C	2131
Benchmark	57.0	1905	61.0	2125
AA 2015	57.0	1922	61.0	2107
H4895	62.0	1996	64.0C	2102
Varget	63.0	2008	65.0C	2075
IMR 4895	62.0	1952	64.0C	2048
Reloder 7	50.0	1867	54.0	2039
IMR 4320	61.0	1902	65.0C	2037
IMR 4198	44.0	1812	48.0	2026
IMR 3031	59.0	1921	61.0C	2013
IMR 4064	61.0	1884	63.0C	1992

0.458"	45 MT SP
Weight, grains	350
Ballistic Coefficient	0.218
Sectional Density	0.238
COAL Tested:	2.710"
Speer Part No.	2478

Propellant	START CHARGE		MAXIMUM CHARGE	
	Weight, grs	Muzzle Velocity, ft/sec	Weight, grs	Muzzle Velocity, ft/sec
AA 2015	54.0	1918	60.0	2132
Viht. N133	56.0	1935	60.0C	2104
IMR 4198	46.5	1933	51.5	2049
H4895	57.0	1771	63.0C	2019
IMR 3031	55.0	1818	61.0C	2016
II322	54.0	1873	60.0	2016
IMR 4895	55.0	1834	61.0C	2016
Reloder 10X	46.0	1886	50.0	1983
4064	56.0	1674	62.0C	1910
IMR 4320	58.0	1748	62.0C	1881
SR 4759 (reduced load)	28.0	1354	32.0	1507

*Maximum Loads should be used with CAUTION • C = Compressed Load • *Magnum Primer used with this powder.*

45-70 Government *(Strong Actions)*

0.458"	45 FNSP
Weight, grains	400
Ballistic Coefficient	0.259
Sectional Density	0.272
COAL Tested:	2.540"
Speer Part No.	2479

Propellant	START CHARGE Weight, grs	Muzzle Velocity, ft/sec	MAXIMUM CHARGE Weight, grs	Muzzle Velocity, ft/sec
AA 2015	52.0	1851	56.0C	2018
H4895	56.0	1831	60.0C	1997
Viht. N133	51.0	1832	55.0	1995
H335	58.0	1839	62.0C	1955
H322	51.0	1722	55.0	1927
Reloder 10X	47.0	1771	51.0	1921
IMR 4198	42.0	1631	46.0	1814
IMR 3031	50.0	1567	54.0C	1786
IMR 4064	52.0	1602	56.0C	1761
IMR 4320	53.0	1616	57.0	1758
SR 4759 (reduced load)	28.0	1357	32.0	1536

*Maximum Loads should be used with CAUTION • C = Compressed Load • *Magnum Primer used with this powder.*

450 Marlin

America's long-standing affection for the lever-action rifle is evidenced by the persistent popularity of Marlin's big-bore lever guns. Marlin has sold thousands of 444 and 45-70 rifles, but some people want more power.

The solution was to come up with a new cartridge compatible with existing rifle actions yet safely tolerate higher peak pressures. In a joint development effort, Marlin and Hornady created a new lever gun and cartridge that safely exceeded the performance of the venerable 45-70.

The 450 Marlin cartridge is best described as an updated 45-70. Bullet diameter and case length are the same but the new case has heavier walls to handle higher pressures. The radical change from conventional lever gun cartridges is that the 450 is a rimless, belted case. The head dimensions are nearly all within H&H head specs with one exception. The belt is .032 inches longer than traditional belts so it impossible to inadvertently fire a 450 Marlin cartridge in another magnum rifle.

The 450 Marlin has a maximum average pressure of 43,500 psi, much higher than the 45-70. Industry specs call for a 350-grain bullet at 2125 ft/sec, producing over 3500 ft/lbs of energy. Factory 45-70 loads with 300-grain bullets produce 2350 ft/lbs.

Speer makes two 45-caliber rifle bullets that work in the 450 Marlin. The 300-grain Uni-Cor® HP has a true bonded core and is an excellent choice for most hunting. The 400-grain soft point, although designed for the 45-70, gives a heavier option and we were able to reach velocities of nearly 2000 ft/sec. The Speer 350-grain Mag-Tip bullet is profiled for the 458 Winchester Magnum and will not feed properly in lever action rifles.

Any rifle with a tubular magazine must be loaded with flat point bullets fitted with a cannelure to permit firm crimping. Failing to crimp can cause the bullet to telescope into the case from the pressure of the magazine spring. This will raise pressures and create malfunctions.

The heavy-walled 450 Marlin case has approximately seven grains less capacity than the Winchester 45-70 cases we have in our lab inventory. For that reason, never attempt to use any 45-70 data to derive 450 Marlin loads. Use published load data only.

450 Marlin

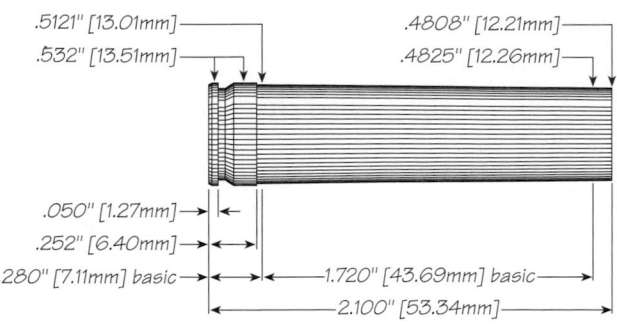

.5121" [13.01mm]
.532" [13.51mm]
.4808" [12.21mm]
.4825" [12.26mm]
.050" [1.27mm]
.252" [6.40mm]
.280" [7.11mm] basic
1.720" [43.69mm] basic
2.100" [53.34mm]

Max. Case Length:	2.100"	Cart. Case:	Hornady
Trim-to Length:	2.090"	Primer:	CCI 200; 250*
Max Cart. OAL:	2.550"	Test Firearm:	Universal Receiver
RCBS Shell Holder:	#4	Barrel Length:	Krieger 24"

0.458"	45 UC FNHP
Weight, grains	300
Ballistic Coefficient	0.206
Sectional Density	0.204
COAL Tested:	2.525"
Speer Part No.	2482

Propellant	START CHARGE		MAXIMUM CHARGE	
	Weight, grs	Muzzle Velocity, ft/sec	Weight, grs	Muzzle Velocity, ft/sec
H322	57.0	2228	61.0C	2405
Reloder 7	52.0	2220	56.0C	2392
Viht. N133	55.0	2206	59.0C	2366
BenchMark	58.0	2229	62.0C	2364
Viht. N120	49.0	2182	53.0	2359
IMR 4198	46.0	2177	50.0	2353
AA 2230*	55.0	2234	59.0	2333
AA 2015	56.0	2132	60.0C	2303
H4227	40.0	2017	44.0	2184
IMR 4895	60.0C	2093	62.0C	2184
AA 5744	36.0	1808	40.0	1996

0.458"	45 FNSP
Weight, grains	400
Ballistic Coefficient	0.259
Sectional Density	0.272
COAL Tested:	2.525"
Speer Part No.	2479

Propellant	START CHARGE		MAXIMUM CHARGE	
	Weight, grs	Muzzle Velocity, ft/sec	Weight, grs	Muzzle Velocity, ft/sec
H322	47.5	1781	51.5C	1990
AA 2230*	47.0	1852	51.0	1978
Benchmark	48.0	1780	52.0C	1974
Viht. N133	46.0	1765	50.0C	1964
Reloder 7	43.0	1819	47.0	1963
Varget	53.0	1821	57.0C	1962
IMR 4198	39.0	1780	43.0	1930
AA 2015	47.0	1735	51.0C	1914
Viht. N120	40.0	1766	44.0	1905
748*	54.0	1745	56.0C	1817
IMR 3031	48.0C	1661	50.0C	1783
H4227	32.0	1563	36.0	1724

*Maximum Loads should be used with CAUTION • C = Compressed Load • *Magnum Primer used with this powder.*

458 Winchester Magnum

In 1956, Winchester gave American sportsmen traveling to Africa their first chance to hunt dangerous game with a factory, large-bore American rifle and cartridge. The 458 Magnum was the first in a successful series of Winchester belted magnum cartridges designed to function in 30-06 length actions. The first rifle for the new cartridge was the Winchester Model 70 African, a deluxe version of the standard Model 70.

The 458 was an immediate success. It turned in impressive performances on African game in spite of its compact size. Equal in power to many of the big English cartridges, the 458 has become a world standard for African hunting. Most U.S. and foreign makers now chamber rifles for the 458, helping it to surpass the expensive English cartridges in popularity.

Factory ammunition is loaded with a 500-grain solid or a 500-grain soft point bullet. Nominal muzzle velocity is around 2025 ft/sec. Like other American cartridges designed to replace traditional British African cartridges, the 458 has less case capacity than its British counterparts but makes up by loading to higher pressures appropriate to modern bolt-action rifles.

Today the 458 is experiencing some competition from a more powerful cartridge, the 458 Lott. Still, the 458 Winchester holds the market advantage at the moment although Ruger has dropped the Winchester version in their bolt rifles in favor of the Lott.

Like other cartridges in this class, the 458 is too much gun with factory loads for North American game other than dangerous bear species. The handloader has more flexibility by reloading lighter jacketed and cast bullets. These also help reduce recoil for more comfortable practice.

The 400-grain soft point, designed for the 45-70 cartridge, has a relatively thin jacket. Rifles with rough bores or a burr at the muzzle may deform the thin jacket enough to cause the jacket to separate in flight. If your rifle is not so affected, it is fine for elk and moose but we prefer the newer 350-grain Mag-Tip for most North American game including large bear. Even though 50 grains lighter, the 350-grain bullet normally out-penetrates the 400-grain due to its tough, heavy jacket that was designed for 458 Magnum velocities.

Stick to 500-grain bullets for the largest and most dangerous African game. Trophy Bonded bullets deliver the world-class strength needed for tough game. Choose either the Bear Claw soft point or the SledgeHammer solid, depending on the target.

Reloading the 458 is the same as for any other straight-wall case. Reducing charges of the listed propellants below our start loads can cause slight ignition delays. If using the ammunition in a bolt-action rifle, bullets should be firmly crimped. The 400-grain Speer soft point was seated to the rear cannelure for a cartridge overall length of 3.12 inches.

The industry maximum average pressure for the 458 Magnum is 53,000 CUP. None of these loads exceed that limit.

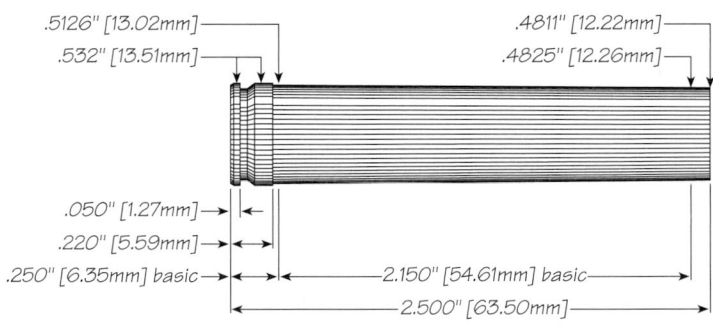

Max. Case Length:	2.500"	**Cart. Case:**	Winchester
Trim-to Length:	2.490"	**Primer:**	CCI 250*
Max Cart. OAL:	3.340"	**Test Firearm:**	Ruger Model 77
RCBS Shell Holder:	#4	**Barrel Length:**	24"

458 Winchester Magnum

0.458"	45 MT SP
Weight, grains	350
Ballistic Coefficient	0.218
Sectional Density	0.238
COAL Tested:	3.105"
Speer Part No.	2478

	START CHARGE		MAXIMUM CHARGE	
Propellant	Weight, grs	Muzzle Velocity, ft/sec	Weight, grs	Muzzle Velocity, ft/sec
AA 2230*	82.0	2499	86.0C	2593
AA 2015*	73.0	2419	77.0C	2560
H322*	78.0	2399	82.0C	2524
IMR 4198*	67.0	2399	71.0C	2505
Viht. N133*	72.0	2233	76.0C	2471
IMR 4895*	76.0	2331	80.0C	2467
H335*	81.0	2227	85.0C	2418
AA 2460*	75.0	2261	79.0C	2371
BL-C(2)*	80.0	2204	84.0C	2343
Reloder 7*	69.0	2186	73.0C	2335
IMR 3031*	71.0	2165	75.0C	2314

Scott DeYoung, age 17, son of Mark DeYoung, ATK Senior Vice President; President, ATK Ammunition Systems Group; 30-06; whitetail deer, Albany, Texas.

0.458"	45 FNSP
Weight, grains	400
Ballistic Coefficient	0.259
Sectional Density	0.272
COAL Tested:	3.125"
Speer Part No.	2479

Propellant	START CHARGE		MAXIMUM CHARGE	
	Weight, grs	Muzzle Velocity, ft/sec	Weight, grs	Muzzle Velocity, ft/sec
AA 2230*	78.0	2290	82.0C	2429
BL-C(2)*	75.0	2269	79.0C	2410
AA 2015BR*	70.0	2269	74.0C	2386
Reloder 7*	70.0	2190	74.0	2316
Viht. N133*	70.0	2174	74.0C	2305
H4198*	60.0	2107	64.0	2231
IMR 3031*	67.0	2055	71.0C	2169
IMR SR4759*	26.0	1262	30.0	1445

*Maximum Loads should be used with CAUTION • C = Compressed Load • *Magnum Primer used with this powder.*

0.458"	45 TBBC SP	45 TBSS (Solid)
Weight, grains	500	500
Ballistic Coefficient	0.340	0.328
Sectional Density	0.341	0.341
COAL Tested:	3.300"	3.250"
Speer Part No.	1790	1791

Propellant	START CHARGE		MAXIMUM CHARGE	
	Weight, grs	Muzzle Velocity, ft/sec	Weight, grs	Muzzle Velocity, ft/sec
H4895*	70.0	2000	72.0C	2059
Ramshot X-Terminator*	70.0	2012	72.0C	2058
BenchMark*	68.0	1996	70.0C	2043
Reloder 10X*	63.0	1988	65.0C	2039
AA 2015*	67.0	1982	69.0	2024
H322*	64.0	1978	66.0	2022
IMR 4895*	70.0	1948	72.0C	2010
Viht. N133*	66.0	1953	68.0C	2002
Reloder 7*	60.0	1936	62.0	1998
IMR 3031*	65.0	1919	67.0C	1976

NOTE: *Trophy Bonded Bear Claw and Trophy Bonded Sledgehammer Solid bullets have unique ballistic behavior compared to conventional bullets. Loads for TBBC and TBSS bullets may not "track" with data for conventional bullets. Use TBBC and TBSS data ONLY for TBBC and TBSS bullets.*

*Maximum Loads should be used with CAUTION • C = Compressed Load • *Magnum Primer used with this powder.*

458 Lott

The 458 Lott started as a wildcat cartridge, gaining popularity in Africa as an improved dangerous game cartridge. Writer and hunter Jack Lott is said to have experienced an "unpleasant encounter" with a wounded Cape buffalo in the 1950's, launching his quest for an improved heavy cartridge for bolt-action rifles.

Although the 458 Winchester Magnum is a fine cartridge, its compact case limits practical muzzle velocity with most 500-grain bullets to just over 2000 ft/sec. Lott and other African hunters and guides felt those bullets should leave the muzzle at 2200 to 2400 ft/sec. In 1971, Lott settled on the full-length (2.850 inch) Holland & Holland belted magnum case. To keep loaded length suitable for bolt-action rifles, he shortened the case to 2.800 inch. That allowed the use of standard 500-grain bullets in magazine rifles.

The 458 Lott became a standard U.S. cartridge in 1998, introduced by A-Square in their semi-custom rifles. A few years later, Hornady began selling ammunition and Ruger offered its M77 Mk2 Magnum bolt-action rifle and its No. 1 Tropical single-shot in 458 Lott. Federal Cartridge also loads the Lott with Trophy Bonded® Bear Claw® soft points and Sledgehammer® solids in its Cape-Shok® ammunition. Industry nominal velocity tables list 500-grain bullets at 2300 ft/sec.

The 500-grain loads can be used for either the Bear Claw or Sledgehammer bullets. Velocities were recorded using Bear Claws. Sledgehammer solids will shoot approximately 50 ft/sec faster than Bear Claws, coming very close to factory nominal velocities.

In addition to Bear Claw and Sledgehammer solids, we show data for the Speer 350-grain Mag-Tip soft point. This bullet is a fine North American option or a nice big cat load for Africa. The 350-grain bullet is plenty tough for such speeds and greatly increases the flexibility of the big cartridge.

We elected to set the 350-grain start loads only two grains under the maximum loads. Long straight cases with light bullets have a rapid pressure drop-off as air space increases. The 500-grain bullets allow a four-grain reduction to get the start charge. We selected propellants that used most of the case. Air space and low pressures can cause inconsistent ignition including apparent delayed firings. With 500-grain bullets, Reloder 15 was the most consistent performer.

Many propellants fill the case, making a powder funnel fitted with a long drop tube, such as the RCBS Quick Change Powder Funnel, almost mandatory. This reduces the amount of force needed to seat bullets. Be sure to apply a firm crimp with all loads shown here.

The loads presented here remain within the 62,500 psi pressure limit established for the 458 Lott.

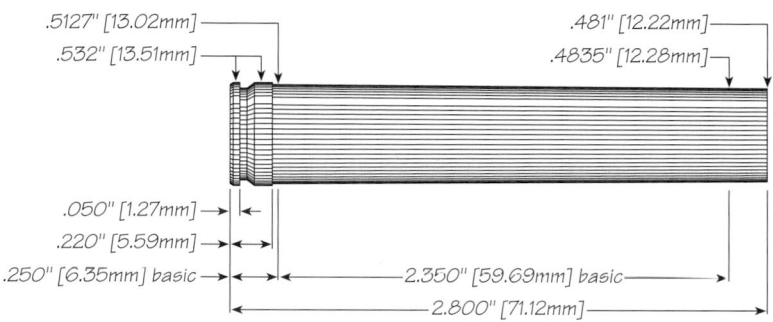

.5127" [13.02mm]
.532" [13.51mm]
.481" [12.22mm]
.4835" [12.28mm]
.050" [1.27mm]
.220" [5.59mm]
.250" [6.35mm] basic
2.350" [59.69mm] basic
2.800" [71.12mm]

Max. Case Length:	2.800"	Cart. Case:	Hornady
Trim-to Length:	2.790"	Primer:	Federal 215*
Max Cart. OAL:	3.600"	Test Firearm:	Universal Receiver
RCBS Shell Holder:	#4	Barrel Length:	Wilson 24"

Mark DeYoung, ATK Senior Vice President; President, ATK Ammunition Systems Group; 45-70 Replica Sharps rifle, Federal ammunition; buffalo, White Horse, South Dakota.

0.458"	45 MT SP
Weight, grains	350
Ballistic Coefficient	0.218
Sectional Density	0.238
COAL Tested:	3.400"
Speer Part No.	2478

Propellant	START CHARGE		MAXIMUM CHARGE	
	Weight, grs	Muzzle Velocity, ft/sec	Weight, grs	Muzzle Velocity, ft/sec
H322*	86.0	2708	88.0C	2749
Ramshot TAC*	91.0	2676	93.0C	2715
BenchMark*	87.0	2672	89.0C	2714
Reloder 10X*	82.0	2662	84.0C	2712
Reloder 7*	79.0	2650	81.0	2699
IMR 4198*	78.0	2645	80.0C	2693
AA 2015*	83.0	2562	85.0C	2603
Viht. N133*	83.0	2534	85.0C	2588

*Maximum Loads should be used with CAUTION • C = Compressed Load • *Magnum Primer used with this powder.*

0.458"	45 TBBC SP	45 TBSS (Solid)
Weight, grains	500	500
Ballistic Coefficient	0.340	0.328
Sectional Density	0.341	0.341
COAL Tested:	3.600"	3.550"
Speer Part No.	1790	1791

	START CHARGE		MAXIMUM CHARGE	
Propellant	Weight, grs	Muzzle Velocity, ft/sec	Weight, grs	Muzzle Velocity, ft/sec
Reloder 15*	76.0	2149	80.0C	2227
Varget*	75.0	2140	79.0C	2225
IMR 4895*	76.0	2125	80.0C	2214
Viht. N540*	78.0	2089	82.0C	2178
Ramshot TAC*	69.0	2037	73.0	2123
Benchmark*	66.0	2024	70.0	2098
Reloder 10X*	63.0	2004	67.0	2097
AA 2015*	66.0	1967	70.0	2085

NOTE: *Trophy Bonded Bear Claw and Trophy Bonded Sledgehammer Solid bullets have unique ballistic behavior compared to conventional bullets. Loads for TBBC and TBSS bullets may not "track" with data for conventional bullets. Use TBBC and TBSS data ONLY for TBBC and TBSS bullets.*

*Maximum Loads should be used with CAUTION • C = Compressed Load • *Magnum Primer used with this powder.*

470 Nitro Express

A century ago the British small arms industry reacted to changes in certain hunting and export regulations. At a time when 45-caliber dangerous game rifles were popular, the British protectorates in both India and the Sudan banned that caliber for hunting. The presumed (and convoluted) reason was that the British overseers feared that anti-government terrorists would pull 45-caliber bullets from sporting ammo for loading in stolen 45-caliber service rifles. The talented inventors working for England's finest gunmakers quickly developed new cartridges including the 470 Nitro Express to get around the 45-caliber ban.

With a 3.25-inch case, the 470 Nitro Express is suitable only for single-shot and double rifles. Still, the cartridge has managed to survive while many of its contemporaries faded into oblivion. It was not loaded in the United States until 1989 when Federal Cartridge® offered the 470 Nitro Express loaded with Woodleigh and Trophy Bonded 500-grain bullets. A nominal muzzle velocity of 2150 ft/sec places the 470 Nitro Express slightly ahead of the popular 458 Winchester Magnum in muzzle energy. Although no U.S. factory rifles are available in 470 Nitro Express, some custom gunmakers have converted Ruger No. 1 single-shot rifles to chamber the big English cartridge.

We offer two world-class 0.474-inch bullets for this venerable cartridge. The Trophy Bonded Bear Claw is a superb bullet for large and dangerous game. Its lead jacket and copper core are 100% bonded for high weight retention and deep penetration. For the toughest game animals, the bonded-bronze Trophy Bonded Sledgehammer Solid provides the ultimate in stopping power. The Sledgehammer's flat nose minimizes deflection for a straight, deep wound cavity.

This is NOT a cartridge for the novice handloader. The massive case requires slow-burning propellants and a nearly full case without exceeding a rather modest pressure limit. You will get best results with slow-burning cylindrical propellants that nearly fill the case like Reloder® 22. Before relying on any handload for hunting, test to ensure that you are getting consistent velocities. For this reason, we strongly recommend a firm crimp even if you are loading for a single-shot rifle. The crimp insures a uniform bullet pull with the modest pressures required of 470 Nitro Express ammunition.

Double rifles must be "regulated" so that bullets from both barrels strike reasonably close to each other. This is a trial-and-error proposition requiring testing of different powder types and charge weights in your rifle. The best starting point for the hand-loader is to start with propellant charges that closely approximate the 2150 ft/sec of factory ammo.

These loads do not exceed the industry maximum average pressure of 41,000 psi.

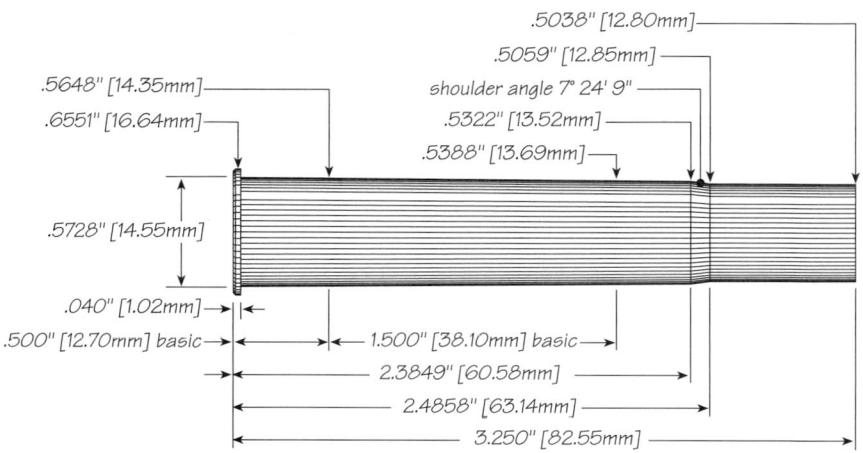

Max. Case Length:	3.250"	Cart. Case:	Norma
Trim-to Length:	3.240"	Primer:	Federal 215
Max Cart. OAL:	3.980"	Test Firearm:	Universal Receiver
RCBS Shell Holder:	Special	Barrel Length:	24"

Lab Notes:

Most British sporting cartridges dating to the beginning of the smokeless propellant era have a nearly straight case and modest pressures. Both exist for the same reason: Cordite propellant.

Cordite is the trade name of an early nitrocellulose propellant that saw nearly universal acceptance by British makers of rifle ammo. Cordite is loaded in stick form; the sticks are as long as the distance from the case web to the base of the bullet for each cartridge in which it was loaded. Loose bundles of sticks make up the proper charge. Getting the bundle into the case during manufacture required a relatively straight case.

Early Cordite had the reputation for producing pressure spikes when fired at ambient temperatures higher than those characterized by England's mild climate. Temperatures in sub-Saharan Africa and most of India, where the cartridges were used, commonly exceeded 100°F causing a significant pressure increase. To avoid gun failures, the pressure at loading was held back so that any temperature-related "spikes" in pressure in hot climates would remain within the design limits of the rifle.

0.474"	470 TBBC SP	470 TBSS (Solid)
Weight, grains	500	500
Ballistic Coefficient	0.330	0.302
Sectional Density	0.318	0.318
COAL Tested:	3.900"	3.885"
Speer Part No.	1795	1796

| Propellant | START CHARGE | | MAXIMUM CHARGE | |
	Weight, grs	Muzzle Velocity, ft/sec	Weight, grs	Muzzle Velocity, ft/sec
Reloder 19*	111.0	2159	**115.0**	2244
Reloder 22*	113.0	2167	**117.0C**	2234
AA 3100*	109.0	2164	**113.0**	2232
Viht. N560*	114.0	2142	**118.0**	2222
H4831SC*	107.0	2080	**111.0**	2167
IMR 7828*	112.0	2089	**116.0C**	2160

NOTE: *Trophy Bonded Bear Claw and Trophy Bonded Sledgehammer Solid bullets have unique ballistic behavior compared to conventional bullets. Loads for TBBC and TBSS bullets may not "track" with data for conventional bullets. Use TBBC and TBSS data ONLY for TBBC and TBSS bullets.*

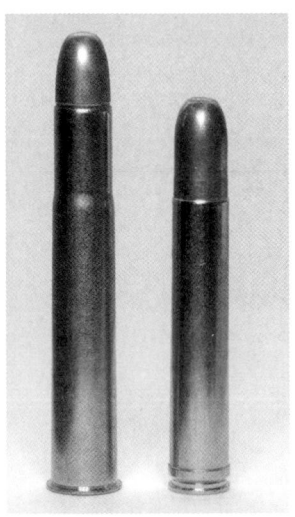

The 470 Nitro Express (left) dwarfs the 458 Winchester Magnum.

*Maximum Loads should be used with CAUTION • C = Compressed Load • *Magnum Primer used with this powder.*

chapter 14

Speer® Handgun Bullets: A Usage Guide

Handgun reloaders enjoy many types of shooting activities that place special demands on their ammunition. Speer® is committed to providing the handgunner with a choice of component bullets to cover most shooting sports. Speer is no newcomer to the field of high-performance handgun bullets. We were the first major bullet manufacturer to provide the reloader with modern handgun projectiles—long before major ammunition companies offered similar designs in factory ammunition.

For years, factory ammunition offered handgunners a very limited choice of bullets. The round nose lead bullet was the standard for revolver cartridges, its form and function virtually unchanged from the earliest days of cartridge firearms. Cartridges for autoloaders were loaded with round-nose, full metal jacket bullets that were believed necessary for reliable feeding. Some target ammunition was loaded with flat-nose "wadcutter" bullets that cut a clean hole in a paper target for maximum score. Because of their low velocities, these bullets were seldom given serious consideration for either hunting or defense use.

It fell to private experimenters like Elmer Keith, Phil Sharpe and Ray Thompson to first suggest that the industry was overlooking the potential of the handgun as a hunting tool. They proved that more powerful loads and improved bullet designs gave quality revolvers the attributes needed to take game.

These men found that loading the 38 Special, 44 Special and 45 Colt cartridges with hard-cast flat point bullets at high velocities (compared to the factory ammo of the time) made a real difference in terminal performance on game. Bullet mould makers offered Keith, Sharpe, and Thompson designs; shooters had to buy the moulds and cast

Elmer Keith

bullets from molten lead alloy. Not everyone had the time or temperament to be a bullet caster.

Other researchers like Jim Harvey of Lakeville Arms realized that the velocity potential was even greater with lighter bullets and, with the right lead alloys, these bullets would give explosive expansion for lighter game and varmints. Harvey developed two versions of light, expanding bullets. The "Prot-X-Bore" was a soft lead bullet with a rigid zinc washer cast (later swaged) onto the base to resist gas cutting and leading. Harvey's "Jugular" bullet was cold-swaged with a partial copper jacket covering the rear half of the bullet. In both designs, soft lead still contacted the bore and lead fouling often occurred unless careful loading techniques were observed.

The high-performance handgun cartridge remained in the realm of the small shop owner or the home bullet caster. Many handgun reloaders did not have access to these bullets through normal channels. In 1958, Vernon Speer began commercial production of a "half-jacketed" revolver bullet that closely followed the original Harvey Jugular design.

Within a year, this bullet was replaced with a superior Speer design that incorporated a longer jacket with a patented edge profile that effectively prevented the lead core from contacting the barrel. This design was offered in .357 and .429-inch diameters for the 38 Special, 357 Magnum, 44 Special and the 44 Magnum in both hollow point and soft point versions. Later, he added bullets of similar design for the 41 Magnum. These accurate, game getting bullets proved extremely popular and several are still in the Speer line today in spite of the many newer designs that have followed.

As you can see, Speer has always been a leader in the handgun bullet field. With modern technology, Speer has continued to provide the handgun shooter with high-quality, high-performance bullets. Today, Speer has nearly 90 different handgun bullets in calibers from 25 to 50.

Speer® Jacketed Handgun Bullets
Uni-Cor®—The Technology at the Heart of the Bullet

Before looking at specific bullet types, we need to look at the underlying technical achievement that keeps Speer the leader in modern handgun bullets—Uni-Cor®. Uni-Cor is Speer's unique technology for manufacturing bonded jacketed pistol bullets that offer the shooter new levels of bullet integrity and accuracy.

Traditional jacketed bullets start as two distinctly separate parts: a lead core and a metal jacket. Bullet jackets are made in one operation and lead cores in another. They are eventually combined to create a finished bullet. Any bullet that starts as two pieces can end up in two or more pieces on impact. This reversion to a two-component state is not what most handgun shooters want whether on the hunt or in a self-defense situation.

Speer's Uni-Cor bullets incorporate a process that builds a true jacket through the electro-chemical bonding of pure copper to a lead core. This bond makes core-jacket separation virtually impossible.

Each bullet begins as a swaged lead core. The lead alloy is chosen for the specific use of the bullet. Expanding bullets have a soft lead core; a harder core is used for target bullets. After swaging and cleaning, the cores are placed in a computer-controlled electro-chemical plating system to receive the copper jacket literally one molecule at a time. Jacket thickness ranges from 0.007 inches to over 0.030 inches depending on the bullet's intended use. Because of the slow and carefully controlled copper deposition, jackets are tougher and more concentric giving bullet integrity not possible with conventional jacketed bullets. The result is better accuracy, more reliable expansion in hollow point and soft point designs, plus incredible weight retention that only true bonded construction can afford.

After the jacket is fully formed, Uni-Cor bullets go through additional operations insuring sharp, square bases and forming other features that determine what kind of Speer bullet it will become. This process also allows very precise diameter control.

Uni-Cor bullets have been put through testing tougher than anything the sport shooter will encounter. In one test, our technicians fired a 9mm Uni-Cor bullet across the edge of a steel plate. The bullet was cut completely in half at 1150 ft/sec, yet the jacket remained firmly bonded to the core sections.

Uni-Cor technology is literally at the core of every Speer Gold Dot®, TMJ®, and Uni-Cor® expanding bullet. Of the 76 Speer jacketed handgun bullets offered at press time, 65 begin with Uni-Cor technology.

Gold Dot®—Serious Technology for Serious Needs

 Speer's Gold Dot is a mission-critical™ bullet that, in hollow point form, is designed to exceed the tough standards for handgun performance set by the Federal Bureau of Investigation. Each bullet is fine-tuned to give optimum expansion and penetration for its intended velocity range. Uni-Cor technology allows Speer to offer the first mass-produced hollow point handgun bullet with a true bonded core. This construction allows Gold Dot bullets to pass through barriers yet function normally when they reach the target.

Gold Dot hollow points typically retain in excess of 95 percent of their weight when fired into ordnance gelatin. The pure copper jacket ensures expansion even at relatively low velocities. Separation of core and jacket, so common with

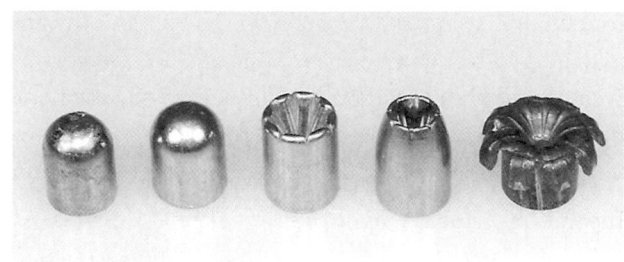

Gold Dot— the manufacturing stages.

other makes of bullets, is a thing of the past with Gold Dot. Because the core cannot slip in the jacket, the expanded bullet holds together for excellent penetration.

Gold Dot technology allows Speer engineers superb flexibility to design bullets for many applications. It is the formation of the hollow-point cavity that sets Gold Dot apart from conventional bullets. Most companies make the cavity in a single operation while doing other forming. Speer has a better way.

We form the cavity in two stages. The first forming stage is dedicated to the cavity alone; no other operations occur in this stage. This preliminary cavity is very large and formed with a series of pleats or folds in its surface, establishing the working surface area of the cavity. We call these folds "memory lines." After final forming, the folds are no longer visible yet remain as permanent guide planes in the lead core. When the bullet expands, it opens evenly following this pre-programmed pattern. By giving the bullet a "memory" early in manufacture, we are able to make bullets that expand symmetrically under conditions that routinely defeat other expanding bullets.

The final cavity shape and volume forms in the final operation. This lets us set the cavity for a particular cartridge and its performance levels. The advanced technology and attention to detail we put into every Gold Dot bullet has made it the most asked-for bullet among law enforcement professionals. Speer ammunition loaded with Gold Dot bullets is a trusted partner for tens of thousands of our nation's first responders.

Gold Dot® Short Barrel Hollow Points

Sub-compact handguns popular for law enforcement and concealed carry place additional demands on bullet design and manufacturing. Standard ammunition designed for full-sized handguns produces less velocity in very short barrels, handicapping the performance of many bullet designs. That's where Gold Dot Short Barrel steps in to bridge the gap. Gold Dot Short Barrel bullets have wide tips and deep cavities—more cavity volume means full expansion at velocities that challenge conventional bullets.

For revolver cartridges, the bullet weights are reduced to allow more velocity and less recoil. This is very beneficial to owners of lightweight 357 and 44 Magnum revolvers. Even though these loads do not produce as much muzzle energy as full-power magnum loads, they are certainly no weaklings; their engineered cavities produce optimum wound cavity profiles for excellent terminal effects.

The .357" 135-grain Gold Dot Short Barrel can be used in both the 38 Special and the 357 Magnum; the 110-grain version is for 38 Special only. Its configuration, necessary for proper 38 Special performance, could suffer in-bore deformation if fired at 357 Magnum pressures.

For 40 and 45-caliber semi-automatic pistol cartridges, Short Barrel bullets are standard weights for reliable function, but have large, cylindrical cavities that mean excellent terminal performance in today's sub-compact pistols.

Gold Dot® Handgun Hunting Bullets

When you build the best law enforcement and self-defense bullets, it's a natural step to use that technology to make the best handgun hunting bullets. Speer has a broad line of fine, bonded-core hunting bullets in 35 through 50-caliber.

We apply the same memory line technology but use heavier jackets tuned for tough game. Our Gold Dot hunting bullets are available in both soft point and hollow point styles to let you match the bullet to the game you seek. Use hollow points on light to medium game, and soft points on large game where greater penetration is required. You get the accuracy, stopping power, and bullet integrity to help you put meat in the freezer.

Other Uni-Cor® Expanding Bullets

Scalable Uni-Cor technology lets us make standard expanding bullets that are as accurate as Gold Dot, but with simpler nose profiles that are excellent for practice and small game hunting. We offer both soft- and hollow-point varieties. Uni-Cor expanding bullets, denoted "UCHP" and "UCSP" in the data tables, typically use the same load data as Gold Dot bullets of the same weight.

This series contains some special purpose bullets. For handgun hunters wanting to enjoy the performance of heavy cast bullets but without the investment in casting equipment, we have 300-grain 44 and 45-caliber Uni-Cor soft points and a 350-grain soft point for the 500 S&W Magnum, all designed for deep penetration and minimal expansion.

TMJ®—The Ultimate Full-Metal-Jacket Bullet

For years full-metal-jacket (FMJ) bullets were the norm for ammunition used in semi-automatic pistols. The nose is completely covered in hard jacket material to allow easy feeding in a wide variety of pistol makes and models. Although now surpassed for hunting and defense purposes by newer hollow point designs, the full jacket bullet is still popular for target shooting and informal practice.

However, most FMJ bullets don't live up to their name. Conventional manufacturing forms a jacket and then inserts a lead core from the rear. This leaves exposed lead at the base along with a folded edge of jacket material. The jacket does not fully cover the core. This exposed lead can be melted by the heat from the burning propellant contributing to airborne lead in indoor ranges. Another disadvantage to traditional "full-jacketed" bullets is that, in near-maximum loads common to a number of modern semi-auto cartridges, the edge of the jacket can be lifted slightly by the expanding gases. This gas damage is rarely symmetrical and accuracy can suffer.

Another problem with old-style open base FMJ's appeared when ported recoil compensators became popular. First fitted to expensive custom handguns, ported compensators are now common in many production pistols and revolvers. Fire conventional FMJ bullets in these guns and lead melts off the base under the heat and pressure of firing and fouls the vents. Such fouling is very difficult to remove.

To overcome all these drawbacks, Speer applied Uni-Cor technology to create the highest evolutionary product among "full jacket" bullets—TMJ®. We swage a hardened lead core and then form a jacket one molecule at a time through chemical electro-plating. The resulting jacket completely and seamlessly encases the lead core including the base. A second swage operation after jacket forming establishes the final profile, reinforces the base and creates a sharp, square heel for accuracy. There are no jacket edges to be deformed by expanding gases and recoil compensators remain lead-free. Shooters in indoor ranges will appreciate the reduction in airborne lead that the protected base affords.

TMJ bullets are available for most popular handgun cartridges between 25 and 50-caliber.

TMJ® Match Semi-Wadcutter

The serious competition shooter will appreciate Speer's TMJ Match bullets for the 45 Auto cartridge. Two weights are offered—a 185-grain bullet for bull's-eye shooting and a 200-grain combat match version for IPSC/USPSA events. Both bullets feature a sharp shoulder for clean, full-caliber holes in paper targets and a long nose for reliable feeding. In the loading data for the 45 Auto, powder charges for the 185-grain bullet are held to the velocities of typical 45 Auto match ammo. The 200-grain bullet is loaded to exceed IPSC major power factor (weight times velocity is greater than 165,000).

TMJ® Silhouette Match

Metallic silhouette competition, whether sanctioned by the International Handgun Metallic Silhouette Association (IHMSA) or the NRA, is one of the most demanding forms of handgun competition. Powerful, accurate handguns are needed to knock down the heavy steel targets at long range. If the plate doesn't fall, it's scored the same as a miss. The wrong bullet can mean you lose the match.

TMJ Silhouette Match bullets start with a hard antimony-lead core. A thick copper jacket is applied with Uni-Cor technology. The bullets then go through a second swaging operation to form the correct point shape for excellent retained velocity and to insure the base is absolutely square with the axis of the bullet.

These specialized Speer bullets have earned a well-deserved reputation for accuracy and plate-toppling power. The tough, fully encased lead core resists initial deformation so the core material remains against the target longer. Unlike conventional full-jacketed silhouette bullets, Speer's version won't extrude lead through a base opening since the base is fully covered.

Our TMJ Silhouette bullet is .357" diameter and weighs 180 grains giving the optimum combination of weight and velocity. See the 357 Magnum Silhouette section for details on using this bullet in a revolver.

Conventional Hollow and Soft-Point Bullets

Speer also manufactures conventional jacketed handgun bullets. These are sometimes called "cup-and-core" bullets; they start as separate copper jackets and lead cores. Speer's knowledge of rifle bullet construction applied the tapered jacket design to handgun bullets. This internal jacket taper limits jacket rollback resulting in better penetration and less chance of a core-jacket separation. Although many of Speer's older cup-and-core bullets have now been superseded by modern Gold Dot and Uni-Cor designs, we retain several of these veterans. Why? Because shooters still like them.

Requiem for a Heavyweight Bullet—the Speer "Flying Ashtray"

Speer shook up the world of 45 Auto shooters in the early 1970's with a newly designed jacketed hollow point bullet. It was a new weight—200 grains—falling between 185-grain match bullets and classic 230-grain FMJ "ball" loads. Its jacket sported internal fluting to assist expansion at modest 45 Auto velocities. It had an unusual nose profile compared to other bullets of its time and gave match-grade accuracy. Yet it wasn't the weight, the fluted jacket, the profile or accuracy that stirred excitement.

It was the hollow point cavity.

In short, it was huge. Hollow points were still taking baby steps when Speer launched the new bullet and shooters had never seen such a cavity. In awe, the shooting public gave the bullet nicknames: the "Flying Ashtray," the "Flying Shot Glass" and, in the South, "Ol' Bucket Mouth."

 "4477" as we called it internally ruled the roost for decades as the most effective projectile for the 45 Auto. We were hard-pressed to keep up with demand for components and loaded ammo. But nothing lasts forever.

Eventually, several factors threatened the absolute monarchy of the Speer 45-200 JHP. When the bullet was designed, the only 45 Autos were military M1911's and their commercial Colt variants. By the late 1980's other companies had designed new 45 Auto pistols. Some had barrels shorter than the Colt Commander, whose typical muzzle velocity was at the lower limit of the Ashtray's expansion capability. Brands other than Colt sometimes had trouble feeding the special bullet designed for the M1911.

Internally, we faced another challenge. The bullet was built on a unique commercial swaging press but the company that made it was out of business and repair and upgrade parts were becoming ever more scarce. It became obvious that the Grand Old Machine was on life support with an unavoidable end clearly in sight. We faced facts: the bullet's clock was running down. We turned to Gold Dot technology to create a worthy successor.

Make that *four* worthy successors.

In making Gold Dot® 45 Auto bullets, we looked to the legacy of the Ashtray as a starting point and considered what we could add without taking anything away. We added true bonded jackets, new profiles suitable for modern firearms,

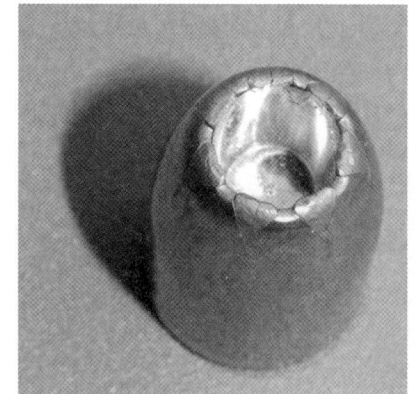

The cavity in the 45 Auto Gold Dot Short Barrel bullet was inspired by the famous "Flying Ashtray."

improved cavities that expand more symmetrically and a range of weights—185, 200, and 230 grains—to cover the needs of every 45 Auto shooter. And that cavity? Gold Dot 45 Auto bullets have retained the "generous cavity" concept. Take a look at the cavity in the new 45-230 Gold Dot Short Barrel bullet; it was inspired by the Ashtray (see photo).

All organizations, including monarchies, have succession plans to insure a smooth transition of power when a leader can no longer serve. A tradition of honoring both the old monarch and his rightful successor led to the famous phrase, "The King is dead; long live the King!" That phrase applies to Speer 45 Auto bullets as well. We say a fond farewell to an old friend and know that its successors will have a long and successful reign.

Considerations Regarding Expanding Handgun Bullets

Most handgun bullets used for hunting and self-defense applications, particularly those of smaller diameter, should be able to increase their diameter after impact. This makes the bullet do its work in stopping the animal, not kicking up dirt behind it. How you achieve that diameter increase depends on how fast the bullet hits the target.

The key to bullet expansion is to balance bullet velocity with the surface area of the expanding portion of the bullet. The rule of thumb is that surface area should increase as velocity decreases. A low-velocity bullet needs more surface area to expand than a high-velocity bullet of the same diameter.

Consider the classic spitzer for high-velocity rifles: although the point is small, high velocity assures full expansion.

These considerations affect your selection of hunting bullets. Although a complex set of factors are involved, we can simplify for most hunting applications. The key number to remember is "1300." Impact velocities under 1300 ft/sec favor

Examples of a low-velocity cavity (l) and a high-velocity cavity(r) in Speer 44-caliber Gold Dot bullets.

the handgun hollow point. However, drive the hollow point much over that point and you risk a bullet loosing too much weight, resulting in a shallow wound that can cripple a fine animal but not put it down. Choose soft points when you expect typical impact velocities to exceed 1300 ft/sec.

As we describe cartridges here we try to suggest when the soft point is more appropriate. You can do some quick checking of downrange velocities using the ballistic tables in the back of this manual or RCBS.LOAD® software on you computer.

Important Note on Jacketed Bullets in Revolvers

Jacketed bullets did not exist when the revolver was invented. Therefore, certain accommodations for the newer projectiles must be employed. Jacketed bullets should not be used in low-velocity revolver loads except as recommended in the loading data. Jacketed bullets create more friction against the barrel wall than lead bullets and more pressure is required to overcome this friction. If the pressure is not great enough, the bullet may become stuck in the barrel causing a risk of gun damage or injury to the shooter. Because it loses some gas from the barrel/cylinder gap, no revolver can use the full power of the powder charge to propel the bullet.

In low-pressure revolver cartridges, do not attempt to reduce powder charges for jacketed bullets below the published starting load. A revolver with excessive barrel/cylinder gap or oversize chamber throats may have bullets stick in the barrel even at the published load levels. If you have any doubts concerning the gap size or chamber throat diameters of your revolver, have them checked before shooting. A barrel/cylinder gap of .008 inches or less is usually satisfactory. A gap in excess of 0.012 inches is out of spec and must be corrected before firing any ammunition type.

Conventional (non-Uni-Cor) rear-jacketed hollow point and soft point bullets can separate the core from the jacket in the barrel at very low velocities. The high frictional force stops the jacket in the bore, but the inertia of the heavy lead core pulls it away and the core exits the barrel. The resulting stuck jacket can be as damaging as a stuck bullet. Most jacketed bullets are intended for high-velocity use. If you want light loads, we recommend the use of lead bullets.

You must never substitute a jacketed bullet with data developed for lead bullets. The increased friction can spike pressures or stick a bullet in the bore.

Lead Handgun Bullets

These are the oldest and most traditional projectiles and remain an inexpensive option for practice or any other high-volume shooting activity. Throughout the history of firearms, two different processes have created lead bullets: swaging (cold-forming) and casting.

Speer® Cold-Swaged Lead Bullets

Before the advent of component bullet manufacturers like Speer, the only component lead bullets were those cast from molten metal. The reloader had to cast them himself or find a small, commercial bullet caster.

Vernon Speer developed lead bullets for handloaders that were formed by cold-forming lead wire into bullets instead of casting from molten lead. This allowed high-speed production and eliminated the voids and slag pockets occasionally found in poorly cast bullets. The first version was a plain-base 38-caliber 148-grain wadcutter that was quickly followed by the 148-grain hollow base wadcutter (HBWC). The deep cavity in the hollow base version allows the low operating pressure typical of 38 Special target loads to expand the base on firing giving a more effective gas seal. For target revolvers, either version works fine; for target semi-autos like the Smith & Wesson model 52, the hollow base version is highly recommended and should be seated flush with the case mouth for reliable feeding.

Later, Speer expanded the line to include round nose, semi-wadcutter and semi-wadcutter hollow points in 38-caliber. A 44-caliber SWC was also introduced along with three 45-caliber bullets—a 200-grain SWC and a 230-grain round nose for the 45 Auto plus a 250-grain SWC for the 45 Colt. Also available is a 98-grain HBWC for target loads in the 32 S&W Long cartridge.

Any lead bullet must be lubricated to pass easily down the gun barrel. In the past, Speer's cold-swaged bullets were lubed by dipping them in a simple mineral wax product. Since *Manual #13* was printed, we changed the lubrication process to one that creates a tough, multi-layer coating that is dry to the touch. It resists the gas cutting that causes barrel leading much better than our previous bullets. In standard leading tests, bullets with the new lube produced so little residue in the barrel that it was difficult to record.

Speer lead revolver bullets (except the two HBWC versions and the 38 round nose) are made with a crimping groove to permit proper seating and crimping. The lead 38 bullet should be crimped over the tapered shoulder. Lead bullets for semi-auto pistols have a shoulder at the transition from the bearing surface to the nose. These bullets should be seated so about 1/32-inch of the bearing surface protrudes above the case mouth; lightly taper-crimping the case completes the process. HBWC bullets should be seated flush with the case mouth before the case is lightly roll-crimped.

Swaged lead bullet velocities should be held to 1000 to 1100 ft/sec. Although some firearms can propel swaged lead bullets at higher velocities without leading, Speer recommends this limit as a good compromise considering the wide range of firearm dimensions, bore finish and propellants available. If you need higher velocities, choose a jacketed bullet or look into hard-cast bullets.

Cast Handgun Bullets

Casting is the melting of a metal alloy and pouring it into a mould shaped to produce a particular bullet style. When the alloy cools and the mould is opened, a fully formed bullet falls out.

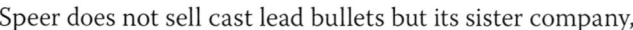

RCBS® Bullet Mould

Speer does not sell cast lead bullets but its sister company, RCBS®, manufacturers a complete line of best-quality bullet moulds and accessories for the hobby bullet caster. Molten lead can be alloyed to greater hardness than cold-swaging on high-speed bullet production equipment permits. Cast bullets often have shapes that are not possible to make with swaged lead bullets. Sharp edges remain sharp because of the harder alloys. Most cast bullet designs have a generous lubrication cannelure that can be filled with large quantities of bullet lube. Hard alloys and the extra capacity for exotic new lubricants allow full-power handgun loads to be developed with many cast bullets.

Economy also plays a big part in bullet casting. Once the cost of the casting equipment has been recovered, the major cost is the lead and lubricant. In some areas, scrap lead such as wheel weights can often be obtained for little or no cost. For maximum hardness, try *linotype* alloy. This mixture of lead, tin and antimony forms very hard bullets that fill out the mould cavities completely. Linotype is often available through printing shops. It can be blended with pure lead or wheel weights to achieve "in-between" alloys. A blend of 50 percent linotype and 50 percent wheel weights yields a very useful magnum revolver bullet alloy.

Cast bullets fall from the mould in a "raw" form; it is fully shaped but oversized. This is by design so that bullets from one mould can be used to service several firearms by adjusting the diameter in a bullet sizing die. Normally, sizing and lubrication are done simultaneously in a special tool known as a *lubrisizer*; RCBS makes one of the best, the Lube-a-Matic®.

For single-shot pistols, size bullets to either exact bore diameter (rounded up to the next 0.001 inch increment) or 0.001 inches over bore diameter. When sizing cast bullets for revolvers, size to the chamber throat diameter, not the bore, whenever possible for best results.

The popularity of Cowboy Action Shooting (CAS) has introduced a new generation of shooters to cast bullets. Jacketed bullets are not permitted in CAS competition. In 1999, RCBS rolled out a line of CAS bullet moulds profiled for the older cartridges. There are eight styles for rifle and handgun from 25 to 45-caliber.

Rifle Cartridges in Handguns

Single-shot hunting handguns such as the Thompson/Center Contender have been very popular in the last two decades. These pistols are as accurate as most hunting rifles and generate surprising velocities considering their barrel lengths. Many are chambered for traditional rifle cartridges. Bullet selection for these cartridges must be matched to the expected velocity levels. A tough bullet like the Grand Slam® in a small-capacity case may give minimum expansion at handgun velocities. With some exceptions, choosing one of the lighter game bullets will keep the velocities high enough for reliable expansion.

For the 22-caliber centerfire cartridges like the 221 Fireball and the 223 Remington, the Speer 50-grain TNT® hollow point is an excellent choice for varmint hunting. Its design allows reliable expansion at velocities as low as 1800 ft/sec. The larger diameter TNT bullets are also excellent varmint bullets in the appropriate cartridges.

For the small 7mm cartridges like the 7mm Remington BR, the 7mm T/CU and the 7-30 Waters, the Speer 130-grain Hot-Cor® spitzers and boat tails are good bullets for small deer. Move to 145-grain bullets for larger deer. The 30-caliber handgun cartridges work well with the 130-grain flat point for similar size game. Larger deer can be taken with Speer 145-grain 7mm bullets or our various 150-grain versions in 30-caliber.

We are often asked if the various Speer rifle bullets will expand at handgun velocities. Most Speer rifle bullets will mushroom to some degree at velocities as low as 1700 ft/sec. If you are shooting at these speeds, the flat point and round nose bullets often give better expansion than spitzers because of their greater frontal area.

Case Forming— A 225 Winchester case (l) is modified by neck expansion (center) and fire-forming (r) to make the 6.5 JDJ pistol cartridge.

Speer Gives You the Bullets You Need

As you can see from this section, Speer is committed to the handgun reloader. You can load no finer hunting or self-defense bullet than Gold Dot. You get a wide selection of weights and style and true bonded-core construction at a popular price and can choose less expensive Uni-Cor expanding bullets, TMJ bullets or lead bullets for economical practice. Whether you're loading a 25 Auto or the massive 500 S&W Magnum, we have a bullet for you.

chapter **15**

Reloading Handgun Cartridges
A Step by Step Guide

Many shooters start reloading handgun cartridges before they move on to loading for a rifle. Economics often plays a major role in choosing to reload for handguns because shooters generally fire more handgun ammo in a session than rifle rounds. Because of the sheer volume of ammunition required, handgun shooters need a cost-effective yet reliable source of ammunition. Unless you're rich, reloading is a terrific solution.

There are other reasons to load handgun cartridges. Cartridges like the 44 Magnum produce heavy recoil with factory ammunition but can be safely handloaded with lighter bullets and powder charges for practice. The handloader has access to a variety of bullet weights and designs that may not be available in over-the-counter ammunition. Custom-tuned ammunition is available to the handgunner, just as it is to the reloading rifleman.

Another factor is improved ballistic performance. Some cartridges developed decades ago for weaker firearms are now chambered in modern versions that can stand substantially higher pressures. Where improved performance is possible, we have noted it in the cartridge introduction or provided a separate section for the high-performance loads.

Most handgun cases are straight-wall designs and loading them is very similar to a rifle case of the same design. Please read chapter 7 of this manual first because there are more similarities than differences between rifle and handgun reloading.

The case must be inspected and then resized (to allow proper chambering) and deprimed. Straight-wall cases are neck-expanded and flared in another operation. Next, the case is primed and then charged with propellant. Bullet seating and crimping followed by final inspection completes the reloading operation.

Like their rifle counterparts, straight-wall handgun cases require three reloading dies.

RCBS® 3-die set for reloading handgun cartridges

Bottleneck handgun cartridges like the 7mm Remington BR and the 221 Remington Fireball are loaded like bottleneck rifle cartridges using a two-die set.

Many high-volume handgun shooters now choose to load on *progressive* or semi-automated equipment. With this sophisticated reloading equipment a reloader can safely produce several hundred rounds per hour. The quality of the ammunition is just as good as that loaded on single-stage equipment. However, the greater complexity of the progressive press requires special attention and experience on the part of the operator. Before using progressive equipment, please read chapter 10, "Automating the Reloading Process".

Step 1—Know Your Firearm and Reloading Equipment

Read the equipment instructions and load data manuals carefully and completely. It is important to understand how your hardware works. Time invested in study now will help avoid headaches and safety hazards later. If you fail to understand the instructions, GET HELP. Most equipment makers have toll-free phone numbers or useful tutorials on their web sites. RCBS® tech support is at 800-533-5000 and on the Internet at www.rcbs.com. Use these resources to insure that you fully understand your equipment before attempting to load.

Understanding your firearm is as critical as understanding the reloading equipment, components and processes. It is your responsibility, and yours alone, to know your firearm and its characteristics. It is vitally important to know what is "normal" based on firing factory ammunition in order to recognize something abnormal that may indicate a problem with your handloads.

Step 2—Case Cleaning (optional)

See chapter 7 for full information on cleaning your cases.

Step 3—Case Inspection

As with rifle cartridges, handgun cases should be inspected for defects before loading. This operation is easier if the cases are clean. Potential defects are similar to those listed in the section on rifle reloading. Case splits in handgun ammunition are usually seen at the case mouth and seldom are longer than 1/8-inch. Even though this is not a safety hazard, these cases should be discarded because they will not allow consistent crimping and bullet pull.

Cases for semi-automatic pistols (especially the 45 Auto) may have bent case mouths from striking the slide during ejection. These cases can be reloaded but the dent should be ironed out with a tapered plug or wooden dowel before sizing. If not removed, the sizing die will turn the dent into a sharp fold and ruin the case. Look for deformed rims in semi-auto cases. These will make inserting the case in the shell holder difficult and could cause a malfunction when fired. Cases with badly deformed rims should be discarded; however, minor burrs caused by the extractor and ejector during previous firings can be quickly removed with a small, fine-cut file.

Step Four—Case Sizing

There are two types of sizing dies for straight-wall cases: steel and carbide. The two types have different adjustment requirements and usage instructions.

Steel Sizing Dies

Standard steel dies are similar to rifle dies because lubricating the cases is required before resizing. Lubricant is applied with a case lube pad in the same manner as for rifle cases. Just as with rifle dies, the sizer die is screwed into the press until it touches the raised shell holder. Unlike bottleneck rifle cartridges, you need not "remove the play" from the press linkage when installing the die. After the cases are sized, you must be sure to remove all lubricant.

Most sizer dies for handgun cartridge incorporate the decapping pin, although in older die sets the decapping pin may be part of the expander die. In either case, the pin should protrude about a quarter-inch below the bottom of the die for proper decapping.

Carbide Sizing Dies

For high-volume reloaders or those of us who don't relish the extra effort of applying and removing case lubricant, carbide dies are a must for sizing straight-wall handgun cartridges. The carbide insert in the steel die body is *tungsten carbide* and is the only portion of the die that touches the case.

Carbide inserts are hard, dense, and highly polished. They reduce sizing friction to such low levels that the need to lubricate the cases is virtually eliminated and produce a smooth, burnished finish. Years ago, carbide dies were practically hand-made and quite expensive. Demand for these premium dies drove manufacturing improvements that reduced production costs. Today,

Cut-away of RCBS® tungsten carbide sizer die. The carbide insert is at the bottom/mouth of die.

there is little reason to forgo the benefits of carbide sizing. The modest additional cost of the carbide sizer is quickly offset by longer case/die life and convenience.

Adjusting the carbide die is accomplished differently from steel dies. Although very hard, carbide is also brittle. If the shell holder strikes the carbide insert, the insert may chip or shatter. To prevent damage to the insert, the die should be installed so that it clears the shell holder by about 1/32-inch (about the thickness of a matchbook cover). You should see a sliver of daylight between the shell holder and the carbide die with the ram fully raised. This small clearance will insure that the die will not be damaged. A carbide die may leave a slight ring just ahead of the case rim. Although this effect is only cosmetic, you can reduce it significantly by backing the die out a little until the ring is reduced. The case body will still be resized enough to permit normal chambering.

Cartridges that routinely operate at high pressure, e.g., the 357 and 44 Magnums, stress the case more than cartridges producing modest pressures. Under these conditions, resizing will often cause a ring regardless of die position. Be sure to size the case far enough back to allow normal chambering. Many reloaders use only new or once-fired brass for maximum loads and afterwards set the cases aside to use for lighter loads.

Step Five—Case Mouth Expanding and Flaring (Straight-wall cases)

The second die in a three-die pistol die set is a combination neck expander and flaring tool. The main body of the expander plug should be at least .001-inch smaller in diameter than the bullet. For heavy-recoil cartridges, the expander may be as much as .003-inch under bullet diameter to ensure the case walls firmly grip a jacketed bullet. Some reloaders keep two expander plugs for a given cartridge—one for lead bullets that is .001-inch undersize and another for jacketed bullets about .002 to .003-inch undersize.

Flaring the case mouth allows you to easily start the bullet into the case. This step is recommended for all straight-wall cases regardless of bullet type and is mandatory when loading lead bullets. A case with little or no flare will cut into the soft alloy of a lead bullet and destroy accuracy. Excessive flare will shorten case life by causing premature mouth splits. The most effective flare is achieved using cases that are trimmed to uniform length. A "short" case (relative to the die setting) will not receive enough flare while a "long" case may be flared too much.

The result of too little mouth flare.

To test for the correct amount of flare, lightly press the bullet you plan to load into the case with your fingers and slowly invert the case. If the bullet enters about 1/32-inch and stays in place, the flare is sufficient.

Step Six—Priming

Priming handgun cases is no different than when reloading rifle ammunition. Therefore, you should review the priming section in chapter 7 to refresh your memory.

CCI® handgun primers give optimum sensitivity when seated .003 to. 005-inch below flush. Failure to follow this simple guideline can result in misfires. Most handguns do not have the firing pin energy available in rifles so anything in the reloading process that optimizes sensitivity will result in more reliable ammunition. Primers must be seated so that the legs of the anvil seat firmly against the bottom of the primer pocket.

High primers can be hazardous in either semi-automatic pistols or revolvers. In semi-autos, a high primer can cause a *slam-fire*—the primer is activated by the slide slamming home. Ignition can occur before the action is fully locked resulting in hot, high-pressure gases being released from the action. Slam-fires may also cause the firearm to "double," firing more than once when the trigger is pulled. Either situation is dangerous.

High primers in revolvers will often cause the cylinder to bind, jamming the firearm. A revolver jammed with live ammo requires great care to disassemble and usually ends the shooting session. When you

RCBS® Universal Hand Priming Tool—A useful tool for the high-volume handgun reloader.

are priming, run your finger across the cartridge base to check for high primers. If detected at this stage (before charging), they can be safely reseated. If you detect a high primer in a loaded round, do not attempt to reseat it without first pulling the bullet and removing the powder.

Handgun shooters seldom worry about cases with crimped primer pockets; however, they do exist. Most U.S. 45 Auto military brass has a light primer crimp that may go unnoticed. Some 38 Special military cases made in Canada (IVI head-stamp) have heavily crimped primers and military surplus 9mm brass is also crimped. For safety's sake, all military 45 Auto, 38 Special and 9mm cases should be processed through the RCBS Primer Pocket Swager before loading.

Because most handguns have less firing pin energy than do rifles, primers for handgun cartridges may have thinner cups. Using a rifle primer in handgun ammo may cause misfires. In addition, rifle primers typically have more priming mix than handgun primers and, if substituted, can cause higher (and potentially dangerous) pressures. However, rifle primers are used for cartridges designed for rifles but later adapted to handguns like the 223 Remington, or for certain high-pressure handgun cartridges. In addition, a large rifle primer is taller than a large pistol primer; unless the case is designed for the large rifle primer, a high-primer condition will occur and you can't correct it. Follow the recommendations of the loading data.

CCI® and Federal® Magnum primers are recommended for charges of slow-burning propellants in large cases. Loads using propellants such as Winchester 296 and Hodgdon H110 were developed with magnum primers as indicated in the data. The magnum primer's longer flame duration insures complete ignition especially in low temperatures. Use magnum primers only when indicated in the data by an asterisk (*) next to the propellant type.

Because of the volume nature of handgun reloading, accessories like the RCBS APS® Priming Tool, the Automatic Priming Tool and Hand Priming Tool are popular options. In addition to speeding the loading operation, these tools allow the reloader to keep primers free of contamination. For a review of priming tool types, see the section on priming in chapter 7.

Step Seven—Powder Selection and Charging

There are many different handgun propellants so you need to carefully consider how you plan to use your handloads before choosing a powder. For light target loads, the "faster" propellants are the best choice to achieve uniform velocities, top accuracy and clean burning. Alliant® Bullseye® is a popular and economical propellant that can be used in most target loads. Other powders such as Winchester 231, Accurate Arms No. 2, and Hodgdon TiteGroup are in this class.

Mid-power loads call for propellants with a "medium" burning rate. There are a number of shotgun propellants that function very well in these loads, including Hercules Unique® and Hodgdon Universal Clays, and handgun propellants like Alliant Power Pistol® and Accurate Arms No. 5. For the heaviest loads and top velocities where the cartridge and gun design permits such power, the slow burning propellants like Winchester 296, Hodgdon H110, Alliant 2400®, VihtaVuori N110, IMR 4227, Ramshot Enforcer and Accurate No. 9 are excellent candidates. Relatively heavy charges of these powders generate the large volume of gas needed to accelerate the bullet to top speed while staying within safe pressure limits.

Slow burning propellants should not be used for light loads, particularly in large cases. These powders operate most efficiently at relatively high pressures. At lower pressures or when significant air space remains in the case, the charge may fail to ignite completely causing the bullet to stick in the bore. If another bullet is fired into the obstructed barrel, it may damage the firearm, and can cause personal injury.

The handgun reloader never starts with a maximum load. He begins with the published starting load and works up incrementally as test firing indicates each increment is safe. If you detect any pressure signs, STOP! You have reached the maximum for your firearm. We discussed pressure signs in general in chapter 5, "Velocity, Energy and Pressure."

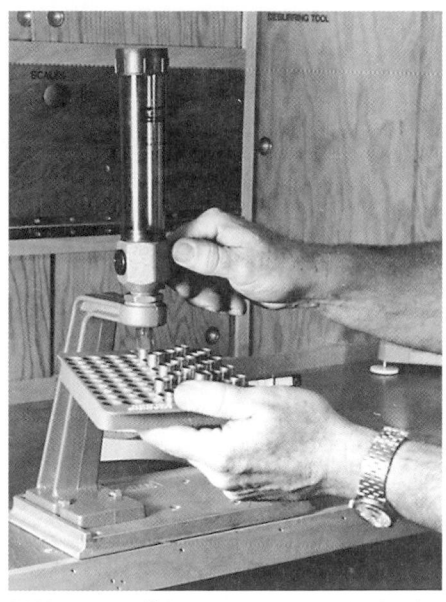

RCBS Little Dandy™ fixed rotor measure was developed for handgun reloading.

In revolvers, one warning of excessive pressure is "sticky" extraction of the case from a revolver's cylinder. Other factors such as soft cases or rough chambers can cause poor extraction with otherwise safe ammo. This combined with badly flattened or loose primers, excessive recoil compared to "normal" or extreme "flyers" on the target probably indicates that you have passed the "safety zone" for your revolver.

It is likewise imprudent to load less than the published starting load. We selected our start loads to remain within the useful pressure range for each cartridge. Overly light loads can lead to bore obstructions, excessive leading, and poor accuracy.

Warning! *Never exceed the maximum loads shown!*

When loading small charges of quick-burning powders, you must be careful to avoid overcharging a case. Small charges occupy very little space so it's possible to get two or more in a case. Reloading rifle ammo seldom poses this hazard because the powders are fairly bulky and a double charge would normally (but not always) overflow the case.

A "squib load" is one in which there is a light or missing powder charge, or when an otherwise normal charge fails to burn completely. A squib load may drive the bullet just far enough into the rifling to cause a bore obstruction. This condition can also occur when a light target load is fired in a revolver with an excessive barrel-cylinder gap. Too much gas is lost through the oversized gap and the next bullet fired can drive into the stuck bullet causing damage to the firearm. Jacketed bullets should not be used in very light loads—especially in revolver cartridges—except as noted in the data. The additional friction against the bore can cause the bullet to stick or to cause the lead core to separate from the jacket. In either circumstance, a dangerous bore obstruction occurs. Any bore obstruction is a hazardous condition.

Normally, the shooter should detect the greatly reduced report and light recoil of a squib load. If this occurs, stop shooting and clear any remaining ammunition from the firearm before removing the obstruction. However, during rapid-fire shooting or when shooting on a busy range, you may not notice the squib. Prevention of squib loads and the double charge *must occur at the loading bench*—not the range. Careful and consistent loading techniques are the best insurance against gun damage or personal injury.

A good technique for preventing charging problems is using two loading blocks. Place one on each side of the powder scale or measure. Primed, empty cases are placed mouth

A deliberate overload blew out this 38 Super case at the feed ramp.

down in one block. With the cases inverted, any debris that may have found its way into the case can fall out. Pick up a case, charge it with powder and put it in the block on the opposite side. After all are charged, pick up the block and visually check each case under a strong light to make certain that it contains ONLY ONE powder charge before seating any bullets.

Because of the high volume of handgun cartridges often loaded at one time, the powder measure is a real time saver for the reloader. If your adjustable powder measure has interchangeable drums, select the smaller size for more accurate metering of small charges. Remember—you must verify that the measure is throwing the correct charge weight by checking it with an accurate handloading scale.

It is common practice when using a powder measure to pass the entire loading block full of primed cases under the mouth of the measure, charging each case in turn. If you use this method, develop a uniform pattern of motion both for moving the block and operating the measure handle. Failure to cycle the measure handle uniformly can result in variations in charge weights that affect the quality of your handloads. Be careful not to miss or double-charge a row of cases.

Again, *you must visually inspect every case.* Inspecting large cases that contain only a small powder charge requires a strong light source and more attention. With either charging method, do not seat bullets until all cases have been charged and visually inspected—twice, if you are prudent.

Current RCBS Uniflow® powder measures come with a special metering screw shaped to accommodate small as well as large charges so no changeover is required. Because many handgun reloaders develop and stick to one basic load, say 2.7 grains of Bullseye for a 38 Special target load, a fixed-cavity measure like the RCBS Little Dandy™ is often used. Twenty-eight different rotors, each calibrated for specific charges of the popular pistol powders, are available for the Little Dandy.

Powder charging should be done at a leisurely pace with frequent inspection to ensure reloading safe ammunition. For additional information on issues of very light loads, read chapter 9, "Reloading for Cowboy Action Shooting."

Step Eight—Bullet Seating and Crimping

Seating bullets and crimping (as required) completes the loading process. Bullet seating depth is fairly critical to proper function in handguns. In revolvers, the cylinder will not rotate if the bullet is seated so long that it protrudes from the cylinder. In semi-auto pistols, feeding will be unreliable if the cartridge is too short yet an overly long cartridge may not fit the magazine or wedge in the rifling. In small capacity, high-pressure cases like the 9mm Luger, excessively deep-seated bullets will raise pressures to potentially unsafe levels. The cartridge overall length that Speer technicians used for load development is shown for each loaded bullet.

If you are loading a bullet with a crimping cannelure, the proper seating length will be achieved by seating to this point. Ammunition for revolvers is typically roll-crimped into the crimping cannelure. Ammunition for semi-automatic pistols is either taper-crimped or requires no crimp at all. Crimping a revolver cartridge is important for proper performance. An uncrimped bullet can unseat due to recoil when other cartridges in the cylinder are fired. If the bullet moves enough, it can tie up the cylinder or its ballistic performance will change. Certain bullets like the Speer 44 and 45-caliber 300-grain Uni-Cor® soft points have two cannelures. Refer to the loading data to determine the correct loading length.

Adjustment for Seating and Roll Crimping

The seater die consists of a die body and a bullet seater plug. Each has a lock ring to preserve its setting. The crimping shoulder is machined into the die body. The position of the seater plug relative to the shell holder determines the bullet seating depth. The position of the die body relative to the shell holder determines the amount of crimp, if any.

Match hollow-base wadcutters must be seated flush for proper feeding in semi-autos.

To set the proper seating depth for a revolver bullet, raise the ram to its highest position and screw the seater die into the loading press until the die body is about a quarter-inch above the shell holder. Screw the lock ring on the die body down against the press but do not tighten the lock screw. Lower the ram, put a bullet on the mouth of a charged case and place it in the shell holder. Raise the ram so the bullet and case enter the die. Continue raising it until you feel a slight resistance. The bullet is now starting into the case.

Lower the ram and check how far the bullet has been seated. The bullet needs to be seated so that almost all of the crimping cannelure is covered by the case mouth. If the bullet needs to be seated deeper, adjust the seater plug in (down) and raise the ram. Check the depth again and repeat the process until the bullet is properly positioned.

To set the crimp, loosen the die body lock ring, screw the seating plug almost all the way out (up) or until it cannot contact the bullet. Raise the ram to its highest point with the cartridge in the shell holder. Slowly screw the die into the press until you feel a slight resistance. The crimp shoulder is now just touching the case mouth. Lower the ram slightly and screw the body in about a quarter turn. Raise the ram fully and check the crimp. Continue until you achieve the desired crimp and then tighten the lock ring on the die body against the press. With the ram at its highest point and the cartridge fully in the die, screw the seater plug into the die body until you feel it touch the seated bullet. Tighten the seater plug lock nut and the die is now set for simultaneous seating and crimping. Check the seating and crimping of the next bullet. Sometimes a slight adjustment is needed to fine-tune the depth and crimp.

This setting procedure works for all RCBS® handgun dies and those of similar design. If you have dies of a different brand, read the instructions from the die manufacturer for proper bullet seating and crimping.

How much crimp is enough? Several factors are involved. When using slow burning propellants, a heavy crimp helps insure that the propellant ignites completely achieving higher velocities and cleaner burning. Light target loads need not be heavily crimped so lightly crimping the case mouth is adequate to prevent bullet jump and gives a "finished" edge for easier chambering. The exception is light loads in large cases. We recommend a heavy crimp to minimize the chances of a squib.

You can have too much crimp. If the crimping operation budges the case, the cartridge may not chamber. Trimming cases to a uniform length is the key to consistent crimping.

More Effective Crimping for the "Big Bruisers"

The extra-wide crimping cannelure featured on all Gold Dot® revolver bullets allows a more robust crimping style known as the *neckdown crimp*. No special or extra equipment is required if you use Gold Dot bullets and RCBS dies. Rather than rolling the case mouth into the groove, neckdown crimping irons a step at the case mouth that nearly fills the cannelure. To produce this crimp, set the seating dies as described in previous paragraphs, leaving only a hairline of the cannelure visible above the case mouth. Seat all the bullets—you will be crimping in a separate operation.

Raise the bullet seating stem to the top of the die. Adjust the die body for crimping, incrementally checking your progress at each step. Continue turning the die in (down) until you produce a step that begins slightly above where the bottom of the groove should be (see photo). Once you've achieved the desired amount of neckdown, tighten the lock ring and crimp the remaining cases.

If you've never done neckdown crimping before, practice on inert rounds until you develop a feel for it. Keeping the revolver cylinder at hand to check for normal chambering helps avoid over-crimping that bulges cases. You can produce a neckdown crimp with any RCBS seating die made since 1984 but you must be using a Gold Dot revolver bullet or one with a cannelure at least 0.060 inches wide and preferably square-bottomed (as opposed to the beveled crimp groove on most cast bullets). This crimp is best used when loading high-recoil revolver cartridges with slow-burning propellants and heavy bullets .

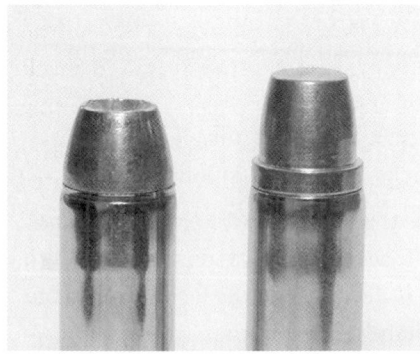

The neckdown crimp (l) compared to the conventional roll crimp (r). Gold Dot revolver bullets allow neckdown crimping in standard dies.

Seating and Taper Crimping for Semi-Autos

Most ammunition for semi-automatic pistols headspaces on the case mouth. If roll crimped, the cartridge may not be firmly supported against the blow of the firing pin and misfires or poor accuracy may occur. Instead, taper crimping is required for cartridges that headspace on the case mouth.

Taper crimping lightly swages the case mouth and part of the case body into the bullet to provide a tighter grip yet still leaves enough of the case mouth edge exposed to permit proper headspacing. Instead of the sharp crimp shoulder found in roll crimp dies, the taper crimp die has a shallow-angle shoulder that performs the necessary forming.

Bullets intended for semi-automatic pistols typically do not have a crimping cannelure. Proper seating depth depends on the individual firearm and its magazine. However, industry standards for maximum and minimum cartridge dimensions take gun variations into consideration. Unless otherwise noted, the data in this manual was developed at cartridge lengths within industry specifications.

Setting the seating depth and taper crimp for a semi-auto pistol cartridge is accomplished by adjusting the seating die like the method for revolver cartridges. Because there is usually no crimping cannelure on the bullet, the length must be carefully checked with a caliper. Once the bullet is seated to the proper depth, setting the taper crimp is accomplished in a manner similar to setting the roll crimp for revolver cartridges except that you will not need to screw in the die body as far. Taper crimping will remove the flare from the case mouth for more reliable feeding. Excessive taper crimping can actually resize the bullet and cause poor accuracy. A light touch is best.

Use the barrel as a gauge to verify that handloads for a semi-auto pistol have the proper taper crimp and seating depth. Unload the pistol, disassemble it and remove the barrel. Clean it and remove any oil. Follow these steps:

- Drop a factory cartridge in the chamber and note the position where the cartridge stops.
- Remove the factory cartridge and drop in a handload. Does it stop where the factory cartridge did?
- Apply thumb pressure to the case head and turn the barrel muzzle-up. Does the handload fall free or does it stick? If it sticks, note the position.

A cartridge that protrudes from the chamber more than the factory cartridge means the case mouth has too much flare or the bullet is seated too long and is jammed in the rifling. A cartridge that sticks in the chamber and is deeper than the factory cartridge has too much crimp. A cartridge that enters the chamber deeper than the factory cartridge but does not stick probably has a short case.

Either extreme is unsatisfactory. Too long means the cartridge may jam or fire at unsafe pressures; too short means it may misfire or be inaccurate. Bullet seating and crimping handloads for semi-auto pistols must be done correctly for reliable and safe performance.

In cartridges that headspace on the case mouth, the case can shorten after many firings. This is due to the blow of the firing pin pushing the case into the chamber shoulder and peening the case mouth. Normally this shortening is not a problem. For critical target work, cases should be of uniform length within industry specifications.

When seating Speer 45 Auto bullets such as the 200-grain lead semi-wadcutter (SWC), the 230-grain lead round nose, and the 185 and 200-grain Uni-Cor TMJ® semi-wad-cutters, leave the shoulder of the bullet exposed about 1/32-inch. This seating position provides improved function, particularly with the lead SWC bullet.

There is a wide variation in handgun bullet profiles. Using a seater punch that's the wrong shape can deform the bullet nose. RCBS die sets for revolver cartridges include seater plugs for wadcutter, semi-wadcutter and round nose bullets. Die sets for semi-auto cartridges have seater plugs for semi-wadcutter and round nose bullets. If none of these plugs fit the profile of the bullet you plan to load, RCBS will adjust theirs if you send them the plug with five sample bullets. If you are using a different brand of die, contact the manufacturer for assistance.

> **Tech Tip:** *When seating lead bullets, lubricant can build up on the seater plug causing successive bullets to seat deeper. Check the seating depth every 20 cartridges to see if the depth is changing. If so, remove the die from the press and clean the plug. A very thin film of light oil or release compound in the seater die and on the plug will help slow the build-up. Don't over-lubricate!*

Step Nine—Final Inspection and Identification

The big commercial makers carefully inspect their ammo—you should also. Before boxing, lay the cartridges on a light-colored cloth and roll them around, carefully examining each one. Look for bulged, dented or split cases, damaged bullets, varying seating depths, irregular crimps or missing primers. As you box the ammo, check once more for high primers by running your finger over the case head. However, *never reseat a high primer in a loaded cartridge!* Set aside any cartridges with high primers for later disassembly and rework.

Cartridges loaded with lead bullets may have excess bullet lubricant on the outside that should be wiped off before boxing. If not removed, the lubricant on the case can cause extra strain on the firearm because the case won't adhere to the chamber walls properly during firing and will thrust harder against the breech.

Before quitting, make sure that all necessary load information is on the ammo boxes. If you are keeping a log, update it at this time.

Rifles Chambered for Handgun Cartridges

The concept of having a handgun and a rifle or carbine that fire the same ammunition dates to the earliest days of cartridge firearms. A rancher in 1880 commonly owned a Colt revolver and a Winchester rifle chambered for the same cartridge. He only needed one type of ammo to fire either firearm. Modern rifles chambered for handgun cartridges fall into two categories:

- **Category 1:** repeating rifles and carbines chambered for powerful revolver cartridges.

- **Category 2:** semi-automatic carbines chambered for compact semi-auto pistol cartridges.

Category One: This includes common lever-action rifles and Ruger gas-operated 44 Magnum semi-autos. The industry pressure limit for a cartridge is the same whether it is to be fired in a rifle or a handgun. A 44 Magnum rifle will use the same loading data as a 44 Magnum revolver. However, there are some considerations the prudent handloader will note:

Bullet shape: A revolver's feed mechanism is the shooters hand—a remarkably adaptive and useful gadget. The feed mechanism in a repeating rifle is a mechanical device that must be carefully fabricated, adjusted and timed to position the cartridge for jam-free feeding. The limitation of this purely mechanical system means that some bullets with sharp shoulders like semi-wadcutters (that easily hand-feed into revolver cylinders) can jam when feeding in a repeating rifle. Cartridges that are considerably shorter or longer than factory ammo may not feed.

Bullet type: an all-lead lead bullet is seldom suitable for gas-operated semi-automatic rifles. Lead shavings and bullet lubricant can foul the gas system and cause malfunctions. Jacketed bullets are the best choice for these rifles.

Propellant type and charge weight: The handloader must remember that the longer rifle barrel will require more gas to expel a bullet than a short handgun barrel. Although pressure is limited by industry standards, the handloader can control the volume of gas through propellant selection. The gas volume produced at firing is proportional to the amount of propellant used. Even though 14.8 grains of Alliant 2400® powder or 7.7 grains of Alliant Unique® under a 158-grain 357 Magnum bullet produce approximately the same peak pressure, the load of 2400 will generate nearly twice the volume of gas and is the better choice when loading for a 357 Magnum rifle.

Category Two: When preparing ammo for a semi-auto carbine chambered for 9mm Luger, 40 S&W and 45 Auto cartridges, the handloader must pay attention to a couple of facts: 1) the cartridges have relatively small cases that limit the amount of propellant, and 2) practically all the carbines are blowback designs, that is, the bolt is not locked. Its mass and a spring or two are all that resist the rearward thrust of firing.

Blowback actions can malfunction or rupture cases with large charges of slow-burning propellants even though the charge weight produces safe pressures. Low-velocity target loads that function fine in a 4-inch handgun barrel may not generate enough gas volume to push the bullet down a barrel that's four times longer.

For these specialized firearms, use load data yielding maximum velocities close to that of factory ammo with the same bullet weight. The 9mm Luger cartridge needs special consideration when you handload for a carbine. 147-grain loads are intended for barrels under 10 inches long. The low propellant weights dictated by the heavier bullet produce relatively low carbine velocities compared to 115 and 124-grain bullets. The risk of a bullet lodging in a carbine bore increases with heavy bullets. You will get the best performance with the lighter 9mm bullets. For the same reason, limit the maximum bullet weight for 40 S&W and 45 Auto carbines to 180 and 230 grains, respectively.

Be sure to test all handloads in your carbine before loading a large number. Load a small test batch first. Watch for feeding or ejection problems and unusual sounds. Be sure to check for bullets lodged in the bore—every pull of the trigger must make a hole in the target. Avoiding very light loads is the best insurance.

Special Considerations for Semi-auto Pistols

The semi-automatic pistol uses the energy from the fired cartridge to operate the action. Ammunition that closely matches the velocities of factory ammunition usually functions best. Very light loads may cause feeding and/or ejection problems because there is not enough energy to operate the mechanism. Heavy loads may accelerate wear or even damage your pistol.

A major factor in pistol wear is slide velocity. The speed at which the slide moves rearward when the pistol fires is proportional to bullet velocity, not pressure. Even though a load produces normal pressures, bullet velocity that is significantly higher than similar factory ammunition increases slide velocity. If the slide velocity exceeds the gun's design limits, battering of the pistol's frame can occur. It is best to keep velocities within the range of factory ammunition.

Low-velocity target loads usually function best with faster-burning propellants. The sharper impulse of these propellants allows the action to operate normally with relatively light charges. Because every firearm is different, you may find that the lighter loads listed may not cycle your pistol. Increasing the powder charge gradually toward the maximum will eventually result in a load which functions reliably.

Taper crimping is best for any cartridge fired in semi-auto pistols. Some cases like the 38 Super Auto are semi-rimmed and, in theory, headspace on the rim. However, this rim is small and there is some variation in dimensions among different brands of cases. Thus, the rim may not control headspace properly. Taper crimping instead of roll crimping insures positive headspace control.

Cartridges for semi-automatic pistols must resist shoving the bullet into the case during feeding. A bullet that telescopes deep into the case will produce excessive pressure. Normally, a properly sized expander plug and a firm taper crimp will provide adequate bullet grip. Test the cartridge by pushing the tip into the edge of a wooden bench. If the bullet moves, you must correct the situation before loading any more cartridges. Case wall thickness often varies considerably. If you are sure that your expander is the correct size but bullets are still loose, try cases of a different brand to see if the setback problem can be eliminated.

9mm Luger Suggestions

The 9mm Luger cartridge was not widely reloaded prior to the 1980's. However, the growing popularity of this cartridge has changed that. Here are some suggestions for better 9mm reloads.

- Cases: the 9mm case is rather small compared to other high-performance pistol cartridges. Propellant space is limited and any variation in capacity among brands may create wide variations in pressure, velocity and reliability. Before reloading, sort your cases by headstamp in addition to brand. Even within one brand there can be variations; however, cases with the same style of headstamp are normally uniform. Mixed cases cause ballistic variations and reloading problems. Neck expansion, bullet seating and crimping operations can all be adversely affected by mixing cases. We strongly recommend you use commercial cases—not military surplus—when reloading the 9mm.

- Bullets: While the industry maximum bullet diameter is .3555-inch, the groove diameter of 9mm pistol barrels varies from .354 inches to .357

inches; the majority of pistols are closer to the larger diameter. The accuracy potential of your pistol depends on how well bullets match the bore diameter. Speer 9mm jacketed bullets are built to the top of the industry diameter specification and are quite accurate in pistols.

Short .355-inch diameter bullets intended for the 380 Auto may not feed in some pistols even with the bullet seated as far out as practical and we did not develop 9mm Luger loads for these bullets for that reason. The best feeding comes with bullets with longer nose sections that were designed for the 9mm Luger.

147-grain bullets are best loaded with a powder having a medium burning rate, such as Unique®, HS-6 and AA No. 7. They generally give better accuracy with heavy bullets than faster powders.

- ◆ Cartridge Length: in the loading data, the cartridge overall length we used for each type of bullet is listed. You must not seat bullets deeper than this without reducing the powder charge. The limited case capacity of the 9mm means that a deep-seated bullet will increase pressures dramatically.

At the Range

Now it's time to test your reloads to see how they shoot. Remember, small groups are more important than the point of impact at this point. Because many handguns have fixed sights or sights that are adjustable for windage only, finding an accurate load that hits close to point-of-aim may require more load development. Here are some suggestions for effective range testing of handgun ammo:

- ◆ *Safety First!* Remember to protect your eyes and ears. Handguns blow unburned powder from the barrel/cylinder gap in revolvers and from the ejection port in semi-autos. Well-designed eye protection keeps this residue out of your eyes. Handguns are quite noisy and continued shooting without proper ear protection can cause immediate and permanent hearing damage. Make certain that the backstop is appropriate and there is an adequate safety zone beyond. A 9mm Luger bullet can travel up to a mile.

- ◆ Testing is more meaningful if you use a rest and shoot from a bench. One of the nicest handgun rests around is the Shooters Ridge® Handgun Rest. It allows the handgun to recoil freely and is steadier than most homemade devices. Sandbags may also be used. When testing powerful revolvers like the 357 and 44 Magnums, be aware that the high-velocity jet of gas from the barrel/cylinder gap can cut through fabric-covered bags and blow sand in your face. When shooting high-pressure revolvers over fabric bags, protect the bags with a layer of heavy leather.

◆ Grip the handgun consistently for each shot. Changing your hand position or grip pressure between shots will change the point of impact and affect the group size. These effects are most apparent when shooting handguns with heavy recoil.

Tech Tip: *When accuracy testing a revolver in single-action mode, you can maintain a constant grip by cocking the hammer for each shot with your non-shooting hand. This helps maintain a consistent grip because it minimizes the need to reposition the revolver for each shot.*

◆ Extended shooting sessions with heavy caliber handguns are more enjoyable if you wear a padded shooting glove. It will distribute recoil and prevent chafing from checkered grips. They are available through several shooting accessory companies.

◆ Firing either two 5-shot groups or one 7-shot group for each load gives an excellent snapshot of the accuracy your ammunition can give. Most handgun accuracy testing is done at 25 yards. However, hunting handguns should be tested at a minimum of 50 yards and even farther if you plan to take longer shots. The bottom line—match your accuracy test distance to the kind of shooting you plan to do.

◆ Relax and take your time when testing loads. Pace your shots and your breathing. Don't try to make a judgment on accuracy based on a group that you shot rapid-fire after jogging back from the 50-yard target holder!

What Kind of Accuracy Should You Expect?

This is a difficult question to answer. The industry accuracy specification for most sporting handgun ammunition is three-inch groups at 25 yards fired from a fixed barrel. A production pistol or revolver of decent quality will generally shoot this well or better if you do your part. Groups under two inches at 25 yards are great in anyone's book from the typical sporting revolver or semi-auto pistol.

However, there are handguns that will routinely shoot well under one inch at this distance. Target handguns for bullseye competition may need to shoot less than two inches at 50 yards. Some rifles can't do that well. Heavy, single-shot pistols like the T/C

Contender and the Remington XP-100 are closer to rifles when it comes to accuracy. It is very possible to shoot 50-yard groups of well under one inch with either gun.

Regardless of what you do as a handloader, each individual firearm will have some finite limit for tightest group size. A good rule of thumb is that the average handgun will shoot better than its owner (many shooters are distressed to discover this!). However, wear, damage or mistreatment can cause even the best-quality handgun to shoot poorly.

Try to be realistic with your expectations. If you are looking for plinking loads, be happy with three-inch groups at 25 yards. However, if you are like most handloaders, knowing that you can adjust loads to give better performance will probably have you back at the bench, looking for just a bit more accuracy.

chapter 16

Speer® Shotshell Capsules

(See the Handgun data section for charge weight information on specific cartridges.)

Speer® component shot capsules have been a popular item for decades for close-range pest control. When first introduced they answered an age-old question among handgun reloaders: "How can I make decent shotshells?"

Historically, making handgun shotshells for close-range pest control was usually more trouble than it was worth. The operations were tedious and the resulting ammo usually performed poorly. When Vernon Speer invested in plastic injection moulding equipment to make bullet boxes, he found the way to make effective handgun shotshells a more pleasant experience.

Speer's solution is a two-part system that allows you to choose a shot size (you supply your favorite shot) and create an easily handled package for loading. We make three diameters so you can load shotshell ammunition for 38 Special, 44 Special and Magnum and 45 Colt. Each capsule has a rigid plastic body and a soft plastic base wad. You fill the capsule body with shot and snap in the base wad. It's then ready to load.

The rigid plastic body is designed to break on contact with the revolver's rifling yet protect the bore from excessive fouling. The flexible base wad is shaped to effectively seal the gas behind the capsule for ballistic efficiency. Standard cleaning methods are usually sufficient to remove any firing residue.

The best way to fill the capsules with shot is to pour a few ounces of pellets into a shallow container. Scoop the capsule through the shot to fill it just below level. You need to leave a little room for the wad to fit. Experiment with a few capsules to find the correct level for the shot size you are using. Overfilling can cause the capsule to break when the wad is inserted. Avoid "loose" loading as well; partially filled capsules will yield inconsistent ballistic performance and poor patterns.

> **NOTE:** *Speer shot capsules are designed for lead shot only. Steel or other lead-free shot can cause bore damage.*

You have control over shot size, but keep a few things in mind. These capsules hold small pellet charges compared to a standard shotgun shell so pattern density is much more important. Smaller shot sizes like #8 and #9 will yield denser patterns perfect for pest control. If you use large shot like #4, your patterns could have pest-size voids.

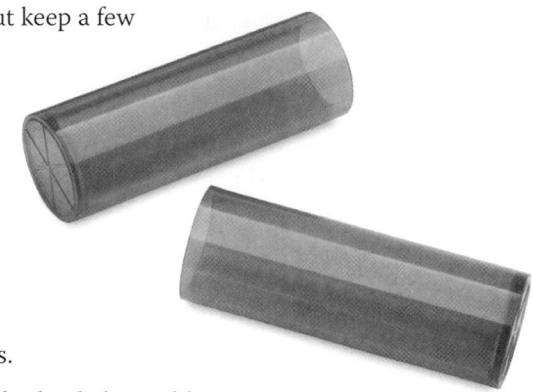

Once assembled, Speer shot capsules load almost like any standard bullet, with a few minor changes:

- Stick to the recommended propellants. Slower-burning propellants give poor results with such light projectiles.
- Seat capsules slowly and with minimum force to avoid breaking them.
- A flat-faced bullet seater plug works best, although a wadcutter-style plug works nearly as well. A deeply cupped punch for seating semi-wadcutter or round nose bullets can break the capsule.
- Crimp lightly separately from seating to avoid breakage.
- We show recommended seating depths in the data section of this manual and you should follow those guidelines. If you seat too long, the blast from one cartridge may break the capsule in an adjacent chamber and spill the payload.
- We found that 38 Special cases originally factory-loaded with wadcutters often have straighter sidewalls internally that better accommodate the long capsules. This reduces seating force—a good thing.
- We urge 357 Magnum shooters to load their shotshells in 38 Special cases. The heavier walls of many magnum cases can present seating problems. There is no real performance advantage to assembling shotshells in the larger case because extra velocity only degrades patterns.

Note that charge weights for shot capsules are relatively light. We limited muzzle velocity to maintain reasonable patterns. When fired from a rifled gun barrel, the shot charge spins and the pattern diameter increases rapidly. The loads we show gave decent patterns in our test firearms. Increasing the velocity will only make the pattern expand faster, reducing its effectiveness. On the other hand, slight charge reductions may improve patterning in your revolver.

Even with careful loading, handgun shotshells are short-range tools when fired from a rifled barrel. Depending on the shot size and the velocity, pattern density thins beyond 15 to 20 feet to the point of being ineffective. Although pattern size will vary with individual firearms and loading practices, we can give you a rough "rule of thumb" for figuring pattern size. Assume one inch of spread for each foot of distance. If you are shooting at ten feet, expect a pattern about ten inches in diameter.

Ported Barrel Advisory

Since our last manual, ported recoil compensators on handguns have graduated from the realm of the custom shops and now come standard on production revolvers. Never fire any shot capsule regardless of make or type in a firearm with a ported barrel or compensator. Slivers of shot or pieces of the capsule can exit the ports at high velocity and in unpredictable directions, causing injury.

Shotshell Capsule Safety

- Show shotshell cartridges the same respect you show any other ammunition product.
- Always be sure of your target and what is beyond. Pellets fired from handgun shotshells can kill at very close range and injure at greater ranges. Pellets may travel up to 200 yards under the right conditions.
- Use only lead shot to fill capsules.
- Avoid shooting at hard surfaces that may cause pellets to ricochet back at the shooter or observers. Although a ricocheting pellet will likely cause only a minor injury to skin, it can cause serious injury to unprotected eyes. Always wear safety glasses when shooting any ammunition.
- NEVER fire any shot cartridge in a handgun fitted with a ported recoil compensator.

Speer® Plastic Training Ammunition
Effective, Low-Cost Training

For years, shooters have sought ways to make accurate, sub-velocity practice ammunition. The most effective way to low-cost training is Speer® Target-38™, Target-44™ and Target-45™ plastic ammunition.

Speer's training ammo for 38/357 and 44 caliber revolvers uses a unique approach. A reusable plastic bullet seats in a reloadable plastic case of special design. The only power required is a large pistol primer; no propellant powder is ever used. You can assemble Speer T-Ammo with a minimum of equipment—even a non-reloader can load and use them.

Speer sells T-Ammo bullets and cases separately because T-cases last a long time but some bullets eventually may be damaged or lost. Separate packaging means you can buy extra bullets to replace those that are lost or no longer serviceable.

Loading is quite simple. Cases come unprimed so you need to insert primers. The loading sequence depends on how you prime the cases.

You use a standard priming tool:

- Install the proper shell holder and a large priming punch in the priming tool.
- Place a large pistol primer on the punch and a T-case in the shell holder.
- Seat the primer, using a minimum of force to avoid damaging the plastic rim. The primer should be flush with the case head.
- Snap a T-bullet into the case with finger pressure. The shoulder on the bullet should contact the case.

You have no priming tool:

- Seat the T-bullet first. This will give you a more effective grip on the case for priming and protect your fingers in the unlikely event that a primer activates when it is seated.

- Place a primer on a hard, smooth surface with the open side up.
- Gently slide the T-case over the primer and press down until the case head touches the flat surface.

When fired T-cases are ready for reloading, you can use a Universal Decapping Die to remove the spent primers. If you are reloading T-Ammo without reloading tools, use a small punch to press out the spent primer. The decapping force required is very low compared to a brass case.

We recommend CCI® 350 Magnum primers for highest velocity. However, misfires may occur in some revolvers due to the thicker primer cup or the cushioning effect of the plastic case. If you get misfires and are certain that the primers were properly seated, try CCI 300 Pistol primers. They are slightly more sensitive than magnum primers in firearms with marginal springs.

Important! *Never use any propellant powder with Speer T-Ammo. Even a small propellant charge could rupture the plastic and vent hot gas into the firearm or onto the shooter.*

T-Ammo with a CCI Magnum primer can post velocities up 400 ft/sec in some revolvers and one-inch groups are possible at twenty feet. However, some makes and models of firearms may not shoot T-Ammo as well as others. T-bullets are designed to ride on the top of the rifling instead of engaging it like a standard bullet. If the bore dimensions of a particular revolver are on the large size, the plastic bullets may not be accurate. If too small, bullets could stick. This is not a condemnation of the guns. They were designed for conventional bullets and perform quite well with them.

A simple test can tell you if your barrel is compatible with Speer T-bullets. Clean and dry the bore and then press a new T-bullet into the muzzle. The bullet should slide in with light finger pressure, but not fall out when the barrel is turned muzzle-down.

T-bullets can be reused if they are fired into a bullet trap that cushions the impact. A wooden or cardboard box with strips of carpet or rubber inner tube hung over the open end and padded with carpet at the back will stop the bullets without deforming them. With care, bullets can be used twenty times or more.

The Target-45 system is slightly different from the 38 and 44 versions. T-45 bullets are loaded in standard brass 45 Auto cases. Bullets are pressed into a primed, resized case with finger pressure until they stop. If primer setback occurs, open the flash hole in the case with a 7/64" drill. Do not use these modified cases for conventional loading. Mark them with a bright, permanent color or notch the rims with a file to clearly identify them as practice cases.

The resulting T-45 ammo will often feed from a M1911 magazine if cycled manually. However, the cartridges do not generate enough energy to operate the action so you need to rack the slide between shots.

Because they produce little or no recoil, T-bullets will usually strike the target below the point of aim used with conventional ammunition. If you don't care to alter your sight settings, paste an auxiliary aiming point on the target to compensate for the lack of recoil.

T-45 bullets perform best when you sort cases by make. Mixed cases can cause variations in seating depth that can degrade accuracy.

Keep the barrel and chambers clean. Primers fired without powder leave residue that must be removed regularly to maintain accuracy and reliability. We recommend dry-brushing the bore and chambers after every 12 to 20 shots. Clean the firearm thoroughly at the end of each shooting session.

Safety With Speer T-Ammo

- Speer T-Ammo is not a toy! It can injure skin and unprotected eyes. Show it the same respect you show any other ammunition product.

- Do not attempt to load T-45 bullets in the 45 Colt cartridge case. The bullet may not seat close enough to the primer pocket, resulting in excessive air space that can cause a bullet to stick in the bore. T-45 bullets are dimensioned for the 45 Auto case only.

- Wear eye and ear protection. Primers alone make a loud noise and repeated exposure can damage hearing. All ammunition emits tiny particles of residue; wear approved safety/shooting glasses while loading and shooting T-Ammo. Provide eye and ear protection to anyone in the area while you are shooting.

- All component primers emit lead residue. We recommend that Speer T-Ammo be used in a well-ventilated area with a smooth, easily cleaned floor such as a garage. Never fire them in a carpeted area. It is nearly impossible to completely remove particulate lead residue from carpeting. Wash your hands thoroughly after shooting. See chapter 6, "Safety in Reloading" for additional information on minimizing lead exposure while reloading and shooting.

- Always use Speer T-Ammo in accordance with applicable local ordinances.

Why Ballisticians Get Gray
By David Andrews

Editor's Note: *Dave Andrews wrote and produced* Speer Manuals 6 *through* 11. *This article was originally featured in the* Speer Reloading Manual Number 9 *published in 1974. It was my intention to write a new section discussing velocity variation among different firearms chambered for the same cartridge. Then I re-read Dave's article and decided that time hasn't aged this information at all. Dave's insightful essay holds as true today as it did in 1974. Thanks to writer Dick Metcalf for his "gentle" urging to reprint this.*

> *"Dear Ballistician:*
>
> *Your reloading manual is all wrong! You say on page 713 that 11.2 grains of Super-Duper powder will push the 125-grain bullet at 1468 fps. My barrel length is the same as yours, but when I tried this load and had my friend chronograph it the velocity was only 1411 fps. Why are you so far off?"*

Letters like this imaginary one are all too common. In an effort to illustrate one reason for such velocity differences, the Speer Ballistic Laboratory selected three lots of 357 Magnum ammunition in different bullet weights. These particular lots of ammunition were selected because of their uniformity, not because of high velocity. This ammunition was fired in all of the 357 Magnum guns available to the lab at the time.

The different handguns were all tested in the same manner with the gun muzzle elevated and then gently lowered to the horizontal for each shot. Every effort was made to make the results as accurate as possible.

The table shows the average velocities of the three different bullet weights in each of the guns tested. Note that in the standard 10" test barrel, made to tight ammunition industry specifications, the extreme variation (EV) in the velocities ranged from 48 fps for the 125-grain hollow point bullet, to 38 fps for the 158-grain soft point bullet.

Why Ballistician Get Gray

Using the 6-inch barrel revolvers as an example, the EV between all 125-grain bullets fired in all the 6-inch barrels was 376 fps, almost 8 times the EV in the test barrel. The EV for all 6-inch revolvers with the 140-grain hollow point ammunition was 275 fps, over 10 times the EV in the test barrel. The 158-grain soft point ammunition showed an EV of 282 fps, almost seven times the test barrel EV of 38 fps.

These large variations are due partly to the relatively very small differences in chamber, bore, forcing cone rifling and barrel-cylinder gap dimensions and in the finish or smoothness of these interior surfaces. Chambers will vary minutely even though cut with the same reamer, as will all other machined surfaces. It is virtually impossible to manufacture two of some machined metal item, even as simple as a revolver, with all dimensions and finishes exactly the same. When hundreds of thousands of 357 Magnum revolvers have been made by thousands of different people in different factories, with different materials and tooling, to different engineering tolerances, it cannot be surprising that there are differences between guns.

These minor differences between guns cause some of the differences in ballistic measurements. Additional variations, due to differences between different makes or lots of bullets, powder, primers, cases, powder charges, loading dies, loading techniques and chronographs complicate the problem. Many times these small differences tend to cancel each other, but when everything goes one way, the resulting variation may be relatively large.

These velocity tests are not presented with any idea of claiming that one particular brand or model of firearm is superior to another. A repeat of the test with different ammunition might well reverse the relative standings shown here. The point we want to make is that even with the very best quality ammunition available, there will always be velocity variations when the ammunition is fired in different guns.

357 Magnum Velocity Variation in Different Guns (ft/sec)				
		Ammunition Used in Test Velocity, ft/sec		
Firearm Description	Barrel Length, inches	125-grain	140-grain	158-grain
S&W M19 #1	2 1/2	1190	1132	1034
Colt Python	2 1/2	1205	1118	989
S&W M19 #2	2 1/2	1209	1118	1018
Ruger Security Six	2 3/4	1233	1154	1075
Colt Trooper Mark III	4	1317	1175	1101
S&W M66	4	1385	1225	1117
S&W M19 #1	4	1368	1227	1153
S&W M19 #2	4	1374	1242	1146
Ruger Security Six #1	4	1370	1242	1130
Ruger Security Six #2	4	1380	1267	1151
Dan Wesson	4	1358	1280	1160
Ruger Blackhawk #1	4 5/8	1361	1266	1159
Ruger Blackhawk #2	4 5/8	1480	1336	1196
Ruger Security Six #3	6	1436	1311	1210
S&W M19 #1	6	1400	1282	1179
S&W M19 #2	6	1372	1281	1154
S&W M19 #3	6	1603	1417	1284
S&W M28 #1	6	1307	1246	1080
S&W M28 #2	6	1499	1353	1178
Colt Python #1	6	1227	1142	1002
Colt Python #2	6	1477	1373	1251
Colt Python #3	6	1468	1364	1207
Ruger Blackhawk (new)	6 1/2	1471	1375	1262
S&W M27	6 1/2	1547	1358	1248
S&W M27	8 3/8	1501	1342	1221
Ruger Blackhawk	10	1738	1544	1365
T/C Contender	10	1944	1726	1587
Martini Rifle	17 3/8	2121	1906	1678
Winchester 92 Rifle	20	2153	1964	1824
Marlin 1894 Rifle	24	2212	1994	1835
Velocity Test Barrel	10	1866	1732	1591
Velocity Test Barrel Extreme Variation	—	48	26	38

handgun **data**

Introduction to the Handgun Data

The following section presents reloading data for Speer® bullets in popular handgun cartridges. We've added new cartridges since printing the previous edition and retested others. If you have used older *Speer Reloading Manuals*, you will notice some differences in the format.

First of all, you will notice that the data table layout is different for #14. The new format was first adopted when we started publishing supplemental reloading data on the revamped Speer Bullets website in 2004 and allows direct export of our internal data files to a publication format, greatly reducing the opportunities for transcription errors. We believe you'll find it easier to read and use. Loads are ranked by maximum charge velocity with the highest at the top.

Starting charges were once set automatically as a fixed increment below the maximum based on case volume and were the same for every propellant used in a cartridge. Now the start charge increment is based on the pressure of the start charge, chosen to avoid low-pressure regions where ballistic uniformity suffers. Not every propellant may have the same weight difference between the start charge and the maximum charge. Read data tables carefully.

Beginning with *Manual #12*, we included the cartridge overall length (COAL) that we used in our testing. This was a much-requested feature and it is shown in the small table below the bullet illustrations. However, understand that this figure is a guideline, not gospel. Your handgun may need a different COAL. It's important not to load compact cartridges like the 9mm Luger shorter than we show. Case length also affects COAL of ammunition requiring a crimp. If your cases are a slightly different length from the lots we used in testing, you will need to make minor changes in COAL to apply a proper crimp. When seating bullets with crimp grooves, seat to the top of the groove. Some Speer handgun bullets have two crimp grooves. The data section will tell you which to use in these cases.

A spent 357 Magnum case that was used in a crusher-type pressure barrel.

It is your responsibility—and yours alone—to determine the proper and safe COAL for your handgun. Please refer to chapter 15 for more information on bullet seating techniques for handgun cartridges.

We show the letter "C" behind the charge weight where compression of the propellant was necessary to assemble the load. However, your propellant charging technique may not be the same as ours and your results may vary. Using a powder funnel with a long drop tube—we like the RCBS Quick Change Powder funnel—will make charging easier and reduce the amount of compression you apply. However, difference in case construction and even propellant lot variation can mean that your loads may compress when ours did not.

Using the Tables

There is a very basic rule for using the tables:

Always start with the minimum load!

All gun authorities recognize there are differences among individual firearms. The maximum loads shown were safe in the test equipment—both pressure barrels and production handguns—that we used during load development. However, your handgun may have some dimensional differences that could result in higher or lower operating pressures. Because you cannot know whether a pressure change will be up or down, using the starting load will give you the margin of safety required due to individual firearm variations. Start charges are generally 4 to 8 percent below maximum, depending on the size of the case.

Some handgun cartridges do not have start loads and are marked "DNR" for "do not reduce." In these cases we want you to use the load shown. This notation means our testing showed that any charge reduction resulted in unacceptable pressure and/or velocity variation.

Maximum loads mean exactly that—MAXIMUM! Under no circumstances should you exceed these loads. They are presented to indicate the maximum performance potential for the cartridge based on industry standards; however, variations in individual handguns may not permit safely using them in every situation.

Here is the bottom line—read it twice:

You must always start with the minimum load and carefully work up toward the maximum in small steps, watching for pressure signs as you shoot each successive increment.

Changing Components

Any change in components—primers, bullets or cases—from those listed requires that you return to the starting load and work up, just as with a new load. We also recommend that you note the propellant lot you are using in your reloading records. If you change lots when assembling maximum loads, we suggest you drop back to the start load and fire several test rounds to make sure the load still is safe for your handgun. Once this is established, you can carefully work up toward the old load level. Modern propellant manufacturing techniques give remarkable lot-to-lot consistency but some minor variations may still occur. We have no control over the manufacturing practices of other component companies. This is another reason why we provide starting loads and emphasize beginning with them.

* * * * *

SAFETY INFORMATION

- All reloading data contained herein is intended for use only by persons familiar with handloading practices, their own firearms and reloading equipment.

- Before using this data to assemble any ammunition, you must read and understand the reloading safety guidelines in chapters 6 and 10 and all safety-related cautions in the individual cartridge sections.

- We strongly urge new reloaders to read and understand the text of this manual. It has been written to give clear instruction in the principles and processes of reloading.

- Use the most current data. Components and cartridge standards change over time and these changes will affect load recommendations in the *Speer Manual*. It is fruitless to compare modern data to that published decades ago. Using old data with current components can create unsafe ammunition.

- If you are uncertain of the operation of your reloading equipment or the properties of any components, contact the manufacturer for additional assistance. Never be afraid to ask for help.

DISCLAIMER

These loads are for Speer® bullets. Bullets of other makes will not produce the same pressures and velocities and can create an unsafe condition if used with loads shown here.

Because ATK has no control over individual loading practices or the quality of the firearms in which the resulting ammunition may be used, we assume no liability—either expressed or implied—for the use of this load data information and instructional materials.

The data contained herein replaces, supersedes and obsoletes all data previously published by Speer, Omark Industries and Blount International, Inc.

22 Hornet

Although originally developed as a rifle cartridge, the compact 22 Hornet has also found favor as a handgun cartridge. Early attempts to convert revolvers were frustrating. In a good single-shot pistol the Hornet is a different story.

Warren Center, the inventor of the Thompson/Center Contender, built his first pistol for the Hornet. It proved a great package for hunting woodchucks in his native Vermont. In the Contender, the Hornet is as accurate as many rifles. Although the shorter pistol barrels give up velocity, the Hornet is still very effective on small varmints out to 100 yards and, with the right wind conditions, a bit more.

Best results in the Contender are gained by dedicating a batch of new cases to the handgun. After the first firing, only neck-size these cases for subsequent reloadings. This will improve both case life and accuracy. The Hornet case is fairly thin and may last for only three to four shots before showing incipient head separations. Inspect cases carefully after every firing.

The 33-grain TNT® hollow point is a natural for the Hornet handgun. Our 10-inch Contender produced velocities of 2700 ft/sec with the top load. 40 and 45-grain bullets generally give the best performance in Hornet pistols. However, the 1-in-14 inch twist in the Contender will usually stabilize the Speer 50-grain TNT bullet. The TNT is one of the few heavy bullets that will expand at lower velocity levels; however, it must be carefully loaded to maximum levels to insure in-flight stability and your pistol barrel must have a long throat. The assembled cartridge length exceeds the industry maximum and is for single-shot firearms only.

The Hornet and the Contender make a flat shooting little varmint combination when the shots aren't too long. Recoil is nearly non-existent but the muzzle blast is quite loud, guaranteed to remind you to wear hearing protection when shooting any firearm. The Hornet's pressure limit is 43,000 CUP.

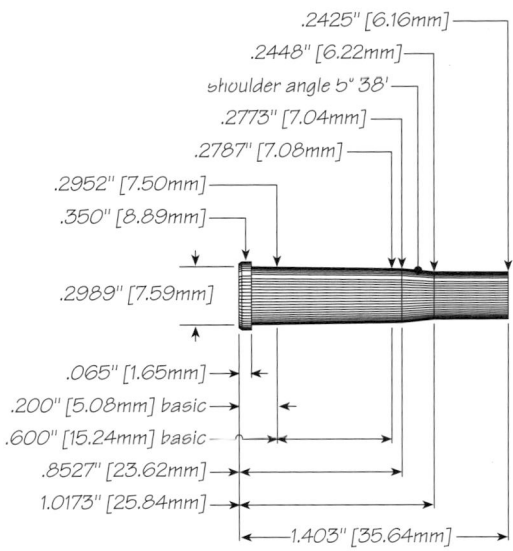

.2425" [6.16mm]
.2448" [6.22mm]
shoulder angle 5° 38'
.2773" [7.04mm]
.2787" [7.08mm]
.2952" [7.50mm]
.350" [8.89mm]
.2989" [7.59mm]
.065" [1.65mm]
.200" [5.08mm] basic
.600" [15.24mm] basic
.8527" [23.62mm]
1.0173" [25.84mm]
1.403" [35.64mm]

Max. Case Length:	1.403"	**Cart. Case:**	Winchester
Trim-to Length:	1.393"	**Primer:**	CCI 500 pistol primer
Max Cart. OAL:	1.723"	**Test Firearm:**	T/C Contender
RCBS Shell Holder:	#12	**Barrel Length:**	10"

IMPORTANT NOTE REGARDING PRIMERS: *This is a totally new data set. Previous data published by Speer used a small rifle primer. The loads here call for CCI 500 small pistol primers. Do not use rifle primers or any magnum primer with these loads or dangerous pressures will result. We found the milder primer significantly improved performance and reduced extreme variations in velocity.*

0.224"	22 TNT
Weight, grains	33
Ballistic Coefficient	0.080
Sectional Density	0.094
COAL Tested:	1.680"
Speer Part No.	1014

	START CHARGE		MAXIMUM CHARGE	
Propellant	Weight, grs	Muzzle Velocity, ft/sec	Weight, grs	Muzzle Velocity, ft/sec
296	12.4	2556	12.8	2703
AA No. 9	10.2	2526	10.8	2674
H110	12.4	2473	12.8	2600
Viht. N110	10.0	2492	10.6C	2580
2400	11.0	2519	11.5C	2554
H. Lil' Gun	13.5C	2342	14.0C	2451

0.224"	22 Spire SP
Weight, grains	40
Ballistic Coefficient	0.144
Sectional Density	0.114
COAL Tested:	1.723"
Speer Part No.	1017

	START CHARGE		MAXIMUM CHARGE	
Propellant	Weight, grs	Muzzle Velocity, ft/sec	Weight, grs	Muzzle Velocity, ft/sec
H110	9.2	2317	10.2	2400
296	9.2	2297	10.2	2375
H. Lil' Gun	12.0	2276	13.0C	2344
Viht. N110	8.1	2136	9.1	2338
2400	8.1	2125	9.1	2306
AA 1680	12.4	2177	13.4C	2258
IMR 4227	10.5	2126	11.3C	2238

0.224"	22 Spitz SP
Weight, grains	45
Ballistic Coefficient	0.143
Sectional Density	0.128
COAL Tested:	1.723"
Speer Part No.	1023

	START CHARGE		MAXIMUM CHARGE	
Propellant	Weight, grs	Muzzle Velocity, ft/sec	Weight, grs	Muzzle Velocity, ft/sec
H. Lil' Gun	12.0	2225	13.0C	2318
296	9.0	2145	10.0	2267
H110	9.0	2083	10.0	2225
AA 1680	12.0	2043	13.0C	2194
2400	8.0	2003	9.0	2190
Viht. N110	8.2	2116	9.0	2188
IMR 4227	10.1	2083	11.1	2183

*Maximum Loads should be used with CAUTION • C = Compressed Load • *Magnum Primer used with this powder.*

0.224"	22 Spitz SP	22 TNT HP
Weight, grains	50	50
Ballistic Coefficient	0.207	0.228
Sectional Density	0.142	0.142
COAL Tested:	1.723"	1.850"†
Speer Part No.	1029	1030

	START CHARGE		MAXIMUM CHARGE	
Propellant	Weight, grs	Muzzle Velocity, ft/sec	Weight, grs	Muzzle Velocity, ft/sec
Lil' Gun	11.0C	2114	12.0C	2251
296	9.0	2141	9.7	2250
H110	9.0	2186	9.6	2240
Viht. N110	7.9	2027	8.6	2099
AA 1680	10.9	1941	11.8	2068
AA 2015	11.5C	1732	12.0C	1860

† — COAL exceeds industry standards; for long-throated single-shots only

Bob & Richard Oliver, husband and father-in-law of Kathy Oliver, maintenance Administrative Assistant, CCI/Speer Operations; 300 Win Mag, 165-grain, Grand Slam® SP; 6 point mule deer; Cottonwood, ID.

0.224"	22 HP
Weight, grains	52
Ballistic Coefficient	0.168
Sectional Density	0.148
COAL Tested:	1.723"
Speer Part No.	1035

Propellant	START CHARGE Weight, grs	START CHARGE Muzzle Velocity, ft/sec	MAXIMUM CHARGE Weight, grs	MAXIMUM CHARGE Muzzle Velocity, ft/sec
H110	7.9	1935	8.9	2125
296	7.9	2011	8.9	2091
Viht. N110	7.4	1899	8.0	2002
H. Lil' Gun	9.0	1852	9.7	1986
IMR 4227	8.6	1817	9.6	1983
IMR 4198	9.7C	1822	10.5C	1960
2400	6.7	1821	7.7	1946
AA 1680	10.1	1833	10.8	1904

*Maximum Loads should be used with CAUTION • C = Compressed Load • *Magnum Primer used with this powder.*

22 K-Hornet

The K-Hornet is a very useful wildcat developed by Lysle Kilbourn prior to World War II. It was quite popular in rifles but got a real boost when Thompson/Center offered its Contender single-shot pistol in this caliber.

The K-Hornet is an "Improved Hornet." In reloading, the term "improved" dates to P. O. Ackley using it to name his wildcat cartridges. Ackley modifications included a straighter case and a steeper shoulder angle than the parent cartridge. Most Ackley wildcats sported a 40° shoulder. These changes increase case capacity.

Wildcats are by definition not standardized, and dimensions will vary. The K-Hornet's variation in neck and shoulder dimensions is rather impressive. In researching various incarnations of the K-Hornet, we found that the neck length varied from 0.238 to 0.375 inches. The shoulder angle can be either 35° or 40°. The dimensions we show in the case drawing represent those we measured from our Contender barrel. The loads here are suitable for any K-Hornet variant with a neck length of .300 inches or less.

Cases are easily formed by firing standard 22 Hornet loads in the K-Hornet chamber. There is a modest performance gain, but the true benefit of the K-Hornet over its parent is better accuracy and case life. The wise reloader will set up his dies so the K-Hornet shoulder—not the rim—becomes the headspace point. The steep shoulder properly fitted to your chamber will minimize stretching so common to the Hornet case. This improved fit also helps accuracy.

"Improved" cartridges with nearly straight case bodies may require full-length sizing. However, if not required for your version of the K-Hornet, we recommend that you neck size only if loading for only one rifle or pistol.

Like the standard Hornet, the K-Hornet is best with 40 and 45-grain bullets. Accuracy is excellent and the K-Hornet is a great 100-yard varmint cartridge in the Contender. There are no pressure standards for the K-Hornet but the loads shown were safe in the test pistol.

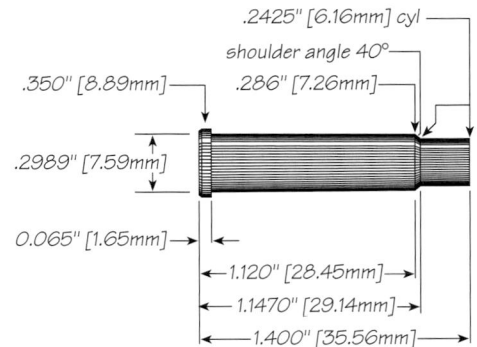

.2425" [6.16mm] cyl
shoulder angle 40°
.350" [8.89mm]
.286" [7.26mm]
.2989" [7.59mm]
0.065" [1.65mm]
1.120" [28.45mm]
1.1470" [29.14mm]
1.400" [35.56mm]

Max. Case Length:	1.400"	**Cart. Case:**	Winchester
Trim-to Length:	1.390"	**Primer:**	CCI 400
Max Cart. OAL:	1.723"	**Test Firearm:**	T/C Contender
RCBS Shell Holder:	#12	**Barrel Length:**	10"

0.224"	22 Spire SP
Weight, grains	40
Ballistic Coefficient	0.144
Sectional Density	0.114
COAL Tested:	1.723"
Speer Part No.	1017

	START CHARGE		MAXIMUM CHARGE	
Propellant	Weight, grs	Muzzle Velocity, ft/sec	Weight, grs	Muzzle Velocity, ft/sec
IMR 4227	11.0	2278	11.7	2439
2400	9.2	2299	9.6	2415
IMR 4198	11.0	1983	11.7C	2119

0.224"	22 Spitz SP
Weight, grains	45
Ballistic Coefficient	0.143
Sectional Density	0.128
COAL Tested:	1.723"
Speer Part No.	1023

	START CHARGE		MAXIMUM CHARGE	
Propellant	Weight, grs	Muzzle Velocity, ft/sec	Weight, grs	Muzzle Velocity, ft/sec
IMR 4227	11.0	2251	11.5	2370
2400	8.4	2156	8.8	2257
IMR 4198	11.0	1995	11.7C	2132

*Maximum Loads should be used with CAUTION • C = Compressed Load • *Magnum Primer used with this powder.*

221 Remington Fireball

In 1962, Remington introduced the innovative XP-100 single-shot, bolt-action pistol. The 221 Fireball cartridge is basically a shortened 222 Remington specifically designed for the new pistol. The combination has proved to be very accurate and has accounted for a lot of varmints over the last thirty years.

An XP-100 or a T/C Contender with a good handgun scope is capable of shooting 100-yard groups under one inch. This kind of accuracy means the effective varmint hunting range is often over 200 yards depending on wind conditions. Although the size and shape of the XP-100 pistol doesn't lend itself to one-handed firing, the pistol is quite easy to support over a convenient rest.

Factory ammo with a 50-grain soft point chronographed at 2620 ft/sec from the 10-3/4-inch barrel. A 10-inch Contender posted nearly identical velocities. Most of the handloads shown will give velocities equal to factory loads. Factory ammo and brass are still available but cases can also be reformed from 222 or 223 Remington brass. If you are using reformed cases, necks must be reamed and loads reduced to accommodate the reduced case capacity.

The Speer 50-grain TNT is probably the best all-around bullet for the Fireball varmint hunter. Its construction will give full bullet disruption over typical varmint-shooting distances.

Remington no longer catalogs the XP-100 but chambers the Fireball in one of its Model 700 variants. Still, the little Fireball lives up to its name in a handgun, coming within 300 ft/sec of the velocities of the 223 Remington pistol.

The industry maximum pressure for the 221 Fireball is 52,000 CUP.

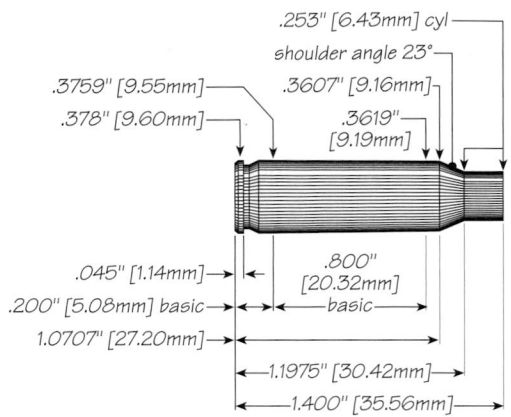

.253" [6.43mm] cyl
shoulder angle 23°
.3759" [9.55mm]
.378" [9.60mm]
.3607" [9.16mm]
.3619" [9.19mm]
.045" [1.14mm]
.200" [5.08mm] basic
1.0707" [27.20mm]
.800" [20.32mm]
basic
1.1975" [30.42mm]
1.400" [35.56mm]

Max. Case Length:	1.400"	Cart. Case:	Remington
Trim-to Length:	1.390"	Primer:	CCI 400; 450*
Max Cart. OAL:	1.830"	Test Firearm:	Remington XP-100
RCBS Shell Holder:	#10	Barrel Length:	10.75"

0.224"	22 Spitz SP
Weight, grains	45
Ballistic Coefficient	0.143
Sectional Density	0.128
COAL Tested:	1.830"
Speer Part No.	1023

Propellant	START CHARGE		MAXIMUM CHARGE	
	Weight, grs	Muzzle Velocity, ft/sec	Weight, grs	Muzzle Velocity, ft/sec
2400	14.0	2599	15.0	2762
Reloder 7	17.3	2603	18.3	2775
H110*	13.0	2555	14.0	2757
IMR 4198	16.8	2556	17.8C	2731
IMR 4227	15.2	2571	16.2	2727

0.224"	22 Spitz SP	22 TNT HP
Weight, grains	50	50
Ballistic Coefficient	0.207	0.228
Sectional Density	0.142	0.142
COAL Tested:	1.830"	1.830"
Speer Part No.	1029	1030

Propellant	START CHARGE Weight, grs	START CHARGE Muzzle Velocity, ft/sec	MAXIMUM CHARGE Weight, grs	MAXIMUM CHARGE Muzzle Velocity, ft/sec
2400	13.5	2521	14.5	2693
IMR 4198	16.5	2503	17.5C	2664
Reloder 7	16.9	2497	17.9	2638
IMR 4227	14.9	2490	15.9	2634
H110*	12.5	2429	13.5	2625

0.224"	22 HP	22 Match BTHP
Weight, grains	52	52
Ballistic Coefficient	0.168	0.230
Sectional Density	0.148	0.148
COAL Tested:	1.830"	1.830"
Speer Part No.	1035	1036

Propellant	START CHARGE Weight, grs	START CHARGE Muzzle Velocity, ft/sec	MAXIMUM CHARGE Weight, grs	MAXIMUM CHARGE Muzzle Velocity, ft/sec
2400	13.3	2411	14.3	2607
Reloder 7	16.7	2441	17.7	2606
IMR 4227	14.7	2404	15.7	2585
IMR 4198	16.0	2330	17.0	2527
H110*	12.2	2268	13.2	2465

*Maximum Loads should be used with CAUTION • C = Compressed Load • *Magnum Primer used with this powder.*

0.224"	22 Spitz SP
Weight, grains	55
Ballistic Coefficient	0.212
Sectional Density	0.157
COAL Tested:	1.830"
Speer Part No.	1047

| | START CHARGE | | MAXIMUM CHARGE | |
Propellant	Weight, grs	Muzzle Velocity, ft/sec	Weight, grs	Muzzle Velocity, ft/sec
IMR 4227	14.5	2419	15.4	2562
IMR 4198	15.5	2317	16.7	2502
Reloder 7	16.4	2348	17.4	2501
2400	12.5	2267	13.5	2477
H110*	12.0	2250	13.0	2432

*Maximum Loads should be used with CAUTION • C = Compressed Load • *Magnum Primer used with this powder.*

223 Remington

The popularity of the 223 Remington in rifles led to its being tried in a handgun and the results were excellent. The most popular handguns are the Remington XP-100 bolt action and the Thompson/Center Contender single-shot pistol. Velocities in 14-inch barrels are surprisingly high—often within 90 percent of rifle velocities—and both pistols are capable of excellent accuracy.

Reloading for a 223 Remington handgun is no different than reloading it for a rifle. Even the slower burning propellants gave good performance and velocities with all loads were quite consistent. Sizing cases is done the same way as with any bottlenecked rifle cartridge. As long as you are shooting cases in only one 223 pistol, neck sizing is strongly recommended. Be sure to use small rifle primers as recommended. Several of the propellants tested gave a dazzling muzzle flash. This is often unavoidable when shooting rifle cartridges in handguns.

There is some variation in the internal construction of 223 cases. As a result, we emphatically repeat the rule that you begin with the starting loads and work up carefully toward the maximum levels. The commercial IMI cases we used to develop these loads have the same capacity as most military cases; therefore, these loads can be safely used in surplus military brass.

Bullets heavier than 55 grains do not stabilize well at 223 pistol velocities so we do not recommend them. The 50-grain TNT® hollow point is ideal for 223 pistols. Its fine accuracy and explosive terminal effects combine to make it an excellent varmint bullet.

These loads are within the industry maximum of 52,000 CUP.

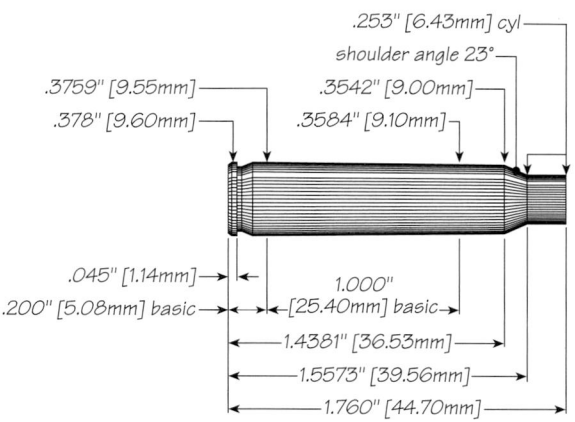

.253" [6.43mm] cyl
shoulder angle 23°
.3759" [9.55mm]
.378" [9.60mm]
.3542" [9.00mm]
.3584" [9.10mm]
.045" [1.14mm]
.200" [5.08mm] basic
1.000"
[25.40mm] basic
1.4381" [36.53mm]
1.5573" [39.56mm]
1.760" [44.70mm]

Max. Case Length:	1.760"	Cart. Case:	IMI
Trim-to Length:	1.750"	Primer:	CCI 400; 450*
Max Cart. OAL:	2.260"	Test Firearm:	T/C Contender
RCBS Shell Holder:	#10	Barrel Length:	14"

0.224"	22 Spitz SP
Weight, grains	45
Ballistic Coefficient	0.143
Sectional Density	0.128
COAL Tested:	2.155"
Speer Part No.	1023

Propellant	START CHARGE Weight, grs	START CHARGE Muzzle Velocity, ft/sec	MAXIMUM CHARGE Weight, grs	MAXIMUM CHARGE Muzzle Velocity, ft/sec
IMR 3031	25.0	2712	27.0C	3121
748*	26.5	2858	28.5C	3097
Viht. N133	22.5	2789	24.5	3065
IMR 4198	21.0	2782	23.0	3061
H322	24.0	2713	26.0	3029
IMR 4895	25.0	2701	27.0C	3022
AA 2015	23.0	2760	25.0	3010
AA 2460*	24.0	2683	26.0	2967
Reloder 7	18.0	2564	20.0	2636

0.224"	22 Spitz SP	22 TNT HP
Weight, grains	50	50
Ballistic Coefficient	0.207	0.228
Sectional Density	0.142	0.142
COAL Tested:	2.185"	2.250"
Speer Part No.	1029	1030

| Propellant | START CHARGE | | MAXIMUM CHARGE | |
	Weight, grs	Muzzle Velocity, ft/sec	Weight, grs	Muzzle Velocity, ft/sec
H322	24.0	2749	26.0	3068
IMR 4895	25.0	2714	27.0C	3037
AA 2520*	26.0	2848	28.0C	3030
IMR 3031	24.0	2571	26.0C	2960
748*	26.0	2728	28.0	2954
H4895	23.5	2537	25.5C	2917
Viht. N133	22.0	2638	24.0	2900
AA 2015	22.5	2651	24.5	2890
IMR 4198	20.0	2608	22.0	2870

*Maximum Loads should be used with CAUTION • C = Compressed Load • *Magnum Primer used with this powder.*

0.224"	22 HP	22 Match BTHP
Weight, grains	52	52
Ballistic Coefficient	0.168	0.230
Sectional Density	0.148	0.148
COAL Tested:	2.185"	2.250"
Speer Part No.	1035	1036

Propellant	START CHARGE		MAXIMUM CHARGE	
	Weight, grs	Muzzle Velocity, ft/sec	Weight, grs	Muzzle Velocity, ft/sec
748*	26.0	2846	28.0	3083
AA 2520	25.5	2892	27.5C	3077
IMR 3031	24.0	2630	26.0C	3027
IMR 4895	24.5	2680	26.5C	2998
H4895	23.5	2600	25.5C	2989
Viht. N133	22.0	2684	24.0	2950
AA 2015	22.0	2662	24.0	2903
IMR 4198	20.0	2598	22.0	2858
H322	22.5	2550	24.5	2846

0.224"	22 Spitz SP
Weight, grains	55
Ballistic Coefficient	0.212
Sectional Density	0.157
COAL Tested:	2.175"
Speer Part No.	1047

	START CHARGE		MAXIMUM CHARGE	
Propellant	Weight, grs	Muzzle Velocity, ft/sec	Weight, grs	Muzzle Velocity, ft/sec
AA 2520*	25.0	2827	27.0C	3008
H4895	23.5	2595	25.5C	2983
748*	26.0	2735	28.0C	2964
IMR 3031	24.0	2574	26.0C	2962
IMR 4895	24.5	2621	26.5C	2932
Viht. N133	21.5	2593	23.5	2849
H322	22.5	2501	24.5	2792
AA 2015	21.5	2535	23.5	2765
IMR 4198	19.0	2473	21.0	2721

*Maximum Loads should be used with CAUTION • C = Compressed Load • *Magnum Primer used with this powder.*

25 Auto

The 25 Automatic cartridge dates to the beginning of the 20th Century, when Fabrique Nationale (FN) of Belgium introduced a small, Browning-designed "vest pocket" semi-automatic pistol for personal defense. Shortly after the FN introduction, Colt licensed the design and made pistols in their Hartford, CT plant as the Colt Model 1908 Hammerless. Both were high-quality firearms. In Europe, the new cartridge was called the 6.35mm Browning; Colt called the cartridge the "25 Automatic Colt Pistol," or 25 ACP; the official name today is simply 25 Auto.

The 25 Auto was loaded with smokeless propellant under a 50-grain full jacket bullet. The bullet was seated conventionally, making the package more rigid for smoother feeding. With minimal case capacity and fired from gun barrels often shorter than two inches, the cartridge produced little velocity—in the 700 to 750-ft/sec range—but enough to wound or kill with proper bullet placement (or dumb luck).

For nearly 80 years, the original 50-grain FMJ load was the only one commonly loaded. A few companies developed soft-point bullets but they did not have enough velocity to expand. Later, improvements in bullet manufacturing led to lighter hollow points including the Speer Gold Dot® that could achieve enough velocity to mushroom.

In spite of its small size, some people reload the 25 Auto. For whatever reason, people buy reloading dies and component bullets for this cartridge so we present load data for it.

The greatest challenge to reloading the 25 Auto is its size, or lack thereof. See the "Lab Notes" in this section for ways to overcome the handling and loading block problems.

The small powder charge problem is harder to handle. Even the best powder measures cannot hold ±0.1 grain tolerance when dispensing tiny charges; velocity variation is hard to avoid regardless of your attention to detail. Worse, metered charge variation can cause some loads to exceed pressure specifications in a tiny cartridge.

We emphatically recommend that you individually weigh each charge and use extra care in your technique. We also recommend that you use the loads shown exactly as shown; do not reduce them as is common with most cartridges. Accurate No. 2 Improved gave the most consistent velocities with either bullet weight. Finding reliable function may mean trying several propellants and bullet weights. All the loads functioned well in our Beretta test pistol.

Quality in 25 Auto pistols varies from excellent to pitiful. Even a pistol once of high quality may have been abused into poor mechanical condition. Have your pistol checked by a good gunsmith before firing it with any ammunition. We recommend these loads be used only in pistols with steel slides and steel or forged (not cast) aluminum frames. Many cheap 25 Autos have major components made of zinc alloys that may not last through more than a few boxes of ammo.

The loads here are within the industry 25,000 psi pressure level established for the 25 Auto cartridge.

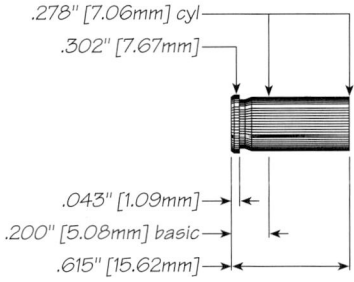

.278" [7.06mm] cyl
.302" [7.67mm]
.043" [1.09mm]
.200" [5.08mm] basic
.615" [15.62mm]

Max. Case Length:	0.615"	Cart. Case:	Speer
Trim-to Length:	n/a	Primer:	CCI 500
Max Cart. OAL:	0.910"	Test Firearm:	Beretta M950
RCBS Shell Holder:	#29	Barrel Length:	2"

Lab Notes:
Handling tiny 25 Auto cases with big fingers may mean modifying a pair of long tweezers to fit around the case. Bend the tips so that they contour to the case body. A bit of thin rubber tubing on the modified tips makes them slip-proof.

"Do it yourself" is also the key to the loading block problem. Cut a sheet of ¼-inch plywood, plastic or fiberboard to the desired length and width, and then drill the desired number of holes completely through it with a 5/16-inch drill. Sand both sides smooth and brad or screw another piece of the same material (without holes) to one side. Sand or plane the edges to make them flush. You now have a block for short cartridges with flat bottom holes to keep the cases level.

0.251"	25 GDHP
Weight, grains	35
Ballistic Coefficient	0.091
Sectional Density	0.079
COAL Tested:	0.870"
Speer Part No.	3985

	START CHARGE		MAXIMUM CHARGE	
Propellant	Weight, grs	Muzzle Velocity, ft/sec	Weight, grs	Muzzle Velocity, ft/sec
Bullseye	DNR	—	1.7	1040
TiteGroup	DNR	—	1.7	1008
AA No. 2 Impr.	DNR	—	1.8	1004
700-X	DNR	—	1.7	971
Red Dot	DNR	—	1.5	966
231	DNR	—	1.7	937

DNR — do not reduce

0.251"	25 TMJ RN
Weight, grains	50
Ballistic Coefficient	0.110
Sectional Density	0.113
COAL Tested:	0.890"
Speer Part No.	3982

	START CHARGE		MAXIMUM CHARGE	
Propellant	Weight, grs	Muzzle Velocity, ft/sec	Weight, grs	Muzzle Velocity, ft/sec
TiteGroup	DNR	—	1.4	822
Bullseye	DNR	—	1.3	812
700-X	DNR	—	1.4	807
231	DNR	—	1.4	797
AA No. 2 Impr.	DNR	—	1.5	792
Red Dot	DNR	—	1.2	755

DNR — do not reduce

*Maximum Loads should be used with CAUTION • C = Compressed Load • *Magnum Primer used with this powder.*

6.5 JDJ

The JDJ in the name of this cartridge stands for J.D. Jones, founder and owner of SSK Industries. J.D. has developed a remarkable family of proprietary hunting cartridges for use in his custom Thompson/Center Contenders and Encores. The entire series has proven their worth in hunting fields around the world.

Early JDJ cartridges are based on two cases. The larger calibers were derived from the 444 Marlin case and the smaller ones from the 225 Winchester case. The 6.5 JDJ falls into the latter group.

The 225 Winchester case is a true rimmed cartridge (despite some early hype about its being semi-rimmed). This makes it a natural for the single-shot Contender. Another attribute of this cartridge is heavy case construction. These cases can contain full-pressure hunting loads to deliver excellent performance. Our loss rate during forming and testing was zero.

The 6.5 JDJ is easily formed by expanding the case neck using the tapered expander furnished with the die set and then fire-forming with a charge at about 90 percent of maximum. The 120-grain Speer bullet with 30.0 grains of IMR 4320 makes an excellent case-forming load. Loss during forming is practically zero and case life is excellent with normal reloading practices. The cartridge features a short neck, minimum body taper and a 40° shoulder, resulting in maximum case capacity.

Because many 6.5mm (.264") component bullets are designed for the 6.5x55mm Mauser cartridge, they give optimum performance at moderate velocities. The 6.5 JDJ falls into the lower end of this velocity range so its terminal performance on game is excellent. It gives proper penetration even with the lighter 120-grain bullets. Typical loads give close to 2400 ft/sec with Speer's 120-grain bullet and over 2200 ft/sec with our 140-grain spitzer.

After the last *Speer Manual* was published, we beefed up the two 6.5mm Hot-Cor bullets but made sure they still performed well in the JDJ. Retained weights went up but the bullets still produce the same expanded diameter as their thinner-jacketed forbears.

A number of powders give excellent ballistics in the 6.5 JDJ, a tribute to its efficient design. Even some of the slow-burning powders give surprising velocities. However, IMR

4320 seems to be the most popular propellant for this cartridge. Reloder 15, VihtaVuori N140 and Accurate Arms 2520 are also good choices.

J.D. states that his 6.5 has taken game up to 400 pounds and that it is an effective deer cartridge out to 275 yards. We see no reason to dispute this claim. The cartridge shows phenomenal accuracy at long range.

Custom JDJ barrels and reloading dies are available directly from SSK Industries (590 Woodvue Lane, Wintersville, OH 43953; www.sskindustries.com).

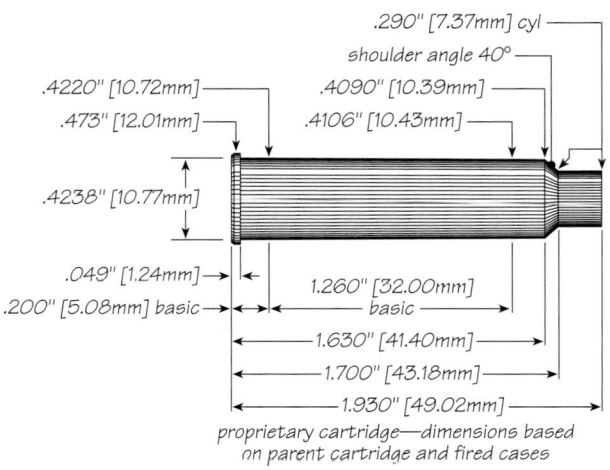

.290" [7.37mm] cyl

shoulder angle 40°

.4090" [10.39mm]

.4106" [10.43mm]

.4220" [10.72mm]

.473" [12.01mm]

.4238" [10.77mm]

.049" [1.24mm]

.200" [5.08mm] basic

1.260" [32.00mm] basic

1.630" [41.40mm]

1.700" [43.18mm]

1.930" [49.02mm]

proprietary cartridge—dimensions based on parent cartridge and fired cases

Max. Case Length:	2.930"	Cart. Case:	Reformed Winchester
Trim-to Length:	2.920"	Primer:	CCI 200
Max Cart. OAL:	2.700"	Test Firearm:	T/C Contender
RCBS Shell Holder:	#11	Barrel Length:	SSK 14"

0.264"	6.5mm Spitz SP
Weight, grains	120
Ballistic Coefficient	0.392
Sectional Density	0.246
COAL Tested:	2.700"
Speer Part No.	1435

| Propellant | START CHARGE | | MAXIMUM CHARGE | |
	Weight, grs	Muzzle Velocity, ft/sec	Weight, grs	Muzzle Velocity, ft/sec
Reloder 15	31.0	2122	35.0	2396
H4350	35.0	2141	39.0C	2386
Viht. N140	30.3	2099	34.3	2376
IMR 4350	35.0	2129	39.0C	2372
760	34.0	2116	38.0	2365
H414	34.0	2104	38.0	2351
IMR 4831	36.0	2116	40.0C	2351
Reloder 22	37.5	2118	41.5C	2344
IMR 4320	30.0	2059	34.0	2333
Reloder 19	36.0	2045	40.0C	2272

*Maximum Loads should be used with CAUTION • C = Compressed Load • *Magnum Primer used with this powder.*

0.264"	6.5mm Spitz SP
Weight, grains	140
Ballistic Coefficient	0.498
Sectional Density	0.287
COAL Tested:	2.700"
Speer Part No.	1441

	START CHARGE		MAXIMUM CHARGE	
Propellant	Weight, grs	Muzzle Velocity, ft/sec	Weight, grs	Muzzle Velocity, ft/sec
Viht. N160	34.5	1998	38.5C	2230
Reloder 15	28.5	1938	32.5	2204
IMR 4064	27.5	1894	31.5	2169
Viht. N140	28.0	1897	32.0	2168
H414	31.5	1918	35.5	2162
AA 2520	26.5	1873	30.5	2155
H380	31.0	1900	35.0	2145
IMR 4350	32.0	1928	36.0C	2140
IMR 4320	28.0	1927	32.0	2136
760	31.0	1880	35.0	2133
Reloder 19	33.5	1872	37.5C	2095
H4831	34.0	1834	38.0C	2050

*Maximum Loads should be used with CAUTION • C = Compressed Load • *Magnum Primer used with this powder.*

7mm Remington BR

The 7mm Remington BR started life as a wildcat cartridge based on another wildcat, the 308x1.5", which is a shortened 308 Winchester. The short, 30-caliber wildcat case was necked down to hold .284" bullets and given a 30° shoulder angle and minimum body taper. A number of experimenters have worked with similar wildcat cartridges, but Remington standardized this one.

An XP-100 Silhouette pistol was introduced in 1980 chambered for the 7mm BR wildcat. Remington furnished a special 308 Winchester match case with a small primer pocket. Because forming BR cases proved to be a chore, the popularity of the cartridge suffered until 1986 when Remington began selling fully-formed 7mm BR cases and loaded ammunition.

This is a very accurate cartridge that is popular with long-range target shooters in silhouette competition where steel targets are shot with handguns out to 200 meters. Most 7mm bullets fired in the 7mm BR have sufficient power to topple steel targets if the shooter scores a solid hit.

For hunting, the 7mm BR is suitable for varmints and the smaller deer species. We have listed loads using bullets up to 160 grains but most hunters will find that the 130 to 145-grain bullets provide a good combination of effective terminal performance without the trajectory becoming too arched. The Speer 110-grain TNT or the 115-grain hollow point are ideal for varmints.

The loads listed were fired from a 10-inch barrel. Newer XP-100 pistols for this cartridge feature 14½-inch barrels. The industry maximum pressure for the 7mm BR is 52,000 CUP.

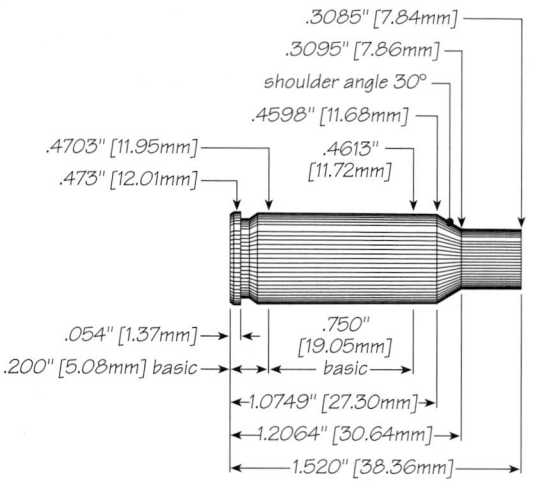

Max. Case Length:	1.520"	Cart. Case:	Remington
Trim-to Length:	1.510"	Primer:	CCI 400; 450*
Max Cart. OAL:	n/a	Test Firearm:	Remington XP-100
RCBS Shell Holder:	#3	Barrel Length:	10"

0.284"	7mm TNT HP	7mm HP
Weight, grains	110	115
Ballistic Coefficient	0.384	0.250
Sectional Density	0.195	0.204
COAL Tested:	2.225"	2.235"
Speer Part No.	1616	1617

	START CHARGE		MAXIMUM CHARGE	
Propellant	Weight, grs	Muzzle Velocity, ft/sec	Weight, grs	Muzzle Velocity, ft/sec
BL-C(2)	32.5	2521	34.5C	2682
H335	30.5	2346	32.5	2518
IMR 4320	31.0	2315	33.0C	2456
748*	32.5	2294	34.5C	2416
Reloder 7	24.4	2234	26.4	2411
IMR 4895	31.0	2212	33.0C	2407
IMR 4064	30.5	2210	32.5C	2387

0.284"	7mm Spitz SP	7mm Spitz BTSP
Weight, grains	130	130
Ballistic Coefficient	0.368	0.424
Sectional Density	0.230	0.230
COAL Tested:	2.235"	2.235"
Speer Part No.	1623	1624

Propellant	START CHARGE		MAXIMUM CHARGE	
	Weight, grs	Muzzle Velocity, ft/sec	Weight, grs	Muzzle Velocity, ft/sec
IMR 4895	29.0	2167	31.0C	2299
748*	31.0	2159	33.0	2295
IMR 4320	30.0	2125	32.0	2295
H335	28.5	2116	30.5	2289
H322	26.0	2059	28.0C	2261
IMR 3031	27.0	2079	29.0C	2242
Reloder 7	23.0	1901	25.0	2074

*Maximum Loads should be used with CAUTION • C = Compressed Load • *Magnum Primer used with this powder.*

0.284"	7mm Spitz BTSP	7mm Spitz SP	7mm Match BTHP
Weight, grains	145	145	145
Ballistic Coefficient	0.472	0.416	0.468
Sectional Density	0.257	0.257	0.257
COAL Tested:	2.225"	2.225"	2.225"
Speer Part No.	1628	1629	1631

	START CHARGE		MAXIMUM CHARGE	
Propellant	Weight, grs	Muzzle Velocity, ft/sec	Weight, grs	Muzzle Velocity, ft/sec
IMR 4064	29.5	2187	31.5	2373
IMR 4320	29.0	2232	31.0C	2333
BL-C(2)	28.0	2166	30.0	2324
H335	27.0	2096	29.0	2248
748*	30.0	2075	32.0C	2228
H322	25.5	2069	27.5	2218
Reloder 7	22.5	1997	24.5	2193

Tom Saleen, Director of International Sales, ATK CCI/Speer Operations and son, Travis; 270 Win 150-grain, Grand Slam®; bull elk; Idaho.

0.284"	7mm Spitz BTSP	7mm Spitz SP	7mm MT SP
Weight, grains	160	160	160
Ballistic Coefficient	0.519	0.504	0.340
Sectional Density	0.283	0.283	0.283
COAL Tested:	2.235"	2.235"	2.225"
Speer Part No.	1634	1635	1637

Propellant	START CHARGE		MAXIMUM CHARGE	
	Weight, grs	Muzzle Velocity, ft/sec	Weight, grs	Muzzle Velocity, ft/sec
IMR 4064	27.5	2023	29.5C	2209
IMR 4320	27.0	1977	29.0C	2126
H335	26.0	1957	28.0	2123
BL-C(2)	26.0	1971	28.0	2116
748*	29.0	1983	31.0C	2116
H322	24.5	1922	26.5	2072
Reloder 7	21.0	1830	23.0	2011

*Maximum Loads should be used with CAUTION • C = Compressed Load • *Magnum Primer used with this powder.*

7mm T/CU

The 7mm T/CU is the most popular of Wes Ugalde's series of wildcat cartridges for handgun metallic silhouette competition in the Thompson/Center Contender. It is based on the 223 Remington case.

Cases are made by expanding the 223's neck with a tapered expander ball and fire-forming using a charge at about 90 percent of the recommended maximum. We strongly recommend sorting cases by brand before forming and firing.

Commercial 223 Remington cases yield the best T/CU cases. We strongly recommend avoiding military cases as a source of T/CU cases; they are heavier with less capacity and don't fire-form as well as their commercial counterparts.

Reloading these cases requires care and attention. The small, narrow shoulder is easily bulged or collapsed. We suggest that you neck size only and thoroughly clean inside the case necks before sizing. When setting the sizer die, make certain that the case shoulder doesn't touch the shoulder in the die. The tiny shoulder is easily displaced, and doing so causes excessive headspace. Case life and accuracy will both suffer and misfires may occur. The case mouth must be properly chamfered before seating bullets to prevent case damage.

The extra attention required to reload the 7 T/CU is more than compensated by the shooting qualities of this fine cartridge. It is quite accurate with the full range of 7mm bullets and has sufficient power for the smaller deer species. On silhouette ranges, the 7mm T/CU has helped earn many awards for IHMSA competitors.

Thompson/Center no longer catalogs 7mm T/CU Contender barrels but their custom shop, Fox Ridge Outfitters, does. There are no pressure standards for this cartridge but the loads here functioned without problems in our Contender.

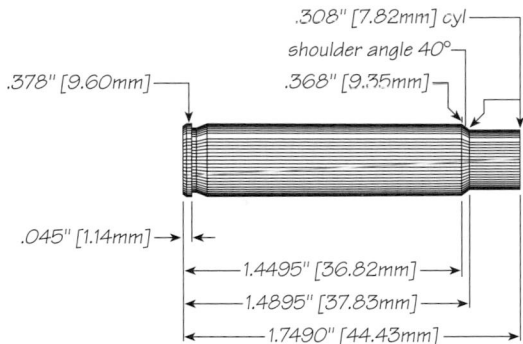

.308" [7.82mm] cyl
shoulder angle 40°
.378" [9.60mm]
.368" [9.35mm]
.045" [1.14mm]
1.4495" [36.82mm]
1.4895" [37.83mm]
1.7490" [44.43mm]

Max. Case Length:	1.749"	Cart. Case:	Federal
Trim-to Length:	1.739"	Primer:	CCI 400
Max Cart. OAL:	n/a	Test Firearm:	Thompson/Center Contender
RCBS Shell Holder:	#10	Barrel Length:	14"

0.284"	7mm TNT HP	7mm HP
Weight, grains	110	115
Ballistic Coefficient	0.384	0.250
Sectional Density	0.195	0.204
COAL Tested:	2.410"	2.410"
Speer Part No.	1616	1617

	START CHARGE		MAXIMUM CHARGE	
Propellant	Weight, grs	Muzzle Velocity, ft/sec	Weight, grs	Muzzle Velocity, ft/sec
H322	27.0	2184	29.0	2346
AA 2015	26.5	2175	28.5	2339
Viht. N130	24.5	2133	26.5	2307
IMR 4895	28.3	2130	30.3C	2281
BL-C(2)	31.0	2139	33.0	2277
AA 2230	27.5	2102	29.5	2255
H335	30.5	2115	32.5	2254
IMR 4198	21.5	1993	23.5	2178
IMR 3031	26.2	1997	28.2C	2149
H4198	21.5	1928	23.5	2107
748	30.5	1971	32.5C	2100
Reloder 7	21.5	1887	23.5	2062

0.284"	7mm Spitz SP	7mm Spitz BTSP
Weight, grains	130	130
Ballistic Coefficient	0.368	0.424
Sectional Density	0.230	0.230
COAL Tested:	2.465"	2.465"
Speer Part No.	1623	1624

Propellant	START CHARGE Weight, grs	START CHARGE Muzzle Velocity, ft/sec	MAXIMUM CHARGE Weight, grs	MAXIMUM CHARGE Muzzle Velocity, ft/sec
AA 2015	26.0	2116	28.0	2279
AA 2230	27.0	2058	29.0	2210
IMR 4895	27.2	2030	29.2C	2201
H322	25.0	2030	27.0	2192
Viht. N130	23.0	1984	25.0	2157
H335	27.4	1999	29.4	2145
748	29.0	1993	31.0	2130
IMR 3031	26.0	1969	28.0	2120
H4895	26.5	1968	28.5C	2117
BL-C(2)	28.0	1968	30.0	2109
IMR 4198	21.0	1917	23.0	2100
Reloder 7	21.0	1882	23.0	2061

*Maximum Loads should be used with CAUTION • C = Compressed Load • *Magnum Primer used with this powder.*

7mm T/CU

0.284"	7mm Spitz BTSP	7mm Spitz SP	7mm Match BTHP
Weight, grains	145	145	145
Ballistic Coefficient	0.472	0.416	0.468
Sectional Density	0.257	0.257	0.257
COAL Tested:	2.475"	2.475"	2.500"
Speer Part No.	1628	1629	1631

Propellant	START CHARGE		MAXIMUM CHARGE	
	Weight, grs	Muzzle Velocity, ft/sec	Weight, grs	Muzzle Velocity, ft/sec
H322	25.0	1961	27.0	2118
AA 2520	27.0	1970	29.0	2116
AA 2015	23.5	1940	25.5	2105
IMR 4895	26.5	1952	28.5	2099
H4895	26.0	1941	28.0	2090
BL-C(2)	27.5	1901	29.5C	2039
Viht. N130	22.0	1855	24.0	2024
H335	26.0	1874	28.0	2018
IMR 3031	25.2	1868	27.2C	2016
748	28.0	1856	30.0C	1989
Reloder 7	20.0	1702	22.0	1872

0.284"	7mm Spitz BTSP	7mm Spitz SP	7mm MT SP
Weight, grains	160	160	160
Ballistic Coefficient	0.519	0.504	0.340
Sectional Density	0.283	0.283	0.283
COAL Tested:	2.670"	2.670"	2.670"
Speer Part No.	1634	1635	1637

	START CHARGE		MAXIMUM CHARGE	
Propellant	Weight, grs	Muzzle Velocity, ft/sec	Weight, grs	Muzzle Velocity, ft/sec
H322	24.5	1838	26.5	1988
IMR 4895	25.5	1828	27.5	1971
H4895	25.5	1797	27.5C	1938
AA 2460	25.5	1792	27.5	1932
IMR 3031	24.5	1770	26.5	1914
748	27.0	1768	29.0	1899
H335	26.0	1754	28.0	1889
BL-C(2)	26.0	1745	28.0	1879
AA 2015	22.5	1725	24.5	1878
Viht. N130	20.0	1615	22.0	1776
Reloder 7	18.5	1553	20.5	1721

*Maximum Loads should be used with CAUTION • C = Compressed Load • *Magnum Primer used with this powder.*

7-30 Waters

Although developed for lever-action rifles, the 7-30 Waters is an effective handgun cartridge in the Thompson/Center Contender. From a 14-inch barrel, the cartridge can be used out to 150 yards on game animals up to the size of whitetail deer. The 110-grain TNT hollow point exiting the muzzle at nearly 2500 ft/sec gives excellent performance on varmints over the same ranges. It is safe to say that the 7-30 is one of the better factory Contender cartridges for the deer hunter and is still listed as a standard chambering at press time.

It's true that many 7mm wildcat pistol cartridges equal or exceed the performance of the 7-30 in a handgun. However, you can use the 7-30 Waters and avoid the extra cost of custom barrels and dies. You will give up little or nothing in real-world game performance. Compare the velocities of 145-grain 7-30 Waters loads in this section with 140-grain loads for the 6.5 JDJ, a successful proprietary hunting cartridge also conceived for Contenders. The handloader has the advantage of being able to use spitzer bullets in the single-shot T/C, something the 7-30 lever-action rifle owner must absolutely avoid.

Velocity differences between our 24-inch Winchester rifle and the 14-inch Contender were small. With several powders, velocity loss in the pistol was less than 200 ft/sec. The overall cartridge length used for these loads was the same as we used in the 7-30 rifle. If your Contender has a relatively long throat, seating the bullets out somewhat may improve accuracy.

We do not list loads for bullets heavier than 145 grains. The velocities of heavy bullets in the pistol are rather low, meaning uncertain expansion and excessive bullet drop over the handgun's effective range. This isn't a concern for the silhouette shooter but the 7-30 is most popular as a hunting cartridge.

Like many other single-shot pistol cartridges, we recommend that you neck size for top accuracy and case life. If factory 7-30 cases are hard to find, 30-30 cases can be full-length sized in a 7-30 Waters sizer die and, if needed, length trimmed.

For background information on the 7-30 Waters, see the Rifle section. The pressure limit is 40,000 CUP and these loads stay within that limit.

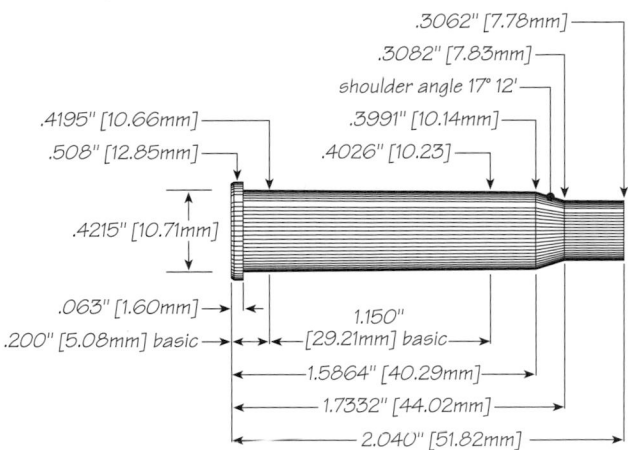

.3062" [7.78mm]
.3082" [7.83mm]
shoulder angle 17° 12'
.4195" [10.66mm]
.508" [12.85mm]
.3991" [10.14mm]
.4026" [10.23]
.4215" [10.71mm]
.063" [1.60mm]
.200" [5.08mm] basic
1.150"
[29.21mm] basic
1.5864" [40.29mm]
1.7332" [44.02mm]
2.040" [51.82mm]

Max. Case Length:	2.040"	Cart. Case:	Federal
Trim-to Length:	2.030"	Primer:	CCI 200; 250*
Max Cart. OAL:	2.550"	Test Firearm:	Thompson/Center Contender
RCBS Shell Holder:	#2	Barrel Length:	14"

0.284"	7mm TNT HP	7mm HP
Weight, grains	110	115
Ballistic Coefficient	0.384	0.250
Sectional Density	0.195	0.204
COAL Tested:	2.550"	2.550"
Speer Part No.	1616	1617

Propellant	START CHARGE		MAXIMUM CHARGE	
	Weight, grs	Muzzle Velocity, ft/sec	Weight, grs	Muzzle Velocity, ft/sec
748*	35.0	2191	39.0	2463
Viht. N135	31.0	2092	35.0	2462
AA 2015	29.0	2253	33.0	2451
H4895	32.0	2147	36.0	2449
H335*	32.0	2216	36.0	2422
Reloder 15	33.0	2079	37.0	2421
IMR 3031	30.0	2124	34.0	2376
AA 2230*	27.5	2163	31.5	2376
IMR 4895	30.5	2155	34.5	2375

David Biery, son-in-law of Tom Saleen, Director of International Sales, ATK CCI/Speer Operations; 270 Win 150-grain, Grand Slam®; bull elk; Idaho.

0.284"	7mm Spitz SP	7mm Spitz BTSP
Weight, grains	130	130
Ballistic Coefficient	0.368	0.424
Sectional Density	0.230	0.230
COAL Tested:	2.550"	2.550"
Speer Part No.	1623	1624

| Propellant | START CHARGE | | MAXIMUM CHARGE | |
	Weight, grs	Muzzle Velocity, ft/sec	Weight, grs	Muzzle Velocity, ft/sec
Reloder 15	31.5	2037	35.5	2327
748*	31.0	2005	35.0	2304
H4895	30.0	2022	34.0	2294
IMR 3031	29.0	1967	33.0	2264
Viht. N135	28.5	1969	32.5	2260
H335*	29.0	1996	33.0	2212
AA 2015	26.0	1976	30.0	2208
AA 2230*	26.0	1951	30.0	2188
Reloder 7	23.0	1914	27.0	2137

*Maximum Loads should be used with CAUTION • C = Compressed Load • *Magnum Primer used with this powder.*

0.284"	7mm Spitz BTSP	7mm Spitz SP	7mm Match BTHP
Weight, grains	145	145	145
Ballistic Coefficient	0.472	0.416	0.468
Sectional Density	0.257	0.257	0.257
COAL Tested:	2.550"	2.550"	2.550"
Speer Part No.	1628	1629	1631

	START CHARGE		MAXIMUM CHARGE	
Propellant	Weight, grs	Muzzle Velocity, ft/sec	Weight, grs	Muzzle Velocity, ft/sec
Reloder 15	35.0	2006	35.0	2294
IMR 4895	33.5	1964	33.5	2237
Viht. N135	33.0	2002	33.0	2225
H4895	33.0	1947	33.0	2202
AA 2015	30.0	1908	30.0	2185
H335*	32.0	1920	32.0	2094
IMR 3031	31.0	1808	31.0	2092
748*	34.0	1937	34.0	2066
AA 2230	28.0	1740	28.0	2034
Reloder 7	25.0	1726	25.0	1967

*Maximum Loads should be used with CAUTION • C = Compressed Load • *Magnum Primer used with this powder.*

30 M1 Carbine

Although not very effective in rifles, the 30 Carbine cartridge qualifies as a high-performance varmint cartridge for handguns. From the cartridge's earliest days, custom gunsmiths have created handguns with varying degrees of success. However, interest spiked when Ruger added the 30 Carbine as a standard chambering for their rugged single-action Blackhawk revolver. Thompson/Center also chambered Contender barrels in 30 Carbine and barrels are still available from T/C's Custom Shop. Ironically, either handgun can shoot tighter groups than the majority of military surplus M1 carbines.

The 30 Carbine is in the same pressure class as the 357 Magnum. The case is slightly tapered requiring you to remove all traces of lubricant from the cartridge and the revolver's chambers before firing. An oily case will slide back when fired and wedge against the breech face, locking up the cylinder. A carbide sizer die eliminates the need for case lube and is well worth the small added cost if you shoot a 30 Carbine revolver.

Speer's 110-grain round nose and spire point bullets can be used but will not give the explosive expansion produced by the 100-grain Plinker and the 110-grain Varminter hollow point at handgun velocities. The 30 Carbine handgun has a well-earned reputation for muzzle blast. You'll only forget your ear protection once!

The 30 Carbine is best used as a varmint cartridge. For this purpose, its flat trajectory and accuracy in a quality handgun make hitting targets easy at longer ranges. The 30 Carbine cartridge should not be used on deer-sized or larger animals.

Some 30 Carbine semi-automatic pistols exist and we recommend your reloads for these closely match factory ballistics for reliable operation. Of the loads here, those with H110 and 296 will most closely approximate commercial and military ammo.

Note that the data shows the use of small rifle primers. The case mouth controls headspace so a taper crimp is required to avoid misfires and accuracy problems. Best accuracy is obtained when cases are of uniform length.

For additional information on the 30 Carbine, see the Rifle section.

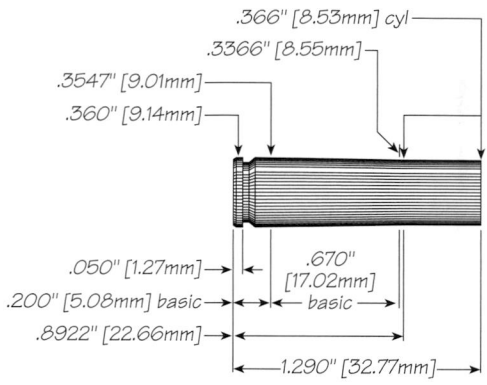

Max. Case Length:	1.290"	Cart. Case:	IMI Commercial
Trim-to Length:	1.280"	Primer:	CCI 400; 450*
Max Cart. OAL:	1.690"	Test Firearm:	Ruger Blackhawk
RCBS Shell Holder:	#17	Barrel Length:	7.5"

0.308"	30 RN SP
Weight, grains	100
Ballistic Coefficient	0.144
Sectional Density	0.151
COAL Tested:	1.620"
Speer Part No.	1805

Propellant	START CHARGE		MAXIMUM CHARGE	
	Weight, grs	Muzzle Velocity, ft/sec	Weight, grs	Muzzle Velocity, ft/sec
H110*	14.5	1475	15.5	1589
296*	14.5	1415	15.5	1527
2400	11.7	1385	12.7	1476
IMR 4227	13.5	1312	14.5	1417
Viht. N110	12.0	1306	13.0C	1394
IMR 4198	14.5	1116	15.5C	1201
Unique	4.5	938	5.5	1142
AA 1680	15.0	1077	16.0C	1126

0.308"	30 HP	30 RN SP
Weight, grains	110	110
Ballistic Coefficient	0.128	0.136
Sectional Density	0.166	0.166
COAL Tested:	1.675"	1.675"
Speer Part No.	1835	1845

Propellant	START CHARGE		MAXIMUM CHARGE	
	Weight, grs	Muzzle Velocity, ft/sec	Weight, grs	Muzzle Velocity, ft/sec
H110*	13.7	1315	14.7	1418
IMR 4227	13.5	1281	14.5	1387
296*	14.0	1259	15.0	1363
2400	10.2	1132	11.2	1261
Viht. N110	11.5	1164	12.5	1253
IMR 4198	14.0	967	15.0	1046
AA 1680	15.0	973	16.0	1040
Unique	4.5	779	5.5	945

*Maximum Loads should be used with CAUTION • C = Compressed Load • *Magnum Primer used with this powder.*

30-30 Winchester

The introduction of 30-30 barrels for the Thompson/Center Contender gave handgun hunting a real boost. Although not as powerful as some wildcat and proprietary 30-caliber pistol cartridges like the 30 Herrett and the 309 JDJ, the 30-30 has the advantage of nearly universal ammo and brass availability. Within its range limitations the 30-30 pistol loaded with soft point bullets is suitable for most deer. The light hollow point bullets have an explosive effect on varmints.

T/C barrels have been available in both 10 and 14-inch lengths. The blast and recoil in the shorter barrel may prove more than some people care to experience. The cartridge offers improved performance and shows much better manners in the longer barrel. Older *Speer Manuals* showed velocities in a 10-inch barrel. We chose the 14-inch tube because it has become more popular. Measured velocities from the 14-inch barrel were surprisingly high—not too far behind typical carbine velocities. This extra velocity means that spitzer bullets not suitable for 30-30 lever-action rifles are effective on game in a handgun.

The overall cartridge lengths we list here for the 125 and 150-grain bullets are greater than those used in a 30-30 rifle and exceed the industry length specification. Because our 30-30 Contender has a generous throat, we seated the bullets out for better accuracy. Since this data was developed, we have seen newer Contender barrels in this caliber with shorter throats. Try the longer length with a dummy round. If it hits the rifling, use the seating lengths we show in the Rifle section of this book. This case requires no charge weight adjustment for minor seating depth changes.

Neck sizing is recommended for the 30-30 Contender. For best results dedicate some new cases to the Contender and separate them from your 30-30 rifle cases.

The 130 and 150-grain flat points and the 150-grain round nose bullets are the better choice for 10-inch barrels. Their jacket construction and large exposed lead tips promote better expansion in short barrels. Like most other rifle cartridges fired in handguns, rifle primers are recommended.

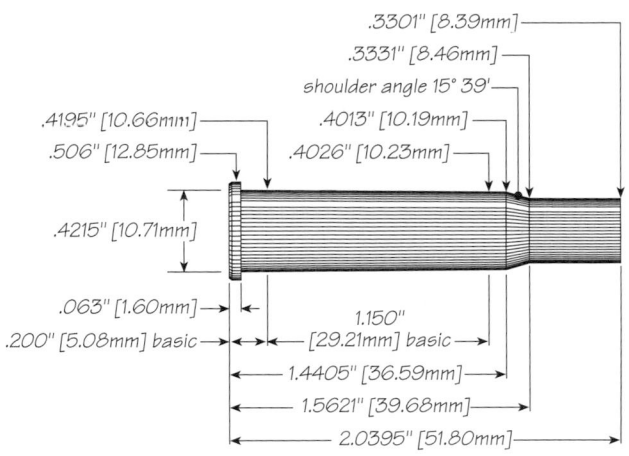

Max. Case Length:	2.039"	Cart. Case:	Winchester
Trim-to Length:	2.029"	Primer:	CCI 200; 250*
Max Cart. OAL:	Sec text	Test Firearm:	T/C Contender
RCBS Shell Holder:	#2	Barrel Length:	14"

0.308"	30 HP	30 RN SP	30 TMJ RN	30 Spire SP
Weight, grains	110	110	110	110
Ballistic Coefficient	0.128	0.136	0.179	0.245
Sectional Density	0.166	0.166	0.166	0.166
COAL Tested:	2.415"	2.415"	2.415"	2.530"
Speer Part No.	1835	1845	1846	1855

	START CHARGE		MAXIMUM CHARGE	
Propellant	Weight, grs	Muzzle Velocity, ft/sec	Weight, grs	Muzzle Velocity, ft/sec
Reloder 7	30.0	2356	**34.0**	2618
H322	31.0	2003	**35.0**	2373
748*	36.0	2111	**40.0C**	2343
AA 2015	30.0	1974	**34.0**	2340
IMR 4064	33.0	1912	**37.0C**	2266
IMR 4895	31.0	1884	**35.0**	2206
H4895	30.0	1853	**34.0**	2165
Viht. N133	27.0	1817	**31.0**	2153

*Maximum Loads should be used with CAUTION • C = Compressed Load • *Magnum Primer used with this powder.*

0.308"	30 TNT HP	30 HP	30 FN SP
Weight, grains	125	130	130
Ballistic Coefficient	0.341	0.244	0.213
Sectional Density	0.188	0.196	0.196
COAL Tested:	2.740"	2.730"	2.550"
Speer Part No.	1986	2005	2007

Propellant	START CHARGE Weight, grs	START CHARGE Muzzle Velocity, ft/sec	MAXIMUM CHARGE Weight, grs	MAXIMUM CHARGE Muzzle Velocity, ft/sec
Reloder 7	27.0	2095	31.0	2328
AA 2460*	30.0	2037	34.0	2313
AA 2520*	31.0	2060	35.0	2296
H322	29.0	1908	33.0	2260
Reloder 10X	26.5	1938	30.5	2131
Varget	31.0	1871	35.0	2106
Viht. N140	31.0	1868	35.0	2101
748*	31.5	1889	35.5	2096
IMR 4895	28.0	1686	32.0	1975
IMR 4064	29.0	1634	33.0	1937

0.308"	30 FN SP	30 RN SP	30 Spitz BTSP	30 Spitz SP	30 MT SP
Weight, grains	150	150	150	150	150
Ballistic Coefficient	0.255	0.235	0.417	0.377	0.278
Sectional Density	0.226	0.226	0.226	0.226	0.226
COAL Tested:	2.550"	2.600"	2.700"	2.700"	2.650"
Speer Part No.	2011	2017	2022	2023	2025

Propellant	START CHARGE		MAXIMUM CHARGE	
	Weight, grs	Muzzle Velocity, ft/sec	Weight, grs	Muzzle Velocity, ft/sec
748*	33.0	1956	37.0	2171
Reloder 7	25.0	1931	29.0	2144
H322	27.0	1780	31.0	2110
Viht. N140	30.0	1847	34.0	2078
AA 2520*	31.0	1853	35.0	2066
H335*	28.0	1841	32.0	2024
Varget	29.0	1776	33.0	2009
Reloder 10X	24.0	1732	28.0	1960
IMR 4895	27.0	1669	31.0	1955
IMR 4198	24.0	1287	26.0	1458

*Maximum Loads should be used with CAUTION • C = Compressed Load • *Magnum Primer used with this powder.*

32 Auto *(7.65mm Browning)*

The 32 Auto is, like the 25 Auto, a cartridge popularized by the efforts of John Browning and Colt. Colt's Model 1903 "Hammerless" pistol was based on a Browning design that proved to be one of the nicest pocket pistols ever built. Known for their compactness and reliability, these Colts are eagerly sought today by both collectors and shooters.

The 32 Auto was also very popular in Europe as the 7.65mm Browning Short. It was a primary European police cartridge for many years and was adopted for secondary military sidearms by some countries. Current ballistic specifications for U.S. ammo show a 71-grain bullet at 905 ft/sec and a 60-grain bullet at about 970 ft/sec.

Compact 9mm Luger and 380 Auto pistols have largely displaced the 32 Auto in the modern pocket pistol market but newer "ultra-compact" 32-caliber pistols such as the Seecamp and Beretta Tomcat have breathed new life into the old cartridge.

Speer makes one component bullet for the 32 Auto, the 60-grain Gold Dot hollow point. Bullseye, Red Dot, 231 and 700-X gave the most consistent velocities in this small case. The seating length we used for testing is the same as Speer Gold Dot ammunition, and is sufficiently short to fit the magazine of the diminutive Seecamp pistol.

Some surplus European military pistols may not give reliable function with light bullets or short cartridge lengths. They were designed for 73 to 77-grain bullets that are common in Europe. They may show sluggish cycling when American ammo with 71-grain bullets and refuse to operate with any 60-grain loads. Knowing what kind of factory ammo your pistol prefers helps when deciding to handload this cartridge. Newer commercial pistols should handle the loads shown here without problems. Our Walther PP fed the short Gold Dot without a hitch.

Many 32 Auto pistols have rudimentary sights and heavy trigger pulls that contribute to less-than-stellar accuracy. A 5-shot group of less than six inches at 25 yards is considered good for this cartridge. Some high-grade pistols are capable of better accuracy and allow the 32 Auto to be used for small game hunting or pest control at realistic distances.

Like the 25 Auto, small charge weight variations in the 32 Auto will make significant pressure changes. *Note that we recommend that the loads presented be used exactly as shown.* Reducing the charges even 0.2 grain results in extreme pressure and velocity variations. We strongly recommend that all charges be carefully hand-weighed to minimize such variations.

These loads are within the industry pressure limit of 20,500 psi.

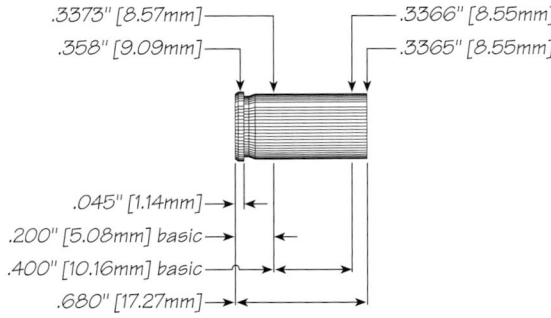

Max. Case Length:	0.680"	Cart. Case:	Speer
Trim-to Length:	0.675"	Primer:	CCI 500
Max Cart. OAL:	0.984"	Test Firearm:	Walter PP
RCBS Shell Holder:	#17	Barrel Length:	3.80"

0.312"	32 GDHP
Weight, grains	60
Ballistic Coefficient	0.118
Sectional Density	0.088
COAL Tested:	0.940"
Speer Part No.	3986

Propellant	START CHARGE Weight, grs	START CHARGE Muzzle Velocity, ft/sec	MAXIMUM CHARGE Weight, grs	MAXIMUM CHARGE Muzzle Velocity, ft/sec
700-X	DNR	—	2.6	1060
TiteGroup	DNR	—	2.6	1058
Power Pistol	DNR	—	3.6	1030
Bullseye	DNR	—	2.6	1030
Red Dot	DNR	—	2.3	1030
H. Universal	DNR	—	3.0	1021
231	DNR	—	2.8	1007
Unique	DNR	—	3.2	971
AA No. 2	DNR	—	2.6	963

DNR — do not reduce

*Maximum Loads should be used with CAUTION • C = Compressed Load • *Magnum Primer used with this powder.*

32 S&W Long *(32 Colt New Police)*

The 32 S&W Long Cartridge dates to the end of the 19th century when it was introduced in Smith & Wesson's First Model Hand Ejector revolver. Colt and other manufacturers—both domestic and European—soon picked up the cartridge and both breaktop and solid frame revolvers were chambered for the new 32 Long.

There was a time when the 32 S&W Long was popular in America as a police service revolver. The 38 Special quickly usurped the 32-caliber for this purpose but the 32 Long stayed popular for snub-nose revolvers until 38 Special "snubbies" appeared. Current factory ammunition is loaded with a 98-grain lead round nose bullet at a nominal velocity of 705 ft/sec. Federal also loads a 98-grain wadcutter for target use. This cartridge is capable of fine accuracy in a quality handgun and the 32 S&W Long wadcutter load is still a popular European target cartridge in high-grade match pistols such as the semi-automatic Walther GSP.

Speer makes three bullets that are appropriate for reloading the 32 S&W Long. The 60-grain Gold Dot hollow point is designed for the 32 Auto but can be used for high-velocity revolver loads. The bullet lacks a crimping cannelure but this can be safely overcome. Use the COAL shown and roll a crimp over the bullet ogive (see photo).

The .312" 100-grain JHP can be used for plinking and small game hunting. Be sure to apply a heavy crimp and use the recommended loads only in quality revolvers that have a barrel/cylinder gap of .008 inches or smaller to avoid leaving a bullet in the bore. Note that several propellants are marked "DNR" meaning "do not reduce." Reduced loads with these propellants produced velocities too low for jacketed bullets fired in revolvers.

The Speer 98-grain hollow base wadcutter is a very accurate bullet designed for target use. The HBWC is seated flush with the case mouth and lightly crimped. The loads shown for this bullet may not reach maximum pressures but produced

The proper seating and crimping of the 60-grain Gold Dot® in the 32 S&W Long.

top accuracy in our test pistol. Do not exceed these load recommendations to avoid deforming the bullet base.

We show new data for bullets cast from RCBS bullet moulds for the 32-caliber 98-grain flat point bullet and the newer 90-grain Cowboy bullet. These bullets are very accurate and their flat point makes them effective on small game like rabbits. We used a Smith & Wesson M31 with a three-inch barrel for the velocity testing with the cast bullets and the 60-grain Gold Dot.

The 32 S&W Long is identical to the 32 Colt New Police cartridge, but is not interchangeable with the 32 Long Colt cartridge. *This reloading data is for the 32 S&W Long and 32 Colt New Police cartridges only.*

Consult a qualified gunsmith if you are unsure which of the various 32 cartridges your revolver requires. These loads are intended for solid-frame revolvers in good condition. Ask the gunsmith to evaluate the revolver's quality before firing the gun. Many older or imported revolvers may be unsafe to fire with any ammunition. The SAAMI maximum pressure for the 32 Long is 15,000 psi.

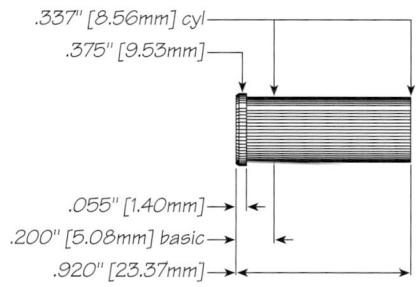

Max. Case Length:	0.920"	**Cart. Case:**	Remington
Trim-to Length:	0.910"	**Primer:**	CCI 500
Max Cart. OAL:	1.280"	**Test Firearm:**	See data blocks
RCBS Shell Holder:	#23	**Barrel Length:**	—

0.314"	32-90 CM
Weight, grains	90
Lead Alloy	hard
Ballistic Coefficient	0.110
Sectional Density	0.130
COAL Tested:	1.190"
RCBS Mould No.	82303

	START CHARGE		MAXIMUM CHARGE	
Propellant	Weight, grs	Muzzle Velocity, ft/sec	Weight, grs	Muzzle Velocity, ft/sec
TiteGroup	2.1	727	2.5	844
700-X	2.2	734	2.5	811
231	2.4	712	2.7	805
AA No. 2 Impr.	2.3	728	2.6	800
Bullseye	1.9	672	2.3	794
Red Dot	1.8	640	2.3	769
Nitro 100	1.8	683	2.1	741

NOTE: *We sell bullet moulds, not cast bullets. These bullets were cast in RCBS moulds. Contact your dealer for more information on the RCBS line of premium bullet casting equipment, or visit on the Internet at www.rcbs.com. Test Firearm: S&W M31 3"*

*Maximum Loads should be used with CAUTION • C = Compressed Load • *Magnum Primer used with this powder.*

0.314"	32-098 SWC
Weight, grains	98
Lead Alloy	hard
Ballistic Coefficient	0.134
Sectional Density	0.141
COAL Tested:	1.280"
RCBS Mould No.	82061

| Propellant | START CHARGE | | MAXIMUM CHARGE | |
	Weight, grs	Muzzle Velocity, ft/sec	Weight, grs	Muzzle Velocity, ft/sec
Viht. 3N37	3.5	752	3.7	838
2400	5.2	705	5.6	801
AA No. 9	5.3	742	5.7	800
231	2.4	722	2.7	797
H. Universal	2.8	748	3.0	785
Bullseye	2.1	705	2.3	770
Unique	2.5	662	2.8	769
WSF	2.5	671	2.8	761
AA No. 5	3.3	663	3.8	755
Red Dot	1.8	635	2.1	700

NOTE: *We sell bullet moulds, not cast bullets. These bullets were cast in RCBS moulds. Contact your dealer for more information on the RCBS line of premium bullet casting equipment, or visit on the Internet at www.rcbs.com. Test Firearm: S&W M31 3"*

0.314"	32 HBWC
Weight, grains	98
Ballistic Coefficient	0.044
Sectional Density	0.142
COAL Tested:	0.920"
Speer Part No.	4600

Propellant	START CHARGE		MAXIMUM CHARGE	
	Weight, grs	Muzzle Velocity, ft/sec	Weight, grs	Muzzle Velocity, ft/sec
Bullseye	1.6	674	1.8	777
Red Dot	1.6	703	1.8	771
HP-38	1.7	689	1.9	765
Herco	2.0	700	2.2	758
AA No. 5	2.5	701	2.7	756
231	1.7	672	1.9	739
PB	1.5	649	1.7	735
Unique	1.8	663	2.0	733
700-X	1.5	720	1.7	733

NOTE: *Test Firearm: Walther GSP 4"*

*Maximum Loads should be used with CAUTION • C = Compressed Load • *Magnum Primer used with this powder.*

0.312"	32 GDHP
Weight, grains	60
Ballistic Coefficient	0.118
Sectional Density	0.088
COAL Tested:	1.105"
Speer Part No.	3986

Propellant	START CHARGE		MAXIMUM CHARGE	
	Weight, grs	Muzzle Velocity, ft/sec	Weight, grs	Muzzle Velocity, ft/sec
700-X	2.5	834	3.2	1025
231	2.7	839	3.4	1014
Bullseye	2.4	836	3.0	1003
TiteGroup	2.5	834	3.0	975
Red Dot	2.1	782	2.7	946
AA No. 2 Impr.	2.5	800	3.0	933

NOTE: *Test Firearm: S&W M31 3"*

0.312"	32 JHP
Weight, grains	100
Ballistic Coefficient	0.167
Sectional Density	0.147
COAL Tested:	1.185"
Speer Part No.	3981

Propellant	START CHARGE		MAXIMUM CHARGE	
	Weight, grs	Muzzle Velocity, ft/sec	Weight, grs	Muzzle Velocity, ft/sec
H110	6.3	629	7.0	769
AA No. 9	5.1	663	5.6	769
296	6.0	635	6.6	742
2400	5.0	660	5.5	733
HS-6	DNR	—	4.1	720
WSF	DNR	—	3.0	715
Viht. 3N37	DNR	—	3.5	700
H. Universal	DNR	—	3.0	694
231	DNR	—	2.6	676
AA No. 5	DNR	—	3.8	675

NOTE: *Test Firearm: S&W K32 6"; DNR — do not reduce*

Maximum Loads should be used with CAUTION • C = Compressed Load • *Magnum Primer used with this powder.

32 H&R Magnum

Harrington & Richardson and Federal Cartridge jointly announced the 32 H&R Magnum in 1983. It is a more powerful version of the 32 S&W Long cartridge with a longer case and a 75 percent higher maximum pressure.

For a time only H&R made 32 Magnum revolvers but soon Ruger modified its popular rimfire Single-Six single-action to centerfire and offered it in 32 Magnum. Smith & Wesson, Dan Wesson and Charter have chambered revolvers for this cartridge. Revolvers chambered for the 32 Magnum can also fire 32 S&W Long ammunition.

Federal loads factory ammunition with either an 85-grain JHP or a 95-grain lead semi-wadcutter. In our test revolver, the 95-grain factory load achieved 1030 ft/sec and the 85-grain load clocked at 1090 ft/sec.

The extra power of the 32 Magnum compared to the 32 S&W Long makes it a nice field cartridge. The .312" Speer 100-grain JHP will expand well at maximum load levels and its flat trajectory is handy for long shots. The little Ruger with its adjustable sights was quite accurate at ranges well beyond 100 yards.

The reloader can safely surpass factory ammo's energy by using the Speer 100-grain JHP bullet. This bullet can exceed 1100 ft/sec and top loads produced nearly 290 ft/lbs of energy. When using the slower burning propellants, be sure to give the bullet a firm crimp to insure reliable ignition and consistent performance. We also list loads for a Speer 85-grain JHP. This bullet was discontinued in 2006 but we include it for those with a supply of them.

Federal discontinued selling new, unprimed H&R Magnum cases but Starline (Sedalia, MO; www.starlinebrass.com) offers 32 Magnum cases to handloaders.

The 98-grain wadcutter loads are not loaded to maximum pressure. However, these are the highest charge weights that avoid deformation of the bullet base and still afford good accuracy. The 98-grain cast flat nose bullet from RCBS mould number 82061 may be used with the 100-grain jacketed bullet data. Bullets for the higher velocity loads should be cast from a hard lead alloy for best results. The quicker-burning propellants like Bullseye and Red Dot produce velocities in the range required for Cowboy Action shooting.

32 H&R Magnum

The SAAMI maximum pressure for the 32 H&R Magnum is 21,000 CUP, slightly higher than the 38 Special +P. These loads remain within this limit.

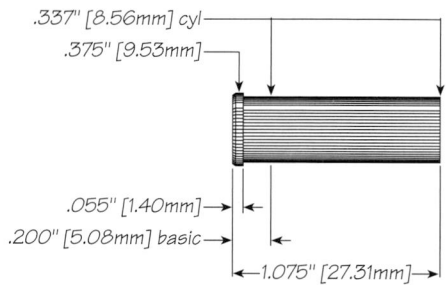

Max. Case Length:	1.075"	**Cart. Case:**	Federal
Trim-to Length:	1.065"	**Primer:**	CCI 500
Max Cart. OAL:	1.350"	**Test Firearm:**	Ruger Single Six
RCBS Shell Holder:	#23	**Barrel Length:**	5.5"

0.312"	32 JHP
Weight, grains	85
Ballistic Coefficient	0.121
Sectional Density	0.125
COAL Tested:	1.340"
Speer Part No.	3987

Propellant	START CHARGE Weight, grs	START CHARGE Muzzle Velocity, ft/sec	MAXIMUM CHARGE Weight, grs	MAXIMUM CHARGE Muzzle Velocity, ft/sec
Unique	4.1	1101	4.7	1240
H. Universal	4.1	1119	4.5	1198
700-X	3.4	1040	4.0	1178
Viht. 3N37	4.7	1091	5.1	1163
Bullseye	3.5	1088	3.9	1162
TiteGroup	3.4	1030	3.9	1157
231	3.7	1064	4.2	1149
AA No. 5	5.3	1047	5.9	1142
American Select	3.3	1002	4.0	1113
AA No. 2 Impr.	3.4	973	4.2	1098

0.312"	32 JHP
Weight, grains	100
Ballistic Coefficient	0.167
Sectional Density	0.147
COAL Tested:	1.345"
Speer Part No.	3981

Propellant	START CHARGE		MAXIMUM CHARGE	
	Weight, grs	Muzzle Velocity, ft/sec	Weight, grs	Muzzle Velocity, ft/sec
H110	9.5	1039	10.5	1140
H. Universal	4.0	998	4.5	1110
Herco	4.3	985	4.7	1104
AA No. 5	5.2	979	5.7	1096
AA No. 7	6.3	1025	6.9	1094
2400	7.0	987	7.7	1091
AA No. 9	7.1	1017	7.8	1090
HS-6	5.5	978	6.1	1088
Viht. N110	8.1	970	9.0	1080
Unique	3.9	978	4.4	1074
Green Dot	3.7	957	4.2	1067
Super Field	4.0	940	4.5	1045
Red Dot	3.2	935	3.6	1018
Bullseye	3.1	899	3.6	1000
231	3.4	892	3.9	991

*Maximum Loads should be used with CAUTION • C = Compressed Load • *Magnum Primer used with this powder.*

0.314"	32 HBWC
Weight, grains	98
Ballistic Coefficient	0.044
Sectional Density	0.142
COAL Tested:	1.075"
Speer Part No.	4600

	START CHARGE		MAXIMUM CHARGE	
Propellant	Weight, grs	Muzzle Velocity, ft/sec	Weight, grs	Muzzle Velocity, ft/sec
AA No. 5	3.2	783	3.4	843
Unique	2.8	770	3.0	814
PB	2.2	760	2.4	812
Bullseye	2.1	752	2.3	810
Red Dot	2.1	735	2.3	805
HP-38	2.3	740	2.5	801
700-X	2.0	735	2.2	792
Green Dot	2.3	751	2.5	791
231	2.2	742	2.4	778

*Maximum Loads should be used with CAUTION • C = Compressed Load • *Magnum Primer used with this powder.*

32-20 Winchester *(Revolver)*

(The loads in this section do not exceed standard pressures)

It was once both fashionable and prudent to pack a revolver and rifle chambered for the same cartridge. Winchester developed a trio of lever-action rifle cartridges—the 32-20, 38-40 and 44-40. Colt soon chambered them in its famous Single Action Army revolver to meet the "dual-gun" concept.

Both Colt and Smith & Wesson sold 32-20 revolvers until the Second World War began. In addition to the Single Action Army, Colt produced both medium- and small-frame double-action revolvers. Smith & Wesson chambered their Military & Police model in 32-20. The 38 Special was so popular by 1940 that the smaller cartridge was dropped. However, there are still many serviceable 32-20 revolvers around that deserve to be shot if they are in good shape.

Cowboy Action Shooting has renewed interest in the dual-gun cartridges like the 32-20 and new revolvers are again available. Fine accuracy, light recoil and the nostalgia of a century-old cartridge keep the 32-20 alive. Match rules require a lead bullet at 1000 ft/sec or less. RCBS makes a bullet mould that casts the perfect lead bullet for CAS competition.

Check the barrel-cylinder gap of any older revolver before shooting it. The industry's maximum allowable gap is 0.012 inches but we feel a maximum of 0.008 inches is better for all-around performance. An oversized gap can cause a bullet to lodge in the barrel. Sizing cast bullets to .001" over chamber throat diameter helps avoid stuck bullets, too. Do not load below the starting loads shown here. The start loads were selected to produce a minimum of about 12,000 CUP to avoid problems with inconsistent performance.

These loads are within the 32-20's 16,000 CUP pressure limit. See the Rifle section for more information.

• • • • •

Editor's Note: *Thanks to Hamilton Bowen of Bowen Classic Arms for his excellent conversion of a "worn-out" 357 Magnum Ruger Blackhawk to 32-20.*

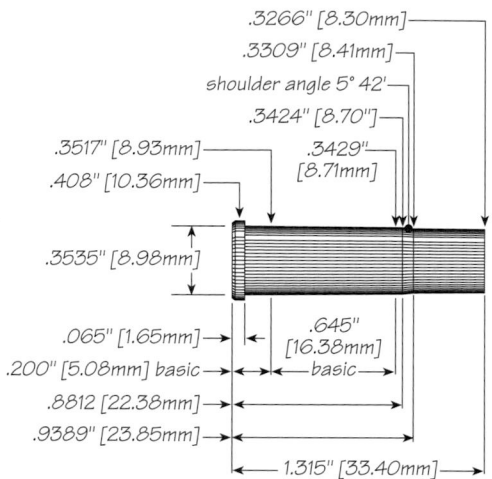

.3266" [8.30mm]
.3309" [8.41mm]
shoulder angle 5° 42'
.3424" [8.70"]
.3517" [8.93mm]
.3429"
[8.71mm]
.408" [10.36mm]
.3535" [8.98mm]
.065" [1.65mm]
.645"
[16.38mm]
.200" [5.08mm] basic
basic
.8812 [22.38mm]
.9389" [23.85mm]
1.315" [33.40mm]

Max. Case Length:	1.315"	**Cart. Case:**	Starline
Trim-to Length:	1.305"	**Primer:**	CCI 500
Max Cart. OAL:	1.592"	**Test Firearm:**	Bowen Classic Arms Custom Ruger
RCBS Shell Holder:	#1	**Barrel Length:**	7.5"

0.314"	32-098 SWC
Weight, grains	98
Lead Alloy	hard
Ballistic Coefficient	0.134
Sectional Density	0.141
COAL Tested:	1.530"
RCBS Mould No.	82061

Propellant	START CHARGE		MAXIMUM CHARGE	
	Weight, grs	Muzzle Velocity, ft/sec	Weight, grs	Muzzle Velocity, ft/sec
AA No. 7	5.4	934	6.1	1072
AA No. 5	4.5	942	5.1	1046
Power Pistol	3.9	915	4.4	1033
Viht. 3N37	3.8	877	4.3	1018
H. Universal	3.4	915	3.8	1016
Unique	3.0	875	3.5	969
700-X	2.7	879	3.1	963
TiteGroup	2.6	848	3.0	956
231	2.9	816	3.3	941
Bullseye	2.4	797	2.9	937

NOTE: *We sell bullet moulds, not cast bullets. These bullets were cast in RCBS moulds. Contact your dealer for more information on the RCBS line of premium bullet casting equipment, or visit on the Internet at www.rcbs.com.*

*Maximum Loads should be used with CAUTION • C = Compressed Load • *Magnum Primer used with this powder.*

32-20 Winchester *(Contender Only)*

Metallic silhouette handgun competition caused shooters to look at different case configurations including some very old cartridges. One of these was the 32-20 Winchester case. For the Field Pistol class where the longest shots are 100 meters, a small 30-caliber cartridge with light recoil and reasonable velocity was needed. The 32-20 case, carefully loaded to pressures appropriate to the Contender action, would topple steel targets with regularity.

Thompson/Center introduced 32-20 barrels for their excellent Contender single-shot pistol. They chose to make the groove diameter .308" (instead of the standard .311" diameter) to allow more flexibility in the choice of bullets. The Contender gives excellent accuracy with Speer 30-caliber bullets from 100 to 130 grains.

To load the 32-20 T/C with 0.308" jacketed bullets you must replace the original expander plug with one no larger than 0.307" for properly bullet grip. Contact your die manufacturer for the correct plug. New cases may require neck sizing before loading 0.308" jacketed bullets.

The 32-20 case is relatively thin compared to more modern cartridges. Use new or once-fired cases when assembling these loads. We recommend neck sizing over full-length sizing to extend case life and improve accuracy.

Important Note: *These loads are for the Thompson/Center Contender ONLY. Do not use them in any other 32-20 firearm. 32-20 T/C pressures are higher than 32-20 Winchester. Do not substitute the Speer .312" 100-grain hollow point for the .308" Plinker.*

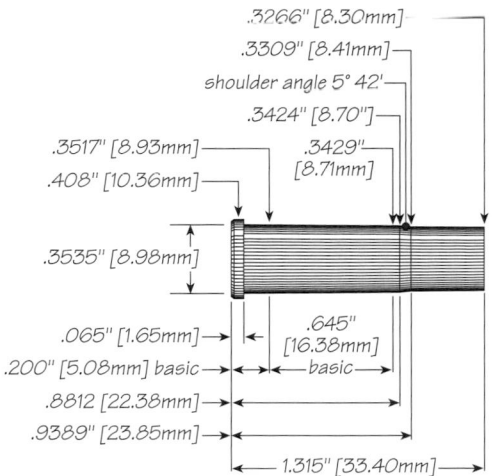

.3266" [8.30mm]

.3309" [8.41mm]

shoulder angle 5° 42'

.3424" [8.70"]

.3517" [8.93mm]

.3429" [8.71mm]

.408" [10.36mm]

.3535" [8.98mm]

.065" [1.65mm]

.645" [16.38mm] basic

.200" [5.08mm] basic

.8812 [22.38mm]

.9389" [23.85mm]

1.315" [33.40mm]

Max. Case Length:	1.315"	Cart. Case:	Winchester
Trim-to Length:	1.305"	Primer:	CCI 500
Max Cart. OAL:	n/a	Test Firearm:	T/C Contender
RCBS Shell Holder:	#1	Barrel Length:	10"

0.308"	30 RNSP
Weight, grains	100
Ballistic Coefficient	0.144
Sectional Density	0.151
COAL Tested:	1.710"
Speer Part No.	1805

	START CHARGE		MAXIMUM CHARGE	
Propellant	Weight, grs	Muzzle Velocity, ft/sec	Weight, grs	Muzzle Velocity, ft/sec
H110	16.0	1734	17.0	1908
296	15.5	1646	16.5	1897
AA No. 9	13.0	1666	14.0	1833
IMR 4227	15.5	1637	16.5C	1831
2400	12.0	1595	13.0	1793
HS-6	9.1	1606	10.1	1713
Herco	8.1	1587	9.1	1712
IMR 4198	17.0	1527	18.0C	1683
SR 4759	12.0	1326	13.0C	1582

NOTE: *Do not substitute the .312" 100-grain JHP (#3981) for the 100-grain RNSP.*

0.308"	30 HP	30 RNSP	30 Spire SP
Weight, grains	110	110	110
Ballistic Coefficient	0.128	0.136	0.245
Sectional Density	0.166	0.166	0.166
COAL Tested:	1.710"	1.710"	1.800"
Speer Part No.	1835	1845	1855

Propellant	START CHARGE		MAXIMUM CHARGE	
	Weight, grs	Muzzle Velocity, ft/sec	Weight, grs	Muzzle Velocity, ft/sec
H110	15.0	1598	16.0	1813
296	14.5	1610	15.5	1765
AA No. 9	12.5	1579	13.5	1739
IMR 4227	15.0	1540	16.0	1730
2400	11.0	1371	12.0	1594
IMR 4198	16.0	1375	17.0C	1576
SR 4759	12.0	1279	13.0C	1566
Herco	7.4	1472	8.4	1552
HS-6	8.1	1484	9.1	1539

*Maximum Loads should be used with CAUTION • C = Compressed Load • *Magnum Primer used with this powder.*

0.308"	30 HP	30 FN SP
Weight, grains	130	130
Ballistic Coefficient	0.244	0.213
Sectional Density	0.196	0.196
COAL Tested:	1.910"	1.865"
Speer Part No.	2005	2007

Propellant	START CHARGE Weight, grs	START CHARGE Muzzle Velocity, ft/sec	MAXIMUM CHARGE Weight, grs	MAXIMUM CHARGE Muzzle Velocity, ft/sec
H110	14.0	1479	15.0	1664
IMR 4227	14.5	1479	15.5C	1645
AA No. 9	12.0	1476	13.0	1632
296	13.5	1443	14.5	1602
SR 4759	12.0	1256	13.0	1489
2400	10.5	1234	11.5	1488
IMR 4198	15.0	1339	16.0C	1453
Herco	6.8	1270	7.8	1387
HS-6	7.6	1246	8.6	1340

*Maximum Loads should be used with CAUTION • C = Compressed Load • *Magnum Primer used with this powder.*

380 Auto

The 380 Auto was introduced to U.S. shooters in 1908 when Colt chambered it in the Pocket Automatic, a compact and well-built pistol designed by John Browning. The cartridge was also introduced in Europe as the 9mm Browning Short. In an era when some people considered a 32-caliber pistol a "big gun," the 380 Auto created quite a splash. It was compact enough to be adapted to any pistol that could handle the 32 Auto cartridge yet offered a distinct ballistic advantage. Remington and Savage— names associated today with rifles and shotguns—designed and produced semi-automatic pistols chambered for the 380 in the decades between the World Wars.

Following the Second World War, no American gun makers chambered pistols for the 380 but there were plenty of new and surplus imported guns available. Factory ammunition was limited to a single load—a 95-grain FMJ bullet with a nominal muzzle velocity of 950 ft/sec. Because there is so much variation in chamber and bore dimensions, many factory loads did not meet this specification in production pistols.

In the 1970's new, high-quality pistols began to appear on the market. At the same time, ammo makers offered hollow point bullets to improve the terminal effects of the cartridge. The 380 Auto has always been a popular back-up gun for peace officers and is often chosen for home defense. It will never challenge the performance of the 9mm Luger but is far ahead of the 32 Auto for defense when loaded with modern JHP ammunition.

Most 380 pistols have rudimentary sights better suited for concealed carry and trigger pulls are often heavy. As a result, the 380 isn't much of a target or hunting pistol. There are exceptions of course: quality Walthers, SIG's, Berettas and others can give exceptional accuracy with good ammo.

Although not as widely reloaded as other centerfire pistol cartridges, the 380 requires few special techniques other than a shorter loading block and a tight case neck fit (to avoid bullet set-back on feeding). There is now a good choice of .355" bullets for the 380, including the high-tech Speer Gold Dot 90-grain hollow point. Do not seat bullets deeper than we show here.

The 380 headspaces on the case mouth so light taper crimping is required. This also produces a nicely finished case mouth that helps feeding reliability. These loads do not exceed the 21,500 psi pressure limit established for the 380 Auto cartridge.

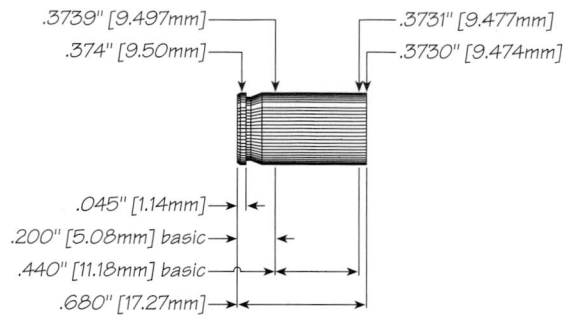

.3739" [9.497mm]
.374" [9.50mm]
.3731" [9.477mm]
.3730" [9.474mm]

.045" [1.14mm]
.200" [5.08mm] basic
.440" [11.18mm] basic
.680" [17.27mm]

Max. Case Length:	0.680"	Cart. Case:	Winchester
Trim-to Length:	0.670"	Primer:	CCI 500
Max Cart. OAL:	0.984"	Test Firearm:	Walther PP
RCBS Shell Holder:	#10	Barrel Length:	3.8"

0.355"	380 Auto GDHP
Weight, grains	90
Ballistic Coefficient	0.101
Sectional Density	0.102
COAL Tested:	0.970"
Speer Part No.	3992

Propellant	START CHARGE		MAXIMUM CHARGE	
	Weight, grs	Muzzle Velocity, ft/sec	Weight, grs	Muzzle Velocity, ft/sec
AA No. 2 Impr.	3.5	982	3.9	1056
AA No. 7	6.3	941	7.0C	1050
Viht. N320	3.1	953	3.4	1044
Unique	4.1	877	4.6C	1034
231	3.6	978	4.0	1031
Power Pistol	4.4	944	4.8C	1020
H. Universal	3.8	821	4.3	994
700-X	3.2	812	3.6	988
AA No. 5	4.8	845	5.4	984
Bullseye	3.0	885	3.4	981
TiteGroup	2.8	885	3.2	976
WSL	3.2	825	3.6	972
American Select	2.8	841	3.3	955

0.355"	380 Auto TMJ RN
Weight, grains	95
Ballistic Coefficient	0.131
Sectional Density	0.108
COAL Tested:	0.970"
Speer Part No.	4001

| Propellant | START CHARGE | | MAXIMUM CHARGE | |
	Weight, grs	Muzzle Velocity, ft/sec	Weight, grs	Muzzle Velocity, ft/sec
231	3.6	945	4.0	1027
AA No. 7	5.9	971	6.5	1019
700-X	3.1	912	3.4	1012
Unique	3.8	918	4.2	1006
Viht. N320	3.0	893	3.4	998
Bullseye	3.0	874	3.3	990
H. Universal	3.6	854	4.1	979
Power Pistol	4.2	883	4.7	974
AA No. 2	3.3	887	3.7	965
WSL	3.1	849	3.5	960
AA No. 5	4.6	871	5.0	949
American Select	2.8	824	3.3	935
TiteGroup	2.7	851	3.1	930

*Maximum Loads should be used with CAUTION • C = Compressed Load • *Magnum Primer used with this powder.*

9x18mm Makarov

9x18mm Makarov pistols and ammo appeared on the surplus market after the break-up of the Soviet Union in the late 1980's. Several Eastern Bloc countries adopted the Makarov pistol following World War II as a standard military and police sidearm. The Stechkin selective-fire machine pistol also used the Makarov cartridge.

The 9x18mm case length is halfway between the 380 Auto and the 9mm Luger cartridges. In terms of performance it is only slightly ahead of the 380 due to a modest advantage in working pressure. Surplus ammunition is loaded with 95 to 96-grain FMJ bullets and velocities are in the 940 to 1000-ft/sec range. Some reference books show Makarov velocities as high as 1115 ft/sec. We have not encountered any surplus lots achieving this velocity in a Makarov pistol.

The 9x18 Makarov does not use the same bullet diameter as most other 9mm cartridges. Its bullets are .364" rather than the more common .355" diameter. Speer sells two bullets designed for reloading the Makarov: a 95-grain TMJ® for plinking and a 90-grain Gold Dot® hollow point suitable for defense or small game hunting.

Blazer® and almost all imported 9x18mm ammunition are Berdan-primed and aren't easily reloaded. Boxer-primed reloadable cases are available from Starline (Sedalia, MO; www.starlinebrass.com).

Most Makarov pistols that we have examined seem to be decently made and reasonably accurate. The sights and trigger pulls are typically military. Bore diameters may vary a few thousandths but you should plan on using .363 to .364-inch bullets for best results. Some pistols have been retrofitted with barrels chambered for the 380 Auto so be sure you are using the correct ammo.

CCI was the first U.S. manufacturer to make Makarov ammunition and established the maximum average pressure limit at 24,100 psi.

• • • • •

Editor's Note: *Our thanks to Bob and Barbara Hayden of Starline Brass for furnishing cases for this testing.*

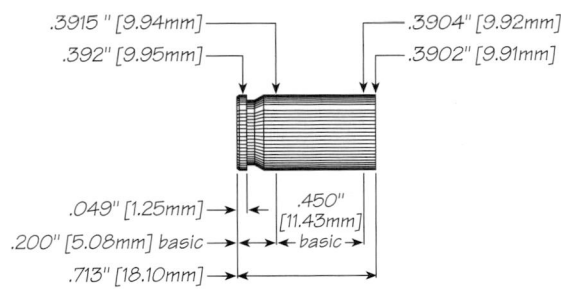

Max. Case Length:	0.713"	Cart. Case: Starline
Trim-to Length:	0.703"	Primer: CCI 500
Max Cart. OAL:	0.984"	Test Firearm: East German Makarov
RCBS Shell Holder:	#16	Barrel Length: 3.625"

0.364"	9mm Mak GDHP
Weight, grains	90
Ballistic Coefficient	0.107
Sectional Density	0.097
COAL Tested:	0.970"
Speer Part No.	3999

Propellant	START CHARGE		MAXIMUM CHARGE	
	Weight, grs	Muzzle Velocity, ft/sec	Weight, grs	Muzzle Velocity, ft/sec
AA No. 5	6.0	970	6.7	1180
Viht. N330	4.2	908	4.7	1097
H. Universal	4.3	930	4.8	1094
231	4.0	971	4.5	1074
Bullseye	3.6	971	4.1	1067
AA No. 2 Impr.	4.0	957	4.5	1058
Viht. N320	3.6	962	4.0	1054
AA No. 7	7.2	935	8.0C	1049
HS-6	5.8	891	6.5	1048

*Maximum Loads should be used with CAUTION • C = Compressed Load • *Magnum Primer used with this powder.*

0.364"	9mm Mak TMJ RN
Weight, grains	95
Ballistic Coefficient	0.127
Sectional Density	0.102
COAL Tested:	0.980"
Speer Part No.	4375

Propellant	START CHARGE		MAXIMUM CHARGE	
	Weight, grs	Muzzle Velocity, ft/sec	Weight, grs	Muzzle Velocity, ft/sec
AA No. 5	5.6	891	6.3	1068
AA No. 2 Impr.	3.9	936	4.4	1042
AA No. 7	7.0	912	7.8	1038
231	3.9	911	4.4	1029
HS-6	5.6	828	6.3	1010
Bullseye	3.5	896	3.9	1010
Viht. N330	4.0	841	4.5	966
H. Universal	4.0	774	4.5	965
Viht. N320	3.3	832	3.7	963

*Maximum Loads should be used with CAUTION • C = Compressed Load • *Magnum Primer used with this powder.*

9mm Luger

The 9mm Luger cartridge is known as the 9mm Parabellum and 9x19mm. Some pistols chambered for this cartridge are marked "9mm/08" or "9mm P/08" to indicate the date (1908) when it was adopted by the German Army. Except for war souvenirs, there were few 9mm pistols in the U.S. until the 1950's.

The U.S. military considered the 9mm Luger as a service pistol cartridge on numerous occasions and finally adopted it in 1985 in the M9 Beretta pistol. Compact pistols and generous magazine capacity have combined to make the 9mm Luger the most popular cartridge in the U.S. law enforcement community.

The 9mm was originally loaded with full metal-jacketed (FMJ) bullets for reliable feeding. To succeed as a police service cartridge, expanding bullets were needed to limit the tremendous penetration of 9mm FMJ bullets. The current trend in law enforcement is toward 124 and 147-grain JHP bullets.

Speer offers a number of bullets that are suitable for the 9mm. For general-purpose shooting and target practice, the three TMJ® bullets and the 124-grain Uni-Cor® soft point bullets are good choices. The 115, 124 and 147-grain Gold Dot hollow points should be chosen for serious defense work.

There is a wide variation in locking mechanisms and spring rates in 9mm pistols. Some may exhibit sluggish function with the lighter 147-grain loads. Sub-compact pistols are more prone to this issue. Load a few rounds and test them for function before settling on a 147-grain load.

Carefully observe the cartridge overall lengths listed in the data when loading the 9mm. Under no conditions should the bullets be loaded shorter than the listed lengths. 9mm case capacity is small and seating a bullet deeper than indicated can cause excessive pressures and the potential for gun damage or injury.

The 9mm Luger headspaces on the case mouth so taper crimping is required. The taper crimp also gives a nicely finished edge to the case mouth for reliable feeding. Refer to the section, "Loading for Semi-automatic Pistols" in the introduction to the Handgun data. There you will find an extended discussion on 9mm Luger reloading containing some helpful tips. Review the section "Rifles Chambered for Handgun Cartridges" in the same chapter if you plan to load for a 9mm carbine. We do not recommend loading 147-grain bullets for carbine use.

The listed loads do not exceed the industry maximum pressure of 35,000 psi.

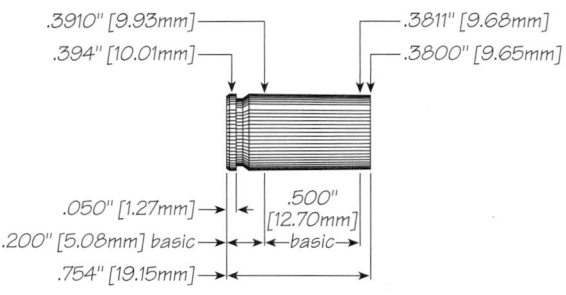

Max. Case Length:	0.754"	Cart. Case:	Speer
Trim-to Length:	0.744"	Primer:	CCI 500
Max Cart. OAL:	1.169"	Test Firearm:	S&W M5906
RCBS Shell Holder:	#16	Barrel Length:	4"

IMPORTANT SAFETY NOTE: *These loads were developed and tested for safe use in HANDGUNS. Not all loads may be suitable for use in a carbine or rifle chambered for this cartridge. If loading for a carbine or rifle, choose from among the loads developing the highest handgun velocities and load just a few rounds. Thoroughly test this small sample in your firearm in slow-fire mode, insuring that you achieve proper feeding and ejection. Be certain that all bullets exit the barrel; watching the target for each bullet strike is the best way to know that the load produces sufficient gas volume for a longer barrel.*

0.355"	9mm GDHP	9mm TMJ RN
Weight, grains	115	115
Ballistic Coefficient	0.125	0.151
Sectional Density	0.130	0.130
COAL Tested:	1.125"	1.135"
Speer Part No.	3994	3995

Propellant	START CHARGE Weight, grs	START CHARGE Muzzle Velocity, ft/sec	MAXIMUM CHARGE Weight, grs	MAXIMUM CHARGE Muzzle Velocity, ft/sec
Blue Dot	7.7	1161	8.5	1258
Unique	5.6	1166	6.3	1244
Viht. 3N37	6.0	1128	6.7	1225
AA No. 7	8.6	1158	9.6C	1220
Power Pistol	6.2	1122	6.7	1212
Viht. N350	5.8	1109	6.5	1210
HS-6	6.6	1048	7.4	1178
H. Universal	4.7	1046	5.3	1172
WSF	5.0	1041	5.6	1156
Bullseye	4.2	1037	4.7	1144
231	4.4	1026	4.9	1133
TiteGroup	4.1	1061	4.5	1121
AA No. 5	6.0	1003	6.7	1102
American Select	4.8	1067	5.4	1102
700-X	4.0	1007	4.4	1101

*Maximum Loads should be used with CAUTION • C = Compressed Load • *Magnum Primer used with this powder.*

0.355"	9mm TMJ RN	9mm UCSP	9mm GDHP
Weight, grains	124	124	124
Ballistic Coefficient	0.159	0.115	0.134
Sectional Density	0.141	0.141	0.141
COAL Tested:	1.135"	1.120"	1.120"
Speer Part No.	3993	3997	3998

Propellant	START CHARGE		MAXIMUM CHARGE	
	Weight, grs	Muzzle Velocity, ft/sec	Weight, grs	Muzzle Velocity, ft/sec
HS-7	8.0	1159	8.9	1249
Blue Dot	7.1	1121	7.9	1238
AA No. 9	9.4	1061	10.5C	1185
Unique	5.2	1080	5.8	1180
AA No. 7	8.1	1077	9.0	1180
Viht. 3N37	5.7	1063	6.4	1179
Power Pistol	5.6	1033	6.4	1157
TiteGroup	4.0	1020	4.4	1095
H. Universal	4.5	993	5.0	1089
AA No. 5	5.7	963	6.4	1069
700-X	3.9	989	4.3	1067
Bullseye	3.9	966	4.4	1059
HS-6	6.0	951	6.7	1059
American Select	4.5	994	5.0	1053
231	4.0	887	4.5	998

0.355"	9mm GDHP	9mm TMJ FN
Weight, grains	147	147
Ballistic Coefficient	0.164	0.188
Sectional Density	0.167	0.167
COAL Tested:	1.130"	1.130"
Speer Part No.	4002	4006

	START CHARGE		MAXIMUM CHARGE	
Propellant	Weight, grs	Muzzle Velocity, ft/sec	Weight, grs	Muzzle Velocity, ft/sec
Blue Dot	5.1	900	5.8	1001
Power Pistol	4.5	872	5.0	975
Viht. 3N37	4.4	886	4.9	969
AA No. 7	6.1	867	6.8	961
SR 4756	4.2	841	4.6	957
HS-6	5.0	845	5.5	956
Unique	3.8	852	4.3	954
HS-7	6.1	866	6.8	953
WSF	3.6	840	4.1	931
AA No. 5	4.5	821	5.1	931

NOTE: *147-grain bullets not recommended for barrels longer than 10 inches.*

Lab Notes:

Reloadable 9mm Luger cases were once hard to find but are now as abundant as flies in most areas. There is little need to use military surplus brass when there are so many good commercial cases available at a reasonable price.

In addition to requiring the extra effort of removing a primer crimp, some military cases have primer pocket profiles slightly different from commercial cases. This can cause repriming difficulties, especially on progressive equipment. Powder capacities may not be the same either and pressure variations can show up.

Our recommendation: don't bother with military 9mm Luger cases.

*Maximum Loads should be used with CAUTION • C = Compressed Load • *Magnum Primer used with this powder.*

9mm Largo *(9mm Bergmann-Bayard)*

The 9mm Largo is the Spanish version of the 9mm Bergmann-Bayard cartridge. This is a very old European pistol cartridge for the Bergmann-Bayard pistol dating to around 1908. The case is 4mm (0.157-inch) longer than the more common 9mm Luger.

Spain adopted the Bergmann-Bayard cartridge in 1913 and called it the 9mm Largo; "largo" is Spanish for "long." Spain mated the cartridge with their first semi-automatic service pistol, the Campo Giro. The Astra Model 1921, known in commercial circles as the Model 400, superseded the Campo Giro. Like its predecessor, the Astra was a blowback design but of more robust construction. Later, Spain adopted the locked-breech Star Model "A" and ultimately the Star Super. These are Colt M1911 look-a-likes chambered for the Largo cartridge.

Used Spanish Largo pistols occasionally showed up on the U.S. surplus market but proper ammo was practically nonexistent so the majority of owners shot 38 Super or 9mm Luger cartridges. Neither is acceptable for Largo pistols, especially the Astra 400. The 38 Super's pressure assignment is higher and the semi-rimmed case causes feed problems in some guns. The 9mm Luger also operates at higher pressures and doesn't headspace correctly in a Largo chamber. Accuracy is usually dismal and fired cases show considerable damage in the form of chipped and torn rims and excessive bulging.

There is considerable variation in 9mm Largo ammo specs. Typical surplus ammo pushes a 124 or 125-grain bullet in the velocity range of 1150 to 1200 ft/sec. Pressures also vary. We tested Spanish military lots that averaged over 35,000 psi. However these were later lots, most likely intended for the locked-breech Star pistols.

This discussion would be a moot point except that large quantities of Star and Astra pistols appeared in the United States in 1993-4. Short supplies of surplus ammo (often having corrosive primers) dampened the renewed interest in the Largo cartridge.

CCI developed Blazer® 9mm Largo ammunition to supply these imports. We set the pressure limit at 30,000 psi in deference to the Astra's low-tech breeching system. The data presented here is loaded to that pressure for the same reason. CCI's Largo offerings were dropped several years ago after demand fell off.

Starline (www.starlinebrass.com) sells reloadable 9mm Largo brass cases. Speer's 115 and 124-grain Gold Dot hollow points are excellent choices for the Largo. The 147-

grain bullets were considered but not tested. The internal case taper caused unacceptable bulging when the long bullets were seated. The bulging was enough to prevent the cartridges from chambering in the pressure barrel.

CAUTION!

Never attempt to fire the 9x23mm Winchester cartridge in any pistol chambered for the 9mm Largo. The Winchester competition cartridge operates at nearly twice the pressure of the Largo and would surely destroy these older pistols. Likewise, 9x23 Winchester cases have heavier walls and must not be used with the data here.

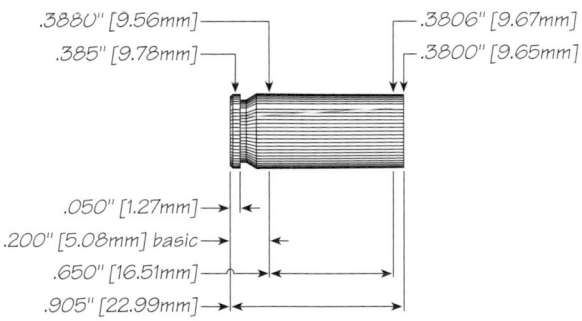

Max. Case Length:	0.905"	**Cart. Case:**	Starline
Trim-to Length:	0.900"	**Primer:**	CCI 500
Max Cart. OAL:	1.300"	**Test Firearm:**	Star "Super"
RCBS Shell Holder:	#16	**Barrel Length:**	5.25"

0.355"	9mm GDHP	9mm TMJ FN
Weight, grains	115	115
Ballistic Coefficient	0.125	0.151
Sectional Density	0.130	0.130
COAL Tested:	1.260"	1.290"
Speer Part No.	3994	3995

Propellant	START CHARGE Weight, grs	START CHARGE Muzzle Velocity, ft/sec	MAXIMUM CHARGE Weight, grs	MAXIMUM CHARGE Muzzle Velocity, ft/sec
Power Pistol	6.0	1063	6.8	1207
HS-6	6.5	1031	7.5	1186
AA No. 5	6.4	1009	7.1	1138
Viht. 3N37	5.6	1051	6.4	1137
700-X	4.1	967	4.7	1110
H. Universal	4.8	1006	5.2	1099
Bullseye	4.4	979	5.1	1093
231	4.8	990	5.3	1082

Lab Notes:

Developing ammo and loading data for a foreign cartridge like the Largo was a learning experience. Ballistically, there were no surprises. However, we learned much about the Largo guns:

• Pistols marked "9mm/38" are chambered for 9mm Largo; those marked "9mm/08" or "9mm/P08" are chambered for 9mm Luger.

• Older Star Model "A" pistols often lack inertial firing pins and therefore must never be carried or stored with the hammer down on a loaded chamber. Star pistols marked "Super" normally have inertial firing pins and are safer. If you're not sure about your pistol's firing pin type, ask a gunsmith to check it.

• Some of the surplus Astra 400 pistols we purchased had minor slide cracks when we received them. They were very small and hard to detect, usually at machine cuts in the slide rails. This indicates hard use before being declared surplus.

• After firing many rounds, even the locked-breech Stars showed some battering where the slide stops against the frame in recoil. Even though the Stars have a stronger lock-up than the Astras, don't think you can exceed the loads shown here!

In spite of these technical issues, both the Stars and Astras proved reliable with the proper ammo. They are relatively inexpensive and make sense for the budget-minded casual shooter.

0.355"	9mm TMJ RN	9mm UCSP	9mm GDHP
Weight, grains	124	124	124
Ballistic Coefficient	0.159	0.115	0.139
Sectional Density	0.141	0.141	0.141
COAL Tested:	1.290"	1.260"	1.260"
Speer Part No.	3993	3997	3998

Propellant	START CHARGE		MAXIMUM CHARGE	
	Weight, grs	Muzzle Velocity, ft/sec	Weight, grs	Muzzle Velocity, ft/sec
Power Pistol	5.6	1040	6.1	1107
H. Universal	4.3	885	4.9	1095
AA No. 7	7.5	989	8.3	1085
AA No. 5	6.0	939	6.7	1069
HS-6	6.4	965	6.9	1065
Unique	4.5	951	5.0	1053
Viht. 3N37	5.2	840	5.8	1037
231	4.3	951	4.7	1013
PB	4.2	882	4.6	990

*Maximum Loads should be used with CAUTION • C = Compressed Load • *Magnum Primer used with this powder.*

357 SIG

Developed jointly by SIG-Arms and Federal Cartridge in 1994, the 357 SIG is a powerful cartridge that can match the performance of a 357 Magnum service revolver loaded with lighter bullets. Factory ammo has a nominal velocity of 1350 ft/sec with a 125-grain bullet —impressive performance for a compact, semi-automatic pistol. The first pistol chambered for this cartridge was the SIG 229. The cartridge has become quite popular and has been adopted by several law enforcement agencies.

The 357 SIG is based on a necked-down 40 S&W case. Other bottleneck pistol cartridges have enjoyed only limited popularity. However, the design offers advantages over the more common straight-taper design. In addition to enhanced powder capacity, the bottleneck case offers very reliable feeding with a variety of bullet shapes.

In spite of its name, this cartridge uses .355" bullets—the same as the 9mm Luger. Larger .357" bullets intended for the 38 Special and 357 Magnum must not be used.

Some 9mm Luger bullets are unsuitable for the 357 SIG. Full-jacketed 9mm Luger bullets having the long NATO-style nose must not be used. At the proper cartridge length, very little of their bearing surface contacts the case neck and the bullet may be pushed into the case during feeding. Rather than spend time deciding which Luger bullet works, choose Speer's .355" 125-grain Gold Dot® and TMJ® bullets. They were designed expressly for the 357 SIG.

The 147-grain Gold Dot allows deeper penetration. The heavy bullets gave impressive velocities and are significantly more potent than when loaded in a 9mm Luger or 38 Super.

This cartridge headspaces on the case mouth, not the shoulder as so many people think. The shoulder angle and surface area are not suitable for shoulder headspacing. Check case length often when firing full-power loads and trim if necessary. When the cartridge was first released, there were few empty cases for handloading so some reloaders made cases from 40 S&W brass. This results in a case that is up to .020 inches short—ignition and accuracy will suffer. Using 10mm Auto cases will result in excessive pressure. Today the ready supply of unprimed brass should eliminate any thoughts of making 357 SIG cases from something else.

Speer sells factory-loaded ammo in reloadable brass cases in both the Gold Dot and Lawman® lines. The industry's maximum average pressure for this cartridge is 40,000 psi. These loads were developed on standard test equipment and do not exceed this pressure level.

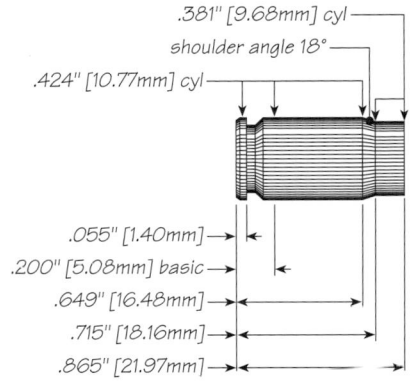

.381" [9.68mm] cyl
shoulder angle 18°
.424" [10.77mm] cyl
.055" [1.40mm]
.200" [5.08mm] basic
.649" [16.48mm]
.715" [18.16mm]
.865" [21.97mm]

Max. Case Length:	0.865"	Cart. Case:	Speer
Trim-to Length:	0.860"	Primer:	CCI 500
Max Cart. OAL:	1.140"	Test Firearm:	SIG 229
RCBS Shell Holder:	#27	Barrel Length:	4"

0.355"	357 SIG GDHP	357 SIG TMJ FN
Weight, grains	125	125
Ballistic Coefficient	0.141	0.147
Sectional Density	0.142	0.142
COAL Tested:	1.135"	1.135"
Speer Part No.	4360	4362

| Propellant | START CHARGE | | MAXIMUM CHARGE | |
	Weight, grs	Muzzle Velocity, ft/sec	Weight, grs	Muzzle Velocity, ft/sec
AA No. 9	13.1	1287	14.6	1437
Blue Dot	9.9	1293	11.0C	1416
AA No. 7	11.1	1264	12.3	1403
Viht. N105	10.1	1257	11.2C	1400
HS-7	10.2	1242	11.3	1359
Viht. N350	7.6	1242	8.5	1350
Unique	7.2	1231	8.0	1344
HS-6	8.6	1199	9.6	1335
Viht. 3N37	7.6	1200	8.5	1301
Herco	7.3	1172	8.1	1277

0.355"	9mm GDHP	9mm TMJ FN
Weight, grains	147	147
Ballistic Coefficient	0.164	0.188
Sectional Density	0.167	0.167
COAL Tested:	1.135"	1.135"
Speer Part No.	4002	4006

Propellant	START CHARGE		MAXIMUM CHARGE	
	Weight, grs	Muzzle Velocity, ft/sec	Weight, grs	Muzzle Velocity, ft/sec
Blue Dot	7.9	1130	8.8	1218
Viht. N105	8.2	1100	9.0	1207
AA No. 9	11.0	1094	12.0	1204
HS-6	7.5	1075	8.3	1170
AA No. 7	9.0	1069	10.0	1169
Power Pistol	6.7	1065	7.5	1152
HS-7	8.3	1034	9.1	1145
Viht. N350	6.2	1040	6.8	1111
Unique	5.8	1008	6.6	1101

*Maximum Loads should be used with CAUTION • C = Compressed Load • *Magnum Primer used with this powder.*

38 Super Auto +P

The 38 Super is an improved version of the Colt 38 Auto (or 38 ACP) cartridge. The original cartridge was introduced in 1900 in the Colt 38 Automatic Pistol and propelled a 130-grain FMJ bullet at a leisurely 1050 ft/sec. The cartridge was capable of better performance but the original Colt pistol could not handle higher pressures.

Colt introduced the 38 Super Auto pistol in 1929 based on the stronger M1911 design, and a higher-pressure version of the original 38 Auto cartridge. With the extra pressure, the cartridge launched the same 130-grain bullet at 1280 ft/sec—very impressive performance in those days. It was renamed the 38 Super Auto, or "38 Super" for short.

The rising popularity of the 9mm Luger between 1975 and 1990 diminished the appeal of the Super in some markets. However, the Super has a tremendous following among action pistol shooters. They want the power of a 45 Auto but with lighter recoil and higher magazine capacity. Because the 9mm Luger cartridge lacks sufficient propellant capacity to accomplish this, competitors and custom pistolsmiths turned to the 38 Super.

To make USPSA/IPSC major power factor, the Super must be loaded well over existing pressure standards. We cannot recommend this practice in stock, or "out-of-the-box," pistols. Nearly every custom pistol firing high-pressure 38 Super loads has a modified frame, high-capacity springs and special barrel features to provide better support of the cartridge case. If you wish to shoot the 38 Super beyond industry pressures, we strongly recommend that you consult a pistolsmith who specializes in building high-performance 38 Super pistols that can deal with pressures in excess of industry recommendations. Many have gone to special cases of heavier construction to reach desired performance goals.

In its standard form, the 38 Super is a fine field pistol cartridge. Loaded with 115-grain hollow points, it is an effective small game and varmint cartridge. The 125 and 147-grain Gold Dot hollow points are excellent for self-defense and provide more energy than the 9mm Luger with similar bullets. 125-grain bullets designed for the 357 SIG cartridge may afford better feeding in some pistols. The SIG bullets are closer to the original 38 Super bullet profile than bullets designed for the 9mm Luger cartridge.

For years, 38 Super pistols seemed capable of only mediocre accuracy. The problem was traced to the way headspace is controlled in the chamber. This has now been remedied.

For an excellent discussion of this subject, please consult Bill Corson's article in Issue #71 of *Handloader* magazine. Reprints are available for sale from Wolfe Publishing (2625 Stearman Rd. Suite A, Prescott, AZ 86301).

In 1974, the industry adopted the +P headstamp for cartridges having two pressure limits. The +P designator was added to the 38 Super case to avoid confusion because the Super is identical in appearance to the older 38 Auto cartridge. The following loads do not exceed the 33,000 CUP pressure limit established for the +P version.

These loads are not for use in Colt Model 1900 and 1902 pistols. These models are distinctive in that the barrel remains attached to the frame when the slide is removed. If in doubt as to your pistol's identity, have it checked by a gunsmith familiar with early Colt pistols.

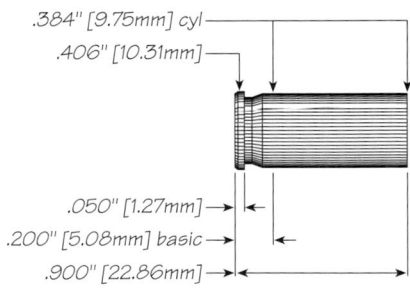

Max. Case Length:	0.900"	**Cart. Case:**	Winchester
Trim-to Length:	0.890"	**Primer:**	CCI 500
Max Cart. OAL:	1.280"	**Test Firearm:**	Colt 38 Super
RCBS Shell Holder:	#39	**Barrel Length:**	5"

0.355"	9mm GDHP	9mm TMJ RN
Weight, grains	115	115
Ballistic Coefficient	0.125	0.151
Sectional Density	0.130	0.130
COAL Tested:	1.260"	1.270"
Speer Part No.	3994	3995

Propellant	START CHARGE		MAXIMUM CHARGE	
	Weight, grs	Muzzle Velocity, ft/sec	Weight, grs	Muzzle Velocity, ft/sec
Blue Dot	9.0	1265	10.0C	1362
AA No. 7	9.5	1219	10.5	1328
AA No. 5	7.8	1229	8.6	1326
AA No. 9	11.7	1222	12.7C	1324
Viht. 3N37	7.0	1188	7.7	1323
WSF	6.2	1164	6.8	1282
H. Universal	5.7	1145	6.3	1278
Herco	7.0	1232	7.8C	1276
HS-6	8.0	1177	8.8	1253

0.355"	9mm TMJ RN	9mm UCSP	9mm GDHP	9mm SIG GDHP	9mm SIG TMJ FN
Weight, grains	124	124	124	125	125
Ballistic Coefficient	0.159	0.115	0.134	0.141	0.147
Sectional Density	0.141	0.141	0.141	0.142	0.142
COAL Tested:	1.280"	1.260"	1.260"	1.260"	1.260"
Speer Part No.	3993	3997	3998	4360	4362

Propellant	START CHARGE		MAXIMUM CHARGE	
	Weight, grs	Muzzle Velocity, ft/sec	Weight, grs	Muzzle Velocity, ft/sec
Blue Dot	8.3	1182	9.2	1312
Herco	6.7	1176	7.3	1272
AA No. 9	11.0	1187	12.0C	1267
HS-6	7.5	1134	8.3	1245
AA No. 5	7.2	1102	8.0	1213
Unique	5.6	1127	6.2	1208
H. Universal	5.3	1078	5.9	1202
Viht. 3N37	6.4	1092	7.1	1198
WSF	5.6	1057	6.1	1184
AA No. 7	9.0	1058	9.9	1169
Bullseye	4.7	1073	5.2	1158
AA No. 2 Impr.	5.3	1079	5.8	1135
700-X	4.5	1050	5.0	1132
Green Dot	4.8	1051	5.3	1125
231	4.8	1021	5.3	1117
Red Dot	4.3	1027	4.8	1086

*Maximum Loads should be used with CAUTION • C = Compressed Load • *Magnum Primer used with this powder.*

0.355"	9mm GDHP	9mm TMJ FP
Weight, grains	147	147
Ballistic Coefficient	0.164	0.188
Sectional Density	0.167	0.167
COAL Tested:	1.275"	1.275"
Speer Part No.	4002	4006

Propellant	START CHARGE		MAXIMUM CHARGE	
	Weight, grs	Muzzle Velocity, ft/sec	Weight, grs	Muzzle Velocity, ft/sec
AA No. 9	9.5	1021	10.5	1122
2400	8.5	960	9.5	1099
Viht. 3N37	5.2	979	6.2	1081
H. Universal	4.7	961	5.2	1065
AA No. 7	7.4	914	8.2	1061
HS-6	6.4	948	7.1	1048
Unique	4.9	984	5.4	1043
Bullseye	4.2	958	4.6	1041
WSF	4.8	938	5.3	1029
AA No. 2 Impr.	4.6	941	5.1	1021
231	4.3	899	4.8	1008
AA No. 5	5.8	910	6.4	1004
HP-38	4.3	919	4.8	992

38 S&W *(38 Colt New Police)*

The 38 S&W (not to be confused with the 38 S&W Special) is an old revolver cartridge dating to 1877 when Smith & Wesson introduced it in a hinged frame or "break-top" revolver. It started as a black powder cartridge but the compact case easily made the transition to modern propellants. It became popular for small, concealable handguns and was adopted as a British service revolver cartridge before World War II.

Much of the 38 S&W's appeal was that it was so well suited to compact revolvers. Not until small-frame 38 Specials like Colt's Detective Special and S&W's Chief Special revolvers became available did the 38 S&W's popularity start to slip. Even with 38 Special snub-nose revolvers available, several firms continued to make inexpensive revolvers chambered for the 38 S&W until recently.

The 38 S&W is also known by other names, including the 38 Colt New Police, the 38 Super Police and the 38/200. The last two cartridges were loaded with 200-grain lead bullets for additional "stopping power." The last British military version was known as the "380 Revolver Mk II Z"; it launched a 178-grain FMJ bullet at about 600 ft/sec. Current factory ammunition uses a 146-grain lead round nose bullet at 685 ft/sec (4-inch test barrel).

The quality of revolvers chambered for this cartridge varies from excellent to dismal. Almost all hinged-frame revolvers produced prior to WWII should be considered unsuitable for shooting modern ammo. Their latching mechanisms are frail and become even less effective when worn. Notable exceptions are the British Enfield and Webley revolvers; they feature heavier frames and very robust latches that resist deformation. The loads shown are intended for use only in modern, solid-frame revolvers or Enfield and Webley revolvers known to be in top condition.

The nominal bullet diameter for the 38 S&W cartridge is .360", so the bullets listed are undersized for this cartridge. However, in revolvers with deep rifling, accuracy is usually fairly good. Smith & Wesson revolvers for this caliber have the rifling pattern best suited for .357-inch jacketed bullets. By comparison, Webley and Enfield revolvers have relatively shallow rifling and may not engage jacketed bullets completely. Cast lead bullets may be the better choice as the caster can size the bullets to an appropriate diameter, usually .359-inch. Of the jacketed bulleted listed, expect expansion only from the 110-grain Gold Dot Short Barrel hollow point.

As of press time, Remington and Winchester are still loading the 38 S&W but only Starline offers unprimed cases. The case is larger in diameter than the 38 Special so Special cases must not be cut off and reloaded. They will bulge and often split on the first shot. The industry pressure limit for the 38 S&W cartridge is 13,000 CUP.

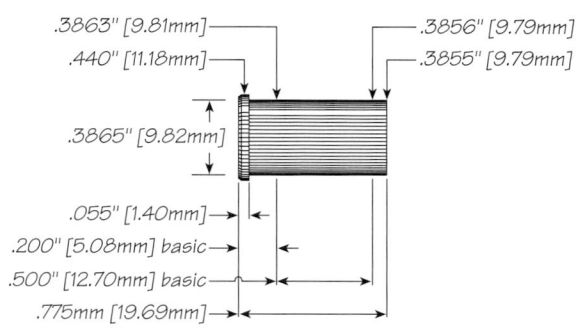

Max. Case Length:	0.775"	Cart. Case:	Winchester
Trim-to Length:	0.765"	Primer:	CCI 500
Max Cart. OAL:	1.240"	Test Firearm:	S&W Model 33
RCBS Shell Holder:	#6	Barrel Length:	4"

0.357"	38	38 GDHP SB
Weight, grains	110	110
Ballistic Coefficient	0.113	0.117
Sectional Density	0.123	0.123
COAL Tested:	1.055"	1.055"
Speer Part No.	4007	4009

	START CHARGE		MAXIMUM CHARGE	
Propellant	Weight, grs	Muzzle Velocity, ft/sec	Weight, grs	Muzzle Velocity, ft/sec
Herco	5.0	1013	5.3	1060
Unique	4.8	938	5.1	1001
Bullseye	3.0	894	3.2	935
Red Dot	3.2	852	3.5	929
SR 7625	3.5	826	3.8	909
231	2.9	725	3.2	797

0.357"	38 UCSP	38 USHP
Weight, grains	125	125
Ballistic Coefficient	0.129	0.129
Sectional Density	0.140	0.140
COAL Tested:	1.055"	1.055"
Speer Part No.	4011	4013

Propellant	START CHARGE Weight, grs	START CHARGE Muzzle Velocity, ft/sec	MAXIMUM CHARGE Weight, grs	MAXIMUM CHARGE Muzzle Velocity, ft/sec
Herco	4.7	914	5.0	986
Unique	4.5	920	4.8	972
Red Dot	3.0	773	3.3	846
SR 7625	3.2	748	3.5	826
Bullseye	2.8	742	3.0	789
231	DNR	—	3.0	662

DNR — do not reduce

0.358"	38 LSWC	38 LSWC HP	38 LRN
Weight, grains	158	158	158
Ballistic Coefficient	0.123	0.121	0.170
Sectional Density	0.176	0.176	0.176
COAL Tested:	1.065"	1.065"	1.065"
Speer Part No.	4623	4627	4647

Propellant	START CHARGE Weight, grs	START CHARGE Muzzle Velocity, ft/sec	MAXIMUM CHARGE Weight, grs	MAXIMUM CHARGE Muzzle Velocity, ft/sec
Red Dot	2.4	667	2.7	765
SR 7625	2.6	683	2.9	752
Herco	2.9	630	3.2	702
Unique	2.8	619	3.1	694
Bullseye	2.2	629	2.4	693
231	2.3	593	2.6	671

*Maximum Loads should be used with CAUTION • C = Compressed Load • *Magnum Primer used with this powder.*

38 Special

Smith & Wesson introduced the 38 Special in 1902 as a ballistic improvement over the 38 Long Colt cartridge. Much of its acceptance was due not to increased power but to its excellent accuracy. Originally loaded with black powder, the cartridge gracefully made the transition to smokeless as the new propellants became available.

The original cartridge fired a 158-grain lead round nose bullet at about 800 ft/sec, a load spec that remains with us today. Wadcutter bullets were also loaded to cut clean, full-caliber holes in paper targets. Other than a handful of specialty loads for law enforcement, these two bullets were the only choices in factory ammunition until the late 1960's when expanding jacketed bullets were first introduced.

During the 1930's, demand for better 38 Special performance led to the introduction of heavy-frame revolvers designed to handle higher pressures and ammunition driving 158-grain bullets at velocities up to 1000 ft/sec. Thus, two 38 Special pressure levels existed in the industry for years but there was little uniformity in case markings. You couldn't always tell a high-pressure load simply by looking at the cartridge.

This confusion was finally eliminated in 1974 when the industry adopted the +P headstamp designator to identify cartridges loaded to the higher pressure limit. As all U.S. ammo makers and most foreign ones agreed to use this system, the shooter could read the headstamp and tell if the pressure level was suitable for his revolver. Because there are differences in the reloading of 38 Special and 38 Special +P cartridges, we have listed data for this cartridge in separate sections. The section on +P loads immediately follows this one.

Reloaders must remember that the 38 Special case is much bigger than necessary for most modern propellants. A maximum-pressure charge of some propellants takes up very little room in the case. Air space is high, especially when loading standard (not +P) loads. You must keep this in mind to avoid accidental double charges.

Lead bullets are best for loading standard pressure 38 Specials. They are easily propelled through the barrel by modest powder charges. Jacketed bullets create more resistance than lead bullets and may lodge in the bore if propellant charges are too light or too slow-burning. This condition is aggravated in revolvers with large chamber throats or excessive barrel/cylinder gaps. To avoid these problems, we are showing jacketed bullet data for only 110 and 125-grain bullets. Heavier bullets may not attain sufficient velocity to reliably overcome both friction and the gap. Note that these loads are marked "DNR," meaning "do not reduce." Reductions of loads below the levels shown can result in a bullet-in-bore condition in revolvers with excessive barrel/cylinder gaps. These jacketed bullet loads must never be used in rifles.

The industry specification for barrel-cylinder gap is 0.001 to 0.012-inch in newly manufactured revolvers. Gaps no larger than 0.008-inch give better ballistic performance. Excessive gaps can result in a dangerous bullet-in-bore condition.

The new 110-grain Gold Dot Short Barrel bullet is the best expanding bullet for standard pressure loadings. Its deep and spacious hollow point cavity allows expansion at low velocities common to standard pressure loads in compact revolvers. We show velocities from both the standard 6-inch revolver as well as from a 2-inch barrel.

We developed loads for Cowboy Action shooting using bullets cast from the RCBS 9mm-147-FN mould. Although intended for the 9mm Luger, this bullet can be sized to .358" to make excellent 38 Special CAS loads. We roll-crimped into the front lube groove.

Wadcutters are popular for target shooting and are also very effective small-game bullets if the ranges do not exceed 50 yards. At greater distances, semi-wadcutters are better due to their superior downrange stability. The Speer hollow-base wadcutter (HBWC) is seated flush with the case mouth; use a light roll or taper crimp to support low-pressure ignition. Wadcutter bullet loads are not necessarily at maximum pressure but are at velocity levels that give good accuracy in target handguns. To avoid bullet base deformation, do not exceed these loads when using HBWC bullets.

We show 38 Special loads for Speer shot capsules in this data set. Please read the text at the beginning of the Handgun data section for additional information on these specialty projectiles.

The industry pressure limit for the 38 Special is 17,000 psi.

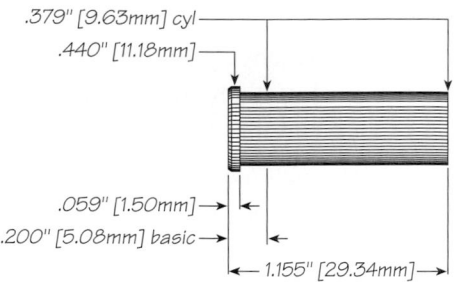

.379" [9.63mm] cyl
.440" [11.18mm]
.059" [1.50mm]
.200" [5.08mm] basic
1.155" [29.34mm]

Max. Case Length:	1.155"	Cart. Case:	Speer
Trim-to Length:	1.145"	Primer:	CCI 500; 550
Max Cart. OAL:	1.550"	Test Firearm:	S&W Model 14
RCBS Shell Holder:	#6	Barrel Length:	6"

0.358"	38 HBWC
Weight, grains	148
Ballistic Coefficient	0.050
Sectional Density	0.165
COAL Tested:	See note
Speer Part No.	4617

	START CHARGE		MAXIMUM CHARGE	
Propellant	Weight, grs	Muzzle Velocity, ft/sec	Weight, grs	Muzzle Velocity, ft/sec
Red Dot	2.7	754	3.0	806
231	3.0	749	3.3	804
HP-38	2.9	752	3.2	801
Bullseye	2.8	741	3.1	799
700-X	2.6	739	2.9	791
AA No. 2 Impr.	2.7	690	3.1	789

NOTE: *Seat bullet flush with case mouth. Use a light roll or taper crimp.*

0.358"	9mm-147 FN
Weight, grains	147
Lead Alloy	hard
Ballistic Coefficient	0.151
Sectional Density	0.167
COAL Tested:	1.530"
RCBS Mould No.	82077

Propellant	START CHARGE		MAXIMUM CHARGE	
	Weight, grs	Muzzle Velocity, ft/sec	Weight, grs	Muzzle Velocity, ft/sec
700-X	3.2	780	3.8	893
AA No. 2 Impr.	3.5	803	4.0	871
HP-38	3.6	768	4.0	852
H. Universal	4.0	765	4.4	846
PB	3.7	761	4.2	840
Bullseye	3.1	768	3.5	838
WSF	3.8	753	4.2	836
Unique	4.0	741	4.6	820
Red Dot	3.0	716	3.4	794

NOTE: *We sell bullet moulds, not cast bullets. These bullets were cast in RCBS moulds. Contact your dealer for more information on the RCBS line of premium bullet casting equipment, or visit on the Internet at www.rcbs.com.*

*Maximum Loads should be used with CAUTION • C = Compressed Load • *Magnum Primer used with this powder.*

0.358"	38 LSWC	38 LSWC HP	38 LRN
Weight, grains	158	158	158
Ballistic Coefficient	0.123	0.121	0.170
Sectional Density	0.176	0.176	0.176
COAL Tested:	1.440"	1.455"	1.510"
Speer Part No.	4623	4627	4647

Propellant	START CHARGE Weight, grs	START CHARGE Muzzle Velocity, ft/sec	MAXIMUM CHARGE Weight, grs	MAXIMUM CHARGE Muzzle Velocity, ft/sec
SR 4756	5.0	844	5.6	967
Power Pistol	4.8	856	5.4	948
AA No. 5	5.8	874	6.2	922
H. Universal	4.2	827	4.6	902
700-X	3.2	774	3.8	877
231	3.8	783	4.3	863
PB	3.7	770	4.2	858
HP-38	3.6	756	4.1	855
WSF	3.8	738	4.3	830
Viht. N350	4.5	717	5.0	818
Unique	4.0	740	4.7	815
Bullseye	3.1	752	3.5	814
Red Dot	3.0	727	3.4	793
AA No. 2	3.6	708	4.0	781

0.358"	38 UCHP	38 GDHP SB
Weight, grains	110	110
Ballistic Coefficient	0.113	0.117
Sectional Density	0.123	0.123
COAL Tested:	1.455"	1.455"
Speer Part No.	4007	4009

Propellant	START CHARGE		MAXIMUM CHARGE	
	Weight, grs	Muzzle Velocity, ft/sec	Weight, grs	Muzzle Velocity, ft/sec
Power Pistol	6.2	1006	6.6	1074
Viht. 3N37	6.5	990	6.9	1071
Unique	5.4	947	5.8	1065
AA No. 5	6.8	979	7.2	1043
TiteGroup	4.1	890	4.5	1002
H. Universal	5.1	829	5.5	998
700-X	4.2	907	4.6	997
Bullseye	4.2	891	4.6	990
231	4.6	871	5.0	971
American Select	DNR	—	4.3	887

DNR — do not reduce

0.357"	38 UCHP	38 GDHP SB
Weight, grains	110	110
Ballistic Coefficient	0.113	0.117
Sectional Density	0.123	0.123
COAL Tested:	1.455"	1.455"
Speer Part No.	4007	4009

SHORT BARREL VELOCITIES
Test Firearm: S&W M15 2"

| Propellant | START CHARGE | | MAXIMUM CHARGE | |
	Weight, grs	Muzzle Velocity, ft/sec	Weight, grs	Muzzle Velocity, ft/sec
Unique	5.4	806	5.8	936
AA No. 5	6.8	860	7.2	900
Viht. 3N37	6.5	845	6.9	895
H. Universal	5.1	760	5.5	882
Power Pistol	6.2	823	6.6	880
700-X	4.2	784	4.6	879
Bullseye	4.2	791	4.6	852
TiteGroup	4.1	782	4.5	850
231	4.6	817	5.0	848
American Select	DNR	—	4.3	784

DNR — do not reduce

0.357"	38 UCSP	38 GDHP	38 UCHP	38 TMJ FN
Weight, grains	125	125	125	125
Ballistic Coefficient	0.129	0.140	0.129	0.146
Sectional Density	0.140	0.140	0.140	0.140
COAL Tested:	1.435"	1.440"	1.435"	1.435"
Speer Part No.	4011	4012	4013	4015

Propellant	START CHARGE Weight, grs	START CHARGE Muzzle Velocity, ft/sec	MAXIMUM CHARGE Weight, grs	MAXIMUM CHARGE Muzzle Velocity, ft/sec
Viht. 3N37	DNR	—	6.8	1037
AA No. 5	DNR	—	7.1	1011
AA No. 2 Impr.	DNR	—	5.4	994
Power Pistol	DNR	—	6.1	986
Unique	DNR	—	5.7	980
H. Universal	DNR	—	5.5	966
WSF	DNR	—	5.3	934
TiteGroup	DNR	—	4.4	933
PB	DNR	—	4.9	927
Bullseye	DNR	—	4.5	914
700-X	DNR	—	4.6	905
American Select	DNR	—	4.1	839

DNR — do not reduce

*Maximum Loads should be used with CAUTION • C = Compressed Load • *Magnum Primer used with this powder.*

0.358"	38/357 Shot Capsule
Weight, grains	109
Ballistic Coefficient	n/a
Sectional Density	n/a
COAL Tested:	1.500"
Speer Part No.	8780

Propellant	Weight, grs	Muzzle Velocity, ft/sec
Unique	5.5	1111
700-X	4.5	1060
HP-38	4.5	1054
Bullseye	4.5	1021
231	5.0	996

NOTE: *Shot capsules must not be used in firearms with ported recoil compensators.*

---

*Maximum Loads should be used with CAUTION • C = Compressed Load • *Magnum Primer used with this powder.*

38 Special +P

Intended only for firearms approved by their manufacturer for +P ammunition. See the previous section for 38 Special loads at standard pressures.

In the 1930's, the performance of the standard 38 Special was enhanced by the addition of loads at higher operating pressures. When first conceived, these loads were intended for firing only in heavy Colt and Smith & Wesson revolvers built on 44 Special frames. Cases were sometimes headstamped "38 HV," "38 HS" or "38/44" to indicate the higher pressure but many of these loads could be identified only if you had the original box or a catalog number.

For consistency in identifying higher-pressure ammo, the firearms industry adopted the +P headstamp in 1974. By agreement, gun makers would determine which of their firearms were suitable for +P ammunition and make that information available to their customers. The three cartridges to which this identifier was first applied were the 38 Super Auto, the 257 Roberts and the 38 Special. The current pressure limit for 38 Special +P ammunition is 20,000 psi compared to 17,000 psi for the standard 38 Special. This allows a bit more flexibility for the handloader using jacketed bullets. When loading Speer jacketed bullets, you must not use charge weights lighter than the starting loads shown here.

At +P velocities, you will obtain the best combination of expansion and penetration with Speer's new 135-grain Gold Dot Short Barrel hollow point. It features a deep, large-volume cavity and will expand reliably in revolver barrels as short as two inches. The 110-grain Gold Dot Short Barrel bullet shares the same cavity and allows much higher velocity at the expense of some penetration. The 125-grain hollow point bullets give less expansion but offer deep penetration. We show velocities for the two Short Barrel bullets both in our standard 6-inch revolver and a 2-inch revolver.

Powders having a moderate burning rate such as Power Pistol and Unique usually give the best performance in the 38 +P. Jacketed bullets heavier than 146 grains yielded very low velocities under current pressure standards and we no longer recommend them in the 38 Special. To fill this weight slot we have developed +P loads for the 158-grain Speer lead bullets.

38 Spl +P 135-gr Gold Dot® Short Barrel bullet fired into ordnance gelatin from a 2-inch revolver (vel. 861 ft/sec)

The new high-tech lube works fine at these speeds. Many researchers still think the 158-grain lead hollow point beats any jacketed 38 Special load for expansion and penetration. The Gold Dot Short Barrel bullets may force them to change their opinions.

Some revolvers are not rated for 38 Special +P ammunition. Contact your firearm's manufacturer—not the ammo makers—and follow their recommendation on the use of this ammunition. Firearms not approved for +P ammunition may show accelerated wear if subjected to continuous firing with +P ammo.

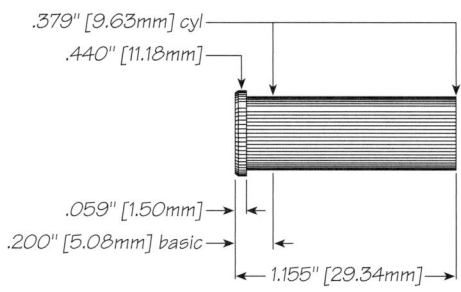

Max. Case Length:	1.155"	Cart. Case:	Speer
Trim-to Length:	1.145"	Primer:	CCI 500; 550*
Max Cart. OAL:	1.550"	Test Firearm:	S&W Model 14
RCBS Shell Holder:	#6	Barrel Length:	6"

0.358"	38 LSWC	38 LSWC HP	38 LRN
Weight, grains	158	158	158
Ballistic Coefficient	0.123	0.121	0.170
Sectional Density	0.176	0.176	0.176
COAL Tested:	1.440"	1.455"	1.510"
Speer Part No.	4623	4627	4647

Propellant	START CHARGE		MAXIMUM CHARGE	
	Weight, grs	Muzzle Velocity, ft/sec	Weight, grs	Muzzle Velocity, ft/sec
Power Pistol	5.4	948	6.0	1037
700-X	3.8	877	4.4	980
AA No. 5	6.2	922	6.6	978
HS-6	6.3	914	6.7	971
H. Universal	4.6	902	5.0	971
PB	4.2	858	4.6	962
231	4.3	863	4.7	935
Unique	4.7	815	5.2	919
HP-38	4.1	855	4.5	918
Viht. N350	5.0	818	5.4	901
WSF	4.3	830	4.7	892
Bullseye	3.5	814	3.9	874
Red Dot	3.4	793	3.8	846
AA No. 2 Impr.	4.0	781	4.3	843

*Maximum Loads should be used with CAUTION • C = Compressed Load • *Magnum Primer used with this powder.*

0.357"	38 UCHP	38 GDHP SB
Weight, grains	110	110
Ballistic Coefficient	0.113	0.117
Sectional Density	0.123	0.123
COAL Tested:	1.455"	1.455"
Speer Part No.	4007	4009

Propellant	START CHARGE Weight, grs	START CHARGE Muzzle Velocity, ft/sec	MAXIMUM CHARGE Weight, grs	MAXIMUM CHARGE Muzzle Velocity, ft/sec
Power Pistol	7.0	1123	7.4	1192
Viht. 3N37	6.9	1071	7.3	1150
AA No. 5	7.5	1099	7.9	1143
Unique	5.9	1090	6.3	1117
H. Universal	5.7	1028	6.1	1100
Bullseye	4.8	1027	5.2	1098
700-X	4.7	1017	5.1	1085
TiteGroup	4.7	1013	5.1	1082
231	5.2	1008	5.6	1059
American Select	4.4	894	4.8	967

0.357"	38 UCHP	38 GDHP SB
Weight, grains	110	110
Ballistic Coefficient	0.113	0.117
Sectional Density	0.123	0.123
COAL Tested:	1.455"	1.455"
Speer Part No.	4007	4009

SHORT BARREL
VELOCITIES
Test Firearm: S&W M15 2"

Propellant	START CHARGE		MAXIMUM CHARGE	
	Weight, grs	Muzzle Velocity, ft/sec	Weight, grs	Muzzle Velocity, ft/sec
Unique	5.9	929	6.3	976
H. Universal	5.7	895	6.1	976
AA No. 5	7.5	915	7.9	969
Power Pistol	7.0	911	7.4	967
Viht. 3N37	6.9	903	7.3	958
700-X	4.7	878	5.1	954
TiteGroup	4.7	875	5.1	945
231	5.2	884	5.6	944
Bullseye	4.8	873	5.2	941
American Select	DNR	—	4.8	879

DNR — do not reduce

---

*Maximum Loads should be used with CAUTION • C = Compressed Load • *Magnum Primer used with this powder.*

0.357"	38 UCSP	38 GDHP	38 UCHP	38 TMJ FN
Weight, grains	125	125	125	125
Ballistic Coefficient	0.129	0.140	0.129	0.146
Sectional Density	0.140	0.140	0.140	0.140
COAL Tested:	1.435"	1.440"	1.455"	1.435"
Speer Part No.	4011	4012	4013	4015

Propellant	START CHARGE		MAXIMUM CHARGE	
	Weight, grs	Muzzle Velocity, ft/sec	Weight, grs	Muzzle Velocity, ft/sec
Viht. 3N37	6.8	1037	7.2	1098
Unique	5.7	980	6.0	1082
Power Pistol	6.1	986	6.8	1082
H. Universal	5.6	976	5.9	1058
AA No. 5	7.5	927	7.8	1030
Bullseye	4.5	914	4.8	1021
PB	4.9	927	5.4	1021
WSF	5.3	934	5.8	1021
AA No. 2 Impr.	5.4	994	5.7	1014
700-X	4.6	905	4.9	1013
TiteGroup	4.4	933	4.9	1012
American Select	DNR	—	4.7	931

DNR — do not reduce

0.357"	38 GDHP SB
Weight, grains	135
Ballistic Coefficient	0.141
Sectional Density	0.151
COAL Tested:	1.450"
Speer Part No.	4014

Propellant	START CHARGE		MAXIMUM CHARGE	
	Weight, grs	Muzzle Velocity, ft/sec	Weight, grs	Muzzle Velocity, ft/sec
Power Pistol	6.0	983	6.4	1065
AA No. 5	6.6	1000	7.0	1052
AA No. 7	7.8	964	8.2	1030
HS-6	6.8	944	7.2	1027
Viht. 3N37	6.0	969	6.4	1007
Unique	4.8	867	5.2	988
H. Universal	5.0	937	5.2	977
PB	DNR	—	4.7	936

DNR — do not reduce

*Maximum Loads should be used with CAUTION • C = Compressed Load • *Magnum Primer used with this powder.*

0.357"	38 GDHP SB
Weight, grains	135
Ballistic Coefficient	0.141
Sectional Density	0.151
COAL Tested:	1.450"
Speer Part No.	4014

SHORT BARREL
VELOCITIES
Test Firearm: S&W M15 2"

Propellant	START CHARGE		MAXIMUM CHARGE	
	Weight, grs	Muzzle Velocity, ft/sec	Weight, grs	Muzzle Velocity, ft/sec
AA No. 7	7.8	838	8.2	882
AA No. 5	6.6	819	7.0	878
HS-6	6.8	780	7.2	856
Power Pistol	6.0	797	6.4	845
Unique	4.8	768	5.2	834
H. Universal	5.0	785	5.2	825
Viht. 3N37	6.0	760	6.4	823
PB	DNR	—	4.7	788

DNR — do not reduce

0.357"	38 UCHP
Weight, grains	140
Ballistic Coefficient	0.145
Sectional Density	0.157
COAL Tested:	1.435"
Speer Part No.	4203

	START CHARGE		MAXIMUM CHARGE	
Propellant	Weight, grs	Muzzle Velocity, ft/sec	Weight, grs	Muzzle Velocity, ft/sec
Blue Dot	7.1	1024	7.4	1053
AA No. 5	6.8	955	7.1	1002
Viht. N350	5.9	924	6.2	982
Power Pistol	5.3	872	6.0	976
WSF	5.3	930	5.5	974
H. Universal	5.0	935	5.3	969
Unique	5.0	902	5.3	960
HS-6	6.4	873	7.0	960
SR 4756	5.4	860	5.9	933
231	4.8	870	5.1	931
Bullseye	4.0	828	4.6	924
TiteGroup	3.7	819	4.2	883

*Maximum Loads should be used with CAUTION • C = Compressed Load • * Magnum Primer used with this powder.*

0.357"	38 JHP-SWC
Weight, grains	146
Ballistic Coefficient	0.159
Sectional Density	0.164
COAL Tested:	1.370"
Speer Part No.	4205

| Propellant | START CHARGE | | MAXIMUM CHARGE | |
	Weight, grs	Muzzle Velocity, ft/sec	Weight, grs	Muzzle Velocity, ft/sec
AA No. 7	7.8	937	8.2	1004
Blue Dot	6.7	971	7.1	1000
Unique	4.8	905	5.1	957
2400	8.3	836	9.0	952
H. Universal	4.6	894	5.0	940
Power Pistol	4.9	832	5.5	935
Viht. N350	5.2	840	5.6	903

*Maximum Loads should be used with CAUTION • C = Compressed Load • *Magnum Primer used with this powder.*

357 Magnum

The 357 Magnum was introduced in 1935 as the result of Smith & Wesson's extensive research with high-performance 38 Special loads. Much of this interest was stimulated by Elmer Keith and Phil Sharpe, who found that heavy charges of certain quick-burning rifle powders in a 38 case could achieve significant increases in velocity, enough for deer-sized game.

Major D.B Wesson wisely noted that a 38 Special cartridge loaded to very high pressures would be a severe hazard if accidentally fired in one of the lighter frame 38 Special revolvers. To avoid this he designed a new cartridge that was physically identical to the 38 Special except for case length. The extra .135 inches of case prevented the potent new cartridge from chambering in 38 Special revolvers.

Thus was born the first "magnum" handgun cartridge. The original Smith & Wesson 357 revolver was a high-grade model made with special steel and careful fitting to handle the new cartridge. Within a year Colt chambered their heavy New Service and Shooting Master revolvers for the 357 Magnum. An added advantage of owning a 357 Magnum revolver is that 38 Special ammunition may be used for practice.

The popularity of the 357 didn't take off until after the Korean War when Smith & Wesson and Colt both introduced lighter, less expensive revolvers. However, factory 357 Magnum ammunition was loaded with only 158-grain lead bullets until the late 1960's when jacketed bullets appeared. The soft lead bullets always caused severe barrel leading so jacketed projectiles were a welcome improvement.

Today's handloader has an excellent selection of bullets. Speer's 110-grain Uni-Cor hollow point at high velocity is an impressive varmint bullet. The 125-grain Gold Dot® hollow point offers excellent expansion and better penetration for defense. The 140-grain Uni-Cor hollow point produces less recoil than the 158-grain bullets yet still offers adequate penetration. For hunting smaller deer species, the 158-grain Gold Dot hollow point and the two 158-grain Uni-Cor bullets are both good choices.

Since we published *Speer #13*, we have introduced several new 35-caliber bullets that add extra flexibility for the 357 Magnum reloader. For compact revolvers, the 135-grain Gold Dot Short Barrel bullet can be loaded to modest velocity for reduced recoil in lightweight "snubbies" yet still expands reliably. The same bullet at maximum safe velocity is a fast-expanding varmint bullet. For medium deer, we have the new Gold

Dot soft point at 170 grains. This bullet is for situations when penetration is more important than expansion. We recommend using this bullet in revolvers with at least six inches of barrel; shorter barrels drop velocity enough to diminish the penetration advantage.

There is one new Speer bullet we don't recommend for the 357 Magnum. It is the 110-grain Gold Dot Short Barrel. It is designed for 38 Special velocities, with a thin jacket and a cavity that comes close to the bullet base. The elevated pressure of the 357 Magnum will deform this bullet in-bore. The 110-grain Uni-Cor hollow point is the one for magnum applications.

Some states have minimum muzzle or downrange energy requirements for handgun hunting that may eliminate the 357 Magnum from consideration. Check with your local game department for applicable regulations.

The 158-grain lead semi-wadcutters, both in solid and hollow point form, make good practice and target loads. To avoid leading, we recommend limiting velocities to around 1000 ft/sec.

Slow-burning pistol powders require a heavy roll crimp to insure proper ignition. Use magnum primers only when they are specified in the data. We found VihtaVuori N110 to be an excellent 357 Magnum propellant with standard CCI primers. Do not use magnum primers with the 2400 or VihtaVuori N110 loads shown here or high pressures will result.

If you wish to load Speer shot capsules for close-range pest control, we recommend you do so in 38 Special cases for best patterning. Shot capsule data is in the 38 Special (non +P) data section.

The industry maximum average pressure for the 357 Magnum is 35,000 psi. These loads do not exceed that level.

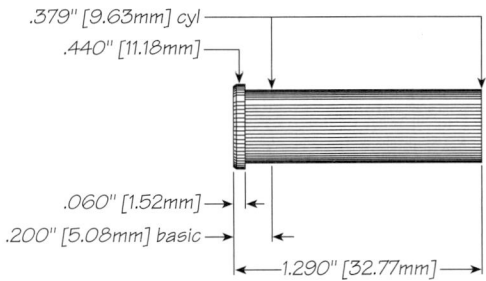

.379" [9.63mm] cyl
.440" [11.18mm]
.060" [1.52mm]
.200" [5.08mm] basic
1.290" [32.77mm]

Max. Case Length:	1.290"	Cart. Case:	Speer
Trim-to Length:	1.280"	Primer:	CCI 500; 550*
Max Cart. OAL:	1.590"	Test Firearm:	S&W Model 19
RCBS Shell Holder:	#6	Barrel Length:	6"

0.358"	38 LSWC	38 LSWC HP
Weight, grains	158	158
Ballistic Coefficient	0.123	0.121
Sectional Density	0.176	0.176
COAL Tested:	1.570"	1.575"
Speer Part No.	4623	4627

	START CHARGE		MAXIMUM CHARGE	
Propellant	Weight, grs	Muzzle Velocity, ft/sec	Weight, grs	Muzzle Velocity, ft/sec
Unique	5.5	970	6.0	1034
SR 7625	4.8	926	5.3	1021
700-X	4.5	904	5.0	1002
231	4.9	897	5.4	989
Bullseye	4.3	848	4.8	939
HP-38	4.5	839	5.0	932

NOTE: *These loads do not reach maximum pressures.*

Maximum Loads should be used with CAUTION • C = Compressed Load • *Magnum Primer used with this powder.*

0.357"	38 UCHP
Weight, grains	110
Ballistic Coefficient	0.113
Sectional Density	0.123
COAL Tested:	1.575"
Speer Part No.	4007

	START CHARGE		MAXIMUM CHARGE	
Propellant	Weight, grs	Muzzle Velocity, ft/sec	Weight, grs	Muzzle Velocity, ft/sec
Viht. N110	19.0	1557	21.0C	1693
Blue Dot	14.0	1548	16.0	1680
2400	17.5	1536	19.5	1670
Power Pistol	9.5	1326	10.5	1451
Unique	8.5	1284	9.7	1447
3N37	9.7	1305	10.8	1433
Bullseye	7.8	1246	8.7	1403
700-X	7.0	1208	8.0	1366
H. Universal	8.0	1264	9.0	1359
HS-7	12.5	1182	14.4	1341
AA No. 5	10.8	1246	12.0	1330
231	8.5	1231	9.5	1319

NOTE: *Do not use the 110-grain Gold Dot SB HP (#4009) in the 357 Magnum.*

0.357"	38 UCSP	38 GDHP	38 UCHP	38 TMJ FN
Weight, grains	125	125	125	125
Ballistic Coefficient	0.129	0.140	0.129	0.146
Sectional Density	0.140	0.140	0.140	0.140
COAL Tested:	1.575"	1.580"	1.575"	1.575"
Speer Part No.	4011	4012	4013	4015

Propellant	START CHARGE Weight, grs	START CHARGE Muzzle Velocity, ft/sec	MAXIMUM CHARGE Weight, grs	MAXIMUM CHARGE Muzzle Velocity, ft/sec
Viht. N110	16.8	1410	17.8	1443
2400	16.5	1335	17.5	1409
Power Pistol	9.5	1273	10.5	1345
Unique	8.6	1259	9.6	1343
296*	18.3	1188	20.3	1336
Blue Dot	11.5	1252	13.0	1333
H110*	18.0	1154	20.0	1282
AA No. 9	12.6	1119	14.6	1238
Viht. N350	9.0	1097	10.0	1226
H. Universal	7.5	1148	8.2	1200
Viht. 3N37	9.0	1035	10.2	1180
HS-7*	11.8	1052	13.3	1169
231	7.6	1129	8.3	1168
AA No. 7	12.0	1045	13.5	1134
HS-6*	10.0	1009	11.3	1124

*Maximum Loads should be used with CAUTION • C = Compressed Load • *Magnum Primer used with this powder.*

0.357"	38 GDHP SB
Weight, grains	135
Ballistic Coefficient	0.141
Sectional Density	0.151
COAL Tested:	1.590"
Speer Part No.	4014

Propellant	START CHARGE		MAXIMUM CHARGE	
	Weight, grs	Muzzle Velocity, ft/sec	Weight, grs	Muzzle Velocity, ft/sec
H110*	17.5	1313	18.5	1387
296*	17.5	1264	18.5	1377
2400	15.0	1219	16.0	1377
AA No. 9	14.5	1234	15.5	1345
Power Pistol	8.6	1192	9.6	1291
Viht. 3N37	7.7	1093	8.7	1185
Unique	6.8	1082	7.8	1185

0.357"	38 GDHP SB
Weight, grains	135
Ballistic Coefficient	0.141
Sectional Density	0.151
COAL Tested:	1.590"
Speer Part No.	4014

SHORT BARREL VELOCITIES

Test Firearm: S&W Model 19 2.5"

Propellant	START CHARGE		MAXIMUM CHARGE	
	Weight, grs	Muzzle Velocity, ft/sec	Weight, grs	Muzzle Velocity, ft/sec
AA No. 9	14.5	1202	15.5	1258
H110*	17.5	1128	18.5	1205
2400	15.0	1124	16.0	1176
Power Pistol	8.6	1046	9.6	1137
296*	17.5	1105	18.5	1130
Unique	6.8	971	7.8	1109
Viht. 3N37	7.7	874	8.7	1012

0.357"	38 UCHP
Weight, grains	140
Ballistic Coefficient	0.145
Sectional Density	0.157
COAL Tested:	1.560"
Speer Part No.	4203

Propellant	START CHARGE		MAXIMUM CHARGE	
	Weight, grs	Muzzle Velocity, ft/sec	Weight, grs	Muzzle Velocity, ft/sec
296*	17.0	1327	18.0	1367
Viht. N110	14.2	1255	15.2	1365
H110*	16.2	1323	17.2	1352
Blue Dot	10.3	1234	11.5	1324
IMR 4227	17.2	1153	19.2C	1298
2400	13.1	1219	15.1	1298
Power Pistol	8.5	1193	9.5	1288
AA No. 9	13.0	1213	14.0	1266
AA No. 7	11.1	1144	12.1	1238
Viht. N350	8.1	1078	9.1	1195
Unique	7.2	1086	8.0	1185
AA No. 5	9.1	1111	10.2	1181
HS-7*	10.7	1041	11.9	1179
HS-6*	8.8	1005	9.8	1142
231	DNR	—	7.1	1105

NOTE: *The 146-gr JHP-SWC (#4205) may be used with these propellants by reducing the charge weights one grain. DNR — do not reduce*

*Maximum Loads should be used with CAUTION • C = Compressed Load • *Magnum Primer used with this powder.*

0.357"	38 TMJ FN	38 UCHP	38 GDHP	38 UCSP
Weight, grains	158	158	158	158
Ballistic Coefficient	0.173	0.163	0.168	0.164
Sectional Density	0.177	0.177	0.177	0.177
COAL Tested:	1.570"	1.570"	1.575"	1.570"
Speer Part No.	4207	4211	4215	4217

Propellant	START CHARGE Weight, grs	START CHARGE Muzzle Velocity, ft/sec	MAXIMUM CHARGE Weight, grs	MAXIMUM CHARGE Muzzle Velocity, ft/sec
2400	13.8	1128	14.8	1265
Viht. N110	13.5	1102	15.0	1253
H110*	13.9	1151	15.5	1217
Blue Dot	9.0	1049	10.2	1188
296*	13.2	1089	14.7	1185
AA No. 5	9.0	1032	10.0	1152
AA No. 7	10.5	1015	11.7	1140
AA No. 9	12.3	1052	13.7	1136
IMR 4227	15.0	1003	17.0	1126
Power Pistol	7.5	963	8.5	1078
Viht. N350	7.7	958	8.6	1072
HS-7*	9.9	895	11.0	1041
HS-6*	8.7	925	9.7	1040
Unique	6.9	978	7.7	1040
H. Universal	6.5	904	7.3	1015

0.357"	357 Mag GDSP
Weight, grains	170
Ballistic Coefficient	0.185
Sectional Density	0.191
COAL Tested:	1.590"
Speer Part No.	4230

Propellant	START CHARGE		MAXIMUM CHARGE	
	Weight, grs	Muzzle Velocity, ft/sec	Weight, grs	Muzzle Velocity, ft/sec
2400	13.9	1100	14.5	1166
Viht. N110	13.2	1046	13.8	1132
H. Lil' Gun*	14.8	1100	15.4	1121
IMR 4227	16.1	1037	16.7	1084
H110*	14.4	1024	15.2	1076
AA No. 9*	11.0	1030	11.7	1071
Blue Dot	8.8	978	9.4	1002

*Maximum Loads should be used with CAUTION • C = Compressed Load • *Magnum Primer used with this powder.*

357 Magnum Silhouette

Toppling heavy steel plates at long range with a 357 Magnum requires tough bullets. The Speer 180-grain TMJ® Silhouette Match bullet fills the bill.

This bullet was developed for single-shot target pistols such as the Thompson/Center Contender that aren't too fussy about cartridge overall length (COAL). Normal seating of these bullets produces a COAL up to 1.690 inches, a tenth-inch over the 357 Magnum's maximum cartridge length. Contender barrels usually have generous throats and loading the Silhouette bullet requires no special reloading steps. Revolvers are another story.

A revolver must have a total cylinder length of at least 1.625 inches (not counting rim recesses, if present) to benefit from this specialty bullet. All cases must be trimmed to 1.275 inches and bullets seated so that the case mouth covers almost all the crimping groove. Apply a very firm crimp to prevent bullet jump during recoil. Make a dummy round (no powder or primer) using the above technique and try it in your cylinder. For proper and safe function the bullet tip must be below—not flush with—the face of the cylinder.

Not all 357 Magnum revolvers have cylinders long enough to use the above loading technique. If your revolver has a short cylinder, we recommend choosing the 357" 158-grain TMJ bullet. It is every bit as accurate as the 180-grain Silhouette TMJ and will fit all 357 cylinders with normal loading techniques. The velocity increase and reduced recoil compared to the heavier bullet will usually offset the difference in weight.

The loads here were developed on copper crusher pressure barrels and approach the industry pressure limit of 45,000 CUP. Use them only in single-shot pistols and heavy-frame revolvers.

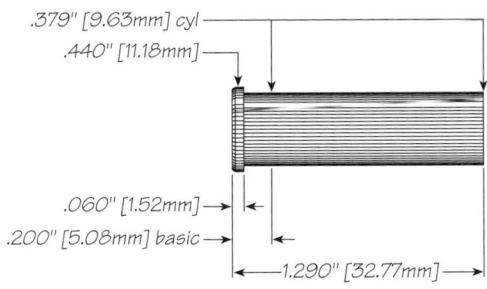

.379" [9.63mm] cyl
.440" [11.18mm]
.060" [1.52mm]
.200" [5.08mm] basic
1.290" [32.77mm]

Max. Case Length:	1.290"	**Cart. Case:**	Speer
Trim-to Length:	1.275"	**Primer:**	CCI 500; 550*
Max Cart. OAL:	See text	**Test Firearm:**	T/C Contender
RCBS Shell Holder:	#6	**Barrel Length:**	10"

0.357"	357 Mag Match TMJ Sil
Weight, grains	180
Ballistic Coefficient	0.230
Sectional Density	0.202
COAL Tested:	1.690"
Speer Part No.	4229

Propellant	START CHARGE		MAXIMUM CHARGE	
	Weight, grs	Muzzle Velocity, ft/sec	Weight, grs	Muzzle Velocity, ft/sec
296*	14.3	1430	**15.9**	1573
H110*	14.5	1396	**16.1**	1528
AA No 9	13.0	1388	**14.4**	1503
IMR 4227*	14.1	1274	**15.7**	1429
2400	12.1	1291	**13.5**	1416
Blue Dot	10.1	1245	**11.2**	1371

*Maximum Loads should be used with CAUTION • C = Compressed Load • * Magnum Primer used with this powder.*

357 Maximum

The 357 Remington Maximum is a joint development of Remington and Sturm-Ruger intended as a flat-shooting silhouette combination. It was announced in 1983 with a single 158-grain JHP load and was chambered only in a "stretched" version of the Ruger Blackhawk revolver. Within a short time, Dan Wesson developed a revolver for the new cartridge and Thompson/Center offered 357 Maximum barrels for their Contender single-shot pistol. The cartridge showed some problems in revolvers and the single-shot pistol proved to be the happier home for this high-performance cartridge.

The Maximum is simply the 357 Magnum case extended to 1.605 inches to provide greater powder capacity. The pressure limit was increased 3000 CUP over the 357 Magnum. When the cartridge moved from the silhouette range to the hunting fields, many shooters opined that the factory 158-grain hollow points were too light for game and several ammo makers reacted with 180-grain factory loads to overcome this objection. Of course, handloaders had already discovered that the cartridge could be loaded with heavier bullets including some designed for rifles.

The Maximum is a superb handgun hunting cartridge. It offers reasonably flat trajectory and good retained energy and has taken plenty of deer and black bear. Hits at 200 yards are surprisingly easy with a scope-sighted 14-inch Contender and 180-grain rifle bullets. A few custom rifles have been made for this cartridge and their owners seem very satisfied with them.

The only hollow point bullet under 180 grains we recommend for smaller deer is the 158-grain Speer Gold Dot. Other hollow points at these velocities act like varmint bullets. For larger deer, the .358" 180-grain Hot-Cor rifle bullet, designed for the 35 Remington, is excellent and very accurate. The .357" 170-grain Gold Dot soft point uses the same data as the 180-grain soft point. The 220-grain FN SP is best suited to game shots at shorter ranges. The 180-grain TMJ Silhouette Match bullet is intended for silhouette competition and should never be used on game animals. Expect higher velocity variations with bullets lighter than 158 grains. This is an unavoidable effect of light bullets in a big case.

At press time, Remington still lists unprimed 357 Maximum brass on their website but not loaded ammo. The 357 Maximum operates at rifle pressures so we recommend using small rifle primers in this cartridge. These loads do not exceed the industry pressure limit of 48,000 CUP.

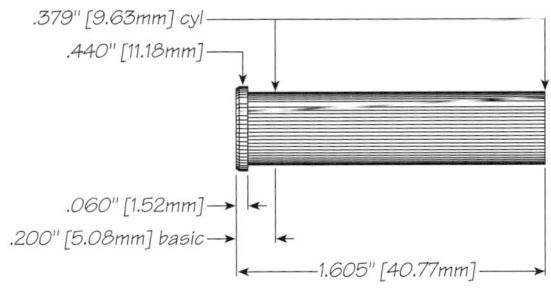

.379" [9.63mm] cyl
.440" [11.18mm]
.060" [1.52mm]
.200" [5.08mm] basic
1.605" [40.77mm]

Max. Case Length:	1.605"	Cart. Case:	Remington
Trim-to Length:	1.595"	Primer:	CCI 400
Max Cart. OAL:	1.990"	Test Firearm:	T/C Contender
RCBS Shell Holder:	#6	Barrel Length:	14"

0.357"	38 UCSP	38 GDHP	38 UCSP	38 TMJ RN
Weight, grains	125	125	125	125
Ballistic Coefficient	0.129	0.140	0.129	0.146
Sectional Density	0.140	0.140	0.140	0.140
COAL Tested:	1.885"	1.885"	1.885"	1.885"
Speer Part No.	4011	4012	4013	4015

	START CHARGE		MAXIMUM CHARGE	
Propellant	Weight, grs	Muzzle Velocity, ft/sec	Weight, grs	Muzzle Velocity, ft/sec
H110	27.0	2205	29.0C	2432
296	26.0	2223	28.0C	2381
Viht. N110	20.5	2066	22.5	2224
2400	19.5	2054	21.5	2188
IMR 4227	24.0	2031	26.0	2148

*Maximum Loads should be used with CAUTION • C = Compressed Load • *Magnum Primer used with this powder.*

0.357"	38 UCHP
Weight, grains	140
Ballistic Coefficient	0.145
Sectional Density	0.157
COAL Tested:	1.885"
Speer Part No.	4203

Propellant	START CHARGE		MAXIMUM CHARGE	
	Weight, grs	Muzzle Velocity, ft/sec	Weight, grs	Muzzle Velocity, ft/sec
H110	25.0	2095	27.0C	2283
296	24.5	2093	26.5C	2261
Viht. N110	19.0	1888	21.0	2029
AA 1680	26.0	1822	28.0C	1996
2400	18.0	1880	20.0	1981
IMR 4227	22.0	1824	24.0C	1977
Viht. N120	23.0	1685	25.0C	1883

0.357"	38 TMJ FN	38 UCHP	38 UCHP
Weight, grains	158	158	158
Ballistic Coefficient	0.173	0.163	0.164
Sectional Density	0.177	0.177	0.177
COAL Tested:	1.875"	1.875"	1.875"
Speer Part No.	4207	4211	4217

Propellant	START CHARGE		MAXIMUM CHARGE	
	Weight, grs	Muzzle Velocity, ft/sec	Weight, grs	Muzzle Velocity, ft/sec
H110	22.0	1896	24.0	2058
296	21.5	1883	23.5	2046
AA 1680	25.0	1796	27.0C	1938
2400	16.5	1747	18.5	1895
IMR 4227	20.5	1735	22.5C	1866
Viht. N120	22.0	1670	24.0C	1857

*Maximum Loads should be used with CAUTION • C = Compressed Load • *Magnum Primer used with this powder.*

0.357-.358"	38 Mag GDSP	38 FN SP
Diameter	.357"	.358"
Weight, grains	170	180
Ballistic Coefficient	0.185	0.236
Sectional Density	0.191	0.201
COAL Tested:	1.875"	2.145"
Speer Part No.	4230	2435

Propellant	START CHARGE		MAXIMUM CHARGE	
	Weight, grs	Muzzle Velocity, ft/sec	Weight, grs	Muzzle Velocity, ft/sec
AA 1680	25.0	1719	27.0C	1884
296	21.0	1708	23.0	1881
H110	20.5	1662	22.5	1820
2400	16.0	1575	18.0	1710
Viht. N120	21.0	1477	23.0C	1678
IMR 4227	19.5	1564	21.5	1677
IMR 4198	21.0	1417	23.0C	1573

NOTE: *180-gr, bullet is for single-shot firearms only.*

0.357"	38 Mag Match TMJ Sil
Weight, grains	180
Ballistic Coefficient	0.230
Sectional Density	0.202
COAL Tested:	1.990"
Speer Part No.	4229

Propellant	START CHARGE		MAXIMUM CHARGE	
	Weight, grs	Muzzle Velocity, ft/sec	Weight, grs	Muzzle Velocity, ft/sec
AA 1680	24.0	1685	26.0C	1849
296	18.5	1572	20.5	1716
H110	18.5	1546	20.5	1699
2400	14.5	1437	16.5	1585
IMR 4227	18.0	1457	20.0	1577
Viht. N120	19.0	1339	21.0C	1540

0.357"	38 FN SP
Weight, grains	220
Ballistic Coefficient	0.286
Sectional Density	0.245
COAL Tested:	2.145"
Speer Part No.	2439

	START CHARGE		MAXIMUM CHARGE	
Propellant	Weight, grs	Muzzle Velocity, ft/sec	Weight, grs	Muzzle Velocity, ft/sec
H110	16.5	1339	18.5	1541
AA 1680	20.0	1342	22.0C	1509
296	16.0	1314	18.0	1500
Viht. N120	18.0	1216	20.0C	1445
IMR 4227	16.5	1255	18.5	1438
2400	13.0	1194	15.0	1361

NOTE: *220-gr bullet is for single-shot firearms only.*

*Maximum Loads should be used with CAUTION • C = Compressed Load • *Magnum Primer used with this powder.*

35 Remington

Metallic silhouette shooters saw the need for a powerful 35-caliber handgun that did not require special case-forming operations. The simple solution was the venerable 35 Remington rifle cartridge. In a 14-inch T/C Contender barrel, the 35 Remington delivered an additional 200 ft/sec over the potent 357 Maximum, even though the older cartridge operates at much lower pressures. The 35 Remington in the Contender turned out to be an excellent hunting combo.

The 35 Remington in a Contender produces velocities quite close to those from a 22-inch rifle barrel, making it a good hunting cartridge. Most people choose the 180-grain flat point for deer hunting because velocities are high enough to keep the trajectory flat.

Firing new cases in the Contender may result in an occasional misfire; some lots of cases have a minimum length shoulder or are a bit soft. The firing pin blow moves the shoulder slightly, cushioning the impact on the primer. This is a case problem, not a gun problem. Once the case is fired the first time, the shoulder position is set for your barrel and the brass is slightly work-hardened; misfires generally do not happen with once-fired cases. These steps will help you avoid misfires on the first firing:

- Try different brands of loaded ammo or cases.
- Try reloading once-fired cases fired in another firearm. Take care in sizing so the shoulder position isn't changed more than needed for chambering in your barrel.
- Use a .375" diameter tapered expander ball (available from RCBS) to expand the neck, then carefully resize only the neck in a 35 Remington sizer until your action will just close on the case. This positions a temporary shoulder at the correct point for your chamber. Load with a near-maximum load and fire-form.

Be careful in sizing after applying these remedies. You worked to put that new shoulder in a certain position and careless sizing can negate your efforts. We recommend neck sizing this cartridge to improve accuracy and extend case life in the T/C.

These loads are within the 35,000 CUP pressure limit established for this cartridge.

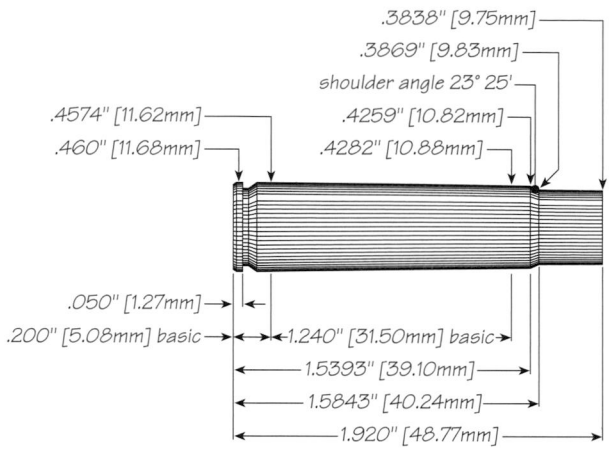

.3838" [9.75mm]
.3869" [9.83mm]
shoulder angle 23° 25'
.4574" [11.62mm]
.460" [11.68mm]
.4259" [10.82mm]
.4282" [10.88mm]
.050" [1.27mm]
.200" [5.08mm] basic
1.240" [31.50mm] basic
1.5393" [39.10mm]
1.5843" [40.24mm]
1.920" [48.77mm]

Max. Case Length:	1.920"	Cart. Case:	Winchester
Trim-to Length:	1.910"	Primer:	CCI 200; 250*
Max Cart. OAL:	2.525"	Test Firearm:	T/C Contender
RCBS Shell Holder:	#9	Barrel Length:	14"

0.357-.358"	38 Mag Match TMJ Sil	38 FN SP
Diameter	0.357"	0.358"
Weight, grains	180	180
Ballistic Coefficient	0.230	0.236
Sectional Density	0.202	0.201
COAL Tested:	2.470"	2.315"
Speer Part No.	4229	2435

Propellant	START CHARGE Weight, grs	START CHARGE Muzzle Velocity, ft/sec	MAXIMUM CHARGE Weight, grs	MAXIMUM CHARGE Muzzle Velocity, ft/sec
H335	36.0	1871	38.0	2023
H322	36.0	1825	38.0	1997
IMR 4895	38.0	1786	40.0	1896
BL-C(2)*	33.0	1736	35.0	1885
748*	40.0	1714	42.0	1879
IMR 3031	36.0	1734	38.0	1837
IMR 4198	28.0	1683	30.0	1806
H380*	42.0	1653	44.0	1782
Reloder 7	28.0	2565	30.0	1739

0.358"	38 FN SP
Weight, grains	220
Ballistic Coefficient	0.286
Sectional Density	0.245
COAL Tested:	2.470"
Speer Part No.	2439

	START CHARGE		MAXIMUM CHARGE	
Propellant	Weight, grs	Muzzle Velocity, ft/sec	Weight, grs	Muzzle Velocity, ft/sec
IMR 4064	34.0	1558	36.0	1638
H414*	38.0	1550	40.0	1626
IMR 4895	33.5	1539	35.5	1620
IMR 3031	31.5	1495	33.5	1611
H335	30.0	1429	32.0	1567
BL-C(2)*	33.0	1460	35.0	1561
748*	33.0	1438	35.0	1550
Reloder 7	22.5	1243	24.5	1421

*Maximum Loads should be used with CAUTION • C = Compressed Load • *Magnum Primer used with this powder.*

375 Winchester

This is yet another rifle cartridge that has found a happy home in the Thompson/Center Contender single-shot pistol. The 375 Winchester is one of T/C's more interesting introductions and is building a good reputation with handgun hunters.

Speer makes only one bullet suitable for the 375 Winchester—the 235-grain semi-spitzer. Because it is designed to tolerate 2900 ft/sec in a 375 H&H Magnum, expansion at handgun velocities is modest but penetration is excellent. Velocities in the 14-inch test pistol approached 1900 ft/sec with Reloder 7. Heavier 375 bullets would yield very low velocities and therefore cannot be recommended.

Because this is a rimmed, straight-taper case, reloading is easily accomplished. We used a cartridge overall length of 2.600 inches, slightly over the 2.560 inch maximum cartridge length specified for lever-action rifles.

These loads do not exceed the industry maximum pressure of 52,000 CUP.

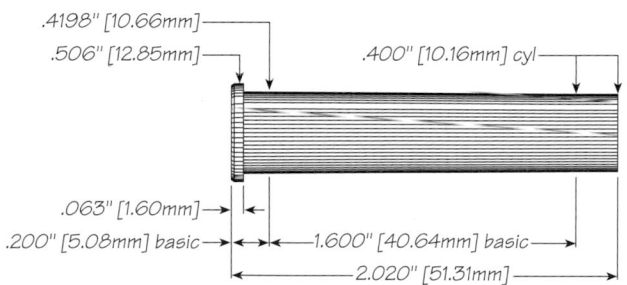

Max. Case Length:	2.020"	Cart. Case:	Winchester
Trim-to Length:	2.010"	Primer:	CCI 200
Max Cart. OAL:	2.560"	Test Firearm:	T/C Contender
RCBS Shell Holder:	#2	Barrel Length:	14"

0.375"	375 Semi-Spitz SP
Weight, grains	235
Ballistic Coefficient	0.301
Sectional Density	0.239
COAL Tested:	2.600"
Speer Part No.	2471

Propellant	START CHARGE		MAXIMUM CHARGE	
	Weight, grs	Muzzle Velocity, ft/sec	Weight, grs	Muzzle Velocity, ft/sec
Reloder 7	31.0	1628	35.0C	1884
IMR 4198	28.0	1543	32.0C	1808
Viht. N133	33.0	1600	37.0C	1793
AA 2015	32.0	1592	36.0C	1776
H322	31.0	1484	35.0C	1737
AA 2230	33.5	1577	37.5C	1711
IMR 4895	32.0	1418	36.0C	1692
IMR 3031	31.0	1375	35.0C	1636

John Garrison, Associated Products; ATK customer; 375 JDJ, 285-grain, Grand Slam®; brown bear.

Maximum Loads should be used with CAUTION • C = Compressed Load • *Magnum Primer used with this powder.

38-40 Winchester *(38 W.C.F.)*

In the Rifle Section we related the background of this old cartridge. It was just as popular in handguns, the most common being the famous Colt Single Action Army. Cowboy Action Shooting has revived interest in many old cartridges including the 38-40.

CAS competition requires a lead bullet at modest velocities. RCBS® makes two moulds that produce suitable cast bullets for the 38-40. The 40-180-FN design is a close copy of original moulds in that it has a "crimp-over" shoulder rather than a true crimp groove. The new 40-180-CM design has a broader point and a conventional crimp groove. This is the bullet of choice when loading for both rifle and revolver.

The 38-40 case has a very thin neck wall. Trimming all cases to uniform length and separating the seating and crimping operations will produce a better crimp and reduce the incidence of crumpled case necks.

We elected to show the velocities from a Colt New Service double-action revolver made in 1923. Its cylinder and barrel dimensions were as close to optimum as possible, and we feel these velocities are quite representative.

We used only the faster-burning handgun propellants. Slower powders produced poor ballistic uniformity unless loaded to considerably over the industry pressure limit of 14,000 CUP. Do not attempt to load lighter charges than the start loads shown here. They were selected to produce a minimum pressure of at least 10,000 CUP. Loading lighter could result in poor performance and risk lodging a bullet in the barrel.

If you choose to load the start loads for reduced recoil consider American Select, Bullseye, TiteGroup, AA No. 2 Improved and Hodgdon Universal. They produced the least velocity variation at the start load levels.

Refer to the Rifle data for additional information on this cartridge.

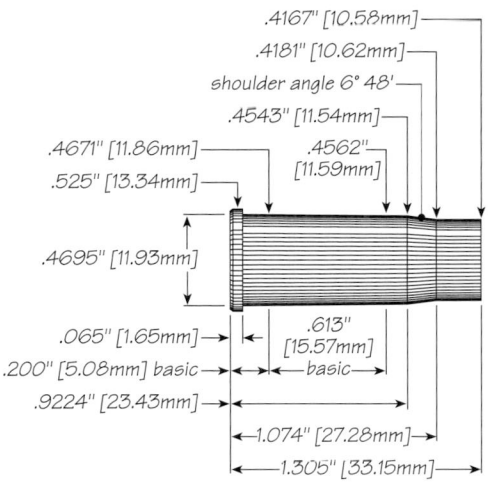

.4167" [10.58mm]
.4181" [10.62mm]
shoulder angle 6° 48'
.4543" [11.54mm]
.4671" [11.86mm]
.4562" [11.59mm]
.525" [13.34mm]
.4695" [11.93mm]
.065" [1.65mm]
.613" [15.57mm] basic
.200" [5.08mm] basic
.9224" [23.43mm]
1.074" [27.28mm]
1.305" [33.15mm]

Max. Case Length:	1.305"	Cart. Case:	Winchester
Trim-to Length:	1.295"	Primer:	CCI 300
Max Cart. OAL:	1.592"	Test Firearm:	Colt New Service
RCBS Shell Holder:	#35	Barrel Length:	4.5"

0.401"	40-180 FN	40-180 CM
Weight, grains	180	180
Lead Alloy	hard	hard
Ballistic Coefficient	0.143	0.135
Sectional Density	0.181	0.181
COAL Tested:	1.560"	1.575"
RCBS Mould No.	82066	82306

Propellant	START CHARGE		MAXIMUM CHARGE	
	Weight, grs	Muzzle Velocity, ft/sec	Weight, grs	Muzzle Velocity, ft/sec
Unique	6.4	776	7.4	846
TiteGroup	4.9	771	5.5	829
AA No.2 Impr.	5.1	744	5.7	828
Red Dot	4.3	726	5.2	817
Bullseye	4.5	726	5.3	810
Viht. N350	7.8	772	8.4	808
AA Nitro 100	4.3	691	5.0	805
H. Universal	6.5	759	7.0	789
700-X	4.6	754	5.1	789
American Select	4.6	732	5.2	788
231	5.2	694	6.0	781
Trail Boss	4.9	717	5.4	744

NOTE: *We sell bullet moulds, not cast bullets. These bullets were cast in RCBS moulds. Contact your dealer for more information on the RCBS line of premium bullet casting equipment, or visit on the Internet at www.rcbs.com.*

*Maximum Loads should be used with CAUTION • C = Compressed Load • *Magnum Primer used with this powder.*

40 Smith &Wesson

The 40 S&W is a relative newcomer to the semi-auto pistol arena. Smith & Wesson and Winchester jointly announced the cartridge in January of 1990.

The 40 S&W resulted from law enforcement interest in the potent 10mm Auto cartridge. Administrators considered full-power 10mm ammo too powerful for typical police applications and 10mm pistols tended to be large. To remedy this, the 10mm was loaded lighter to fire 180-grain bullets at 980 ft/sec. This modification reduced recoil and gave excellent ballistic performance but did not address the issue of pistol bulk for plain-clothes officers or those with small hands.

What they wanted was a more powerful cartridge that fit the smaller 9mm pistol frame. Winchester developed a shortened 10mm loaded to the law enforcement velocity specification (180-grain bullet at 980 ft/sec). Operating pressures and loaded cartridge length of the 40 S&W are essentially the same as the 9mm Luger. Thus a cartridge having energy levels approaching the 45 Auto cartridge was available in a package not much different from standard 9mm pistols.

The new combo was an immediate success. Factory ammunition is available with a wide choice of bullet weights and types. Speer offers three weights in the Gold Dot hollow point for hunting and defense, and in its TMJ line for plinking and target practice.

Gunwriter Charles Petty has done extensive accuracy testing with the 40 S&W. He found that quick-burning powders seldom give top accuracy unless downloaded and that propellants in the middle range of burning rates performed best. Our tests here at Speer substantiate Petty's findings.

The first 165-grain factory loads were reduced-pressure loads for law enforcement but the current practice is to load 165-grain bullets to full pressures. The 165-grain loads here reflect that trend. However, several of our 165-grain start loads meet the 980 ft/sec velocity level of the older "40 Lite" loads and are so marked. As such, they are quite useful for accuracy loading and to reduce recoil in the newer 40-caliber subcompacts.

The trend to ultra-compact 40 S&W pistols for concealed carry meant the 40 suffered the same problems in short barrels as the 45 Auto—jacketed hollow points that expand nicely in longer barrels did not behave as well at sub-compact pistol velocities. This led Speer to develop Gold Dot Short Barrel ammo and component bullets. The 40-caliber

180-grain Gold Dot Short Barrel hollow point has a greater cavity volume than other Gold Dots for excellent expansion at short-barrel velocities.

Reloading the 40 S&W is no different from reloading the 45 Auto. As with other semi-auto cartridges, taper crimping is recommended. Note that the 40 S&W uses small pistol primers compared to the 10mm, which uses large primers. The loads shown do not exceed the industry pressure maximum of 35,000 psi.

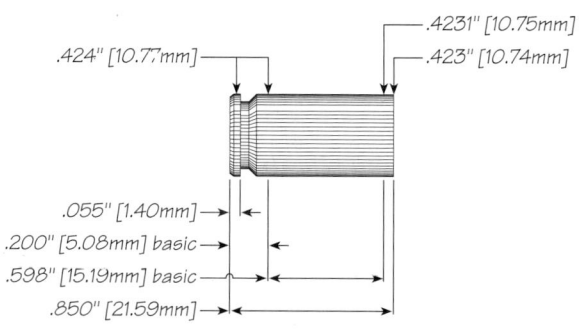

Max. Case Length:	0.850"	Cart. Case:	Speer
Trim-to Length:	0.840"	Primer:	CCI 500
Max Cart. OAL:	1.135"	Test Firearm:	Smith & Wesson M4006
RCBS Shell Holder:	#27	Barrel Length:	4"

IMPORTANT SAFETY NOTE: *These loads were developed and tested for safe use in HANDGUNS. Not all loads may be suitable for use in a carbine or rifle chambered for this cartridge. If loading for a carbine or rifle, choose from among the loads developing the highest handgun velocities and load just a few rounds. Thoroughly test this small sample in your firearm in slow-fire mode, insuring that you achieve proper feeding and ejection. Be certain that all bullets exit the barrel; watching the target for each bullet strike is the best way to know that the load produces sufficient gas volume for a longer barrel.*

0.400"	40/10mm TMJ FN	40/10mm GDHP
Weight, grains	155	155
Ballistic Coefficient	0.125	0.123
Sectional Density	0.138	0.138
COAL Tested:	1.120"	1.120"
Speer Part No.	4399	4400

Propellant	START CHARGE Weight, grs	Muzzle Velocity, ft/sec	MAXIMUM CHARGE Weight, grs	Muzzle Velocity, ft/sec
Blue Dot	10.0	1113	11.0	1221
Power Pistol	8.0	1112	9.0	1213
Unique	7.2	1048	8.0	1207
H. Universal	6.2	995	7.0	1159
TiteGroup	5.4	1011	6.2	1144
AA No. 5	7.9	956	8.7	1116
WSF	6.7	981	7.5	1090
AA No. 7	10.0	984	11.0	1089
Viht. N350	6.8	858	7.6	1061
HS-7	9.0	921	10.0	1051
231	5.8	867	6.5	1038
HS-6	7.3	786	9.0	1033
Bullseye	5.4	905	6.0	1023
American Select	5.0	931	5.6	1001
AA No. 2 Impr.	5.8	840	6.5	956

*Maximum Loads should be used with CAUTION • C = Compressed Load • *Magnum Primer used with this powder.*

0.400"	40/10mm TMJ FN	40/10mm GDHP
Weight, grains	165	165
Ballistic Coefficient	0.135	0.138
Sectional Density	0.147	0.147
COAL Tested:	1.120"	1.120"
Speer Part No.	4410	4397

Propellant	START CHARGE		MAXIMUM CHARGE	
	Weight, grs	Muzzle Velocity, ft/sec	Weight, grs	Muzzle Velocity, ft/sec
Viht. N350	6.7†	989	7.5	1106
HS-7	9.0	1008	9.8	1085
WSF	6.2	1007	6.8	1082
Power Pistol	7.0†	978	7.8	1081
H. Universal	5.7†	999	6.2	1074
AA No. 5	7.6	916	8.5	1067
Unique	6.2	882	7.2	1064
HS-6	8.0	1012	8.5	1060
AA No. 7	9.6†	951	10.5	1041
TiteGroup	5.0†	957	5.4	1035
231	5.8†	955	6.3	1031
Bullseye	5.3†	949	5.8	1022

NOTE: Loads marked "†" approximate 165-gr law enforcement loads ("40 Lite")

0.400"	40/10mm GDHP SB	40/10mm TMJ FN	40/10mm GDHP
Weight, grains	180	180	180
Ballistic Coefficient	0.148	0.143	0.143
Sectional Density	0.161	0.161	0.161
COAL Tested:	1.120"	1.120"	1.120"
Speer Part No.	4401	4402	4406

Propellant	START CHARGE		MAXIMUM CHARGE	
	Weight, grs	Muzzle Velocity, ft/sec	Weight, grs	Muzzle Velocity, ft/sec
HS-7	8.3	894	9.3	1027
700-X	5.0	953	5.5	1020
Blue Dot	8.0	922	8.9	1018
Power Pistol	6.2	890	7.2	1013
Unique	6.0	849	6.7	1000
Viht. N350	6.2	804	6.9	987
SR 7625	5.4	884	6.0	981
AA No. 7	8.7	895	9.7	972
AA No. 5	7.0	791	7.8	969
Viht. 3N37	6.6	841	7.2	960
HS-6	7.3	786	8.2	942
Bullseye	4.9	783	5.5	929
TiteGroup	4.0	793	4.7	917
H. Universal	5.3	802	5.9	904
Amer. Select	4.3	770	5.1	865

*Maximum Loads should be used with CAUTION • C = Compressed Load • *Magnum Primer used with this powder.*

10mm Auto

The idea of a 40-caliber semi-auto pistol cartridge has been around for many years and some wildcat versions have briefly held the interest of pistol shooters. It wasn't until 1983 that a commercial version appeared.

In that year, the firm of Dornaus & Dixon announced the introduction of the 10mm Auto cartridge in a heavy combat pistol, the Bren Ten. Norma of Sweden developed the new cartridge for D&D. The cartridge pushed a 200-grain bullet at 1200 ft/sec making it just a little less powerful than hunting loads in the potent 41 Magnum revolver.

Manufacturing problems resulted in few Bren Tens (and fewer magazines) actually reaching consumers. Colt announced production guns in this caliber in 1987. The Delta Elite was a basic M1911 design beefed up to handle the high-pressure 10mm cartridge. Within 18 months most other U.S. pistol makers offered a 10mm and several ammo companies were producing the ammunition.

The 10mm received a lot of attention when the FBI looked for a new service pistol to replace its 9mm and 38 Special handguns. They experimented with reduced loads driving a 180-grain bullet at 980 ft/sec and found a cartridge that combined tolerable recoil with excellent terminal ballistics. There isn't an official name for this reduced 10mm load but it is variously referred to as "Subsonic," the "FBI load" or occasionally, the "10 Lite." However, the 10mm subsonic load is no weakling—it is an excellent law enforcement cartridge for departments that choose large-frame semi-autos.

The 10mm Auto is among just a few semi-auto pistol cartridges that can be used on deer. Check your local hunting regulations—your state may place limitations on the handgun cartridges that can be used on game. Generally, 180-grain Gold Dot hollow point bullets offer sufficient penetration to handle smaller whitetail at close range. The 155-grain Gold Dot hollow point allows very high velocity but shouldn't be used on deer because its penetration at such speeds is less than the heavier bullets.

One of the most overlooked applications of the 10mm was as a trail gun. It is more compact than a heavy-frame revolver, holds more cartridges and its performance exceeds that of the 357 Magnum in typical revolvers. For this application, we feel that Speer's tough 180-grain TMJ is an excellent choice for deep penetration.

The quick acceptance of the 40 S&W by sports shooters and law enforcement has decimated the 10mm's market position in the last ten years. At press time, Glock was the only firm still producing 10mm pistols. The selection of factory ammo has also diminished compared to the 40 S&W. As long as cases remain available, this should have little effect on the handloader.

These loads do not exceed the 10mm's 37,500 psi pressure limit established by the industry.

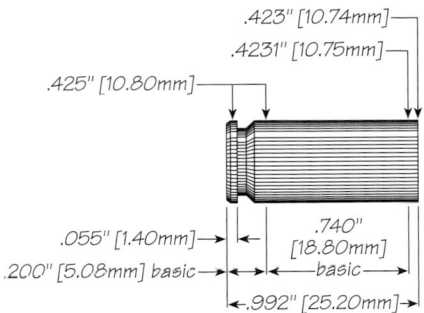

Max. Case Length:	0.992"	**Cart. Case:**	Hornady	
Trim-to Length:	0.982"	**Primer:**	CCI 300; 350*	
Max Cart. OAL:	1.260"	**Test Firearm:**	Smith & Wesson M1006	
RCBS Shell Holder:	#27	**Barrel Length:**	5"	

0.400"	40/10mm TMJ FN	40/10mm GDHP
Weight, grains	155	155
Ballistic Coefficient	0.125	0.123
Sectional Density	0.138	0.138
COAL Tested:	1.250"	1.250"
Speer Part No.	4399	4400

Propellant	START CHARGE		MAXIMUM CHARGE	
	Weight, grs	Muzzle Velocity, ft/sec	Weight, grs	Muzzle Velocity, ft/sec
AA No. 7	12.0	1187	13.0	1320
Blue Dot	11.0	1164	12.0	1291
HS-7*	11.0	1094	12.0	1254
Unique	7.5	1091	8.5	1246
HS-6*	9.5	1095	10.5	1223
231	7.0	1062	7.7	1183
Viht. N340	7.2	1034	8.0	1180
AA No. 5	9.2	1004	10.2	1176
WSF	7.6	1017	8.4	1162

0.400"	40/10mm GDHP	40/10mm TMJ FN
Weight, grains	165	165
Ballistic Coefficient	0.138	0.135
Sectional Density	0.147	0.147
COAL Tested:	1.255"	1.255"
Speer Part No.	4397	4410

Propellant	START CHARGE		MAXIMUM CHARGE	
	Weight, grs	Muzzle Velocity, ft/sec	Weight, grs	Muzzle Velocity, ft/sec
AA No. 9*	14.5	1277	15.5	1344
Power Pistol	9.0	1204	10.0	1314
AA No. 7	11.2	1177	12.2	1278
Blue Dot	10.5	1181	11.5	1273
2400	13.8	1159	14.8	1234
Viht. 3N37	8.3	1091	9.2	1228
H. Universal	6.8	1100	7.5	1205
Unique	7.4	1126	8.3	1194
HS-6*	9.0	1071	10.0	1185
WSF	7.2	1065	8.0	1177
231	6.3	1043	7.0	1143

*Maximum Loads should be used with CAUTION • C = Compressed Load • *Magnum Primer used with this powder.*

0.400"	40/10mm TMJ FN	40/10mm GDHP
Weight, grains	180	180
Ballistic Coefficient	0.143	0.143
Sectional Density	0.161	0.161
COAL Tested:	1.250"	1.250"
Speer Part No.	4402	4406

	START CHARGE		MAXIMUM CHARGE	
Propellant	Weight, grs	Muzzle Velocity, ft/sec	Weight, grs	Muzzle Velocity, ft/sec
Blue Dot	10.0	1105	11.0	1295
2400	11.5	1051	12.8	1214
AA No. 7	11.0	1065	12.0	1180
Viht. N350	8.9	1077	9.7	1152
HS-7*	9.7	1037	10.6	1150
Viht. 3N37	9.0	1027	10.0	1150
Unique	7.2	1043	8.0	1138
WSF	6.8	1001	7.5	1120
AA No. 5	8.5	1015	9.5	1116
HS-6*	8.2	1001	9.1	1099

*Maximum Loads should be used with CAUTION • C = Compressed Load • *Magnum Primer used with this powder.*

41 Remington Magnum

The 41 Magnum answered the call of gunwriters and law enforcement officials wanting a new revolver cartridge falling between the power of the 357 and 44 Magnums. In 1964, Remington announced the cartridge and Smith & Wesson introduced a new revolver, the Model 57. It was identical to the 44 Magnum Model 29 except for caliber. S&W later introduced the less expensive Model 58 with fixed sights for the law enforcement market. Ruger also chambers its popular Blackhawk revolver for the 41 Magnum.

The first factory ammunition offered two performance levels: a hunting load with a 210-grain jacketed soft point with a velocity close to 1350 ft/sec and a "police" load with a 210-grain lead semi-wadcutter at around 1000 ft/sec.

The police community never fully embraced the 41 Magnum in spite of its excellent "street" performance. Many officers found the recoil difficult to control and those with small hands couldn't get a secure grip on the big revolvers. Another problem: for years the cartridge suffered from a lack of hollow point factory loads. The factory semi-wadcutters and soft points could stop a bad guy in his tracks but almost always exited with enough energy to do property damage or injury downrange.

The 41 Magnum is much more successful among handgun hunters. Hunting loads are nearly as effective on deer as 44 Magnum full-power loads and its supporters feel its trajectory is flatter. In the 1980's, there was enough new interest in the 41 Magnum to entice the major ammunition companies to bring out additional loads including hollow points as light as 170 grains.

Since the last *Speer Manual*, we have developed a new 210-grain Gold Dot Hunting hollow point bullet for 41 Magnum reloaders. The Gold Dot has a significantly different internal construction from the 200 and 220-grain bullets so loads do not necessarily "track" with those bullets.

The older Speer 200-grain hollow point and the 220-grain soft point are both very effective deer bullets. Like the 44 Magnum, full-power loads are best assembled with slow-burning handgun powders. A heavy roll crimp must be applied when using these powders. See the Rifle section for information on this cartridge in a carbine.

These loads are within the cartridge's 36,000 psi pressure limit established by the industry.

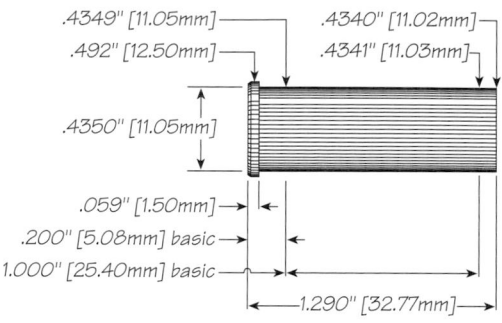

.4349" [11.05mm]
.492" [12.50mm]
.4340" [11.02mm]
.4341" [11.03mm]
.4350" [11.05mm]
.059" [1.50mm]
.200" [5.08mm] basic
1.000" [25.40mm] basic
1.290" [32.77mm]

Max. Case Length:	1.290"	Cart. Case:	Winchester
Trim-to Length:	1.280"	Primer:	CCI 300; 350*
Max Cart. OAL:	1.590"	Test Firearm:	S&W Model 57
RCBS Shell Holder:	#30	Barrel Length:	6"

0.410"	41 JHP-SWC
Weight, grains	200
Ballistic Coefficient	0.113
Sectional Density	0.170
COAL Tested:	1.590"
Speer Part No.	4405

Propellant	START CHARGE Weight, grs	START CHARGE Muzzle Velocity, ft/sec	MAXIMUM CHARGE Weight, grs	MAXIMUM CHARGE Muzzle Velocity, ft/sec
296*	20.0	1302	22.0	1428
H110*	20.0	1290	22.0	1412
Viht. N110	16.1	1197	17.9	1328
2400	15.1	1203	16.8	1311
AA No. 9	14.6	1155	16.3	1280
Blue Dot	10.8	1177	12.1	1279
IMR 4227	18.0	1133	20.0	1254
Unique	8.5	1117	9.0	1181
Viht. N350	9.0	1049	10.0	1172

0.410"	41 GDHP
Weight, grains	210
Ballistic Coefficient	0.183
Sectional Density	0.178
COAL Tested:	1.575"
Speer Part No.	4430

Propellant	START CHARGE		MAXIMUM CHARGE	
	Weight, grs	Muzzle Velocity, ft/sec	Weight, grs	Muzzle Velocity, ft/sec
296*	20.5	1251	21.5	1295
H110*	20.5	1237	21.5	1265
AA No. 9	17.0	1199	18.0	1265
Viht. N110	17.0	1136	18.0	1244
2400	18.0	1176	19.0	1223
IMR 4227	21.0	1117	22.0	1203
Blue Dot	12.0	1126	13.0	1193
Unique	8.7	1034	9.7	1123
Viht. N350	9.8	1035	10.5	1110

Tom Hill (r), Speer® Bullet Manager, CCI/Speer Operations and Earl Landrus (l); 41 Magnum Revolver, 200-grain, JHP-SWC; 150 pound mountain lion; Powell, Idaho.

Maximum Loads should be used with CAUTION • C = Compressed Load • *Magnum Primer used with this powder.

0.410"	41 JSP-SWC
Weight, grains	220
Ballistic Coefficient	0.137
Sectional Density	0.178
COAL Tested:	1.590"
Speer Part No.	4417

| Propellant | START CHARGE | | MAXIMUM CHARGE | |
	Weight, grs	Muzzle Velocity, ft/sec	Weight, grs	Muzzle Velocity, ft/sec
296*	18.5	1247	20.5	1360
H110*	18.5	1235	20.5	1352
IMR 4227	17.0	1197	19.0	1240
2400	14.2	1139	15.8	1215
AA No. 9	14.3	1089	15.9	1212
Blue Dot	10.2	1068	11.4	1203
Viht. N110	13.3	963	14.8	1155
Unique	8.0	1023	8.5	1081
Viht. N350	8.6	960	9.6	1076

*Maximum Loads should be used with CAUTION • C = Compressed Load • *Magnum Primer used with this powder.*

44 Russian

This is a very old cartridge dating to 1870 when Smith & Wesson developed a 44-caliber service revolver for the Czarist Russian Army. The 44 Russian case was somewhat shorter than some of its contemporaries to fit the shorter cylinder of the S&W break-top action. Although developed as a military cartridge, it was its performance on the target range rather than the battlefield that sealed the 44 Russian's place in history.

Target shooters quickly flock to an accurate cartridge and the 44 Russian proved a winner on all counts. Soon Colt also chambered target models of the Single Action Army for 44 Russian. Colt revolvers chambered for 44 Special were marked "44 Russian and Special" until the onset of World War II. Any revolver chambered for the 44 Special will also accept the shorter Russian cartridge.

An original 44 Russian black powder cartridge (l), our 44 Russian CAS load (center), and a 44 Special cast bullet load (r).

Although the Russian was considered inefficient with the earliest smokeless propellants, it managed to survive the transition. The Winchester catalog for 1911 showed 44 Russian loads with 246-grain bullets in both lead and full metal patched versions, plus two "gallery" loads with a 115-grain conical bullet or a 105-grain round ball for indoor target shooting. Both black powder and "semi-smokeless" propellant versions were cataloged. The nominal velocity of the heavier bullets was usually listed as 750 ft/sec. The Russian became the inspiration for the excellent 44 Special cartridge in the early 1900's and, ultimately, the 44 Magnum in 1956.

Were it not for Cowboy Action shooting, the 44 Russian would be a dead issue. Cowboy shooters looked to older, smaller cartridge cases to produce efficient reduced loads. Starline (www.starlinebrass.com) introduced newly made 44 Russian brass cases and Black Hills Ammo offers loaded ammo aimed at the Cowboy market.

In our testing, we found that the small case does very well for reduced loads. We picked the RCBS 44-200-FN mould and sized the bullets to 0.430-inch. All the propellants listed gave consistent performance with the 200-grain bullet and produced very mild recoil. If your Cowboy Action revolver is a 44 Special or Magnum, you can use the Russian case to improve the consistency of reduced loads.

Light bullets at modest velocity seldom "hit where the gun's looking." Always check point-of-impact to learn what corrections will be needed before the big match.

There are no U.S. pressure standards for the 44 Russian. The charge levels were scaled from pressure-tested 44 Special data with the same bullet. These smokeless powder loads are intended for use in modern firearms only.

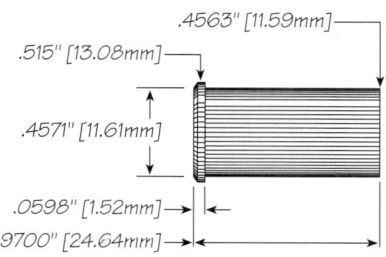

Max. Case Length:	0.970"	Cart. Case:	Starline
Trim-to Length:	0.960"	Primer:	CCI 300
Max Cart. OAL:	1.430"	Test Firearm:	Cimarron SAA
RCBS Shell Holder:	#18	Barrel Length:	5.5"

0.430"	44-200 FN	44-200 CM
Weight, grains	200	200
Lead Alloy	hard	hard
Ballistic Coefficient	0.136	0.124
Sectional Density	0.155	0.155
COAL Tested:	1.260"	1.245"
RCBS Mould No.	82036	82307

Cowboy ACTION SHOOTING DATA

Propellant	START CHARGE Weight, grs	START CHARGE Muzzle Velocity, ft/sec	MAXIMUM CHARGE Weight, grs	MAXIMUM CHARGE Muzzle Velocity, ft/sec
Unique	4.9	813	5.4	887
Viht. N320	3.6	743	4.0	850
H. Universal	4.5	761	5.0	847
Bullseye	3.6	747	4.0	826
TiteGroup	3.5	761	3.9	814
HP-38	3.9	738	4.3	798
700-X	3.5	753	3.9	796
Red Dot	3.4	720	3.8	796
231	3.9	698	4.3	786
American Select	3.3	704	3.7	763
Nitro 100	3.0	679	3.3	748
AA No. 2 Impr.	3.2	640	3.5	713
Trail Boss	2.5	568	2.9	617

NOTE: *We sell bullet moulds, not cast bullets. These bullets were cast in RCBS moulds. Contact your dealer for more information on the RCBS line of premium bullet casting equipment, or visit on the Internet at www.rcbs.com.*

*Maximum Loads should be used with CAUTION • C = Compressed Load • *Magnum Primer used with this powder.*

44 S&W Special

This fine old cartridge evolved from an even older cartridge, the 44 S&W Russian that enjoyed an excellent reputation as a target cartridge (see previous section). The stubby Russian case proved to be too small for early smokeless propellants that tended to be bulky. Smith & Wesson engineers lengthened the Russian case by 0.190-inch to increase propellant space.

Smith & Wesson developed a new, large-frame revolver as the platform for the improved cartridge. The 44 Hand Ejector and the 44 S&W Special appeared in 1908. This basic revolver design became the first in S&W's successful line of N-frame revolvers. Colt also made high-quality 44 Special service and target revolvers using their large-frame New Service model.

The 44 Special is every bit as accurate as its predecessor and the larger case capacity caught the interest of experimenters. Elmer Keith and others combined certain fast-burning rifle propellants and flat-point cast bullets that gave excellent game performance. Ultimately, Keith's work with heavy 44 Special loads saw the light of day in 1956 as the 44 Magnum. Today, the 44 Special is still popular with 44 Magnum owners who use the older cartridge for low-recoil practice.

For years, the only available factory load was a 246-grain lead round nose that seldom broke 700 ft/sec from a 4-inch barrel. Renewed interest in the 44 Special in the last decades of the 20th century led to the introduction of compact, 5-shot revolvers from Smith & Wesson, Charter Arms, Taurus and others. Commonly sporting 3-inch barrels, these little powerhouses promised big performance in a small package but needed modern bullet designs. Today, several ammo makers including CCI, Speer, and Federal offer 200 to 225-grain loads with modern bullet designs that safely increase the effectiveness of the cartridge.

Handloaders looking for bullet expansion should pick the 200-grain Gold Dot® hollow point. It was designed expressly for the 44 Special and helps to keep recoil down and velocity up. It is, without a doubt, the most effective expanding 44 Special bullet. The 240-grain lead SWC is also a good choice for low-velocity loads. The 240-grain hollow- and soft-point bullets will not expand at 44 Special velocities, but are quite accurate when loaded to maximum safe velocities. Do not load jacketed bullets with charges less than we show here.

Cowboy Action shooting has also helped the 44 Special's popularity. The case is smaller than the 44-40 and 45 Colt and the maximum pressure level is slightly higher making efficient reduced loads easier to develop. Even so, care must be exercised in picking a propellant that will produce consistent velocities. The start loads here were set to maintain at least 11,000 psi; do not load lighter than the start charges listed here to avoid inconsistent performance and bullets stuck in the barrel.

We recommend bullets cast from the RCBS® 44-200-FN and 44-200-CM moulds for Cowboy competition. The listed start loads for 231, Red Dot, AA #2 Improved, American Select, and AA Nitro 100 make excellent, mild loads for Cowboy Action shooting.

We also include data for two other cast bullets including the classic 250-grain Keith bullet. This bullet is very accurate in a wide variety of revolvers.

The industry pressure limit for the 44 Special is 15,500 psi. These loads are within these guidelines.

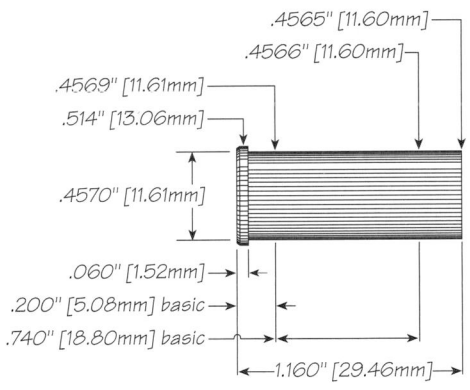

Max. Case Length:	1.160"	Cart. Case:	Remington
Trim-to Length:	1.150"	Primer:	CCI 300; 350*
Max Cart. OAL:	1.615"	Test Firearm:	Cimarron SAA
RCBS Shell Holder:	#18	Barrel Length:	5.5"

0.430"	44-200 FN	44-200 CM
Weight, grains	200	200
Lead Alloy	hard	hard
Ballistic Coefficient	0.136	0.124
Sectional Density	0.155	0.155
COAL Tested:	1.440"	1.435"
RCBS Mould No.	82036	82307

Cowboy ACTION SHOOTING DATA

Propellant	START CHARGE		MAXIMUM CHARGE	
	Weight, grs	Muzzle Velocity, ft/sec	Weight, grs	Muzzle Velocity, ft/sec
Unique	7.8	1043	8.7	1143
H. Universal	7.2	1007	8.0	1079
Bullseye	5.4	927	6.4	1032
Viht. N320	5.9	931	6.5	1022
TiteGroup	5.5	945	6.2	1020
700-X	5.4	908	6.2	1014
HP-38	6.0	904	6.8	1005
Red Dot	5.4	897	6.0	999
231	6.0	888	6.8	964
AA No. 2 Impr.	5.5	864	6.1	947
Nitro 100	4.8	864	5.2	939
American Select	5.2	865	5.8	933
Trail Boss	3.9	696	4.6	778

NOTE: *We sell bullet moulds, not cast bullets. These bullets were cast in RCBS moulds. Contact your dealer for more information on the RCBS line of premium bullet casting equipment, or visit on the Internet at www.rcbs.com.*

0.430"	44-225 SWC GC
Weight, grains	225
Lead Alloy	hard
Ballistic Coefficient	0.157
Sectional Density	0.175
COAL Tested:	1.500"
RCBS Mould No.	82041

	START CHARGE		MAXIMUM CHARGE	
Propellant	Weight, grs	Muzzle Velocity, ft/sec	Weight, grs	Muzzle Velocity, ft/sec
Unique	6.8	942	7.8	1043
N350	8.0	935	8.7	1025
AA No. 7	11.0	956	11.7	975
Power Pistol	6.8	860	7.7	952
H. Universal	6.2	849	6.8	950
Bullseye	4.7	806	5.5	903
700-X	4.8	828	5.5	895
231	5.4	775	6.2	886

NOTE: *RCBS crimp-on gas check used. We sell bullet moulds, not cast bullets. These bullets were cast in RCBS moulds. Contact your dealer for more information on the RCBS line of premium bullet casting equipment, or visit on the Internet at www.rcbs.com.*

---

*Maximum Loads should be used with CAUTION • C = Compressed Load • *Magnum Primer used with this powder.*

0.430"	44-250 K
Weight, grains	250
Lead Alloy	hard
Ballistic Coefficient	0.185
Sectional Density	0.193
COAL Tested:	1.580"
RCBS Mould No.	82080

	START CHARGE		MAXIMUM CHARGE	
Propellant	Weight, grs	Muzzle Velocity, ft/sec	Weight, grs	Muzzle Velocity, ft/sec
SR 4756	7.3	917	8.0	1014
2400	12.0	856	13.0	965
Power Pistol	7.2	842	8.0	954
AA No. 7	10.6	874	11.5	948
AA No. 5	8.4	868	9.3	936
Unique	6.4	816	6.9	921
HS-6*	8.2	829	9.0	889
Viht. N350	7.0	774	7.7	883
H. Universal	5.9	769	6.5	880
231	5.4	732	6.2	849
Bulseye	4.5	734	5.3	835
TiteGroup	4.5	772	5.2	816

NOTE: *We sell bullet moulds, not cast bullets. These bullets were cast in RCBS moulds. Contact your dealer for more information on the RCBS line of premium bullet casting equipment, or visit on the Internet at www.rcbs.com.*

0.430"	44 LSWC
Weight, grains	240
Ballistic Coefficient	0.151
Sectional Density	0.185
COAL Tested:	1.475"
Speer Part No.	4660

Propellant	START CHARGE		MAXIMUM CHARGE	
	Weight, grs	Muzzle Velocity, ft/sec	Weight, grs	Muzzle Velocity, ft/sec
Unique	5.7	746	6.3	820
Herco	5.8	730	6.4	816
HS-6*	7.0	695	8.0	815
231	5.2	701	5.7	796
Bullseye	4.7	691	5.2	793
Red Dot	4.5	658	5.0	750
Green Dot	5.2	672	5.7	749
700-X	4.1	640	4.6	734

NOTE: *Velocities determined using a Taurus revolver with 3" barrel.*

*Maximum Loads should be used with CAUTION • C = Compressed Load • *Magnum Primer used with this powder.*

0.429"	44 GDHP SB
Weight, grains	200
Ballistic Coefficient	0.145
Sectional Density	0.155
COAL Tested:	1.490"
Speer Part No.	4427

Propellant	START CHARGE		MAXIMUM CHARGE	
	Weight, grs	Muzzle Velocity, ft/sec	Weight, grs	Muzzle Velocity, ft/sec
Power Pistol	7.6	872	8.6	976
Viht. N350	8.0	823	8.8	952
H. Universal	7.0	842	7.6	950
AA No. 5	8.8	805	9.9	935
700-X	5.3	800	6.1	902
TiteGroup	5.3	795	6.1	902
231	6.0	730	6.9	886
Bullseye	5.1	766	5.9	884
Red Dot	5.4	801	5.9	868
Unique	7.0	788	7.8	855
AA No. 2 Impr.	DNR	—	5.9	828
American Select	DNR	—	5.7	821

DNR — do not reduce

0.429"	44 Mag JHP	44 Mag JSP
Weight, grains	240	240
Ballistic Coefficient	0.165	0.164
Sectional Density	0.186	0.186
COAL Tested:	1.465"	1.465"
Speer Part No.	4453	4457

	START CHARGE		MAXIMUM CHARGE	
Propellant	Weight, grs	Muzzle Velocity, ft/sec	Weight, grs	Muzzle Velocity, ft/sec
Blue Dot	9.2	775	10.2	871
Unique	6.8	760	7.6	836
Power Pistol	6.8	744	7.6	819
AA No. 7	10.0	722	11.0	814
Viht. 3N37	7.6	719	8.5	813
HS-6*	8.2	727	9.0	812
AA No. 5	8.0	700	0.9	806
H. Universal	6.3	662	6.8	803
SR 7625	DNR	—	6.9	764
231	DNR	—	6.3	717

DNR — do not reduce

*Maximum Loads should be used with CAUTION • C = Compressed Load • *Magnum Primer used with this powder.*

0.430"	44 Shot Capsule
Weight, grains	~ 140
Ballistic Coefficient	n/a
Sectional Density	n/a
COAL Tested:	1.600"
Speer Part No.	8782

Propellant	Weight, grs	Muzzle Velocity, ft/sec
HP-38	5.8	1055
231	6.3	1045
HS-6*	8.2	1029
700-X	5.3	1014
Unique	6.7	1005

NOTE: *Shot capsules must not be used in firearms with ported recoil compensators. Test Firearm: S&W Model 29 4"*

Maximum Loads should be used with CAUTION • C = Compressed Load • *Magnum Primer used with this powder.

44-40 Winchester

The 44-40 Winchester was the second most potent revolver cartridge on the American frontier, only slightly behind the 45 Colt in power. It was popular with civilians because it was also chambered in lever-action rifles. Pushing a 200-grain flat point bullet in excess of 900 ft/sec from a revolver was mighty good performance for a black powder cartridge in 1873.

For much of the 20th Century, newer revolver cartridges largely overshadowed the 44-40 in most areas. However, there were holdouts; an old U.S. Border Patrol armorer told this writer that they had some 44-40 Colt New Service revolvers and kept them in service long after Colt discontinued that model. Until recently, no new 44-40 revolvers were on the market.

The popularity of Cowboy Action Shooting helped many old cartridges make new friends. Today, a number of single-action revolvers, both domestic and foreign, are available for this cartridge.

Loading the 44-40 takes some attention. Although called a 44-caliber, the bullets are normally .427" to .428" in diameter, slightly smaller than those for other 44-caliber handgun cartridges. Jacketed bullet selection is limited, but CAS competition calls for lead bullets. Thus, the 44-40 is a prime candidate for cast bullets.

A 44-40 factory soft point load (l) and a handload with the RCBS 44-200-FN bullet (r).

RCBS makes two bullet moulds for the 44-40, including the new CM design introduced in 1999. Both designs feature a deep crimp groove; plan to use it! A good crimp is one secret to consistent loads with this big case. As the case neck is quite thin by modern standards, plan to seat and crimp in separate operations to avoid ruined cases.

The loads here use fast- to medium-burning rate powders. The higher velocity loads listed are for those who wish to get maximum performance from the 44-40 at safe pressures. Do not attempt to load less than our recommended starting loads. They were selected to produce at least 10,000 CUP. Loading lighter than the start loads will induce excessive velocity variation and risk lodging a bullet in the bore.

To record velocities, we used a Colt New Service double-action revolver made in 1940 because its barrel and cylinder were dimensionally correct in all respects. The industry's maximum average pressure for the 44-40 is 13,000 CUP.

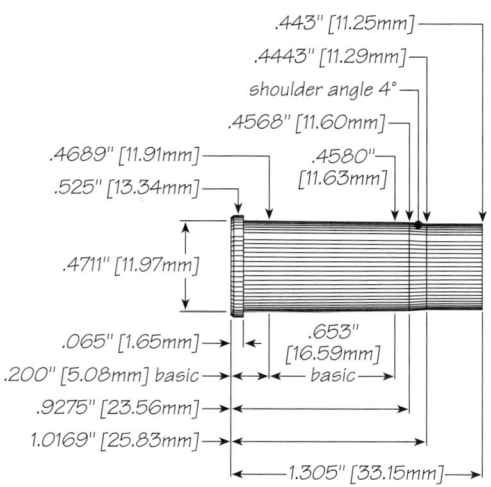

Max. Case Length:	1.305"	**Cart. Case:**	Remington
Trim-to Length:	1.295"	**Primer:**	CCI 300
Max Cart. OAL:	1.590"	**Test Firearm:**	Colt New Service
RCBS Shell Holder:	#35	**Barrel Length:**	5.5"

0.428"	44-200 FN	44-200 CM
Weight, grains	200	200
Lead Alloy	hard	hard
Ballistic Coefficient	0.136	0.124
Sectional Density	0.156	0.156
COAL Tested:	1.590"	1.580"
RCBS Mould No.	82036	82307

Propellant	START CHARGE		MAXIMUM CHARGE	
	Weight, grs	Muzzle Velocity, ft/sec	Weight, grs	Muzzle Velocity, ft/sec
Viht. N350	9.0	848	9.5	952
Unique	7.8	865	8.6	951
TiteGroup	5.8	826	6.3	905
700-X	5.5	824	6.1	903
231	6.4	817	7.1	892
Nitro 100	5.0	802	5.0	892
Bullseye	5.5	804	6.1	885
AA No.2 Impr.	6.1	825	6.6	882
Red Dot	5.4	814	5.9	866
American Select	5.5	808	6.0	856
Trail Boss	5.9	772	6.4	814
H. Universal	6.5	714	6.9	770

NOTE: *We sell bullet moulds, not cast bullets. These bullets were cast in RCBS moulds. Contact your dealer for more information on the RCBS line of premium bullet casting equipment, or visit on the Internet at www.rcbs.com.*

*Maximum Loads should be used with CAUTION • C = Compressed Load • *Magnum Primer used with this powder.*

44 Remington Magnum

In a preceding section on the 44 Special we talked about Elmer Keith and others, who experimented for years with heavy 44 Special handloads in the search for an effective handgun hunting cartridge. A commercial version of these high-performance loads was introduced in 1956 as the 44 Remington Magnum. Remington and Smith & Wesson teamed up to develop the cartridge and the new revolver to handle it. The result was a winning combination in anyone's book.

The cartridge was envisioned as the ultimate handgun hunting cartridge and also stimulated some interest from law enforcement. The cost of the revolvers and ammunition combined with heavy recoil diminished police interest but handgun hunters had found the gun and cartridge of their dreams.

Original factory loads featured a 240-grain lead semi-wadcutter bullet fitted with a unique gas check to protect and stiffen the bullet base. In spite of this, barrel leading was (and is) a problem in factory lead-bullet ammo. Thanks to pioneers like Vernon Speer and others, handloaders were shooting jacketed bullets long before similar factory loads were available.

For small to medium deer, the Speer 210-grain Gold Dot® gives excellent performance combined with tolerable recoil. For taking larger deer species, the 240-grain Gold Dot hollow point or soft point should be used. The 270-grain Gold Dot soft point is an excellent choice for most large game. When extreme penetration is required, the Speer 300 grain Uni-Cor® soft point fills the niche. It was designed to perform much like a hard-cast lead bullet on game animals, sacrificing expansion for straight-line penetration.

When loading the 300-grain bullet in most revolvers, crimp in the rear cannelure. The Colt Anaconda and Wesson Arms revolvers have rather tight chamber throats and 300-grain bullets may not fully enter these revolvers' chamber throats when seated long. Seat the bullet to the front cannelure using the 300-grain data in the 44 Magnum rifle section of this manual. Be sure to begin with the starting loads.

There are several light-weight 44 Magnum revolvers today and some weigh less than a 38 Special service revolver. You can assemble effective handloads that give superb terminal performance with greatly reduced recoil. Choose the 200-grain 44 Special Gold Dot hollow point using the loads here. They do not represent maximum pressure loads; rather, they are loaded to leave a 4-inch revolver barrel in the 1000 to 1100-ft/sec range. These loads were the inspiration for the popular Gold Dot Short Barrel ammo and bullet lines.

Cast bullets and the 44 Magnum seem to belong together. Two cast bullets from RCBS® moulds are represented here. The 225-grain gas check is an excellent all-round bullet. The 250-grain Keith bullet makes a classic 44 Magnum hunting load that delivers outstanding accuracy. Both cast bullets exceed the maximum cartridge length specification but function fine in revolvers and single-shot firearms.

Lead bullets should not be used in gas-operated 44 Magnum firearms like the Desert Eagle pistol. Bullet lubricant and lead particles can foul the gas system.

Speer's 240-grain lead semi-wadcutter at 900 to 1000 ft/sec makes a nice plinking and small game load. All Speer lead bullets now feature a unique, multi-layer lube that resists leading much better than traditional lubes. We recommend loading swaged lead bullets no faster than 1000 ft/sec for best performance.

The industry maximum average pressure for the 44 Magnum is 36,000 psi.

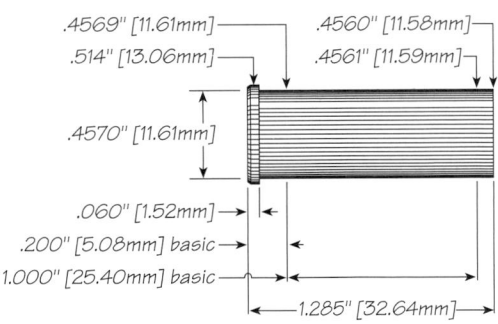

	Max. Case Length:	1.285"	Cart. Case:	Speer
	Trim-to Length:	1.275"	Primer:	CCI 300; 350*
	Max Cart. OAL:	1.610"	Test Firearm:	Ruger Redhawk
	RCBS Shell Holder:	#18	Barrel Length:	7.5"

0.430"	44 LSWC
Weight, grains	240
Ballistic Coefficient	0.141
Sectional Density	0.185
COAL Tested:	1.605"
Speer Part No.	4660

Propellant	START CHARGE		MAXIMUM CHARGE	
	Weight, grs	Muzzle Velocity, ft/sec	Weight, grs	Muzzle Velocity, ft/sec
HS-6	8.5	822	9.5	947
SR 4756	6.5	751	7.5	923
SR 7625	6.0	834	7.0	912
Red Dot	6.0	871	6.5	905
Green Dot	6.0	804	7.0	901
Unique	6.5	720	7.0	899
Bullseye	5.5	828	6.0	894
700-X	5.5	836	6.0	871
231	6.0	808	6.5	867

0.430"	44-225 SWC GC
Weight, grains	225
Lead Alloy	hard
Ballistic Coefficient	0.157
Sectional Density	0.175
COAL Tested:	1.635"
RCBS Mould No.	82041

Propellant	START CHARGE		MAXIMUM CHARGE	
	Weight, grs	Muzzle Velocity, ft/sec	Weight, grs	Muzzle Velocity, ft/sec
H110*	22.0	1379	24.0	1512
2400	19.0	1401	21.0	1482
296*	22.0	1399	24.0	1471
AA No. 9	17.0	1305	19.0	1430
Viht. N110	18.0	1278	20.0	1407
IMR 4227	21.0	1192	23.0	1329
Unique	9.0	1056	11.0	1259

NOTE: *For revolvers only. We sell bullet moulds, not cast bullets. These bullets were cast in RCBS moulds. Contact your dealer for more information on the RCBS line of premium bullet casting equipment, or visit on the Internet at www.rcbs.com.*

*Maximum Loads should be used with CAUTION • C = Compressed Load • *Magnum Primer used with this powder.*

0.430"	44-250 K
Weight, grains	250
Lead Alloy	hard
Ballistic Coefficient	0.185
Sectional Density	0.193
COAL Tested:	1.710"
RCBS Mould No.	82080

Propellant	START CHARGE		MAXIMUM CHARGE	
	Weight, grs	Muzzle Velocity, ft/sec	Weight, grs	Muzzle Velocity, ft/sec
296*	21.0	1343	23.0	1439
H110*	21.0	1356	23.0	1435
2400	18.0	1290	20.0	1390
Viht. N110	17.0	1238	19.0	1346
AA No. 9	16.0	1219	18.0	1344
IMR 4227	20.0	1141	22.0	1272
Unique	9.0	1029	11.0	1211

NOTE: *For revolvers only. We sell bullet moulds, not cast bullets. These bullets were cast in RCBS moulds. Contact your dealer for more information on the RCBS line of premium bullet casting equipment, or visit on the Internet at www.rcbs.com.*

0.429"	44 Mag JHP
Weight, grains	200
Ballistic Coefficient	0.122
Sectional Density	0.155
COAL Tested:	1.590"
Speer Part No.	4425

Propellant	START CHARGE		MAXIMUM CHARGE	
	Weight, grs	Muzzle Velocity, ft/sec	Weight, grs	Muzzle Velocity, ft/sec
H110*	26.5	1590	28.5	1688
Viht. N110	22.0	1513	24.0	1662
296*	26.0	1521	28.0	1639
IMR 4227	26.0	1473	28.0	1596
2400	22.0	1447	24.0	1589
Power Pistol	13.5	1434	15.5	1573
Blue Dot	14.4	1402	16.0	1495
AA No. 7	16.5	1295	18.5	1446
Unique	11.1	1299	12.4	1399
HS-7*	15.0	1258	17.0	1397
Viht. N350	11.7	1267	13.0	1378
231	10.5	1219	11.5	1295

*Maximum Loads should be used with CAUTION • C = Compressed Load • *Magnum Primer used with this powder.*

0.429"	44 Special GDHP SB
Weight, grains	200
Ballistic Coefficient	0.145
Sectional Density	0.115
COAL Tested:	1.610"
Speer Part No.	4427

SHORT BARREL
VELOCITIES
Test Firearm: S&W M29 4"

Propellant	START CHARGE		MAXIMUM CHARGE	
	Weight, grs	Muzzle Velocity, ft/sec	Weight, grs	Muzzle Velocity, ft/sec
H. Universal	8.9	999	10.0	1132
Unique	9.0	990	11.0	1122
American Select	8.6	1005	10.0	1120
700-X	7.9	997	9.0	1109
Red Dot	8.2	1033	9.2	1096
TiteGroup	7.9	989	9.0	1084
231	8.9	989	10.0	1083
Bullseye	8.0	1014	9.0	1080

NOTE: *These loads do not produce maximum pressure.*

*Maximum Loads should be used with CAUTION • C = Compressed Load • *Magnum Primer used with this powder.*

0.429"	44 Mag GDHP
Weight, grains	210
Ballistic Coefficient	0.154
Sectional Density	0.163
COAL Tested:	1.600"
Speer Part No.	4428

Propellant	START CHARGE		MAXIMUM CHARGE	
	Weight, grs	Muzzle Velocity, ft/sec	Weight, grs	Muzzle Velocity, ft/sec
296*	25.5	1562	27.5	1664
H110*	25.5	1533	27.5	1645
Viht. N110	21.0	1434	23.0	1607
AA No. 9	21.0	1504	23.0	1587
Ramshot Enforcer*	22.0	1491	24.0	1577
2400	21.5	1428	23.5	1566
H. Lil' Gun*	26.0	1509	28.0	1566
Power Pistol	12.5	1324	14.5	1504
HS-7*	14.0	1282	16.0	1437
Unique	10.5	1212	12.5	1392
H. Universal	9.0	1132	11.0	1320

0.429"	44 JHP-SWC
Weight, grains	225
Ballistic Coefficient	0.146
Sectional Density	0.175
COAL Tested:	1.575"
Speer Part No.	4435

Propellant	START CHARGE		MAXIMUM CHARGE	
	Weight, grs	Muzzle Velocity, ft/sec	Weight, grs	Muzzle Velocity, ft/sec
Viht. N110	20.0	1471	22.0C	1557
H110*	22.5	1450	24.5	1544
2400	19.4	1331	21.4	1526
AA No. 9	19.5	1367	21.5	1523
296*	22.0	1398	24.0	1512
IMR 4227	22.0	1276	24.0	1388

0.429"	44 Mag JHP	44 Mag GDHP	44 Mag GDSP	44 Mag JSP
Weight, grains	240	240	240	240
Ballistic Coefficient	0.165	0.175	0.175	0.164
Sectional Density	0.186	0.186	0.186	0.186
COAL Tested:	1.575"	1.575"	1.575"	1.575"
Speer Part No.	4453	4455	4456	4457

	START CHARGE		MAXIMUM CHARGE	
Propellant	Weight, grs	Muzzle Velocity, ft/sec	Weight, grs	Muzzle Velocity, ft/sec
H110*	22.0	1362	24.0	1451
2400	19.0	1269	21.0	1434
296*	22.0	1344	24.0	1420
AA No. 9	18.0	1222	20.0	1404
H. Lil' Gun*	21.0	1325	23.0	1383
Viht. N110	18.0	1307	20.0	1382
Ramshot Enforcer*	18.5	1269	20.5	1344
IMR 4227	21.4	1252	23.4	1340
AA No. 7	15.5	1183	17.5	1319
Blue Dot	12.3	1186	13.7	1285
HS-6*	12.3	1172	13.7	1271
Viht. N350	10.4	1155	11.6	1212
Unique	9.2	1077	10.3	1175

NOTE: *These loads may be used with the 240-gr JSP-SWC (#4447) by reducing maximum charges but ONE grain.*

0.429"	44 Mag GDSP
Weight, grains	270
Ballistic Coefficient	0.193
Sectional Density	0.210
COAL Tested:	1.585"
Speer Part No.	4461

Propellant	START CHARGE		MAXIMUM CHARGE	
	Weight, grs	Muzzle Velocity, ft/sec	Weight, grs	Muzzle Velocity, ft/sec
H110*	19.0	1205	21.0	1309
296*	18.5	1198	20.5	1283
Viht. N110	16.0	1184	18.0	1265
Ramshot Enforcer*	17.0	1166	19.0	1255
H. Lil' Gun*	17.5	1178	19.5	1241
2400	15.5	1083	17.5	1182
IMR 4227	10.5	1101	20.5	1182
AA 1680*	22.5	1067	24.5C	1176
AA No. 9	14.0	1026	16.0	1172

*Maximum Loads should be used with CAUTION • C = Compressed Load • * Magnum Primer used with this powder.*

0.429"	44 Mag UCSP
Weight, grains	300
Ballistic Coefficient	0.213
Sectional Density	0.233
COAL Tested:	1.665"
Speer Part No.	4463

Propellant	START CHARGE		MAXIMUM CHARGE	
	Weight, grs	Muzzle Velocity, ft/sec	Weight, grs	Muzzle Velocity, ft/sec
296*	20.2	1038	22.5	1187
H110*	20.2	1040	22.5	1187
AA No. 9	16.6	1024	18.5	1176
IMR 4227	20.7	1000	23.0C	1172
2400	17.1	1003	19.0	1088
AA 1680*	22.5	942	25.0C	1056

NOTE: *For revolvers only. Crimp in rear cannelure. See text for additional information.*

Lab Notes:

We developed the 300-grain Uni-Cor® SP loads on copper crusher test equipment to accommodate the extra bullet length. All other bullets were tested on the transducer system. The UCSP's lead core is harder than lighter Speer bullets resulting in lower pressure. These are the reasons that the 300-grain loads do not "track" with loads for the lighter bullets. These loads have been thoroughly tested in production handguns.

Remember to crimp the big bullet in the rear cannelure for most revolvers. See the cartridge text if you plan to use them in a Colt Anaconda or Wesson Arms revolver.

0.430"	44 Shot Capsule
Weight, grains	~ 140
Ballistic Coefficient	n/a
Sectional Density	n/a
COAL Tested:	1.600"
Speer Part No.	8782

Propellant	Weight, grs	Muzzle Velocity, ft/sec
231	7.3	1133
700-X	5.7	1105
Bullseye	6.0	1101
Unique	6.8	1097
HP-38	6.0	1061

NOTE: *Shot capsules must not be used in firearms with ported recoil compensators. Test Firearm: S&W Model 29 6"*

*Maximum Loads should be used with CAUTION • C = Compressed Load • *Magnum Primer used with this powder.*

45 Auto Rim

World War I found the U.S. Army short of the relatively new Model 1911 service pistols. As a stopgap measure, both Colt and Smith &Wesson dedicated their manufacturing resources to building large-frame revolvers that could accommodate the rimless 45-caliber service cartridge. The Army designated these new firearms the Model 1917 revolvers. Historical records indicate the two firms made more than 300,000 of these revolvers.

To permit normal ejection of the rimless case, a thin metal clip was developed to hold three cartridges in alignment with the chambers. This device (called a "half-moon clip" because of its shape) snapped into the cartridges' extraction cannelure to allow the extractor to lift the cases and to provide headspace support. The ammo was packaged in clips so the soldiers did not have to worry about them.

When you look at a M1917 from the side, you notice the unusually large gap between the cylinder and the breechface. The cylinders were relieved enough at the rear to leave room for both the clips and the cartridge rims.

After the war, the revolvers were declared surplus and sold on the civilian market. Sport shooters found the clips to be a nuisance—hard to load with fresh cartridges, harder to remove spent cases, and easily bent if mishandled. A badly bent clip means a disabled revolver.

In 1922 the Peters Cartridge Company created the 45 Auto Rim cartridge, designed to fire in 1917 revolvers without clips. It was physically the same as the 45 Auto case except for the rim. The 45 AR is a true rimmed case but the rim is nearly 50 percent thicker than traditional ones to fill the space in the revolver normally occupied by the clip, putting the primer in the proper position for reliable ignition. The new cartridge was loaded with a 230-grain lead round nose bullet. For years, only Remington made 45 Auto Rim ammunition and cases. However, neither is listed on their 2007 website. Remington seems to make runs of 45 AR cases from time to time for Midway (www. midwayusa.com) and Starline (www.starlinebrass.com) also makes 45 AR cases for reloaders.

This combination proved popular and both Smith & Wesson and Colt built commercial service and target revolvers chambered for 45 Auto Rim. Of course, 45 Auto ammo could still be used with or without clips. The 45 Auto Rim received a lower pressure limit than the 45 Auto to reduce gas cutting when firing primitive lead bullets. As the revolvers were designed for the 45 Auto's higher pressures, safe 45 Auto handloads can be used in the revolvers as well as any standard-pressure 45 Auto factory ammo.

Handloading the 45 AR cartridge is no different from any other rimmed revolver cartridge. 45 Auto dies can be used with a 45 AR shell holder. Cartridges can be roll crimped with the proper die and when the bullet has a crimping groove. If no groove is present, then light taper crimping will suffice. All the jacketed bullets we list shoot very well in revolvers in good condition. The 250-grain lead semi-wadcutter is a good choice for accurate, low-cost plinking. Loads for the 200-grain lead SWC are held back to velocity levels popular for target shooting.

---

45 AR Accuracy Tip

Bullets with the military ball ammo profile are often less accurate in 45 AR revolvers than in semi-autos. Their short bearing surfaces may let the bullet tip slightly in the long chamber throat before entering the barrel. Most jacketed hollow points have enough bearing surface to avoid this problem.

The industry maximum pressure for the 45 Auto Rim is 15,000 CUP. These loads are within the 45 Auto pressure limit of 21,000 psi.

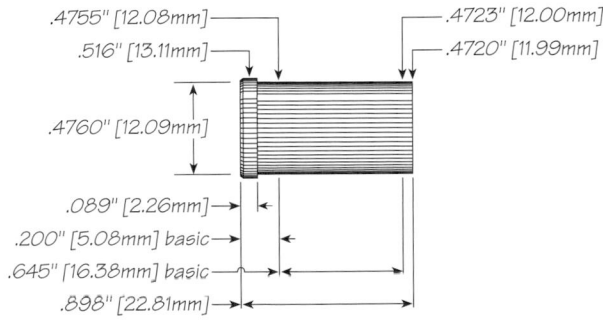

Max. Case Length:	0.898"
Trim-to Length:	0.888"
Max Cart. OAL:	1.275"
RCBS Shell Holder:	#8

Cart. Case:	Remington
Primer:	CCI 300
Test Firearm:	S&W Model 25-2
Barrel Length:	6.5"

0.452"	45 LSWC
Weight, grains	200
Ballistic Coefficient	0.078
Sectional Density	0.139
COAL Tested:	1.185"
Speer Part No.	4677

Propellant	START CHARGE		MAXIMUM CHARGE	
	Weight, grs	Muzzle Velocity, ft/sec	Weight, grs	Muzzle Velocity, ft/sec
SR 4756	5.5	708	6.0	770
Unique	5.0	701	5.5	767
231	4.5	671	5.0	749
Herco	5.3	686	5.8	748
Bullseye	4.1	667	4.6	745
700-X	3.8	666	4.3	743
SR 7625	4.7	659	5.2	735
Green Dot	4.6	672	5.1	733
Red Dot	4.0	643	4.5	717

0.452"	45 LRN
Weight, grains	230
Ballistic Coefficient	0.160
Sectional Density	0.161
COAL Tested:	1.250"
Speer Part No.	4690

Propellant	START CHARGE		MAXIMUM CHARGE	
	Weight, grs	Muzzle Velocity, ft/sec	Weight, grs	Muzzle Velocity, ft/sec
HS-6	8.1	806	8.6	872
231	5.0	743	5.5	813
Unique	6.1	723	6.6	787
700-X	4.3	687	4.8	761
Red Dot	4.5	671	5.0	749
Bullseye	4.0	627	4.5	696

0.452"	45 LSWC
Weight, grains	250
Ballistic Coefficient	0.117
Sectional Density	0.175
COAL Tested:	1.240"
Speer Part No.	4683

Propellant	START CHARGE		MAXIMUM CHARGE	
	Weight, grs	Muzzle Velocity, ft/sec	Weight, grs	Muzzle Velocity, ft/sec
Herco	6.2	791	6.6	842
Blue Dot	8.6	789	9.0	824
Unique	5.8	772	6.2	824
HS-6	7.4	700	7.8	787
SR 4756	6.3	691	6.7	782

0.451"	45 GDHP
Weight, grains	200
Ballistic Coefficient	0.138
Sectional Density	0.140
COAL Tested:	1.120"
Speer Part No.	4478

Propellant	START CHARGE		MAXIMUM CHARGE	
	Weight, grs	Muzzle Velocity, ft/sec	Weight, grs	Muzzle Velocity, ft/sec
Herco	7.0	890	7.5	951
Unique	6.5	858	7.0	925
231	5.5	819	6.0	899
Red Dot	4.7	769	5.2	863
700-X	4.5	772	5.0	860
Bullseye	4.4	699	4.9	775

*Maximum Loads should be used with CAUTION • C = Compressed Load • *Magnum Primer used with this powder.*

0.451"	45 Colt JHP	45 GDHP	45 GDHP SB
Weight, grains	225	230	230
Ballistic Coefficient	0.169	0.143	0.148
Sectional Density	0.158	0.162	0.162
COAL Tested:	1.250"	1.275"	1.275"
Speer Part No.	4479	4483	4482

Propellant	START CHARGE		MAXIMUM CHARGE	
	Weight, grs	Muzzle Velocity, ft/sec	Weight, grs	Muzzle Velocity, ft/sec
Unique	6.4	837	6.9	900
SR 7625	5.4	791	5.9	866
HS-6	8.0	806	8.6	865
Herco	6.6	807	7.1	863
SR 4756	6.5	782	7.0	850
Bullseye	5.0	768	5.5	841
231	5.4	769	5.9	836
Red Dot	4.5	726	5.0	810
700-X	4.4	724	4.9	809
Green Dot	5.0	671	5.5	736

*Maximum Loads should be used with CAUTION • C = Compressed Load • *Magnum Primer used with this powder.*

45 G.A.P.

The 45 Glock Automatic Pistol cartridge was designed to provide 45-caliber performance in compact handguns. The development process is the same one that bought the 40 S&W cartridge from the 10mm Auto: take a cartridge designed for a full-sized pistol and shorten it to fit a smaller frame. In the case of the 40 S&W and the 45 Glock, the target platform was pistols chambered for the 9mm Luger cartridge. At our end, development engineer Ernest Durham worked on the new cartridge and let Speer ship the first G.A.P. factory loads.

The maximum average pressure of the 45 Glock is set at 23,000 psi, the same as 45 Auto +P and 2000 psi higher than the standard 45 Auto. With this slight pressure difference, the newer cartridge delivers virtually identical performance to its venerable predecessor when you review nominal velocities. "Nominal velocity" means the velocity called out in industry standards for the cartridge.

In real production pistols, the G.A.P. cartridge compares favorably with 45 Auto ammo fired from barrels of equivalent length. A Glock M37 will produce similar velocities to a 45 Auto Colt Commander. Speer factory ammo is loaded with 185-grain and 200-grain bullets.

The 45 Glock case is now reasonably available as a component. It is important that you not use shortened 45 Auto cases when reloading the Glock cartridge. The Glock case was inspired by the Auto case but is not identical in construction. The Glock case has a slightly rebated rim, and its internal taper and the height of the web are different from the 45 Auto, but the big difference is that the Glock cartridge uses a small pistol primer. Safe handloads as we present here, developed with small pistol primers, can generate excessive pressure if assembled in a cut-down 45 Auto case with a large primer.

Reloading the 45 Glock is no different from loading the 45 Auto cartridge. The propellant selection and loading sequences are the same. If you are loading very light loads for target use or for low-recoil practice, move to the faster-burning propellants such as Bullseye, 231, TiteGroup, or Accurate No. 2 to preserve reliable function.

Note that we show the TMJ and Gold Dot hollow points separately. In such a small case, construction differences between the two bullet types were apparent. We felt that showing separate tables for TMJ and Gold Dot bullets will give you more flexibility in reloading the 45 G.A.P.

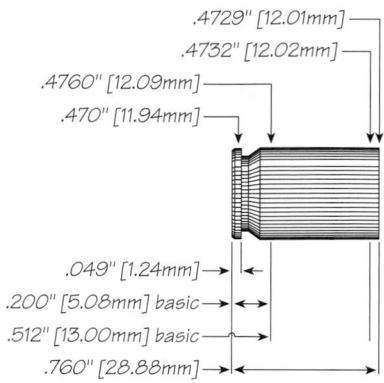

.4729" [12.01mm]
.4732" [12.02mm]
.4760" [12.09mm]
.470" [11.94mm]

.049" [1.24mm]
.200" [5.08mm] basic
.512" [13.00mm] basic
.760" [28.88mm]

Max. Case Length:	0.760"	Cart. Case:	Speer
Trim-to Length:	0.750"	Primer:	CCI 500
Max Cart. OAL:	1.137"	Test Firearm:	Glock Model 37
RCBS Shell Holder:	#3	Barrel Length:	4.5"

0.451"	45 TMJ FN
Weight, grains	185
Ballistic Coefficient	0.094
Sectional Density	0.130
COAL Tested:	1.070"
Speer Part No.	4476

	START CHARGE		MAXIMUM CHARGE	
Propellant	Weight, grs	Muzzle Velocity, ft/sec	Weight, grs	Muzzle Velocity, ft/sec
H. Universal	6.7	1007	7.1	1089
Bullseye	5.7	981	6.4	1072
Power Pistol	7.9	994	8.5	1061
Unique	7.2	1002	7.7	1061
TiteGroup	5.3	956	5.9	1041
AA No. 5	8.4	953	9.2	1035
Ramshot True Blue	7.8	940	8.6	1033
Viht. 3N37	8.0	919	8.6	1011
231	5.7	912	6.3	1001
AA No. 2 Improved	5.0	882	5.5	946

0.451"	45 GDHP
Weight, grains	185
Ballistic Coefficient	0.109
Sectional Density	0.130
COAL Tested:	1.070"
Speer Part No.	4470

Propellant	START CHARGE		MAXIMUM CHARGE	
	Weight, grs	Muzzle Velocity, ft/sec	Weight, grs	Muzzle Velocity, ft/sec
H. Universal	6.3	938	6.8	1044
Bullseye	5.5	950	6.1	1037
Viht. 3N37	7.7	881	8.4	1018
Unique	7.1	984	7.7	1009
Ramshot True Blue	7.4	908	8.2	1005
231	5.5	892	6.2	1000
AA No. 5	8.1	922	8.8	999
TiteGroup	5.1	934	5.6	994
Power Pistol	7.2	927	7.8	993
AA No. 2 Improved	4.6	807	5.2	897

*Maximum Loads should be used with CAUTION • C = Compressed Load • *Magnum Primer used with this powder.*

0.451"	45 TMJ FN
Weight, grains	200
Ballistic Coefficient	0.102
Sectional Density	0.140
COAL Tested:	1.070"
Speer Part No.	4471

Propellant	START CHARGE		MAXIMUM CHARGE	
	Weight, grs	Muzzle Velocity, ft/sec	Weight, grs	Muzzle Velocity, ft/sec
H. Universal	6.4	970	7.0	1072
Power Pistol	7.5	941	8.2	1023
Unique	6.7	948	7.3	1002
AA No. 5	7.7	862	8.6	979
TiteGroup	4.9	891	5.4	965
Bullseye	5.1	886	5.6	964
Viht. 3N37	7.4	863	8.0	963
Ramshot True Blue	7.3	887	8.1	959
231	5.3	860	5.7	921
AA No. 2 Impr.	4.6	813	5.1	882

0.451"	45 GDHP
Weight, grains	200
Ballistic Coefficient	0.138
Sectional Density	0.140
COAL Tested:	1.070"
Speer Part No.	4478

Propellant	START CHARGE		MAXIMUM CHARGE	
	Weight, grs	Muzzle Velocity, ft/sec	Weight, grs	Muzzle Velocity, ft/sec
Unique	6.3	918	6.8	988
H. Universal	5.8	893	6.2	988
Power Pistol	6.9	903	7.6	977
Bullseye	4.9	859	5.4	943
TiteGroup	4.6	865	5.1	940
AA No. 5	7.3	848	8.0	921
Ramshot True Blue	6.8	851	7.4	912
231	5.0	840	5.5	900
Viht. 3N37	6.8	811	7.2	863
AA No. 2 Impr.	4.3	783	4.7	838

*Maximum Loads should be used with CAUTION • C = Compressed Load • *Magnum Primer used with this powder.*

45 Auto

The 45 Automatic is among one of the most popular handgun cartridges ever and among the most widely reloaded. John Browning developed the cartridge around 1905 for a prototype service pistol. The 1905 version propelled a 200-grain full-jacket bullet at 900 ft/sec. However, U.S. Army Ordnance wanted a pistol with additional safeties and a heavier bullet. They were still stinging from the poor performance of the 38 Colt cartridge during the Philippine insurrection.

Browning designed a stronger pistol and chose a 230-grain bullet at 850 ft/sec, virtually identical to the 45 Colt cartridge's performance in barrels of equivalent length. The military named the new version, "Pistol, 45-Caliber, Model of 1911." The rest, as they say, is history.

Although born for battle, both the pistol and the cartridge proved popular for target shooting. In a modified M1911, the 45 Auto cartridge is capable of outstanding accuracy. Well-worn military issue pistols seldom let the cartridge reveal its accuracy potential.

The M1911 45 Auto pistol is not as difficult to master as rumor has it. It is a big handful with a pronounced but manageable recoil. The handloader can assemble light target or practice loads to reduce recoil. The Speer® 200-grain lead semi-wadcutter and the 185-grain TMJ® bullets are excellent choices for target practice and Bullseye competition.

For light game hunting or defense, the 185, 200 and 230-grain Gold Dot® hollow points are designed for optimum penetration and expansion. For economical practice, we make our renowned TMJ bullets in the same three weights.

We developed Gold Dot Short Barrel ammo and bullets to address the new generation of sub-compact pistols. The 230-grain Gold Dot Short Barrel bullet has a very large cavity to yield optimum terminal effects when fired from barrels as short as 3¾ inches. It uses the same loading data as the regular Gold Dot of the same weight.

We recommend taper crimping all 45 Auto loads shown. Observe the loading lengths we show for best feeding and do not load shorter than the lengths we list.

In the past few years, a number of factory 45 Auto cartridges were fitted with small primer pockets for lead-free priming. There is no safety hazard in reloading these cases with standard primers but the loads here were developed with standard large pistol primers. A small primer should have no trouble igniting a 45 Auto charge but may produce slightly less pressure, something to keep in mind when loading target loads. Avoid mixing small- and large-pocket cases when loading for accuracy.

In spite of many new cartridges for semi-auto pistols, the 45 Auto has remained strong. Some pundits predicted that new 9mm and 40 S&W pistols would ultimately "kill off" the 45 Auto and the 1911 but, as with many predictions, this one seems far off the mark. There are more 1911-type 45 Auto pistols on the market today than at any other time.

The industry pressure limit for the 45 Auto is established at 21,000 psi; these loads are within that limit.

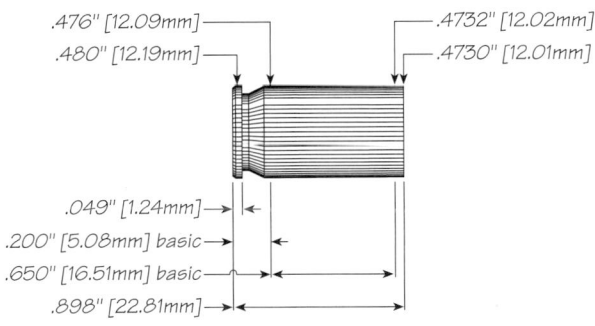

Max. Case Length:	0.898"	Cart. Case:	Speer
Trim-to Length:	0.888"	Primer:	CCI 300
Max Cart. OAL:	1.275"	Test Firearm:	SIG P220
RCBS Shell Holder:	#3	Barrel Length:	4.4"

IMPORTANT SAFETY NOTE: *These loads were developed and tested for safe use in HANDGUNS. Not all loads may be suitable for use in a carbine or rifle chambered for this cartridge. If loading for a carbine or rifle, choose from among the loads developing the highest handgun velocities and load just a few rounds. Thoroughly test this small sample in your firearm in slow-fire mode, insuring that you achieve proper feeding and ejection. Be certain that all bullets exit the barrel; watching the target for each bullet strike is the best way to know that the load produces sufficient gas volume for a longer barrel.*

0.452"	45 LSWC
Weight, grains	200
Ballistic Coefficient	0.078
Sectional Density	0.140
COAL Tested:	1.190"
Speer Part No.	4677

Propellant	START CHARGE Weight, grs	START CHARGE Muzzle Velocity, ft/sec	MAXIMUM CHARGE Weight, grs	MAXIMUM CHARGE Muzzle Velocity, ft/sec
Red Dot	4.1	749	4.5	831
Herco	5.5	750	6.0	826
SR 7625	4.7	726	5.2	811
Bullseye	4.2	744	4.6	807
H. Universal	4.9	710	5.4	804
231	4.6	739	5.0	803
SR 4756	5.3	728	5.8	800
Unique	4.9	716	5.4	790
700-X	3.8	715	4.2	790

NOTE: *These loads are not necessarily at maximum pressure. They are held to velocities popular for target shooting.*

0.452"	45 LRN
Weight, grains	230
Ballistic Coefficient	0.160
Sectional Density	0.161
COAL Tested:	1.270"
Speer Part No.	4690

Propellant	START CHARGE Weight, grs	START CHARGE Muzzle Velocity, ft/sec	MAXIMUM CHARGE Weight, grs	MAXIMUM CHARGE Muzzle Velocity, ft/sec
Unique	5.3	764	5.8	849
SR 4756	6.0	783	6.5	848
Herco	5.9	779	6.4	845
Green Dot	4.8	772	5.3	842
Red Dot	4.7	765	5.1	841
700-X	4.3	767	4.7	838
H. Universal	5.2	748	5.5	837
231	5.1	760	5.6	831

0.451"	45 TMJ Match SWC
Weight, grains	185
Ballistic Coefficient	0.090
Sectional Density	0.130
COAL Tested:	1.275"
Speer Part No.	4473

	START CHARGE		MAXIMUM CHARGE	
Propellant	Weight, grs	Muzzle Velocity, ft/sec	Weight, grs	Muzzle Velocity, ft/sec
231	5.0	717	5.5	807
Red Dot	4.5	758	4.9	803
700-X	4.3	731	4.7	798
Unique	5.0	671	5.8	796
Bullseye	4.5	770	4.9	795
AA No. 5	7.2	691	8.0	793
SR 7625	5.1	705	5.6	793
HP-38	4.9	730	5.4	792
PB	5.0	719	5.5	770

NOTE: *These loads are not necessarily at maximum pressure. They are held to velocities popular for target shooting.*

*Maximum Loads should be used with CAUTION • C = Compressed Load • *Magnum Primer used with this powder.*

0.451"	45 GDHP	45 TMJ FN
Weight, grains	185	185
Ballistic Coefficient	0.109	0.094
Sectional Density	0.130	0.130
COAL Tested:	1.200"	1.200"
Speer Part No.	4470	4476

Propellant	START CHARGE Weight, grs	START CHARGE Muzzle Velocity, ft/sec	MAXIMUM CHARGE Weight, grs	MAXIMUM CHARGE Muzzle Velocity, ft/sec
Power Pistol	8.2	939	9.5	1047
AA No. 5	9.5	956	10.6	1034
Unique	7.3	904	8.2	1015
700-X	5.8	889	6.5	997
H. Universal	6.9	851	7.7	991
Bullseye	5.7	874	6.4	986
SR 7625	7.0	810	7.8	981
AA No. 2	6.0	850	6.7	970
231	6.6	837	7.4	954
AA No. 7	10.8	825	12.0	947
American Select	5.5	834	6.2	941
HS-6	8.9	832	9.9	926
Viht. 3N37	8.1	804	9.0	915
WSF	6.9	814	7.7	885

0.451"	45 TMJ FN	45 TMJ Match SWC	45 GDHP
Weight, grains	200	200	200
Ballistic Coefficient	0.102	0.128	0.138
Sectional Density	0.140	0.140	0.140
COAL Tested:	1.200"	1.275"	1.200"
Speer Part No.	4471	4475	4478

Propellant	START CHARGE		MAXIMUM CHARGE	
	Weight, grs	Muzzle Velocity, ft/sec	Weight, grs	Muzzle Velocity, ft/sec
Blue Dot	9.4	877	10.5	1010
Unique	6.5	860	7.3	984
H. Universal	6.3	829	7.0	967
HS-6	8.5	823	9.5	956
Viht. N340	6.3	818	7.0	953
Power Pistol	7.0	823	8.3	952
Bullseye	5.2	845	5.8	934
WSF	6.4	824	7.2	934
Viht. 3N37	7.3	769	8.2	910
AA No. 5	8.1	798	9.0	900
AA No. 7	9.9	791	11.0	891
231	5.6	769	6.3	857

*Maximum Loads should be used with CAUTION • C = Compressed Load • *Magnum Primer used with this powder.*

0.451"	45 Colt JHP
Weight, grains	225
Ballistic Coefficient	0.169
Sectional Density	0.158
COAL Tested:	1.200"
Speer Part No.	4479

Propellant	START CHARGE		MAXIMUM CHARGE	
	Weight, grs	Muzzle Velocity, ft/sec	Weight, grs	Muzzle Velocity, ft/sec
Blue Dot	9.0	814	10.0	935
Power Pistol	7.3	814	8.2	920
Viht. N350	7.2	797	8.0	907
Unique	6.4	835	7.2	906
AA No. 5	8.1	773	9.0	887
AA No. 7	9.7	736	10.7	877
WSF	6.3	774	7.0	860
Bullseye	5.0	782	5.6	856
H. Universal	5.8	725	6.5	845
HS-6	8.0	740	9.0	841
Viht. 3N37	7.2	730	8.0	840
231	5.4	787	6.0	787

0.451"	45 TMJ RN
Weight, grains	230
Ballistic Coefficient	0.153
Sectional Density	0.162
COAL Tested:	1.260"
Speer Part No.	4480

Propellant	START CHARGE		MAXIMUM CHARGE	
	Weight, grs	Muzzle Velocity, ft/sec	Weight, grs	Muzzle Velocity, ft/sec
Power Pistol	7.0	806	8.1	916
Viht. N340	5.5	760	6.3	872
HS-6	7.8	773	8.5	863
231	5.6	789	6.2	858
H. Universal	5.5	730	6.3	841
Bullseye	5.2	779	5.7	840
Red Dot	4.8	770	5.3	839
Unique	5.5	728	6.5	832
700-X	4.6	710	5.1	815

SAFETY NOTICE: *Do not use these loads with the 230-grain Gold Dot HP (#4483). Gold Dot loads are in the next data block.*

*Maximum Loads should be used with CAUTION • C = Compressed Load • *Magnum Primer used with this powder.*

0.451"	45 GDHP SB	45 GDHP
Weight, grains	230	230
Ballistic Coefficient	0.148	0.143
Sectional Density	0.162	0.162
COAL Tested:	1.200"	1.200"
Speer Part No.	4482	4483

	START CHARGE		MAXIMUM CHARGE	
Propellant	Weight, grs	Muzzle Velocity, ft/sec	Weight, grs	Muzzle Velocity, ft/sec
Blue Dot	8.1	796	9.0	893
Power Pistol	6.3	759	7.4	881
HS-7	8.5	724	9.5	849
Viht. N340	5.4	709	6.1	836
Viht. N350	6.3	730	7.1	826
700-X	4.5	748	5.0	818
Bullseye	4.5	742	5.0	812
H. Universal	5.4	704	6.0	806
Unique	5.4	721	6.0	806
HS-6	7.2	702	8.0	799
SR 7625	5.4	664	6.0	796
AA No. 7	8.6	690	9.6	794
AA No. 5	7.0	687	7.8	792
231	5.0	683	5.6	765

*Maximum Loads should be used with CAUTION • C = Compressed Load • *Magnum Primer used with this powder.*

45 S&W Schofield

In the 1870's, the Army of the United States had two 45-caliber cartridge revolvers in their arsenal. The most famous is the 45 Colt Single Action Army (SAA) revolver. Less recognized is the Smith & Wesson Model 3 "Schofield" revolver chambered for the 45 S&W cartridge.

The revolver was a modification of S&W's 44-caliber, hinged-frame Model 3 revolver. Major George W. Schofield of the 10th Cavalry suggested certain changes in the Model 3 to make it a better sidearm for horse soldiers. S&W incorporated many of Schofield's ideas including strengthening the latch mechanism and moving it from the topstrap to the frame. Ultimately, Major Schofield's name was used to describe both the revolver and the cartridge.

The Smith & Wesson revolver had one major advantage over the Colt design—simultaneous ejection of the fired cases afforded by the hinged-frame design. The revolver could be quickly opened and emptied one-handed at full gallop, a task that's much more difficult with a Colt Single Action. Hinged-frame, or "break-top," designs

Copper-cased 45 S&W military issue cartridge with inside priming (l), a commercial black powder 45 S&W, our CAS load, and the 45 Colt (r).

are typically more delicate than their solid-frame counterparts but the Schofield latch made the S&W revolver tough enough to serve alongside the Colt.

The shorter S&W cylinder required a shorter cartridge than the 45 Colt. The bullet weight was reduced from 255 to 230 grains and the charge of black powder went from 40 to 28 grains. Schofield ammo would chamber and fire in the Colt. As a result, units might be issued Schofield ammo even though some soldiers were armed with Colts. It was no different than a police department issuing only 38 Special ammo even though some officers carry 357 Magnum revolvers. There's a performance penalty for some but everyone has ammo.

The cartridge faded into obscurity before World War II and would have remained only a fond memory were it not for Cowboy Action shooting. The need for smaller, more efficient cases for lighter loads resulted in the resurrection of several obsolete cartridges including the Schofield. Black Hills Ammo sells Schofield ammo and Starline sells empty cases.

The loads presented here are loaded with bullets cast from the RCBS 45-225-CAV mould, designed for the 45 Colt by Jim Huber for Cowboy competition. They may also be used with the newer RCBS 45-230-CM bullet design.

The cartridge drawing shows C.I.P. (European) cartridge maximum dimensions and may not match current Starline case dimensions. Starline rim diameters run closer to 0.520-inch.

As the Schofield is technically obsolete, there are no pressure standards. The loads shown were derived volumetrically from safe 45 Colt data with the same bullet.

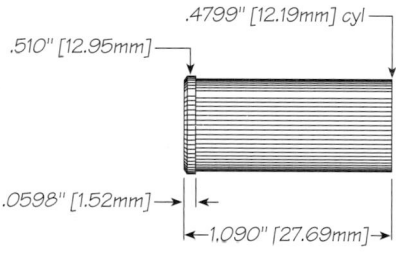

Max. Case Length:	1.090"	Cart. Case:	Starline
Trim-to Length:	1.080"	Primer:	CCI 300
Max Cart. OAL:	1.430"	Test Firearm:	Colt Single Action Army
RCBS Shell Holder:	#35	Barrel Length:	5.5"

0.454"	45-225 CAV	45-230 CM
Weight, grains	225	230
Lead Alloy	hard	hard
Ballistic Coefficient	0.128	0.126
Sectional Density	0.156	0.159
COAL Tested:	1.425"	1.410"
RCBS Mould No.	82081	82308

Propellant	START CHARGE		MAXIMUM CHARGE	
	Weight, grs	Muzzle Velocity, ft/sec	Weight, grs	Muzzle Velocity, ft/sec
Unique	5.5	689	6.1	728
231	4.6	670	5.1	726
700-X	3.9	669	4.3	719
TiteGroup	4.0	648	4.4	713
American Select	3.9	671	4.3	707
Nitro 100	3.8	642	4.2	703
Trail Boss	4.2	638	4.6	702
Bullseye	3.9	662	4.3	697
SR 4756	6.5	606	7.2	692
AA No. 2 Impr.	4.2	620	4.7	685
Viht. N350	5.9	570	6.6	655
H Universal	5.0	551	5.5	628

NOTE: *We sell bullet moulds, not cast bullets. These bullets were cast in RCBS moulds. Contact your dealer for more information on the RCBS line of premium bullet casting equipment, or visit on the Internet at www.rcbs.com.*

*Maximum Loads should be used with CAUTION • C = Compressed Load • *Magnum Primer used with this powder.*

45 Colt

In 1873, the U.S. Army adopted the famous Colt Single Action Army revolver as its service sidearm. It was chambered for the new 45 Colt cartridge that held an impressive quantity of black powder under a 255-grain lead bullet. The new combination proved both powerful and accurate, serving for nearly 20 years before being replaced by a 38-caliber revolver. Like other service cartridges, the 45 Colt became popular with civilians as well. It produced more muzzle energy than any other cartridge handgun until the 357 Magnum appeared in 1935.

Today the 45 Colt is gaining new fans among sport shooters. Cowboy Action Shooting competition calls for single-action firearms and the 45 Colt is certainly the most nostalgic. There are many well-made copies of the Colt Single Action on the market, and Ruger has sold thousands of their modern Blackhawk and Vaquero revolvers chambered for 45 Colt. In the 1970's, Smith & Wesson introduced the double-action Model 25-5 in their large "N-frame" series that stayed in the line until 1991, and still catalogs a "Mountain Gun" in 45 Colt today.

Factory ammunition was limited to a 250 or 255-grain lead bullet for many years. Velocities run 770 to 850 ft/sec in a six-inch barrel. Increased interest in the cartridge convinced ammo makers to design newer bullet styles including hollow points starting in the 1970's.

Prior to World War II, most Colt revolvers had a bore diameter of .454". Postwar guns measure .451" to .452"—the same as the 45 Auto. Many older loading dies are designed for use with the larger bullets and may not size or expand the case properly to grip the smaller bullets properly. Your expander ball should be no larger than .450" diameter to properly load .451" bullets. We found that new cases will not properly grip a jacketed bullet unless partially sized. Sizing the first half-inch of the case in a carbide die easily remedies this.

In 2004, Speer introduced a 250-grain Gold Dot hollow point designed for standard-pressure 45 Colt loads. The weight helps fixed-sight revolvers stay close to point of aim and the large cavity is designed for expansion at low velocities. Due to its weight and the 45 Colt's low pressure, we do not show starting loads for this bullet. Do not load lighter than shown. Other popular Speer jacketed bullets for standard pressure loads in the 45 Colt are the 225 and 260-grain jacketed hollow points but will not afford the bullet expansion of the Gold Dot.

Speer's 200 and 250-grain lead semi-wadcutters make nice practice and target loads. The 200-grain bullet should be should be firmly roll-crimped over the shoulder. Do not try to load this bullet too light.

Bullets designed for the 45 Auto usually lack a crimping groove and are more difficult to load in a revolver cartridge. When crimping the Gold Dot bullets, use a 45 Auto taper crimp die to adequately grip the bullet without deforming the jacket. Loading these to higher velocities than shown may cause taper-crimped bullets to "jump crimp" resulting in poor performance.

We show CAS loads for bullets from two RCBS moulds. We also tested the excellent 45-255-SWC Keith design bullet. This is probably the best general-purpose lead bullet in the 45 Colt. We sized cast bullets to .454" to create a better fit in the chamber throat. Our start loads produce at least 11,000 psi and we emphatically recommend that you not load these bullets lighter.

Although within industry pressure limits, these loads must be used only in revolvers originally made for smokeless propellant. If in doubt, check with the firearm manufacturer or a qualified gunsmith before firing older revolvers with any modern ammo. We strongly recommend that the jacketed bullet loads here not be fired in any revolver having a barrel-cylinder greater than 0.009-inch. You can check the gap in your revolver with an automotive feeler gauge but be certain the gun is unloaded and clean. Hold the cylinder as far to the rear as possible while taking the reading.

The industry maximum average pressure for the 45 Colt is 14,000 psi.

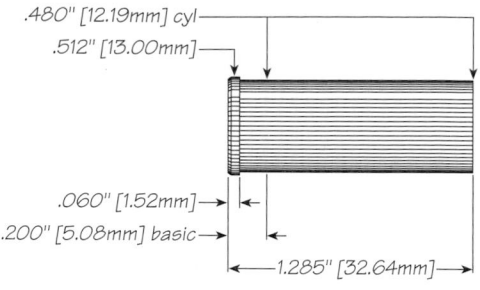

.480" [12.19mm] cyl
.512" [13.00mm]
.060" [1.52mm]
.200" [5.08mm] basic
1.285" [32.64mm]

Max. Case Length:	1.285"	Cart. Case:	Winchester
Trim-to Length:	1.275"	Primer:	CCI 300; 350*
Max Cart. OAL:	1.600"	Test Firearm:	Colt Single Action Army
RCBS Shell Holder:	#20	Barrel Length:	5.5"

0.452"	45 LSWC
Weight, grains	200
Ballistic Coefficient	0.078
Sectional Density	0.140
COAL Tested:	1.515"
Speer Part No.	4677

Propellant	START CHARGE		MAXIMUM CHARGE	
	Weight, grs	Muzzle Velocity, ft/sec	Weight, grs	Muzzle Velocity, ft/sec
Unique	8.0	896	9.5	1061
HS-6	10.7	898	12.2	1036
Herco	8.0	855	9.5	1021
Red Dot	6.3	859	7.3	1001
231	7.3	854	8.3	998
Bullseye	6.5	835	7.5	988
Green Dot	7.3	834	8.3	980
SR 7625	7.1	860	8.1	959
700-X	5.9	795	6.9	959

NOTE: *Firmly roll-crimp over the bullet shoulder for reliable performance.*

0.452"	45 LSWC
Weight, grains	250
Ballistic Coefficient	0.117
Sectional Density	0.175
COAL Tested:	1.600"
Speer Part No.	4683

	START CHARGE		MAXIMUM CHARGE	
Propellant	Weight, grs	Muzzle Velocity, ft/sec	Weight, grs	Muzzle Velocity, ft/sec
Blue Dot	11.9	912	12.9	1028
Viht. 3N37	10.5	889	11.5	1012
2400	13.4	838	15.4	972
HS-6*	11.0	917	12.0	945
H. Universal	8.3	826	9.2	942
Unique	8.6	891	9.5	941
AA No. 5	10.6	840	11.8	927
HS-7*	11.2	812	12.2	906
IMR 4227	17.0	775	19.0	904
Bullseye	6.3	810	7.0	879
231	7.2	780	8.0	852

*Maximum Loads should be used with CAUTION • C = Compressed Load • *Magnum Primer used with this powder.*

0.454"	45-225 CAV	45-230 CM
Weight, grains	225	230
Lead Alloy	hard	hard
Ballistic Coefficient	0.128	0.126
Sectional Density	0.156	0.159
COAL Tested:	1.600"	1.585"
RCBS Mould No.	82081	82308

Propellant	START CHARGE Weight, grs	START CHARGE Muzzle Velocity, ft/sec	MAXIMUM CHARGE Weight, grs	MAXIMUM CHARGE Muzzle Velocity, ft/sec
SR 4756	9.5	793	10.3	917
H. Universal	7.8	813	8.5	887
Viht. N350	8.8	783	9.7	857
231	6.5	788	7.2	852
Unique	7.8	804	8.5	850
TiteGroup	5.6	775	6.2	832
Nitro 100	5.1	782	5.9	831
700-X	5.2	767	6.0	816
Bullseye	5.0	709	6.0	815
AA No. 2 Impr.	6.4	735	6.8	799
Trail Boss	5.8	743	6.5	797
American Select	5.5	724	6.0	782

NOTE: *We sell bullet moulds, not cast bullets. These bullets were cast in RCBS moulds. Contact your dealer for more information on the RCBS line of premium bullet casting equipment, or visit on the Internet at www.rcbs.com.*

0.454"	45-225 SWC
Weight, grains	255
Lead Alloy	hard
Ballistic Coefficient	0.165
Sectional Density	0.165
COAL Tested:	1.665"†
RCBS Mould No.	82050

Propellant	START CHARGE Weight, grs	START CHARGE Muzzle Velocity, ft/sec	MAXIMUM CHARGE Weight, grs	MAXIMUM CHARGE Muzzle Velocity, ft/sec
Viht. N110	15.8	809	16.8	914
H. Universal	7.2	815	8.0	883
SR 4756	9.0	808	10.0	865
Viht. N350	8.6	717	9.5	847
Unique	7.7	789	8.5	846
Power Pistol	7.3	763	8.3	810
231	6.1	700	7.0	784
Nitro 100	5.0	675	5.5	752

NOTE: *We sell bullet moulds, not cast bullets. These bullets were cast in RCBS moulds. Contact your dealer for more information on the RCBS line of premium bullet casting equipment, or visit on the Internet at www.rcbs.com. † — exceeds industry max. cartridge length but will fit most revolvers. Not for use in repeating rifles.*

*Maximum Loads should be used with CAUTION • C = Compressed Load • *Magnum Primer used with this powder.*

0.451"	45 GDHP
Weight, grains	200
Ballistic Coefficient	0.138
Sectional Density	0.140
COAL Tested:	1.555"
Speer Part No.	4478

Propellant	START CHARGE		MAXIMUM CHARGE	
	Weight, grs	Muzzle Velocity, ft/sec	Weight, grs	Muzzle Velocity, ft/sec
HS-6*	11.0	945	12.5	1081
Unique	8.8	940	9.8	1048
Herco	9.0	928	10.0	1032
SR 7625	7.7	880	8.7	1002
Bullseye	7.4	920	7.9	994
Green Dot	7.8	868	8.8	991
H. Universal	8.4	892	9.2	985
Red Dot	7.1	911	7.6	981
700-X	6.1	852	7.1	921
Power Pistol	8.6	829	9.2	885
TiteGroup	6.2	788	6.8	865

0.451"	45 JHP	45 GDHP SB	45 GDHP
Weight, grains	225	230	230
Ballistic Coefficient	0.169	0.148	0.143
Sectional Density	0.158	0.162	0.162
COAL Tested:	1.590"	1.600"	1.600"
Speer Part No.	4479	4482	4483

Propellant	START CHARGE		MAXIMUM CHARGE	
	Weight, grs	Muzzle Velocity, ft/sec	Weight, grs	Muzzle Velocity, ft/sec
Blue Dot	12.0	967	13.0	1036
SR 4756	10.3	836	11.0	962
Viht. N110	16.0	778	18.0	946
HS-6*	10.8	876	11.8	936
Unique	8.1	827	9.0	932
Herco	8.4	839	9.4	918
AA No. 5	10.8	840	11.8	912
Bullseye	6.4	825	7.1	890
Power Pistol	8.5	823	9.5	878
H. Universal	8.2	819	9.0	873
231	7.5	804	8.3	870

*Maximum Loads should be used with CAUTION • C = Compressed Load • *Magnum Primer used with this powder.*

0.452"	45 Colt GDHP
Weight, grains	250
Ballistic Coefficient	0.165
Sectional Density	0.175
COAL Tested:	1.600"
Speer Part No.	4484

Propellant	START CHARGE		MAXIMUM CHARGE	
	Weight, grs	Muzzle Velocity, ft/sec	Weight, grs	Muzzle Velocity, ft/sec
AA No. 9*	DNR	—	14.0	874
HS-7*	DNR	—	11.6	848
Power Pistol	DNR	—	8.8	845
Viht. N110	DNR	—	16.0	843
Unique	DNR	—	7.8	840
AA No. 5	DNR	—	10.0	835
2400	DNR	—	15.0	826

DNR — do not reduce

0.451"	45 JHP
Weight, grains	260
Ballistic Coefficient	0.183
Sectional Density	0.183
COAL Tested:	1.590"
Speer Part No.	4481

Propellant	START CHARGE		MAXIMUM CHARGE	
	Weight, grs	Muzzle Velocity, ft/sec	Weight, grs	Muzzle Velocity, ft/sec
Blue Dot	DNR	—	13.0	941
HS-6*	DNR	—	11.5	925
H. Universal	DNR	—	8.9	897
Viht. 3N37	DNR	—	10.4	875
Power Pistol	DNR	—	8.4	852
231	DNR	—	8.0	843
Bullseye	DNR	—	7.1	841

DNR — do not reduce

---

*Maximum Loads should be used with CAUTION • C = Compressed Load • *Magnum Primer used with this powder.*

45 Colt

0.452"	45 Colt Shot Capsule
Weight, grains	~ 150
Ballistic Coefficient	n/a
Sectional Density	n/a
COAL Tested:	1.575"
Speer Part No.	8785

Propellant	Weight, grs	Muzzle Velocity, ft/sec
Unique	7.5	975
231	6.0	925
TiteGroup	5.7	920
700-X	5.5	915
Bullseye	5.5	875

NOTE: *Shot capsules must not be used in firearms with ported recoil compensators. Test Firearm: S&W Model 25-5 6"*

*Maximum Loads should be used with CAUTION • C = Compressed Load • * Magnum Primer used with this powder.*

45 Colt *(Ruger & Contender Only)*

With the introduction of massively strong revolvers and pistols chambered for the 45 Colt cartridge, handloaders wanted to enhanced the performance of the cartridge. The Ruger Blackhawk and the Thompson/Center Contender can both handle somewhat higher pressures than traditional 45 Colt revolvers. The resulting increase in velocity makes the 45 Colt a potent hunting handgun.

Important Safety Note

Since we published the last manual, Ruger has replaced the original Vaquero revolver with a smaller version called the New Vaquero. Ruger has advised the industry that the New Vaquero must not be fired with loads exceeding industry pressure standards (14,000 psi). If loading for a New Vaquero, use the standard pressure data in the previous data section.

However, there are limitations. A few handloaders have assembled 45 Colt loads that exceed the pressures of the 44 Magnum. Some 45 Colt cases are not as strong as the 44 Magnum case and you must not attempt to load it as high, regardless of the gun model. The loads Speer developed are roughly halfway between standard 45 Colt and 44 Magnum pressures. This results in a significant increase in energy yet the loads were safe in Speer's test firearms. If you need more power than this, buy a 44 Magnum or a 454 Casull.

The bullets we selected for these loads are designed for high-velocity use. Do not use bullets intended for the 45 Auto at these velocities. Their lack of a crimping groove makes obtaining enough crimp for heavy recoil difficult.

Although the new 250-grain Gold Dot hollow point was designed for standard-pressure velocities, it is quite happy in these loads. It is suited to hunting smaller deer but will expand very violently at these velocities, reducing penetration.

All bullets shown should be heavily crimped; use a neckdown crimp (see chapter 15) for the Gold Dot hollow point and the Uni-Cor soft point. We crimped the 300-grain Uni-Cor soft point to the rear cannelure for a cartridge length of 1.640 inches. Do not seat them to the front cannelure with these charge weights as excessive pressure will result. Loads for the 300-grain bullet were developed in a copper crusher test barrel; they operate at higher pressure than those for lighter bullets. Even so, they showed no pressure signs in our test revolver.

When expanding case necks, make sure that your expander plug is no larger than .450" to insure a firm grip on the bullet. We recommend that these loads be used in new or once-fired cases known to be of recent manufacture.

Do not use in any other make or model of firearm.

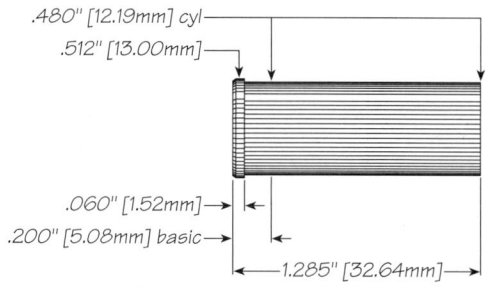

Max. Case Length:	1.285"	**Cart. Case:**	Winchester	
Trim-to Length:	1.275"	**Primer:**	CCI 300; 350*	
Max Cart. OAL:	1.600"	**Test Firearm:**	Ruger Blackhawk	
RCBS Shell Holder:	#20	**Barrel Length:**	7.5"	

0.451"	45 JHP
Weight, grains	225
Ballistic Coefficient	0.169
Sectional Density	0.158
COAL Tested:	1.590"
Speer Part No.	4479

Propellant	START CHARGE		MAXIMUM CHARGE	
	Weight, grs	Muzzle Velocity, ft/sec	Weight, grs	Muzzle Velocity, ft/sec
Blue Dot	14.0	1216	16.0	1343
Viht. N110	21.0	1209	23.0C	1339
2400	17.0	1156	19.0	1259
HS-6*	13.0	1146	14.0	1198
† SR 4759	21.5	1094	23.5C	1198
Unique	10.5	1107	11.5	1191
AA No. 5	12.5	1085	13.5	1157
231	9.5	1011	10.5	1127

† — DO NOT confuse with SR 4756 or excessive pressure will result

*Maximum Loads should be used with CAUTION • C = Compressed Load • *Magnum Primer used with this powder.*

0.452"	45 Colt GDHP
Weight, grains	250
Ballistic Coefficient	0.165
Sectional Density	0.175
COAL Tested:	1.600"
Speer Part No.	4484

	START CHARGE		MAXIMUM CHARGE	
Propellant	Weight, grs	Muzzle Velocity, ft/sec	Weight, grs	Muzzle Velocity, ft/sec
296*	19.0	1118	21.0	1203
H110*	19.0	1091	21.0	1200
AA No. 9*	16.0	1052	18.0	1182
Viht. N110	18.0	1003	20.0	1148
2400	18.0	1058	20.0	1145
Power Pistol	11.0	1039	12.0	1112
Viht. N350	11.0	973	12.0	1105
HS-7*	13.4	1012	14.4	1094
Unique	9.8	995	10.8	1075

*Maximum Loads should be used with CAUTION • C = Compressed Load • *Magnum Primer used with this powder.*

0.451"	45 JHP
Weight, grains	260
Ballistic Coefficient	0.183
Sectional Density	0.183
COAL Tested:	1.590"
Speer Part No.	4481

Propellant	START CHARGE		MAXIMUM CHARGE	
	Weight, grs	Muzzle Velocity, ft/sec	Weight, grs	Muzzle Velocity, ft/sec
296*	19.0	1096	20.5	1183
2400*	16.0	1045	18.0	1180
H110*	18.5	1042	20.0	1151
HS-7*	13.7	1021	14.7	1123
Herco	10.0	996	11.0	1082
Unique	9.5	987	10.5	1079
231	9.2	987	10.2	1067
Bullseye	8.5	1005	9.4	1064

0.451"	45 UCSP
Weight, grains	300
Ballistic Coefficient	0.199
Sectional Density	0.211
COAL Tested:	1.640"
Speer Part No.	4485

Propellant	START CHARGE		MAXIMUM CHARGE	
	Weight, grs	Muzzle Velocity, ft/sec	Weight, grs	Muzzle Velocity, ft/sec
296*	20.7	1084	23.0	1193
H110*	21.1	974	23.5	1156
HS-7*	14.0	975	15.5	1057
2400*	15.8	938	17.5	1048
AA No. 9*	15.0	959	15.5	1041
† SR 4759	20.3	825	22.5	1029

NOTE: *Seat bullet to REAR cannelure and use a neckdown crimp. † — DO NOT confuse with SR 4756 or excessive pressure will*

454 Casull

The powerful 454 Casull has been with us for a long time but did not become a standard industry cartridge until 1998. Prior to that, it was a proprietary (privately held) cartridge of Freedom Arms. Freedom was the only source of ammo and cases and the only revolvers were single-action. Industry adoption of the cartridge, changes to cartridge cases and introduction of double-action revolvers have created new handloading guidelines.

The 454 started with Dick Casull's research into high-pressure 45 Colt loads in highly modified Colt Single Action Army revolvers. It became apparent that such a cartridge needed a strong new revolver not based on existing models. Freedom Arms developed the revolver that is still with us today. It is one of the finest revolvers on the market, tough and finely fitted.

The new industry pressure standard for the 454 Casull is transducer-based and a whopping 65,000 psi, the same as the most powerful rifle cartridges. Current cases are not the same as older Freedom cases (headstamp "F-A"). Cases are now available from Winchester and Starline.

In the real world, 65,000 psi is not a practical working pressure. We (and others) found that this cartridge cannot be loaded to max pressure and still extract smoothly from most revolvers, especially double-action models. The lot of Winchester factory ammunition we tested was just over 55,000 psi. We held our maximum loads to similar levels and experienced no extraction problems.

Extraction issues extend to the stiffness of the cases you use. Winchester 454 cases are much stiffer than typical handgun brass. In case wall deflection tests done as part of calibrating our pressure barrel, the Winchester cases needed 5,000 psi more pressure to deflect the same amount as Starline cases that showed case wall stiffness normal for magnum handgun cases. This means the harder cases extract easier, but may not last as long. See the "Lab Notes" for additional reloading tips.

The new Speer 300-grain Gold Dot® hollow point was designed expressly for the 454 Casull. It has a massive 0.030-inch copper jacket to resist deformation in the barrel throat, a very likely occurrence with thinner jackets at these pressures. Such deformation can cause premature erosion of the barrel throat and topstrap. Because of this, you must not use the 300-grain Gold Dot hollow point loads with any other bullet, including the Speer 300-grain Uni-Cor® soft point.

Full-power 454 Casull loads generate wicked recoil but reloaders can safely produce milder loads that make shooting more pleasant. We show three sets of reduced recoil loads: one with a 270-grain lead bullet cast from an RCBS mould and two for 250 to 300-grain Speer jacketed bullets. The lead bullet loads can produce pressures up to 27,000 psi and the jacketed bullet loads range up to 44 Magnum pressures, 36,000 psi. These are still quite powerful but the pressures remain within the design criteria for those bullets. For comfortable practice, look to the lead bullet start loads.

Note that we used CCI 400 small rifle primers for these loads. Do not attempt to use pistol primers; they are not appropriate to this cartridge.

The data and cartridge drawing presented here replaces, supersedes, and obsoletes all data for this cartridge previously published in *Speer Reloading Manuals* when the 454 Casull was a proprietary cartridge and the only production revolvers were Freedom Arms models. Substituting bullets of other makes may create dangerously high pressures.

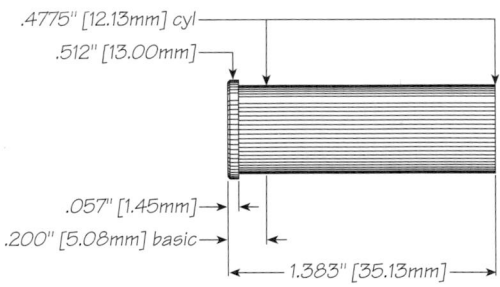

Max. Case Length:	1.383"	Cart. Case:	Winchester and Starline
Trim-to Length:	1.373"	Primer:	CCI 400
Max Cart. OAL:	1.765"	Test Firearm:	Freedom Arms
RCBS Shell Holder:	#20	Barrel Length:	7.5"

0.452"	45-270 SAA
Weight, grains	270
Lead Alloy	hard
Ballistic Coefficient	0.172
Sectional Density	0.189
COAL Tested:	1.750"
RCBS Mould No.	82092

Propellant	START CHARGE		MAXIMUM CHARGE	
	Weight, grs	Muzzle Velocity, ft/sec	Weight, grs	Muzzle Velocity, ft/sec
Ramshot True Blue	11.0	1032	13.0	1178
XMP 5744	21.0	1062	23.0	1166
Unique	9.0	993	11.0	1155
TiteGroup	7.0	960	9.0	1135
Power Pistol	9.0	953	11.0	1114
H. Universal	8.0	906	10.0	1111
IMR Trail Boss	9.0	977	11.0C	1098
Viht. N350	10.0	930	12.0	1087
AA No. 7	12.0	933	14.0	1053
231	7.0	872	9.0	1049

NOTE: *We sell bullet moulds, not cast bullets. These bullets were cast in RCBS moulds. Contact your dealer for more information on the RCBS linc of premium bullet casting equipment, or visit on the Internet at www.rcbs.com. REDUCED RECOIL LOADS: Starline cases*

---

*Maximum Loads should be used with CAUTION • C = Compressed Load • *Magnum Primer used with this powder.*

0.451" (260 gr) 0.452" (250 gr)	45 Colt GDHP	45 JHP
Weight, grains	250	260
Ballistic Coefficient	0.165	0.183
Sectional Density	0.175	0.183
COAL Tested:	1.670"	1.670"
Speer Part No.	4484	4481

	START CHARGE		MAXIMUM CHARGE	
Propellant	Weight, grs	Muzzle Velocity, ft/sec	Weight, grs	Muzzle Velocity, ft/sec
2400	24.0	1422	26.0	1531
Viht. N110	23.0	1381	25.0	1499
IMR 4227	27.0	1248	29.0C	1399
AA No. 9	23.0	1323	25.0	1375
AA 5744	26.0	1225	28.0	1341
Ramshot True Blue	14.0	1164	16.0	1325
Viht. N350	13.0	1129	15.0	1277

NOTE: *REDUCED RECOIL LOADS: Starline cases*

Lab Notes:

Reloading the Casull cartridge changed significantly with its industry adoption in 1998. These guidelines will help:

- Do not use any cases bearing the Freedom Arms headstamp (F-A) with the 300-grain Gold Dot loads shown here. Relegate them to lighter loads.
- Use new cases for maximum loads with the 300-grain Gold Dot HP. Fire them once and then use them with lighter loads.
- Bullets for maximum pressure loads must have thick jackets. The 300-grain Gold Dot HP qualifies in every respect.
- If you experience hard extraction in double-action revolvers using Starline cases, reduce the charge weight one grain and test again.
- NEVER exceed the loads listed here. This cartridge has a steep pressure-to-charge curve; adding one more grain of powder will quickly put them out of the pressure range that allows normal extraction and could result in premature barrel throat erosion with some bullets.

0.451"	45 UCSP
Weight, grains	300
Ballistic Coefficient	0.199
Sectional Density	0.211
COAL Tested:	1.760"
Speer Part No.	4485

Propellant	START CHARGE		MAXIMUM CHARGE	
	Weight, grs	Muzzle Velocity, ft/sec	Weight, grs	Muzzle Velocity, ft/sec
H110	26.5	1328	28.5	1452
296	26.0	1298	28.0	1426
AA No. 9	21.5	1218	23.5	1349
IMR 4227	25.5	1142	27.5	1327
2400	22.0	1209	24.0	1325
Viht. N110	20.0	1220	22.0	1322

NOTE: *REDUCED RECOIL LOADS: Winchester cases*

0.452"	45 GDHP
Weight, grains	300
Ballistic Coefficient	0.233
Sectional Density	0.210
COAL Tested:	1.750"
Speer Part No.	3974

Propellant	START CHARGE		MAXIMUM CHARGE	
	Weight, grs	Muzzle Velocity, ft/sec	Weight, grs	Muzzle Velocity, ft/sec
H110	29.5	1506	31.5C	1630
296	29.0	1475	31.0C	1587
Viht. N110	25.5	1446	27.5	1549
AA No. 9	24.5	1403	26.5	1535
2400	25.0	1379	27.0	1479
IMR 4227	28.0	1320	30.0C	1426

NOTE: *FULL POWER LOADS: Winchester cases*

Maximum Loads should be used with CAUTION • C = Compressed Load • *Magnum Primer used with this powder.

460 S&W Magnum

The 460 Smith & Wesson Magnum followed the 500 S&W Magnum as the second chambering of S&W's big X-Frame revolver. Although its name sounds like a new diameter, the 460 uses the same bullet diameter as the 45 Colt and 454 Casull.

For a high-pressure cartridge, jacketed bullets must be built with thick tough jackets not only for proper integrity on game but also to avoid premature erosion of the top strap and forcing cone. The Speer 300-grain Gold Dot was designed for the 454 Casull, and works fine in the 460 because they operate at roughly the same pressures.

The selection of Speer 45-caliber bullets lets us show some reduced recoil loads. The jackets on our 250 and 260-grain hollow points and the 300-grain Uni-Cor soft point are rated to a little over 44 Magnum pressures so they can be used for practice or even hunting as long as pressures are held back. Loads here for those bullets produce less than 37,000 psi and should not be increased to avoid erosion of critical gun parts.

The 250-grain Gold Dot was designed for the 45 Colt and has a very large hollow point cavity. It should not be used on game animals in the 460 S&W. At these velocities it will produce explosive expansion better suited for large varmints than deer.

Every load here needs a heavy crimp. See the section "More Effective Crimping for the Big Bruisers" in chapter 15 for how to produce a neckdown crimp if you're loading either the Gold Dot bullet or the 300-grain soft point. The 260-grain hollow point should receive a conventional roll crimp.

On average, our 8-3/8-inch revolver shot about 250 ft/sec slower than the unvented 10-inch pressure barrel. Still, the performance is impressive with muzzle energies approaching 2100 ft/lbs. The maximum average pressure set for the 460 S&W is 65,000 psi. However, if loaded close to this pressure cases may exhibit hard extraction. We held even our full-power loads to that of factory ammunition—around 55,000 psi—for reliable extraction. We recommend that you not try to "creep" up any loads shown here.

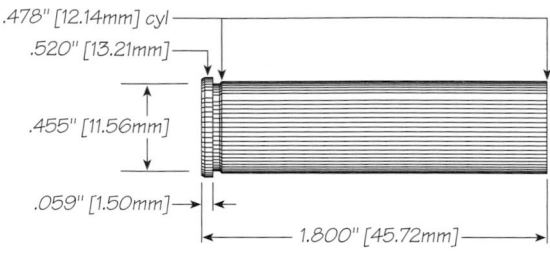

.478" [12.14mm] cyl
.520" [13.21mm]
.455" [11.56mm]
.059" [1.50mm]
1.800" [45.72mm]

Max. Case Length:	1.800"	Cart. Case:	Hornady
Trim-to Length:	1.790"	Primer:	Federal 210
Max Cart. OAL:	2.290"	Test Firearm:	Smith & Wesson X-Frame
RCBS Shell Holder:	#14	Barrel Length:	8.375"

0.452" - .452"	45 Colt GDHP	45 JHP
Weight, grains	250	260
Ballistic Coefficient	0.165	0.183
Sectional Density	0.175	0.183
COAL Tested:	2.090"	2.090"
Speer Part No.	4484	4481

Propellant	START CHARGE Weight, grs	START CHARGE Muzzle Velocity, ft/sec	MAXIMUM CHARGE Weight, grs	MAXIMUM CHARGE Muzzle Velocity, ft/sec
AA No. 9	28.0	1403	30.0	1591
2400	29.0	1499	31.0	1553
Viht. N110	29.0	1498	31.0	1551
Power Pistol	19.0	1400	21.0	1514
Ramshot True Blue	19.0	1332	21.0	1436
AA 5744	33.0	1282	35.0	1366

NOTE: *REDUCED RECOIL LOADS*

0.452"	45 UCSP
Weight, grains	300
Ballistic Coefficient	0.199
Sectional Density	0.211
COAL Tested:	2.170"
Speer Part No.	4485

Propellant	START CHARGE		MAXIMUM CHARGE	
	Weight, grs	Muzzle Velocity, ft/sec	Weight, grs	Muzzle Velocity, ft/sec
AA 1680	42.0	1478	44.0	1591
2400	28.0	1392	30.0	1551
H. Lil' Gun	29.0	1464	31.0	1545
AA No. 9	25.0	1420	27.0	1527
Ramshot Enforcer	30.0	1457	32.0	1515
H110	29.0	1406	31.0	1475
IMR 4227	33.0	1375	35.0	1471
296	32.0	1504	34.0	1469
Viht. N110	29.0	1394	31.0	1458
Power Pistol	18.0	1292	20.0	1359

NOTE: *REDUCED RECOIL LOADS*

*Maximum Loads should be used with CAUTION • C = Compressed Load • *Magnum Primer used with this powder.*

0.452"	454 Casull GDHP
Weight, grains	300
Ballistic Coefficient	0.233
Sectional Density	0.210
COAL Tested:	2.150"
Speer Part No.	3974

	START CHARGE		MAXIMUM CHARGE	
Propellant	Weight, grs	Muzzle Velocity, ft/sec	Weight, grs	Muzzle Velocity, ft/sec
AA No. 9	33.0	1669	35.0	1784
2400	34.0	1610	36.0	1782
AA 1680	46.0	1614	48.0C	1715
H. Lil' Gun	34.0	1634	36.0	1703
Ramshot Enforcer	34.0	1627	36.0	1677
IMR 4227	38.0	1567	40.0C	1656
H110	34.0	1581	36.0	1645
Viht. N110	34.0	1563	36.0	1625
296	36.0	1539	38.0	1597
Power Pistol	22.0	1457	24.0	1525

NOTE: *FULL PRESSURE LOADS*

*Maximum Loads should be used with CAUTION • C = Compressed Load • *Magnum Primer used with this powder.*

480 Ruger

Ruger and Hornady jointly introduced the 480 Ruger in 2001. For all practical purposes, it is a shortened 475 Linebaugh® revolver cartridge (see next section). The Linebaugh case was reduced from 1.400 to 1.285 inches and the loaded length was adjusted accordingly; all other important dimensions are virtually identical. Like firing a 38 Special in a 357 Magnum, the 480 can be safely fired in 475 Linebaugh revolvers.

In spite of the smaller case, the 480 Ruger is no pipsqueak; its muzzle energy is on par with the potent 50 Action Express cartridge. Factory ammo drives a 325-grain bullet at 1350 ft/sec (7.5-inch vented test barrel). With proper bullets, the 480 can take nearly any game animal within handgun range.

Speer has three Gold Dot bullets for the 480: a 275-grain hollow point and two soft points weighting 325 and 400 grains. The 400-grain bullet may not expand when fired from a 480 Ruger, but will duplicate the proven performance of hard-cast lead hunting bullets: terrific penetration on heavy game.

The 325-grain soft point duplicates factory bullets and was designed for the velocities of the 480 Ruger. The 275-grain hollow point is Speer's response to requests for a fast-expanding bullet for small to medium deer.

Our only test revolver is fitted with a 9½-inch barrel, so velocities for the 325-grain bullet are understandably faster than the same bullet from our 475 Linebaugh revolver with a 6-inch barrel. Hornady factory ammunition posted an average muzzle velocity of 1377 ft/sec in our long-barreled Ruger.

As with any revolver cartridge producing heavy recoil, you must apply a heavy crimp to the case to prevent bullet jump, and the neckdown crimp is the best choice. Go to chapter 15 and review the section, "More Effective Crimping for the Big Bruisers." All three Speer .475" bullets have the extra wide crimping groove required for a neckdown crimp.

Most of the propellants shown were selected to produce high velocity hunting loads. However, practice without pain is nice so we included several propellants including Unique, HS-7, AA 1680, and VihtaVuori N350 that reduce recoil. Use magnum primers only where indicated by an asterisk (*) next to the propellant name.

These loads remain within the 48,000 psi pressure limit established for the 480 Ruger.

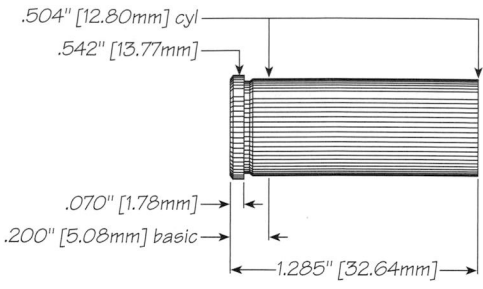

.504" [12.80mm] cyl
.542" [13.77mm]
.070" [1.78mm]
.200" [5.08mm] basic
1.285" [32.64mm]

Max. Case Length:	1.285"	Cart. Case:	Hornady
Trim-to Length:	1.275"	Primer:	CCI 300; 350*
Max Cart. OAL:	1.650"	Test Firearm:	Ruger Redhawk
RCBS Shell Holder:	#40	Barrel Length:	9.5"

0.475"	475 GDHP
Weight, grains	275
Ballistic Coefficient	0.162
Sectional Density	0.174
COAL Tested:	1.640"
Speer Part No.	3973

| Propellant | START CHARGE | | MAXIMUM CHARGE | |
	Weight, grs	Muzzle Velocity, ft/sec	Weight, grs	Muzzle Velocity, ft/sec
296*	32.0	1590	34.0	1695
H110*	32.0	1554	34.0	1663
Viht. N110	25.5	1461	27.5	1575
AA No. 9	26.0	1474	28.0	1566
2400	27.0	1454	29.0	1560
IMR 4227	31.0	1424	33.0	1523
AA No. 7	20.0	1314	22.0	1493
Power Pistol	15.5	1324	17.5	1465
HS-7*	18.0	1332	20.0	1426
Unique	14.0	1275	16.0	1400
Viht. N350	14.0	1205	16.0	1341

0.475"	475 GDSP
Weight, grains	325
Ballistic Coefficient	0.191
Sectional Density	0.206
COAL Tested:	1.650"
Speer Part No.	3978

Propellant	START CHARGE		MAXIMUM CHARGE	
	Weight, grs	Muzzle Velocity, ft/sec	Weight, grs	Muzzle Velocity, ft/sec
H. Lil' Gun*	26.0	1427	28.0	1492
296*	26.0	1366	28.0	1464
Viht. N110	22.5	1349	24.5C	1457
H110*	26.0	1368	28.0	1445
AA No. 9	23.0	1360	25.0	1444
2400	23.0	1319	25.0	1435
IMR 4227	27.0C	1263	29.0C	1389
AA 1680*	28.0	1138	30.0C	1239
Unique	10.0	991	13.0	1178

*Maximum Loads should be used with CAUTION • C = Compressed Load • *Magnum Primer used with this powder.*

0.475"	475 GDSP
Weight, grains	400
Ballistic Coefficient	0.242
Sectional Density	0.253
COAL Tested:	1.650"
Speer Part No.	3976

	START CHARGE		MAXIMUM CHARGE	
Propellant	Weight, grs	Muzzle Velocity, ft/sec	Weight, grs	Muzzle Velocity, ft/sec
H110*	19.5	1100	21.5	1188
296*	19.0	1067	21.0	1165
H. Lil' Gun*	18.0	1073	20.0	1133
Viht. N110	15.5	965	17.5	1115
AA No. 9	16.0	1014	18.0	1102
2400	16.0	975	18.0	1081
IMR 4227	19.0	915	21.0	1041
AA 1680*	22.0	936	24.0C	1018

*Maximum Loads should be used with CAUTION • C = Compressed Load • *Magnum Primer used with this powder.*

475 Linebaugh®

Custom pistolsmith John Linebaugh developed this powerful cartridge in the 1980's and expertly converted large-frame single-action revolvers to fire it. The parent case is the 45-70 Government, shortened to 1.400-inches and straightened so a 0.475-inch bullet can be seated.

Tim Sundles of Buffalo Bore Ammunition (www.buffalobore.com) improved the original case design. He reduced the rim diameter to a more manageable 0.542-inch and beefed up the cartridge case to better handle high pressures. Buffalo Bore sells ammunition as well as unprimed cases for handloading.

> **Important Safety Note**
>
> *Older reloading data developed in cut-down 45-70 cases must not be used in new Buffalo Bore or Hornady cases, as high pressures will result.*

Speer makes three 475-caliber bullets weighing 275, 325, and 400 grains. Screening tests showed the 275-grain Gold Dot® hollow point did not produce consistent ballistic performance in the capacious Linebaugh case. The 325 and 400-grain bullets are Gold Dot soft points for deep penetration. Full-power 475 Linebaugh loads can take their toll on your wrist so we developed lighter loads with both bullet weights using medium-burning propellants. The start load of Unique® with the 400-grain bullet was almost fun to shoot!

A firm neck-down crimp is mandatory and Speer Gold Dot bullets have a wide crimp cannelure to make this crimp possible. See the section on crimping in chapter 15.

The loads here do not exceed 50,000 psi, the established maximum average pressure for this cartridge.

475 Linebaugh is a registered trademark of Timothy R. Sundles.

The 400-gr Gold Dot® soft point fired from a 475 Linebaugh revolver into expansion medium. The perfect combination for expansion and deep penetration.

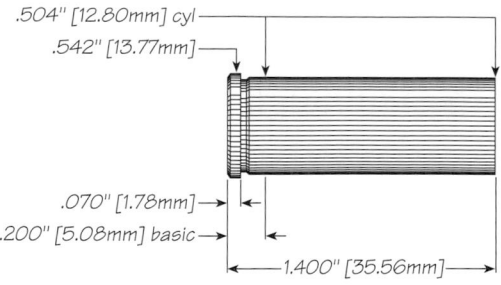

.504" [12.80mm] cyl
.542" [13.77mm]
.070" [1.78mm]
.200" [5.08mm] basic
1.400" [35.56mm]

Max. Case Length:	1.400"	Cart. Case:	Buffalo Bore
Trim-to Length:	1.390"	Primer:	CCI 300
Max Cart. OAL:	1.765"	Test Firearm:	Freedom Arms M767
RCBS Shell Holder:	#40	Barrel Length:	6"

0.475"	475 GDSP
Weight, grains	325
Ballistic Coefficient	0.191
Sectional Density	0.206
COAL Tested:	1.750"
Speer Part No.	3978

	START CHARGE		MAXIMUM CHARGE	
Propellant	Weight, grs	Muzzle Velocity, ft/sec	Weight, grs	Muzzle Velocity, ft/sec
AA No. 9	26.0	1324	28.0	1429
Viht. N110	25.5	1308	27.5	1412
2400	25.0	1262	27.0	1371
AA No. 7	19.0	1153	23.0	1363
Blue Dot	18.0	1159	20.0	1324
Power Pistol	15.5	1168	17.5	1302
Unique	13.5	1107	15.5	1221
Viht. N350	14.5	1065	16.5	1220

0.475"	475 GDSP
Weight, grains	400
Ballistic Coefficient	0.242
Sectional Density	0.253
COAL Tested:	1.750"
Speer Part No.	3976

Propellant	START CHARGE		MAXIMUM CHARGE	
	Weight, grs	Muzzle Velocity, ft/sec	Weight, grs	Muzzle Velocity, ft/sec
H. Lil' Gun*	24.0	1239	26.0	1319
Viht. N110	21.0	1200	23.0	1283
2400	21.0	1130	23.0	1254
296*	23.5	1161	25.5	1226
H110*	23.0	1126	25.0	1212
IMR 4227	25.0	1114	27.0	1209
AA No. 9	21.0	1143	23.0	1209
Unique	11.5	987	13.0	1074
AA 1680*	27.0	1021	28.0C	1059

Gun Week's Jim Taylor dropped this large feral hog with his 475 Linebaugh revolver and a Speer 400-grain Gold Dot SP.

Maximum Loads should be used with CAUTION • C = Compressed Load • *Magnum Primer used with this powder.

50 Action Express

With the rising interest in handgun hunting, shooters continue to demand more powerful combinations of guns and ammunition to take larger game. Although much of this development centers on revolver cartridges, fans of the semi-automatic pistol can find a new level of power in the 50 Action Express cartridge.

The 50 Action Express began as an experimental cartridge developed by Evan Whildin of Action Arms, Ltd. Working with Israeli Military Industries (IMI), he used the massive Desert Eagle gas-operated pistol as the design platform. The 50 Action Express is a true rebated-rim case—the rim is the same diameter as a 44 Magnum but the case body is large enough to accept a .500" diameter bullet. The result is a powerful, flat shooting cartridge for semi-auto pistol enthusiasts. Engineers at CCI-Speer worked with IMI to bring the 50 Action Express cartridge to the market as a commercial cartridge in 1991.

Recoil is impressive but tolerable for the experienced magnum handgun shooter. The heavy pistol's broad grip helps spread the "felt" recoil and the gas system helps to soften the blow. The pistol twists upward noticeably but can be controlled with practice. Prototype pistols and ammunition used a .510" bullet. However, production pistols require a .500" diameter bullet. Do not attempt to use the larger diameter bullets in production pistols, as excessive pressures will result.

Factory ammunition is available in the Speer Gold Dot line, loaded with a 300-grain Gold Dot hollow point at 1550 ft/sec and a 325-grain Uni-Cor hollow point bullet at 1400 ft/sec (6-inch test barrel). At 100 yards the 50 Action Express has almost as much retained energy as the typical 44 Magnum revolver has at the muzzle.

Several other 50 Action Express pistols were introduced in 1993. LAR and AMT produced semi-auto pistols based on the Browning design, and Freedom Arms manufactures its large, single-action revolver in 50 Action Express.

Reloaders can choose among three bullets: a 300-grain Gold Dot® for lighter game, a 300-grain TMJ® for economical practice, and a 325-grain Uni-Cor hollow point for large game. All require taper-crimping for reliable headspace control. The new 350-grain Uni-Cor® soft point is profiled for the 500 S&W and is not suitable for the 50 Action Express.

In 1998, RCBS developed a mould for a 340-grain cast revolver bullet. Lead bullets should not be used in the Desert Eagle because lead and bullet lube residue can clog the gas system. We used a Freedom Arms revolver to test this bullet. Revolver velocities are also shown for the 325-grain jacketed bullet. Loaded with the new cast bullet, a Freedom revolver can handle almost any large game in North America.

The RCBS cast bullet has a shallow, square-profile crimp groove. Applying a heavy taper crimp firmly holds the bullet, yet still leaves enough case mouth exposed for proper headspace control. Lead bullets should be cast from a hard alloy such as linotype to resist the stress of engaging the rifling. We recommend a .500" sizing diameter for the Freedom Arms Revolver; an increase in sizing diameter of only .001" is enough to prevent cartridges from chambering in the FA.

Winchester 296 and Hodgdon H110 powders gave excellent results in both test guns. Do not use magnum primers with the 2400 loads as high pressure will result.

The industry maximum pressure of the 50 Action Express is 35,000 psi.

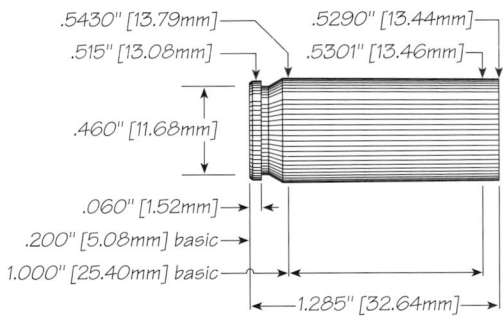

Max. Case Length:	1.286"	**Cart. Case:**	Speer
Trim-to Length:	1.276"	**Primer:**	CCI 300; 250*
Max Cart. OAL:	1.595"	**Test Firearm:**	Magnum Research Desert Eagle
RCBS Shell Holder:	#33	**Barrel Length:**	6"

50 Action Express

0.500"	50 AE TMJ FN	50 AE GDHP
Weight, grains	300	300
Ballistic Coefficient	0.157	0.155
Sectional Density	0.171	0.171
COAL Tested:	1.580"	1.580"
Speer Part No.	4490	4493

Propellant	START CHARGE		MAXIMUM CHARGE	
	Weight, grs	Muzzle Velocity, ft/sec	Weight, grs	Muzzle Velocity, ft/sec
296*	33.5	1466	34.5	1567
H110*	33.5	1482	34.5	1510
Viht. N110	28.0	1418	29.0	1501
2400	28.0	1368	29.0	1435
AA No. 9*	25.0	1343	26.0	1380
IMR 4227*	31.5	1266	32.5	1303

0.500"	50 AE UCHP
Weight, grains	325
Ballistic Coefficient	0.169
Sectional Density	0.186
COAL Tested:	1.575"
Speer Part No.	4495

Propellant	START CHARGE		MAXIMUM CHARGE	
	Weight, grs	Muzzle Velocity, ft/sec	Weight, grs	Muzzle Velocity, ft/sec
H110*	29.4	1298	32.6	1437
296*	29.5	1279	32.7	1409
2400	26.0	1259	28.0	1377
Viht. N110	25.0	1229	27.0	1376
AA 1680*	34.0	1155	37.8C	1305
IMR 4227*	29.5	1224	31.1	1289
AA No. 9*	22.6	1157	23.8	1247

0.500"	50 AE TMJ FN	50 AE GDHP
Weight, grains	300	300
Ballistic Coefficient	0.157	0.155
Sectional Density	0.171	0.171
COAL Tested:	1.580"	1.580"
Speer Part No.	4490	4493

| Propellant | START CHARGE | | MAXIMUM CHARGE | |
	Weight, grs	Muzzle Velocity, ft/sec	Weight, grs	Muzzle Velocity, ft/sec
296*	33.5	1465	34.5	1526
Viht. N110	28.0	1445	29.0	1509
H110*	33.5	1448	34.5	1505
2400	28.0	1435	29.0	1483
AA No. 7	21.5	1282	23.5	1437
AA No. 9*	25.0	1404	26.0	1426
IMR 4227*	31.5	1284	32.5	1334

NOTE: *REVOLVER VELOCITIES: Freedom Arms M555 7.5"*

---

*Maximum Loads should be used with CAUTION • C = Compressed Load • *Magnum Primer used with this powder.*

0.500"	50 AE UCHP
Weight, grains	325
Ballistic Coefficient	0.169
Sectional Density	0.186
COAL Tested:	1.575"
Speer Part No.	4495

Propellant	START CHARGE		MAXIMUM CHARGE	
	Weight, grs	Muzzle Velocity, ft/sec	Weight, grs	Muzzle Velocity, ft/sec
H110*	29.4	1324	32.6	1475
296*	29.5	1321	32.7	1461
2400	26.0	1345	28.0	1461
Viht. N110	25.0	1283	27.0	1444
AA 1680*	34.0	1243	37.8C	1374
IMR 4227*	29.5	1256	31.1	1344
AA No. 9*	22.6	1270	23.8	1318

NOTE: *REVOLVER VELOCITIES: Freedom Arms M555 7.5"*

0.500"	50-340 SWC
Weight, grains	340
Lead Alloy	hard
Ballistic Coefficient	0.147
Sectional Density	0.194
COAL Tested:	1.595"
RCBS Mould No.	82087

| Propellant | START CHARGE | | MAXIMUM CHARGE | |
	Weight, grs	Muzzle Velocity, ft/sec	Weight, grs	Muzzle Velocity, ft/sec
296*	29.0	1412	31.0C	1498
2400	24.0	1333	26.0C	1453
Viht. N110	23.0	1311	25.0	1446
H110*	28.0	1372	30.0C	1445
IMR 4227*	26.5	1230	28.5C	1319
AA 1680*	31.5	1223	33.5C	1318

NOTE: *We sell bullet moulds, not cast bullets. These bullets were cast in RCBS moulds. Contact your dealer for more information on the RCBS line of premium bullet casting equipment, or visit on the Internet at www.rcbs.com. REVOLVER VELOCITIES: Freedom Arms M555 7.5"*

*Maximum Loads should be used with CAUTION • C = Compressed Load • *Magnum Primer used with this powder.*

500 S&W Magnum

The 500 Smith & Wesson Magnum is a massive handgun cartridge that required Smith & Wesson to create a completely new handgun in 2003—the X-frame revolver. Bullet diameter is the same as the 50 Action Express at 0.500-inch but the case is not directly derived from the older 50 Action Express case. The 500 S&W case body is a true cylinder, not the straight taper of the 50 Action Express. It's also a third of an inch longer at 1.625-inch. The cartridge case alone is longer than the maximum loaded length of the 44 Magnum.

Although the 500 S&W shares the bullet diameter of the 50 Action Express, Speer 50 Action Express bullets should never be used for maximum pressure loads. The jacket design of 50 Action Express bullets was tuned to the maximum pressure of the 50 Action Express—36,000 psi. The maximum pressure for the 500 is nearly double. The Speer 350-grain Uni-Cor® soft point has a heavier jacket rated for 500 S&W pressure levels. Thin-jacketed 50 Action Express bullets at full 500 S&W pressures can cause premature erosion to the revolver's forcing cone and topstrap.

Early 500 S&W cases used large pistol primers, but today nearly all are fitted with pockets for large rifle primers. There is a difference in pocket depth so, should you find that rifle primers refuse to seat below flush, you probably have older cases. We recommend you replace those with new cases fitted with rifle primer pockets. When reloading any high-recoil cartridge, proper and accurate primer seating is mandatory for safety. We recommend that primers 0.003 to 0.005 inch below flush with the case head. The wise 500 S&W reloader will clean primer pockets after every firing. Excessive primer residue in the pocket can cause high primers. We used Federal 215 Magnum rifle primers for load development. The large case leaves airspace with some propellants, and the magnum primer helped maintain uniform performance. CCI 250 Magnum primers can be safely substituted for the Federal 215 in this cartridge.

In spite of its large case capacity, the 500 S&W turns in the best velocities with traditional, slow-burning handgun propellants. Hodgdon Lil' Gun used most of the case volume, eliminating serious airspace issues, and produced very high velocities. The velocities from the 8-3/8-inch test revolver averaged 220 ft/sec less than those recorded from the unvented 10-inch pressure barrel.

Case capacity—too much of it—limits what you can do with very light practice loads with jacketed bullets. Lighter 50 Action Express bullets, even when loaded to lower pressures, did not give consistent loads in such a large case and the bullets lack the crimping cannelure required for this cartridge. For reasonable practice loads, we recommend you consider the starting load we show for Alliant Power Pistol propellant. It will still kick but will be much more tolerable than the top loads listed.

The industry maximum average pressure for the 500 S&W is 60,000 psi. However, factory ammo and most published handloads are held somewhat below this to permit reliable extraction of fired cases from double-action revolvers. The loads here gave no extraction problems in our test revolver. Should you experience extraction problems, try a different brand of case or reduce loads by one grain. Most propellants have a rapid pressure drop-off in this case; we recommend that you observe the start charge weights carefully and not load lighter with this bullet.

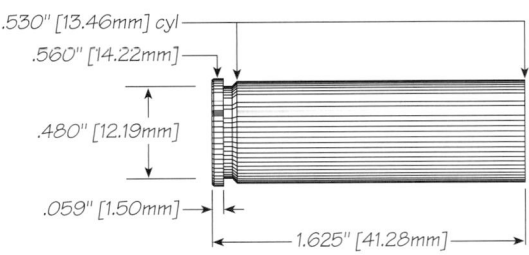

Max. Case Length:	1.625"	Cart. Case:	Starline
Trim-to Length:	1.615"	Primer:	Federal 215*
Max Cart. OAL:	2.250"	Test Firearm:	Smith & Wesson X-Frame
RCBS Shell Holder:	#44	Barrel Length:	8.875"

0.500"	50 S&W UCSP
Weight, grains	350
Ballistic Coefficient	0.178
Sectional Density	0.200
COAL Tested:	2.250"
Speer Part No.	4491

Propellant	START CHARGE		MAXIMUM CHARGE	
	Weight, grs	Muzzle Velocity, ft/sec	Weight, grs	Muzzle Velocity, ft/sec
H. Lil' Gun*	45.0	1667	49.0	1739
Ramshot Enforcer*	40.0	1585	44.0	1673
AA 1680*	49.0	1550	53.0C	1667
Viht. N110	36.0	1534	40.0	1649
AA No. 9*	34.0	1441	38.0	1643
2400*	38.0	1565	42.0	1642
296*	44.0	1585	46.0	1639
H110*	44.0	1598	46.0	1631
IMR 4227*	43.0	1554	45.0C	1608
Power Pistol*	23.0	1446	27.0	1564

*Maximum Loads should be used with CAUTION • C = Compressed Load • *Magnum Primer used with this powder.*

reference **section**

Metric Conversion Tables

Handloaders and shooters constantly make measurements of many kinds in preparing ammunition and in testing the results. They measure cartridges and cartridge cases for length and for possible expansion. They weigh propellant charges and bullets. If they have a chronograph, they measure velocities. They need to know distances to the target and measure group sizes.

These measurements can be made in either "English" units (the system most commonly used in the United States) or the metric system. The metric system was conceived as a measurement system to the base 10. The units of the system, their multiples, and submultiples are related to each other by simple factors of 10. This conforms to our common system of numerals that is a "base-10" system. Changing metric units, e.g., grams to kilograms involves only multiplying or dividing by tens. You simply move the decimal point the correct number of places. Changing English units means memorizing individual conversion units (12 inches to the foot; three feet to the yard, etc.)

The United States is the only industrialized country in the world not using the metric system of weights and measures. The rest of the world is committed to the metric system. The following tables give conversion guidelines for most of the common units of measure you may encounter in your shooting and reloading activities.

With the explosion of resources on the Internet, it's often faster to use Web-based conversion calculators. Open your favorite search engine and search for "conversion calculator" or "conversion units." You will be presented with a wealth of choices. Try several and, if you find one you like, bookmark it for future reference.

Length

Multiply...	by...	to get...
inches	2.540	centimeters
inches	25.40	millimeters
feet	30.48	centimeters
feet	0.3048	meters
yards	0.9144	meters
millimeters	0.03937	inches
centimeters	0.3937	inches
centimeters	0.01	meters
centimeters	10	millimeters
meters	100	centimeters
meters	3.281	feet
meters	1.094	yards
meters	39.37	inches
kilometers	3281	feet
kilometers	1094	yards
kilometers	0.6214	miles
miles	1609	meters
miles	1.609	kilometers

Velocity

Multiply...	by...	to get...
feet per second	0.3048	meters per second
feet per second	0.6818	miles per hour
meters per second	3.281	feet per second
kilometers per hour	0.6214	miles per hour
miles per hour	1.467	feet per second
miles per hour	1.609	kilometers per hour

Weight

Multiply...	by...	to get...
grains (troy)	1	grains (avoirdupois)
grains	64.8	milligrams
grains	0.0648	grams
grains	0.002286	ounces
grams	15.43	grains
grams	0.03527	ounces
ounces	437.5	grains
ounces	0.0625	pounds (avoirdupois)
ounces	28.35	grams
pounds	7000	grains
pounds	16	ounces

Weight

Multiply...	by...	to get...
pounds	453.6	grams
pounds	0.4536	kilograms
kilograms	1000	grams
kilograms	2.205	pounds (avoirdupois)
tons	907.2	kilograms
metric tons	2205	pounds

Volume

Multiply...	by...	to get...
cubic inches	16.39	cubic centimeters
cubic centimeters	0.0610	cubic inches
liters	1000	milliliters or cubic centimeters
liters	0.2642	gallons
liters	1.057	quarts
gallons	3.785	liters
quarts	0.9463	liters

Area

Multiply...	by...	to get...
square inches	6.452	square centimeters
square centimeters	0.1550	square inches

Energy

Multiply...	by...	to get...
foot-pounds	0.1383	kilogram meters
kilogram meters	7.233	foot pounds
foot-pounds	1.3558	joules
joules	0.7375	foot pounds

Pressure

Multiply...	by...	to get...
atmospheres	14.70	pounds per square inch
bars	14.504	pounds per square inch
pounds per square inch	0.0689	bars
pounds per square inch	0.07032	kilograms per square centimeter
kilograms per square centimeter	14.23	pounds per square inch

Temperature

The United States uses the Fahrenheit (F) scale to measure temperature. Most other countries and nearly all science disciplines use the Celsius (C) scale. The Celsius scale sets the freezing point of water as 0°C and the boiling point of water as 100°C.

- To convert degrees Celsius (C°) to degrees Fahrenheit (F°):

$$F° = (9/5)\ C° + 32$$

- To convert degrees Fahrenheit (F°) to degress Celsius (C°)

$$C° = (F° - 32)\ x\ (5/9)$$

trajectory **tables**

Speer® Ballistic Tables Introduction

If you have not yet read chapter 12, please do so. There we discuss exterior ballistics in detail and the information gives you some technical background to better understand the use of the tables that follow. These tables are calculated to give trajectory information about a bullet at different velocities. They allow you to learn about the path of your loads without access to a computer.

Using the Tables

First of all, find the ballistic coefficient (BC) of the bullet you are using. The BC is listed just under the bullet pictures in the loading data. These are the BC values for Speer® bullets. If you choose a bullet other than Speer, the BC will likely be different. Contact that bullet maker for BC information.

Next, decide if you need path information for short-range (0 to 250 yards) or long-range (0 to 500 yards) situations. Speer has two sets of tables corresponding to these categories. The table type, either short or long-range, is printed at the top of each page of tables. Short-range tables are listed first. Now determine the muzzle velocity either from the loading data or from your own chronograph testing.

Here is an example problem: You are using Speer's .284" 160-grain Hot-Cor spitzer bullet with a muzzle velocity of 2734 ft/sec. In the chart above the data, you find that the BC of this bullet is 0.504. Remember that the velocities shown in the data were measured in temperatures between 68° and 72° F. If you want path information in this temperature range, you can skip the next step. However, if you wish to see the effect on the path of a different temperature, refer to the chart at the end of this section. It is labeled "Variation of Muzzle Velocity with Temperature."

In that chart, look under the 70° column and note that there is an entry of 2722 ft/sec in the top row. To get an estimate of muzzle velocity at another temperature, scan across the row containing 2722 to the desired new temperature. At 0° F, the load that clocked 2722 will be down to 2631, a loss of 91 ft/sec. For our example, we would use 2734 − 91, or 2643 ft/sec as a working muzzle velocity at 0° F. Because velocity variation with temperature also depends on other factors such as powder burning rate, these values are approximate and rounding to 2600 won't significantly affect the accuracy of the results.

With a working velocity in hand you can find the path of your load. Let's say you want the rifle sighted for 300 yards. Go to the Long-range Tables and find the one for BC = .500. Within that table are a number of blocks, each corresponding to a velocity increment of 100 ft/sec. Let's use the 70° velocity of 2734 ft/sec. This is very close to 2700. Scan for the block within the "BC = .500" table that shows a velocity of 2700 ft/sec. For this bullet it's the seventh section from the top. Go to the right and find the remaining velocity at 300 yards, 2178 ft/sec. The lower part of this section is labeled "Path (inches)" and "Zero Range." We are zeroing at 300 yards, so we see the value 0.0 where the 300-yard range column meets the row for a 300 yard zero. To find the path at 100, 200, 400 and 500 yards, scan across the 300-yard row. You can also scan right and left in other rows to find the velocity and time-of-flight (TOF) at the same ranges.

These tables assume you have a scope-sighted firearm with the center of the scope 1.5 inches over the center of the bore. That's why the path point at the muzzle is -1.5 inches at the muzzle. Now you have the path plus other data about this load over typical hunting ranges.

There is yet another useful piece of information to be gleaned. The tables let you calculate the remaining energy at any of the above ranges. Find the row, "Energy, ft/lbs per grain" in the same section. Go across to the 300-yard range column and find the number "10.53." This means a one-grain bullet with a remaining velocity of 2178 ft/sec would have an energy of 10.53 ft/lbs. Our example uses a 160-grain bullet, so multiplying 10.53 by 160 gives our bullet a remaining energy of 1684.8 ft/lbs at 300 yards.

With a little practice you'll soon find these tables to be a useful tool for making you a more confident shooter. If you're a "computer shooter," consider picking up a copy of RCBS.LOAD® ballistic and reloading software. It uses computer power to display greatly expanded bullet path information that we cannot show in these space-constrained tables. Chapter 12 has information on this fine product.

Velocity Variation with Temperature

The following data was not obtained from high velocity firing tests of rifle cartridges but rather were calculated to roughly indicate what may be generally expected from progressive burning smokeless powder with normal density. They are in approximate agreement with scattered and meager data available for rifle cartridges. Cartridges with very high loading density and high chamber pressures may vary quite considerably with temperature changes from the values shown below. Remember that even carefully loaded cartridges fired at constant temperature may show variations in muzzle velocities from 10 to 80 ft/sec from one shot to the next. This table will help you approximate the direction and approximate amount of velocity change with temperature.

Computer owners may find that modern ballistics software like RCBS.LOAD may give better temperature correction numbers. This table is included to help those without a computer.

0°	10°	20°	30°	40°	50°	60°	70°	80°	90°	100°
2631	2641	2648	2657	2668	2682	2700	2722	2750	2784	2827
2733	2738	2746	2755	2767	2782	2800	2823	2851	2887	2931
2830	2836	2846	2854	2866	2881	2900	2924	2953	2990	3036
2928	2934	2942	2952	2965	2981	3000	3025	3055	3093	3141
3025	3032	3040	3051	3064	3080	3100	3125	3157	3196	3246
3127	3130	3138	3149	3163	3179	3200	3226	3258	3299	3350
3221	3228	3236	3248	3261	3279	3300	3327	3360	3402	3453
3318	3325	3334	3346	3360	3378	3400	3428	3462	3505	3560
3416	3423	3433	3444	3459	3477	3500	3529	3564	3608	3664
3514	3521	3531	3543	3558	3577	3600	3629	3666	3711	3769
3611	3619	3629	3641	3657	3676	3700	3730	3768	3814	3874
3709	3717	3727	3740	3756	3775	3800	3831	3870	3918	3978
3806	3814	3825	3838	3854	3875	3900	3932	3971	4021	4083
3904	3912	3923	3936	3953	3974	4000	4033	4073	4124	4188
4001	4010	4021	4035	4052	4073	4100	4133	4173	4227	4292
4099	4108	4119	4133	4151	4173	4200	4234	4277	4330	4398

short range tables

Exterior Ballistic Table for Ballistic Coefficient 0.12

		Muzzle	50 yds	100 yds	150 yds	200 yds	250 yds
Velocity, ft/sec		2900	2515	2161	1837	1549	1307
Energy, ft/lbs per grain		18.67	14.04	10.37	7.49	5.33	3.79
Time of Flight, sec		0.0000	0.0556	0.1199	0.1952	0.2842	0.3898
Path, inches Relative to Line of Sight	50 yds	-1.5	0.0	0.1	-1.7	-6.0	-14.0
ZERO RANGE	100 yds	-1.5	-0.1	0.0	-1.8	-6.2	-14.3
	150 yds	-1.5	0.6	1.2	0.0	-3.8	-11.3
Velocity, ft/sec		2800	2423	2077	1761	1483	1255
Energy, ft/lbs per grain		17.41	13.03	9.58	6.88	4.88	3.50
Time of Flight, sec		0.0000	0.0576	0.1245	0.2029	0.2958	0.4060
Path, inches Relative to Line of Sight	50 yds	-1.5	0.0	0.0	-2.0	-6.9	-15.7
ZERO RANGE	100 yds	-1.5	0.0	0.0	-2.0	-6.9	-15.7
	150 yds	-1.5	0.7	1.4	0.0	-4.2	-12.4
Velocity, ft/sec		2700	2331	1992	1686	1419	1206
Energy, ft/lbs per grain		16.18	12.06	8.81	6.31	4.47	3.23
Time of Flight, sec		0.0000	0.0598	0.1294	0.2113	0.3084	0.4234
Path, inches Relative to Line of Sight	50 yds	-1.5	0.0	-0.1	-2.4	-7.9	-17.6
ZERO RANGE	100 yds	-1.5	0.1	0.0	-2.3	-7.6	-17.3
	150 yds	-1.5	0.8	1.5	0.0	-4.6	-13.6
Velocity, ft/sec		2600	2239	1908	1611	1357	1161
Energy, ft/lbs per grain		15.01	11.13	8.08	5.76	4.09	2.99
Time of Flight, sec		0.0000	0.0622	0.1348	0.2204	0.3219	0.4419
Path, inches. Relative to Line of Sight	50 yds	-1.5	0.0	-0.2	-2.9	-9.0	-19.7
ZERO RANGE	100 yds	-1.5	0.1	0.0	-2.5	-8.5	-19.1
	150 yds	-1.5	1.0	1.7	0.0	-5.1	-14.9
Velocity, ft/sec		2500	2147	1825	1538	1298	1121
Energy, ft/lbs per grain		13.88	10.23	7.39	5.25	3.74	2.79
Time of Flight, sec		0.0000	0.0647	0.1406	0.2302	0.3365	0.4614
Path, inches Relative to Line of Sight	50 yds	-1.5	0.0	-0.4	-3.4	-10.2	-22.1
ZERO RANGE	100 yds	-1.5	0.2	0.0	-2.8	-9.4	-21.1
	150 yds	-1.5	1.1	1.9	0.0	-5.6	-16.4
Velocity, ft/sec		2400	2055	1742	1467	1242	1084
Energy, ft/lbs per grain		12.79	9.38	6.74	4.78	3.42	2.61
Time of Flight, sec		0.0000	0.0675	0.1469	0.2408	0.3522	0.4820
Path, inches Relative to Line of Sight	50 yds	-1.5	0.0	-0.6	-4.0	-11.6	-24.8
ZERO RANGE	100 yds	-1.5	0.3	0.0	-3.2	-10.4	-23.3
	150 yds	-1.5	1.4	2.1	0.0	-6.2	-18.0
Velocity, ft/sec		2300	1964	1660	1398	1190	1052
Energy, ft/lbs per grain		11.74	8.56	6.12	4.34	3.14	2.46
Time of Flight, sec		0.0000	0.0706	0.1537	0.2523	0.3689	0.5036
Path, inches Relative to Line of Sight	50 yds	-1.5	0.0	-0.8	-4.7	-13.2	-27.8
ZERO RANGE	100 yds	-1.5	0.4	0.0	-3.6	-11.6	-25.8
	150 yds	-1.5	1.6	2.4	0.0	-6.9	-19.9
Velocity, ft/sec		2200	1873	1580	1332	1144	1022
Energy, ft/lbs per grain		10.75	7.79	5.54	3.94	2.91	2.32
Time of Flight, sec		0.0000	0.0739	0.1612	0.2648	0.3868	0.5261
Path, inches Relative to Line of Sight	50 yds	-1.5	0.0	-1.0	-5.5	-15.0	-31.1
ZERO RANGE	100 yds	-1.5	0.5	0.0	-4.0	-13.0	-28.5
	150 yds	-1.5	1.8	2.7	0.0	-7.6	-21.8

Exterior Ballistic Table for Ballistic Coefficient 0.12

	Muzzle	50 yds	100 yds	150 yds	200 yds	250 yds
			RANGE			
Velocity, ft/sec	2100	1782	1502	1269	1102	995
Energy, ft/lbs per grain	9.79	7.05	5.01	3.58	2.70	2.20
Time of Flight, sec	0.0000	0.0776	0.1693	0.2783	0.4057	0.5494
Path, inches — ZERO RANGE 50 yds	-1.5	0.0	-1.3	-6.4	-17.0	-34.7
Relative to — ZERO RANGE 100 yds	-1.5	0.6	0.0	-4.5	-11.5	-31.5
Line of Sight — ZERO RANGE 150 yds	-1.5	2.1	3.0	0.0	-8.4	-24.0
Velocity, ft/sec	2000	1693	1425	1210	1064	970
Energy, ft/lbs per grain	8.88	6.36	4.51	3.25	2.51	2.09
Time of Flight, sec	0.0000	0.0816	0.1783	0.2928	0.4255	0.5736
Path, inches — ZERO RANGE 50 yds	-1.5	0.0	-1.6	-7.4	-19.3	-38.7
Relative to — ZERO RANGE 100 yds	-1.5	0.8	0.0	-5.1	-16.1	-34.8
Line of Sight — ZERO RANGE 150 yds	-1.5	2.5	3.4	0.0	-9.3	-26.3
Velocity, ft/sec	1900	1604	1351	1157	1031	947
Energy, ft/lbs per grain	8.01	5.71	4.05	2.97	2.36	1.99
Time of Flight, sec	0.0000	0.0860	0.1880	0.3084	0.4463	0.5985
Path, inches — ZERO RANGE 50 yds	-1.5	0.0	-1.9	-8.6	-21.8	-43.1
Relative to — ZERO RANGE 100 yds	-1.5	1.0	0.0	-5.7	-18.0	-38.4
Line of Sight — ZERO RANGE 150 yds	-1.5	2.9	3.8	0.0	-10.3	-28.8
Velocity, ft/sec	1800	1517	1281	1110	1000	925
Energy, ft/lbs per grain	7.19	5.11	3.64	2.74	2.22	1.90
Time of Flight, sec	0.0000	0.0909	0.1987	0.3250	0.4679	0.6241
Path, inches — ZERO RANGE 50 yds	-1.5	0.0	-2.3	-9.9	-24.6	-48.0
Relative to — ZERO RANGE 100 yds	-1.5	1.2	0.0	-6.5	-20.0	-42.2
Line of Sight — ZERO RANGE 150 yds	-1.5	3.3	4.3	0.0	-11.4	-31.4
Velocity, ft/sec	1700	1431	1215	1067	972	903
Energy, ft/lbs per grain	6.42	4.55	3.28	2.53	2.10	1.81
Time of Flight, sec	0.0000	0.0963	0.2103	0.3426	0.4903	0.6506
Path, inches — ZERO RANGE 50 yds	-1.5	0.0	-2.8	-11.4	-27.7	-53.2
Relative to — ZERO RANGE 100 yds	-1.5	1.4	0.0	-7.3	-22.2	-46.2
Line of Sight — ZERO RANGE 150 yds	-1.5	3.8	4.9	0.0	-12.5	-34.1
Velocity, ft/sec	1600	1348	1155	1029	946	883
Energy, ft/lbs per grain	5.68	4.03	2.96	2.35	1.99	1.73
Time of Flight, sec	0.0000	0.1023	0.2230	0.3611	0.5135	0.6778
Path, inches — ZERO RANGE 50 yds	-1.5	0.0	-3.3	-13.1	-31.1	-58.9
Relative to — ZERO RANGE 100 yds	-1.5	1.7	0.0	-8.2	-24.5	-50.6
Line of Sight — ZERO RANGE 150 yds	-1.5	4.4	5.4	0.0	-13.6	-37.0
Velocity, ft/sec	1500	1268	1101	995	921	862
Energy, ft/lbs per grain	5.00	3.57	2.69	2.20	1.88	1.65
Time of Flight, sec	0.0000	0.1090	0.2365	0.3804	0.5374	0.7060
Path, inches — ZERO RANGE 50 yds	-1.5	0.0	-3.9	-15.0	-34.9	-65.0
Relative to — ZERO RANGE 100 yds	-1.5	2.0	0.0	-9.1	-27.0	-55.2
Line of Sight — ZERO RANGE 150 yds	-1.5	5.0	6.1	0.0	-14.9	-40.0
Velocity, ft/sec	1400	1192	1053	962	896	641
Energy, ft/lbs per grain	4.35	3.15	2.46	2.05	1.78	1.57
Time of Flight, sec	0.0000	0.1165	0.2510	0.4004	0.5622	0.7352
Path, inches — ZERO RANGE 50 yds	-1.5	0.0	-4.6	-17.1	-38.9	-71.5
Relative to — ZERO RANGE 100 yds	-1.5	2.3	0.0	-10.1	-29.6	-60.0
Line of Sight — ZERO RANGE 150 yds	-1.5	5.7	6.8	0.0	-16.1	-43.1

short range tables

Exterior Ballistic Table for Ballistic Coefficient 0.12

		Muzzle	50 yds	100 yds	150 yds	200 yds	250 yds
Velocity, ft/sec		1300	1122	1008	931	870	819
Energy, ft/lbs per grain		3.75	2.79	2.26	1.92	1.68	1.49
Time of Flight, sec		0.0000	0.1247	0.2662	0.4213	0.5882	0.7660
Path, inches	50 yds	-1.5	0.0	-5.4	-19.3	-43.2	-78.7
Relative to	100 yds	-1.5	2.7	0.0	-11.2	-32.5	-65.2
Line of Sight	150 yds	-1.5	6.4	7.5	0.0	-17.5	-46.5
Velocity, ft/sec		1200	1058	966	898	843	795
Energy, ft/lbs per grain		3.20	2.49	2.07	1.79	1.58	1.40
Time of Flight, sec		0.0000	0.1337	0.2825	0.4438	0.6163	0.7996
Path, inches	50 yds	-1.5	0.0	-6.3	-21.8	-48.1	-86.7
Relative to	100 yds	-1.5	3.1	0.0	-12.4	-35.6	-71.1
Line of Sight	150 yds	-1.5	7.3	8.3	0.0	-19.1	-50.4
Velocity, ft/sec		1100	994	920	861	811	767
Energy, ft/lbs per grain		2.69	2.19	1.88	1.65	1.46	1.31
Time of Flight, sec		0.0000	0.1439	0.3010	0.4697	0.6492	0.8395
Path, inches	50 yds	-1.5	0.0	-7.3	-24.8	-54.1	-96.6
Relative to	100 yds	-1.5	3.6	0.0	-13.9	-39.5	-78.4
Line of Sight	150 yds	-1.5	8.3	9.3	0.0	-21.0	-55.2
Velocity, ft/sec		1000	925	865	815	770	729
Energy, ft/lbs per grain		2.22	1.90	1.66	1.47	1.32	1.18
Time of Flight, sec		0.0000	0.1563	0.3242	0.5029	0.6925	0.8928
Path, inches	50 yds	-1.5	0.0	-8.7	-28.9	-62.3	-110.4
Relative to	100 yds	-1.5	4.3	0.0	-15.9	-45.0	-88.7
Line of Sight	150 yds	-1.5	9.6	10.6	0.0	-23.7	-62.1

(ZERO RANGE applies to Path rows: 50 yds, 100 yds, 150 yds)

Exterior Ballistic Table for Ballistic Coefficient 0.13

		Muzzle	50 yds	100 yds	150 yds	200 yds	250 yds
Velocity, ft/sec		2900	2543	2213	1909	1633	1394
Energy, ft/lbs per grain		18.67	14.36	10.87	8.09	5.92	4.31
Time of Flight, sec		0.0000	0.0552	0.1185	0.1914	0.2764	0.3760
Path, inches	50 yds	-1.5	0.0	0.1	-1.5	-5.5	-12.9
Relative to	100 yds	-1.5	0.1	0.0	-1.7	-5.8	-13.2
Line of Sight	150 yds	-1.5	0.5	1.1	0.0	-3.5	-10.4
Velocity, ft/sec		2800	2451	2128	1831	1564	1336
Energy, ft/lbs per grain		17.41	13.34	10.05	7.44	5.43	3.96
Time of Flight, sec		0.0000	0.0573	0.1230	0.1990	0.2877	0.3916
Path, inches	50 yds	-1.5	0.0	0.0	-1.8	-6.4	-14.4
Relative to	100 yds	-1.5	0.0	0.0	-1.9	-6.4	-14.6
Line of Sight	150 yds	-1.5	0.6	1.3	0.0	-3.9	11.4
Velocity, ft/sec		2700	2359	2042	1753	1496	1281
Energy, ft/lbs per grain		16.18	12.35	9.26	6.82	4.97	3.64
Time of Flight, sec		0.0000	0.0594	0.1278	0.2071	0.2998	0.4084
Path, inches	50 yds	-1.5	0.0	0.1	-2.2	-7.3	16.2
Relative to	100 yds	-1.5	0.0	0.0	-2.1	-7.1	16.0
Line of Sight	150 yds	-1.5	0.7	1.4	0.0	-4.3	-12.5

(ZERO RANGE applies to Path rows: 50 yds, 100 yds, 150 yds)

short range tables

Exterior Ballistic Table for Ballistic Coefficient 0.13

	Muzzle	50 yds	100 yds	150 yds	200 yds	250 yds
			RANGE			
Velocity, ft/sec	2600	2266	1957	1676	1430	1229
Energy, ft/lbs per grain	15.01	11.40	8.50	6.24	4.54	3.35
Time of Flight, sec	0.0000	0.0618	0.1330	0.2159	0.3129	0.4263
Path, inches — ZERO RANGE 50 yds	-1.5	0.0	-0.2	-2.7	-8.3	-18.2
Relative to — ZERO RANGE 100 yds	-1.5	0.1	0.0	-2.4	-7.9	-17.7
Line of Sight — ZERO RANGE 150 yds	-1.5	0.9	1.6	0.0	-4.7	-13.7
Velocity, ft/sec	2500	2173	1872	1601	1366	1180
Energy, ft/lbs per grain	13.88	10.48	7.78	5.69	4.14	3.09
Time of Flight, sec	0.0000	0.0644	0.1387	0.2254	0.3270	0.4455
Path, inches — ZERO RANGE 50 yds	-1.5	0.0	-0.4	-3.2	-9.5	-20.4
Relative to — ZERO RANGE 100 yds	-1.5	0.2	0.0	-2.7	-8.8	-19.6
Line of Sight — ZERO RANGE 150 yds	-1.5	1.1	1.8	0.0	-5.2	-15.1
Velocity, ft/sec	2400	2081	1788	1527	1305	1137
Energy, ft/lbs per grain	12.79	9.61	7.10	5.18	3.78	2.87
Time of Flight, sec	0.0000	0.0671	0.1449	0.2358	0.3422	0.4658
Path, inches — ZERO RANGE 50 yds	-1.5	0.0	-0.5	-3.8	-10.8	-23.0
Relative to — ZERO RANGE 100 yds	-1.5	0.3	0.0	-3.0	-9.8	-21.7
Line of Sight — ZERO RANGE 150 yds	-1.5	1.3	2.0	0.0	-5.8	-16.6
Velocity, ft/sec	2300	1988	1704	1454	1247	1097
Energy, ft/lbs per grain	11.74	8.77	6.45	4.69	3.45	2.67
Time of Flight, sec	0.0000	0.0701	0.1517	0.2470	0.3586	0.4873
Path, inches — ZERO RANGE 50 yds	-1.5	0.0	-0.7	-4.5	-12.3	-25.8
Relative to — ZERO RANGE 100 yds	-1.5	0.4	0.0	-3.4	-10.9	-24.0
Line of Sight — ZERO RANGE 150 yds	-1.5	1.5	2.3	0.0	-6.4	-18.4
Velocity, ft/sec	2200	1897	1622	1384	1194	1062
Energy, ft/lbs per grain	10.75	7.99	5.84	4.25	3.17	2.50
Time of Flight, sec	0.0000	0.0734	0.1590	0.2592	0.3762	0.5099
Path, inches — ZERO RANGE 50 yds	-1.5	0.0	-0.9	-5.2	-14.0	-29.0
Relative to — ZERO RANGE 100 yds	-1.5	0.5	0.0	-3.8	-12.2	-26.6
Line of Sight — ZERO RANGE 150 yds	-1.5	1.7	2.5	0.0	-7.1	-20.3
Velocity, ft/sec	2100	1805	1542	1317	1145	1031
Energy, ft/lbs per grain	9.79	7.23	5.28	3.85	2.91	2.36
Time of Flight, sec	0.0000	0.0771	0.1670	0.2724	0.3949	0.5335
Path, inches — ZERO RANGE 50 yds	-1.5	0.0	-1.2	-6.1	-16.0	-32.5
Relative to — ZERO RANGE 100 yds	-1.5	0.6	0.0	-4.3	-13.6	-29.5
Line of Sight — ZERO RANGE 150 yds	-1.5	2.0	2.9	0.0	-7.9	-22.4
Velocity, ft/sec	2000	1715	1463	1254	1102	1002
Energy, ft/lbs per grain	8.88	6.53	4.75	3.49	2.70	2.23
Time of Flight, sec	0.0000	0.0810	0.1758	0.2868	0.4148	0.5580
Path, inches — ZERO RANGE 50 yds	-1.5	0.0	-1.5	-7.1	-18.2	-36.4
Relative to — ZERO RANGE 100 yds	-1.5	0.7	0.0	-4.8	-15.2	-32.7
Line of Sight — ZERO RANGE 150 yds	-1.5	2.4	3.2	0.0	-8.8	-24.7
Velocity, ft/sec	1900	1625	1387	1196	1064	976
Energy, ft/lbs per grain	8.01	5.86	4.27	3.18	2.51	2.11
Time of Flight, sec	0.0000	0.0854	0.1854	0.3022	0.4357	0.5833
Path, inches — ZERO RANGE 50 yds	-1.5	0.0	-1.8	-8.2	-20.6	-40.7
Relative to — ZERO RANGE 100 yds	-1.5	0.9	0.0	-5.5	-17.0	-36.2
Line of Sight — ZERO RANGE 150 yds	-1.5	2.7	3.6	0.0	-9.7	-27.1

Exterior Ballistic Table for Ballistic Coefficient 0.13

	Muzzle	50 yds	100 yds	150 yds	200 yds	250 yds
Velocity, ft/sec	1800	1537	1314	1143	1029	951
Energy, ft/lbs per grain	7.19	5.24	3.83	2.90	2.35	2.01
Time of Flight, sec	0.0000	0.0902	0.1960	0.3188	0.4576	0.6095
Path, inches — Zero Range 50 yds	-1.5	0.0	-2.2	-9.5	-23.4	-45.5
Relative to — Zero Range 100 yds	-1.5	1.1	0.0	-6.2	-19.0	-40.0
Line of Sight — Zero Range 150 yds	-1.5	3.2	4.1	0.0	-10.8	-29.7
Velocity, ft/sec	1700	1450	1244	1095	998	928
Energy, ft/lbs per grain	6.42	4.67	3.44	2.66	2.21	1.91
Time of Flight, sec	0.0000	0.0956	0.2075	0.3365	0.4804	0.6365
Path, inches — Zero Range 50 yds	-1.5	0.0	-2.7	-10.9	-26.5	-50.7
Relative to — Zero Range 100 yds	-1.5	1.3	0.0	-7.0	-21.1	-44.0
Line of Sight — Zero Range 150 yds	-1.5	3.6	4.6	0.0	-11.9	-32.4
Velocity, ft/sec	1600	1365	1180	1053	969	905
Energy, ft/lbs per grain	5.68	4.14	3.09	2.46	2.08	1.82
Time of Flight, sec	0.0000	0.1016	0.2201	0.3552	0.5040	0.46644
Path, inches — Zero Range 50 yds	-1.5	0.0	-3.2	-12.6	-29.9	-56.4
Relative to — Zero Range 100 yds	-1.5	1.6	0.0	-7.8	-23.5	-48.4
Line of Sight — Zero Range 150 yds	-1.5	4.2	5.2	0.0	-13.0	-35.3
Velocity, ft/sec	1500	1283	1122	1015	941	883
Energy, ft/lbs per grain	5.00	3.65	2.79	2.29	1.97	1.73
Time of Flight, sec	0.0000	0.1083	0.2338	0.3747	0.5285	0.6932
Path, inches — Zero Range 50 yds	-1.5	0.0	-3.8	-14.5	-33.6	-62.5
Relative to — Zero Range 100 yds	-1.5	1.9	0.0	-8.8	-26.0	-53.0
Line of Sight — Zero Range 150 yds	-1.5	4.8	5.9	0.0	-14.3	-38.4
Velocity, ft/sec	1400	1206	1070	980	914	861
Energy, ft/lbs per grain	4.35	3.23	2.54	2.13	1.85	1.65
Time of Flight, sec	0.0000	0.1158	0.2483	0.3951	0.5538	0.7230
Path, inches — Zero Range 50 yds	-1.5	0.0	-4.5	-16.5	-37.6	-69.1
Relative to — Zero Range 100 yds	-1.5	2.2	0.0	-9.8	-28.7	-57.9
Line of Sight — Zero Range 150 yds	-1.5	5.5	6.5	0.0	-15.6	-41.5
Velocity, ft/sec	1300	1133	1023	947	888	830
Energy, ft/lbs per grain	3.75	2.85	2.32	1.99	1.75	1.56
Time of Flight, sec	0.0000	0.1240	0.2638	0.4165	0.5803	0.7544
Path, inches — Zero Range 50 yds	-1.5	0.0	-5.3	-18.8	-42.0	-76.3
Relative to — Zero Range 100 yds	-1.5	2.6	0.0	-10.9	-31.5	-63.2
Line of Sight — Zero Range 150 yds	-1.5	6.3	7.3	0.0	-17.0	-45.0
Velocity, ft/sec	1200	1066	978	912	859	813
Energy, ft/lbs per grain	3.20	2.52	2.12	1.85	1.64	1.47
Time of Flight, sec	0.0000	0.1331	0.2804	0.4394	0.6089	0.7885
Path, inches — Zero Range 50 yds	-1.5	0.0	-6.1	-21.3	-47.0	-84.4
Relative to — Zero Range 100 yds	-1.5	3.1	0.0	-12.1	-34.7	-69.1
Line of Sight — Zero Range 150 yds	-1.5	7.1	8.1	0.0	-18.5	-48.8
Velocity, ft/sec	1100	1001	930	874	826	784
Energy, ft/lbs per grain	2.69	2.22	1.92	1.70	1.51	1.36
Time of Flight, sec	0.0000	0.1434	0.2991	0.4656	0.6422	0.8288
Path, inches — Zero Range 50 yds	-1.5	0.0	-7.2	-24.4	-52.9	-94.3
Relative to — Zero Range 100 yds	-1.5	3.6	0.0	-13.6	-38.6	-76.4
Line of Sight — Zero Range 150 yds	-1.5	8.1	9.1	0.0	-20.5	-53.7

short range tables

Exterior Ballistic Table for Ballistic Coefficient 0.13

			RANGE			
	Muzzle	50 yds	100 yds	150 yds	200 yds	250 yds
Velocity, ft/sec	1000	930	874	826	783	745
Energy, ft/lbs per grain	2.22	1.92	1.70	1.51	1.36	1.23
Time of Flight, sec	0.0000	0.1558	0.3224	0.4991	0.6858	0.8824
Path, inches ZERO RANGE 50 yds	-1.5	0.0	-8.6	-28.5	-61.2	-108.1
Relative to ZERO RANGE 100 yds	-1.5	4.3	0.0	-15.7	-44.1	-86.7
Line of Sight ZERO RANGE 150 yds	-1.5	9.5	10.4	0.0	-23.2	-60.6

Exterior Ballistic Table for Ballistic Coefficient 0.14

			RANGE			
	Muzzle	50 yds	100 yds	150 yds	200 yds	250 yds
Velocity, ft/sec	2900	2568	2259	1972	1709	1475
Energy, ft/lbs per grain	18.67	14.64	11.33	8.63	6.48	4.83
Time of Flight, sec	0.0000	0.0550	0.1173	0.1883	0.2701	0.3646
Path, inches 50 yds	-1.5	0.0	0.2	-1.4	-5.2	-11.9
Relative to 100 yds	-1.5	-0.1	0.0	-1.6	-5.5	-12.4
Line of Sight 150 yds	-1.5	0.5	1.1	0.0	-3.3	-9.7
Velocity, ft/sec	2800	2475	2173	1892	1637	1412
Energy, ft/lbs per grain	17.41	13.60	10.48	7.95	5.95	4.43
Time of Flight, sec	0.0000	0.0570	0.1217	0.1957	0.2809	0.3797
Path, inches 50 yds	-1.5	0.0	0.1	-1.7	-5.9	-13.4
Relative to 100 yds	-1.5	0.0	0.0	-1.8	-6.1	-13.6
Line of Sight 150 yds	-1.5	0.6	1.2	0.0	-3.7	-10.6
Velocity, ft/sec	2700	2382	2086	1813	1566	1352
Energy, ft/lbs per grain	16.18	12.60	9.66	7.30	5.44	4.06
Time of Flight, sec	0.0000	0.0592	0.1264	0.2030	0.2927	0.3959
Path, inches 50 yds	-1.5	0.0	0.0	-2.1	-6.8	-15.1
Relative to 100 yds	-1.5	0.0	0.0	-2.0	-6.7	-18.0
Line of Sight 150 yds	-1.5	0.7	1.4	0.0	-4.0	-11.6
Velocity, ft/sec	2600	2289	2000	1734	1242	1294
Energy, ft/lbs per grain	15.01	11.63	8.88	6.68	4.98	3.72
Time of Flight, sec	0.0000	0.0615	0.1316	0.2122	0.3054	0.4133
Path, inches 50 yds	-1.5	0.0	0.2	-2.5	-7.8	-17.0
Relative to 100 yds	-1.5	0.1	0.0	-2.3	-7.5	-16.6
Line of Sight 150 yds	-1.5	0.8	1.5	0.0	-4.4	-12.8
Velocity, ft/sec	2500	2196	1913	1656	1429	1240
Energy, ft/lbs per grain	13.88	10.71	8.12	6.09	4.53	3.41
Time of Flight, sec	0.0000	0.0640	0.1372	0.2215	0.3191	0.4320
Path, inches 50 yds	-1.5	0.0	-0.3	-3.0	-8.9	-19.1
Relative to 100 yds	-1.5	0.2	0.0	-2.5	-8.3	-18.3
Line of Sight 150 yds	-1.5	1.0	1.7	0.0	-4.9	-14.1
Velocity, ft/sec	2400	2103	1828	1580	1363	1190
Energy, ft/lbs per grain	12.79	9.82	7.42	5.54	4.12	3.14
Time of Flight, sec	0.0000	0.0668	0.1433	0.2316	0.3340	0.4520
Path, inches 50 yds	-1.5	0.0	-0.5	-3.6	-10.2	-21.5
Relative to 100 yds	-1.5	0.2	0.0	-2.9	-9.2	-20.3
Line of Sight 150 yds	-1.5	1.2	1.9	0.0	-5.4	-15.5

Exterior Ballistic Table for Ballistic Coefficient 0.14

		RANGE				
	Muzzle	50 yds	100 yds	150 yds	200 yds	250 yds
Velocity, ft/sec	2300	2010	1734	1505	1301	1144
Energy, ft/lbs per grain	11.74	8.97	6.74	5.03	3.76	2.91
Time of Flight, sec	0.0000	0.0696	0.1499	0.2426	0.3500	0.4733
Path, inches — Relative to Line of Sight — ZERO RANGE 50 yds	-1.5	0.0	-0.7	-4.2	-11.6	-24.2
100 yds	-1.5	0.3	0.0	-3.2	-10.3	-22.5
150 yds	-1.5	1.4	2.1	0.0	-6.0	-17.2
Velocity, ft/sec	2200	1917	1660	1432	1243	1103
Energy, ft/lbs per grain	10.75	8.16	6.12	4.55	3.43	2.70
Time of Flight, sec	0.0000	0.0730	0.1572	0.2546	0.3672	0.4956
Path, inches — Relative to Line of Sight — ZERO RANGE 50 yds	-1.5	0.0	-0.9	-4.9	-13.3	-27.2
100 yds	-1.5	0.4	0.0	-3.9	-11.5	-25.0
150 yds	-1.5	1.6	2.4	0.0	-6.7	-19.0
Velocity, ft/sec	2100	1825	1577	1362	1188	1066
Energy, ft/lbs per grain	9.79	7.39	5.52	4.12	3.13	2.52
Time of Flight, sec	0.0000	0.0766	0.1651	0.2675	0.3858	0.5194
Path, inches — Relative to Line of Sight — ZERO RANGE 50 yds	-1.5	0.0	-1.1	-5.8	-15.1	-30.6
100 yds	-1.5	0.6	0.0	-4.1	-12.9	-27.8
150 yds	-1.5	1.9	2.7	0.0	-7.4	-21.0
Velocity, ft/sec	2000	1734	1497	1295	1139	1033
Energy, ft/lbs per grain	8.88	6.68	4.98	3.72	2.88	2.37
Time of Flight, sec	0.0000	0.0806	0.1737	0.2816	0.4055	0.5442
Path, inches — Relative to Line of Sight — ZERO RANGE 50 yds	-1.5	0.0	-1.4	-6.7	-17.2	-34.4
100 yds	-1.5	0.7	0.0	-4.6	-14.4	-30.9
150 yds	-1.5	2.2	3.1	0.0	-8.3	-23.2
Velocity, ft/sec	1900	1644	1418	1232	1096	1004
Energy, ft/lbs per grain	8.01	6.00	4.46	3.37	2.67	2.24
Time of Flight, sec	0.0000	0.0849	0.1832	0.2969	0.4265	0.5699
Path, inches — Relative to Line of Sight — ZERO RANGE 50 yds	-1.5	0.0	-1.7	-7.8	-19.6	-38.7
100 yds	-1.5	0.9	0.0	-5.2	-16.2	-34.3
150 yds	-1.5	2.6	3.5	0.0	-9.2	-25.6
Velocity, ft/sec	1800	1555	1343	1174	1057	976
Energy, ft/lbs per grain	7.19	5.37	4.00	3.06	2.48	2.11
Time of Flight, sec	0.0000	0.0897	0.1937	0.3134	0.4485	0.5965
Path, inches — Relative to Line of Sight — ZERO RANGE 50 yds	-1.5	0.0	-2.1	-9.1	-22.3	-43.4
100 yds	-1.5	1.1	0.0	-5.9	-18.1	-38.1
150 yds	-1.5	3.0	3.9	0.0	-10.2	-28.2
Velocity, ft/sec	1700	1467	1270	1122	1022	951
Energy, ft/lbs per grain	6.42	4.78	3.58	2.79	2.32	2.01
Time of Flight, sec	0.0000	0.0951	0.2051	0.3311	0.4716	0.6240
Path, inches — Relative to Line of Sight — ZERO RANGE 50 yds	-1.5	0.0	-2.6	-10.5	-25.4	-48.5
100 yds	-1.5	1.3	0.0	-6.7	-20.2	-42.1
150 yds	-1.5	3.5	4.5	0.0	-11.3	-31.0
Velocity, ft/sec	1600	1381	1203	1076	990	926
Energy, ft/lbs per grain	5.68	4.23	3.21	2.57	2.18	1.90
Time of Flight, sec	0.0000	0.1010	0.2177	0.3500	0.4956	0.6525
Path, inches — Relative to Line of Sight — ZERO RANGE 50 yds	-1.5	0.0	-3.1	-12.2	-28.8	-54.2
100 yds	-1.5	1.5	0.0	-7.5	-22.6	-46.5
150 yds	-1.5	4.1	5.0	0.0	-12.5	-33.9

short range tables

Exterior Ballistic Table for Ballistic Coefficient 0.14

		Muzzle	50 yds	100 yds	150 yds	200 yds	250 yds
Velocity, ft/sec		1500	1297	1141	1035	960	903
Energy, ft/lbs per grain		5.00	3.73	2.89	2.38	2.05	1.81
Time of Flight, sec		0.0000	0.1077	0.2313	0.3698	0.5206	0.6819
Path, inches	50 yds	-1.5	0.0	-3.7	-14.0	-32.5	-60.3
Relative to	100 yds	-1.5	1.8	0.0	-8.5	-25.1	-51.1
Line of Sight	150 yds	-1.5	4.7	5.7	0.0	-13.8	-37.0
Velocity, ft/sec		1400	1218	1086	997	932	879
Energy, ft/lbs per grain		4.35	3.29	2.62	2.21	1.93	1.72
Time of Flight, sec		0.0000	0.1151	0.2460	0.3905	0.5464	0.7123
Path, inches	50 yds	-1.5	0.0	-4.4	-16.1	-36.5	-67.0
Relative to	100 yds	-1.5	2.2	0.0	-9.5	-27.8	-56.1
Line of Sight	150 yds	-1.5	5.4	6.4	0.0	-15.1	-40.2
Velocity, ft/sec		1300	1143	1036	961	903	855
Energy, ft/lbs per grain		3.75	2.90	2.38	2.05	1.81	1.62
Time of Flight, sec		0.0000	0.1234	0.2616	0.4122	0.5734	0.7442
Path, inches	50 yds	-1.5	0.0	-5.1	-18.4	-41.0	-74.3
Relative to	100 yds	-1.5	2.6	0.0	-10.7	-30.7	-61.4
Line of Sight	150 yds	-1.5	6.1	7.1	0.0	-16.5	-43.7
Velocity, ft/sec		1200	1074	989	925	874	829
Energy, ft/lbs per grain		3.20	2.56	2.17	1.90	1.70	1.53
Time of Flight, sec		0.0000	0.1326	0.2784	0.4355	0.6025	0.7789
Path, inches	50 yds	-1.5	0.0	-6.0	-20.9	-46.0	-82.4
Relative to	100 yds	-1.5	3.0	0.0	-11.9	-33.9	-67.4
Line of Sight	150 yds	-1.5	7.0	7.9	0.0	-18.1	-47.6
Velocity, ft/sec		1100	1007	939	885	839	798
Energy, ft/lbs per grain		2.69	2.25	1.96	1.74	1.56	1.41
Time of Flight, sec		0.0000	0.1429	0.2974	0.4620	0.6362	0.8195
Path, inches	50 yds	-1.5	0.0	-7.1	-24.0	-52.0	-92.3
Relative to	100 yds	-1.5	3.5	0.0	-13.4	-37.8	-74.7
Line of Sight	150 yds	-1.5	8.0	8.9	0.0	-20.0	-52.4
Velocity, ft/sec		1000	934	881	835	795	758
Energy, ft/lbs per grain		2.22	1.94	1.72	1.55	1.40	1.28
Time of Flight, sec		0.0000	0.1554	0.3209	0.4958	0.6800	0.8734
Path, inches	50 yds	-1.5	0.0	-8.5	-28.1	-60.2	-106.1
Relative to	100 yds	-1.5	4.2	0.0	-15.4	-43.3	-85.0
Line of Sight	150 yds	-1.5	9.4	10.3	0.0	-22.7	-59.3

Exterior Ballistic Table for Ballistic Coefficient 0.15

		Muzzle	50 yds	100 yds	150 yds	200 yds	250 yds
Velocity, ft/sec		2900	2589	2299	2028	1776	1549
Energy, ft/lbs per grain		18.67	14.88	11.73	9.13	7.00	5.33
Time of Flight, sec		0.0000	0.0547	0.1162	0.1857	0.2648	0.3552
Path, inches	50 yds	-1.5	0.0	0.2	-1.3	-4.8	-11.2
Relative to	100 yds	-1.5	-0.1	0.0	-1.6	-5.2	-11.7
Line of Sight	150 yds	-1.5	0.4	1.0	0.0	-3.2	-9.1

short range tables

Exterior Ballistic Table for Ballistic Coefficient 0.15

	Muzzle	50 yds	100 yds	150 yds	200 yds	250 yds
RANGE						
Velocity, ft/sec	2800	2496	2212	1946	1702	1483
Energy, ft/lbs per grain	17.41	13.83	10.86	8.41	6.43	4.88
Time of Flight, sec	0.0000	0.0567	0.1206	0.1929	0.2753	0.3698
Path, inches — ZERO RANGE 50 yds	-1.5	0.0	0.1	-1.6	-5.6	-12.6
Relative to — ZERO RANGE 100 yds	-1.5	0.0	0.0	-1.7	-5.8	-12.9
Line of Sight — ZERO RANGE 150 yds	-1.5	0.5	1.2	0.0	-3.5	-10.0
Velocity, ft/sec	2700	2403	2124	1865	1629	1419
Energy, ft/lbs per grain	16.18	12.82	10.02	7.72	5.89	4.47
Time of Flight, sec	0.0000	0.0589	0.1253	0.2007	0.2868	0.3855
Path, inches — ZERO RANGE 50 yds	-1.5	0.0	0.0	-2.0	-6.4	-14.2
Relative to — ZERO RANGE 100 yds	-1.5	0.0	0.0	-1.9	-6.4	-14.2
Line of Sight — ZERO RANGE 150 yds	-1.5	0.7	1.3	0.0	-3.8	-10.9
Velocity, ft/sec	2600	2309	2037	1785	1557	1357
Energy, ft/lbs per grain	15.01	11.84	9.21	7.07	5.38	4.09
Time of Flight, sec	0.0000	0.0612	0.1304	0.2091	0.2991	0.4024
Path, inches — ZERO RANGE 50 yds	-1.5	0.0	-0.1	-2.4	-7.4	-16.0
Relative to — ZERO RANGE 100 yds	-1.5	0.1	0.0	-2.2	-7.1	-15.6
Line of Sight — ZERO RANGE 150 yds	-1.5	0.8	1.5	0.0	-4.2	-12.0
Velocity, ft/sec	2500	2215	1950	1705	1486	1298
Energy, ft/lbs per grain	13.88	10.89	8.44	6.45	4.90	3.74
Time of Flight, sec	0.0000	0.0637	0.1359	0.2182	0.3125	0.4207
Path, inches — ZERO RANGE 50 yds	-1.5	0.0	-0.3	-2.9	-8.5	-18.0
Relative to — ZERO RANGE 100 yds	-1.5	0.1	0.0	-2.4	-7.9	-17.3
Line of Sight — ZERO RANGE 150 yds	-1.5	1.0	1.6	0.0	-4.6	-13.2
Velocity, ft/sec	2400	2122	1863	1627	1417	1242
Energy, ft/lbs per grain	12.79	10.00	7.71	5.88	4.46	3.42
Time of Flight, sec	0.0000	0.0665	0.1419	0.2281	0.3270	0.4402
Path, inches — ZERO RANGE 50 yds	-1.5	0.0	-0.4	-3.4	-9.7	-20.3
Relative to — ZERO RANGE 100 yds	-1.5	0.2	0.0	-2.7	-8.8	-19.2
Line of Sight — ZERO RANGE 150 yds	-1.5	1.1	1.8	0.0	5.1	-14.6
Velocity, ft/sec	2300	2028	1777	1550	1351	1190
Energy, ft/lbs per grain	11.74	9.13	7.01	5.33	4.05	3.14
Time of Flight, sec	0.0000	0.0695	0.1485	0.2389	0.3127	0.4612
Path, inches — ZERO RANGE 50 yds	-1.5	0.0	-0.6	-4.0	-11.1	-22.9
Relative to — ZERO RANGE 100 yds	-1.5	0.3	0.0	-3.1	-9.8	-21.3
Line of Sight — ZERO RANGE 150 yds	-1.5	1.3	2.1	0.0	-5.7	-16.2
Velocity, ft/sec	2200	1935	1692	1475	1289	1144
Energy, ft/lbs per grain	10.75	8.31	6.36	4.83	3.69	2.91
Time of Flight, sec	0.0000	0.0727	0.1556	0.2506	0.3596	0.4835
Path, inches — ZERO RANGE 50 yds	-1.5	0.0	-0.8	-4.7	-12.6	-25.8
Relative to — ZERO RANGE 100 yds	-1.5	0.4	0.0	-3.5	-11.0	-23.7
Line of Sight — ZERO RANGE 150 yds	-1.5	1.6	2.3	0.0	-6.3	-17.9
Velocity, ft/sec	2100	1843	1609	1402	1230	1102
Energy, ft/lbs per grain	9.79	7.54	5.75	4.36	3.36	2.70
Time of Flight, sec	0.0000	0.0763	0.1634	0.2634	0.3778	0.5071
Path, inches — ZERO RANGE 50 yds	-1.5	0.0	-1.1	-5.6	-14.7	-29.1
Relative to — ZERO RANGE 100 yds	-1.5	0.5	0.0	-3.9	-12.3	-26.4
Line of Sight — ZERO RANGE 150 yds	-1.5	1.8	2.6	0.0	-7.1	-19.9

short range tables

Exterior Ballistic Table for Ballistic Coefficient 0.15

		Muzzle	50 yds	100 yds	150 yds	200 yds	250 yds
Velocity, ft/sec		2000	1751	1527	1332	1176	1064
Energy, ft/lbs per grain		8.88	6.81	5.18	3.94	3.07	2.51
Time of Flight, sec		0.0000	0.0802	0.1720	0.2773	0.3974	0.5319
Path, inches	50 yds	-1.5	0.0	-1.4	-6.5	-16.5	-32.8
Relative to ZERO RANGE	100 yds	-1.5	0.7	0.0	-4.4	-13.8	-29.4
Line of Sight	150 yds	-1.5	2.2	3.0	0.0	-7.9	-22.0
Velocity, ft/sec		1900	1660	1447	1265	1127	1031
Energy, ft/lbs per grain		8.01	6.12	4.65	3.55	2.82	2.36
Time of Flight, sec		0.0000	0.0845	0.1814	0.2924	0.4184	0.5579
Path, inches	50 yds	-1.5	0.0	-1.7	-7.5	-18.8	-36.9
Relative to ZERO RANGE	100 yds	-1.5	0.8	0.0	-5.0	-15.5	-32.7
Line of Sight	150 yds	-1.5	2.5	3.3	0.0	-8.8	-24.4
Velocity, ft/sec		1800	1570	1369	1204	1084	1000
Energy, ft/lbs per grain		7.19	5.47	4.16	3.22	2.61	2.22
Time of Flight, sec		0.0000	0.0893	0.1917	0.3088	0.4405	0.5849
Path, inches	50 yds	-1.5	0.0	-2.0	-8.8	-21.5	-41.5
Relative to ZERO RANGE	100 yds	-1.5	1.0	0.0	-5.7	-17.4	-36.4
Line of Sight	150 yds	-1.5	2.9	3.8	0.0	-9.8	-27.0
Velocity, ft/sec		1700	1482	1294	1148	1045	972
Energy, ft/lbs per grain		6.42	4.88	3.72	2.93	2.42	2.10
Time of Flight, sec		0.0000	0.0946	0.2031	0.3265	0.4638	0.6129
Path, inches	50 yds	-1.5	0.0	-2.5	-10.2	-24.4	-46.7
Relative to ZERO RANGE	100 yds	-1.5	1.2	0.0	-6.4	-19.5	-40.5
Line of Sight	150 yds	-1.5	3.4	4.3	0.0	-10.9	-29.7
Velocity, ft/sec		1600	1394	1224	1097	1010	946
Energy, ft/lbs per grain		5.68	4.31	3.33	2.67	2.26	1.99
Time of Flight, sec		0.0000	0.1005	0.2156	0.3454	0.4882	0.6418
Path, inches	50 yds	-1.5	0.0	-3.0	-11.8	-27.8	-52.3
Relative to ZERO RANGE	100 yds	-1.5	1.5	0.0	-7.3	-21.8	-44.8
Line of Sight	150 yds	-1.5	3.9	4.9	0.0	-12.1	-32.7
Velocity, ft/sec		1500	1309	1159	1053	978	921
Energy, ft/lbs per grain		5.00	3.80	2.98	2.46	2.21	1.88
Time of Flight, sec		0.0000	0.1072	0.2292	0.3654	0.5135	0.6718
Path, inches	50 yds	-1.5	0.0	-3.6	-13.6	-31.5	-58.5
Relative to ZERO RANGE	100 yds	-1.5	1.8	0.0	-8.3	-24.3	-49.5
Line of Sight	150 yds	-1.5	4.5	5.5	0.0	-13.3	-35.7
Velocity, ft/sec		1400	1228	1101	1012	948	896
Energy, ft/lbs per grain		4.35	3.35	2.69	2.27	2.00	1.78
Time of Flight, sec		0.0000	0.1146	0.2440	0.3864	0.5398	0.7028
Path, inches	50 yds	-1.5	0.0	-4.3	-15.7	-35.6	-65.2
Relative to ZERO RANGE	100 yds	-1.5	2.1	0.0	-9.3	-27.1	-54.5
Line of Sight	150 yds	-1.5	5.2	6.2	0.0	-14.7	-39.0
Velocity, ft/sec		1300	1152	1048	974	918	870
Energy, ft/lbs per grain		3.75	2.95	2.44	2.11	1.87	1.68
Time of Flight, sec		0.0000	0.1229	0.2598	0.4085	0.5672	0.7352
Path, inches	50 yds	-1.5	0.0	-5.0	-18.0	-40.1	-72.5
Relative to ZERO RANGE	100 yds	-1.5	2.5	0.0	-10.4	-30.0	-59.9
Line of Sight	150 yds	-1.5	6.0	6.9	0.0	-16.1	-42.5

short range tables

Exterior Ballistic Table for Ballistic Coefficient 0.15

		Muzzle	50 yds	100 yds	150 yds	200 yds	250 yds
Velocity, ft/sec		1200	1081	998	937	887	843
Energy, ft/lbs per grain		3.20	2.59	2.21	1.95	1.75	1.58
Time of Flight, sec		0.0000	0.1321	0.2768	0.4320	0.5968	0.7704
Path, inches	50 yds	-1.5	0.0	-5.9	-20.6	-45.1	-80.7
Relative to / ZERO RANGE	100 yds	-1.5	3.0	0.0	-11.7	-33.2	-65.9
Line of Sight	150 yds	-1.5	6.9	7.8	0.0	-17.7	-46.4
Velocity, ft/sec		1100	1012	947	895	851	812
Energy, ft/lbs per grain		269	2.27	1.99	1.78	1.61	1.46
Time of Flight, sec		0.0000	0.1425	0.2959	0.4589	0.6309	0.8116
Path, inches	50 yds	-1.5	0.0	-7.0	-23.6	-51.1	-90.6
Relative to / ZERO RANGE	100 yds	-1.5	3.5	0.0	-13.2	-37.2	-73.2
Line of Sight	150 yds	-1.5	7.9	8.8	0.0	-19.6	-51.3
Velocity, ft/sec		1000	938	888	844	805	770
Energy, ft/lbs per grain		2.22	1.95	1.75	1.58	1.44	1.32
Time of Flight, sec		0.0000	0.1551	0.3196	0.4930	0.6751	0.8656
Path, inches	50 yds	-1.5	0.0	-8.4	-27.8	-59.4	-104.4
Relative to / ZERO RANGE	100 yds	-1.5	4.2	0.0	-15.2	-42.6	-83.5
Line of Sight	150 yds	-1.5	9.3	10.1	0.0	-22.4	-58.1

Exterior Ballistic Table for Ballistic Coefficient 0.16

		Muzzle	50 yds	100 yds	150 yds	200 yds	250 yds
Velocity, ft/sec		2300	2045	1807	1590	1398	1236
Energy, ft/lbs per grain		11.74	9.28	7.25	5.61	4.34	3.39
Time of Flight, sec		0.0000	0.0692	0.1472	0.2357	0.3364	0.4507
Path, inches	50 yds	-1.5	0.0	-0.6	-3.9	-10.6	-21.8
Relative to / ZERO RANGE	100 yds	-1.5	0.3	0.0	-3.0	-9.4	-20.3
Line of Sight	150 yds	-1.5	1.3	2.0	0.0	-5.4	-15.3
Velocity, ft/sec		2200	1951	1721	1513	1332	1184
Energy, ft/lbs per grain		10.75	8.45	6.58	5.08	3.94	3.11
Time of Flight, sec		0.0000	0.0724	0.1543	0.2473	0.3530	0.4727
Path, inches	50 yds	-1.5	0.0	-0.8	-4.5	-12.1	-24.6
Relative to / ZERO RANGE	100 yds	-1.5	0.4	0.0	-3.3	-10.5	-22.6
Line of Sight	150 yds	-1.5	1.5	2.2	0.0	-6.0	17.0
Velocity, ft/sec		2100	1858	1637	1438	1269	1137
Energy, ft/lbs per grain		9.79	7.66	4.59	3.58	3.58	2.87
Time of Flight, sec		0.0000	0.0759	0.1620	0.2598	0.3710	0.4962
Path, inches	50 yds	-1.5	0.0	-1.0	-5.3	-13.8	-27.8
Relative to / ZERO RANGE	100 yds	-1.5	0.5	0.0	-3.8	-11.8	-25.2
Line of Sight	150 yds	-1.5	1.8	2.5	0.0	-6.7	-18.9
Velocity, ft/sec		2000	1766	1553	1366	1210	1095
Energy, ft/lbs per grain		8.88	6.92	5.35	4.14	3.25	2.66
Time of Flight, sec		0.0000	0.0798	0.1704	0.2735	0.3904	0.5210
Path, inches	50 yds	-1.5	0.0	-1.3	-6.2	-15.8	-31.4
Relative to / ZERO RANGE	100 yds	-1.5	0.7	0.0	-4.3	-13.2	-28.1
Line of Sight	150 yds	-1.5	2.1	2.8	0.0	-7.5	-21.0

short range tables

Exterior Ballistic Table for Ballistic Coefficient 0.16

		Muzzle	50 yds	100 yds	150 yds	200 yds	250 yds
				RANGE			
Velocity, ft/sec		1900	1674	1472	1296	1157	1057
Energy, ft/lbs per grain		8.01	6.22	4.81	3.73	2.97	2.48
Time of Flight, sec		0.0000	0.0841	0.1797	0.2885	0.4112	0.5472
Path, inches	50 yds	-1.5	0.0	-1.6	-7.3	-18.1	-35.4
Relative to ZERO RANGE	100 yds	-1.5	0.8	0.0	-4.8	-14.9	-31.4
Line of Sight	150 yds	-1.5	2.4	3.2	0.0	-8.4	-23.3
Velocity, ft/sec		1800	1584	1392	1231	1110	1023
Energy, ft/lbs per grain		7.19	5.57	4.30	3.36	2.74	2.32
Time of Flight, sec		0.0000	0.0889	0.1900	0.3047	0.4334	0.5744
Path, inches	50 yds	-1.5	0.0	-2.0	-8.5	-20.7	-40.0
Relative to ZERO RANGE	100 yds	-1.5	1.0	0.0	-5.5	-16.7	-35.0
Line of Sight	150 yds	-1.5	2.8	3.7	0.0	-9.4	-25.8
Velocity, ft/sec		1700	1494	1316	1172	1067	993
Energy, ft/lbs per grain		6.42	4.96	3.84	3.05	2.53	2.19
Time of Flight, sec		0.0000	0.0942	0.2013	0.3223	0.4568	0.6028
Path, inches	50 yds	-1.5	0.0	-2.4	-9.9	-23.6	-45.0
Relative to ZERO RANGE	100 yds	-1.5	1.2	0.0	-6.2	-18.8	-39.0
Line of Sight	150 yds	-1.5	3.3	4.2	0.0	-10.5	-28.6
Velocity, ft/sec		1600	1406	1243	1118	1029	964
Energy, ft/lbs per grain		5.68	4.39	3.43	2.77	2.35	2.06
Time of Flight, sec		0.0000	0.1001	0.2137	0.3413	0.4815	0.6323
Path, inches	50 yds	-1.5	0.0	-2.9	-11.5	-27.0	-50.6
Relative to ZERO RANGE	100 yds	-1.5	1.5	0.0	-7.1	-21.1	-43.4
Line of Sight	150 yds	-1.5	3.0	4.7	0.0	11.7	-31.5
Velocity, ft/sec		1500	1320	1175	1070	995	937
Energy, ft/lbs per grain		5.00	3.87	3.07	2.54	2.20	1.95
Time of Flight, sec		0.0000	0.1067	0.2274	0.3615	0.5072	0.6627
Path, inches	50 yds	-1.5	0.0	-3.5	-13.3	-30.7	-56.8
Relative to ZERO RANGE	100 yds	-1.5	1.7	0.0	-8.0	-23.7	-48.1
Line of Sight	150 yds	-1.5	4.4	5.4	0.0	-12.9	-34.7
Velocity, ft/sec		1400	1238	1114	1027	962	911
Energy, ft/lbs per grain		4.35	3.40	2.76	2.34	2.05	1.84
Time of Flight, sec		0.0000	0.1141	0.2422	0.3827	0.5339	0.6942
Path, inches	50 yds	-1.5	0.0	-4.2	-15.3	-34.8	-63.5
Relative to ZERO RANGE	100 yds	-1.5	2.1	0.0	-9.1	-26.4	-53.1
Line of Sight	150 yds	-1.5	5.1	6.1	0.0	-14.3	-38.0
Velocity, ft/sec		1300	1160	1059	987	931	884
Energy, ft/lbs per grain		3.75	2.99	2.49	2.16	1.92	1.73
Time of Flight, sec		0.0000	0.1224	0.2581	0..4051	0.5618	0.7272
Path, inches	50 yds	-1.5	0.0	-5.0	-17.6	-39.3	-70.9
Relative to ZERO RANGE	100 yds	-1.5	-2.5	0.0	-10.2	-29.4	-58.5
Line of Sight	150 yds	-1.5	5.9	6.8	0.0	-15.7	-41.5
Velocity, ft/sec		1200	1087	1007	947	898	856
Energy, ft/lbs per grain		3.20	2.62	2.25	1.99	1.79	1.63
Time of Flight, sec		0.0000	0.1317	0.2753	0.4290	0.5918	0.7629
Path, inches	50 yds	-1.5	0.0	-5.8	-20.2	-44.3	-79.2
Relative to ZERO RANGE	100 yds	-1.5	2.9	0.0	-11.5	-32.6	-64.6
Line of Sight	150 yds	-1.5	6.7	7.6	0.0	-17.3	-45.4

short range tables

Exterior Ballistic Table for Ballistic Coefficient 0.16

				RANGE		
	Muzzle	50 yds	100 yds	150 yds	200 yds	250 yds
Velocity, ft/sec	1100	1017	954	904	861	823
Energy, ft/lbs per grain	2.69	2.30	2.02	1.81	1.65	1.50
Time of Flight, sec	0.0000	0.1421	0.2946	0.4561	0.6262	0.8045
Path, inches — Relative to Line of Sight — ZERO RANGE 50 yds	-1.5	0.0	-6.9	-23.3	-50.4	-89.2
100 yds	-1.5	3.4	0.0	-13.0	-36.6	-71.9
150 yds	-1.5	7.8	8.7	0.0	-19.3	-50.3
Velocity, ft/sec	1000	941	893	852	815	781
Energy, ft/lbs per grain	2.22	1.97	1.77	1.61	1.47	1.35
Time of Flight, sec	0.0000	0.1548	0.3184	0.4905	0.6706	0.8589
Path, inches — Relative to Line of Sight — ZERO RANGE 50 yds	-1.5	0.0	-8.3	-27.5	-58.7	-102.9
100 yds	-1.5	4.1	0.0	-15.0	-42.1	-82.2
150 yds	-1.5	9.2	10.0	0.0	-22.0	-57.1

Exterior Ballistic Table for Ballistic Coefficient 0.17

				RANGE		
	Muzzle	50 yds	100 yds	150 yds	200 yds	250 yds
Velocity, ft/sec	2900	2625	2366	2121	1892	1680
Energy, ft/lbs per grain	18.67	15.30	12.43	9.99	7.95	6.27
Time of Flight, sec	0.0000	0.0544	0.1146	0.1815	0.2564	0.3406
Path, inches — Relative to Line of Sight — ZERO RANGE 50 yds	-1.5	0.0	0.2	-1.1	-4.4	-10.1
100 yds	-1.5	-0.1	0.0	-1.4	-4.8	-10.6
150 yds	-1.5	0.4	1.0	0.0	-2.9	-8.2
Velocity, ft/sec	2800	2531	2277	2038	1814	1609
Energy, ft/lbs per grain	17.41	14.22	11.51	9.22	7.31	5.75
Time of Flight, sec	0.0000	0.0564	0.1188	0.1885	0.2665	0.3544
Path, inches — Relative to Line of Sight — ZERO RANGE 50 yds	-1.5	0.0	0.1	-1.4	-5.1	-11.4
100 yds	-1.5	-0.1	0.0	-1.6	-5.3	-11.7
150 yds	-1.5	0.5	1.1	0.0	-3.2	-9.0
Velocity, ft/sec	2700	2437	2188	1954	1737	1539
Energy, ft/lbs per grain	16.18	13.18	10.63	8.48	6.70	5.26
Time of Flight, sec	0.0000	0.0585	0.1235	0.1960	0.2774	0.3692
Path, inches — Relative to Line of Sight — ZERO RANGE 50 yds	-1.5	0.0	0.0	-1.8	-5.8	-12.8
100 yds	-1.5	0.0	0.0	-1.8	-5.9	-12.9
150 yds	-1.5	0.6	1.2	0.0	-3.5	-9.9
Velocity, ft/sec	2600	2342	2099	1871	1661	1471
Energy, ft/lbs per grain	15.01	12.18	9.78	7.77	6.12	4.80
Time of Flight, sec	0.0000	0.0608	0.1284	0.2041	0.2892	0.3853
Path, inches — Relative to Line of Sight — ZERO RANGE 50 yds	-1.5	0.0	-0.1	-2.2	-6.7	-14.5
100 yds	-1.5	0.0	0.0	-2.0	-6.5	-14.2
150 yds	-1.5	0.7	1.4	0.0	-3.8	-10.9
Velocity, ft/sec	2500	2248	2010	1789	1586	1404
Energy, ft/lbs per grain	13.88	11.22	8.97	7.11	5.58	4.38
Time of Flight, sec	0.0000	0.0633	0.1338	0.2130	0.3021	0.4026
Path, inches — Relative to Line of Sight — ZERO RANGE 50 yds	-1.5	0.0	-0.2	-2.6	-7.7	-16.3
100 yds	-1.5	0.1	0.0	-2.3	-7.3	-15.8
150 yds	-1.5	0.9	1.5	0.0	-4.2	-12.0

short range tables

Exterior Ballistic Table for Ballistic Coefficient 0.17

	Muzzle	50 yds	100 yds	150 yds	200 yds	250 yds
RANGE						
Velocity, ft/sec	2400	2154	1922	1707	1512	1341
Energy, ft/lbs per grain	12.79	10.30	8.20	6.47	5.08	3.99
Time of Flight, sec	0.0000	0.0841	0.1797	0.2885	0.4112	0.5472
Path, inches — Relative to Line of Sight — ZERO RANGE 50 yds	-1.5	0.0	-0.4	-3.1	-8.9	-18.4
ZERO RANGE 100 yds	-1.5	0.2	0.0	-2.6	-8.1	-17.5
ZERO RANGE 150 yds	-1.5	1.0	1.7	0.0	-4.7	-13.2
Velocity, ft/sec	2300	2059	1834	1627	1441	1280
Energy, ft/lbs per grain	11.74	9.41	7.47	5.88	4.61	3.64
Time of Flight, sec	0.0000	0.0689	0.1461	0.2330	0.3310	0.4416
Path, inches — Relative to Line of Sight — ZERO RANGE 50 yds	-1.5	0.0	-0.6	-3.7	-10.2	-20.8
ZERO RANGE 100 yds	-1.5	0.3	0.0	-2.9	-9.0	-19.4
ZERO RANGE 150 yds	-1.5	1.2	1.9	0.0	-5.2	-14.6
Velocity, ft/sec	2200	1966	1747	1548	1372	1223
Energy, ft/lbs per grain	10.75	8.58	6.78	5.32	4.18	3.32
Time of Flight, sec	0.0000	0.0721	0.1531	0.2443	0.3473	0.4633
Path, inches — Relative to Line of Sight — ZERO RANGE 50 yds	-1.5	0.0	-0.8	-4.4	-11.6	-23.5
ZERO RANGE 100 yds	-1.5	0.4	0.0	-3.2	-10.1	-21.6
ZERO RANGE 150 yds	-1.5	1.5	2.2	0.0	-5.8	-16.2
Velocity, ft/sec	2100	1872	1662	1471	1306	1171
Energy, ft/lbs per grain	9.79	7.78	6.13	4.80	3.79	3.04
Time of Flight, sec	0.0000	0.0757	0.1607	0.2567	0.3651	0.4866
Path, inches — Relative to Line of Sight — ZERO RANGE 50 yds	-1.5	0.0	-1.0	-5.1	-13.3	-26.6
ZERO RANGE 100 yds	-1.5	0.5	0.0	-3.7	-11.3	-24.1
ZERO RANGE 150 yds	-1.5	1.7	2.4	0.0	6.5	-18.1
Velocity, ft/sec	2000	1779	1577	1397	1244	1125
Energy, ft/lbs per grain	8.88	7.03	5.52	4.33	3.44	2.81
Time of Flight, sec	0.0000	0.0795	0.1691	0.2703	0.3842	0.5113
Path, inches — Relative to Line of Sight — ZERO RANGE 50 yds	-1.5	0.0	-1.3	-6.0	-15.3	-30.1
ZERO RANGE 100 yds	-1.5	0.6	0.0	-4.1	-12.8	-27.0
ZERO RANGE 150 yds	-1.5	2.0	2.8	0.0	-7.2	-20.1
Velocity, ft/sec	1900	1687	1494	1325	1186	1083
Energy, ft/lbs per grain	8.01	6.32	4.96	3.90	3.12	2.60
Time of Flight, sec	0.0000	0.0838	0.1783	0.2850	0.4049	0.5375
Path, inches — Relative to Line of Sight — ZERO RANGE 50 yds	-1.5	0.0	-1.6	-7.0	-17.5	-34.1
ZERO RANGE 100 yds	-1.5	0.8	0.0	-4.7	-14.3	-30.2
ZERO RANGE 150 yds	-1.5	2.3	3.1	0.0	-8.1	-22.4
Velocity, ft/sec	1800	1596	1413	1257	1135	1046
Energy, ft/lbs per grain	7.19	5.65	4.43	3.51	2.86	2.43
Time of Flight, sec	0.0000	0.0885	0.1885	0.3012	0.4270	0.5650
Path, inches — Relative to Line of Sight — ZERO RANGE 50 yds	-1.5	0.0	-1.9	-8.2	-20.0	-38.6
ZERO RANGE 100 yds	-1.5	1.0	0.0	-5.3	-16.2	-33.8
ZERO RANGE 150 yds	-1.5	2.7	3.6	0.0	-9.1	-24.9
Velocity, ft/sec	1700	1506	1335	1194	1088	1012
Energy, ft/lbs per grain	6.42	5.04	3.96	3.17	2.63	2.27
Time of Flight, sec	0.0000	0.0938	0.1997	0.3187	0.4506	0.5937
Path, inches — Relative to Line of Sight — ZERO RANGE 50 yds	-1.5	0.0	-2.3	-9.6	-22.9	-43.6
ZERO RANGE 100 yds	-1.5	1.2	0.0	-6.1	-18.2	-37.7
ZERO RANGE 150 yds	-1.5	3.2	4.0	0.0	-10.1	-27.6

short range tables

Exterior Ballistic Table for Ballistic Coefficient 0.17

	Muzzle	50 yds	100 yds	150 yds	200 yds	250 yds
Velocity, ft/sec	1600	1417	1260	1137	1047	982
Energy, ft/lbs per grain	5.68	4.46	3.52	2.87	2.43	2.14
Time of Flight, sec	0.0000	0.0997	0.2121	0.3377	0.4754	0.6236
Path, inches — ZERO RANGE 50 yds	-1.5	0.0	-2.8	-11.2	-26.2	-49.2
Relative to — ZERO RANGE 100 yds	-1.5	1.4	0.0	-6.9	-20.5	-42.1
Line of Sight — ZERO RANGE 150 yds	-1.5	3.7	4.6	0.0	-11.3	-30.5
Velocity, ft/sec	1500	1330	1190	1086	1010	953
Energy, ft/lbs per grain	5.00	3.93	3.14	2.62	2.26	2.02
Time of Flight, sec	0.0000	0.1063	0.2257	0.3580	0.5014	0.6545
Path, inches — ZERO RANGE 50 yds	-1.5	0.0	-3.4	-13.0	-29.9	-55.3
Relative to — ZERO RANGE 100 yds	-1.5	1.7	0.0	-7.8	-23.1	-46.8
Line of Sight — ZERO RANGE 150 yds	-1.5	4.3	5.2	0.0	-12.6	-33.7
Velocity, ft/sec	1400	1246	1126	1040	976	925
Energy, ft/lbs per grain	4.35	3.45	2.81	2.40	2.11	1.90
Time of Flight, sec	0.0000	0.1137	0.2406	0.3794	0.5285	0.6865
Path, inches — ZERO RANGE 50 yds	-1.5	0.0	-4.1	-15.0	-34.0	-62.1
Relative to — ZERO RANGE 100 yds	-1.5	2.1	0.0	-8.9	-25.8	-51.8
Line of Sight — ZERO RANGE 150 yds	-1.5	5.0	5.9	0.0	-14.0	-37.0
Velocity, ft/sec	1300	1167	1069	998	943	897
Energy, ft/lbs per grain	3.75	3.02	2.54	2.21	1.97	1.79
Time of Flight, sec	0.0000	0.1220	0.2566	0.4021	0.5569	0.7200
Path, inches — ZERO RANGE 50 yds	-1.5	0.0	-4.9	-17.3	-38.5	-69.5
Relative to — ZERO RANGE 100 yds	1.5	2.4	0.0	-10.0	-28.8	-57.3
Line of Sight — ZERO RANGE 150 yds	-1.5	5.8	6.7	0.0	-15.4	-40.6
Velocity, ft/sec	1200	1093	1015	957	909	868
Energy, ft/lbs per grain	3.20	2.65	2.29	2.03	1.83	1.67
Time of Flight, sec	0.0000	0.1313	0.2739	0.4263	0.5873	0.7562
Path, inches — ZERO RANGE 50 yds	-1.5	0.0	-5.8	-20.0	-43.6	-77.8
Relative to — ZERO RANGE 100 yds	-1.5	2.9	0.0	-11.3	-32.1	-63.4
Line of Sight — ZERO RANGE 150 yds	-1.5	6.7	7.5	0.0	-17.0	-44.6
Velocity, ft/sec	1100	1021	961	913	871	834
Energy, ft/lbs per grain	2.69	2.31	2.05	1.85	1.68	1.54
Time of Flight, sec	0.0000	0.1418	0.2934	0.4537	0.6220	0.7981
Path, inches — ZERO RANGE 50 yds	-1.5	0.0	-6.8	-23.1	-49.7	-87.9
Relative to — ZERO RANGE 100 yds	-1.5	3.4	0.0	-12.8	-36.1	-70.8
Line of Sight — ZERO RANGE 150 yds	-1.5	7.7	8.5	0.0	-19.0	-49.4
Velocity, ft/sec	1000	9.45	899	859	823	791
Energy, ft/lbs per grain	2.22	1.98	1.79	1.64	1.50	1.39
Time of Flight, sec	0.0000	0.1545	0.3174	0.4883	0.6667	0.8528
Path, inches — ZERO RANGE 50 yds	-1.5	0.0	-8.2	-27.2	-58.0	-101.6
Relative to — ZERO RANGE 100 yds	-1.5	4.1	0.0	-14.9	-41.5	-81.0
Line of Sight — ZERO RANGE 150 yds	-1.5	9.1	9.9	0.0	-21.7	-56.2

short range tables

Exterior Ballistic Table for Ballistic Coefficient 0.18

	Muzzle	50 yds	100 yds	150 yds	200 yds	250 yds
			RANGE			
Velocity, ft/sec	2800	2545	2304	2077	1862	1664
Energy, ft/lbs per grain	17.41	14.38	11.79	9.58	7.70	6.15
Time of Flight, sec	0.0000	0.0562	0.1181	0.1867	0.2630	0.3482
Path, inches — ZERO RANGE 50 yds	-1.5	0.0	0.2	-1.3	-4.8	-10.9
Relative to — ZERO RANGE 100 yds	-1.5	-0.1	0.0	-1.6	-5.2	-11.3
Line of Sight — ZERO RANGE 150 yds	-1.5	0.4	1.0	0.0	-3.1	-8.7
Velocity, ft/sec	2700	2451	2215	1992	1784	1592
Energy, ft/lbs per grain	16.18	13.34	10.89	8.81	7.07	5.63
Time of Flight, sec	0.0000	0.0583	0.1227	0.1941	0.2737	0.3627
Path, inches — ZERO RANGE 50 yds	-1.5	0.0	0.0	-1.7	-5.6	-12.3
Relative to — ZERO RANGE 100 yds	-1.5	0.0	0.0	-1.8	-5.7	-12.4
Line of Sight — ZERO RANGE 150 yds	-1.5	0.6	1.2	0.0	-3.4	-9.5
Velocity, ft/sec	2600	2356	2125	1908	1706	1521
Energy, ft/lbs per grain	15.01	12.32	10.02	8.08	6.46	5.14
Time of Flight, sec	0.0000	0.0606	0.1276	0.2021	0.2853	0.3784
Path, inches — ZERO RANGE 50 yds	-1.5	0.0	-0.1	-2.1	-6.5	-13.9
Relative to — ZERO RANGE 100 yds	-1.5	0.0	0.0	-2.0	-6.3	-13.7
Line of Sight — ZERO RANGE 150 yds	-1.5	0.7	1.3	0.0	-3.7	-10.4
Velocity, ft/sec	2500	2261	2036	1825	1629	1452
Energy, ft/lbs per grain	13.88	11.35	9.20	7.39	5.89	4.68
Time of Flight, sec	0.0000	0.0631	0.1330	0.2108	0.2979	0.3954
Path, inches — ZERO RANGE 50 yds	-1.5	0.0	-0.2	-2.5	-7.5	-15.7
Relative to — ZERO RANGE 100 yds	-1.5	0.1	0.0	-2.2	-7.0	-15.2
Line of Sight — ZERO RANGE 150 yds	-1.5	0.8	1.5	0.0	-4.1	-11.5
Velocity, ft/sec	2400	2167	1947	1742	1554	1386
Energy, ft/lbs per grain	12.79	10.43	8.42	6.74	5.36	4.26
Time of Flight, sec	0.0000	0.0658	0.1388	0.2203	0.3115	0.4138
Path, inches — ZERO RANGE 50 yds	-1.5	0.0	-0.4	-3.0	-8.6	-17.7
Relative to — ZERO RANGE 100 yds	-1.5	0.2	0.0	-2.5	-7.8	-16.8
Line of Sight — ZERO RANGE 150 yds	-1.5	1.0	1.7	0.0	-4.5	-12.7
Velocity, ft/sec	2300	2072	1859	1660	1480	1322
Energy, ft/lbs per grain	11.74	9.53	7.67	6.12	4.86	3.88
Time of Flight, sec	0.0000	0.0687	0.1452	0.2306	0.3263	0.4336
Path, inches — ZERO RANGE 50 yds	-1.5	0.0	-0.5	-3.6	-9.8	-20.0
Relative to — ZERO RANGE 100 yds	-1.5	0.3	0.0	-2.8	-8.8	-18.7
Line of Sight — ZERO RANGE 150 yds	-1.5	1.2	1.9	0.0	-5.0	-14.0
Velocity, ft/sec	2200	1978	1771	1580	1409	1261
Energy, ft/lbs per grain	10.75	8.69	6.96	5.54	4.41	3.53
Time of Flight, sec	0.0000	0.0719	0.1521	0.2418	0.3424	0.4551
Path, inches — ZERO RANGE 50 yds	-1.5	0.0	-0.7	-4.2	-11.3	-22.7
Relative to — ZERO RANGE 100 yds	-1.5	0.4	0.0	-3.1	-9.8	-20.8
Line of Sight — ZERO RANGE 150 yds	-1.5	1.4	2.1	0.0	-5.6	-15.6
Velocity, ft/sec	2100	1884	1684	1502	1340	1205
Energy, ft/lbs per grain	9.79	7.88	6.30	5.01	3.99	3.22
Time of Flight, sec	0.0000	0.0754	0.1596	0.2540	0.3598	0.4781
Path, inches — ZERO RANGE 50 yds	-1.5	0.0	-1.0	-5.0	-12.9	-25.7
Relative to — ZERO RANGE 100 yds	-1.5	0.5	0.0	-3.6	-11.0	-23.3
Line of Sight — ZERO RANGE 150 yds	-1.5	1.7	2.4	0.0	-6.2	-17.3

Exterior Ballistic Table for Ballistic Coefficient 0.18

		Muzzle	50 yds	100 yds	150 yds	200 yds	250 yds
Velocity, ft/sec		2000	1791	1599	1425	1275	1154
Energy, ft/lbs per grain		8.88	7.12	5.68	4.51	3.61	2.96
Time of Flight, sec		0.0000	0.0793	0.1679	0.2674	0.3788	0.5027
Path, inches	50 yds	-1.5	0.0	-1.2	-5.9	-14.8	-29.1
Relative to	100 yds	-1.5	0.6	0.0	-4.0	-12.3	-26.0
Line of Sight ZERO RANGE	150 yds	-1.5	2.0	2.7	0.0	-7.0	-19.3
Velocity, ft/sec		1900	1698	1515	1351	1214	1108
Energy, ft/lbs per grain		8.01	6.40	5.10	4.05	3.27	2.73
Time of Flight, sec		0.0000	0.0835	0.1771	0.2820	0.3993	0.5289
Path, inches	50 yds	-1.5	0.0	-1.5	-6.9	-17.0	-33.0
Relative to	100 yds	-1.5	0.8	0.0	-4.6	-13.9	-29.1
Line of Sight ZERO RANGE	150 yds	-1.5	2.3	3.0	0.0	-7.8	-21.5
Velocity, ft/sec		1800	1607	1432	1281	1159	1068
Energy, ft/lbs per grain		7.19	5.73	4.55	3.64	2.98	2.53
Time of Flight, sec		0.0000	0.0882	0.1872	0.2980	0.4214	0.5565
Path, inches	50 yds	-1.5	0.0	-1.9	-8.0	-19.4	-37.3
Relative to	100 yds	-1.5	0.9	0.0	-5.2	-15.7	-32.6
Line of Sight ZERO RANGE	150 yds	-1.5	2.7	3.5	0.0	-8.8	-24.0
Velocity, ft/sec		1700	1516	1353	1215	1109	1031
Energy, ft/lbs per grain		6.42	5.10	4.06	3.28	2.73	2.36
Time of Flight, sec		0.0000	0.0935	0.1983	0.3155	0.4450	0.5855
Path, inches	50 yds	-1.5	0.0	-2.3	-9.4	-22.3	-42.3
Relative to	100 yds	-1.5	1.1	0.0	-5.9	-17.7	-36.6
Line of Sight ZERO RANGE	150 yds	-1.5	3.1	3.9	0.0	-9.8	-26.7
Velocity, ft/sec		1600	1426	1276	1155	1065	998
Energy, ft/lbs per grain		5.68	4.51	3.61	2.96	2.52	2.21
Time of Flight, sec		0.0000	0.0993	0.2107	0.3344	0.4700	0.6157
Path, inches	50 yds	-1.5	0.0	-2.8	-10.9	-25.6	-47.9
Relative to	100 yds	1.5	1.4	0.0	-6.7	-20.0	-40.9
Line of Sight ZERO RANGE	150 yds	-1.5	3.6	4.5	0.0	-11.0	-29.7
Velocity, ft/sec		1500	1339	1204	1101	1025	968
Energy, ft/lbs per grain		5.00	3.98	3.22	2.69	2.33	2.08
Time of Flight, sec		0.0000	0.1059	0.2243	0.3548	0.4963	0.6471
Path, inches	50 yds	-1.5	0.0	-3.4	-12.7	-29.2	-54.0
Relative to	100 yds	-1.5	1.7	0.0	-7.7	-22.5	-45.6
Line of Sight ZERO RANGE	150 yds	-1.5	4.2	5.1	0.0	-12.3	-32.8
Velocity, ft/sec		1400	1254	1138	1053	989	938
Energy, ft/lbs per grain		4.35	3.49	2.88	2.46	2.17	1.95
Time of Flight, sec		0.0000	0.1133	0.2391	0.3765	0.5237	0.6796
Path, inches	50 yds	-1.5	0.0	-4.0	-14.8	-33.3	-60.8
Relative to	100 yds	-1.5	2.0	0.0	-8.7	-25.3	-50.7
Line of Sight ZERO RANGE	150 yds	-1.5	4.9	5.8	0.0	-13.6	-36.2
Velocity, ft/sec		1300	1173	1078	1008	954	909
Energy, ft/lbs per grain		3.75	3.05	2.58	2.26	2.02	1.83
Time of Flight, sec		0.0000	0.1217	0.2553	0.3993	0.5524	0.7136
Path, inches	50 yds	-1.5	0.0	-4.8	-17.1	-37.9	-68.3
Relative to	100 yds	-1.5	2.4	0.0	-9.9	-28.3	-56.2
Line of Sight ZERO RANGE	150 yds	-1.5	5.7	6.6	0.0	-15.1	-39.8

short range tables

Exterior Ballistic Table for Ballistic Coefficient 0.18

		Muzzle	50 yds	100 yds	150 yds	200 yds	250 yds
				RANGE			
Velocity, ft/sec		1200	1098	1023	966	919	879
Energy, ft/lbs per grain		3.20	2.68	2.32	2.07	1.87	1.72
Time of Flight, sec		0.0000	0.1310	0.2727	0.4238	0.5931	0.7501
Path, inches	50 yds	-1.5	0.0	-5.7	-19.7	-43.0	-76.6
Relative to	100 yds	-1.5	2.9	0.0	-11.1	-31.6	-62.3
Line of Sight	150 yds	-1.5	6.6	7.4	0.0	-16.7	-43.8
Velocity, ft/sec		1100	1025	967	920	880	844
Energy, ft/lbs per grain		2.69	2.33	2.08	1.88	1.72	1.58
Time of Flight, sec		0.0000	0.1415	0.2924	0.4515	0.6183	0.7925
Path, inches	50 yds	-1.5	0.0	-6.8	-22.8	-49.1	-86.7
Relative to	100 yds	-1.5	3.4	0.0	-12.7	-35.6	-69.8
Line of Sight	150 yds	-1.5	7.6	8.4	0.0	-18.7	-48.6
Velocity, ft/sec		1000	947	903	865	831	799
Energy, ft/lbs per grain		2.22	1.99	1.81	1.66	1.53	1.42
Time of Flight, sec		0.0000	0.1542	0.3165	0.4863	0.6633	0.8474
Path, inches	50 yds	-1.5	0.0	-8.2	-27.0	-57.5	-100.5
Relative to	100 yds	-1.5	4.1	0.0	-14.7	-41.1	-80.0
Line of Sight	150 yds	-1.5	9.0	9.8	0.0	-21.4	-55.5

Exterior Ballistic Table for Ballistic Coefficient 0.19

		Muzzle	50 yds	100 yds	150 yds	200 yds	250 yds
				RANGE			
Velocity, ft/sec		2900	2653	2419	2197	1986	1789
Energy, ft/lbs per grain		18.67	15.63	12.99	10.72	8.76	7.11
Time of Flight, sec		0.0000	0.0541	0.1133	0.1784	0.2502	0.3298
Path, inches	50 yds	-1.5	0.0	0.3	-1.0	-4.0	-9.2
Relative to	100 yds	-1.5	-0.1	0.0	-1.4	-4.5	-9.9
Line of Sight	150 yds	-1.5	0.3	0.9	0.0	-2.7	-7.6
Velocity, ft/sec		2800	2558	2329	2112	1906	1714
Energy, ft/lbs per grain		17.41	14.53	12.04	9.90	8.07	6.52
Time of Flight, sec		0.0000	0.0560	0.1175	0.1851	0.2599	0.3429
Path, inches	50 yds	-1.5	0.0	0.2	-1.3	-4.7	-10.5
Relative to	100 yds	-1.5	0.1	0.0	-1.5	-5.0	-10.9
Line of Sight	150 yds	-1.5	0.4	1.0	0.0	-3.0	-8.3
Velocity, ft/sec		2700	2464	2239	2026	1826	1641
Energy, ft/lbs per grain		16.18	13.48	11.13	9.11	7.40	5.98
Time of Flight, sec		0.0000	0.0582	0.1220	0.1925	0.2704	0.3571
Path, inches	50 yds	-1.5	0.0	0.1	-1.6	-5.4	-11.8
Relative to	100 yds	-1.5	0.0	0.0	-1.7	-5.5	-12.0
Line of Sight	150 yds	-1.5	0.5	1.1	0.0	-3.3	-9.1
Velocity, ft/sec		2600	2369	2149	1941	1747	1568
Energy, ft/lbs per grain		15.01	12.46	10.25	8.36	6.78	5.46
Time of Flight, sec		0.0000	0.0604	0.1269	0.2004	0.2818	0.3725
Path, inches	50 yds	-1.5	0.0	-0.1	-2.0	-6.3	-13.4
Relative to	100 yds	-1.5	0.0	-1.9	-6.1	-32.6	-13.2
Line of Sight	150 yds	-1.5	0.7	1.3	0.0	-3.6	-10.0

short range tables

Exterior Ballistic Table for Ballistic Coefficient 0.19

			RANGE			
	Muzzle	50 yds	100 yds	150 yds	200 yds	250 yds
Velocity, ft/sec	2500	2274	2059	1857	1669	1497
Energy, ft/lbs per grain	13.88	11.48	9.41	7.66	6.18	4.98
Time of Flight, sec	0.0000	0.0629	0.1322	0.2090	0.2942	0.3891
Path, inches Relative to Line of Sight — ZERO RANGE 50 yds	-1.5	0.0	-0.2	-2.4	-7.2	-15.1
100 yds	-1.5	0.1	0.0	-2.2	-6.8	-14.6
150 yds	-1.5	0.8	1.4	0.0	-4.0	-11.1
Velocity, ft/sec	2400	2179	1969	1773	1592	1428
Energy, ft/lbs per grain	12.79	10.54	8.61	6.98	5.63	4.53
Time of Flight, sec	0.0000	0.0656	0.1380	0.2183	0.3076	0.4072
Path, inches Relative to Line of Sight — ZERO RANGE 50 yds	-1.5	0.0	-0.3	-2.9	-8.3	-17.1
100 yds	-1.5	0.2	0.0	-2.4	-7.6	-16.2
150 yds	-1.5	1.0	1.6	0.0	-4.4	-12.2
Velocity, ft/sec	2300	2084	1880	1690	1516	1361
Energy, ft/lbs per grain	11.74	9.64	7.85	6.34	5.10	4.11
Time of Flight, sec	0.0000	0.0685	0.1443	0.2285	0.3222	0.4267
Path, inches Relative to Line of Sight — ZERO RANGE 50 yds	-1.5	0.0	-0.5	-3.5	-9.5	-19.3
100 yds	-1.5	0.3	0.0	-2.7	-8.5	-18.1
150 yds	-1.5	1.2	1.8	0.0	-4.9	-13.5
Velocity, ft/sec	2200	1990	1792	1609	1443	1297
Energy, ft/lbs per grain	10.75	8.79	7.13	5.75	4.62	3.73
Time of Flight, sec	0.0000	0.0717	0.1512	0.2395	0.3380	0.4478
Path, inches Relative to Line of Sight — ZERO RANGE 50 yds	-1.5	0.0	-0.7	-4.1	-10.9	-21.9
100 yds	-1.5	0.4	0.0	-3.1	-9.5	-20.1
150 yds	-1.5	1.4	2.0	0.0	-5.4	-15.0
Velocity, ft/sec	2100	1895	1704	1529	1372	1238
Energy, ft/lbs per grain	9.79	7.97	6.45	5.19	4.18	3.40
Time of Flight, sec	0.0000	0.0752	0.1587	0.2516	0.3553	0.4705
Path, inches Relative to Line of Sight — ZERO RANGE 50 yds	-1.5	0.0	-0.9	-4.9	-12.5	-24.8
100 yds	-1.5	0.5	0.0	-3.5	-10.7	-22.5
150 yds	-1.5	1.6	2.3	0.0	-6.0	-16.7
Velocity, ft/sec	2000	1802	1618	1451	1304	1183
Energy, ft/lbs per grain	8.88	7.21	5.81	4.67	3.78	3.11
Time of Flight, sec	0.0000	0.0790	0.1669	0.2649	0.3740	0.4949
Path, inches Relative to Line of Sight — ZERO RANGE 50 yds	-1.5	0.0	-1.2	-5.7	-14.4	-28.1
100 yds	-1.5	0.6	0.0	-3.9	-12.0	-25.2
150 yds	-1.5	1.9	2.6	0.0	-6.8	-18.6
Velocity, ft/sec	1900	1709	1533	1376	1241	1133
Energy, ft/lbs per grain	8.01	6.48	5.22	4.20	3.42	2.85
Time of Flight, sec	0.0000	0.0833	0.1760	0.2794	0.3943	0.5211
Path, inches Relative to Line of Sight — ZERO RANGE 50 yds	-1.5	0.0	-1.5	-6.7	-16.5	-31.9
100 yds	-1.5	0.7	0.0	-4.5	-13.5	-28.2
150 yds	-1.5	2.2	3.0	0.0	-7.6	-20.8
Velocity, ft/sec	1800	1616	1450	1303	1182	1089
Energy, ft/lbs per grain	7.19	5.80	4.67	3.77	3.10	2.63
Time of Flight, sec	0.0000	0.0880	0.1860	0.2952	0.4163	0.5488
Path, inches Relative to Line of Sight — ZERO RANGE 50 yds	-1.5	0.0	-1.8	-7.8	-18.9	-36.3
100 yds	-1.5	0.9	0.0	-5.1	-15.3	-31.7
150 yds	-1.5	2.6	3.4	0.0	-8.5	-23.2

Exterior Ballistic Table for Ballistic Coefficient 0.19

	Zero Range	Muzzle	50 yds	100 yds	150 yds	200 yds	250 yds
Velocity, ft/sec		1700	1525	1369	1235	1129	1050
Energy, ft/lbs per grain		6.42	5.16	4.16	3.39	2.83	2.45
Time of Flight, sec		0.0000	0.0932	0.1971	0.3126	0.4399	0.5779
Path, inches	50 yds	-1.5	0.0	-2.2	-9.1	-21.8	-41.2
Relative to	100 yds	-1.5	1.1	0.0	-5.8	-17.3	-35.5
Line of Sight	150 yds	-1.5	3.0	3.9	0.0	-9.6	-25.9
Velocity, ft/sec		1600	1435	1291	1172	1081	1014
Energy, ft/lbs per grain		5.68	4.57	3.70	3.05	2.59	2.28
Time of Flight, sec		0.0000	0.0990	0.2094	0.3315	0.4650	0.6085
Path, inches	50 yds	-1.5	0.0	-2.7	-10.7	-25.0	-46.7
Relative to	100 yds	-1.5	1.4	0.0	-6.6	-19.5	-39.9
Line of Sight	150 yds	-1.5	3.6	4.4	0.0	-10.7	-28.9
Velocity, ft/sec		1500	1347	1217	1115	1039	981
Energy, ft/lbs per grain		5.00	4.03	3.29	2.76	2.40	2.14
Time of Flight, sec		0.0000	0.1056	0.2230	0.3520	0.4915	0.6402
Path, inches	50 yds	-1.5	0.0	-3.3	-12.5	-28.6	-52.8
Relative to	100 yds	-1.5	1.7	0.0	-7.5	-22.0	-44.6
Line of Sight	150 yds	-1.5	4.2	5.0	0.0	-12.0	-32.0
Velocity, ft/sec		1400	1261	1149	1064	1001	951
Energy, ft/lbs per grain		4.35	3.53	2.93	2.51	2.22	2.01
Time of Flight, sec		0.0000	0.1130	0.2379	0.3738	0.5193	0.6732
Path, inches	50 yds	-1.5	0.0	-4.0	-14.5	-32.7	-59.6
Relative to	100 yds	-1.5	2.0	0.0	-8.6	-24.8	-49.7
Line of Sight	150 yds	-1.5	4.8	5.7	0.0	-13.4	-35.4
Velocity, ft/sec		1300	1179	1087	1018	965	920
Energy, ft/lbs per grain		3.75	3.09	2.62	2.30	2.07	1.88
Time of Flight, sec		0.0000	0.1213	0.2540	0.3968	0.5483	0.7077
Path, inches	50 yds	-1.5	0.0	-4.7	-16.8	-37.3	-67.1
Relative to	100 yds	-1.5	2.4	0.0	-9.7	-27.8	-55.2
Line of Sight	150 yds	-1.5	5.6	6.5	0.0	-14.9	-39.1
Velocity, ft/sec		1200	1102	1030	974	928	889
Energy, ft/lbs per grain		3.20	2.70	2.36	2.11	1.91	1.75
Time of Flight, sec		0.0000	0.1307	0.2716	0.4216	0.5794	0.7447
Path, inches	50 yds	-1.5	0.0	-5.6	-19.5	-42.5	-75.5
Relative to	100 yds	-1.5	2.8	0.0	-11.0	-31.2	-61.4
Line of Sight	150 yds	-1.5	6.5	7.3	0.0	-16.5	-43.1
Velocity, ft/sec		1100	1028	972	927	888	853
Energy, ft/lbs per grain		2.69	2.35	2.10	1.91	1.75	1.62
Time of Flight, sec		0.0000	0.1413	0.2914	0.4495	0.6150	0.7875
Path, inches	50 yds	-1.5	0.0	-6.7	-22.6	-48.6	-85.7
Relative to	100 yds	-1.5	3.4	0.0	-12.5	-35.2	-68.9
Line of Sight	150 yds	-1.5	7.5	8.4	0.0	-18.5	-48.0
Velocity, ft/sec		1000	950	908	871	838	807
Energy, ft/lbs per grain		2.22	2.00	1.83	1.68	1.56	1.45
Time of Flight, sec		0.0000	0.1540	0.3157	0.4844	0.6602	0.8426
Path, inches	50 yds	-1.5	0.0	-8.1	-26.8	-56.9	-99.4
Relative to	100 yds	-1.5	4.1	0.0	-14.6	-40.7	-79.1
Line of Sight	150 yds	-1.5	8.9	9.7	0.0	-21.2	-54.8

Exterior Ballistic Table for Ballistic Coefficient 0.21

	Muzzle	50 yds	100 yds	150 yds	200 yds	250 yds
Velocity, ft/sec	2900	2676	2463	2259	2065	1881
Energy, ft/lbs per grain	18.67	15.90	13.47	11.33	9.47	7.85
Time of Flight, sec	0.0000	0.0539	0.1123	0.1759	0.2453	0.3214
Path, inches — ZERO RANGE 50 yds	-1.5	0.0	0.3	-0.9	-3.7	-8.6
Relative to — ZERO RANGE 100 yds	-1.5	-0.1	0.0	-1.3	-4.3	-9.3
Line of Sight — ZERO RANGE 150 yds	-1.5	0.3	0.9	0.0	-2.6	-7.2
Velocity, ft/sec	2800	2581	2372	2173	1983	1804
Energy, ft/lbs per grain	17.41	14.79	12.49	10.48	8.73	7.23
Time of Flight, sec	0.0000	0.0558	0.1164	0.1825	0.2548	0.3341
Path, inches — ZERO RANGE 50 yds	-1.5	0.0	0.2	-1.2	-4.4	-9.8
Relative to — ZERO RANGE 100 yds	-1.5	-0.1	0.0	-1.5	-4.8	-10.3
Line of Sight — ZERO RANGE 150 yds	-1.5	0.4	1.0	0.0	-2.8	-7.8
Velocity, ft/sec	2700	2486	2281	2086	1901	1727
Energy, ft/lbs per grain	16.18	13.72	11.55	9.66	8.02	6.62
Time of Flight, sec	0.0000	0.0579	0.1209	0.1897	0.2650	0.3478
Path, inches — ZERO RANGE 50 yds	-1.5	0.0	0.1	-1.5	-5.1	-11.1
Relative to — ZERO RANGE 100 yds	-1.5	0.0	0.0	-1.6	-5.3	-11.3
Line of Sight — ZERO RANGE 150 yds	-1.5	0.5	1.1	0.0	-3.1	-8.6
Velocity, ft/sec	2600	2390	2190	2000	1819	1651
Energy, ft/lbs per grain	15.01	12.68	10.65	8.88	7.35	6.05
Time of Flight, sec	0.0000	0.0602	0.1257	0.1975	0.2761	0.3626
Path, inches — ZERO RANGE 50 yds	-1.5	0.0	0.0	-1.9	-5.9	-12.5
Relative to — ZERO RANGE 100 yds	-1.5	0.0	0.0	1.8	-5.8	-12.5
Line of Sight — ZERO RANGE 150 yds	-1.5	0.6	1.2	0.0	-3.4	-9.4
Velocity, ft/sec	2500	2295	2099	1913	1739	1577
Energy, ft/lbs per grain	13.88	11.69	9.78	8.12	6.71	5.52
Time of Flight, sec	0.0000	0.0626	0.1310	0.2058	0.2881	0.3787
Path, inches — ZERO RANGE 50 yds	-1.5	0.0	-0.2	-2.3	-6.8	-14.2
Relative to — ZERO RANGE 100 yds	-1.5	0.1	0.0	2.1	-6.5	-13.8
Line of Sight — ZERO RANGE 150 yds	-1.5	0.8	1.4	0.0	-3.8	-10.4
Velocity, ft/sec	2400	2199	2008	1828	1659	1504
Energy, ft/lbs per grain	12.79	10.74	8.95	7.42	6.11	5.02
Time of Flight, sec	0.0000	0.0653	0.1367	0.2150	0.3011	0.3961
Path, inches — ZERO RANGE 50 yds	-1.5	0.0	-0.3	-2.8	-7.8	-16.1
Relative to — ZERO RANGE 100 yds	-1.5	0.2	0.0	-2.3	-7.2	-15.3
Line of Sight — ZERO RANGE 150 yds	-1.5	0.9	1.5	0.0	-4.2	-11.5
Velocity, ft/sec	2300	2104	1918	1743	1581	1433
Energy, ft/lbs per grain	11.74	9.83	8.17	6.74	5.55	4.56
Time of Flight, sec	0.0000	0.0682	0.1429	0.2249	0.3153	0.4150
Path, inches — ZERO RANGE 50 yds	-1.5	0.0	-0.5	-3.3	-9.0	-18.2
Relative to — ZERO RANGE 100 yds	-1.5	0.2	0.0	-2.6	-8.1	-17.0
Line of Sight — ZERO RANGE 150 yds	-1.5	1.1	1.7	0.0	-4.6	-12.7
Velocity, ft/sec	2200	2009	1828	1660	1504	1364
Energy, ft/lbs per grain	10.75	8.96	7.42	6.12	5.02	4.13
Time of Flight, sec	0.0000	0.0714	0.1496	0.2358	0.3307	0.4355
Path, inches — ZERO RANGE 50 yds	-1.5	0.0	-0.7	-3.9	-10.4	-20.6
Relative to — ZERO RANGE 100 yds	-1.5	0.3	0.0	-2.9	-9.0	-19.0
Line of Sight — ZERO RANGE 150 yds	-1.5	1.3	2.0	0.0	-5.1	-14.1

Exterior Ballistic Table for Ballistic Coefficient 0.21

			RANGE			
	Muzzle	50 yds	100 yds	150 yds	200 yds	250 yds
Velocity, ft/sec	2100	1914	1739	1577	1430	1299
Energy, ft/lbs per grain	9.79	8.13	6.71	5.52	4.54	3.75
Time of Flight, sec	0.0000	0.0748	0.1570	0.2476	0.3475	0.4577
Path, inches — Relative to Line of Sight — ZERO RANGE 50 yds	-1.5	0.0	-0.9	-4.6	-11.9	-23.4
100 yds	-1.5	0.4	0.0	-3.3	-10.1	-21.2
150 yds	-1.5	1.5	2.2	0.0	-5.7	-15.7
Velocity, ft/sec	2000	1820	1652	1497	1358	1237
Energy, ft/lbs per grain	8.88	7.35	6.06	4.98	4.09	3.40
Time of Flight, sec	0.0000	0.0786	0.1652	0.2606	0.3659	0.4818
Path, inches — Relative to Line of Sight — ZERO RANGE 50 yds	-1.5	0.0	-1.1	-5.5	-13.7	-26.6
100 yds	-1.5	0.6	0.0	-3.8	-11.4	-23.8
150 yds	-1.5	1.8	2.5	0.0	-6.4	-17.5
Velocity, ft/sec	1900	1726	1565	1418	1289	1181
Energy, ft/lbs per grain	8.01	6.61	5.44	4.46	3.69	3.10
Time of Flight, sec	0.0000	0.0828	0.1741	0.2748	0.3859	0.5076
Path, inches — Relative to Line of Sight — ZERO RANGE 50 yds	-1.5	0.0	-1.4	-6.4	-15.7	-30.3
100 yds	-1.5	0.7	0.0	-4.3	-12.9	-26.7
150 yds	-1.5	2.1	2.8	0.0	-7.2	-19.6
Velocity, ft/sec	1800	1633	1480	1343	1225	1130
Energy, ft/lbs per grain	7.19	5.92	4.86	4.00	3.33	2.83
Time of Flight, sec	0.0000	0.0875	0.1840	0.2905	0.4076	0.5353
Path, inches — Relative to Line of Sight — ZERO RANGE 50 yds	-1.5	0.0	-1.8	-7.5	-18.1	-34.5
100 yds	-1.5	0.9	0.0	-4.9	-14.6	-30.0
150 yds	-1.5	2.5	3.2	0.0	-8.1	-21.9
Velocity, ft/sec	1700	1541	1397	1270	1166	1084
Energy, ft/lbs per grain	6.42	5.27	4.33	3.58	3.02	2.61
Time of Flight, sec	0.0000	0.0927	0.1950	0.3077	0.4311	0.5647
Path, inches — Relative to Line of Sight — ZERO RANGE 50 yds	-1.5	0.0	-2.2	-8.8	-20.8	-39.2
100 yds	-1.5	1.1	0.0	-5.5	-16.5	-33.8
150 yds	-1.5	2.9	3.7	0.0	-9.1	-24.6
Velocity, ft/sec	1600	1450	1316	1203	1113	1044
Energy, ft/lbs per grain	5.68	4.67	3.84	3.21	2.75	2.42
Time of Flight, sec	0.0000	0.0985	0.2072	0.3265	0.4564	0.5958
Path, inches — Relative to Line of Sight — ZERO RANGE 50 yds	-1.5	0.0	-2.6	-10.3	-24.0	-44.7
100 yds	-1.5	1.3	0.0	-6.3	-18.7	-38.1
150 yds	-1.5	3.4	4.2	0.0	-10.2	-27.5
Velocity, ft/sec	1500	1360	1239	1141	1066	1007
Energy, ft/lbs per grain	5.00	4.11	3.41	2.89	2.52	2.25
Time of Flight, sec	0.0000	0.1051	0.2207	0.3470	0.4832	0.6282
Path, inches — Relative to Line of Sight — ZERO RANGE 50 yds	-1.5	0.0	-3.2	-12.1	-27.6	-50.8
100 yds	-1.5	1.6	0.0	-7.3	-21.2	-42.8
150 yds	-1.5	4.0	4.8	0.0	-11.5	-30.7
Velocity, ft/sec	1400	1273	1168	1086	1023	973
Energy, ft/lbs per grain	4.35	3.60	3.03	2.62	2.32	2.10
Time of Flight, sec	0.0000	0.1125	0.2356	0.3690	0.5115	0.6620
Path, inches — Relative to Line of Sight — ZERO RANGE 50 yds	-1.5	0.0	-3.9	-14.1	-31.7	-57.6
100 yds	-1.5	1.9	0.0	-8.3	-24.0	-47.9
150 yds	-1.5	4.7	5.5	0.0	-12.9	-34.1

short range tables

Exterior Ballistic Table for Ballistic Coefficient 0.21

RANGE

		Muzzle	50 yds	100 yds	150 yds	200 yds	250 yds
Velocity, ft/sec		1300	1190	1102	1036	984	941
Energy, ft/lbs per grain		3.75	3.14	2.70	2.38	2.15	1.97
Time of Flight, sec		0.0000	0.1208	0.2519	0.3925	0.5412	0.6973
Path, inches Relative to Line of Sight	ZERO RANGE 50 yds	-1.5	0.0	-4.6	-16.4	-36.3	-65.1
	100 yds	-1.5	2.3	0.0	-9.5	-27.0	-53.5
	150 yds	-1.5	5.5	6.3	0.0	-14.4	-37.8
Velocity, ft/sec		1200	1110	1042	989	945	907
Energy, ft/lbs per grain		3.20	2.74	2.41	2.17	1.98	1.83
Time of Flight, sec		0.0000	0.1301	0.2697	0.4177	0.5730	0.7351
Path, inches Relative to Line of Sight	ZERO RANGE 50 yds	-1.5	0.0	-5.5	-19.1	-41.5	-73.7
	100 yds	-1.5	2.8	0.0	-10.8	-30.4	-59.8
	150 yds	-1.5	6.4	7.2	0.0	-16.1	-41.9
Velocity, ft/sec		1100	1034	982	939	902	869
Energy, ft/lbs per grain		2.69	2.37	2.14	1.96	1.81	1.68
Time of Flight, sec		0.0000	0.1408	0.2898	0.4461	0.6091	0.7786
Path, inches Relative to Line of Sight	ZERO RANGE 50 yds	-1.5	0.0	-6.6	-22.2	-47.7	-83.9
	100 yds	-1.5	3.3	0.0	-12.3	-34.5	-67.3
	150 yds	-1.5	7.4	8.2	0.0	-18.1	-46.8
Velocity, ft/sec		1000	954	915	881	850	822
Energy, ft/lbs per grain		2.22	2.02	1.86	1.72	1.60	1.50
Time of Flight, sec		0.0000	0.1537	0.3142	0.4814	0.6548	0.8344
Path, inches Relative to Line of Sight	ZERO RANGE 50 yds	-1.5	0.0	-8.0	-26.5	-56.1	-97.7
	100 yds	-1.5	4.0	0.0	-14.4	-40.0	-77.6
	150 yds	-1.5	8.8	9.6	0.0	-20.8	-53.6

Exterior Ballistic Table for Ballistic Coefficient 0.22

RANGE

		Muzzle	50 yds	100 yds	150 yds	200 yds	250 yds
Velocity, ft/sec		2900	2686	2482	2286	2100	1922
Energy, ft/lbs per grain		18.67	16.02	13.68	11.60	9.79	8.20
Time of Flight, sec		0.0000	0.0538	0.1110	0.1748	0.2433	0.3180
Path, inches Relative to Line of Sight	ZERO RANGE 50 yds	-1.5	0.0	0.3	-0.8	-3.6	-8.4
	100 yds	-1.5	-0.1	0.0	-1.3	-4.2	-9.1
	150 yds	-1.5	0.3	0.8	0.0	-2.5	-7.0
Velocity, ft/sec		2800	2591	2390	2199	2017	1844
Energy, ft/lbs per grain		17.41	14.90	12.68	10.74	9.03	7.55
Time of Flight, sec		0.0000	0.0557	0.1160	0.1814	0.2526	0.3304
Path, inches Relative to Line of Sight	ZERO RANGE 50 yds	-1.5	0.0	0.2	-1.1	-4.2	-9.5
	100 yds	-1.5	0.1	0.0	-1.4	-4.6	-10.0
	150 yds	-1.5	0.4	0.9	0.0	-2.8	-7.6
Velocity, ft/sec		2700	2495	2299	2112	1934	1766
Energy, ft/lbs per grain		16.18	13.82	11.73	9.90	8.30	6.92
Time of Flight, sec		0.0000	0.0578	0.1204	0.1885	0.2627	0.3439
Path, inches Relative to Line of Sight	ZERO RANGE 50 yds	-1.5	0.0	0.1	-1.4	-4.9	-10.8
	100 yds	-1.5	0.1	0.0	-1.6	-5.1	-11.0
	150 yds	-1.5	0.5	1.1	0.0	-3.0	-8.4

short range tables

Exterior Ballistic Table for Ballistic Coefficient 0.22

	Muzzle	50 yds	100 yds	150 yds	200 yds	250 yds
Velocity, ft/sec	2600	2400	2208	2025	1851	1688
Energy, ft/lbs per grain	15.01	12.79	10.82	9.10	7.61	6.33
Time of Flight, sec	0.0000	0.0601	0.1252	0.1962	0.2737	0.3585
Path, inches — ZERO RANGE 50 yds	-1.5	0.0	0.0	-1.8	-5.7	-12.2
Relative to — ZERO RANGE 100 yds	-1.5	0.0	0.0	-1.8	-5.7	-12.2
Line of Sight — ZERO RANGE 150 yds	-1.5	0.6	1.2	0.0	-3.3	-9.2
Velocity, ft/sec	2500	2304	2116	1938	1770	1612
Energy, ft/lbs per grain	13.88	11.79	9.94	8.34	6.96	5.77
Time of Flight, sec	0.0000	0.0625	0.2045	0.2855	0.3743	0.3743
Path, inches — ZERO RANGE 50 yds	-1.5	0.0	-0.1	-2.2	-6.6	-13.8
Relative to — ZERO RANGE 100 yds	-1.5	0.1	0.0	-2.0	-6.4	-13.5
Line of Sight — ZERO RANGE 150 yds	-1.5	0.7	1.3	0.0	-3.7	-10.1
Velocity, ft/sec	2400	2208	2025	1852	1689	1538
Energy, ft/lbs per grain	12.79	10.82	9.10	7.61	6.33	5.25
Time of Flight, sec	0.0000	0.0652	0.1361	0.2136	0.2984	0.3915
Path, inches — ZERO RANGE 50 yds	-1.5	0.0	-0.3	-2.7	-7.7	-15.7
Relative to — ZERO RANGE 100 yds	-1.5	0.1	0.0	-2.3	-7.1	-14.9
Line of Sight — ZERO RANGE 150 yds	-1.5	0.9	1.5	0.0	-4.1	-11.2
Velocity, ft/sec	2300	2113	1935	1766	1609	1465
Energy, ft/lbs per grain	11.74	9.91	8.31	6.92	5.75	4.76
Time of Flight, sec	0.0000	0.0680	0.1422	0.2234	0.3124	0.4101
Path, inches — ZERO RANGE 50 yds	-1.5	0.0	-0.5	-3.2	-8.8	-17.7
Relative to — ZERO RANGE 100 yds	-1.5	0.2	0.0	-2.6	-7.9	-16.6
Line of Sight — ZERO RANGE 150 yds	-1.5	1.1	1.7	0.0	-4.6	-12.4
Velocity, ft/sec	2200	2017	1844	1682	1531	1394
Energy, ft/lbs per grain	10.75	9.03	7.55	6.28	5.20	4.31
Time of Flight, sec	0.0000	0.0712	0.1490	0.2342	0.3277	0.4304
Path, inches — ZERO RANGE 50 yds	-1.5	0.0	-0.6	-3.8	-10.1	-20.1
Relative to — ZERO RANGE 100 yds	-1.5	0.3	0.0	-2.9	-8.8	-18.5
Line of Sight — ZERO RANGE 150 yds	-1.5	1.3	1.9	0.0	-5.0	-13.7
Velocity, ft/sec	2100	1922	1755	1599	1455	1327
Energy, ft/lbs per grain	9.79	8.20	6.84	5.68	4.70	3.91
Time of Flight, sec	0.0000	0.0747	0.1563	0.2459	0.3443	0.4523
Path, inches — ZERO RANGE 50 yds	-1.5	0.0	-0.9	-4.5	-11.6	-22.9
Relative to — ZERO RANGE 100 yds	-1.5	0.4	0.0	-3.3	-9.9	-20.7
Line of Sight — ZERO RANGE 150 yds	-1.5	1.5	2.2	0.0	-5.6	-15.3
Velocity, ft/sec	2000	1828	1666	1517	1382	1263
Energy, ft/lbs per grain	8.88	7.42	6.16	5.11	4.24	3.54
Time of Flight, sec	0.0000	0.0785	0.1644	0.2588	0.3624	0.4761
Path, inches — ZERO RANGE 50 yds	-1.5	0.0	-1.1	-5.4	-13.4	-26.0
Relative to — ZERO RANGE 100 yds	-1.5	0.6	0.0	-3.7	-11.2	-23.2
Line of Sight — ZERO RANGE 150 yds	-1.5	1.8	2.5	0.0	-6.2	-17.1
Velocity, ft/sec	1900	1734	1579	1438	1311	1203
Energy, ft/lbs per grain	8.01	6.68	5.54	4.59	3.82	3.21
Time of Flight, sec	0.0000	0.0827	0.1733	0.2729	0.3823	0.5018
Path, inches — ZERO RANGE 50 yds	-1.5	0.0	-1.4	-6.3	-15.4	-29.6
Relative to — ZERO RANGE 100 yds	-1.5	0.7	0.0	-4.2	-12.6	-26.1
Line of Sight — ZERO RANGE 150 yds	-1.5	2.1	2.8	0.0	-7.0	-19.1

short range tables

Exterior Ballistic Table for Ballistic Coefficient 0.22

	Muzzle	50 yds	100 yds	150 yds	200 yds	250 yds
			RANGE			
Velocity, ft/sec	1800	1641	1493	1360	1245	1149
Energy, ft/lbs per grain	7.19	5.98	4.95	4.11	3.44	2.93
Time of Flight, sec	0.0000	0.0873	0.1832	0.2885	0.4039	0.5294
Path, inches — ZERO RANGE 50 yds	-1.5	0.0	-1.7	-7.4	-17.7	-33.7
Relative to Line of Sight — ZERO RANGE 100 yds	-1.5	0.9	0.0	-4.8	-14.3	-29.3
— ZERO RANGE 150 yds	-1.5	2.5	3.2	0.0	-7.9	-21.4
Velocity, ft/sec	1700	1548	1409	1287	1183	1101
Energy, ft/lbs per grain	6.42	5.32	4.41	3.68	3.11	2.69
Time of Flight, sec	0.0000	0.0925	0.1941	0.3056	0.4273	0.5589
Path, inches — ZERO RANGE 50 yds	-1.5	0.0	-2.1	-8.7	-20.4	-38.4
Relative to Line of Sight — ZERO RANGE 100 yds	-1.5	1.1	0.0	-5.5	-16.2	-33.1
— ZERO RANGE 150 yds	-1.5	2.9	3.6	0.0	-8.9	-24.0
Velocity, ft/sec	1600	1456	1328	1217	1127	1058
Energy, ft/lbs per grain	5.68	4.71	3.92	3.29	2.82	2.49
Time of Flight, sec	0.0000	0.0983	0.2062	0.3244	0.4568	0.5901
Path, inches — ZERO RANGE 50 yds	-1.5	0.0	-2.6	-10.2	-23.6	-43.8
Relative to Line of Sight — ZERO RANGE 100 yds	-1.5	1.3	0.0	-6.2	-18.4	-37.3
— ZERO RANGE 150 yds	-1.5	3.4	4.2	0.0	-10.0	-26.9
Velocity, ft/sec	1500	1366	1250	1153	1078	1019
Energy, ft/lbs per grain	5.00	4.14	3.47	2.95	2.58	2.31
Time of Flight, sec	0.0000	0.1048	0.2197	0.3449	0.4796	0.6229
Path, inches — ZERO RANGE 50 yds	-1.5	0.0	-3.2	-11.9	-27.2	-49.9
Relative to Line of Sight — ZERO RANGE 100 yds	-1.5	1.6	0.0	-7.2	-20.8	-42.0
— ZERO RANGE 150 yds	-1.5	4.0	4.8	0.0	-11.3	-30.1
Velocity, ft/sec	1400	1278	1176	1096	1033	984
Energy, ft/lbs per grain	4.35	3.63	3.07	2.67	2.37	2.15
Time of Flight, sec	0.0000	0.1122	0.2347	0.3669	0.5081	0.6570
Path, inches — ZERO RANGE 50 yds	-1.5	0.0	-3.8	-13.9	-31.2	-56.7
Relative to Line of Sight — ZERO RANGE 100 yds	-1.5	1.9	0.0	-8.2	-23.6	-47.2
— ZERO RANGE 150 yds	-1.5	4.6	5.5	0.0	-12.7	-33.5
Velocity, ft/sec	1300	1194	1109	1044	992	950
Energy, ft/lbs per grain	3.75	3.17	2.73	2.42	2.18	2.00
Time of Flight, sec	0.0000	0.1205	0.2510	0.3906	0.5381	0.6927
Path, inches — ZERO RANGE 50 yds	-1.5	0.0	-4.6	-16.2	-35.9	-64.3
Relative to Line of Sight — ZERO RANGE 100 yds	-1.5	2.3	0.0	-9.3	-26.7	-52.8
— ZERO RANGE 150 yds	-1.5	5.4	6.2	0.0	-14.2	-37.2
Velocity, ft/sec	1200	1114	1048	995	952	915
Energy, ft/lbs per grain	3.20	2.76	2.44	2.20	2.01	1.86
Time of Flight, sec	0.0000	0.1299	0.2689	0.4160	0.5702	0.7309
Path, inches — ZERO RANGE 50 yds	-1.5	0.0	-5.5	-18.9	-41.1	-72.8
Relative to Line of Sight — ZERO RANGE 100 yds	-1.5	2.7	0.0	-10.7	-30.1	-59.1
— ZERO RANGE 150 yds	-1.5	6.3	7.1	0.0	-15.9	-41.3
Velocity, ft/sec	1100	1037	986	945	909	877
Energy, ft/lbs per grain	2.69	2.39	2.16	1.98	1.83	1.71
Time of Flight, sec	0.0000	0.1406	0.2891	0.4446	0.6065	0.7747
Path, inches — ZERO RANGE 50 yds	-1.5	0.0	-6.6	-22.1	-47.3	-83.1
Relative to Line of Sight — ZERO RANGE 100 yds	-1.5	3.3	0.0	-12.2	-34.2	-66.7
— ZERO RANGE 150 yds	-1.5	7.4	8.1	0.0	-17.9	-46.3

short range tables

Exterior Ballistic Table for Ballistic Coefficient 0.22

			RANGE			
	Muzzle	50 yds	100 yds	150 yds	200 yds	250 yds
Velocity, ft/sec	1000	956	919	885	855	828
Energy, ft/lbs per grain	2.22	2.03	1.87	1.74	1.62	1.52
Time of Flight, sec	0.0000	0.1535	0.3136	0.4800	0.6525	0.8308
Path, inches — Relative to Line of Sight — ZERO RANGE 50 yds	-1.5	0.0	-8.0	-26.3	-55.7	-97.0
100 yds	-1.5	4.0	0.0	-14.3	-39.7	-77.0
150 yds	-1.5	8.8	9.5	0.0	-20.6	-53.1

Exterior Ballistic Table for Ballistic Coefficient 0.23

			RANGE			
	Muzzle	50 yds	100 yds	150 yds	200 yds	250 yds
Velocity, ft/sec	2900	2695	2499	2311	2131	1960
Energy, ft/lbs per grain	18.67	16.12	13.86	11.86	10.08	8.53
Time of Flight, sec	0.0000	0.0537	0.1115	0.1739	0.2415	0.3149
Path, inches — ZERO RANGE 50 yds	-1.5	0.0	0.3	-0.8	-3.5	-8.2
Relative to 100 yds	-1.5	-0.2	0.0	-1.2	-4.1	-8.9
Line of Sight 150 yds	-1.5	0.3	0.8	0.0	-2.5	-6.8
Velocity, ft/sec	2800	2599	2408	2224	2048	1880
Energy, ft/lbs per grain	17.41	15.00	12.87	10.98	9.31	7.85
Time of Flight, sec	0.0000	0.0556	0.1156	0.1804	0.2507	0.3271
Path, inches — ZERO RANGE 50 yds	-1.5	0.0	0.2	-1.1	-4.1	-9.3
Relative to 100 yds	-1.5	-0.1	0.0	-1.4	-4.6	-9.8
Line of Sight 150 yds	-1.5	0.4	0.9	0.0	-2.7	-7.5
Velocity, ft/sec	2700	2504	2316	2136	1964	1801
Energy, ft/lbs per grain	16.18	13.92	11.91	10.13	8.56	7.20
Time of Flight, sec	0.0000	0.0577	0.1200	0.1874	0.2607	0.3404
Path, inches — ZERO RANGE 50 yds	-1.5	0.0	0.1	-1.4	-4.8	-10.5
Relative to 100 yds	-1.5	4.1	0.0	-1.6	-5.0	-10.8
Line of Sight 150 yds	-1.5	0.5	1.0	0.0	-3.0	-8.2
Velocity, ft/sec	2600	2408	2224	2048	1881	1723
Energy, ft/lbs per grain	15.01	12.87	10.98	9.31	7.85	6.59
Time of Flight, sec	0.0000	0.0599	0.1248	0.1950	0.2715	0.3548
Path, inches — ZERO RANGE 50 yds	-1.5	0.0	0.0	-1.8	-5.6	-11.9
Relative to 100 yds	-1.5	0.0	0.0	-1.8	-5.6	-11.9
Line of Sight 150 yds	-1.5	0.6	1.2	0.0	-3.3	-9.0
Velocity, ft/sec	2500	2312	2132	1961	1798	1645
Energy, ft/lbs per grain	13.88	11.87	10.09	8.54	7.18	6.01
Time of Flight, sec	0.0000	0.0624	0.1299	0.2033	0.2832	0.3704
Path, inches — ZERO RANGE 50 yds	-1.5	0.0	-0.1	-2.2	-6.5	-13.5
Relative to 100 yds	-1.5	0.1	0.0	-2.0	-6.2	-13.2
Line of Sight 150 yds	-1.5	0.7	1.3	0.0	-3.6	-9.9
Velocity, ft/sec	2400	2216	2041	1874	1716	1569
Energy, ft/lbs per grain	12.79	10.90	9.25	7.80	6.54	5.47
Time of Flight, sec	0.0000	0.0650	0.1356	0.2123	0.2959	0.3874
Path, inches — ZERO RANGE 50 yds	-1.5	0.0	-0.3	-2.6	-7.5	-15.3
Relative to 100 yds	-1.5	0.1	0.0	-2.2	-6.9	-14.6
Line of Sight 150 yds	-1.5	0.9	1.5	0.0	-4.0	-10.9

Exterior Ballistic Table for Ballistic Coefficient 0.23

	Zero Range	Muzzle	50 yds	100 yds	150 yds	200 yds	250 yds
Velocity, ft/sec		2300	2121	1950	1788	1636	1495
Energy, ft/lbs per grain		11.74	9.99	8.44	7.10	5.94	4.96
Time of Flight, sec		0.0000	0.0679	0.1417	0.2220	0.3098	0.4057
Path, inches	50 yds	-1.5	0.0	-0.4	-3.2	-8.6	-17.3
Relative to	100 yds	-1.5	0.2	0.0	-2.5	-7.7	-16.2
Line of Sight	150 yds	-1.5	1.1	1.7	0.0	-4.4	-12.1
Velocity, ft/sec		2200	2025	1859	1702	1557	1423
Energy, ft/lbs per grain		10.75	9.10	7.67	6.43	5.38	4.50
Time of Flight, sec		0.0000	0.0711	0.1484	0.2327	0.3249	0.4257
Path, inches	50 yds	-1.5	0.0	-0.6	-3.8	-9.9	-19.7
Relative to	100 yds	-1.5	0.3	0.0	-2.8	-8.7	-18.1
Line of Sight	150 yds	-1.5	1.3	1.9	0.0	-4.9	-13.4
Velocity, ft/sec		2100	1930	1769	1618	1479	1353
Energy, ft/lbs per grain		9.79	8.27	6.95	5.81	4.86	4.06
Time of Flight, sec		0.0000	0.0745	0.1557	0.2444	0.3413	0.4474
Path, inches	50 yds	-1.5	0.0	-0.8	-4.5	-11.4	-22.3
Relative to	100 yds	-1.5	0.4	0.0	-3.2	-9.7	-20.2
Line of Sight	150 yds	-1.5	1.5	2.1	0.0	-5.5	-14.9
Velocity, ft/sec		2000	1835	1680	1536	1404	1287
Energy, ft/lbs per grain		8.88	7.48	6.27	5.24	4.38	3.68
Time of Flight, sec		0.0000	0.0783	0.1637	0.2572	0.3593	0.4710
Path, inches	50 yds	-1.5	0.0	-1.1	-5.3	-13.1	-25.4
Relative to	100 yds	-1.5	0.5	0.0	-3.6	-11.0	22.7
Line of Sight	150 yds	-1.5	1.8	2.4	0.0	-6.1	-16.6
Velocity, ft/sec		1900	1741	1592	1455	1332	1225
Energy, ft/lbs per grain		8.01	6.73	5.63	4.70	3.94	3.33
Time of Flight, sec		0.0000	0.0825	0.1726	0.2712	0.3790	0.4965
Path, inches	50 yds	-1.5	0.0	-1.4	-6.2	-15.1	-28.9
Relative to	100 yds	-1.5	0.7	0.0	-4.1	-12.4	25.5
Line of Sight	150 yds	-1.5	2.1	2.7	0.0	-6.9	-18.6
Velocity, ft/sec		1800	1647	1506	1377	1263	1168
Energy, ft/lbs per grain		7.19	6.02	5.04	4.21	3.54	3.03
Time of Flight, sec		0.0000	0.0871	0.1824	0.2866	0.4005	0.5241
Path, inches	50 yds	-1.5	0.0	-1.7	-7.3	-17.4	-33.0
Relative to	100 yds	-1.5	0.9	0.0	-4.7	-14.0	-28.7
Line of Sight	150 yds	-1.5	2.4	3.1	0.0	-7.7	-20.9
Velocity, ft/sec		1700	1554	1421	1302	1200	1117
Energy, ft/lbs per grain		6.42	5.36	4.48	3.76	3.20	2.77
Time of Flight, sec		0.0000	0.0923	0.1933	0.3037	0.4238	0.5536
Path, inches	50 yds	-1.5	0.0	-2.1	-8.5	-20.1	-37.7
Relative to	100 yds	-1.5	1.1	0.0	-5.4	-15.9	-32.4
Line of Sight	150 yds	-1.5	2.8	3.6	0.0	-8.7	-23.5
Velocity, ft/sec		1600	1462	1338	1230	1141	1072
Energy, ft/lbs per grain		5.68	4.75	3.97	3.36	2.89	2.55
Time of Flight, sec		0.0000	0.0981	0.2054	0.3224	0.4491	0.5849
Path, inches	50 yds	-1.5	0.0	-2.6	-10.0	-23.2	-43.0
Relative to	100 yds	-1.5	1.3	0.0	-6.1	-18.0	-36.6
Line of Sight	150 yds	-1.5	3.3	4.1	0.0	-9.8	-26.3

short range tables

Exterior Ballistic Table for Ballistic Coefficient 0.23

			RANGE			
	Muzzle	50 yds	100 yds	150 yds	200 yds	250 yds
Velocity, ft/sec	1500	1372	1259	1164	1090	1031
Energy, ft/lbs per grain	5.00	4.18	3.52	3.01	2.64	2.36
Time of Flight, sec	0.0000	0.1046	0.2189	0.3429	0.4762	0.6179

Path, inches	50 yds	-1.5	0.0	-3.1	-11.7	-26.8	-49.1
Relative to / ZERO RANGE	100 yds	-1.5	1.6	0.0	-7.0	-20.5	-41.3
Line of Sight	150 yds	-1.5	3.9	4.7	0.0	-11.1	-29.5

Velocity, ft/sec	1400	1283	1184	1105	1043	994
Energy, ft/lbs per grain	4.35	3.65	3.11	2.71	2.42	2.19
Time of Flight, sec	0.0000	0.1120	0.2338	0.3650	0.5049	0.6524

Path, inches	50 yds	-1.5	0.0	-3.8	-13.8	-30.8	-55.9
Relative to / ZERO RANGE	100 yds	-1.5	1.9	0.0	-8.1	-23.3	-46.4
Line of Sight	150 yds	-1.5	4.6	5.4	0.0	-12.5	-33.0

Velocity, ft/sec	1300	1198	1116	1052	1001	959
Energy, ft/lbs per grain	3.75	3.19	2.76	2.46	2.22	2.04
Time of Flight, sec	0.0000	0.1203	0.2502	0.3888	0.5351	0.6884

Path, inches	50 yds	-1.5	0.0	-4.6	-16.1	-35.4	-63.5
Relative to / ZERO RANGE	100 yds	-1.5	2.3	0.0	-9.2	-26.3	-52.1
Line of Sight	150 yds	-1.5	5.4	6.2	0.0	-14.0	-36.7

Velocity, ft/sec	1200	1117	1053	1001	959	923
Energy, ft/lbs per grain	3.20	2.77	2.46	2.22	2.04	1.89
Time of Flight, sec	0.0000	0.1297	0.2682	0.4144	0.5675	0.7270

Path, inches	50 yds	-1.5	0.0	-5.5	-18.7	-40.7	-72.1
Relative to / ZERO RANGE	100 yds	-1.5	2.7	0.0	-10.6	-29.8	-58.4
Line of Sight	150 yds	-1.5	6.2	7.0	0.0	-15.7	-40.8

Velocity, ft/sec	1100	1039	990	950	915	883
Energy, ft/lbs per grain	2.69	2.40	2.18	2.00	1.86	1.73
Time of Flight, sec	0.0000	0.1404	0.2884	0.4432	0.6042	0.7712

Path, inches	50 yds	-1.5	0.0	-6.5	-21.9	-47.0	-82.4
Relative to / ZERO RANGE	100 yds	-1.5	3.3	0.0	-12.1	-33.9	-66.0
Line of Sight	150 yds	-1.5	7.3	8.1	0.0	-17.7	-45.8

Velocity, ft/sec	1000	958	922	890	861	834
Energy, ft/lbs per grain	2.22	2.04	1.89	1.76	1.65	1.54
Time of Flight, sec	0.0000	0.1533	0.3131	0.4788	0.6504	0.8275

Path, inches	50 yds	-1.5	0.0	-8.0	-26.2	-55.4	-96.3
Relative to / ZERO RANGE	100 yds	-1.5	4.0	0.0	-14.2	-39.4	-76.3
Line of Sight	150 yds	-1.5	8.7	9.5	0.0	-20.5	-52.7

Exterior Ballistic Table for Ballistic Coefficient 0.24

			RANGE			
	Muzzle	50 yds	100 yds	150 yds	200 yds	250 yds
Velocity, ft/sec	2900	2703	2515	2334	2161	1995
Energy, ft/lbs per grain	18.67	16.22	14.04	12.09	10.37	8.84
Time of Flight, sec	0.0000	0.0536	0.1111	0.1730	0.2398	0.3121

Path, inches	50 yds	-1.5	0.0	0.3	-0.8	-3.4	-8.0
Relative to / ZERO RANGE	100 yds	-1.5	-0.2	0.0	-1.2	-4.0	-8.7
Line of Sight	150 yds	-1.5	0.3	0.8	0.0	-2.4	-6.7

short range tables

	Muzzle	50 yds	100 yds	150 yds	200 yds	250 yds
				RANGE		
Velocity, ft/sec	2800	2608	2423	2246	2077	1915
Energy, ft/lbs per grain	17.41	15.10	13.03	11.20	9.58	8.14
Time of Flight, sec	0.0000	0.0555	0.1152	0.1795	0.2489	0.3242
Path, inches / Relative to Line of Sight — ZERO RANGE 50 yds	-1.5	0.0	0.2	-1.0	-4.0	-9.0
ZERO RANGE 100 yds	-1.5	-0.1	0.0	-1.4	-4.5	-9.6
ZERO RANGE 150 yds	-1.5	0.3	0.9	0.0	-2.6	-7.3
Velocity, ft/sec	2700	2512	2331	2158	1992	1834
Energy, ft/lbs per grain	16.18	14.01	12.06	10.34	8.81	7.47
Time of Flight, sec	0.0000	0.0576	0.1196	0.1865	0.2588	0.3373
Path, inches — ZERO RANGE 50 yds	-1.5	0.0	0.1	-1.4	-4.7	-10.3
ZERO RANGE 100 yds	-1.5	-0.1	0.0	-1.5	-5.0	-10.6
ZERO RANGE 150 yds	-1.5	0.5	1.0	0.0	-2.9	-8.0
Velocity, ft/sec	2600	2416	2239	2070	1908	1755
Energy, ft/lbs per grain	15.01	12.96	11.13	9.51	8.08	6.84
Time of Flight, sec	0.0000	0.0599	0.1243	0.1940	0.2695	0.3515
Path, inches — ZERO RANGE 50 yds	-1.5	0.0	0.0	-1.7	-5.5	-11.6
ZERO RANGE 100 yds	-1.5	0.0	0.0	-1.7	-5.5	-11.7
ZERO RANGE 150 yds	-1.5	0.6	1.2	0.0	-3.2	-8.8
Velocity, ft/sec	2500	2320	2147	1982	1825	1676
Energy, ft/lbs per grain	13.88	11.95	10.23	8.72	7.39	6.24
Time of Flight, sec	0.0000	0.0623	0.1295	0.2022	0.2811	0.3669
Path, inches — ZERO RANGE 50 yds	-1.5	0.0	-0.1	-2.1	-6.3	-13.2
ZERO RANGE 100 yds	-1.5	0.1	0.0	-1.9	-6.1	-12.9
ZERO RANGE 150 yds	-1.5	0.7	1.3	0.0	-3.5	-9.6
Velocity, ft/sec	2400	2224	2055	1894	1742	1599
Energy, ft/lbs per grain	12.79	10.98	9.38	7.96	6.74	5.68
Time of Flight, sec	0.0000	0.0649	0.1351	0.2111	0.2937	0.3836
Path, inches — ZERO RANGE 50 yds	-1.5	0.0	-0.3	-2.6	-7.3	-15.0
ZERO RANGE 100 yds	-1.5	0.1	0.0	-2.2	-6.8	-14.3
ZERO RANGE 150 yds	-1.5	0.9	1.5	0.0	-3.9	-10.6
Velocity, ft/sec	2300	2128	1964	1807	1660	1523
Energy, ft/lbs per grain	11.74	10.05	8.56	7.25	6.12	5.15
Time of Flight, sec	0.0000	0.0678	0.1412	0.2208	0.3074	0.4018
Path, inches — ZERO RANGE 50 yds	-1.5	0.0	-0.4	-3.1	-8.5	-17.0
ZERO RANGE 100 yds	-1.5	0.2	0.0	-2.5	-7.6	-15.9
ZERO RANGE 150 yds	-1.5	1.0	1.6	0.0	-4.3	-11.8
Velocity, ft/sec	2200	2032	1873	1721	1580	1450
Energy, ft/lbs per grain	10.75	9.17	7.79	6.58	5.54	4.67
Time of Flight, sec	0.0000	0.0709	0.1478	0.2314	0.3224	0.4215
Path, inches — ZERO RANGE 50 yds	-1.5	0.0	-0.6	-3.7	-9.7	-19.3
ZERO RANGE 100 yds	-1.5	0.3	0.0	-2.8	-8.5	-17.7
ZERO RANGE 150 yds	-1.5	1.2	1.9	0.0	-4.8	-13.1
Velocity, ft/sec	2100	1937	1782	1637	1502	1378
Energy, ft/lbs per grain	9.79	8.33	7.05	5.95	5.01	4.22
Time of Flight, sec	0.0000	0.0744	0.1551	0.2430	0.3387	0.4430
Path, inches — ZERO RANGE 50 yds	-1.5	0.0	-0.8	-4.4	-11.2	-21.9
ZERO RANGE 100 yds	-1.5	0.4	0.0	-3.2	-9.6	-19.8
ZERO RANGE 150 yds	-1.5	1.5	2.1	0.0	-5.4	-14.6

short range tables

Exterior Ballistic Table for Ballistic Coefficient 0.24

			RANGE			
	Muzzle	50 yds	100 yds	150 yds	200 yds	250 yds
Velocity, ft/sec	2000	1842	1693	1553	1425	1310
Energy, ft/lbs per grain	8.88	7.53	6.36	5.35	4.51	3.81
Time of Flight, sec	0.0000	0.0782	0.1631	0.2557	0.3565	0.4664
Path, inches — Relative to Line of Sight — ZERO RANGE 50 yds	-1.5	0.0	-1.1	-5.5	-12.9	-24.9
100 yds	-1.5	0.5	0.0	-3.6	-10.8	-22.2
150 yds	-1.5	1.7	2.4	0.0	-6.0	-16.3
Velocity, ft/sec	1900	1747	1604	1472	1351	1246
Energy, ft/lbs per grain	8.01	6.78	5.71	4.81	4.05	3.45
Time of Flight, sec	0.0000	0.0823	0.1720	0.2696	0.3760	0.4917
Path, inches — Relative to Line of Sight — ZERO RANGE 50 yds	-1.5	0.0	-1.4	-6.1	-14.8	-28.4
100 yds	-1.5	0.7	0.0	-4.1	-12.1	-25.0
150 yds	-1.5	2.0	2.7	0.0	-6.7	-18.2
Velocity, ft/sec	1800	1653	1517	1392	1281	1186
Energy, ft/lbs per grain	7.19	6.07	5.11	4.30	3.64	3.12
Time of Flight, sec	0.0000	0.0870	0.1817	0.2850	0.3974	0.5192
Path, inches — Relative to Line of Sight — ZERO RANGE 50 yds	-1.5	0.0	-1.7	-7.2	-17.1	-32.4
100 yds	-1.5	0.8	0.0	-4.6	-13.7	-28.2
150 yds	-1.5	2.4	3.1	0.0	-7.6	-20.5
Velocity, ft/sec	1700	1560	1431	1316	1215	1133
Energy, ft/lbs per grain	6.42	5.40	4.55	3.84	3.28	2.85
Time of Flight, sec	0.0000	0.0921	0.1925	0.3019	0.4206	0.5486
Path, inches — Relative to Line of Sight — ZERO RANGE 50 yds	-1.5	0.0	-2.1	-8.4	-19.8	-37.0
100 yds	-1.5	1.0	0.0	-5.3	-15.6	-31.8
150 yds	-1.5	2.8	3.5	0.0	-8.6	-23.0
Velocity, ft/sec	1600	1468	1348	1243	1155	1085
Energy, ft/lbs per grain	5.68	4.78	4.03	3.43	2.96	2.61
Time of Flight, sec	0.0000	0.0979	0.2046	0.3206	0.4459	0.5801
Path, inches — Relative to Line of Sight — ZERO RANGE 50 yds	-1.5	0.0	-2.5	-9.9	-22.8	-42.3
100 yds	-1.5	1.3	0.0	-6.1	-17.7	-35.9
150 yds	-1.5	3.3	4.0	0.0	-9.7	-25.8
Velocity, ft/sec	1500	1377	1268	1175	1101	1042
Energy, ft/lbs per grain	5.00	4.21	3.57	3.07	2.69	2.41
Time of Flight, sec	0.0000	0.1044	0.2180	0.3411	0.4731	0.6133
Path, inches — Relative to Line of Sight — ZERO RANGE 50 yds	-1.5	0.0	-3.1	-11.6	-26.4	-48.3
100 yds	-1.5	1.5	0.0	-7.0	-20.2	-40.6
150 yds	-1.5	3.9	4.6	0.0	-10.9	-29.0
Velocity, ft/sec	1400	1288	1192	1114	1053	1003
Energy, ft/lbs per grain	4.35	3.68	3.15	2.76	2.46	2.23
Time of Flight, sec	0.0000	0.118	0.2330	0.3633	0.5019	0.6481
Path, inches — Relative to Line of Sight — ZERO RANGE 50 yds	-1.5	0.0	-3.7	-13.6	-30.5	-55.2
100 yds	-1.5	1.9	0.0	-8.0	-23.0	-45.8
150 yds	-1.5	4.5	5.3	0.0	-12.3	-32.5
Velocity, ft/sec	1300	1202	1122	1059	1008	967
Energy, ft/lbs per grain	3.75	3.21	2.79	2.49	2.26	2.08
Time of Flight, sec	0.0000	0.1201	0.2494	0.3872	0.5324	0.6845
Path, inches — Relative to Line of Sight — ZERO RANGE 50 yds	-1.5	0.0	-4.5	-15.9	-35.1	-62.8
100 yds	-1.5	2.3	0.0	-9.2	-26.0	-51.5
150 yds	-1.5	5.3	6.1	0.0	-13.8	-36.2

short range tables

Exterior Ballistic Table for Ballistic Coefficient 0.24

		Muzzle	50 yds	100 yds	150 yds	200 yds	250 yds
Velocity, ft/sec		1200	1120	1058	1007	966	930
Energy, ft/lbs per grain		3.20	2.78	2.49	2.25	2.07	1.92
Time of Flight, sec		0.0000	0.1295	0.2675	0.4129	0.5651	0.7234
Path, inches	50 yds	-1.5	0.0	-5.4	-18.6	-40.3	-71.4
Relative to	100 yds	-1.5	2.7	0.0	-10.5	-29.5	-57.8
Line of Sight (ZERO RANGE)	150 yds	-1.5	6.2	7.0	0.0	-15.5	-40.4
Velocity, ft/sec		1100	1041	994	955	920	890
Energy, ft/lbs per grain		2.69	2.41	2.19	2.02	1.88	1.76
Time of Flight, sec		0.0000	0.1403	0.2878	0.4419	0.6021	0.7679
Path, inches	50 yds	-1.5	0.0	-6.5	-21.8	-46.6	-81.7
Relative to	100 yds	-1.5	3.3	0.0	-12.0	-33.6	-65.6
Line of Sight (ZERO RANGE)	150 yds	-1.5	7.3	8.0	0.0	-17.6	-45.4
Velocity, ft/sec		1000	960	925	893	865	839
Energy, ft/lbs per grain		2.22	2.05	1.90	1.77	1.66	1.56
Time of Flight, sec		0.0000	0.1532	0.3126	0.4776	0.6484	0.8244
Path, inches	50 yds	-1.5	0.0	-7.9	-26.0	-55.0	-95.6
Relative to	100 yds	-1.5	4.0	0.0	-14.1	-33.2	-75.8
Line of Sight (ZERO RANGE)	150 yds	-1.5	8.7	9.4	0.0	-20.3	-52.2

Exterior Ballistic Table for Ballistic Coefficient 0.25

		Muzzle	50 yds	100 yds	150 yds	200 yds	250 yds
Velocity, ft/sec		2900	2711	2530	2356	2188	2028
Energy, ft/lbs per grain		18.67	16.32	14.21	12.32	10.63	9.13
Time of Flight, sec		0.0000	0.0535	0.1108	0.1722	0.2383	0.3095
Path, inches	50 yds	-1.5	0.0	0.3	-0.7	-3.3	-7.8
Relative to	100 yds	-1.5	-0.2	0.0	-1.2	-4.0	-8.6
Line of Sight (ZERO RANGE)	150 yds	-1.5	0.2	0.8	0.0	-2.4	-6.6
Velocity, ft/sec		2800	2615	2438	2267	2103	1946
Energy, ft/lbs per grain		17.41	15.18	13.20	11.41	9.82	8.41
Time of Flight, sec		0.0000	0.0554	0.1148	0.1787	0.2474	0.3215
Path, inches	50 yds	-1.5	0.0	0.2	-1.0	-3.9	-8.8
Relative to	100 yds	-1.5	-0.1	0.0	-1.4	-4.4	-9.4
Line of Sight (ZERO RANGE)	150 yds	-1.5	0.3	0.9	0.0	-2.6	-7.2
Velocity, ft/sec		2700	2519	2345	2178	2018	1865
Energy, ft/lbs per grain		16.18	14.09	12.21	10.53	9.04	7.72
Time of Flight, sec		0.0000	0.0575	0.1192	0.1856	0.2571	0.3344
Path, inches	50 yds	-1.5	0.0	0.1	-1.3	-4.6	-10.0
Relative to	100 yds	-1.5	-0.1	0.0	-1.5	-4.9	-10.4
Line of Sight (ZERO RANGE)	150 yds	-1.5	0.4	1.0	0.0	-2.8	-7.8
Velocity, ft/sec		2600	2423	2253	2090	1933	1785
Energy, ft/lbs per grain		15.01	13.03	11.27	9.70	8.30	7.07
Time of Flight, sec		0.0000	0.0598	0.1240	0.1931	0.2677	0.3485
Path, inches	50 yds	-1.5	0.0	0.0	-1.7	-5.4	-11.4
Relative to	100 yds	-1.5	0.0	0.0	-1.7	-5.4	-11.4
Line of Sight (ZERO RANGE)	150 yds	-1.5	0.6	1.1	0.0	-3.1	-8.6

short range tables

	Muzzle	50 yds	100 yds	150 yds	200 yds	250 yds
RANGE						

		Muzzle	50 yds	100 yds	150 yds	200 yds	250 yds
Velocity, ft/sec		2500	2327	2161	2001	1849	1705
Energy, ft/lbs per grain		13.88	12.02	10.37	8.89	7.59	6.45
Time of Flight, sec		0.0000	0.0622	0.1291	0.2012	0.2792	0.3637
Path, inches	50 yds	-1.5	0.0	-0.1	-2.1	-6.2	12.9
Relative to	100 yds	-1.5	0.1	0.0	-1.9	-6.0	-12.7
Line of Sight ZERO RANGE	150 yds	-1.5	0.7	1.3	0.0	-3.5	-9.5
Velocity, ft/sec		2400	2231	2068	1913	1766	1627
Energy, ft/lbs per grain		12.79	11.05	9.49	8.12	6.92	5.88
Time of Flight, sec		0.0000	0.0648	0.1347	0.2101	0.2917	0.3802
Path, inches	50 yds	-1.5	0.0	-0.2	-2.5	-7.2	-14.7
Relative to	100 yds	-1.5	0.1	0.0	-2.2	-6.7	-14.0
Line of Sight ZERO RANGE	150 yds	-1.5	0.8	1.4	0.0	-3.8	-10.4
Velocity, ft/sec		2300	2135	1976	1826	1683	1550
Energy, ft/lbs per grain		11.74	10.12	8.67	7.40	6.29	5.33
Time of Flight, sec		0.0000	0.0677	0.1407	0.2197	0.3053	0.3982
Path, inches	50 yds	-1.5	0.0	-0.4	-3.1	-8.3	-16.6
Relative to	100 yds	-1.5	0.2	0.0	-2.4	-7.5	-15.6
Line of Sight ZERO RANGE	150 yds	-1.5	1.0	1.6	0.0	-4.2	-11.5
Velocity, ft/sec		2200	2039	1885	1739	1602	1475
Energy, ft/lbs per grain		10.75	9.23	7.89	6.71	5.70	4.83
Time of Flight, sec		0.0000	0.0708	0.1473	0.2302	0.3201	0.4177
Path, inches	50 yds	-1.5	0.0	-0.6	-3.6	-9.6	-18.9
Relative to	100 yds	-1.5	0.3	0.0	-2.7	-8.4	-17.4
Line of Sight ZERO RANGE	150 yds	-1.5	1.2	1.8	0.0	-4.7	-12.8
Velocity, ft/sec		2100	1943	1794	1654	1522	1402
Energy, ft/lbs per grain		9.79	8.38	7.15	6.07	5.14	4.36
Time of Flight, sec		0.0000	0.0743	0.1546	0.2417	0.3363	0.4390
Path, inches	50 yds	-1.5	0.0	-0.8	-4.3	-11.0	-21.5
Relative to	100 yds	-1.5	0.4	0.0	-3.1	-9.4	-19.5
Line of Sight ZERO RANGE	150 yds	-1.5	1.4	2.1	0.0	-5.3	-14.3
Velocity, ft/sec		2000	1848	1704	1569	1445	1332
Energy, ft/lbs per grain		8.88	7.58	6.45	5.47	4.64	3.94
Time of Flight, sec		0.0000	0.0780	0.1626	0.2543	0.3540	0.4621
Path, inches	50 yds	-1.5	0.0	-1.0	-5.1	-12.7	-24.4
Relative to	100 yds	-1.5	0.5	0.0	-3.5	-10.6	-21.8
Line of Sight ZERO RANGE	150 yds	-1.5	1.7	2.3	0.0	-5.9	-15.9
Velocity, ft/sec		1900	1753	1615	1487	1370	1266
Energy, ft/lbs per grain		8.01	6.82	5.79	4.91	4.17	3.56
Time of Flight, sec		0.0000	0.0822	0.1714	0.2682	0.3733	0.4873
Path, inches	50 yds	-1.5	0.0	-1.3	-6.0	-14.6	-27.9
Relative to	100 yds	-1.5	0.7	0.0	-4.0	-11.9	-24.5
Line of Sight ZERO RANGE	150 yds	-1.5	2.0	2.7	0.0	-6.6	-17.9
Velocity, ft/sec		1800	1659	1528	1406	1298	1204
Energy, ft/lbs per grain		7.19	6.11	5.18	4.39	3.74	3.27
Time of Flight, sec		0.0000	0.0868	0.1811	0.2834	0.3945	0.5140
Path, inches	50 yds	-1.5	0.0	-1.7	-7.1	-16.9	-31.8
Relative to	100 yds	-1.5	0.8	0.0	-4.6	-13.5	-27.7
Line of Sight ZERO RANGE	150 yds	-1.5	2.4	3.0	0.0	-7.4	-20.0

Exterior Ballistic Table for Ballistic Coefficient 0.25

		Muzzle	50 yds	100 yds	150 yds	200 yds	250 yds
Velocity, ft/sec		1700	1566	1441	1329	1230	1148
Energy, ft/lbs per grain		6.42	5.44	4.61	3.92	3.35	2.93
Time of Flight, sec		0.0000	0.0920	0.1919	0.3003	0.4177	0.5441
Path, inches	50 yds	-1.5	0.0	-2.1	-8.3	-19.5	-36.4
Relative to	100 yds	-1.5	1.0	0.0	-5.2	-15.4	-31.2
Line of Sight	150 yds	-1.5	2.8	3.5	0.0	-8.4	-22.6
Velocity, ft/sec		1600	1473	1357	1255	1168	1097
Energy, ft/lbs per grain		5.68	4.82	4.09	3.50	3.03	2.67
Time of Flight, sec		0.0000	0.0977	0.2039	0.3189	0.4430	0.5756
Path, inches	50 yds	-1.5	0.0	-2.5	-9.8	-22.5	-41.6
Relative to	100 yds	-1.5	1.3	0.0	-6.0	-17.5	-35.4
Line of Sight	150 yds	-1.5	3.3	4.0	0.0	-9.5	-25.4
Velocity, ft/sec		1500	1381	1276	1185	1112	1053
Energy, ft/lbs per grain		5.00	4.23	3.61	3.12	2.75	2.46
Time of Flight, sec		0.0000	0.1042	0.2173	0.3394	0.4702	0.6090
Path, inches	50 yds	-1.5	0.0	-3.1	-11.5	-26.0	-47.7
Relative to	100 yds	-1.5	1.5	0.0	-6.9	-19.9	-40.0
Line of Sight	150 yds	-1.5	3.8	4.6	0.0	-10.8	-28.6
Velocity, ft/sec		1400	1292	1199	1122	1061	1012
Energy, ft/lbs per grain		4.35	3.71	3.19	2.79	2.50	2.27
Time of Flight, sec		0.0000	0.1116	0.2322	0.3616	0.4992	0.6440
Path, inches	50 yds	-1.5	0.0	-3.7	-13.5	-30.1	-54.5
Relative to	100 yds	-1.5	1.9	0.0	-7.9	-22.7	-45.2
Line of Sight	150 yds	-1.5	4.5	5.3	0.0	-12.2	-32.0
Velocity, ft/sec		1300	1206	1128	1066	1016	975
Energy, ft/lbs per grain		3.75	3.23	2.82	2.52	2.29	2.11
Time of Flight, sec		0.0000	0.1199	0.2487	0.3856	0.5299	0.6808
Path, inches	50 yds	-1.5	0.0	-4.5	-15.8	-34.7	-62.1
Relative to	100 yds	-1.5	2.2	0.0	-9.1	-25.8	-50.9
Line of Sight	150 yds	-1.5	5.3	6.0	0.0	-13.7	-35.8
Velocity, ft/sec		1200	1123	1062	1013	972	937
Energy, ft/lbs per grain		3.20	2.80	2.50	2.28	2.10	1.95
Time of Flight, sec		0.0000	0.1293	0.2668	0.4115	0.5628	0.7201
Path, inches	50 yds	-1.5	0.0	-5.4	-18.5	-40.0	-70.7
Relative to	100 yds	-1.5	2.7	0.0	-10.4	-29.2	-57.3
Line of Sight	150 yds	-1.5	6.2	6.9	0.0	-15.4	-40.0
Velocity, ft/sec		1100	1043	998	959	925	895
Energy, ft/lbs per grain		2.69	2.42	2.21	2.04	1.90	1.78
Time of Flight, sec		0.0000	0.1401	0.2872	0.4407	0.6000	0.7650
Path, inches	50 yds	-1.5	0.0	-6.5	-21.7	-46.3	-81.2
Relative to	100 yds	-1.5	3.2	0.0	-12.0	-33.4	-65.0
Line of Sight	150 yds	-1.5	7.2	8.0	0.0	-17.4	-45.0
Velocity, ft/sec		1000	961	927	897	870	844
Energy, ft/lbs per grain		2.22	2.05	1.91	1.79	1.68	1.58
Time of Flight, sec		0.0000	0.1531	0.3121	0.4766	0.6465	0.8216
Path, inches	50 yds	-1.5	0.0	-7.9	-25.9	-54.7	-95.0
Relative to	100 yds	-1.5	4.0	0.0	-14.1	-38.9	-75.3
Line of Sight	150 yds	-1.5	8.6	9.4	0.0	-20.2	-51.8

The "Path, inches / Relative to / Line of Sight" blocks are labeled ZERO RANGE.

Exterior Ballistic Table for Ballistic Coefficient 0.26

	Muzzle	50 yds	100 yds	150 yds	200 yds	250 yds
			RANGE			
Velocity, ft/sec	2300	2141	1988	1843	1704	1575
Energy, ft/lbs per grain	11.74	10.18	8.77	7.54	6.45	5.51
Time of Flight, sec	0.0000	0.0676	0.1403	0.2187	0.3033	0.3949
Path, inches — ZERO RANGE 50 yds	-1.5	0.0	-0.4	-3.0	-8.2	-16.3
Relative to — 100 yds	-1.5	0.2	0.0	-2.4	-7.4	-15.3
Line of Sight — 150 yds	-1.5	1.0	1.6	0.0	-4.2	-11.3
Velocity, ft/sec	2200	2045	1897	1755	1622	1498
Energy, ft/lbs per grain	10.75	9.28	7.99	6.84	5.84	4.98
Time of Flight, sec	0.0000	0.0707	0.1469	0.2291	0.3180	0.4142
Path, inches — ZERO RANGE 50 yds	-1.5	0.0	-0.6	-3.6	-9.4	-18.5
Relative to — 100 yds	-1.5	0.3	0.0	-2.7	-8.2	-17.1
Line of Sight — 150 yds	-1.5	1.2	1.8	0.0	-4.6	-12.6
Velocity, ft/sec	2100	1949	1805	1669	1542	1424
Energy, ft/lbs per grain	9.79	8.43	7.23	6.18	5.28	4.50
Time of Flight, sec	0.0000	0.0741	0.1541	0.2405	0.3341	0.4353
Path, inches — ZERO RANGE 50 yds	-1.5	0.0	-0.8	-4.3	-10.8	-21.1
Relative to — 100 yds	-1.5	0.4	0.0	-3.1	-9.3	-19.1
Line of Sight — 150 yds	-1.5	1.4	2.0	0.0	-5.2	-14.0
Velocity, ft/sec	2000	1854	1715	1584	1463	1353
Energy, ft/lbs per grain	8.88	7.63	6.53	5.57	4.75	4.06
Time of Flight, sec	0.0000	0.0779	0.1621	0.2531	0.3516	0.4583
Path, inches — ZERO RANGE 50 yds	-1.5	0.0	-1.0	-5.0	-12.5	-24.0
Relative to — 100 yds	-1.5	0.5	0.0	-3.5	-10.4	-21.4
Line of Sight — 150 yds	-1.5	1.7	2.3	0.0	-5.8	-15.6
Velocity, ft/sec	1900	1759	1625	1501	1387	1284
Energy, ft/lbs per grain	8.01	6.87	5.86	5.00	4.27	3.66
Time of Flight, sec	0.0000	0.0821	0.1708	0.2668	0.3708	0.4833
Path, inches — ZERO RANGE 50 yds	-1.5	0.0	-1.3	-5.9	-14.4	-27.4
Relative to — 100 yds	-1.5	0.7	0.0	-4.0	-11.8	-24.1
Line of Sight — 150 yds	-1.5	2.0	2.6	0.0	-6.5	-17.5
Velocity, ft/sec	1800	1664	1537	1420	1314	1221
Energy, ft/lbs per grain	7.19	6.15	5.24	4.48	3.83	3.31
Time of Flight, sec	0.0000	0.0867	0.1805	0.2820	0.3919	0.5105
Path, inches — ZERO RANGE 50 yds	-1.5	0.0	-1.6	-7.0	-16.6	-31.3
Relative to — 100 yds	-1.5	0.8	0.0	-4.5	-13.3	-27.2
Line of Sight — 150 yds	-1.5	2.3	3.0	0.0	-7.3	-29.7
Velocity, ft/sec	1700	1571	1450	1341	1244	1162
Energy, ft/lbs per grain	6.42	5.48	4.67	3.99	3.44	3.00
Time of Flight, sec	0.0000	0.0918	0.1912	0.2988	0.4150	0.5399
Path, inches — ZERO RANGE 50 yds	-1.5	0.0	-2.0	-8.2	-19.2	-35.8
Relative to — 100 yds	-1.5	1.0	0.0	-5.2	-15.1	-30.7
Line of Sight — 150 yds	-1.5	2.7	3.4	0.0	-8.3	-22.2
Velocity, ft/sec	1600	1478	1365	1266	1180	1110
Energy, ft/lbs per grain	5.68	4.85	4.14	3.56	3.09	2.74
Time of Flight, sec	0.0000	0.0976	0.2032	0.3174	0.4402	0.5715
Path, inches — ZERO RANGE 50 yds	-1.5	0.0	-2.5	-9.6	-22.2	-41.0
Relative to — 100 yds	-1.5	1.2	0.0	-5.9	-17.2	-34.8
Line of Sight — 150 yds	-1.5	3.2	3.9	0.0	-9.4	-25.0

Exterior Ballistic Table for Ballistic Coefficient 0.27

			RANGE			
	Muzzle	50 yds	100 yds	150 yds	200 yds	250 yds
Velocity, ft/sec	2900	2725	2556	2394	2237	2086
Energy, ft/lbs per grain	18.67	16.49	14.50	12.72	11.11	9.66
Time of Flight, sec	0.0000	0.0534	0.1102	0.1708	2357	0.3051
Path, inches — ZERO RANGE 50 yds	-1.5	0.0	0.3	-0.7	-3.2	-7.5
Relative to — ZERO RANGE 100 yds	-1.5	-0.2	0.0	-1.2	-3.9	-8.3
Line of Sight — ZERO RANGE 150 yds	-1.5	0.2	0.8	0.0	-2.3	-6.3
Velocity, ft/sec	2800	2629	2464	2304	2151	2004
Energy, ft/lbs per grain	17.41	15.34	13.48	11.79	10.27	8.92
Time of Flight, sec	0.0000	0.0553	0.1142	0.1772	0.2446	0.3168
Path, inches — ZERO RANGE 50 yds	-1.5	0.0	0.2	-1.0	-3.8	-8.5
Relative to — ZERO RANGE 100 yds	-1.5	-0.1	0.0	-1.3	-4.3	-9.1
Line of Sight — ZERO RANGE 150 yds	-1.5	0.3	0.9	0.0	-2.5	-6.9
Velocity, ft/sec	2700	2532	2371	2215	2065	1921
Energy, ft/lbs per grain	16.18	14.23	12.48	10.89	9.47	8.19
Time of Flight, sec	0.0000	0.0574	0.1186	0.1840	0.2542	0.3295
Path, inches — ZERO RANGE 50 yds	-1.5	0.0	0.1	-1.3	-4.4	-9.7
Relative to — ZERO RANGE 100 yds	-1.5	-0.1	0.0	-1.5	-4.7	-10.0
Line of Sight — ZERO RANGE 150 yds	-1.5	0.4	1.0	0.0	-2.8	-7.6
Velocity, ft/sec	2600	2436	2278	2125	1979	1839
Energy, ft/lbs per grain	15.01	13.17	11.52	10.02	6.69	7.51
Time of Flight, sec	0.0000	0.0596	0.1233	0.1915	0.2646	0.3432
Path, inches — ZERO RANGE 50 yds	-1.5	0.0	0.0	-1.6	-5.2	-11.0
Relative to — ZERO RANGE 100 yds	-1.5	0.0	0.0	-1.7	-5.2	-11.1
Line of Sight — ZERO RANGE 150 yds	-1.5	0.5	1.1	0.0	-3.0	-8.3
Velocity, ft/sec	2500	2340	2185	2036	1893	1758
Energy, ft/lbs per grain	13.88	12.16	10.60	9.20	7.96	6.86
Time of Flight, sec	0.0000	0.0620	0.1284	0.1995	0.2759	0.3581
Path, inches — ZERO RANGE 50 yds	-1.5	0.0	-0.1	-2.0	-6.0	-12.5
Relative to — ZERO RANGE 100 yds	-1.5	0.0	0.0	-1.9	-5.8	-12.2
Line of Sight — ZERO RANGE 150 yds	-1.5	0.7	1.2	0.0	-3.3	-9.1
Velocity, ft/sec	2400	2243	2092	1947	1808	1677
Energy, ft/lbs per grain	12.79	11.17	9.72	8.42	7.26	6.24
Time of Flight, sec	0.0000	0.0646	0.1339	0.2082	0.2882	0.3743
Path, inches — ZERO RANGE 50 yds	-1.5	0.0	-0.2	-2.4	-7.0	-14.1
Relative to — ZERO RANGE 100 yds	-1.5	0.1	0.0	-2.1	-6.5	-13.6
Line of Sight — ZERO RANGE 150 yds	-1.5	0.8	1.4	0.0	-3.7	-10.1
Velocity, ft/sec	2300	2147	1999	1859	1724	1598
Energy, ft/lbs per grain	11.74	10.23	8.87	7.67	6.60	5.67
Time of Flight, sec	0.0000	0.0675	0.1399	0.2177	0.3015	0.3919
Path, inches — ZERO RANGE 50 yds	-1.5	0.0	-0.4	-3.0	-8.0	-16.1
Relative to — ZERO RANGE 100 yds	-1.5	0.2	0.0	-2.4	-7.3	-15.1
Line of Sight — ZERO RANGE 150 yds	-1.5	1.0	1.6	0.0	-4.1	-11.1
Velocity, ft/sec	2200	2051	1907	1771	1642	1521
Energy, ft/lbs per grain	10.75	9.34	8.07	6.96	5.99	5.14
Time of Flight, sec	0.0000	0.0706	0.1465	0.2281	0.3161	0.4111
Path, inches — ZERO RANGE 50 yds	-1.5	0.0	-0.6	-3.5	-9.3	-18.2
Relative to — ZERO RANGE 100 yds	-1.5	0.3	0.0	-2.7	-8.1	-16.8
Line of Sight — ZERO RANGE 150 yds	-1.5	1.2	1.8	0.0	-4.6	-12.4

short range tables

		Muzzle	50 yds	100 yds	150 yds	200 yds	250 yds
				RANGE			
Velocity, ft/sec		2100	1955	1816	1684	1560	1445
Energy, ft/lbs per grain		9.79	8.49	7.32	6.30	5.40	4.64
Time of Flight, sec		0.0000	0.0740	0.1537	0.2395	0.3320	0.4319
Path, inches	50 yds	-1.5	0.0	-0.8	-4.2	-10.7	-20.8
Relative to ZERO RANGE	100 yds	-1.5	0.4	0.0	-3.0	-9.1	-18.8
Line of Sight	150 yds	-1.5	1.4	2.0	0.0	-5.1	-13.8
Velocity, ft/sec		2000	1859	1725	1599	1481	1372
Energy, ft/lbs per grain		8.88	7.67	6.61	5.68	4.87	4.18
Time of Flight, sec		0.0000	0.0778	0.1616	0.2519	0.3495	0.4547
Path, inches	50 yds	-1.5	0.0	-1.0	-5.0	-12.3	-23.6
Relative to ZERO RANGE	100 yds	-1.5	0.5	0.0	-3.4	-10.3	-21.1
Line of Sight	150 yds	-1.5	1.7	2.3	0.0	-5.7	-15.4
Velocity, ft/sec		1900	1764	1635	1515	1403	1302
Energy, ft/lbs per grain		8.01	6.91	5.93	5.10	4.37	3.76
Time of Flight, sec		0.0000	0.0819	0.1703	0.2656	0.3686	0.4796
Path, inches	50 yds	-1.5	0.0	-1.3	-5.9	-14.2	-27.0
Relative to ZERO RANGE	100 yds	-1.5	0.6	0.0	-3.9	-11.6	-23.7
Line of Sight	150 yds	-1.5	2.0	2.6	0.0	-6.4	-17.2
Velocity, ft/sec		1800	1669	1546	1432	1329	1237
Energy, ft/lbs per grain		7.19	6.18	5.31	4.55	3.92	3.40
Time of Flight, sec		0.0000	0.0866	0.1799	0.2808	0.3895	0.5066
Path, inches	50 yds	-1.5	0.0	-1.6	-6.9	-16.4	-30.8
Relative to ZERO RANGE	100 yds	-1.5	0.8	0.0	-4.5	-13.1	-26.8
Line of Sight	150 yds	-1.5	2.3	3.0	0.0	-7.2	-19.3
Velocity, ft/sec		1700	1575	1459	1353	1258	1176
Energy, ft/lbs per grain		6.42	5.51	4.73	4.06	3.51	3.07
Time of Flight, sec		0.0000	0.0917	0.1906	0.2975	0.4125	0.5360
Path, inches	50 yds	-1.5	0.0	-2.0	-8.1	-19.0	-35.5
Relative to ZERO RANGE	100 yds	-1.5	1.0	0.0	-5.1	-14.9	-30.3
Line of Sight	150 yds	-1.5	2.7	3.4	0.0	-8.1	-21.8
Velocity, ft/sec		1600	1482	1373	1276	1192	1122
Energy, ft/lbs per grain		5.68	4.88	4.19	3.61	3.15	2.79
Time of Flight, sec		0.0000	0.0974	0.2026	0.3160	0.4377	0.5676
Path, inches	50 yds	-1.5	0.0	-2.5	-9.5	-22.0	-40.5
Relative to ZERO RANGE	100 yds	-1.5	1.2	0.0	-5.8	-17.0	-34.3
Line of Sight	150 yds	-1.5	3.2	3.9	0.0	-9.2	24.6
Velocity, ft/sec		1500	1390	1291	1204	1132	1073
Energy, ft/lbs per grain		5.00	4.29	3.70	3.22	2.84	2.56
Time of Flight, sec		0.0000	0.1039	0.2160	0.3364	0.4650	0.6013
Path, inches	50 yds	-1.5	0.0	-3.0	-11.2	-25.4	-46.5
Relative to ZERO RANGE	100 yds	-1.5	1.5	0.0	-6.7	-19.4	-38.9
Line of Sight	150 yds	-1.5	3.7	4.5	0.0	-10.5	-27.7
Velocity, ft/sec		1400	1300	1212	1138	1078	1029
Energy, ft/lbs per grain		4.35	3.75	3.26	2.88	2.58	2.35
Time of Flight, sec		0.0000	0.1113	0.2309	0.3587	0.4943	0.6368
Path, inches	50 yds	-1.5	0.0	-3.6	-13.2	-29.5	-53.2
Relative to ZERO RANGE	100 yds	-1.5	1.8	0.0	-7.7	-22.2	-44.1
Line of Sight	150 yds	-1.5	4.4	5.2	0.0	-11.9	-31.2

short range tables

Exterior Ballistic Table for Ballistic Coefficient 0.27

		Muzzle	50 yds	100 yds	150 yds	200 yds	250 yds
Velocity, ft/sec		1300	1212	1138	1078	1030	989
Energy, ft/lbs per grain		3.75	3.26	2.88	2.58	2.36	2.17
Time of Flight, sec		0.0000	0.1196	0.2474	0.3829	0.5254	0.6741
Path, inches	50 yds	-1.5	0.0	-4.4	-15.5	-34.1	-60.9
Relative to	100 yds	-1.5	2.2	0.0	-8.9	-25.3	-49.9
Line of Sight	150 yds	-1.5	5.2	5.9	0.0	-13.4	-35.0
Velocity, ft/sec		1200	1128	1070	1023	983	949
Energy, ft/lbs per grain		3.20	2.82	2.54	2.32	2.15	2.00
Time of Flight, sec		0.0000	0.1290	0.2656	0.4091	0.5588	0.7141
Path, inches	50 yds	-1.5	0.0	-5.3	-18.2	-39.4	-69.9
Relative to	100 yds	-1.5	2.7	0.0	-10.2	-28.8	-56.3
Line of Sight	150 yds	-1.5	6.1	6.8	0.0	-15.1	-39.2
Velocity, ft/sec		1100	1047	1004	967	935	906
Energy, ft/lbs per grain		2.69	2.43	2.24	2.08	1.94	1.82
Time of Flight, sec		0.0000	0.1399	0.2863	0.4386	0.5964	0.7595
Path, inches	50 yds	-1.5	0.0	-6.4	-21.5	-45.8	-80.1
Relative to	100 yds	-1.5	3.2	0.0	-11.8	-32.9	-64.0
Line of Sight	150 yds	-1.5	7.2	7.9	0.0	-17.2	-44.3
Velocity, ft/sec		1000	964	932	903	878	853
Energy, ft/lbs per grain		2.22	2.06	1.93	1.81	1.71	1.62
Time of Flight, sec		0.0000	0.1529	0.3112	0.4748	0.6433	0.8168
Path, inches	50 yds	-1.5	0.0	-7.9	-25.7	-54.2	-94.0
Relative to	100 yds	-1.5	3.9	0.0	13.9	-38.5	-74.4
Line of Sight	150 yds	-1.5	8.6	9.3	0.0	-19.9	-51.2

Exterior Ballistic Table for Ballistic Coefficient 0.30

		Muzzle	50 yds	100 yds	150 yds	200 yds	250 yds
Velocity, ft/sec		2400	2259	2122	1990	1863	1742
Energy, ft/lbs per grain		12.79	11.33	10.00	8.79	7.71	6.74
Time of Flight, sec		0.0000	0.0644	0.1330	0.2060	0.2839	0.3671
Path, inches	50 yds	-1.5	0.0	-0.2	-2.3	-6.7	-13.5
Relative to	100 yds	-1.5	0.1	0.0	-2.0	-6.3	-13.0
Line of Sight	150 yds	-1.5	0.8	1.4	0.0	-3.6	-9.6
Velocity, ft/sec		2300	2162	2028	1900	1777	1660
Energy, ft/lbs per grain		11.74	10.38	913	8.01	7.01	6.12
Time of Flight, sec		0.0000	0.0673	0.1389	0.2153	0.2969	0.3843
Path, inches	50 yds	-1.5	0.0	-0.4	-2.8	-7.7	-15.4
Relative to	100 yds	-1.5	0.2	0.0	-2.3	-7.0	-14.5
Line of Sight	150 yds	-1.5	0.9	1.5	0.0	-3.9	-10.6
Velocity, ft/sec		2200	2065	1935	1811	1692	1580
Energy, ft/lbs per grain		10.75	9.47	8.31	7.28	6.36	5.54
Time of Flight, sec		0.0000	0.0704	0.1454	0.2255	0.3112	0.4030
Path, inches	50 yds	-1.5	0.0	-0.5	-3.4	-8.9	-17.5
Relative to	100 yds	-1.5	0.3	0.0	-2.6	-7.8	-16.1
Line of Sight	150 yds	-1.5	1.1	1.7	0.0	-4.4	-11.8

Exterior Ballistic Table for Ballistic Coefficient 0.30

RANGE

		Muzzle	50 yds	100 yds	150 yds	200 yds	250 yds
Velocity, ft/sec		2100	1969	1843	1723	1609	1502
Energy, ft/lbs per grain		9.79	8.61	7.54	6.59	5.75	5.01
Time of Flight, sec		0.0000	0.0738	0.1525	0.2367	0.3268	0.4234
Path, inches	50 yds	-1.5	0.0	-0.7	-4.1	-10.3	-19.9
Relative to ZERO RANGE	100 yds	-1.5	0.4	0.0	-2.9	-8.8	-18.0
Line of Sight	150 yds	-1.5	1.4	2.0	0.0	-4.9	-13.1
Velocity, ft/sec		2000	1873	1751	1636	1527	1425
Energy, ft/lbs per grain		8.88	7.79	6.81	5.94	5.18	4.51
Time of Flight, sec		0.0000	0.0775	0.1603	0.2490	0.3439	0.4457
Path, inches	50 yds	-1.5	0.0	-1.0	-4.9	-11.9	-22.7
Relative to ZERO RANGE	100 yds	-1.5	0.5	0.0	-3.3	-9.9	-20.2
Line of Sight	150 yds	-1.5	1.6	2.2	0.0	-5.5	-14.7
Velocity, ft/sec		1900	1777	1660	1550	1447	1351
Energy, ft/lbs per grain		8.01	7.01	6.12	5.33	4.65	4.05
Time of Flight, sec		0.0000	0.0816	0.1690	0.2625	0.3627	0.4700
Path, inches	50 yds	-1.5	0.0	-1.3	-5.7	-13.7	-25.9
Relative to ZERO RANGE	100 yds	-1.5	0.6	0.0	-3.8	-11.2	-22.8
Line of Sight	150 yds	-1.5	1.9	2.5	0.0	-6.1	-16.4
Velocity, ft/sec		1800	1682	1570	1466	1369	1281
Energy, ft/lbs per grain		7.19	6.28	5.47	4.77	4.16	3.64
Time of Flight, sec		0.0000	0.0862	0.1785	0.2774	0.3834	0.4967
Path, inches	50 yds	-1.5	0.0	-1.6	-6.7	-15.8	-29.6
Relative to ZERO RANGE	100 yds	-1.5	0.8	0.0	-4.3	-12.7	-25.7
Line of Sight	150 yds	-1.5	2.2	2.9	0.0	-6.9	-18.5
Velocity, ft/sec		1700	1587	1482	1383	1294	1215
Energy, ft/lbs per grain		6.42	5.59	4.88	4.25	3.72	3.28
Time of Flight, sec		0.0000	0.0913	0.1892	0.2940	0.4061	0.5258
Path, inches	50 yds	-1.5	0.0	-2.0	-7.9	-18.3	-34.0
Relative to ZERO RANGE	100 yds	-1.5	1.0	0.0	-4.9	-14.4	-29.1
Line of Sight	150 yds	-1.5	2.6	3.3	0.0	-7.8	-20.9
Velocity, ft/sec		1600	1493	1394	1304	1224	1155
Energy, ft/lbs per grain		5.68	4.95	4.31	3.78	3.33	2.96
Time of Flight, sec		0.0000	0.0971	0.2010	0.3123	0.4311	0.5574
Path, inches	50 yds	-1.5	0.0	-2.4	-9.3	-21.3	-39.1
Relative to ZERO RANGE	100 yds	-1.5	1.2	0.0	-5.7	-16.5	-33.1
Line of Sight	150 yds	-1.5	3.1	3.8	0.0	-8.9	-23.6
Velocity, ft/sec		1500	1400	1309	1229	1159	1101
Energy, ft/lbs per grain		5.00	4.35	3.80	3.35	2.98	2.69
Time of Flight, sec		0.0000	0.1035	0.2143	0.3327	0.4585	0.5914
Path, inches	50 yds	-1.5	0.0	-2.9	-10.9	-24.7	-44.5
Relative to ZERO RANGE	100 yds	-1.5	1.5	0.0	-6.5	-18.8	-37.6
Line of Sight	150 yds	-1.5	3.6	4.4	0.0	-10.1	-26.7
Velocity, ft/sec		1400	1309	1228	1159	1101	1053
Energy, ft/lbs per grain		4.35	3.80	3.35	2.98	2.69	2.46
Time of Flight, sec		0.0000	0.1108	0.2292	0.3550	0.4880	0.6274
Path, inches	50 yds	-1.5	0.0	-3.6	-12.9	-28.7	-51.7
Relative to ZERO RANGE	100 yds	-1.5	1.8	0.0	-7.5	-21.6	-42.8
Line of Sight	150 yds	-1.5	4.3	5.0	0.0	-11.5	-30.2

short range tables

Exterior Ballistic Table for Ballistic Coefficient 0.30

		Muzzle	50 yds	100 yds	150 yds	200 yds	250 yds
Velocity, ft/sec		1300	1220	1152	1095	1048	1008
Energy, ft/lbs per grain		3.75	3.30	2.95	2.66	2.44	2.26
Time of Flight, sec		0.0000	0.1192	0.2458	0.3794	0.5195	0.6656
Path, inches	50 yds	-1.5	0.0	-4.3	-15.2	-33.3	-59.4
Relative to	100 yds	-1.5	2.2	0.0	-8.7	-24.7	-48.5
Line of Sight	150 yds	-1.5	5.1	5.8	0.0	-13.1	-34.0
Velocity, ft/sec		1200	1135	1081	1036	998	966
Energy, ft/lbs per grain		3.20	2.86	2.59	2.38	2.21	2.07
Time of Flight, sec		0.0000	0.1286	0.2642	0.4060	0.5535	0.7064
Path, inches	50 yds	-1.5	0.0	-5.2	-17.9	-38.7	-68.2
Relative to	100 yds	-1.5	2.6	0.0	-10.1	-28.2	-55.1
Line of Sight	150 yds	-1.5	6.0	6.7	0.0	-14.8	-38.3
Velocity, ft/sec		1100	1052	1012	978	947	920
Energy, ft/lbs per grain		2.69	2.46	2.27	2.12	1.99	1.88
Time of Flight, sec		0.0000	0.1395	0.2850	0.4359	0.5918	0.7526
Path, inches	50 yds	-1.5	0.0	-6.3	-21.2	-45.1	-78.7
Relative to	100 yds	-1.5	3.2	0.0	-11.7	-32.4	-62.8
Line of Sight	150 yds	-1.5	7.1	7.8	0.0	-16.9	-43.4
Velocity, ft/sec		1000	967	938	912	888	865
Energy, ft/lbs per grain		2.22	2.08	1.95	1.85	1.75	1.66
Time of Flight, sec		0.0000	0.1526	0.3102	0.4724	0.6393	0.8105
Path, inches	50 yds	-1.5	0.0	-7.8	-25.4	-53.6	-92.7
Relative to	100 yds	-1.5	3.9	0.0	-13.8	-38.0	-73.3
Line of Sight	150 yds	-1.5	8.5	9.2	0.0	-19.7	-50.3

Exterior Ballistic Table for Ballistic Coefficient 0.32

		Muzzle	50 yds	100 yds	150 yds	200 yds	250 yds
Velocity, ft/sec		2400	2267	2139	2014	1894	1779
Energy, ft/lbs per grain		12.79	11.41	10.16	9.01	7.96	7.03
Time of Flight, sec		0.0000	0.0643	0.1324	0.2047	0.2815	0.3632
Path, inches	50 yds	-1.5	0.0	-0.2	-2.3	-6.5	-13.2
Relative to	100 yds	-1.5	0.1	0.0	-2.0	-6.1	-12.7
Line of Sight	150 yds	-1.5	0.8	1.3	0.0	-3.5	9.4
Velocity, ft/sec		2300	2170	2045	1924	1807	1696
Energy, ft/lbs per grain		11.74	10.45	9.28	8.22	7.25	6.39
Time of Flight, sec		0.0000	0.0671	0.1383	0.2140	0.2944	0.3801
Path, inches	50 yds	-1.5	0.0	-0.3	-2.8	-7.6	-15.0
Relative to	100 yds	-1.5	0.2	0.0	-2.3	-6.9	-14.1
Line of Sight	150 yds	-1.5	0.9	1.5	0.0	-3.9	-10.4
Velocity, ft/sec		2200	2074	1951	1834	1721	1614
Energy, ft/lbs per grain		10.75	9.55	8.45	7.47	6.58	5.78
Time of Flight, sec		0.0000	0.0702	0.1448	0.2241	0.3085	0.3985
Path, inches	50 yds	-1.5	0.0	-0.5	-3.3	-8.7	-17.1
Relative to	100 yds	-1.5	0.3	0.0	-2.5	-7.7	-15.7
Line of Sight	150 yds	-1.5	1.1	1.7	0.0	-4.3	-11.5

short range tables

Exterior Ballistic Table for Ballistic Coefficient 0.32

	Muzzle	50 yds	100 yds	150 yds	200 yds	250 yds
			RANGE			
Velocity, ft/sec	2100	1977	1858	1745	1637	1534
Energy, ft/lbs per grain	9.79	8.68	7.66	6.76	5.95	5.22
Time of Flight, sec	0.0000	0.0736	0.1519	0.2352	0.3240	0.4186
Path, inches / Relative to / Line of Sight — ZERO RANGE 50 yds	-1.5	0.0	-0.7	-4.0	-10.1	-19.4
100 yds	-1.5	0.4	0.0	-2.9	-8.6	-17.6
150 yds	-1.5	1.3	1.9	0.0	-4.8	-12.8
Velocity, ft/sec	2000	1881	1766	1657	1553	1456
Energy, ft/lbs per grain	8.88	7.85	6.92	6.10	5.35	4.71
Time of Flight, sec	0.0000	0.0773	0.1597	0.2474	0.3409	0.4407
Path, inches / Relative to / Line of Sight — ZERO RANGE 50 yds	-1.5	0.0	-1.0	-4.7	-11.6	-22.2
100 yds	-1.5	0.5	0.0	-3.3	-9.7	-19.8
150 yds	-1.5	1.6	2.2	0.0	-5.3	-14.3
Velocity, ft/sec	1900	1785	1674	1570	1472	1380
Energy, ft/lbs per grain	8.01	7.07	6.22	5.47	4.81	4.23
Time of Flight, sec	0.0000	0.0815	0.1683	0.2608	0.3595	0.4648
Path, inches / Relative to / Line of Sight — ZERO RANGE 50 yds	-1.5	0.0	-1.2	-5.6	-13.4	-25.3
100 yds	-1.5	0.6	0.0	-3.7	-11.0	-22.2
150 yds	-1.5	1.9	2.5	0.0	-6.0	-16.0
Velocity, ft/sec	1800	1689	1584	1485	1392	1307
Energy, ft/lbs per grain	7.19	6.33	5.57	4.90	4.30	3.79
Time of Flight, sec	0.0000	0.0860	0.1778	0.2756	0.3800	0.4912
Path, inches / Relative to / Line of Sight — ZERO RANGE 50 yds	-1.5	0.0	-1.0	-5.1	-12.7	-24.4
100 yds	-1.5	0.5	0.0	-3.5	-10.6	-21.8
150 yds	-1.5	1.7	2.3	0.0	-5.9	-15.9
Velocity, ft/sec	1700	1594	1494	1401	1316	1239
Energy, ft/lbs per grain	6.42	4.64	4.96	4.36	3.84	3.41
Time of Flight, sec	0.0000	0.0911	0.1883	0.2920	0.4025	0.5201
Path, inches / Relative to / Line of Sight — ZERO RANGE 50 yds	-1.5	0.0	-1.9	-7.7	-18.0	-33.3
100 yds	-1.5	1.0	0.0	-4.9	-14.1	-28.5
150 yds	-1.5	2.6	3.2	0.0	-7.7	-20.4
Velocity, ft/sec	1600	1500	1406	1320	1243	1175
Energy, ft/lbs per grain	5.68	5.00	4.39	3.87	3.43	3.07
Time of Flight, sec	0.0000	0.0968	0.2002	0.3103	0.4274	0.5516
Path, inches / Relative to / Line of Sight — ZERO RANGE 50 yds	-1.5	0.0	-2.4	-9.1	-20.9	-38.3
100 yds	-1.5	1.2	0.0	-5.6	-16.2	-32.3
150 yds	-1.5	3.0	3.7	0.0	-8.7	-23.0
Velocity, ft/sec	1500	1406	1320	1243	1175	1118
Energy, ft/lbs per grain	5.00	4.39	3.87	3.43	3.07	2.77
Time of Flight, sec	0.0000	0.1033	0.2134	0.3306	0.4548	0.5857
Path, inches / Relative to / Line of Sight — ZERO RANGE 50 yds	-1.5	0.0	-2.9	-10.8	-24.3	-44.1
100 yds	-1.5	1.4	0.0	-6.4	-18.5	-36.9
150 yds	-1.5	3.6	4.3	0.0	-9.9	-26.1

short range tables

	Muzzle	50 yds	100 yds	150 yds	200 yds	250 yds
Velocity, ft/sec	2900	2778	2659	2543	2431	2321
Energy, ft/lbs per grain	18.67	17.13	15.70	14.36	13.12	11.96
Time of Flight, sec	0.0000	0.0528	0.1080	0.1657	0.2260	0.2892
Path, inches — Relative to Line of Sight — ZERO RANGE 50 yds	-1.5	0.0	0.4	-0.5	-2.7	-6.4
100 yds	-1.5	-0.2	0.0	-1.0	-3.4	-7.3
150 yds	-1.5	0.2	0.7	0.0	-2.0	-5.5

	Muzzle	50 yds	100 yds	150 yds	200 yds	250 yds
Velocity, ft/sec	2800	2681	2564	2451	2341	2233
Energy, ft/lbs per grain	17.41	15.96	14.59	13.34	12.17	11.07
Time of Flight, sec	0.0000	0.0548	0.1120	0.1718	0.2344	0.3000
Path, inches — Relative to Line of Sight — ZERO RANGE 50 yds	-1.5	0.0	0.3	-0.7	-3.2	-7.3
100 yds	-1.5	-0.1	0.0	-1.2	-3.8	-8.0
150 yds	-1.5	0.2	0.8	0.0	-2.2	-6.1

	Muzzle	50 yds	100 yds	150 yds	200 yds	250 yds
Velocity, ft/sec	2700	2583	2469	2359	2250	2145
Energy, ft/lbs per grain	16.18	14.81	13.53	12.35	11.24	10.21
Time of Flight, sec	0.0000	0.0568	0.1162	0.1783	0.2435	0.3117
Path, inches — Relative to Line of Sight — ZERO RANGE 50 yds	-1.5	0.0	0.2	-1.0	-3.8	-8.3
100 yds	-1.5	-0.1	0.0	-1.3	-4.2	-8.8
150 yds	-1.5	0.3	0.9	0.0	-2.4	-6.6

	Muzzle	50 yds	100 yds	150 yds	200 yds	250 yds
Velocity, ft/sec	2600	2486	2374	2266	2160	2057
Energy, ft/lbs per grain	15.01	13.72	12.51	11.40	10.36	9.39
Time of Flight, sec	0.0000	0.0590	0.1207	0.1854	0.2532	0.3244
Path, inches — Relative to Line of Sight — ZERO RANGE 50 yds	-1.5	0.0	0.1	-1.4	-4.5	-9.5
100 yds	-1.5	0.0	0.0	-1.5	-4.7	-9.7
150 yds	-1.5	0.5	1.0	0.0	-2.7	-7.2

	Muzzle	50 yds	100 yds	150 yds	200 yds	250 yds
Velocity, ft/sec	2500	2388	2279	2173	2070	1969
Energy, ft/lbs per grain	13.88	12.66	11.53	10.48	9.51	8.61
Time of Flight, sec	0.0000	0.0614	0.1257	0.1931	0.2638	0.3381
Path, inches — Relative to Line of Sight — ZERO RANGE 50 yds	-1.5	0.0	0.0	-1.7	-5.3	-10.8
100 yds	-1.5	0.0	0.0	-1.7	-5.2	-10.8
150 yds	-1.5	0.6	1.1	0.0	-3.0	-8.0

	Muzzle	50 yds	100 yds	150 yds	200 yds	250 yds
Velocity, ft/sec	2400	2291	2184	2081	1980	1882
Energy, ft/lbs per grain	12.79	11.65	10.59	9.61	8.70	7.86
Time of Flight, sec	0.0000	0.0640	0.1310	0.2014	0.2753	0.3530
Path, inches — Relative to Line of Sight — ZERO RANGE 50 yds	-1.5	0.0	-0.2	-2.1	-6.1	-12.3
100 yds	-1.5	0.1	0.0	-1.9	-5.8	-11.9
150 yds	-1.5	0.7	1.3	0.0	-3.3	-8.8

	Muzzle	50 yds	100 yds	150 yds	200 yds	250 yds
Velocity, ft/sec	2300	2193	2089	1988	1890	1796
Energy, ft/lbs per grain	11.74	10.68	9.69	8.77	7.93	7.16
Time of Flight, sec	0.0000	0.0668	0.1369	0.2104	0.2878	0.3692
Path, inches — Relative to Line of Sight — ZERO RANGE 50 yds	-1.5	0.0	-0.3	-2.6	-7.1	-14.0
100 yds	-1.5	0.2	0.0	-2.1	-6.5	-13.3
150 yds	-1.5	0.9	1.4	0.0	-3.6	-9.7

	Muzzle	50 yds	100 yds	150 yds	200 yds	250 yds
Velocity, ft/sec	2200	2096	1995	1897	1802	1710
Energy, ft/lbs per grain	10.75	9.75	8.84	7.99	7.21	6.49
Time of Flight, sec	0.0000	0.0699	0.1432	0.2203	0.3015	0.3870
Path, inches — Relative to Line of Sight — ZERO RANGE 50 yds	-1.5	0.0	-0.5	-3.1	-8.2	-16.0
100 yds	-1.5	0.2	0.0	-2.4	-7.3	-14.8
150 yds	-1.5	1.0	1.6	0.0	-4.0	-10.7

Exterior Ballistic Table for Ballistic Coefficient 0.39

	Muzzle	50 yds	100 yds	150 yds	200 yds	250 yds
			RANGE			
Velocity, ft/sec	2100	1999	1900	1805	1714	1626
Energy, ft/lbs per grain	9.79	8.87	8.01	7.23	6.52	5.87
Time of Flight, sec	0.0000	0.0732	0.1502	0.2312	0.3165	0.4063
Path, inches — Relative to Line of Sight — ZERO RANGE 50 yds	-1.5	0.0	-0.7	-3.8	-9.5	-18.2
100 yds	-1.5	0.3	0.0	-2.7	-8.2	-16.5
150 yds	-1.5	1.3	1.8	0.0	-4.5	-12.0
Velocity, ft/sec	2000	1902	1807	1715	1627	1543
Energy, ft/lbs per grain	8.88	8.03	7.25	6.53	5.88	5.29
Time of Flight, sec	0.0000	0.0769	0.1578	0.2431	0.3329	0.4276
Path, inches — Relative to Line of Sight — ZERO RANGE 50 yds	-1.5	0.0	-0.9	-4.5	-11.0	-20.9
100 yds	-1.5	0.5	0.0	-3.1	-9.2	-18.5
150 yds	-1.5	1.5	2.1	0.0	-5.0	-13.4
Velocity, ft/sec	1900	1805	1713	1625	1542	1462
Energy, ft/lbs per grain	8.01	7.23	6.51	5.86	5.28	4.75
Time of Flight, sec	0.0000	0.0810	0.1663	0.2562	0.3510	0.4509
Path, inches — Relative to Line of Sight — ZERO RANGE 50 yds	-1.5	0.0	-1.2	-5.3	-12.7	-23.8
100 yds	-1.5	0.6	0.0	-3.5	-10.4	-20.9
150 yds	-1.5	1.8	2.4	0.0	-5.7	-15.0
Velocity, ft/sec	1800	1709	1621	1537	1458	1383
Energy, ft/lbs per grain	7.19	6.48	5.83	5.24	4.72	4.25
Time of Flight, sec	0.0000	0.0855	0.1757	0.2707	0.3709	0.4766
Path, inches — Relative to Line of Sight — ZERO RANGE 50 yds	-1.5	0.0	-1.5	-6.3	-14.7	-27.3
100 yds	-1.5	0.7	0.0	-4.0	-11.8	-23.6
150 yds	-1.5	2.1	2.7	0.0	-6.4	-16.8
Velocity, ft/sec	1700	1613	1529	1450	1376	1307
Energy, ft/lbs per grain	6.42	5.78	5.19	4.67	4.20	3.79
Time of Flight, sec	0.0000	0.0906	0.1861	0.2868	0.3930	0.5049
Path, inches — Relative to Line of Sight — ZERO RANGE 50 yds	-1.5	0.0	-1.8	-7.4	-17.1	-31.4
100 yds	-1.5	0.9	0.0	-4.6	-13.4	-26.8
150 yds	-1.5	2.5	3.1	0.0	-7.2	-19.0
Velocity, ft/sec	1600	1517	1439	1366	1297	1235
Energy, ft/lbs per grain	5.68	5.11	4.60	4.14	3.73	3.39
Time of Flight, sec	0.0000	0.0963	0.1978	0.3048	0.4176	0.5361
Path, inches — Relative to Line of Sight — ZERO RANGE 50 yds	-1.5	0.0	-2.3	-8.8	-19.9	-36.2
100 yds	-1.5	1.1	0.0	-5.3	-15.3	-30.5
150 yds	-1.5	2.9	3.6	0.0	-8.2	-21.6
Velocity, ft/sec	1500	1423	1350	1283	1223	1169
Energy, ft/lbs per grain	5.00	4.50	4.05	3.65	3.32	3.03
Time of Flight, sec	0.0000	0.1027	0.2109	0.3249	0.4447	0.5702
Path, inches — Relative to Line of Sight — ZERO RANGE 50 yds	-1.5	0.0	-2.8	-10.4	-23.2	-41.9
100 yds	-1.5	1.4	0.0	-6.2	-17.6	-34.9
150 yds	-1.5	3.5	4.1	0.0	-9.4	-24.6

Exterior Ballistic Table for Ballistic Coefficient 0.14

		Muzzle	100 yds	200 yds	RANGE 300 yds	400 yds	500 yds
Velocity, ft/sec		4000	3185	2505	1917	1432	1103
Energy, ft/lbs per grain		35.52	22.52	13.93	8.16	4.55	2.70
Time of Flight, sec		0.0000	0.0842	0.1905	0.3274	0.5089	0.7502
Path, inches	100 yds	-1.5	0.0	-2.0	-9.7	-27.1	-61.9
Relative to	200 yds	-1.5	1.0	0.0	-6.7	-23.1	-56.9
Line of Sight ZERO RANGE	300 yds	-1.5	3.2	4.5	0.0	-14.2	-45.8
Velocity, ft/sec		3900	3103	2434	1857	1386	1078
Energy, ft/lbs per grain		33.77	21.38	13.15	7.66	4.26	2.58
Time of Flight, sec		0.0000	0.0864	0.1956	0.3368	0.5244	0.7726
Path, inches	100 yds	-1.5	0.0	-2.2	-10.4	-29.0	-66.1
Relative to	200 yds	-1.5	1.1	0.0	-7.1	-24.6	-60.6
Line of Sight ZERO RANGE	300 yds	-1.5	3.5	4.7	0.0	-15.1	-48.7
Velocity, ft/sec		3800	3021	2363	1797	1340	1056
Energy, ft/lbs per grain		32.06	20.26	12.40	7.17	3.99	2.48
Time of Flight, sec		0.0000	0.0887	0.2010	0.3467	0.5407	0.7960
Path, inches	100 yds	-1.5	0.0	-2.4	-11.2	-31.1	-70.6
Relative to	200 yds	-1.5	1.2	0.0	-7.6	-26.3	-64.7
Line of Sight ZERO RANGE	300 yds	-1.5	3.7	5.1	0.0	-16.2	-52.0
Velocity, ft/sec		3700	2938	2292	1736	1296	1034
Energy, ft/lbs per grain		30.39	19.16	11.66	6.69	3.73	2.37
Time of Flight, sec		0.0000	0.0911	0.2068	0.3573	0.5581	0.8204
Path, inches	100 yds	-1.5	0.0	-2.6	-12.0	-33.3	-75.6
Relative to	200 yds	-1.5	1.3	0.0	-8.1	-28.1	-69.1
Line of Sight ZERO RANGE	300 yds	-1.5	4.0	5.4	0.0	-17.3	-55.5
Velocity, ft/sec		3600	2855	2220	1676	1254	1014
Energy, ft/lbs per grain		28.77	18.10	10.94	6.24	3.49	2.28
Time of Flight, sec		0.0000	0.0937	0.2129	0.3686	0.5766	0.8459
Path, inches	100 yds	-1.5	0.0	-2.9	-13.0	-35.9	-81.0
Relative to	200 yds	-1.5	1.4	0.0	-8.7	-30.1	-73.9
Line of Sight ZERO RANGE	300 yds	-1.5	4.3	5.8	0.0	-18.5	-59.4
Velocity, ft/sec		3500	2771	2147	1616	1213	995
Energy, ft/lbs per grain		27.20	17.05	10.23	5.80	3.27	2.20
Time of Flight, sec		0.0000	0.0964	0.2195	0.3807	0.5963	0.8724
Path, inches	100 yds	-1.5	0.0	-3.1	-14.0	-38.6	-86.9
Relative to	200 yds	-1.5	1.6	0.0	-9.3	-32.4	-79.1
Line of Sight ZERO RANGE	300 yds	-1.5	4.7	6.2	0.0	-19.9	-63.5
Velocity, ft/sec		3400	2687	2074	1557	1175	977
Energy, ft/lbs per grain		25.66	16.03	9.55	5.38	3.07	2.12
Time of Flight, sec		0.0000	0.0994	0.2265	0.3937	0.6172	0.9000
Path, inches	100 yds	-1.5	0.0	-3.4	-15.2	-41.7	-93.4
Relative to	200 yds	-1.5	1.7	0.0	-10.0	-34.8	-84.8
Line of Sight ZERO RANGE	300 yds	-1.5	5.1	6.7	0.0	-21.4	-68.0
Velocity, ft/sec		3300	2602	2001	1498	1140	960
Energy, ft/lbs per grain		24.18	15.03	8.89	4.98	2.89	2.05
Time of Flight, sec		0.0000	0.1025	0.2340	0.4076	0.6392	0.9287
Path, inches	100 yds	-1.5	0.0	-3.8	-16.5	-45.1	-100.3
Relative to	200 yds	-1.5	1.9	0.0	-10.8	-37.6	-90.9
Line of Sight ZERO RANGE	300 yds	-1.5	5.5	7.2	0.0	-23.1	-72.9

long range tables

	Muzzle	100 yds	200 yds	300 yds	400 yds	500 yds
Velocity, ft/sec	3200	2517	1928	1440	1107	943
Energy, ft/lbs per grain	22.73	14.06	8.25	4.60	2.72	1.97
Time of Flight, sec	0.0000	0.1058	0.2420	0.4225	0.6625	0.9584
Path, inches — Relative to Line of Sight — ZERO RANGE 100 yds	-1.5	0.0	-4.1	-17.9	-48.8	-108.0
200 yds	-1.5	2.1	0.0	-11.7	-40.6	-97.6
300 yds	-1.5	6.0	7.8	0.0	-25.0	-78.1
Velocity, ft/sec	3100	2431	1855	1384	1077	927
Energy, ft/lbs per grain	21.33	13.12	7.64	4.25	2.58	1.91
Time of Flight, sec	0.0000	0.1093	0.2507	0.4385	0.6870	0.9892
Path, inches — Relative to Line of Sight — ZERO RANGE 100 yds	-1.5	0.0	-4.5	-19.5	-53.0	-116.2
200 yds	-1.5	2.3	0.0	-12.7	-43.9	-104.9
300 yds	-1.5	6.5	8.5	0.0	-27.0	-83.7
Velocity, ft/sec	3000	2345	1781	1329	1050	912
Energy, ft/lbs per grain	19.98	12.21	7.04	3.92	2.45	1.85
Time of Flight, sec	0.0000	0.1132	0.2600	0.4557	0.7127	1.0212
Path, inches — Relative to Line of Sight — ZERO RANGE 100 yds	-1.5	0.0	-5.0	-21.3	57.6	-125.2
200 yds	-1.5	2.5	0.0	-13.8	-47.6	-112.7
300 yds	-1.5	7.1	9.2	0.0	-29.2	-89.7
Velocity, ft/sec	2900	2259	1709	1277	1025	897
Energy, ft/lbs per grain	18.67	11.33	6.48	3.62	2.33	1.79
Time of Flight, sec	0.0000	0.1173	0.2701	0.4742	0.7396	1.0541
Path, inches — Relative to Line of Sight — ZERO RANGE 100 yds	-1.5	0.0	-5.5	-23.3	-42.6	-134.9
200 yds	-1.5	2.8	0.0	-15.0	-51.6	-121.1
300 yds	-1.5	7.8	10.0	0.0	-31.6	-96.1
Velocity, ft/sec	2800	2173	1637	1227	1001	882
Energy, ft/lbs per grain	17.41	10.48	5.95	3.34	2.22	1.73
Time of Flight, sec	0.0000	0.1217	0.2809	0.4939	0.7676	1.0882
Path, inches — Relative to Line of Sight — ZERO RANGE 100 yds	-1.5	0.0	-6.1	-25.5	-48.2	-145.3
200 yds	-1.5	3.0	0.0	-16.4	-56.0	-130.1
300 yds	-1.5	8.5	10.9	0.0	-34.1	-102.8
Velocity, ft/sec	2700	2086	1566	1181	980	868
Energy, ft/lbs per grain	16.18	9.66	5.44	3.10	2.13	1.67
Time of Flight, sec	0.0000	0.1264	0.2927	0.5149	0.7967	1.1233
Path, inches — Relative to Line of Sight — ZERO RANGE 100 yds	-1.5	0.0	-6.7	-28.0	-74.3	-156.6
200 yds	-1.5	3.4	0.0	-17.9	-40.8	-139.8
300 yds	-1.5	9.3	12.0	0.0	-36.9	-109.9
Velocity, ft/sec	2600	2000	1497	1139	959	854
Energy, ft/lbs per grain	15.01	8.88	4.98	2.88	2.04	1.62
Time of Flight, sec	0.0000	0.1316	0.3054	0.5372	0.8269	1.1594
Path, inches — Relative to Line of Sight — ZERO RANGE 100 yds	-1.5	0.0	-7.5	-30.9	-81.0	-168.7
200 yds	-1.5	3.7	0.0	-19.7	-66.0	-150.1
300 yds	-1.5	10.3	13.1	0.0	-39.8	-117.3
Velocity, ft/sec	2500	1913	1429	1101	940	840
Energy, ft/lbs per grain	13.88	8.12	4.53	2.69	1.96	1.57
Time of Flight, sec	0.0000	0.1372	0.3191	0.5608	0.8580	1.1966
Path, inches — Relative to Line of Sight — ZERO RANGE 100 yds	-1.5	0.0	-8.3	-34.0	-88.2	-181.7
200 yds	-1.5	4.1	0.0	-21.6	-71.6	-161.0
300 yds	-1.5	11.3	14.4	0.0	-42.9	-125.1

long range tables

	Muzzle	100 yds	200 yds	300 yds	400 yds	500 yds
			RANGE			
Velocity, ft/sec	2400	1828	1363	1067	921	826
Energy, ft/lbs per grain	12.79	7.42	4.12	2.53	1.88	1.51
Time of Flight, sec	0.0000	0.1433	0.3340	0.5856	0.8901	1.2348
Path, inches — 100 yds	-1.5	0.0	-9.2	-37.5	-96.1	-195.6
Relative to — ZERO RANGE 200 yds	-1.5	4.6	0.0	-23.7	-77.7	-172.6
Line of Sight — 300 yds	-1.5	12.5	15.8	0.0	-46.1	-133.1
Velocity, ft/sec	2300	1743	1301	1037	904	813
Energy, ft/lbs per grain	11.74	6.74	3.76	2.39	1.81	1.47
Time of Flight, sec	0.0000	0.1499	0.3500	0.6115	0.9231	1.2739
Path, inches — 100 yds	-1.5	0.0	-10.3	-41.4	-104.7	-210.5
Relative to — ZERO RANGE 200 yds	-1.5	5.1	0.0	-25.9	-84.1	-184.8
Line of Sight — 300 yds	-1.5	13.8	17.3	0.0	-49.5	-141.5
Velocity, ft/sec	2200	1660	1243	1009	887	800
Energy, ft/lbs per grain	10.75	6.12	3.43	2.26	1.75	1.42
Time of Flight, sec	0.0000	0.1572	0.3672	0.6384	0.9570	1.3142
Path, inches — 100 yds	-1.5	0.0	-11.5	-45.7	-113.9	-226.3
Relative to — ZERO RANGE 200 yds	-1.5	5.8	0.0	-28.4	-90.9	-197.6
Line of Sight — 300 yds	-1.5	15.2	18.9	0.0	-53.0	-150.2
Velocity, ft/sec	2100	1577	1188	983	870	786
Energy, ft/lbs per grain	9.79	5.52	3.13	2.15	1.68	1.37
Time of Flight, sec	0.0000	0.1651	0.3858	0.6663	0.9919	1.3554
Path, inches — 100 yds	-1.5	0.0	-12.9	-50.4	-123.8	-243.1
Relative to — ZERO RANGE 200 yds	-1.5	6.4	0.0	-31.1	-98.0	-211.0
Line of Sight — 300 yds	-1.5	16.8	20.7	0.0	-56.6	-159.1
Velocity, ft/sec	2000	1497	1139	959	854	773
Energy, ft/lbs per grain	8.88	4.98	2.88	2.04	1.62	1.33
Time of Flight, sec	0.0000	0.1737	0.4055	0.6951	1.0276	1.3976
Path, inches — 100 yds	-1.5	0.0	-14.4	-55.5	-134.3	-260.9
Relative to — ZERO RANGE 200 yds	-1.5	7.2	0.0	-33.9	-105.5	-224.9
Line of Sight — 300 yds	-1.5	18.5	22.6	0.0	-60.3	-168.3
Velocity, ft/sec	1900	1418	1096	937	838	760
Energy, ft/lbs per grain	8.01	4.46	2.67	1.95	1.556	1.28
Time of Flight, sec	0.0000	0.1832	0.4265	0.7248	1.0644	1.4411
Path, inches — 100 yds	-1.5	0.0	-16.2	-61.1	-145.6	-279.8
Relative to — ZERO RANGE 200 yds	-1.5	8.1	0.0	-36.9	-113.3	-239.4
Line of Sight — 300 yds	-1.5	20.4	24.6	0.0	-64.2	-177.9
Velocity, ft/sec	1800	1343	1057	916	822	747
Energy, ft/lbs per grain	7.19	4.00	2.48	1.86	1.50	1.24
Time of Flight, sec	0.0000	0.1937	0.4485	0.7553	1.1021	1.4859
Path, inches — 100 yds	-1.5	0.0	-18.1	-67.1	-157.7	-299.8
Relative to — ZERO RANGE 200 yds	-1.5	9.1	0.0	-40.0	-121.5	-254.6
Line of Sight — 300 yds	-1.5	22.4	26.7	0.0	-68.1	-187.9
Velocity, ft/sec	1700	1270	1022	895	806	733
Energy, ft/lbs per grain	6.42	3.58	2.32	1.78	1.44	1.19
Time of Flight, sec	0.0000	0.2051	0.4716	0.7868	1.1409	1.5319
Path, inches — 100 yds	-1.5	0.0	-20.2	-73.6	-170.4	-320.9
Relative to — ZERO RANGE 200 yds	-1.5	10.1	0.0	-43.2	-129.9	-270.3
Line of Sight — 300 yds	-1.5	24.5	28.8	0.0	-72.3	-198.2

long range tables

Exterior Ballistic Table for Ballistic Coefficient 0.14

		Muzzle	100 yds	200 yds	300 yds	400 yds	500 yds
				RANGE			
Velocity, ft/sec		1600	1203	990	875	790	720
Energy, ft/lbs per grain		5.68	3.21	2.18	1.70	1.39	1.15
Time of Flight, sec		0.0000	0.2177	0.4956	0.8193	1.1811	1.5796
Path, inches	100 yds	-1.5	0.0	-22.6	-80.5	-184.0	-343.2
Relative to	200 yds	-1.5	11.3	0.0	-46.6	-138.8	-286.7
Line of Sight	300 yds	-1.5	26.8	31.1	0.0	-76.6	-209.0
Velocity, ft/sec		1500	1141	960	854	774	705
Energy, ft/lbs per grain		5.00	2.89	2.05	1.62	1.33	1.10
Time of Flight, sec		0.0000	0.2313	0.5205	0.8528	1.2225	1.6296
Path, inches	100 yds	-1.5	0.0	-25.1	-87.8	-198.3	-367.1
Relative to	200 yds	-1.5	12.6	0.0	-50.2	-148.0	-304.3
Line of Sight	300 yds	-1.5	29.3	33.4	0.0	-81.1	-220.7

Exterior Ballistic Table for Ballistic Coefficient 0.17

		Muzzle	100 yds	200 yds	300 yds	400 yds	500 yds
				RANGE			
Velocity, ft/sec		4200	3487	2879	2347	1876	1474
Energy, ft/lbs per grain		39.16	26.99	18.40	12.23	7.81	4.82
Time of Flight, sec		0.0000	0.0785	0.1732	0.2887	0.4317	0.6124
Path, inches	100 yds	-1.5	0.0	-1.4	-7.0	-19.1	-41.3
Relative to	200 yds	-1.5	0.7	0.0	-5.0	-16.3	-37.8
Line of Sight	300 yds	-1.5	2.3	3.3	0.0	-9.7	-29.5
Velocity, ft/sec		4100	3403	2806	2283	1819	1429
Energy, ft/lbs per grain		37.32	25.71	17.48	11.57	7.35	4.53
Time of Flight, sec		0.0000	0.0804	0.1776	0.2961	0.4434	0.6299
Path, inches	100 yds	-1.5	0.0	-1.5	-7.6	-20.4	-43.9
Relative to	200 yds	-1.5	0.8	0.0	-5.3	-17.3	-40.1
Line of Sight	300 yds	-1.5	2.5	3.5	0.0	-10.3	-31.3
Velocity, ft/sec		4000	3318	2733	2217	1762	1383
Energy, ft/lbs per grain		35.52	24.44	16.58	10.91	6.89	4.25
Time of Flight, sec		0.0000	0.0824	0.1821	0.3040	0.4559	0.6485
Path, inches	100 yds	-1.5	0.0	-1.7	-8.1	-21.8	-46.8
Relative to	200 yds	-1.5	0.8	0.0	-5.6	-18.4	-42.6
Line of Sight	300 yds	-1.5	2.7	3.7	0.0	-10.9	-33.3
Velocity, ft/sec		3900	3233	2659	2151	1706	1339
Energy, ft/lbs per grain		33.77	23.20	15.70	10.27	6.46	3.98
Time of Flight, sec		0.0000	0.0846	0.1870	0.3124	0.4691	0.6682
Path, inches	100 yds	-1.5	0.0	-1.9	-8.7	-23.3	-50.0
Relative to	200 yds	-1.5	0.9	0.0	-5.9	-19.5	-45.3
Line of Sight	300 yds	-1.5	2.9	4.0	0.0	-11.6	-35.4
Velocity, ft/sec		3800	3148	2584	2085	1649	1296
Energy, ft/lbs per grain		32.06	22.00	14.82	9.65	6.04	3.73
Time of Flight, sec		0.0000	0.0868	0.1921	0.3213	0.4832	0.6891
Path, inches	100 yds	-1.5	0.0	-2.1	-9.4	-24.9	-53.5
Relative to	200 yds	-1.5	1.0	0.0	-6.3	-20.8	-48.3
Line of Sight	300 yds	-1.5	3.1	4.2	0.0	-12.4	-37.8

long range tables

Exterior Ballistic Table for Ballistic Coefficient 0.17

			RANGE			
	Muzzle	100 yds	200 yds	300 yds	400 yds	500 yds
Velocity, ft/sec	3700	3063	2509	2019	1593	1255
Energy, ft/lbs per grain	30.39	20.83	13.98	9.05	5.63	3.50
Time of Flight, sec	0.0000	0.0892	0.1975	0.3308	0.4983	0.7113
Path, inches — ZERO RANGE 100 yds	-1.5	0.0	-2.3	-10.1	-26.7	-57.3
Relative to — ZERO RANGE 200 yds	-1.5	1.1	0.0	-6.7	-22.2	-51.6
Line of Sight — ZERO RANGE 300 yds	-1.5	3.4	4.5	0.0	-13.2	-40.4
Velocity, ft/sec	3600	2977	2434	1952	1537	1215
Energy, ft/lbs per grain	28.77	19.68	13.15	8.46	5.24	3.28
Time of Flight, sec	0.0000	0.0917	0.2032	0.3409	0.5144	0.7349
Path, inches — ZERO RANGE 100 yds	-1.5	0.0	-2.5	-10.9	-28.7	-61.5
Relative to — ZERO RANGE 200 yds	-1.5	1.2	0.0	-7.2	-23.7	-55.3
Line of Sight — ZERO RANGE 300 yds	-1.5	3.6	4.8	0.0	-14.4	-43.2
Velocity, ft/sec	3500	2891	2357	1885	1482	1178
Energy, ft/lbs per grain	27.20	18.56	12.33	7.89	4.88	3.08
Time of Flight, sec	0.0000	0.0944	0.2093	0.3517	0.5316	0.7599
Path, inches — ZERO RANGE 100 yds	-1.5	0.0	-2.7	-11.8	-30.9	-66.1
Relative to — ZERO RANGE 200 yds	-1.5	1.4	0.0	-7.7	-25.5	-59.3
Line of Sight — ZERO RANGE 300 yds	-1.5	3.9	5.2	0.0	-15.1	-46.4
Velocity, ft/sec	3400	2804	2281	1817	1427	1143
Energy, ft/lbs per grain	25.66	17.46	11.55	7.33	4.52	2.90
Time of Flight, sec	0.0000	0.0972	0.2159	0.3633	0.5499	0.7864
Path, inches — ZERO RANGE 100 yds	-1.5	0.0	-3.0	-12.8	-33.3	-71.2
Relative to — ZERO RANGE 200 yds	-1.5	1.5	0.0	-8.3	-27.4	-63.7
Line of Sight — ZERO RANGE 300 yds	-1.5	4.3	5.5	0.0	-16.3	-49.9
Velocity, ft/sec	3300	2717	2203	1750	1374	1111
Energy, ft/lbs per grain	24.18	16.39	10.77	6.80	4.19	2.74
Time of Flight, sec	0.0000	0.1002	0.2229	0.3757	0.5696	0.8143
Path, inches — ZERO RANGE 100 yds	-1.5	0.0	-3.3	-13.9	-36.0	76.9
Relative to — ZERO RANGE 200 yds	-1.5	1.6	0.0	-8.9	-29.5	-48.7
Line of Sight — ZERO RANGE 300 yds	-1.5	4.6	6.0	0.0	-17.5	-53.7
Velocity, ft/sec	3200	2630	2126	1684	1322	1081
Energy, ft/lbs per grain	22.73	15.36	10.03	6.30	3.88	2.59
Time of Flight, sec	0.0000	0.1035	0.2304	0.3891	0.5907	0.8437
Path, inches — ZERO RANGE 100 yds	-1.5	0.0	-3.6	-15.1	-39.0	-83.1
Relative to — ZERO RANGE 200 yds	-1.5	1.8	0.0	-9.7	-31.8	-74.1
Line of Sight — ZERO RANGE 300 yds	-1.5	5.0	6.4	0.0	-19.0	-58.0
Velocity, ft/sec	3100	2542	2048	1617	1273	1054
Energy, ft/lbs per grain	21.33	14.35	9.31	5.80	3.60	2.47
Time of Flight, sec	0.0000	0.1069	0.2384	0.4034	0.6133	0.8745
Path, inches — ZERO RANGE 100 yds	-1.5	0.0	-4.0	-16.4	-42.4	-90.0
Relative to — ZERO RANGE 200 yds	-1.5	2.0	0.0	-10.4	-34.4	-80.1
Line of Sight — ZERO RANGE 300 yds	-1.5	5.5	7.0	0.0	-20.5	-62.6
Velocity, ft/sec	3000	2454	1970	1552	1226	1029
Energy, ft/lbs per grain	19.98	13.37	8.62	5.35	3.34	2.35
Time of Flight, sec	0.0000	0.1106	0.2471	0.4189	0.6374	0.9067
Path, inches — ZERO RANGE 100 yds	-1.5	0.0	-4.4	-17.9	-46.1	-97.6
Relative to — ZERO RANGE 200 yds	-1.5	2.2	0.0	-11.3	-37.4	-86.6
Line of Sight — ZERO RANGE 300 yds	-1.5	6.0	7.6	0.0	-22.3	-67.7

Exterior Ballistic Table for Ballistic Coefficient 0.17

	Muzzle	100 yds	200 yds	300 yds	400 yds	500 yds
Velocity, ft/sec	2900	2366	1892	1488	1182	1006
Energy, ft/lbs per grain	18.67	12.43	7.95	4.92	3.10	2.25
Time of Flight, sec	0.0000	0.1146	0.2564	0.4355	0.6631	0.9403
Path, inches — ZERO RANGE 100 yds	-1.5	0.0	-4.8	-19.6	-50.3	-105.9
Relative to Line of Sight — ZERO RANGE 200 yds	-1.5	2.4	0.0	-12.3	-40.6	-93.9
ZERO RANGE 300 yds	-1.5	6.5	8.2	0.0	-24.2	-73.3
Velocity, ft/sec	2800	2277	1814	1425	1142	984
Energy, ft/lbs per grain	17.41	11.51	7.31	4.51	2.90	2.15
Time of Flight, sec	0.0000	0.1188	0.2665	0.4535	0.6903	0.9753
Path, inches — 100 yds	-1.5	0.0	-5.3	-21.4	-55.0	-115.1
Relative to — 200 yds	-1.5	2.7	0.0	-13.5	-44.3	-101.8
Line of Sight — 300 yds	-1.5	7.2	9.0	0.0	-26.4	-79.3
Velocity, ft/sec	2700	2188	1737	1364	1105	964
Energy, ft/lbs per grain	16.18	10.63	6.70	4.13	2.71	2.06
Time of Flight, sec	0.0000	0.1235	0.2774	0.4728	0.7191	1.0116
Path, inches — 100 yds	-1.5	0.0	-5.9	-23.6	-60.2	-125.1
Relative to — 200 yds	-1.5	3.0	0.0	-14.7	-48.4	-110.4
Line of Sight — 300 yds	-1.5	7.9	9.8	0.0	-28.7	-85.9
Velocity, ft/sec	2600	2099	1661	1305	1072	945
Energy, ft/lbs per grain	15.01	9.78	6.12	3.78	2.55	1.98
Time of Flight, sec	0.0000	0.1284	0.2892	0.4937	0.7494	1.0491
Path, inches — 100 yds	-1.5	0.0	-6.5	-26.0	-66.0	-136.1
Relative to — 200 yds	-1.5	3.3	0.0	-16.1	-52.9	-119.7
Line of Sight — 300 yds	-1.5	8.7	10.8	0.0	-31.4	-92.8
Velocity, ft/sec	2500	2010	1586	1250	1042	926
Energy, ft/lbs per grain	13.88	8.97	5.58	3.47	2.41	1.90
Time of Flight, sec	0.0000	0.1338	0.3021	0.5160	0.7811	1.0878
Path, inches — 100 yds	-1.5	0.0	-7.3	-28.7	-72.4	-148.0
Relative to — 200 yds	-1.5	3.6	0.0	-17.7	-57.8	-129.8
Line of Sight — 300 yds	-1.5	9.6	11.8	0.0	-34.2	-100.3
Velocity, ft/sec	2400	1922	-8.1	-31.7	-79.5	-161.0
Energy, ft/lbs per grain	12.79	8.20	5.08	3.19	2.29	1.83
Time of Flight, sec	0.0000	0.1397	0.3159	0.5399	0.8141	1.1277
Path, inches — 100 yds	-1.5	0.0	-8.1	-31.7	-79.5	-161.0
Relative to — 200 yds	-1.5	4.1	0.0	-19.5	-63.3	-140.7
Line of Sight — 300 yds	-1.5	10.6	13.0	0.0	-37.3	-108.2
Velocity, ft/sec	2300	1834	1441	1152	990	892
Energy, ft/lbs per grain	11.74	7.47	4.61	2.95	2.18	1.77
Time of Flight, sec	0.0000	0.1461	0.3310	0.5654	0.8484	1.1687
Path, inches — 100 yds	-1.5	0.0	-9.0	-35.1	-87.3	-175.0
Relative to — 200 yds	-1.5	4.5	0.0	-21.5	-69.2	-152.4
Line of Sight — 300 yds	-1.5	11.7	14.4	0.0	-40.5	-116.5
Velocity, ft/sec	2200	1747	1372	1110	967	875
Energy, ft/lbs per grain	10.75	6.78	4.18	2.74	2.08	1.70
Time of Flight, sec	0.0000	0.1531	0.3473	0.5924	0.8838	1.2108
Path, inches — 100 yds	-1.5	0.0	-10.1	-39.0	-95.9	-190.1
Relative to — 200 yds	-1.5	5.1	0.0	-23.8	-75.7	-164.7
Line of Sight — 300 yds	-1.5	13.0	15.9	0.0	-44.0	-125.1

Exterior Ballistic Table for Ballistic Coefficient 0.17

	Muzzle	100 yds	200 yds	300 yds	400 yds	500 yds
Velocity, ft/sec	2100	1662	1306	1072	945	859
Energy, ft/lbs per grain	9.79	6.13	3.79	2.55	1.98	1.64
Time of Flight, sec	0.0000	0.1607	0.3651	0.6207	0.9203	1.2540
Path, inches — Relative to Line of Sight, ZERO RANGE 100 yds	-1.5	0.0	-11.3	-43.3	-105.3	-206.3
200 yds	-1.5	5.7	0.0	-26.3	-82.6	-177.9
300 yds	-1.5	14.4	17.5	0.0	-47.6	-134.1
Velocity, ft/sec	2000	1577	1244	1039	924	843
Energy, ft/lbs per grain	8.88	5.52	3.44	2.40	1.90	1.58
Time of Flight, sec	0.0000	0.1691	0.3842	0.6504	0.9579	1.2984
Path, inches — Relative to Line of Sight, ZERO RANGE 100 yds	-1.5	0.0	-12.8	-48.1	-115.5	-223.6
200 yds	-1.5	6.4	0.0	-29.0	-90.0	-191.8
300 yds	-1.5	16.0	19.3	0.0	-51.4	-143.5
Velocity, ft/sec	1900	1494	1186	1008	904	828
Energy, ft/lbs per grain	8.01	4.96	3.12	2.26	1.81	1.52
Time of Flight, sec	0.0000	0.1783	0.4049	0.6813	0.9966	1.3440
Path, inches — Relative to Line of Sight, ZERO RANGE 100 yds	-1.5	0.0	-14.3	-53.4	-126.6	-242.2
200 yds	-1.5	7.2	0.0	-31.9	-97.9	-206.4
300 yds	-1.5	17.8	21.3	0.0	-55.4	-153.2
Velocity, ft/sec	1800	1413	1135	980	885	812
Energy, ft/lbs per grain	7.19	4.43	2.86	2.13	1.74	1.46
Time of Flight, sec	0.0000	0.1885	0.4270	0.7134	1.0363	1.3908
Path, inches — Relative to Line of Sight, ZERO RANGE 100 yds	-1.5	0.0	-16.2	-59.3	-138.4	-262.1
200 yds	-1.5	8.1	0.0	-35.0	-106.1	-221.6
300 yds	-1.5	19.8	23.3	0.0	-59.4	-163.3
Velocity, ft/sec	1700	1335	1088	954	866	797
Energy, ft/lbs per grain	6.42	3.96	2.63	2.02	1.66	1.41
Time of Flight, sec	0.0000	0.1997	0.4506	0.7465	1.0772	1.4391
Path, inches — Relative to Line of Sight, ZERO RANGE 100 yds	-1.5	0.0	-18.2	-65.7	-151.2	-283.2
200 yds	-1.5	9.1	0.0	-38.3	-114.8	237.6
300 yds	-1.5	21.9	25.6	0.0	-63.7	-173.8
Velocity, ft/sec	1600	1260	1047	930	848	781
Energy, ft/lbs per grain	5.68	3.52	2.43	1.92	1.60	1.35
Time of Flight, sec	0.0000	0.2121	0.4754	0.7808	1.1194	1.4887
Path, inches — Relative to Line of Sight, ZERO RANGE 100 yds	-1.5	0.0	-20.5	-72.6	-164.9	-305.6
200 yds	-1.5	10.3	0.0	-41.8	-123.8	-254.3
300 yds	-1.5	24.2	27.9	0.0	-68.1	-184.6
Velocity, ft/sec	1500	1190	1010	906	829	765
Energy, ft/lbs per grain	5.00	3.14	2.26	1.82	1.53	1.30
Time of Flight, sec	0.0000	0.2257	0.5015	0.8161	1.1630	1.5405
Path, inches — Relative to Line of Sight, ZERO RANGE 100 yds	-1.5	0.0	-23.1	-80.1	-179.4	-329.6
200 yds	-1.5	11.5	0.0	-45.5	-133.3	-272.0
300 yds	-1.5	26.7	30.3	0.0	-72.7	-196.2

long range tables

Exterior Ballistic Table for Ballistic Coefficient 0.19

			Muzzle	100 yds	200 yds	300 yds	400 yds	500 yds
Velocity, ft/sec			4000	3385	2850	2374	1964	1572
Energy, ft/lbs per grain			35.52	25.44	18.03	12.51	8.41	5.49
Time of Flight, sec			0.0000	0.0816	0.1783	0.2936	0.4333	0.6050
Path, inches	ZERO RANGE	100 yds	-1.5	0.0	-1.6	-7.5	-19.6	41.1
Relative to		200 yds	-1.5	0.8	0.0	-5.1	-16.5	-37.2
Line of Sight		300 yds	-1.5	2.5	3.4	0.0	-9.7	-28.7
Velocity, ft/sec			3900	3298	2774	2305	1885	1521
Energy, ft/lbs per grain			33.77	24.15	17.08	11.80	7.89	5.14
Time of Flight, sec			0.0000	0.0837	0.1830	0.3016	0.4456	0.6230
Path, inches	ZERO RANGE	100 yds	-1.5	0.0	-1.7	-8.0	-21.0	-43.9
Relative to		200 yds	-1.5	0.9	0.0	-5.4	-17.5	-39.5
Line of Sight		300 yds	-1.5	2.7	3.6	0.0	-10.3	-30.5
Velocity, ft/sec			3800	3212	2697	2237	1824	1470
Energy, ft/lbs per grain			32.06	22.90	16.15	11.11	7.39	1470
Time of Flight, sec			0.0000	0.0859	0.1879	0.3101	0.4587	0.6422
Path, inches	ZERO RANGE	100 yds	-1.5	0.0	-1.9	-8.6	-22.4	-46.9
Relative to		200 yds	-1.5	1.0	0.0	-5.8	-18.6	-42.1
Line of Sight		300 yds	-1.5	2.9	3.9	0.0	-10.9	-32.5
Velocity, ft/sec			3700	3125	2620	2167	1763	1420
Energy, ft/lbs per grain			30.39	21.68	15.24	10.43	6.90	4.48
Time of Flight, sec			0.0000	0.0883	0.1932	0.3191	0.4726	0.6626
Path, inches	ZERO RANGE	100 yds	-1.5	0.0	-2.1	-9.3	-24.1	-50.2
Relative to		200 yds	-1.5	1.0	0.0	-6.2	-19.9	-44.9
Line of Sight		300 yds	-1.5	3.1	4.1	0.0	11.6	-34.6
Velocity, ft/sec			3600	3038	2543	2097	1702	1370
Energy, ft/lbs per grain			28.77	20.49	14.36	9.76	6.43	4.17
Time of Flight, sec			0.0000	0.0908	0.1988	0.3287	0.4876	0.6844
Path, inches	ZERO RANGE	100 yds	-1.5	0.0	-2.3	-10.1	-25.9	-53.8
Relative to		200 yds	-1.5	1.2	0.0	-6.6	-21.2	-48.1
Line of Sight		300 yds	-1.5	3.4	4.4	0.0	-12.4	-37.1
Velocity, ft/sec			3500	2951	2465	2027	1641	1322
Energy, ft/lbs per grain			27.20	19.33	13.49	9.12	5.98	3.88
Time of Flight, sec			0.0000	0.0934	0.2047	0.3389	0.5035	0.7077
Path, inches	ZERO RANGE	100 yds	-1.5	0.0	-2.5	-10.9	-27.8	-57.9
Relative to		200 yds	-1.5	1.3	0.0	-7.1	-22.7	-51.5
Line of Sight		300 yds	-1.5	3.6	4.7	0.0	-13.3	-39.7
Velocity, ft/sec			3400	2863	2386	1957	1581	1276
Energy, ft/lbs per grain			25.66	18.20	12.64	8.50	5.55	3.61
Time of Flight, sec			0.0000	0.0962	0.2110	0.3499	0.5206	0.7325
Path, inches	ZERO RANGE	100 yds	-1.5	0.0	-2.8	-11.8	-30.0	-62.3
Relative to		200 yds	-1.5	1.4	0.0	-7.6	-24.4	-55.4
Line of Sight		300 yds	-1.5	3.9	5.1	0.0	-14.3	-42.7
Velocity, ft/sec			3300	2775	2307	1886	1521	1232
Energy, ft/lbs per grain			24.18	17.10	11.82	7.90	5.14	3.37
Time of Flight, sec			0.0000	0.0992	0.2178	0.3617	0.5390	0.7589
Path, inches	ZERO RANGE	100 yds	-1.5	0.0	-3.1	-12.8	-32.4	-67.3
Relative to		200 yds	-1.5	1.5	0.0	-8.2	-26.3	-59.6
Line of Sight		300 yds	1.5	4.3	5.4	0.0	-15.4	-46.0

long range tables

Exterior Ballistic Table for Ballistic Coefficient 0.19

		Muzzle	100 yds	200 yds	300 yds	400 yds	500 yds
				RANGE			
Velocity, ft/sec		3200	2687	2227	1816	1463	1191
Energy, ft/lbs per grain		22.73	16.03	11.01	7.32	4.75	3.15
Time of Flight, sec		0.0000	0.1024	0.2250	0.3743	0.5586	0.7870
Path, inches	100 yds	-1.5	0.0	-3.4	-13.9	-35.1	-72.8
Relative to ZERO RANGE	200 yds	-1.5	1.7	0.0	-8.8	-28.3	-64.3
Line of Sight	300 yds	-1.5	4.6	5.9	0.0	-16.6	-49.7
Velocity, ft/sec		3100	2598	2147	1745	1405	1152
Energy, ft/lbs per grain		21.33	14.98	10.23	6.76	4.38	2.95
Time of Flight, sec		0.0000	0.1058	0.2328	0.3879	0.5798	0.8169
Path, inches	100 yds	-1.5	0.0	-3.7	-15.1	-38.1	-78.9
Relative to ZERO RANGE	200 yds	-1.5	1.9	0.0	-9.5	-30.6	-69.6
Line of Sight	300 yds	-1.5	5.0	6.3	0.0	-17.9	-53.7
Velocity, ft/sec		3000	2509	2067	1675	1349	1117
Energy, ft/lbs per grain		19.98	13.98	9.49	6.23	4.04	2.77
Time of Flight, sec		0.0000	0.1094	0.2412	0.4025	0.6025	0.8484
Path, inches	100 yds	-1.5	0.0	-4.1	-16.5	-41.4	-85.7
Relative to ZERO RANGE	200 yds	-1.5	2.1	0.0	-10.3	-33.2	-75.4
Line of Sight	300 yds	-1.5	5.5	6.9	0.0	-19.5	-58.2
Velocity, ft/sec		2900	2419	1986	1606	1295	1084
Energy, ft/lbs per grain		18.67	12.99	8.76	5.73	3.72	2.61
Time of Flight, sec		0.0000	0.1133	0.2502	0.4183	0.6268	0.8817
Path, inches	100 yds	-1.5	0.0	-4.5	-18.0	-45.2	-93.2
Relative to ZERO RANGE	200 yds	-1.5	2.3	0.0	-11.2	-36.1	-81.9
Line of Sight	300 yds	-1.5	6.0	7.5	0.0	-21.2	-63.2
Velocity, ft/sec		2800	2329	1906	1538	1244	1055
Energy, ft/lbs per grain		17.41	12.04	8.07	5.25	3.44	2.47
Time of Flight, sec		0.0000	0.1175	0.2599	0.4353	0.6529	0.9166
Path, inches	100 yds	-1.5	0.0	-5.0	-19.7	-49.4	-101.6
Relative to ZERO RANGE	200 yds	-1.5	2.5	0.0	-12.2	-39.4	-89.1
Line of Sight	300 yds	-1.5	6.6	8.2	0.0	-23.1	-68.7
Velocity, ft/sec		2700	2239	1826	1472	1197	1028
Energy, ft/lbs per grain		16.18	11.13	7.40	4.81	3.18	2.35
Time of Flight, sec		0.0000	0.1220	0.2704	0.4537	0.6804	0.9530
Path, inches	100 yds	-1.5	0.0	-5.5	-21.7	-54.1	-110.8
Relative to ZERO RANGE	200 yds	-1.5	2.8	0.0	-13.4	-43.0	-97.0
Line of Sight	300 yds	-1.5	7.2	8.9	0.0	-25.2	-74.7
Velocity, ft/sec		2600	2149	1747	1407	1153	1003
Energy, ft/lbs per grain		15.01	10.25	6.78	4.39	2.95	2.23
Time of Flight, sec		0.0000	0.1269	0.2818	0.4736	0.7104	0.9910
Path, inches	100 yds	-1.5	0.0	-6.1	-23.9	-59.4	-121.0
Relative to ZERO RANGE	200 yds	-1.5	3.1	0.0	-14.7	-47.1	-105.6
Line of Sight	300 yds	-1.5	8.0	9.8	0.0	-27.6	-81.2
Velocity, ft/sec		2500	2059	1669	1344	1113	981
Energy, ft/lbs per grain		13.88	9.41	6.18	4.01	2.75	2.14
Time of Flight, sec		0.0000	0.1322	0.2942	0.4950	0.7418	1.0304
Path, inches	100 yds	-1.5	0.0	-6.8	-26.3	-65.3	-132.2
Relative to ZERO RANGE	200 yds	-1.5	3.4	0.0	-16.1	-51.6	-115.1
Line of Sight	300 yds	-1.5	8.8	10.7	0.0	-30.2	-88.3

Exterior Ballistic Table for Ballistic Coefficient 0.19

		Muzzle	100 yds	200 yds	300 yds	400 yds	500 yds
				RANGE			
Velocity, ft/sec		2400	1969	1592	1284	1078	959
Energy, ft/lbs per grain		12.79	8.61	5.63	3.66	2.58	2.04
Time of Flight, sec		0.0000	0.1380	0.3076	0.5180	0.7747	1.0711
Path, inches	100 yds	-1.5	0.0	-7.6	-29.2	-71.9	-144.5
Relative to	200 yds	-1.5	3.8	0.0	-17.7	-56.7	-125.5
Line of Sight ZERO RANGE	300 yds	-1.5	9.7	11.8	0.0	-33.0	-95.9
Velocity, ft/sec		2300	1880	1516	1229	1046	939
Energy, ft/lbs per grain		11.74	7.85	5.10	3.35	2.43	1.96
Time of Flight, sec		0.0000	0.1443	0.3220	0.5428	0.8093	1.1131
Path, inches	100 yds	-1.5	0.0	-8.5	-32.3	-79.3	-157.9
Relative to	200 yds	-1.5	4.2	0.0	-19.6	-62.3	-136.6
Line of Sight ZERO RANGE	300 yds	-1.5	10.8	13.1	0.0	-36.2	-104.0
Velocity, ft/sec		2200	1792	1443	1177	1017	920
Energy, ft/lbs per grain		10.75	7.13	4.62	3.08	2.30	1.88
Time of Flight, sec		0.0000	0.1512	0.3380	0.5693	0.8452	1.1564
Path, inches	100 yds	-1.5	0.0	-9.5	-35.9	-87.4	-172.4
Relative to	200 yds	-1.5	4.8	0.0	-21.7	-68.4	-148.7
Line of Sight ZERO RANGE	300 yds	-1.5	12.0	14.4	0.0	-39.5	-112.6
Velocity, ft/sec		2100	1704	1372	1131	991	901
Energy, ft/lbs per grain		9.79	6.45	4.18	2.84	2.18	1.80
Time of Flight, sec		0.0000	0.1587	0.3553	0.5975	0.8825	1.2009
Path, inches	100 yds	-1.5	0.0	-10.7	-40.0	-96.4	-188.3
Relative to	200 yds	-1.5	5.3	0.0	-24.0	-75.1	-161.6
Line of Sight ZERO RANGE	300 yds	-1.5	13.3	16.0	0.0	-43.1	-121.6
Velocity, ft/sec		2000	1618	1304	1090	966	883
Energy, ft/lbs per grain		8.88	5.81	3.78	2.64	2.07	1.73
Time of Flight, sec		0.0000	0.1669	0.3740	0.6273	0.9211	1.2466
Path, inches	100 yds	-1.5	0.0	-12.0	-44.6	-106.3	-205.3
Relative to	200 yds	-1.5	6.0	0.0	-26.6	-82.4	-175.3
Line of Sight ZERO RANGE	300 yds	-1.5	14.9	17.7	0.0	-46.9	-131.0
Velocity, ft/sec		1900	1533	1241	1053	943	866
Energy, ft/lbs per grain		8.01	5.22	3.42	2.46	1.97	1.66
Time of Flight, sec		0.0000	0.1760	0.3943	0.6586	0.9609	1.2935
Path, inches	100 yds	-1.5	0.0	-13.5	-49.7	-117.2	-223.7
Relative to	200 yds	-1.5	6.8	0.0	-29.4	-90.1	-189.9
Line of Sight ZERO RANGE	300 yds	-1.5	16.6	19.6	0.0	-50.9	-140.8
Velocity, ft/sec		1800	1450	1182	1020	921	849
Energy, ft/lbs per grain		7.19	4.67	3.10	2.31	1.88	1.60
Time of Flight, sec		0.0000	0.1860	0.4163	0.6913	1.0018	1.3417
Path, inches	100 yds	-1.5	0.0	-15.3	-55.4	-128.9	-243.4
Relative to	200 yds	-1.5	7.6	0.0	-32.5	-98.4	-205.2
Line of Sight ZERO RANGE	300 yds	-1.5	18.5	21.7	0.0	-55.0	-151.0
Velocity, ft/sec		1700	1369	1129	989	900	832
Energy, ft/lbs per grain		6.42	4.16	2.83	2.17	1.80	1.54
Time of Flight, sec		0.0000	0.1971	0.4399	0.7253	1.0440	1.3913
Path, inches	100 yds	-1.5	0.0	-17.3	-61.7	-141.6	-264.5
Relative to	200 yds	-1.5	8.6	0.0	-35.8	-107.1	-221.3
Line of Sight ZERO RANGE	300 yds	-1.5	20.6	23.9	0.0	-59.3	-161.6

long range tables

Exterior Ballistic Table for Ballistic Coefficient 0.19

		Muzzle	100 yds	200 yds	300 yds	400 yds	500 yds
Velocity, ft/sec		1600	1291	1081	961	880	815
Energy, ft/lbs per grain		5.68	3.70	2.59	2.05	1.72	1.47
Time of Flight, sec		0.0000	0.2094	0.4650	0.7605	1.0875	1.4426
Path, inches	100 yds	-1.5	0.0	-19.5	-68.6	-155.3	-287.1
Relative to	200 yds	-1.5	9.8	0.0	-39.4	-116.3	-238.3
Line of Sight	300 yds	-1.5	22.9	26.2	0.0	-63.8	-172.7
Velocity, ft/sec		1500	1217	1039	935	859	798
Energy, ft/lbs per grain		5.00	3.29	2.40	1.94	1.64	1.41
Time of Flight, sec		0.0000	0.2230	0.4915	0.7970	1.1324	1.4954
Path, inches	100 yds	-1.5	0.0	-22.0	-76.1	-170.0	-311.1
Relative to	200 yds	-1.5	11.0	0.0	-43.1	-126.0	-256.0
Line of Sight	300 yds	-1.5	25.4	28.7	0.0	-68.5	-184.2

Exterior Ballistic Table for Ballistic Coefficient 0.21

		Muzzle	100 yds	200 yds	300 yds	400 yds	500 yds
Velocity, ft/sec		3300	2822	2392	2001	1653	1359
Energy, ft/lbs per grain		24.18	17.68	12.70	8.89	6.07	4.10
Time of Flight, sec		0.0000	0.0983	0.2138	0.3510	0.5160	0.7166
Path, inches	100 yds	-1.5	0.0	-2.9	-12.0	-29.8	-60.5
Relative to	200 yds	-1.5	1.5	0.0	-7.6	-24.0	-53.3
Line of Sight	300 yds	-1.5	4.0	5.1	0.0	-13.9	-40.6
Velocity, ft/sec		3200	2733	2311	1928	1589	1308
Energy, ft/lbs per grain		22.73	16.58	11.86	8.25	5.61	3.80
Time of Flight, sec		0.0000	0.1015	0.2209	0.3630	0.5346	0.7431
Path, inches	100 yds	-1.5	0.0	-3.2	-13.0	-32.3	-65.5
Relative to	200 yds	-1.5	1.6	0.0	-8.2	-25.9	-57.5
Line of Sight	300 yds	-1.5	4.3	5.5	0.0	-14.9	-43.8
Velocity, ft/sec		3100	2643	2229	1855	1526	1259
Energy, ft/lbs per grain		21.33	15.51	11.03	7.64	5.17	3.52
Time of Flight, sec		0.0000	0.1048	0.2284	0.3760	0.5545	0.7715
Path, inches	100 yds	-1.5	0.0	-3.6	-15.1	-39.0	-83.1
Relative to	200 yds	-1.5	1.8	0.0	-9.7	-31.8	-74.1
Line of Sight	300 yds	-1.5	5.0	6.4	0.0	-19.0	-58.0
Velocity, ft/sec		3000	2553	2147	1781	1465	1213
Energy, ft/lbs per grain		19.98	14.47	10.23	7.04	4.76	3.27
Time of Flight, sec		0.0000	0.1084	0.2366	0.3900	0.5760	0.8018
Path, inches	100 yds	-1.5	0.0	-3.9	-15.4	-38.0	-77.1
Relative to	200 yds	-1.5	1.9	0.0	-9.6	-30.3	-67.3
Line of Sight	300 yds	-1.5	5.1	6.4	0.0	-17.5	-51.4
Velocity, ft/sec		2900	2463	2065	1709	1404	1171
Energy, ft/lbs per grain		18.67	13.47	9.47	6.48	4.38	3.04
Time of Flight, sec		0.0000	0.1123	0.2453	0.4051	0.5991	0.8341
Path, inches	100 yds	-1.5	0.0	-4.3	-16.9	-41.5	-83.9
Relative to	200 yds	-1.5	2.1	0.0	-10.4	-32.9	-73.2
Line of Sight	300 yds	-1.5	5.6	6.9	0.0	-19.0	-55.8

long range tables

	Muzzle	100 yds	200 yds	300 yds	400 yds	500 yds
Velocity, ft/sec	2800	2372	1983	1637	1346	1132
Energy, ft/lbs per grain	17.41	12.49	8.73	5.95	4.02	2.84
Time of Flight, sec	0.0000	0.1164	0.2548	0.4214	0.6240	0.8683
Path, inches — 100 yds (ZERO RANGE)	1.5	0.0	-4.8	-18.5	-45.3	-91.5
Relative to — 200 yds	-1.5	2.4	0.0	-11.3	-35.8	-79.6
Line of Sight — 300 yds	-1.5	6.2	7.6	0.0	-20.7	-60.8
Velocity, ft/sec	2700	2281	1901	1566	1290	1096
Energy, ft/lbs per grain	16.18	11.55	8.02	5.44	3.69	2.67
Time of Flight, sec	0.0000	0.1209	0.2650	0.4390	0.6507	0.9044
Path, inches — 100 yds (ZERO RANGE)	-1.5	0.0	-5.3	-20.3	-49.6	-100.0
Relative to — 200 yds	-1.5	2.6	0.0	-12.4	-39.1	-86.9
Line of Sight — 300 yds	-1.5	6.8	8.3	0.0	-22.6	-66.2
Velocity, ft/sec	2600	2190	1819	1497	1237	1064
Energy, ft/lbs per grain	15.01	10.65	7.35	4.98	3.40	2.51
Time of Flight, sec	0.0000	0.1257	0.2761	0.4581	0.6793	0.9423
Path, inches — 100 yds (ZERO RANGE)	-1.5	0.0	-5.6	-22.3	-54.5	-109.5
Relative to — 200 yds	-1.5	2.9	0.0	-13.6	-42.8	-94.9
Line of Sight — 300 yds	-1.5	7.4	9.0	0.0	-24.7	-72.3
Velocity, ft/sec	2500	2099	1739	1429	1188	1035
Energy, ft/lbs per grain	13.88	9.78	6.71	4.53	3.13	2.38
Time of Flight, sec	0.0000	0.1310	0.2881	0.4787	0.7099	0.9819
Path, inches — 100 yds (ZERO RANGE)	-1.5	0.0	-6.5	-24.6	-60.0	-120.0
Relative to — 200 yds	-1.5	3.2	0.0	-14.9	-47.0	-103.8
Line of Sight — 300 yds	-1.5	8.2	9.9	0.0	-27.1	-78.9
Velocity, ft/sec	2400	2008	1659	1363	1143	1009
Energy, ft/lbs per grain	12.79	8.95	6.11	4.12	2.90	2.26
Time of Flight, sec	0.0000	0.1367	0.3011	0.5010	0.7424	1.0232
Path, inches — 100 yds (ZERO RANGE)	-1.5	0.0	-7.2	-27.3	-66.2	-131.6
Relative to — 200 yds	-1.5	3.6	0.0	-16.4	-51.7	-113.5
Line of Sight — 300 yds	-1.5	9.1	10.9	0.0	-29.8	-86.2
Velocity, ft/sec	2300	1918	1581	1301	1103	984
Energy, ft/lbs per grain	11.74	8.17	5.55	3.76	2.70	2.15
Time of Flight, sec	0.0000	0.1429	0.3153	0.5250	0.7768	1.0659
Path, inches — 100 yds (ZERO RANGE)	-1.5	0.0	-8.1	-30.2	-73.1	-144.4
Relative to — 200 yds	-1.5	4.0	0.0	-18.1	-56.9	-124.2
Line of Sight — 300 yds	-1.5	10.1	12.1	0.0	-32.7	-94.0
Velocity, ft/sec	2200	1828	1504	1243	1067	962
Energy, ft/lbs per grain	10.75	7.42	5.02	3.43	2.53	2.05
Time of Flight, sec	0.0000	0.1496	0.3307	0.5509	0.8129	1.1100
Path, inches — 100 yds (ZERO RANGE)	-1.5	0.0	-9.0	-33.6	-80.8	-158.4
Relative to — 200 yds	-1.5	4.5	0.0	-20.1	-62.7	-135.8
Line of Sight — 300 yds	-1.5	11.2	13.4	0.0	-36.0	-102.4
Velocity, ft/sec	2100	1739	1430	1188	1035	940
Energy, ft/lbs per grain	9.79	6.71	4.54	3.13	2.38	1.96
Time of Flight, sec	0.0000	0.1570	0.3475	0.5786	0.8506	1.1556
Path, inches — 100 yds (ZERO RANGE)	-1.5	0.0	-10.1	-37.5	-89.4	-173.7
Relative to — 200 yds	-1.5	5.1	0.0	-22.3	-69.1	-148.4
Line of Sight — 300 yds	-1.5	12.5	14.8	0.0	-39.5	-111.3

Exterior Ballistic Table for Ballistic Coefficient 0.21

		Muzzle	100 yds	200 yds	300 yds	400 yds	500 yds
	RANGE						
Velocity, ft/sec		2000	1652	1358	1139	1006	920
Energy, ft/lbs per grain		8.88	6.06	4.09	2.88	2.25	1.88
Time of Flight, sec		0.0000	0.1652	0.3659	0.6083	0.8898	1.2024
Path, inches	100 yds	-1.5	0.0	-11.4	-41.8	-99.0	-190.4
Relative to	200 yds	-1.5	5.7	0.0	-24.7	-76.2	-161.9
Line of Sight	ZERO RANGE 300 yds	-1.5	13.9	16.5	0.0	-43.2	-120.7
Velocity, ft/sec		1900	1565	1289	1096	980	900
Energy, ft/lbs per grain		8.01	5.44	3.69	2.67	2.13	1.80
Time of Flight, sec		0.0000	0.1741	0.2859	0.6397	0.9305	1.2507
Path, inches	100 yds	-1.5	0.0	-12.9	-46.8	-109.6	-208.6
Relative to	200 yds	-1.5	6.4	0.0	-27.5	-83.8	-176.4
Line of Sight	ZERO RANGE 300 yds	-1.5	15.6	18.3	0.0	-47.2	-130.6
Velocity, ft/sec		1800	1480	1225	1057	955	881
Energy, ft/lbs per grain		7.19	4.86	3.33	2.48	2.02	1.72
Time of Flight, sec		0.0000	0.1840	0.4076	0.6728	0.9725	1.3002
Path, inches	100 yds	-1.5	0.0	-14.6	-52.3	-121.1	-228.1
Relative to	200 yds	-1.5	7.3	0.0	-30.5	-92.0	-191.7
Line of Sight	ZERO RANGE 300 yds	-1.5	17.4	20.3	0.0	-51.4	-140.9
Velocity, ft/sec		1700	1397	1166	1022	931	863
Energy, ft/lbs per grain		6.42	4.33	3.02	2.32	1.92	1.65
Time of Flight, sec		0.0000	0.1950	0.4311	0.7074	1.0158	1.3512
Path, inches	100 yds	-1.5	0.0	-16.5	-58.5	-133.8	-249.2
Relative to	200 yds	-1.5	8.2	0.0	-33.8	-100.8	-208.0
Line of Sight	ZERO RANGE 300 yds	-1.5	19.5	22.5	0.0	-55.7	-151.6
Velocity, ft/sec		1600	1316	1113	990	908	844
Energy, ft/lbs per grain		5.68	3.84	2.75	2.18	1.83	1.58
Time of Flight, sec		0.0000	0.2072	0.4564	0.7435	1.0606	1.4038
Path, inches	100 yds	-1.5	0.0	-18.7	-65.4	-147.5	-271.8
Relative to	200 yds	-1.5	9.3	0.0	-37.4	-110.1	-225.1
Line of Sight	ZERO RANGE 300 yds	-1.5	21.8	24.9	0.0	-60.3	-102.0
Velocity, ft/sec		1500	1239	1066	960	886	826
Energy, ft/lbs per grain		5.00	3.41	2.52	2.05	1.74	1.51
Time of Flight, sec		0.0000	0.2207	0.4832	0.7808	1.1068	1.4583
Path, inches	100 yds	-1.5	0.0	-21.2	-72.9	-162.3	-296.1
Relative to	200 yds	-1.5	10.6	0.0	-41.1	-119.9	-243.1
Line of Sight	ZERO RANGE 300 yds	-1.5	24.3	27.4	0.0	-65.1	-174.6

Exterior Ballistic Table for Ballistic Coefficient 0.22

		Muzzle	100 yds	200 yds	300 yds	400 yds	500 yds
	RANGE						
Velocity, ft/sec		3600	3110	2672	2274	1911	1589
Energy, ft/lbs per grain		28.77	21.47	15.85	11.48	8.11	5.61
Time of Flight, sec		0.0000	0.0897	0.1938	0.3155	0.4595	0.6318
Path, inches	100 yds	-1.5	0.0	-2.1	-9.2	-23.0	-46.5
Relative to	200 yds	-1.5	1.1	0.0	-6.0	-18.7	-41.2
Line of Sight	ZERO RANGE 300 yds	-1.5	3.1	4.0	0.0	-10.8	-31.2

long range tables

	Muzzle	100 yds	200 yds	300 yds	400 yds	500 yds
Velocity, ft/sec	3500	3110	2672	2274	1911	1589
Energy, ft/lbs per grain	28.77	21.47	15.85	11.48	8.11	5.61
Time of Flight, sec	0.0000	0.0897	0.1938	0.3155	0.4595	0.6318
Path, inches — ZERO RANGE 100 yds	-1.5	0.0	-2.3	-9.9	-24.7	-49.9
Relative to — ZERO RANGE 200 yds	-1.5	1.2	0.0	-6.4	-20.0	-44.0
Line of Sight — ZERO RANGE 300 yds	-1.5	3.3	4.3	0.0	-11.5	-33.4
Velocity, ft/sec	3400	2932	2511	2127	1779	1475
Energy, ft/lbs per grain	25.66	19.09	14.00	10.04	7.03	4.83
Time of Flight, sec	0.0000	0.0951	0.2056	0.3355	0.4898	0.6752
Path, inches — ZERO RANGE 100 yds	-1.5	0.0	-2.6	-10.7	-26.6	-53.7
Relative to — ZERO RANGE 200 yds	-1.5	1.3	0.0	-6.9	-21.5	-47.3
Line of Sight — ZERO RANGE 300 yds	-1.5	3.6	4.6	0.0	-12.3	-35.8
Velocity, ft/sec	3300	2843	2430	2052	1713	1420
Energy, ft/lbs per grain	24.18	17.94	13.11	9.35	6.51	4.48
Time of Flight, sec	0.0000	0.0980	0.2122	0.3465	0.5066	0.6993
Path, inches — ZERO RANGE 100 yds	-1.5	0.0	-2.8	-11.6	-28.8	-57.9
Relative to — ZERO RANGE 200 yds	-1.5	1.4	0.0	-7.4	-23.1	-50.8
Line of Sight — ZERO RANGE 300 yds	-1.5	3.9	4.9	0.0	-13.3	-38.5
Velocity, ft/sec	3200	2753	2348	1978	1647	1366
Energy, ft/lbs per grain	22.73	16.83	12.24	8.69	6.02	4.14
Time of Flight, sec	0.0000	0.1011	0.2191	0.3584	0.5247	0.7251
Path, inches — ZERO RANGE 100 yds	-1.5	0.0	-3.1	-12.6	-31.1	-62.6
Relative to — ZERO RANGE 200 yds	-1.5	1.6	0.0	-7.9	-24.9	-54.8
Line of Sight — ZERO RANGE 300 yds	-1.5	4.2	5.3	0.0	-14.3	-41.5
Velocity, ft/sec	3100	2663	2265	1903	1582	1313
Energy, ft/lbs per grain	21.33	15.74	11.39	8.04	5.56	3.33
Time of Flight, sec	0.0000	0.1044	0.2266	0.3711	0.5441	0.7527
Path, inches — ZERO RANGE 100 yds	-1.5	0.0	-3.4	-13.7	-33.8	-67.8
Relative to — ZERO RANGE 200 yds	-1.5	1.7	0.0	-8.6	-26.9	-59.2
Line of Sight — ZERO RANGE 300 yds	-1.5	4.6	5.7	0.0	-15.4	-44.9
Velocity, ft/sec	3000	2572	2183	1829	1518	1263
Energy, ft/lbs per grain	19.98	14.69	10.58	7.43	5.12	3.54
Time of Flight, sec	0.0000	0.1080	0.2346	0.3848	0.5651	0.7823
Path, inches — ZERO RANGE 100 yds	-1.5	0.0	-3.8	-15.0	-36.7	-73.7
Relative to — ZERO RANGE 200 yds	-1.5	1.9	0.0	-9.3	-29.1	-64.2
Line of Sight — ZERO RANGE 300 yds	-1.5	5.0	6.2	0.0	-16.7	-48.7
Velocity, ft/sec	2900	2482	2100	1755	1455	1216
Energy, ft/lbs per grain	18.67	13.68	9.79	6.84	4.70	3.28
Time of Flight, sec	0.0000	0.1119	0.2433	0.3997	0.5876	0.8139
Path, inches — ZERO RANGE 100 yds	-1.5	0.0	-4.2	-16.4	-40.0	-80.2
Relative to — ZERO RANGE 200 yds	-1.5	2.1	0.0	-10.1	-31.6	-69.7
Line of Sight — ZERO RANGE 300 yds	-1.5	5.5	6.7	0.0	-18.2	-52.9
Velocity, ft/sec	2800	2390	2017	1681	1394	1172
Energy, ft/lbs per grain	17.41	12.68	9.03	6.27	4.31	3.05
Time of Flight, sec	0.0000	0.1160	0.2526	0.4156	0.6119	0.8476
Path, inches — ZERO RANGE 100 yds	-1.5	0.0	-4.6	-17.9	-43.7	-87.5
Relative to — ZERO RANGE 200 yds	-1.5	2.3	0.0	-11.0	-34.4	-75.9
Line of Sight — ZERO RANGE 300 yds	-1.5	6.0	7.3	0.0	-19.8	-51.6

Exterior Ballistic Table for Ballistic Coefficient 0.22

		Muzzle	100 yds	200 yds	300 yds	400 yds	500 yds
				RANGE			
Velocity, ft/sec		2700	2299	1934	1609	1335	1132
Energy, ft/lbs per grain		16.18	11.73	8.30	5.75	3.96	2.84
Time of Flight, sec		0.0000	0.1204	0.2627	0.4329	0.6381	0.8833
Path, inches	100 yds	-1.5	0.0	-5.1	-19.7	-47.9	-95.7
Relative to ZERO RANGE	200 yds	-1.5	2.6	0.0	-12.0	-37.6	-82.8
Line of Sight	300 yds	-1.5	6.6	8.0	0.0	-21.6	-62.8
Velocity, ft/sec		2600	2208	1851	1537	1278	1096
Energy, ft/lbs per grain		15.01	10.82	7.61	5.24	3.63	2.67
Time of Flight, sec		0.0000	0.1252	0.2737	0.4516	0.6662	0.9210
Path, inches	100 yds	-1.5	0.0	-5.7	-21.7	-52.6	-104.8
Relative to ZERO RANGE	200 yds	-1.5	2.9	0.0	-13.1	-41.1	-90.5
Line of Sight	300 yds	-1.5	7.2	8.7	0.0	-23.6	-68.6
Velocity, ft/sec		2500	2116	1770	1468	1225	1063
Energy, ft/lbs per grain		13.88	9.94	6.69	4.78	3.33	2.51
Time of Flight, sec		0.0000	0.1304	0.2855	0.4719	0.6963	0.9606
Path, inches	100 yds	-1.5	0.0	-6.4	-23.9	-57.8	-114.9
Relative to ZERO RANGE	200 yds	-1.5	3.2	0.0	-14.4	-45.1	-99.1
Line of Sight	300 yds	-1.5	8.0	9.6	0.0	-25.9	-75.0
Velocity, ft/sec		2400	2025	1689	1400	1177	1034
Energy, ft/lbs per grain		12.79	9.10	6.33	4.35	3.08	2.37
Time of Flight, sec		0.0000	0.1361	0.2984	0.4938	0.7285	1.0019
Path, inches	100 yds	-1.5	0.0	-7.1	-26.5	-63.8	-126.2
Relative to ZERO RANGE	200 yds	-1.5	3.5	0.0	-15.9	-49.6	-108.5
Line of Sight	300 yds	-1.5	8.8	10.6	0.0	-28.5	-82.1
Velocity, ft/sec		2300	1935	1609	1335	1132	1007
Energy, ft/lbs per grain		11.74	8.31	5.75	3.96	2.84	2.25
Time of Flight, sec		0.0000	0.1422	0.3124	0.5175	0.7626	1.0448
Path, inches	100 yds	-1.5	0.0	-7.9	-29.4	-70.5	-138.7
Relative to ZERO RANGE	200 yds	-1.5	4.0	0.0	-17.5	-54.7	-118.9
Line of Sight	300 yds	-1.5	9.8	11.7	0.0	-31.3	-89.7
Velocity, ft/sec		2200	1844	1531	1274	1093	982
Energy, ft/lbs per grain		10.75	7.55	5.20	3.60	2.65	2.14
Time of Flight, sec		0.0000	0.1490	0.3277	0.5430	0.7986	1.0894
Path, inches	100 yds	-1.5	0.0	-8.8	-32.7	-78.0	-152.4
Relative to ZERO RANGE	200 yds	-1.5	4.4	0.0	-19.4	-60.4	-130.3
Line of Sight	300 yds	-1.5	10.9	12.9	0.0	-34.5	-98.0
Velocity, ft/sec		2100	1755	1455	1216	1057	959
Energy, ft/lbs per grain		9.79	6.84	4.70	3.28	2.48	2.04
Time of Flight, sec		0.0000	0.1563	0.3443	0.5705	0.8365	1.1354
Path, inches	100 yds	-1.5	0.0	-9.9	-36.4	-86.5	-167.5
Relative to ZERO RANGE	200 yds	-1.5	5.0	0.0	-21.5	-66.6	-142.7
Line of Sight	300 yds	-1.5	12.1	14.4	0.0	-37.9	-106.8
Velocity, ft/sec		2000	1666	1382	1164	1026	937
Energy, ft/lbs per grain		8.88	6.16	4.24	3.01	2.34	1.95
Time of Flight, sec		0.0000	0.1644	0.3624	0.6000	0.8759	1.1828
Path, inches	100 yds	-1.5	0.0	-11.2	-40.7	-95.9	-184.0
Relative to ZERO RANGE	200 yds	-1.5	5.6	0.0	-23.9	-73.5	-156.1
Line of Sight	300 yds	-1.5	13.6	16.0	0.0	-41.6	-116.2

long range tables

Exterior Ballistic Table for Ballistic Coefficient 0.22

		Muzzle	100 yds	200 yds	300 yds	400 yds	500 yds
Velocity, ft/sec		1900	1579	1311	1117	997	917
Energy, ft/lbs per grain		8.01	5.54	3.82	2.77	2.21	1.87
Time of Flight, sec		0.0000	0.1733	0.3823	0.6314	0.9170	1.2315
Path, inches	100 yds	-1.5	0.0	-12.6	-45.5	-106.3	-202.0
Relative to	ZERO RANGE 200 yds	-1.5	6.3	0.0	-26.6	-81.1	-170.5
Line of Sight	300 yds	-1.5	15.2	17.8	0.0	-45.6	-126.1
Velocity, ft/sec		1800	1493	1245	1075	970	897
Energy, ft/lbs per grain		7.19	4.95	3.44	2.57	2.09	1.79
Time of Flight, sec		0.0000	0.1832	0.4039	0.6646	0.9594	1.2817
Path, inches	100 yds	-1.5	0.0	-14.3	-51.0	-117.8	-221.5
Relative to	ZERO RANGE 200 yds	-1.5	7.1	0.0	-29.6	-89.3	-185.8
Line of Sight	300 yds	-1.5	17.0	19.8	0.0	-49.8	-136.5
Velocity, ft/sec		1700	1409	1183	1037	945	877
Energy, ft/lbs per grain		6.42	4.41	3.11	2.39	1.98	1.71
Time of Flight, sec		0.0000	0.1941	0.4273	0.6994	1.0032	1.3334
Path, inches	100 yds	-1.5	0.0	-16.2	-57.2	-130.4	-242.5
Relative to	ZERO RANGE 200 yds	-1.5	8.1	0.0	-32.9	-98.1	-202.1
Line of Sight	300 yds	-1.5	19.1	21.9	0.0	-54.2	-147.3
Velocity, ft/sec		1600	1328	1127	1004	921	858
Energy, ft/lbs per grain		5.68	3.92	2.82	2.24	1.88	1.63
Time of Flight, sec		0.0000	0.2062	0.4526	0.7359	1.0486	1.3867
Path, inches	100 yds	-1.5	0.0	-18.3	-64.0	-144.1	-265.2
Relative to	ZERO RANGE 200 yds	-1.5	9.2	0.0	-36.5	-107.4	-219.3
Line of Sight	300 yds	-1.5	21.3	24.3	0.0	-58.8	-158.5
Velocity, ft/sec		1500	1250	1078	972	898	839
Energy, ft/lbs per grain		5.00	3.47	2.58	2.10	1.79	1.56
Time of Flight, sec		0.0000	0.2197	0.4796	0.7737	1.0954	1.4418
Path, inches	100 yds	-1.5	0.0	-20.8	-71.5	-158.9	-289.5
Relative to	ZERO RANGE 200 yds	-1.5	10.4	0.0	-40.3	-117.3	-237.5
Line of Sight	300 yds	-1.5	23.8	26.8	0.0	-63.6	-170.4

Exterior Ballistic Table for Ballistic Coefficient 0.23

		Muzzle	100 yds	200 yds	300 yds	400 yds	500 yds
Velocity, ft/sec		4000	3485	3028	2616	2238	1894
Energy, ft/lbs per grain		35.52	26.96	20.36	15.19	11.12	7.96
Time of Flight, sec		0.0000	0.0804	0.1728	0.2794	0.4034	0.5492
Path, inches	100 yds	-1.5	0.0	-1.4	-6.6	-16.9	-34.2
Relative to	ZERO RANGE 200 yds	-1.5	0.7	0.0	-4.5	-14.1	-30.8
Line of Sight	300 yds	-1.5	2.2	3.0	0.0	-8.1	-23.3
Velocity, ft/sec		3900	3397	2949	2544	2172	1834
Energy, ft/lbs per grain		33.77	25.62	19.31	14.37	10.47	7.47
Time of Flight, sec		0.0000	0.0825	0.1773	0.2869	0.4145	0.5649
Path, inches	100 yds	-1.5	0.0	-1.5	-7.1	-18.1	-36.5
Relative to	ZERO RANGE 200 yds	-1.5	0.8	0.0	-4.8	-15.0	-32.7
Line of Sight	300 yds	-1.5	2.4	3.2	0.0	-8.6	-24.7

Exterior Ballistic Table for Ballistic Coefficient 0.23

	Muzzle	100 yds	200 yds	300 yds	400 yds	500 yds
			RANGE			
Velocity, ft/sec	3800	3308	2869	2471	2106	1774
Energy, ft/lbs per grain	32.06	24.29	18.27	13.56	9.85	6.99
Time of Flight, sec	0.0000	0.0847	0.1821	0.2948	0.4263	0.5816
Path, inches — 100 yds	-1.5	0.0	-1.7	-7.7	-19.4	-39.0
Relative to / ZERO RANGE — 200 yds	-1.5	0.8	0.0	-5.1	-16.0	-34.7
Line of Sight — 300 yds	-1.5	2.6	3.4	0.0	-9.2	-26.2
Velocity, ft/sec	3700	3220	2789	2398	2039	1714
Energy, ft/lbs per grain	30.39	23.02	17.27	12.77	9.23	6.52
Time of Flight, sec	0.0000	0.0870	0.1871	0.3031	0.4388	0.5994
Path, inches — 100 yds	-1.5	0.0	-1.9	-8.3	-20.7	-41.7
Relative to / ZERO RANGE — 200 yds	-1.5	0.9	0.0	-5.4	-17.0	-37.0
Line of Sight — 300 yds	-1.5	2.8	3.6	0.0	-9.7	-27.9
Velocity, ft/sec	3600	3131	2709	2324	1971	1655
Energy, ft/lbs per grain	28.77	21.76	16.29	11.99	8.62	6.08
Time of Flight, sec	0.0000	0.0894	0.1925	0.3121	0.4522	0.6184
Path, inches — 100 yds	-1.5	0.0	-2.1	-8.9	-22.3	-44.7
Relative to / ZERO RANGE — 200 yds	-1.5	1.0	0.0	-5.8	-18.1	-39.5
Line of Sight — 300 yds	-1.5	3.0	3.9	0.0	-10.4	-29.8
Velocity, ft/sec	3500	3041	2628	2250	1904	1596
Energy, ft/lbs per grain	27.20	20.53	15.33	11.24	8.05	5.65
Time of Flight, sec	0.0000	0.0920	0.1981	0.3216	0.4665	0.6388
Path, inches — 100 yds	-1.5	0.0	-2.3	-9.7	-24.0	-48.0
Relative to / ZERO RANGE — 200 yds	-1.5	1.1	0.0	-6.2	-19.4	-42.2
Line of Sight — 300 yds	-1.5	3.2	4.1	0.0	-11.1	-31.9
Velocity, ft/sec	3400	2952	2546	2175	1836	1537
Energy, ft/lbs per grain	25.66	19.35	14.39	10.50	7.48	5.24
Time of Flight, sec	0.0000	0.0947	0.2042	0.3317	0.4819	0.6606
Path, inches — 100 yds	-1.5	0.0	-2.5	-10.5	-25.8	-51.6
Relative to / ZERO RANGE — 200 yds	-1.5	1.3	0.0	-6.7	-20.8	-45.3
Line of Sight — 300 yds	-1.5	3.5	4.4	0.0	-11.9	-34.2
Velocity, ft/sec	3300	2862	2464	2100	1769	1479
Energy, ft/lbs per grain	24.18	18.18	13.8	9.79	6.95	4.86
Time of Flight, sec	0.0000	0.0977	0.2107	0.3426	0.4983	0.6840
Path, inches — 100 yds	-1.5	0.0	-2.8	-11.3	-27.9	-55.6
Relative to / ZERO RANGE — 200 yds	-1.5	1.4	0.0	-7.2	-22.3	-48.7
Line of Sight — 300 yds	-1.5	3.8	4.8	0.0	-12.7	-36.7
Velocity, ft/sec	3200	2772	2382	2024	1701	1422
Energy, ft/lbs per grain	22.73	17.06	12.60	9.09	6.42	4.49
Time of Flight, sec	0.0000	0.1008	0.2176	0.3542	0.5160	0.7091
Path, inches — 100 yds	-1.5	0.0	-3.1	-12.3	-30.1	-60.1
Relative to / ZERO RANGE — 200 yds	-1.5	1.5	0.0	-7.7	-24.0	-52.5
Line of Sight — 300 yds	-1.5	4.1	5.1	0.0	-13.7	-39.6
Velocity, ft/sec	3100	2681	2299	1948	1634	1366
Energy, ft/lbs per grain	21.33	15.96	11.73	8.42	5.93	4.14
Time of Flight, sec	0.0000	0.1041	0.2250	0.3667	0.5350	0.7360
Path, inches — 100 yds	-1.5	0.0	-3.4	-13.4	-32.7	-65.1
Relative to / ZERO RANGE — 200 yds	-1.5	1.7	0.0	-8.3	-25.9	-56.7
Line of Sight — 300 yds	-1.5	4.5	5.6	0.0	-14.8	-42.8

long range tables

Exterior Ballistic Table for Ballistic Coefficient 0.23

	Muzzle	100 yds	200 yds	300 yds	400 yds	500 yds
RANGE						
Velocity, ft/sec	3000	2590	2215	1873	1568	1313
Energy, ft/lbs per grain	19.98	14.89	10.89	7.79	5.46	3.83
Time of Flight, sec	0.0000	0.1076	0.2329	0.3802	0.5554	0.7649
Path, inches — Relative to Line of Sight — ZERO RANGE 100 yds	-1.5	0.0	-3.7	-14.6	-35.5	-70.7
ZERO RANGE 200 yds	-1.5	1.9	0.0	-9.0	-28.1	-61.4
ZERO RANGE 300 yds	-1.5	4.9	6.0	0.0	-16.0	-46.4

	Muzzle	100 yds	200 yds	300 yds	400 yds	500 yds
Velocity, ft/sec	2900	2499	2131	1797	1503	1262
Energy, ft/lbs per grain	18.67	13.86	10.08	7.17	5.02	3.54
Time of Flight, sec	0.0000	0.1115	0.2415	0.3948	0.5775	0.7959
Path, inches — ZERO RANGE 100 yds	-1.5	0.0	-4.1	-16.0	-38.7	-77.0
ZERO RANGE 200 yds	-1.5	2.1	0.0	-9.8	-30.5	-66.7
ZERO RANGE 300 yds	-1.5	5.3	6.5	0.0	-17.4	-50.4

	Muzzle	100 yds	200 yds	300 yds	400 yds	500 yds
Velocity, ft/sec	2800	2408	2048	1722	1440	1213
Energy, ft/lbs per grain	17.41	12.87	9.31	6.58	4.60	3.27
Time of Flight, sec	0.0000	0.1156	0.2507	0.4105	0.6012	0.8289
Path, inches — ZERO RANGE 100 yds	-1.5	0.0	-4.6	-17.5	-42.3	-84.0
ZERO RANGE 200 yds	-1.5	2.3	0.0	-10.7	-33.2	-72.6
ZERO RANGE 300 yds	-1.5	5.8	7.1	0.0	-19.0	-54.8

	Muzzle	100 yds	200 yds	300 yds	400 yds	500 yds
Velocity, ft/sec	2700	2316	1964	1648	1378	1169
Energy, ft/lbs per grain	16.18	11.91	8.56	6.03	4.22	3.03
Time of Flight, sec	0.0000	0.1200	0.2607	0.4275	0.6269	0.8642
Path, inches — ZERO RANGE 100 yds	-1.5	0.0	-5.0	-19.2	-46.3	-91.8
ZERO RANGE 200 yds	-1.5	2.5	0.0	-11.6	-36.2	-79.2
ZERO RANGE 300 yds	-1.5	6.4	7.8	0.0	-20.7	-59.8

	Muzzle	100 yds	200 yds	300 yds	400 yds	500 yds
Velocity, ft/sec	2600	2224	1881	1576	1318	1128
Energy, ft/lbs per grain	15.01	10.98	7.85	5.51	3.86	2.82
Time of Flight, sec	0.0000	0.1248	0.2715	0.4459	0.6544	0.9015
Path, inches — ZERO RANGE 100 yds	-1.5	0.0	-5.6	-21.1	-50.8	-100.6
ZERO RANGE 200 yds	-1.5	2.8	0.0	-12.7	-39.6	-86.6
ZERO RANGE 300 yds	-1.5	7.0	8.5	0.0	-22.6	-65.4

	Muzzle	100 yds	200 yds	300 yds	400 yds	500 yds
Velocity, ft/sec	2500	2132	1798	1504	1262	1092
Energy, ft/lbs per grain	13.88	10.09	7.18	5.02	3.54	2.65
Time of Flight, sec	0.0000	0.1299	0.2832	0.4658	0.6841	0.9409
Path, inches — ZERO RANGE 100 yds	-1.5	0.0	-6.2	-23.3	-55.9	-110.5
ZERO RANGE 200 yds	-1.5	3.1	0.0	-14.0	-43.5	-94.9
ZERO RANGE 300 yds	-1.5	7.8	9.3	0.0	-24.8	-71.6

	Muzzle	100 yds	200 yds	300 yds	400 yds	500 yds
Velocity, ft/sec	2400	2041	1716	1435	1210	1059
Energy, ft/lbs per grain	12.79	9.25	6.54	4.57	3.25	2.49
Time of Flight, sec	0.0000	0.1356	0.2959	0.4874	0.7158	0.9822
Path, inches — ZERO RANGE 100 yds	-1.5	0.0	-6.9	-25.8	-61.7	-121.4
ZERO RANGE 200 yds	-1.5	3.5	0.0	-15.4	-47.8	-104.1
ZERO RANGE 300 yds	-1.5	8.6	10.3	0.0	-27.3	-78.4

	Muzzle	100 yds	200 yds	300 yds	400 yds	500 yds
Velocity, ft/sec	2300	1950	636	1367	1161	1029
Energy, ft/lbs per grain	11.74	8.44	5.94	4.15	2.99	2.35
Time of Flight, sec	0.0000	0.1417	0.3098	0.5107	0.7497	1.0253
Path, inches — ZERO RANGE 100 yds	-1.5	0.0	-7.7	-28.6	-68.2	-133.6
ZERO RANGE 200 yds	-1.5	3.9	0.0	-17.0	-52.7	-114.2
ZERO RANGE 300 yds	-1.5	9.5	11.3	0.0	-30.1	-85.9

long range tables

Exterior Ballistic Table for Ballistic Coefficient 0.23

	Muzzle	100 yds	200 yds	300 yds	400 yds	500 yds
Velocity, ft/sec	2200	1859	1557	1303	1118	1002
Energy, ft/lbs per grain	10.75	7.67	5.38	3.77	2.77	2.23
Time of Flight, sec	0.0000	0.1484	0.3249	0.5359	0.7856	1.0701
Path, inches — ZERO RANGE 100 yds	-1.5	0.0	-8.7	-31.8	-75.6	-147.1
Relative to — ZERO RANGE 200 yds	-1.5	4.3	0.0	-18.8	-48.2	-125.4
Line of Sight — ZERO RANGE 300 yds	-1.5	10.6	12.6	0.0	-33.1	-94.0
Velocity, ft/sec	2100	1769	1479	1243	1080	977
Energy, ft/lbs per grain	9.79	6.95	4.86	3.43	2.59	2.12
Time of Flight, sec	0.0000	0.1557	0.3414	0.5632	0.8234	1.1165
Path, inches — ZERO RANGE 100 yds	-1.5	0.0	-9.7	-35.5	-83.8	-161.9
Relative to — ZERO RANGE 200 yds	-1.5	4.9	0.0	-20.9	-64.4	-137.6
Line of Sight — ZERO RANGE 300 yds	-1.5	11.8	13.9	0.0	-36.5	-102.7
Velocity, ft/sec	2000	1680	1404	1187	1045	954
Energy, ft/lbs per grain	8.88	6.27	4.38	3.13	2.42	2.02
Time of Flight, sec	0.0000	0.1637	0.3593	0.5925	0.8631	1.1644
Path, inches — ZERO RANGE 100 yds	-1.5	0.0	-11.0	-39.7	-93.1	-178.2
Relative to — ZERO RANGE 200 yds	-1.5	5.5	0.0	-23.3	-71.2	-150.8
Line of Sight — ZERO RANGE 300 yds	-1.5	13.2	15.5	0.0	-40.2	-112.1
Velocity, ft/sec	1900	1592	1332	1137	1014	932
Energy, ft/lbs per grain	8.01	5.63	3.94	2.87	2.28	1.93
Time of Flight, sec	0.0000	0.1726	0.3790	0.6238	0.9044	1.2137
Path, inches — ZERO RANGE 100 yds	-1.5	0.0	-12.4	-44.4	-103.4	-196.0
Relative to — ZERO RANGE 200 yds	-1.5	6.2	0.0	-25.9	-78.6	-165.1
Line of Sight — ZERO RANGE 300 yds	-1.5	14.8	17.3	0.0	-44.1	-122.0
Velocity, ft/sec	1800	1506	1263	1092	986	911
Energy, ft/lbs per grain	7.19	5.04	3.54	2.65	2.16	1.84
Time of Flight, sec	0.0000	0.1824	0.4005	0.6570	0.9472	1.2645
Path, inches — ZERO RANGE 100 yds	-1.5	0.0	-14.0	-49.8	-114.7	-215.4
Relative to — ZERO RANGE 200 yds	-1.5	7.0	0.0	-28.8	-86.8	-180.5
Line of Sight — ZERO RANGE 300 yds	-1.5	16.6	19.2	0.0	-48.3	-132.4
Velocity, ft/sec	1700	1421	1200	1053	959	891
Energy, ft/lbs per grain	6.42	4.48	3.20	2.46	2.04	1.76
Time of Flight, sec	0.0000	0.1933	0.4238	0.6921	0.9916	1.3168
Path, inches — ZERO RANGE 100 yds	-1.5	0.0	-15.9	-55.9	-127.3	-236.4
Relative to — ZERO RANGE 200 yds	-1.5	7.9	0.0	-32.1	-95.5	-196.7
Line of Sight — ZERO RANGE 300 yds	-1.5	18.6	21.4	0.0	-52.7	-143.2
Velocity, ft/sec	1600	1338	1141	1017	934	871
Energy, ft/lbs per grain	5.68	3.97	2.89	2.30	1.94	1.68
Time of Flight, sec	0.0000	0.2054	0.4491	0.7288	1.0374	1.3707
Path, inches — ZERO RANGE 100 yds	-1.5	0.0	-18.0	-62.7	-141.0	-259.1
Relative to — ZERO RANGE 200 yds	-1.5	9.0	0.0	-35.7	-104.9	-214.0
Line of Sight — ZERO RANGE 300 yds	-1.5	20.9	23.8	0.0	-57.3	-154.6
Velocity, ft/sec	1500	1259	1090	984	910	851
Energy, ft/lbs per grain	5.00	3.52	2.64	2.15	1.84	1.61
Time of Flight, sec	0.0000	0.2189	0.4762	0.7670	1.0848	1.4265
Path, inches — ZERO RANGE 100 yds	-1.5	0.0	-20.5	-70.2	-155.8	-283.5
Relative to — ZERO RANGE 200 yds	-1.5	10.3	0.0	-39.5	-114.8	-232.2
Line of Sight — ZERO RANGE 300 yds	-1.5	23.4	26.3	0.0	-62.2	-166.5

long range tables

Exterior Ballistic Table for Ballistic Coefficient 0.24

	Muzzle	100 yds	200 yds	300 yds	400 yds	500 yds
			RANGE			
Velocity, ft/sec	2800	2423	2077	1761	1483	1255
Energy, ft/lbs per grain	17.41	13.03	9.58	6.88	4.88	3.50
Time of Flight, sec	0.0000	0.1152	0.2489	0.4059	0.5917	0.8121
Path, inches — ZERO RANGE 100 yds	-1.5	0.0	-4.5	-17.1	-41.0	-80.9
Relative to — ZERO RANGE 200 yds	-1.5	2.2	0.0	-10.4	-32.1	-69.7
Line of Sight — ZERO RANGE 300 yds	-1.5	5.7	6.9	0.0	-18.2	-52.4
Velocity, ft/sec	2700	2331	1992	1686	1419	1206
Energy, ft/lbs per grain	16.18	12.06	8.81	6.31	4.47	3.23
Time of Flight, sec	0.0000	0.1196	0.2588	0.4226	0.6168	0.8468
Path, inches — ZERO RANGE 100 yds	-1.5	0.0	-5.0	-18.8	-44.9	-88.5
Relative to — ZERO RANGE 200 yds	-1.5	2.5	0.0	-11.3	-32.0	-76.1
Line of Sight — ZERO RANGE 300 yds	-1.5	6.3	7.6	0.0	-19.9	-57.2
Velocity, ft/sec	2600	2239	1908	1611	1357	1161
Energy, ft/lbs per grain	15.01	11.13	8.08	5.76	4.09	2.99
Time of Flight, sec	0.0000	0.1243	0.2695	0.4407	0.6439	0.8837
Path, inches — ZERO RANGE 100 yds	-1.5	0.0	-5.5	-20.6	-49.3	-97.0
Relative to — ZERO RANGE 200 yds	-1.5	2.7	0.0	-12.4	-38.3	-83.2
Line of Sight — ZERO RANGE 300 yds	-1.5	6.9	8.3	0.0	-21.8	-62.6
Velocity, ft/sec	2500	2147	1825	1538	1298	1121
Energy, ft/lbs per grain	13.88	10.23	7.39	5.25	3.74	2.79
Time of Flight, sec	0.0000	0.1295	0.2811	0.4603	0.6731	0.9228
Path, inches — ZERO RANGE 100 yds	-1.5	0.0	-6.1	-22.8	-54.3	-106.5
Relative to — ZERO RANGE 200 yds	-1.5	3.1	0.0	-13.6	-42.0	-91.2
Line of Sight — ZERO RANGE 300 yds	-1.5	7.6	9.1	0.0	-23.9	-68.5
Velocity, ft/sec	2400	2055	1742	1467	1242	1084
Energy, ft/lbs per grain	12.79	9.38	6.74	4.78	3.42	2.61
Time of Flight, sec	0.0000	0.1351	0.2937	0.4816	0.7044	0.9640
Path, inches — ZERO RANGE 100 yds	-1.5	0.0	-6.8	-25.2	-59.9	-117.1
Relative to — ZERO RANGE 200 yds	-1.5	3.4	0.0	-15.0	-46.3	-100.0
Line of Sight — ZERO RANGE 300 yds	-1.5	8.4	10.0	0.0	-26.3	-75.1
Velocity, ft/sec	2300	1964	1660	1398	1191	1052
Energy, ft/lbs per grain	11.74	8.56	6.12	4.34	3.15	2.46
Time of Flight, sec	0.0000	0.1412	0.3074	0.5046	0.7379	1.0072
Path, inches — ZERO RANGE 100 yds	-1.5	0.0	-7.6	-28.0	-66.2	-129.0
Relative to — ZERO RANGE 200 yds	-1.5	3.8	0.0	-16.5	-51.0	-110.0
Line of Sight — ZERO RANGE 300 yds	-1.5	9.3	11.0	0.0	-28.9	-82.4
Velocity, ft/sec	2200	1873	1580	1332	1144	1022
Energy, ft/lbs per grain	10.75	7.79	5.54	3.94	2.91	2.32
Time of Flight, sec	0.0000	0.1478	0.3224	0.5295	0.7736	1.0522
Path, inches — ZERO RANGE 100 yds	-1.5	0.0	-8.5	-31.1	-73.4	-142.2
Relative to — ZERO RANGE 200 yds	-1.5	4.3	0.0	-18.3	-56.4	-120.9
Line of Sight — ZERO RANGE 300 yds	-1.5	10.4	12.2	0.0	-31.9	-90.4
Velocity, ft/sec	2100	1782	1502	1269	1102	995
Energy, ft/lbs per grain	9.79	7.05	5.01	3.58	2.70	2.20
Time of Flight, sec	0.0000	0.1551	0.3387	0.5565	0.8114	1.0989
Path, inches — ZERO RANGE 100 yds	-1.5	0.0	-9.6	-34.7	-81.5	-156.8
Relative to — ZERO RANGE 200 yds	-1.5	4.8	0.0	-20.3	-62.3	-132.9
Line of Sight — ZERO RANGE 300 yds	-1.5	11.6	13.6	0.0	-35.2	-99.0

long range tables

Exterior Ballistic Table for Ballistic Coefficient 0.24

			RANGE			
	Muzzle	100 yds	200 yds	300 yds	400 yds	500 yds
Velocity, ft/sec	2000	1693	1425	1211	1064	970
Energy, ft/lbs per grain	8.88	6.36	4.51	3.26	2.51	2.09
Time of Flight, sec	0.0000	0.1631	0.3565	0.5856	0.8511	1.1472
Path, inches — 100 yds	-1.5	0.0	-10.8	-38.8	-90.5	-172.9
Relative to — ZERO RANGE 200 yds	-1.5	5.4	0.0	-22.6	-69.0	-146.0
Line of Sight — 300 yds	-1.5	12.9	15.1	0.0	-38.8	-108.3

Exterior Ballistic Table for Ballistic Coefficient 0.25

			RANGE			
	Muzzle	100 yds	200 yds	300 yds	400 yds	500 yds
Velocity, ft/sec	4000	3524	3098	2711	2356	2028
Energy, ft/lbs per grain	35.52	27.57	21.31	16.32	12.32	9.13
Time of Flight, sec	0.0000	0.0799	0.1708	0.2743	0.3931	0.5303
Path, inches — 100 yds	-1.5	0.0	-1.3	-6.3	-16.0	-32.0
Relative to — ZERO RANGE 200 yds	-1.5	0.7	0.0	-4.3	-13.4	-28.7
Line of Sight — 300 yds	-1.5	2.1	2.9	0.0	-7.6	-21.6
Velocity, ft/sec	3900	3435	3017	2637	2288	1965
Energy, ft/lbs per grain	33.77	26.20	20.21	15.44	11.62	8.57
Time of Flight, sec	0.0000	0.0820	0.1752	0.2816	0.4037	0.5453
Path, inches — 100 yds	-1.5	0.0	-1.5	-6.8	-17.1	-34.1
Relative to — ZERO RANGE 200 yds	-1.5	0.7	0.0	-4.6	-14.2	-30.5
Line of Sight — 300 yds	-1.5	2.3	3.0	0.0	-8.1	-22.9
Velocity, ft/sec	3800	3345	2936	2563	2219	1902
Energy, ft/lbs per grain	32.06	24.84	19.14	14.58	10.93	8.03
Time of Flight, sec	0.0000	0.0842	0.1799	0.2893	0.4151	0.5611
Path, inches — 100 yds	-1.5	0.0	-1.6	-7.3	-18.3	-36.4
Relative to — ZERO RANGE 200 yds	-1.5	0.8	0.0	-4.9	-15.1	-32.4
Line of Sight — 300 yds	-1.5	2.4	3.2	0.0	-8.6	-24.3
Velocity, ft/sec	3700	3256	2855	2489	2150	1840
Energy, ft/lbs per grain	30.39	23.54	18.10	13.75	10.26	7.52
Time of Flight, sec	0.0000	0.0865	0.1849	0.2975	0.4272	0.5781
Path, inches — 100 yds	-1.5	0.0	-1.8	-7.9	-19.6	-39.0
Relative to — ZERO RANGE 200 yds	-1.5	0.9	0.0	-5.2	-16.0	-34.5
Line of Sight — 300 yds	-1.5	2.6	3.5	0.0	-9.1	-25.8
Velocity, ft/sec	3600	3166	2773	2413	2081	1777
Energy, ft/lbs per grain	28.77	22.25	17.07	12.93	9.61	7.01
Time of Flight, sec	0.0000	0.0889	0.1902	0.3061	0.4400	0.5961
Path, inches — 100 yds	-1.5	0.0	-2.0	-8.5	-21.1	-41.7
Relative to — ZERO RANGE 200 yds	-1.5	1.0	0.0	-5.5	-17.1	-36.8
Line of Sight — 300 yds	-1.5	2.8	3.7	0.0	-9.7	-27.5
Velocity, ft/sec	3500	3076	2691	2337	2011	1714
Energy, ft/lbs per grain	27.20	21.01	16.08	12.13	8.98	6.52
Time of Flight, sec	0.0000	0.0915	0.1958	0.3154	0.4538	0.6155
Path, inches — 100 yds	-1.5	0.0	-2.2	-9.2	-22.7	-44.8
Relative to — ZERO RANGE 200 yds	-1.5	1.1	0.0	-5.9	-18.3	-39.3
Line of Sight — 300 yds	-1.5	3.1	4.0	0.0	-10.4	-29.4

long range tables

	Muzzle	100 yds	200 yds	300 yds	400 yds	500 yds
RANGE						
Velocity, ft/sec	3400	2986	2609	2261	1941	1651
Energy, ft/lbs per grain	25.66	19.79	15.11	11.35	8.36	6.05
Time of Flight, sec	0.0000	0.0942	0.2017	0.3253	0.4685	0.6362
Path, inches / Relative to Line of Sight ZERO RANGE 100 yds	-1.5	0.0	-2.4	-10.0	-24.4	-48.2
200 yds	-1.5	1.2	0.0	-6.4	-19.6	-42.1
300 yds	-1.5	3.3	4.2	0.0	-11.1	-31.5
Velocity, ft/sec	3300	2895	2525	2184	1871	1589
Energy, ft/lbs per grain	24.18	18.61	14.15	10.59	7.77	5.61
Time of Flight, sec	0.0000	0.0971	0.2081	0.3358	0.4843	0.6584
Path, inches / Relative to Line of Sight ZERO RANGE 100 yds	-1.5	0.0	-2.7	-10.8	-26.4	-51.9
200 yds	-1.5	1.3	0.0	-6.8	-21.0	-45.2
300 yds	-1.5	3.6	4.6	0.0	-11.9	-33.8
Velocity, ft/sec	3200	2804	2442	2107	1800	1528
Energy, ft/lbs per grain	22.73	17.46	13.24	9.86	7.19	5.18
Time of Flight, sec	0.0000	0.1002	0.2148	0.3471	0.5012	0.6822
Path, inches / Relative to Line of Sight ZERO RANGE 100 yds	-1.5	0.0	-3.0	-11.8	-28.5	-56.1
200 yds	-1.5	1.5	0.0	-7.4	-22.6	-48.7
300 yds	-1.5	3.9	4.9	0.0	-12.8	-36.4
Velocity, ft/sec	3100	2713	2358	2029	1730	1467
Energy, ft/lbs per grain	21.33	16.34	12.34	9.14	6.64	4.78
Time of Flight, sec	0.0000	0.1035	0.2221	0.3593	0.5194	0.7079
Path, inches / Relative to Line of Sight ZERO RANGE 100 yds	-1.5	0.0	-3.3	-12.8	-30.9	-60.7
200 yds	-1.5	1.6	0.0	-7.9	-24.4	-52.7
300 yds	-1.5	4.3	5.3	0.0	-13.8	-39.3
Velocity, ft/sec	3000	2622	2273	1952	1661	1408
Energy, ft/lbs per grain	19.98	15.26	11.47	8.46	6.12	4.40
Time of Flight, sec	0.0000	0.1070	0.2299	0.3724	0.5391	0.7354
Path, inches / Relative to Line of Sight ZERO RANGE 100 yds	-1.5	0.0	-3.6	-14.0	-33.6	-65.9
200 yds	-1.5	1.8	0.0	-8.6	-26.4	-56.9
300 yds	-1.5	4.7	5.7	0.0	-14.9	-42.6
Velocity, ft/sec	2900	2530	2188	1874	1592	1351
Energy, ft/lbs per grain	18.67	14.21	10.63	7.80	5.63	4.05
Time of Flight, sec	0.0000	0.1108	0.2383	0.3865	0.5602	0.7651
Path, inches / Relative to Line of Sight ZERO RANGE 100 yds	-1.5	0.0	-4.0	-15.3	-36.6	-71.7
200 yds	-1.5	2.0	0.0	-9.3	-28.6	-61.7
300 yds	-1.5	5.1	6.2	0.0	-16.2	-46.2
Velocity, ft/sec	2800	2438	2103	1797	1525	1296
Energy, ft/lbs per grain	17.41	13.20	9.82	7.17	5.16	3.73
Time of Flight, sec	0.0000	0.1148	0.2474	0.4017	0.5831	0.7969
Path, inches / Relative to Line of Sight ZERO RANGE 100 yds	-1.5	0.0	-4.4	-16.7	-39.9	-78.2
200 yds	-1.5	2.2	0.0	-10.1	-31.1	-67.2
300 yds	-1.5	5.6	6.8	0.0	-17.6	-50.3
Velocity, ft/sec	2700	2345	2018	1720	1459	1244
Energy, ft/lbs per grain	16.18	12.21	9.04	6.57	4.73	3.44
Time of Flight, sec	0.0000	0.1192	0.2571	0.4182	0.6077	0.8310
Path, inches / Relative to Line of Sight ZERO RANGE 100 yds	-1.5	0.0	-4.9	-18.4	-43.7	-85.5
200 yds	-1.5	2.4	0.0	-11.0	-34.0	-73.3
300 yds	-1.5	6.1	7.4	0.0	-19.2	-54.9

long range tables

Exterior Ballistic Table for Ballistic Coefficient 0.25

		Muzzle	100 yds	200 yds	300 yds	400 yds	500 yds
				RANGE			
Velocity, ft/sec		2600	2253	1933	1645	1395	1195
Energy, ft/lbs per grain		15.01	11.27	8.30	6.01	4.32	3.17
Time of Flight, sec		0.0000	0.1240	0.2677	0.4360	0.6344	0.8675
Path, inches	100 yds	-1.5	0.0	-5.4	-20.2	-48.0	-93.7
Relative to ZERO RANGE	200 yds	-1.5	2.7	0.0	-12.1	-37.1	-80.2
Line of Sight	300 yds	-1.5	6.7	8.1	0.0	-21.0	-60.1
Velocity, ft/sec		2500	2161	1849	1570	1333	1150
Energy, ft/lbs per grain		13.88	10.37	7.59	5.47	3.94	2.94
Time of Flight, sec		0.0000	0.1291	0.2792	0.4554	0.6631	0.9062
Path, inches	100 yds	-1.5	0.0	-6.0	-22.3	-52.8	-103.0
Relative to ZERO RANGE	200 yds	-1.5	3.0	0.0	-13.3	-40.8	-87.9
Line of Sight	300 yds	-1.5	7.4	8.8	0.0	-23.1	-65.8
Velocity, ft/sec		2400	2068	1766	1498	1274	1110
Energy, ft/lbs per grain		12.79	9.49	6.92	4.98	3.60	2.74
Time of Flight, sec		0.0000	0.1347	0.2917	0.4763	0.6940	0.9472
Path, inches	100 yds	-1.5	0.0	-6.7	-24.7	-58.2	-113.3
Relative to ZERO RANGE	200 yds	-1.5	3.3	0.0	-14.6	-44.8	-96.6
Line of Sight	300 yds	-1.5	8.2	9.7	0.0	-25.4	-72.2
Velocity, ft/sec		2300	1976	1683	1427	1219	1075
Energy, ft/lbs per grain		11.74	8.67	6.29	4.52	3.30	2.57
Time of Flight, sec		0.0000	0.1407	0.3053	0.4997	0.7271	0.9903
Path, inches	100 yds	-1.5	0.0	-7.5	-27.3	-64.4	-124.9
Relative to ZERO RANGE	200 yds	-1.5	3.7	0.0	-16.1	-49.5	-106.2
Line of Sight	300 yds	-1.5	9.1	10.8	0.0	28.0	-79.3
Velocity, ft/sec		2200	1885	1602	1359	1169	1042
Energy, ft/lbs per grain		10.75	7.89	5.70	4.10	3.03	2.41
Time of Flight, sec		0.0000	0.1473	0.3201	0.5237	0.7626	1.0354
Path, inches	100 yds	-1.5	0.0	-8.4	-30.4	-71.4	-137.8
Relative to ZERO RANGE	200 yds	-1.5	4.2	0.0	-17.9	-54.7	-116.9
Line of Sight	300 yds	-1.5	10.1	11.9	0.0	-30.8	-87.1
Velocity, ft/sec		2100	1794	1522	1294	1124	1013
Energy, ft/lbs per grain		9.79	7.15	5.14	3.72	2.80	2.28
Time of Flight, sec		0.0000	0.1546	0.3363	0.5504	0.8002	1.0824
Path, inches	100 yds	-1.5	0.0	-9.4	-33.9	-79.3	-152.2
Relative to ZERO RANGE	200 yds	-1.5	4.7	0.0	-19.8	-60.5	-128.7
Line of Sight	300 yds	-1.5	11.3	13.2	0.0	-34.1	-95.6
Velocity, ft/sec		2000	1704	1445	1233	1083	987
Energy, ft/lbs per grain		8.88	6.45	4.64	3.38	2.60	2.16
Time of Flight, sec		0.0000	0.1626	0.3540	0.5793	0.8400	1.1311
Path, inches	100 yds	-1.5	0.0	-10.6	-37.9	-88.2	-168.1
Relative to ZERO RANGE	200 yds	-1.5	5.3	0.0	-22.1	-67.1	-141.6
Line of Sight	300 yds	-1.5	12.6	14.7	0.0	-37.6	-104.8

long range tables

Exterior Ballistic Table for Ballistic Coefficient 0.26

	Muzzle	100 yds	200 yds	300 yds	400 yds	500 yds
			RANGE			
Velocity, ft/sec	3600	3182	2802	2452	2130	1833
Energy, ft/lbs per grain	28.77	22.48	17.43	13.36	10.07	7.46
Time of Flight, sec	0.0000	0.0887	0.1892	0.3036	0.4348	0.5867
Path, inches Relative to Line of Sight — ZERO RANGE 100 yds	-1.5	0.0	2.0	-8.4	-20.6	-40.5
200 yds	-1.5	1.0	0.0	-5.4	-16.7	-35.6
300 yds	-1.5	2.8	3.6	0.0	-9.4	-26.6
Velocity, ft/sec	3500	3092	2720	2377	2059	1768
Energy, ft/lbs per grain	27.20	21.22	16.42	12.54	9.41	6.94
Time of Flight, sec	0.0000	0.0912	0.1947	0.3127	0.4483	0.6056
Path, inches Relative to Line of Sight — ZERO RANGE 100 yds	-1.5	0.0	-2.2	-9.0	-22.1	-43.5
200 yds	-1.5	1.1	0.0	-5.8	-17.8	-38.1
300 yds	-1.5	3.0	3.9	0.0	-10.1	-28.4
Velocity, ft/sec	3400	3001	2636	2300	1988	1704
Energy, ft/lbs per grain	25.66	19.99	15.43	11.74	8.77	6.45
Time of Flight, sec	0.0000	0.0940	0.2006	0.3225	0.4628	0.6258
Path, inches Relative to Line of Sight — ZERO RANGE 100 yds	-1.5	0.0	-2.4	-9.8	-23.8	-46.8
200 yds	-1.5	1.2	0.0	-6.2	-19.1	-40.8
300 yds	-1.5	3.3	4.2	0.0	-10.8	-30.4
Velocity, ft/sec	3300	2910	2553	2222	1917	1640
Energy, ft/lbs per grain	24.18	18.80	14.47	10.96	8.16	5.97
Time of Flight, sec	0.0000	0.0968	0.2069	0.3329	0.4783	0.6476
Path, inches Relative to Line of Sight — ZERO RANGE 100 yds	-1.5	0.0	-2.6	-10.6	-25.7	-50.4
200 yds	-1.5	1.3	0.0	-6.7	-20.5	-43.8
300 yds	-1.5	3.5	4.5	0.0	-11.6	-32.7
Velocity, ft/sec	3200	2819	2469	2144	1846	1577
Energy, ft/lbs per grain	22.73	17.64	13.53	10.21	7.57	5.52
Time of Flight, sec	0.0000	0.0999	0.2137	0.3441	0.4949	0.6709
Path, inches Relative to Line of Sight — ZERO RANGE 100 yds	-1.5	0.0	-2.9	-11.5	-27.8	-54.4
200 yds	-1.5	1.5	0.0	-7.2	-22.0	-47.1
300 yds	-1.5	3.8	4.8	0.0	-12.4	-35.1
Velocity, ft/sec	3100	2727	2384	2066	1774	1515
Energy, ft/lbs per grain	21.33	16.51	12.62	9.48	6.99	5.10
Time of Flight, sec	0.0000	0.1032	0.2209	0.3561	0.5128	0.6959
Path, inches Relative to Line of Sight — ZERO RANGE 100 yds	-1.5	0.0	-3.2	-12.6	-30.1	-58.9
200 yds	-1.5	1.6	0.0	-7.8	-23.7	-50.9
300 yds	-1.5	4.2	5.2	0.0	-13.4	-37.9
Velocity, ft/sec	3000	2636	2299	1987	1704	1454
Energy, ft/lbs per grain	19.98	15.43	11.73	8.77	6.45	4.69
Time of Flight, sec	0.0000	0.1067	0.2286	0.3690	0.5321	0.7229
Path, inches Relative to Line of Sight — ZERO RANGE 100 yds	-1.5	0.0	-3.5	-13.7	-32.7	-63.9
200 yds	-1.5	1.8	0.0	-8.4	-25.7	-55.0
300 yds	-1.5	4.6	5.6	0.0	-14.5	-41.0
Velocity, ft/sec	2900	2543	2213	1909	1633	1394
Energy, ft/lbs per grain	18.67	14.36	10.87	8.09	5.92	4.31
Time of Flight, sec	0.0000	0.1105	0.2369	0.3829	0.5529	0.7520
Path, inches Relative to Line of Sight — ZERO RANGE 100 yds	-1.5	0.0	-3.9	-15.0	-35.7	-69.5
200 yds	-1.5	2.0	0.0	-9.1	-27.8	-59.7
300 yds	-1.5	5.0	6.1	0.0	-15.7	-44.5

Exterior Ballistic Table for Ballistic Coefficient 0.26

		Muzzle	100 yds	200 yds	RANGE 300 yds	400 yds	500 yds
Velocity, ft/sec		2800	2451	2128	1831	1564	1336
Energy, ft/lbs per grain		17.41	13.34	10.05	7.44	5.43	3.96
Time of Flight, sec		0.0000	0.1145	0.2459	0.3979	0.5753	0.7832
Path, inches	100 yds	-1.5	0.0	-4.3	-16.4	-38.9	-75.8
Relative to	200 yds	-1.5	2.2	0.0	-9.9	-30.3	-65.0
Line of Sight	300 yds	-1.5	5.5	6.6	0.0	-17.1	-48.5
Velocity, ft/sec		2700	2359	2042	1753	1496	1281
Energy, ft/lbs per grain		16.18	12.35	9.26	6.82	4.97	3.64
Time of Flight, sec		0.0000	0.1189	0.2556	0.4142	0.5996	0.8167
Path, inches	100 yds	-1.5	0.0	-4.8	-18.0	-42.6	-82.9
Relative to	200 yds	-1.5	2.4	0.0	-10.8	-33.0	-70.9
Line of Sight	300 yds	-1.5	6.0	7.2	0.0	-18.6	-52.9
Velocity, ft/sec		2600	2266	1957	1676	1430	1229
Energy, ft/lbs per grain		15.01	11.40	8.50	6.24	4.54	3.35
Time of Flight, sec		0.0000	0.1236	0.2661	0.4318	0.6258	0.8526
Path, inches	100 yds	-1.5	0.0	-5.3	-19.8	-46.8	-90.8
Relative to	200 yds	-1.5	2.7	0.0	-11.8	-36.1	-77.5
Line of Sight	300 yds	-1.5	6.6	7.9	0.0	-20.4	-57.8
Velocity, ft/sec		2500	2173	1872	1601	1366	1180
Energy, ft/lbs per grain		13.88	10.48	7.78	5.69	4.14	3.09
Time of Flight, sec		0.0000	0.1287	0.2775	0.4509	0.6540	0.8910
Path, inches	100 yds	-1.5	0.0	-5.9	-21.8	-51.5	-99.8
Relative to	200 yds	-1.5	3.0	0.0	-13.0	-39.6	-85.0
Line of Sight	300 yds	-1.5	7.3	8.6	0.0	-22.3	-63.4

Path rows labeled with ZERO RANGE.

Exterior Ballistic Table for Ballistic Coefficient 0.27

		Muzzle	100 yds	200 yds	RANGE 300 yds	400 yds	500 yds
Velocity, ft/sec		3800	3377	2995	2644	2318	2016
Energy, ft/lbs per grain		32.06	25.32	19.91	15.52	11.93	9.02
Time of Flight, sec		0.0000	0.0838	0.1781	0.2848	0.4060	0.5448
Path, inches	100 yds	-1.5	0.0	-1.6	-7.0	-17.5	-34.5
Relative to	200 yds	-1.5	0.8	0.0	-4.7	-14.4	-30.6
Line of Sight	300 yds	-1.5	2.3	3.1	0.0	-8.1	-22.8
Velocity, ft/sec		3700	3287	2912	2567	2248	1951
Energy, ft/lbs per grain		30.39	23.99	18.83	14.63	11.22	8.45
Time of Flight, sec		0.0000	0.0861	0.1830	0.2928	0.4177	0.5610
Path, inches	100 yds	-1.5	0.0	-1.7	-7.6	-18.7	-36.8
Relative to	200 yds	-1.5	0.9	0.0	-5.0	-15.3	-32.5
Line of Sight	300 yds	-1.5	2.5	3.3	0.0	-8.6	-24.2
Velocity, ft/sec		3600	3197	2829	2491	2176	1886
Energy, ft/lbs per grain		28.77	22.69	17.77	13.78	10.51	7.90
Time of Flight, sec		0.0000	0.0885	0.1882	0.3013	0.4301	0.5782
Path, inches	100 yds	-1.5	0.0	-1.9	-8.2	-20.1	-39.4
Relative to	200 yds	-1.5	1.0	0.0	-5.3	-16.3	-34.7
Line of Sight	300 yds	-1.5	2.7	3.6	0.0	-9.2	-25.8

Path rows labeled with ZERO RANGE.

long range tables

Exterior Ballistic Table for Ballistic Coefficient 0.27

		Muzzle	100 yds	200 yds	300 yds	400 yds	500 yds
				RANGE			
Velocity, ft/sec		3500	3106	2746	2414	2105	1820
Energy, ft/lbs per grain		27.20	21.42	16.74	12.94	9.84	7.35
Time of Flight, sec		0.0000	0.0910	0.1938	0.3103	0.4434	0.5967
Path, inches	100 yds	-1.5	0.0	-2.1	-8.9	-21.6	-42.3
Relative to ZERO RANGE	200 yds	-1.5	1.1	0.0	-5.7	-17.4	-37.0
Line of Sight	300 yds	-1.5	3.0	3.8	0.0	-9.8	-27.5
Velocity, ft/sec		3400	3015	2662	2336	2033	1754
Energy, ft/lbs per grain		25.66	20.18	15.73	12.11	9.18	6.83
Time of Flight, sec		0.0000	0.0937	0.1996	0.3199	0.4576	0.6165
Path, inches	100 yds	-1.5	0.0	-2.3	-9.6	-23.3	-45.5
Relative to ZERO RANGE	200 yds	-1.5	1.2	0.0	-6.1	-18.6	-39.6
Line of Sight	300 yds	-1.5	3.2	4.1	0.0	-10.5	-29.5
Velocity, ft/sec		3300	2924	2578	2258	1960	1689
Energy, ft/lbs per grain		24.18	18.98	14.75	11.32	8.53	6.33
Time of Flight, sec		0.0000	0.0966	0.2059	0.3302	0.4729	0.6378
Path, inches	100 yds	-1.5	0.0	-2.6	-10.4	-25.2	-49.0
Relative to ZERO RANGE	200 yds	-1.5	1.3	0.0	-6.6	-20.0	-42.5
Line of Sight	300 yds	-1.5	3.5	4.4	0.0	-11.2	-31.6
Velocity, ft/sec		3200	2832	2494	2179	1888	1624
Energy, ft/lbs per grain		22.73	17.81	13.81	10.54	7.91	5.86
Time of Flight, sec		0.0000	0.0997	0.2126	0.3413	0.4892	0.6606
Path, inches	100 yds	-1.5	0.0	-2.9	-11.3	-27.2	-52.9
Relative to ZERO RANGE	200 yds	-1.5	1.4	0.0	-7.1	-21.5	-45.8
Line of Sight	300 yds	-1.5	3.8	4.7	0.0	-12.1	-34.0
Velocity, ft/sec		3100	2741	2408	2100	1816	1560
Energy, ft/lbs per grain		21.33	16.68	12.87	9.79	7.32	5.40
Time of Flight, sec		0.0000	0.1029	0.2197	0.3531	0.5068	0.6852
Path, inches	100 yds	-1.5	0.0	-3.2	-12.3	-29.5	-57.2
Relative to ZERO RANGE	200 yds	-1.5	1.6	0.0	-7.6	-23.2	-49.4
Line of Sight	300 yds	-1.5	4.1	5.1	0.0	-13.0	-36.7
Velocity, ft/sec		3000	2649	2323	2021	1744	1497
Energy, ft/lbs per grain		19.98	15.58	11.98	9.07	6.75	4.98
Time of Flight, sec		0.0000	0.1064	0.2274	0.3659	0.5258	0.7116
Path, inches	100 yds	-1.5	0.0	-3.5	-13.5	-32.0	-62.1
Relative to ZERO RANGE	200 yds	-1.5	1.7	0.0	-8.2	-25.0	-53.4
Line of Sight	300 yds	-1.5	4.5	5.5	0.0	-14.1	-39.7
Velocity, ft/sec		2900	2556	2237	1941	1672	1435
Energy, ft/lbs per grain		18.67	14.50	11.11	8.36	6.21	4.57
Time of Flight, sec		0.0000	0.1102	0.2357	0.3796	0.5462	0.7401
Path, inches	100 yds	-1.5	0.0	-3.9	-14.7	-34.9	-67.5
Relative to ZERO RANGE	200 yds	-1.5	1.9	0.0	-8.9	-27.1	-57.9
Line of Sight	300 yds	-1.5	4.9	5.9	0.0	-15.2	-43.0
Velocity, ft/sec		2800	2464	2151	1862	1602	1375
Energy, ft/lbs per grain		17.41	13.48	10.27	7.70	5.70	4.20
Time of Flight, sec		0.0000	0.1142	0.2446	0.3945	0.5683	0.7707
Path, inches	100 yds	-1.5	0.0	-4.3	-16.1	-38.0	-73.6
Relative to ZERO RANGE	200 yds	-1.5	2.1	0.0	-9.7	-29.5	-63.0
Line of Sight	300 yds	-1.5	5.4	6.5	0.0	-16.6	-46.8

Exterior Ballistic Table for Ballistic Coefficient 0.27

		Muzzle	100 yds	200 yds	300 yds	400 yds	500 yds
Velocity, ft/sec		2700	2371	2065	1784	1532	1317
Energy, ft/lbs per grain		16.18	12.48	9.47	7.07	5.21	3.85
Time of Flight, sec		0.0000	0.1186	0.2542	0.4105	0.5921	0.8037
Path, inches	100 yds	-1.5	0.0	-4.7	-17.7	-41.6	-80.5
Relative to	200 yds	-1.5	2.4	0.0	-10.6	-32.2	-68.7
Line of Sight (ZERO RANGE)	300 yds	-1.5	5.9	7.1	0.0	-18.1	-51.1
Velocity, ft/sec		2600	2278	1979	1706	1464	1262
Energy, ft/lbs per grain		15.01	11.52	8.69	6.46	4.76	3.54
Time of Flight, sec		0.0000	0.1233	0.2646	0.4279	0.6179	0.8391
Path, inches	100 yds	-1.5	0.0	-5.2	-19.4	-45.7	-88.2
Relative to	200 yds	-1.5	2.6	0.0	-11.6	-35.2	-75.1
Line of Sight (ZERO RANGE)	300 yds	-1.5	6.5	7.7	0.0	-19.8	-55.8
Velocity, ft/sec		2500	2185	1896	1629	1398	1210
Energy, ft/lbs per grain		13.88	10.60	7.96	5.89	4.34	3.25
Time of Flight, sec		0.0000	0.1284	0.2759	0.4468	0.6458	0.8770
Path, inches	100 yds	-1.5	0.0	-5.8	-21.4	-50.3	-97.0
Relative to	200 yds	-1.5	2.9	0.0	-12.7	-38.6	-82.4
Line of Sight (ZERO RANGE)	300 yds	-1.5	7.1	8.5	0.0	-21.7	-61.2
Velocity, ft/sec		2400	2092	1808	1554	1335	1163
Energy, ft/lbs per grain		12.79	9.72	7.26	5.36	3.96	3.00
Time of Flight, sec		0.0000	0.1339	0.2882	0.4672	0.6759	0.9173
Path, inches	100 yds	-1.5	0.0	-6.5	-23.7	-55.4	-106.8
Relative to	200 yds	-1.5	3.3	0.0	-14.0	-42.4	-90.5
Line of Sight (ZERO RANGE)	300 yds	-1.5	7.9	9.3	0.0	-23.8	-67.2
Velocity, ft/sec		2300	1999	1724	1480	1275	1121
Energy, ft/lbs per grain		11.74	8.87	6.60	4.86	3.61	2.79
Time of Flight, sec		0.0000	0.1399	0.3015	0.4895	0.7083	0.9601
Path, inches	100 yds	-1.5	0.0	-7.3	-26.3	-61.3	-117.8
Relative to	200 yds	-1.5	3.6	0.0	-15.4	-46.8	-99.7
Line of Sight (ZERO RANGE)	300 yds	-1.5	8.8	10.3	0.0	-26.3	-74.0
Velocity, ft/sec		2200	1907	1642	1409	1219	1083
Energy, ft/lbs per grain		10.75	8.07	5.99	4.41	3.30	2.60
Time of Flight, sec		0.0000	0.1465	0.3161	0.5136	0.7431	1.0052
Path, inches	100 yds	-1.5	0.0	-8.1	-29.3	-68.0	-130.2
Relative to	200 yds	-1.5	4.1	0.0	-17.1	-51.8	-109.9
Line of Sight (ZERO RANGE)	300 yds	-1.5	9.8	11.4	0.0	-29.0	-81.4
Velocity, ft/sec		2100	1816	1560	1340	1167	1049
Energy, ft/lbs per grain		9.79	7.32	5.40	3.99	3.02	2.44
Time of Flight, sec		0.0000	0.1537	0.3320	0.5398	0.7804	1.0525
Path, inches	100 yds	-1.5	0.0	-9.1	-32.6	-75.6	-144.1
Relative to	200 yds	-1.5	4.6	0.0	-19.0	-57.4	-121.3
Line of Sight (ZERO RANGE)	300 yds	-1.5	10.9	12.6	0.0	-32.1	-89.7
Velocity, ft/sec		2000	1725	1481	1275	1121	1018
Energy, ft/lbs per grain		8.88	6.61	4.87	3.61	2.79	2.30
Time of Flight, sec		0.0000	0.1616	0.3495	0.5682	0.8200	1.1017
Path, inches	100 yds	-1.5	0.0	-10.3	-36.5	-84.2	-159.5
Relative to	200 yds	-1.5	5.1	0.0	-21.1	-63.7	-133.8
Line of Sight (ZERO RANGE)	300 yds	-1.5	12.2	14.1	0.0	-35.5	-98.7

Exterior Ballistic Table for Ballistic Coefficient 0.27

		Muzzle	100 yds	200 yds	300 yds	400 yds	500 yds
					RANGE		
Velocity, ft/sec		1900	1635	1403	1214	1080	990
Energy, ft/lbs per grain		8.01	5.93	4.37	3.27	2.59	2.18
Time of Flight, sec		0.0000	0.1703	0.3686	0.5990	0.8619	1.1529
Path, inches	100 yds	-1.5	0.0	-11.6	-41.0	-93.9	-176.7
Relative to	200 yds	-1.5	5.8	0.0	-23.6	-70.7	-147.7
Line of Sight (ZERO RANGE)	300 yds	-1.5	13.7	15.7	0.0	-39.3	-108.4
Velocity, ft/sec		1800	1546	1329	1159	1043	964
Energy, ft/lbs per grain		7.19	5.31	3.92	2.98	2.42	2.06
Time of Flight, sec		0.0000	0.1799	0.3895	0.6320	0.9058	1.2057
Path, inches	100 yds	-1.5	0.0	-13.1	-46.1	-104.9	-195.6
Relative to	200 yds	-1.5	6.6	0.0	-26.4	-78.6	-162.7
Line of Sight (ZERO RANGE)	300 yds	-1.5	15.4	17.6	0.0	-43.4	-118.8
Velocity, ft/sec		1700	1459	1258	1109	1010	940
Energy, ft/lbs per grain		6.42	4.73	3.51	2.73	2.26	1.96
Time of Flight, sec		0.0000	0.1906	0.4125	0.6674	0.9517	1.2602
Path, inches	100 yds	-1.5	0.0	-14.9	-51.9	-117.1	-216.3
Relative to	200 yds	-1.5	7.5	0.0	-29.5	-87.2	-178.9
Line of Sight (ZERO RANGE)	300 yds	-1.5	17.3	19.7	0.0	-47.9	-129.8
Velocity, ft/sec		1600	1373	1192	1065	980	916
Energy, ft/lbs per grain		5.68	4.19	3.15	2.52	2.13	1.86
Time of Flight, sec		0.0000	0.2026	0.4377	0.7050	0.9994	1.3167
Path, inches	100 yds	-1.5	0.0	-17.0	-58.5	-130.6	-239.0
Relative to	200 yds	-1.5	8.5	0.0	-33.0	-96.6	-196.4
Line of Sight (ZERO RANGE)	300 yds	-1.5	19.5	22.0	0.0	-52.6	-141.4
Velocity, ft/sec		1500	1291	1132	1025	951	893
Energy, ft/lbs per grain		5.00	3.70	2.84	2.33	2.01	1.77
Time of Flight, sec		0.0000	0.2160	0.4650	0.7444	1.0489	1.3749
Path, inches	100 yds	-1.5	0.0	-19.4	-66.0	-145.6	-263.6
Relative to	200 yds	-1.5	9.7	0.0	-36.8	-106.7	-215.0
Line of Sight (ZERO RANGE)	300 yds	-1.5	22.0	24.5	0.0	-57.6	-153.6

Exterior Ballistic Table for Ballistic Coefficient 0.30

		Muzzle	100 yds	200 yds	300 yds	400 yds	500 yds
					RANGE		
Velocity, ft/sec		3800	3418	3068	2746	2446	2164
Energy, ft/lbs per grain		32.06	25.94	20.90	16.74	13.28	10.40
Time of Flight, sec		0.0000	0.0833	0.1759	0.2793	0.3951	0.5255
Path, inches	100 yds	-1.5	0.0	-1.5	-6.7	-16.5	-32.2
Relative to	200 yds	-1.5	0.7	0.0	-4.5	-13.5	-28.5
Line of Sight (ZERO RANGE)	300 yds	-1.5	2.2	3.0	0.0	-7.6	-21.0
Velocity, ft/sec		3700	3327	2985	2668	2373	2096
Energy, ft/lbs per grain		30.39	24.57	19.78	15.80	12.50	9.75
Time of Flight, sec		0.0000	0.0855	0.1808	0.2871	0.4063	0.5409
Path, inches	100 yds	-1.5	0.0	-1.7	-7.2	-17.7	-34.4
Relative to	200 yds	-1.5	0.8	0.0	-4.7	-14.4	-30.3
Line of Sight (ZERO RANGE)	300 yds	-1.5	2.4	3.2	0.0	-8.1	-22.3

Exterior Ballistic Table for Ballistic Coefficient 0.30

			Muzzle	100 yds	200 yds	300 yds	400 yds	500 yds
Velocity, ft/sec			3600	3235	2900	2590	2299	2028
Energy, ft/lbs per grain			28.77	23.23	18.67	14.89	11.73	9.13
Time of Flight, sec			0.0000	0.0879	0.1859	0.2954	0.4183	0.5573
Path, inches	ZERO RANGE	100 yds	-1.5	0.0	-1.8	-7.8	-19.0	-36.8
Relative to		200 yds	-1.5	0.9	0.0	-5.1	-15.3	-32.2
Line of Sight		300 yds	-1.5	2.6	3.4	0.0	-8.6	-23.8
Velocity, ft/sec			3500	3144	2816	2511	2225	1959
Energy, ft/lbs per grain			27.20	21.94	17.60	14.00	10.99	8.52
Time of Flight, sec			0.0000	0.0905	0.1913	0.3042	0.4311	0.5748
Path, inches	ZERO RANGE	100 yds	-1.5	0.0	-2.0	-8.5	-20.4	-39.5
Relative to		200 yds	-1.5	1.0	0.0	-5.4	-16.4	-34.4
Line of Sight		300 yds	-1.5	2.8	3.6	0.0	-9.2	-25.4
Velocity, ft/sec			3400	3052	2731	2431	2151	1890
Energy, ft/lbs per grain			25.99	20.68	16.56	13.12	10.27	7.93
Time of Flight, sec			0.0000	0.0932	0.1971	0.3135	0.4447	0.5935
Path, inches	ZERO RANGE	100 yds	-1.5	0.0	-2.2	-9.2	-22.0	-42.4
Relative to		200 yds	-1.5	1.1	0.0	-5.8	-17.5	-36.8
Line of Sight		300 yds	-1.5	3.1	3.9	0.0	-9.8	-27.1
Velocity, ft/sec			3300	2960	2645	2351	2076	1821
Energy, ft/lbs per grain			24.18	19.45	15.53	12.27	9.57	7.36
Time of Flight, sec			0.0000	0.0960	0.2032	0.3235	0.4593	0.6136
Path, inches	ZERO RANGE	100 yds	-1.5	0.0	-2.5	-10.0	-23.8	-45.7
Relative to		200 yds	-1.5	1.2	0.0	-6.2	-18.8	-39.5
Line of Sight		300 yds	-1.5	3.3	4.2	0.0	-10.5	-29.1
Velocity, ft/sec			3200	2868	2559	2271	2001	1752
Energy, ft/lbs per grain			22.73	18.26	14.54	11.45	8.89	6.81
Time of Flight, sec			0.0000	0.0991	0.2098	0.3342	0.4750	0.6352
Path, inches	ZERO RANGE	100 yds	-1.5	0.0	-2.7	-10.8	-25.7	-49.3
Relative to		200 yds	-1.5	1.4	0.0	-6.7	-20.2	-42.4
Line of Sight		300 yds	-1.5	3.6	4.5	0.0	-11.3	-31.2
Velocity, ft/sec			3100	2775	2473	2190	1926	1684
Energy, ft/lbs per grain			21.33	17.10	13.58	10.65	8.24	6.30
Time of Flight, sec			0.0000	0.1023	0.2168	0.3457	0.4918	0.6585
Path, inches	ZERO RANGE	100 yds	-1.5	0.0	-3.0	-11.8	-27.8	-53.3
Relative to		200 yds	-1.5	1.5	0.0	-7.2	-21.8	-45.7
Line of Sight		300 yds	-1.5	3.9	4.8	0.0	-12.1	-33.7
Velocity, ft/sec			3000	2682	2386	2109	1851	1616
Energy, ft/lbs per grain			19.98	15.97	12.64	9.87	7.61	5.80
Time of Flight, sec			0.0000	0.1058	0.2244	0.3581	0.5100	0.6835
Path, inches	ZERO RANGE	100 yds	-1.5	0.0	-3.4	-12.8	-30.2	-57.8
Relative to		200 yds	-1.5	1.7	0.0	-7.8	-23.5	-49.4
Line of Sight		300 yds	-1.5	4.3	5.2	0.0	-13.1	-36.4
Velocity, ft/sec			2900	2589	2299	2028	1776	1549
Energy, ft/lbs per grain			18.67	14.88	11.73	9.13	7.00	5.33
Time of Flight, sec			0.0000	0.1095	0.2325	0.3714	0.5295	0.7105
Path, inches	ZERO RANGE	100 yds	-1.5	0.0	-3.7	-14.0	-32.9	-62.8
Relative to		200 yds	-1.5	1.9	0.0	-8.5	-25.4	-53.5
Line of Sight		300 yds	-1.5	4.7	5.6	0.0	-14.2	-39.4

Exterior Ballistic Table for Ballistic Coefficient 0.30

	Zero Range	Muzzle	100 yds	200 yds	300 yds	400 yds	500 yds
Velocity, ft/sec		2800	2496	2212	1946	1702	1483
Energy, ft/lbs per grain		17.41	13.83	10.86	8.41	6.43	4.88
Time of Flight, sec		0.0000	0.1135	0.2412	0.3858	0.5507	0.7396
Path, inches	100 yds	-1.5	0.0	-4.1	-15.4	-35.9	-68.4
Relative to	200 yds	-1.5	2.1	0.0	-9.2	-27.6	-58.4
Line of Sight	300 yds	-1.5	5.1	6.1	0.0	-15.4	-42.8
Velocity, ft/sec		2700	2403	2124	1865	1629	1419
Energy, ft/lbs per grain		16.18	12.82	10.02	7.72	5.89	4.47
Time of Flight, sec		0.0000	0.1178	0.2506	0.4013	0.5735	0.7710
Path, inches	100 yds	-1.5	0.0	-4.6	-16.9	-39.2	-74.8
Relative to	200 yds	-1.5	2.3	0.0	-10.0	-30.1	-63.4
Line of Sight	300 yds	-1.5	5.6	6.7	0.0	-16.7	-46.7
Velocity, ft/sec		2600	2309	2037	1785	1557	1357
Energy, ft/lbs per grain		15.01	11.84	9.21	7.07	5.38	4.09
Time of Flight, sec		0.0000	0.1224	0.2608	0.4182	0.5983	0.8049
Path, inches	100 yds	-1.5	0.0	-5.1	-18.5	-43.0	-81.9
Relative to	200 yds	-1.5	2.5	0.0	-11.0	-32.9	-69.3
Line of Sight	300 yds	-1.5	6.2	7.3	0.0	-18.3	-51.0
Velocity, ft/sec		2500	2215	1950	1705	1486	1298
Energy, ft/lbs per grain		13.88	10.89	8.44	6.45	4.90	3.74
Time of Flight, sec		0.0000	0.1275	0.2719	0.4364	0.6250	0.8413
Path, inches	100 yds	-1.5	0.0	-5.6	-20.5	-47.3	-90.0
Relative to	200 yds	-1.5	2.8	0.0	-12.0	-36.1	-75.9
Line of Sight	300 yds	-1.5	6.8	8.0	0.0	-20.0	-55.9
Velocity, ft/sec		2400	2122	1863	1627	1418	1242
Energy, ft/lbs per grain		12.79	10.00	7.71	5.88	4.46	3.42
Time of Flight, sec		0.0000	0.1330	0.2839	0.4563	0.6540	0.8805
Path, inches	100 yds	-1.5	0.0	-6.3	-22.6	-52.2	-99.1
Relative to	200 yds	-1.5	3.1	0.0	-13.2	-39.6	-83.5
Line of Sight	300 yds	-1.5	7.5	8.8	0.0	-22.0	-61.4
Velocity, ft/sec		2300	2028	1777	1550	1351	1191
Energy, ft/lbs per grain		11.74	9.13	7.01	5.33	4.05	3.15
Time of Flight, sec		0.0000	0.1389	0.2969	0.4778	0.6853	0.9224
Path, inches	100 yds	-1.5	0.0	-7.0	-25.1	-57.7	-109.5
Relative to	200 yds	-1.5	3.5	0.0	-14.6	-43.7	-92.0
Line of Sight	300 yds	-1.5	8.4	9.7	0.0	-24.3	-67.7
Velocity, ft/sec		2200	1935	1692	1475	1289	1144
Energy, ft/lbs per grain		10.75	8.31	6.36	4.83	3.69	2.91
Time of Flight, sec		0.0000	0.1454	0.3112	0.5013	0.7192	0.9670
Path, inches	100 yds	-1.5	0.0	-7.8	-27.9	-64.0	-121.1
Relative to	200 yds	-1.5	3.9	0.0	-16.1	-48.3	-101.5
Line of Sight	300 yds	-1.5	9.3	10.8	0.0	-26.8	-74.7
Velocity, ft/sec		2100	1843	1609	1402	1230	1102
Energy, ft/lbs per grain		9.79	7.54	5.75	4.36	3.36	2.70
Time of Flight, sec		0.0000	0.1525	0.3268	0.5268	0.7557	1.0142
Path, inches	100 yds	-1.5	0.0	-8.8	-31.1	-71.2	-134.3
Relative to	200 yds	-1.5	4.4	0.0	-17.9	-53.6	-112.3
Line of Sight	300 yds	-1.5	10.4	11.9	0.0	-29.7	-82.5

Exterior Ballistic Table for Ballistic Coefficient 0.30

	Muzzle	100 yds	200 yds	300 yds	400 yds	500 yds
			RANGE			
Velocity, ft/sec	2000	1751	1527	1332	1176	1064
Energy, ft/lbs per grain	8.88	6.81	5.18	3.94	3.07	2.51
Time of Flight, sec	0.0000	0.1603	0.3439	0.5546	0.7949	1.0639
Path, inches — 100 yds	-1.5	0.0	-9.9	-34.8	-79.4	-149.1
Relative to ZERO RANGE 200 yds	-1.5	5.0	0.0	-20.0	-59.6	-124.4
Line of Sight — 300 yds	-1.5	11.6	13.3	0.0	-33.0	-91.1
Velocity, ft/sec	1900	1660	1447	1266	1127	1031
Energy, ft/lbs per grain	8.01	6.12	4.65	3.56	2.82	2.36
Time of Flight, sec	0.0000	0.1690	0.3627	0.5848	0.8367	1.1158
Path, inches — 100 yds	-1.5	0.0	-11.2	-39.1	-88.7	-165.7
Relative to ZERO RANGE 200 yds	-1.5	5.6	0.0	-22.3	-66.3	-137.7
Line of Sight — 300 yds	-1.5	13.0	14.9	0.0	-36.6	-100.6
Velocity, ft/sec	1800	1570	1369	1204	1084	1001
Energy, ft/lbs per grain	7.19	5.47	4.16	3.22	2.61	2.22
Time of Flight, sec	0.0000	0.1785	0.3834	0.6176	0.8810	1.1698
Path, inches — 100 yds	-1.5	0.0	-12.7	-44.0	-99.3	-184.2
Relative to ZERO RANGE 200 yds	-1.5	6.3	0.0	-25.0	-73.9	-152.5
Line of Sight — 300 yds	-1.5	14.7	16.7	0.0	-40.6	-110.9
Velocity, ft/sec	1700	1482	1294	1148	1045	973
Energy, ft/lbs per grain	6.42	4.88	3.72	2.93	2.42	2.10
Time of Flight, sec	0.0000	0.1892	0.4061	0.6529	0.9276	1.2258
Path, inches — 100 yds	-1.5	0.0	-14.4	-49.7	-11.3	-204.7
Relative to ZERO RANGE 200 yds	-1.5	7.2	0.0	-28.0	-82.4	-168.6
Line of Sight — 300 yds	1.5	16.6	18.7	0.0	-45.1	-121.9
Velocity, ft/sec	1600	1394	1224	1097	1010	946
Energy, ft/lbs per grain	5.68	4.31	3.33	2.67	2.26	1.99
Time of Flight, sec	0.0000	0.2010	0.4311	0.6908	0.9764	1.2838
Path, inches — 100 yds	-1.5	0.0	-16.5	-56.2	-124.7	-227.3
Relative to ZERO RANGE 200 yds	-1.5	8.2	0.0	-31.5	-91.8	-186.1
Line of Sight — 300 yds	1.5	18.7	21.0	0.0	-49.8	-133.7
Velocity, ft/sec	1500	1309	1159	1053	978	921
Energy, ft/lbs per grain	5.00	3.80	2.98	2.46	2.12	1.88
Time of Flight, sec	0.0000	0.2143	0.4585	0.7308	1.0271	1.3437
Path, inches — 100 yds	-1.5	0.0	-18.8	-63.5	-139.6	-251.9
Relative to ZERO RANGE 200 yds	-1.5	9.4	0.0	-35.3	-101.9	-204.8
Line of Sight — 300 yds	-1.5	21.2	23.5	0.0	-54.9	-146.0

Exterior Ballistic Table for Ballistic Coefficient 0.32

	Muzzle	100 yds	200 yds	300 yds	400 yds	500 yds
			RANGE			
Velocity, ft/sec	3600	3257	2941	2646	2370	2111
Energy, ft/lbs per grain	28.77	23.55	19.20	15.54	12.47	9.89
Time of Flight, sec	0.0000	0.0876	0.1846	0.2921	0.4119	0.5461
Path, inches — 100 yds	-1.5	0.0	-1.8	-7.6	-18.4	-35.4
Relative to ZERO RANGE 200 yds	-1.5	0.9	0.0	-4.9	-14.8	-31.0
Line of Sight — 300 yds	-1.5	2.5	3.3	0.0	-8.3	-22.8

long range tables

Exterior Ballistic Table for Ballistic Coefficient 0.32

		Muzzle	100 yds	200 yds	300 yds	400 yds	500 yds
Velocity, ft/sec		3500	3165	2855	2566	2295	2040
Energy, ft/lbs per grain		27.20	22.24	18.10	14.62	11.69	9.24
Time of Flight, sec		0.0000	0.0902	0.1900	0.3008	0.4244	0.5631
Path, inches	100 yds	-1.5	0.0	-2.0	-8.2	-19.8	-38.0
Relative to	200 yds	-1.5	1.0	0.0	-5.3	-15.8	-33.0
Line of Sight	300 yds	-1.5	2.7	3.5	0.0	-8.8	-24.3
Velocity, ft/sec		3400	3073	2770	2486	2219	1970
Energy, ft/lbs per grain		25.66	20.96	17.03	13.72	10.93	8.62
Time of Flight, sec		0.0000	0.0928	0.1957	0.3100	0.4377	0.5813
Path, inches	100 yds	-1.5	0.0	-2.2	-8.9	-21.3	-40.8
Relative to	200 yds	-1.5	1.1	0.0	-5.6	-16.9	-35.3
Line of Sight	300 yds	-1.5	3.0	3.8	0.0	-9.4	-25.9
Velocity, ft/sec		3300	2980	2683	2405	2143	1899
Energy, ft/lbs per grain		24.18	19.72	15.98	12.84	10.20	8.01
Time of Flight, sec		0.0000	0.0957	0.2018	0.3199	0.4520	0.6008
Path, inches	100 yds	-1.5	0.0	-2.4	-9.7	-23.0	-43.9
Relative to	200 yds	-1.5	1.2	0.0	-6.1	-18.2	-37.9
Line of Sight	300 yds	-1.5	3.2	4.0	0.0	-10.1	-27.8
Velocity, ft/sec		3200	2888	2597	2324	2067	1828
Energy, ft/lbs per grain		22.73	18.52	14.97	11.99	9.49	7.42
Time of Flight, sec		0.0000	0.0987	0.2083	0.3304	0.4673	0.6217
Path, inches	100 yds	-1.5	0.0	-2.7	-10.5	-24.9	-47.4
Relative to	200 yds	-1.5	1.3	0.0	-6.5	-19.5	-40.7
Line of Sight	300 yds	-1.5	3.5	4.3	0.0	-10.8	-29.8
Velocity, ft/sec		3100	2795	2510	2242	1990	1757
Energy, ft/lbs per grain		21.33	17.34	13.99	11.16	8.79	6.85
Time of Flight, sec		0.0000	0.1019	0.2152	0.3417	0.4838	0.6442
Path, inches	100 yds	-1.5	0.0	-3.0	-11.5	-26.9	-51.2
Relative to	200 yds	-1.5	1.5	0.0	-7.0	-21.0	-43.8
Line of Sight	300 yds	-1.5	3.8	4.7	0.0	-11.6	-32.1
Velocity, ft/sec		3000	2702	2422	2159	1914	1687
Energy, ft/lbs per grain		19.98	16.21	13.02	10.35	8.13	6.32
Time of Flight, sec		0.0000	0.1054	0.227	0.3539	0.5015	0.6685
Path, inches	100 yds	-1.5	0.0	-3.3	-12.5	-29.2	-55.5
Relative to	200 yds	-1.5	1.6	0.0	-7.6	-22.7	-47.3
Line of Sight	300 yds	-1.5	4.2	5.1	0.0	-12.6	-34.7
Velocity, ft/sec		2900	2608	2337	2077	1837	1617
Energy, ft/lbs per grain		18.67	15.10	12.09	9.58	7.49	5.80
Time of Flight, sec		0.0000	0.1091	0.2307	0.3669	0.5205	0.6947
Path, inches	100 yds	-1.5	0.0	-3.6	-13.7	-31.8	-60.3
Relative to	200 yds	-1.5	1.8	0.0	-8.2	-24.6	-51.2
Line of Sight	300 yds	-1.5	4.6	5.5	0.0	-13.6	-37.5
Velocity, ft/sec		2800	2514	2246	1995	1761	1549
Energy, ft/lbs per grain		17.41	14.03	11.20	8.84	6.88	5.33
Time of Flight, sec		0.0000	0.1131	0.2393	0.3811	0.5412	0.7229
Path, inches	100 yds	-1.5	0.0	-4.0	-15.0	-34.7	-65.7
Relative to	200 yds	-1.5	2.0	0.0	-8.9	-26.7	-55.7
Line of Sight	300 yds	-1.5	5.0	6.0	0.0	-14.7	-40.9

long range tables

Exterior Ballistic Table for Ballistic Coefficient 0.32
RANGE

		Muzzle	100 yds	200 yds	300 yds	400 yds	500 yds
Velocity, ft/sec		2700	2421	2158	1912	1686	1482
Energy, ft/lbs per grain		16.18	13.01	10.34	8.12	6.31	4.88
Time of Flight, sec		0.0000	0.1174	0.2486	0.3963	0.5635	0.7534
Path, inches	100 yds	-1.5	0.0	-4.5	-16.4	-38.0	-71.8
Relative to ZERO RANGE	200 yds	-1.5	2.2	0.0	-9.7	-29.0	-60.6
Line of Sight	300 yds	-1.5	5.5	6.5	0.0	-16.0	-44.4
Velocity, ft/sec		2600	2327	2070	1830	1611	1416
Energy, ft/lbs per grain		15.01	12.02	9.51	7.43	5.76	4.45
Time of Flight, sec		0.0000	0.1220	0.2587	0.4129	0.5876	0.7864
Path, inches	100 yds	-1.5	0.0	-5.0	-18.1	-41.6	-78.6
Relative to ZERO RANGE	200 yds	-1.5	2.5	0.0	-10.6	-31.7	-66.2
Line of Sight	300 yds	-1.5	6.0	7.1	0.0	-17.5	-48.5
Velocity, ft/sec		2500	2233	1982	1749	1538	1353
Energy, ft/lbs per grain		13.88	11.07	8.72	6.79	5.25	4.06
Time of Flight, sec		0.0000	0.1270	0.2696	0.4308	0.6138	0.8219
Path, inches	100 yds	-1.5	0.0	-5.5	-19.9	-45.8	-86.4
Relative to ZERO RANGE	200 yds	-1.5	2.8	0.0	-11.7	-34.7	-72.6
Line of Sight	300 yds	-1.5	6.6	7.8	0.0	-19.2	-53.2

Exterior Ballistic Table for Ballistic Coefficient 0.33
RANGE

		Muzzle	100 yds	200 yds	300 yds	400 yds	500 yds
Velocity, ft/sec		3400	3082	2787	2511	2251	2006
Energy, ft/lbs per grain		25.66	21.09	17.24	14.00	11.25	8.93
Time of Flight, sec		0.0000	0.0927	0.1951	0.3085	0.4347	0.5785
Path, inches	100 yds	-1.5	0.0	-2.2	-8.8	-21.0	-40.1
Relative to ZERO RANGE	200 yds	-1.5	1.1	0.0	-5.6	-16.7	-34.7
Line of Sight	300 yds	-1.5	2.9	3.7	0.0	-9.3	-25.4
Velocity, ft/sec		3300	2990	2701	2430	2174	1935
Energy, ft/lbs per grain		24.18	19.85	16.20	13.11	10.49	8.31
Time of Flight, sec		0.0000	0.0955	0.2011	0.3182	0.4488	0.5951
Path, inches	100 yds	-1.5	0.0	-2.4	-9.6	-22.7	-43.2
Relative to ZERO RANGE	200 yds	-1.5	1.2	0.0	-6.0	-17.9	-37.2
Line of Sight	300 yds	-1.5	3.2	4.0	0.0	-9.9	-27.2
Velocity, ft/sec		3200	2897	2614	2348	2097	1863
Energy, ft/lbs per grain		22.73	18.63	15.17	12.24	9.76	7.71
Time of Flight, sec		0.0000	0.0986	0.2076	0.3287	0.4639	0.6157
Path, inches	100 yds	-1.5	0.0	-2.7	-10.4	-24.5	-46.6
Relative to ZERO RANGE	200 yds	-1.5	1.3	0.0	-6.4	-19.2	-39.9
Line of Sight	300 yds	-1.5	3.5	4.3	0.0	-10.6	-29.2
Velocity, ft/sec		3100	2804	2526	2265	2020	1791
Energy, ft/lbs per grain		21.33	17.46	14.17	11.39	9.06	7.12
Time of Flight, sec		0.0000	0.1018	0.2145	0.3399	0.4802	0.6379
Path, inches	100 yds	-1.5	0.0	-2.9	-11.3	-26.6	-50.3
Relative to ZERO RANGE	200 yds	-1.5	1.5	0.0	-6.9	-20.7	-43.0
Line of Sight	300 yds	-1.5	3.8	4.6	0.0	-11.4	-31.4

Exterior Ballistic Table for Ballistic Coefficient 0.33

	Muzzle	100 yds	200 yds	300 yds	400 yds	500 yds
RANGE						
Velocity, ft/sec	3000	2710	2439	2183	1942	1720
Energy, ft/lbs per grain	19.98	16.30	13.21	10.58	8.37	6.57
Time of Flight, sec	0.0000	0.1052	0.2219	0.3520	0.4977	0.6619
Path, inches — ZERO RANGE 100 yds	-1.5	0.0	-3.3	-12.4	-28.8	-54.5
Relative to — ZERO RANGE 200 yds	-1.5	1.6	0.0	-7.5	-22.3	-46.4
Line of Sight — ZERO RANGE 300 yds	-1.5	4.1	5.0	0.0	-12.3	-33.9
Velocity, ft/sec	2900	2617	2350	2100	1865	1649
Energy, ft/lbs per grain	18.67	15.20	12.26	9.79	7.72	6.04
Time of Flight, sec	0.0000	0.1089	0.2299	0.3649	0.5166	0.6877
Path, inches — ZERO RANGE 100 yds	-1.5	0.0	-3.6	-13.5	-31.4	-59.2
Relative to — ZERO RANGE 200 yds	-1.5	1.8	0.0	-8.1	-24.2	-50.3
Line of Sight — ZERO RANGE 300 yds	-1.5	4.5	5.4	0.0	-13.3	-36.7
Velocity, ft/sec	2800	2523	2262	2017	1788	1579
Energy, ft/lbs per grain	17.41	14.13	11.36	9.03	7.10	5.54
Time of Flight, sec	0.0000	0.1129	0.2385	0.3789	0.5370	0.7155
Path, inches — ZERO RANGE 100 yds	-1.5	0.0	-4.0	-14.8	-34.2	-64.5
Relative to — ZERO RANGE 200 yds	-1.5	2.0	0.0	-8.8	-26.2	-54.6
Line of Sight — ZERO RANGE 300 yds	-1.5	4.9	5.9	0.0	-14.5	-39.9
Velocity, ft/sec	2700	2429	2173	1934	1712	1511
Energy, ft/lbs per grain	16.18	13.10	10.48	8.30	6.51	5.07
Time of Flight, sec	0.0000	0.1172	0.2477	0.3941	0.5590	0.7456
Path, inches — ZERO RANGE 100 yds	-1.5	0.0	-4.4	-16.2	-37.4	-70.5
Relative to — ZERO RANGE 200 yds	-1.5	2.2	0.0	-9.6	-28.6	-59.4
Line of Sight — ZERO RANGE 300 yds	-1.5	5.4	6.4	0.0	-15.7	-43.4
Velocity, ft/sec	2600	2335	2085	1851	1637	1444
Energy, ft/lbs per grain	15.01	12.10	9.65	7.61	5.95	4.63
Time of Flight, sec	0.0000	0.1218	0.2578	0.4105	0.5829	0.7782
Path, inches — ZERO RANGE 100 yds	-1.5	0.0	-4.9	-17.9	-41.0	-77.2
Relative to — ZERO RANGE 200 yds	-1.5	2.5	0.0	-10.5	-31.2	-64.9
Line of Sight — ZERO RANGE 300 yds	-1.5	6.0	7.0	0.0	-17.2	-47.4
Velocity, ft/sec	2500	2240	1997	1770	1563	1379
Energy, ft/lbs per grain	13.88	11.14	8.85	6.96	5.42	4.20
Time of Flight, sec	0.0000	0.1268	0.2686	0.4283	0.6088	0.8130
Path, inches — ZERO RANGE 100 yds	-1.5	0.0	-5.5	-19.7	-45.1	-84.8
Relative to — ZERO RANGE 200 yds	-1.5	2.7	0.0	-11.5	-34.2	-71.7
Line of Sight — ZERO RANGE 300 yds	-1.5	6.6	7.7	0.0	-18.8	-52.0

Exterior Ballistic Table for Ballistic Coefficient 0.34

	Muzzle	100 yds	200 yds	300 yds	400 yds	500 yds
RANGE						
Velocity, ft/sec	3300	2999	2717	2453	2203	1969
Energy, ft/lbs per grain	24.18	19.97	16.39	13.36	10.77	8.61
Time of Flight, sec	0.0000	0.0954	0.2005	0.3167	0.4458	0.5898
Path, inches — ZERO RANGE 100 yds	-1.5	0.0	-2.4	-9.5	-22.4	-42.5
Relative to — ZERO RANGE 200 yds	-1.5	1.2	0.0	-5.9	-17.6	-36.5
Line of Sight — ZERO RANGE 300 yds	-1.5	3.2	3.9	0.0	-9.7	-26.7

Exterior Ballistic Table for Ballistic Coefficient 0.34

			RANGE					
			Muzzle	100 yds	200 yds	300 yds	400 yds	500 yds
Velocity, ft/sec			3200	2906	2630	2371	2126	1896
Energy, ft/lbs per grain			22.73	18.75	15.36	12.48	10.03	7.98
Time of Flight, sec			0.0000	0.0984	0.2069	0.3271	0.4607	0.6102
Path, inches	ZERO RANGE	100 yds	-1.5	0.0	-2.6	-10.3	-24.2	-45.8
Relative to		200 yds	-1.5	1.3	0.0	-6.4	-18.9	-39.2
Line of Sight		300 yds	-1.5	3.4	4.2	0.0	-10.5	-28.6
Velocity, ft/sec			3100	2812	2542	2288	2048	1824
Energy, ft/lbs per grain			21.33	17.55	14.35	11.62	9.31	7.39
Time of Flight, sec			0.0000	0.1016	0.2138	0.3382	0.4768	0.6321
Path, inches	ZERO RANGE	100 yds	-1.5	0.0	-2.9	-11.2	-26.2	-49.5
Relative to		200 yds	-1.5	1.5	0.0	-6.9	-20.4	-42.2
Line of Sight		300 yds	-1.5	3.7	4.6	0.0	-11.2	-30.8
Velocity, ft/sec			3000	2719	2454	2205	1970	1751
Energy, ft/lbs per grain			19.98	16.41	13.37	10.79	8.62	6.81
Time of Flight, sec			0.0000	0.1051	0.2212	0.3502	0.4942	0.6557
Path, inches	ZERO RANGE	100 yds	-1.5	0.0	-3.2	-12.2	-28.4	-53.6
Relative to		200 yds	-1.5	1.6	0.0	-7.4	-22.0	-45.6
Line of Sight		300 yds	-1.5	4.1	4.9	0.0	-12.1	-33.2
Velocity, ft/sec			2900	2625	2366	2121	1892	1680
Energy, ft/lbs per grain			18.67	15.30	12.43	9.99	7.95	6.27
Time of Flight, sec			0.0000	0.1087	0.2291	0.3631	0.5129	0.6812
Path, inches	ZERO RANGE	100 yds	-1.5	0.0	-3.6	-13.4	-30.9	-58.3
Relative to		200 yds	-1.5	1.8	0.0	-8.0	-23.8	-49.3
Line of Sight		300 yds	-1.5	4.5	5.3	0.0	-13.1	-36.0
Velocity, ft/sec			2800	2531	2277	2038	1814	1609
Energy, ft/lbs per grain			17.41	14.22	11.51	9.22	7.31	5.75
Time of Flight, sec			0.0000	0.1127	0.2377	0.3770	0.5330	0.7087
Path, inches	ZERO RANGE	100 yds	-1.5	0.0	-3.9	-14.6	-33.7	-63.4
Relative to		200 yds	-1.5	2.0	0.0	-8.7	-25.8	-53.6
Line of Sight		300 yds	-1.5	4.9	5.8	0.0	-14.2	-39.1
Velocity, ft/sec			2700	2437	2188	1954	1737	1539
Energy, ft/lbs per grain			16.18	13.18	10.63	8.48	6.70	5.26
Time of Flight, sec			0.0000	0.1170	0.2469	0.3920	0.5549	0.7384
Path, inches	ZERO RANGE	100 yds	-1.5	0.0	-4.4	-16.1	-36.9	-69.3
Relative to		200 yds	-1.5	2.2	0.0	-9.5	-28.1	-58.3
Line of Sight		300 yds	-1.5	5.4	6.3	0.0	-15.5	-42.5
Velocity, ft/sec			2600	2342	2099	1871	1661	1471
Energy, ft/lbs per grain			15.01	12.18	9.78	7.77	6.12	4.80
Time of Flight, sec			0.0000	0.1216	0.2569	0.4083	0.5785	0.7706
Path, inches	ZERO RANGE	100 yds	-1.5	0.0	-4.9	-17.7	-40.4	-75.9
Relative to		200 yds	-1.5	2.4	0.0	-10.4	-30.7	-63.7
Line of Sight		300 yds	-1.5	5.9	6.9	0.0	-16.9	-46.4
Velocity, ft/sec			2500	2248	2010	1789	1586	1404
Energy, ft/lbs per grain			13.88	11.22	8.97	7.11	5.58	4.38
Time of Flight, sec			0.0000	0.1266	0.2677	0.4259	0.6041	0.8053
Path, inches	ZERO RANGE	100 yds	-1.5	0.0	-5.4	-19.5	-44.4	-83.3
Relative to		200 yds	-1.5	2.7	0.0	-11.3	-33.6	-69.8
Line of Sight		300 yds	-1.5	6.5	7.9	0.0	-18.5	-50.9

Exterior Ballistic Table for Ballistic Coefficient 0.35

		RANGE					
		Muzzle	100 yds	200 yds	300 yds	400 yds	500 yds
Velocity, ft/sec		3200	2914	2645	2392	2153	1928
Energy, ft/lbs per grain		22.73	18.85	15.53	12.70	10.29	8.25
Time of Flight, sec		0.0000	0.0983	0.2063	0.3256	0.4578	0.6051
Path, inches	ZERO RANGE 100 yds	-1.5	0.0	-2.6	-10.2	-23.9	-45.1
Relative to	ZERO RANGE 200 yds	-1.5	1.3	0.0	-6.3	-18.7	-38.6
Line of Sight	ZERO RANGE 300 yds	-1.5	3.4	4.2	0.0	-10.3	-28.1
Velocity, ft/sec		3100	2820	2557	2309	2075	1855
Energy, ft/lbs per grain		21.33	17.65	14.52	11.84	9.56	7.64
Time of Flight, sec		0.0000	0.1015	0.2132	0.3367	0.4737	0.6267
Path, inches	ZERO RANGE 100 yds	-1.5	0.0	-2.9	-11.1	-25.9	-48.8
Relative to	ZERO RANGE 200 yds	-1.5	1.4	0.0	-6.8	-20.1	-41.5
Line of Sight	ZERO RANGE 300 yds	-1.5	3.7	4.5	0.0	-11.1	-30.2
Velocity, ft/sec		3000	2726	2469	2225	1996	1781
Energy, ft/lbs per grain		19.98	16.50	13.53	10.99	8.84	7.04
Time of Flight, sec		0.0000	0.1049	0.2205	0.3485	0.4909	0.4900
Path, inches	ZERO RANGE 100 yds	-1.5	0.0	-3.2	-12.1	-28.1	-52.8
Relative to	ZERO RANGE 200 yds	-1.5	1.6	0.0	-7.3	-21.7	-44.8
Line of Sight	ZERO RANGE 300 yds	-1.5	4.0	4.9	0.0	-11.9	-32.6
Velocity, ft/sec		2900	2632	2380	2142	1917	1709
Energy, ft/lbs per grain		18.67	15.38	12.58	10.19	8.16	6.48
Time of Flight, sec		0.0000	0.1086	0.2284	0.3613	0.5094	0.6752
Path, inches	ZERO RANGE 100 yds	-1.5	0.0	-3.5	-13.2	-30.5	-57.3
Relative to	ZERO RANGE 200 yds	-1.5	1.8	0.0	-7.9	-23.5	-48.5
Line of Sight	ZERO RANGE 300 yds	-1.5	4.4	5.3	0.0	-12.9	-35.3
Velocity, ft/sec		2800	2538	2291	2058	1839	1637
Energy, ft/lbs per grain		17.41	14.30	11.65	9.40	7.51	5.95
Time of Flight, sec		0.0000	0.1125	0.2370	0.3751	0.5294	0.7024
Path, inches	ZERO RANGE 100 yds	-1.5	0.0	-3.9	-14.5	-33.3	-62.4
Relative to	ZERO RANGE 200 yds	-1.5	2.0	0.0	-8.6	-25.5	-52.6
Line of Sight	ZERO RANGE 300 yds	-1.5	4.8	5.7	0.0	-14.0	-38.3
Velocity, ft/sec		2700	2444	2202	1974	1761	1566
Energy, ft/lbs per grain		16.18	13.26	10.76	8.65	6.88	5.44
Time of Flight, sec		0.0000	0.1168	0.2461	0.3900	0.5510	0.7317
Path, inches	ZERO RANGE 100 yds	-1.5	0.0	-4.3	-15.9	-36.4	-68.2
Relative to	ZERO RANGE 200 yds	-1.5	2.2	0.0	-9.4	-27.7	-57.3
Line of Sight	ZERO RANGE 300 yds	-1.5	5.3	6.2	0.0	-15.2	-41.7
Velocity, ft/sec		2600	2349	2113	1890	1684	1497
Energy, ft/lbs per grain		15.01	12.25	9.91	7.93	6.30	4.98
Time of Flight, sec		0.0000	0.1214	0.2561	0.4062	0.5744	0.7635
Path, inches	ZERO RANGE 100 yds	-1.5	0.0	-4.8	-17.5	-39.9	-74.6
Relative to	ZERO RANGE 200 yds	-1.5	2.4	0.0	-10.2	-30.2	-42.6
Line of Sight	ZERO RANGE 300 yds	-1.5	5.8	6.8	0.0	-16.6	-45.5
Velocity, ft/sec		2500	2255	2024	1807	1608	1429
Energy, ft/lbs per grain		13.88	11.29	9.09	7.25	5.74	4.53
Time of Flight, sec		0.0000	0.1264	0.2668	0.4237	0.5998	0.7678
Path, inches	ZERO RANGE 100 yds	-1.5	0.0	-5.4	-19.3	-43.8	-81.9
Relative to	ZERO RANGE 200 yds	-1.5	2.7	0.0	-11.2	-33.1	-68.5
Line of Sight	ZERO RANGE 300 yds	-1.5	6.4	7.5	0.0	-18.2	-49.8

Exterior Ballistic Table for Ballistic Coefficient 0.35

		Muzzle	100 yds	200 yds	300 yds	400 yds	500 yds
Velocity, ft/sec		2400	2160	1935	1725	1534	1364
Energy, ft/lbs per grain		12.79	10.36	8.31	6.61	5.22	4.13
Time of Flight, sec		0.0000	0.1318	0.2785	0.4428	0.6273	0.8349
Path, inches	100 yds	-1.5	0.0	-6.0	-21.3	-48.3	-90.2
Relative to	200 yds	-1.5	3.0	0.0	-12.3	-36.4	-75.3
Line of Sight	300 yds	-1.5	7.1	8.2	0.0	-19.9	-54.7
Velocity, ft/sec		2300	2066	1847	1644	1461	1301
Energy, ft/lbs per grain		11.74	9.48	7.57	6.00	4.74	3.76
Time of Flight, sec		0.0000	0.1376	0.2912	0.4635	0.6571	0.8750
Path, inches	100 yds	-1.5	0.0	-6.7	-23.6	-53.4	-99.6
Relative to	200 yds	-1.5	3.3	0.0	-13.6	-40.1	-82.9
Line of Sight	300 yds	-1.5	7.9	9.1	0.0	-22.0	-40.3
Velocity, ft/sec		2200	1972	1759	1565	1391	1243
Energy, ft/lbs per grain		10.75	8.63	6.87	5.44	4.30	3.43
Time of Flight, sec		0.0000	0.1440	0.3051	0.4860	0.6896	0.9181
Path, inches	100 yds	-1.5	0.0	-7.5	-26.2	-59.3	-110.3
Relative to	200 yds	-1.5	3.7	0.0	-15.0	-44.3	-91.6
Line of Sight	300 yds	-1.5	8.7	10.0	0.0	-24.3	-66.6
Velocity, ft/sec		2100	1878	1673	1487	1323	1189
Energy, ft/lbs per grain		9.79	7.83	6.21	4.91	3.89	3.14
Time of Flight, sec		0.0000	0.1511	0.3203	0.5107	0.7247	0.9644
Path, inches	100 yds	-1.5	0.0	-8.4	-29.3	-45.9	-122.5
Relative to	200 yds	-1.5	4.2	0.0	-16.7	-49.1	-101.5
Line of Sight	300 yds	-1.5	9.8	11.1	0.0	-26.9	-73.7

Exterior Ballistic Table for Ballistic Coefficient 0.36

		Muzzle	100 yds	200 yds	300 yds	400 yds	500 yds
Velocity, ft/sec		3700	3387	3096	2823	2568	2325
Energy, ft/lbs per grain		30.39	25.47	21.28	17.69	14.64	12.00
Time of Flight, sec		0.0000	0.0848	0.1774	0.2789	0.3904	0.5132
Path, inches	100 yds	-1.5	0.0	-1.5	-6.7	-16.3	-31.1
Relative to	200 yds	-1.5	0.8	0.0	-4.4	-13.2	-27.3
Line of Sight	300 yds	-1.5	2.2	2.9	0.0	-7.3	-19.9
Velocity, ft/sec		3600	3294	3009	2742	2491	2253
Energy, ft/lbs per grain		28.77	24.09	20.10	16.69	13.78	11.27
Time of Flight, sec		0.0000	0.0871	0.1824	0.2869	0.4017	0.5283
Path, inches	100 yds	-1.5	0.0	-1.7	-7.3	-17.5	-33.3
Relative to	200 yds	-1.5	0.9	0.0	-4.7	-14.0	-29.0
Line of Sight	300 yds	-1.5	2.4	3.1	0.0	-7.8	-21.2
Velocity, ft/sec		3500	3201	2922	2661	2414	2180
Energy, ft/lbs per grain		27.20	22.75	18.96	15.72	12.94	10.55
Time of Flight, sec		0.0000	0.0896	0.1877	0.2953	0.4137	0.5445
Path, inches	100 yds	-1.5	0.0	-1.9	-7.9	-18.8	-35.7
Relative to	200 yds	-1.5	1.0	0.0	-5.0	-15.0	-30.9
Line of Sight	300 yds	-1.5	2.6	3.4	0.0	-8.3	-22.6

long range tables

	Muzzle	100 yds	200 yds	300 yds	400 yds	500 yds
			RANGE			
Velocity, ft/sec	3400	3108	2835	2579	2336	2106
Energy, ft/lbs per grain	25.66	21.45	17.84	14.77	12.11	9.85
Time of Flight, sec	0.0000	0.0923	0.1934	0.3043	0.4266	0.5618
Path, inches — Relative to Line of Sight, ZERO RANGE 100 yds	-1.5	0.0	-2.1	-8.6	-20.2	-38.3
200 yds	-1.5	1.1	0.0	-5.4	-16.0	-33.1
300 yds	-1.5	2.9	3.6	0.0	-8.8	-24.1
Velocity, ft/sec	3300	3015	2748	2496	2258	2032
Energy, ft/lbs per grain	24.18	20.18	16.76	13.83	11.32	9.17
Time of Flight, sec	0.0000	0.0951	0.1994	0.3139	0.4403	0.5804
Path, inches — Relative to Line of Sight, ZERO RANGE 100 yds	-1.5	0.0	-2.3	-9.3	-21.8	-41.2
200 yds	-1.5	1.2	0.0	-5.8	-17.2	-35.4
300 yds	-1.5	3.1	3.9	0.0	-9.5	-25.8
Velocity, ft/sec	3200	2921	2660	2413	2179	1958
Energy, ft/lbs per grain	22.73	18.94	15.71	12.93	10.54	8.51
Time of Flight, sec	0.0000	0.0981	0.2058	0.3242	0.4550	0.6003
Path, inches — Relative to Line of Sight, ZERO RANGE 100 yds	-1.5	0.0	-2.6	-10.1	-23.6	-44.5
200 yds	-1.5	1.3	0.0	-6.2	-18.4	-38.0
300 yds	-1.5	3.4	4.1	0.0	-10.1	-27.6
Velocity, ft/sec	3100	2828	2571	2329	2100	1884
Energy, ft/lbs per grain	21.33	17.76	14.67	12.04	9.79	7.88
Time of Flight, sec	0.0000	0.1013	0.2126	0.3352	0.4709	0.6217
Path, inches — Relative to Line of Sight, ZERO RANGE 100 yds	-1.5	0.0	-2.9	-11.0	-25.6	-48.0
200 yds	-1.5	1.4	0.0	-6.7	-19.8	-40.9
300 yds	-1.5	3.7	4.5	0.0	-10.9	-29.7
Velocity, ft/sec	3000	2734	2483	2245	2021	1810
Energy, ft/lbs per grain	19.98	16.59	13.69	11.19	9.07	7.27
Time of Flight, sec	0.0000	0.1048	0.2199	0.3470	0.4879	0.6447
Path, inches — Relative to Line of Sight, ZERO RANGE 100 yds	-1.5	0.0	-3.2	-12.0	-27.7	-52.0
200 yds	-1.5	1.6	0.0	-7.2	-21.4	-44.1
300 yds	-1.5	4.0	4.8	0.0	-11.8	-32.1
Velocity, ft/sec	2900	2640	2394	2161	1941	1737
Energy, ft/lbs per grain	18.67	15.47	12.72	10.37	8.36	6.70
Time of Flight, sec	0.0000	0.1084	0.2278	0.3597	0.5032	0.6696
Path, inches — Relative to Line of Sight, ZERO RANGE 100 yds	-1.5	0.0	-3.5	-13.1	-30.2	-56.5
200 yds	-1.5	1.8	0.0	-7.8	-23.2	-47.7
300 yds	-1.5	4.4	5.2	0.0	-12.7	-34.7
Velocity, ft/sec	2800	2545	2304	2077	1862	1664
Energy, ft/lbs per grain	17.41	14.38	11.79	9.58	7.70	6.15
Time of Flight, sec	0.0000	0.1124	0.2363	0.3734	0.5260	0.6965
Path, inches — Relative to Line of Sight, ZERO RANGE 100 yds	-1.5	0.0	-3.9	-14.3	-32.9	-61.5
200 yds	-1.5	1.9	0.0	-8.5	-25.1	-51.8
300 yds	-1.5	4.8	5.7	0.0	-13.8	-37.6
Velocity, ft/sec	2700	2451	2215	1992	1784	1592
Energy, ft/lbs per grain	16.18	13.34	10.89	8.81	7.07	5.63
Time of Flight, sec	0.0000	0.1166	0.2454	0.3882	0.5474	0.7255
Path, inches — Relative to Line of Sight, ZERO RANGE 100 yds	-1.5	0.0	-4.3	-15.7	-35.9	-67.1
200 yds	-1.5	2.2	0.0	-9.3	-27.3	-56.4
300 yds	-1.5	5.2	6.2	0.0	-15.0	-40.9

long range tables

Exterior Ballistic Table for Ballistic Coefficient 0.36

			RANGE			
	Muzzle	100 yds	200 yds	300 yds	400 yds	500 yds
Velocity, ft/sec	2600	2356	2125	1908	1706	1521
Energy, ft/lbs per grain	15.01	12.32	10.02	8.08	6.46	5.14
Time of Flight, sec	0.0000	0.1212	0.2553	0.4043	0.5706	0.7569
Path, inches — 100 yds	-1.5	0.0	-4.2	-17.3	-39.4	-73.5
Relative to ZERO RANGE — 200 yds	-1.5	2.4	0.0	-10.1	-29.8	-61.5
Line of Sight — 300 yds	-1.5	5.8	6.7	0.0	-16.3	-44.7
Velocity, ft/sec	2500	2261	2036	1825	1629	1452
Energy, ft/lbs per grain	13.88	11.35	9.20	7.39	5.89	4.68
Time of Flight, sec	0.0000	0.1262	0.2660	0.4217	0.5957	0.7909
Path, inches — 100 yds	-1.5	0.0	-5.2	-19.4	-45.7	-88.2
Relative to ZERO RANGE — 200 yds	-1.5	2.6	0.0	-11.6	-35.2	-75.1
Line of Sight — 300 yds	-1.5	6.5	7.7	0.0	-19.8	-55.8

Exterior Ballistic Table for Ballistic Coefficient 0.37

			RANGE			
	Muzzle	100 yds	200 yds	300 yds	400 yds	500 yds
Velocity, ft/sec	3500	3209	2937	2681	2440	2211
Energy, ft/lbs per grain	27.20	22.86	19.15	15.96	13.22	10.85
Time of Flight, sec	0.0000	0.0895	0.1873	0.2942	0.4115	0.5407
Path, inches — 100 yds	-1.5	0.0	-1.9	-7.8	-18.6	-35.2
Relative to ZERO RANGE — 200 yds	-1.5	0.9	0.0	-5.0	-14.8	-30.5
Line of Sight — 300 yds	-1.5	2.6	3.3	0.0	-8.2	-22.2
Velocity, ft/sec	3400	3116	2850	2599	2361	2137
Energy, ft/lbs per grain	25.66	21.56	18.03	15.00	12.38	10.14
Time of Flight, sec	0.0000	0.0922	0.1929	0.3031	0.4242	0.5578
Path, inches — 100 yds	-1.5	0.0	-2.1	-8.5	-20.2	-37.8
Relative to ZERO RANGE — 200 yds	-1.5	1.0	0.0	-5.3	-15.8	-32.6
Line of Sight — 300 yds	-1.5	2.8	3.6	0.0	-8.7	-23.7
Velocity, ft/sec	3300	3022	2762	2516	2283	2062
Energy, ft/lbs per grain	24.18	20.27	16.94	14.05	11.57	9.44
Time of Flight, sec	0.0000	0.0950	0.1989	0.3127	0.4379	0.5762
Path, inches — 100 yds	-1.5	0.0	-2.3	-9.2	-21.6	-40.7
Relative to ZERO RANGE — 200 yds	-1.5	1.2	0.0	-5.7	-17.0	-34.9
Line of Sight — 300 yds	-1.5	3.1	3.8	0.0	-9.3	-25.4
Velocity, ft/sec	3200	2929	2674	2432	2204	1987
Energy, ft/lbs per grain	22.73	19.05	15.87	13.13	10.78	8.77
Time of Flight, sec	0.0000	0.0980	0.2052	0.3229	0.4525	0.5958
Path, inches — 100 yds	-1.5	0.0	-2.6	-10.0	-23.3	-43.9
Relative to ZERO RANGE — 200 yds	-1.5	1.3	0.0	-6.2	-18.2	-37.5
Line of Sight — 300 yds	-1.5	3.3	4.1	0.0	-10.0	-27.2
Velocity, ft/sec	3100	2835	2585	2348	2124	1913
Energy, ft/lbs per grain	21.33	17.84	14.83	12.24	10.02	8.12
Time of Flight, sec	0.0000	0.1012	0.2120	0.3338	0.4681	0.6170
Path, inches — 100 yds	-1.5	0.0	-2.8	-10.9	-25.3	-47.4
Relative to ZERO RANGE — 200 yds	-1.5	1.4	0.0	-6.6	-19.6	-40.3
Line of Sight — 300 yds	-1.5	3.6	4.4	0.0	-10.8	-29.2

long range tables

Exterior Ballistic Table for Ballistic Coefficient 0.37

	Muzzle	100 yds	200 yds	300 yds	400 yds	500 yds
			RANGE			
Velocity, ft/sec	3000	2741	2496	2264	2044	1838
Energy, ft/lbs per grain	19.98	16.68	13.83	11.38	9.28	7.50
Time of Flight, sec	0.0000	0.1046	0.2193	0.3455	0.4850	0.6398
Path, inches — ZERO RANGE 100 yds	-1.5	0.0	-3.1	-11.9	-27.4	-51.3
Relative to — 200 yds	-1.5	1.6	0.0	-7.2	-21.1	-43.5
Line of Sight — 300 yds	-1.5	4.0	4.8	0.0	-11.6	-31.5
Velocity, ft/sec	2900	2647	2407	2179	1965	1763
Energy, ft/lbs per grain	18.67	15.56	12.86	10.54	8.57	6.90
Time of Flight, sec	0.0000	0.1083	0.2272	0.3582	0.5032	0.6644
Path, inches — ZERO RANGE 100 yds	-1.5	0.0	-3.5	-13.0	-29.8	-55.7
Relative to — 200 yds	-1.5	1.7	0.0	-7.8	-22.9	-47.0
Line of Sight — 300 yds	-1.5	4.3	5.2	0.0	-12.5	-34.1
Velocity, ft/sec	2800	2552	2317	2095	1885	1690
Energy, ft/lbs per grain	17.41	14.46	11.92	9.74	7.89	6.34
Time of Flight, sec	0.0000	0.1122	0.2356	0.3718	0.5228	0.6910
Path, inches — ZERO RANGE 100 yds	-1.5	0.0	-3.9	-14.2	-32.5	-60.6
Relative to — 200 yds	-1.5	1.9	0.0	-8.4	-24.8	-51.0
Line of Sight — 300 yds	-1.5	4.7	5.6	0.0	-13.6	-37.0
Velocity, ft/sec	2700	2457	2227	2010	1806	1617
Energy, ft/lbs per grain	16.18	13.40	11.01	8.97	7.24	5.80
Time of Flight, sec	0.0000	0.1165	0.2447	0.3865	0.5440	0.7197
Path, inches — ZERO RANGE 100 yds	-1.5	0.0	-4.3	-15.6	-35.5	-66.2
Relative to — 200 yds	-1.5	2.1	0.0	-9.2	-27.0	-55.5
Line of Sight — 300 yds	-1.5	5.2	6.1	0.0	-14.8	-40.2
Velocity, ft/sec	2600	2363	2138	1925	1727	1545
Energy, ft/lbs per grain	15.01	12.40	10.15	8.23	6.62	5.30
Time of Flight, sec	0.0000	0.1210	0.2546	0.4025	0.5670	0.7507
Path, inches — ZERO RANGE 100 yds	-1.5	0.0	-4.7	-17.1	-38.9	-72.5
Relative to — 200 yds	-1.5	2.4	0.0	-10.0	-29.4	-60.6
Line of Sight — 300 yds	-1.5	5.7	6.7	0.0	-16.1	-43.9
Velocity, ft/sec	2500	2268	2048	1841	1649	1475
Energy, ft/lbs per grain	13.88	11.42	9.31	7.52	6.04	4.83
Time of Flight, sec	0.0000	0.1260	0.2652	0.4179	0.5919	0.7844
Path, inches — ZERO RANGE 100 yds	-1.5	0.0	-5.3	-18.9	-42.8	-79.5
Relative to — 200 yds	-1.5	2.6	0.0	-11.0	-32.2	-66.3
Line of Sight — 300 yds	-1.5	6.3	7.3	0.0	-17.6	-48.0
Velocity, ft/sec	2400	2173	1959	1758	1573	1407
Energy, ft/lbs per grain	12.79	10.48	8.52	6.86	5.49	4.39
Time of Flight, sec	0.0000	0.1314	0.2768	0.4385	0.6190	0.8207
Path, inches — ZERO RANGE 100 yds	-1.5	0.0	-5.9	-20.9	-47.2	-87.5
Relative to — 200 yds	-1.5	2.9	0.0	-12.0	-35.4	-72.8
Line of Sight — 300 yds	-1.5	7.0	8.0	0.0	-19.3	-52.8
Velocity, ft/sec	2300	2078	1870	1676	1499	1342
Energy, ft/lbs per grain	11.74	9.59	7.76	6.24	4.99	4.00
Time of Flight, sec	0.0000	0.1372	0.2894	0.4590	0.6484	0.8601
Path, inches — ZERO RANGE 100 yds	-1.5	0.0	-6.6	-23.1	-52.1	-96.7
Relative to — 200 yds	-1.5	3.3	0.0	-13.3	-39.0	-80.2
Line of Sight — 300 yds	-1.5	7.7	8.9	0.0	-21.3	-58.1

Exterior Ballistic Table for Ballistic Coefficient 0.37

		Muzzle	100 yds	200 yds	300 yds	400 yds	500 yds
Velocity, ft/sec		2200	1984	1782	1595	1426	1280
Energy, ft/lbs per grain		10.75	8.74	7.05	5.65	4.51	3.64
Time of Flight, sec		0.0000	0.1436	0.3032	0.4812	0.6803	0.9026
Path, inches	100 yds	-1.5	0.0	-7.4	-25.7	-57.8	-107.0
Relative to	ZERO RANGE 200 yds	-1.5	3.7	0.0	-14.7	-43.1	-88.6
Line of Sight	300 yds	-1.5	8.6	9.8	0.0	-23.5	-64.2
Velocity, ft/sec		2100	1890	1694	1516	1356	1222
Energy, ft/lbs per grain		9.79	7.93	6.37	5.10	4.08	3.32
Time of Flight, sec		0.0000	0.1506	0.3183	0.5056	0.7150	0.9484
Path, inches	100 yds	-1.5	0.0	-8.3	-28.7	-64.3	-118.9
Relative to	ZERO RANGE 200 yds	-1.5	4.1	0.0	-16.3	-47.8	-98.2
Line of Sight	300 yds	-1.5	9.6	10.9	0.0	-26.1	-71.1

Exterior Ballistic Table for Ballistic Coefficient 0.38

		Muzzle	100 yds	200 yds	300 yds	400 yds	500 yds
Velocity, ft/sec		3400	3123	2860	2618	2386	2165
Energy, ft/lbs per grain		25.66	21.65	18.20	15.22	12.64	10.41
Time of Flight, sec		0.0000	0.0921	0.1924	0.3020	0.4220	0.5540
Path, inches	100 yds	-1.5	0.0	-2.1	-8.4	-19.8	-37.3
Relative to	ZERO RANGE 200 yds	-1.5	1.0	0.0	-5.3	-15.7	-32.3
Line of Sight	300 yds	-1.5	2.8	3.5	0.0	-8.6	-23.4
Velocity, ft/sec		3300	3029	2775	2535	2307	2090
Energy, ft/lbs per grain		24.18	20.37	17.10	14.27	11.82	9.70
Time of Flight, sec		0.0000	0.0949	0.1984	0.3115	0.4356	0.5722
Path, inches	100 yds	-1.5	0.0	-2.3	-9.1	-21.4	-40.2
Relative to	ZERO RANGE 200 yds	-1.5	1.1	0.0	-5.7	-16.8	-34.4
Line of Sight	300 yds	-1.5	3.0	3.8	0.0	-9.2	-25.0
Velocity, ft/sec		3200	2936	2687	2451	2227	2015
Energy, ft/lbs per grain		22.73	19.14	16.03	13.34	11.01	9.01
Time of Flight, sec		0.0000	0.0979	0.2047	0.3216	0.4501	0.5917
Path, inches	100 yds	-1.5	0.0	-2.5	-9.9	-23.1	-43.3
Relative to	ZERO RANGE 200 yds	-1.5	1.3	0.0	-6.1	-18.0	-37.0
Line of Sight	300 yds	-1.5	3.3	4.1	0.0	-9.9	26.8
Velocity, ft/sec		3100	2842	2598	2367	2147	1940
Energy, ft/lbs per grain		21.33	17.93	14.98	12.44	10.23	8.36
Time of Flight, sec		0.0000	0.1011	0.2115	0.3325	0.4656	0.6126
Path, inches	100 yds	-1.5	0.0	-2.8	-10.8	-25.0	-46.8
Relative to	ZERO RANGE 200 yds	-1.5	1.4	0.0	-6.6	-19.4	-39.7
Line of Sight	300 yds	-1.5	3.6	4.4	0.0	-10.6	-28.8
Velocity, ft/sec		3000	2747	2509	2282	2067	1864
Energy, ft/lbs per grain		19.98	16.75	13.98	11.56	9.49	7.71
Time of Flight, sec		0.0000	0.1045	0.2188	0.3442	0.4823	0.6352
Path, inches	100 yds	-1.5	0.0	-3.1	-11.8	-27.1	-50.7
Relative to	ZERO RANGE 200 yds	-1.5	1.6	0.0	-7.1	-20.9	-42.9
Line of Sight	300 yds	-1.5	3.9	4.7	0.0	-11.4	-31.0

Exterior Ballistic Table for Ballistic Coefficient 0.38

	Muzzle	100 yds	200 yds	300 yds	400 yds	500 yds
			RANGE			
Velocity, ft/sec	2900	2653	2419	2197	1987	1789
Energy, ft/lbs per grain	18.67	15.63	12.99	10.72	8.77	7.11
Time of Flight, sec	0.0000	0.1082	0.2266	0.3567	0.5004	0.6595
Path, inches — 100 yds (ZERO RANGE)	-1.5	0.0	-3.5	-12.9	-29.5	-55.0
Relative to — 200 yds	-1.5	1.7	0.0	-7.7	-22.6	-46.4
Line of Sight — 300 yds	-1.5	4.3	5.1	0.0	-12.4	-33.5
Velocity, ft/sec	2800	2558	2329	2112	1906	1714
Energy, ft/lbs per grain	17.41	14.53	12.04	9.90	8.07	6.52
Time of Flight, sec	0.0000	0.1121	0.2350	0.3703	0.5198	0.6858
Path, inches — 100 yds	-1.5	0.0	-3.8	-14.1	-32.2	-59.9
Relative to — 200 yds	-1.5	1.9	0.0	-8.3	-24.5	-50.3
Line of Sight — 300 yds	-1.5	4.7	5.6	0.0	-13.4	-36.4
Velocity, ft/sec	2700	2464	2239	2026	1826	1641
Energy, ft/lbs per grain	16.18	13.48	11.13	9.11	7.40	5.98
Time of Flight, sec	0.0000	0.1163	0.2441	0.3849	0.5409	0.7142
Path, inches — 100 yds	-1.5	0.0	-4.2	-15.4	-35.2	-65.3
Relative to — 200 yds	-1.5	2.1	0.0	-9.1	-26.7	-54.7
Line of Sight — 300 yds	-1.5	5.1	6.1	0.0	-14.6	-39.6
Velocity, ft/sec	2600	2369	2149	1942	1747	1568
Energy, ft/lbs per grain	15.01	12.46	10.25	8.37	6.78	5.46
Time of Flight, sec	0.0000	0.1209	0.2539	0.4007	0.5637	0.7450
Path, inches — 100 yds	-1.5	0.0	-4.7	-17.0	-38.5	-71.5
Relative to — 200 yds	-1.5	2.4	0.0	-9.9	-29.1	-59.7
Line of Sight — 300 yds	-1.5	5.7	6.6	0.0	-15.9	-43.2
Velocity, ft/sec	2500	2274	2059	1857	1669	1497
Energy, ft/lbs per grain	13.88	11.48	9.41	7.66	6.18	4.98
Time of Flight, sec	0.0000	0.1258	0.2645	0.4179	0.5884	0.7783
Path, inches — 100 yds	-1.5	0.0	-5.2	-18.7	-42.3	-78.4
Relative to — 200 yds	-1.5	2.6	0.0	-10.9	-31.8	-65.3
Line of Sight — 300 yds	-1.5	6.2	7.2	0.0	-17.4	-47.2
Velocity, ft/sec	2400	2179	1970	1773	1592	1428
Energy, ft/lbs per grain	12.79	10.54	8.62	6.98	5.63	4.53
Time of Flight, sec	0.0000	0.1312	0.2760	0.4366	0.6152	0.8143
Path, inches — 100 yds	-1.5	0.0	-5.8	-20.7	-46.6	-86.4
Relative to — 200 yds	-1.5	2.9	0.0	-11.9	-34.9	-71.7
Line of Sight — 300 yds	-1.5	6.9	7.9	0.0	-19.0	-51.9
Velocity, ft/sec	2300	2084	1880	1690	1517	1361
Energy, ft/lbs per grain	11.74	9.64	7.85	6.34	5.11	4.11
Time of Flight, sec	0.0000	0.1370	0.2886	0.4569	0.6444	0.8533
Path, inches — 100 yds	-1.5	0.0	-6.5	-22.9	-51.6	-95.3
Relative to — 200 yds	-1.5	3.3	0.0	-13.1	-38.5	-79.0
Line of Sight — 300 yds	-1.5	7.6	8.8	0.0	-21.0	-57.1
Velocity, ft/sec	2200	1990	1792	1609	1443	1298
Energy, ft/lbs per grain	10.75	8.79	7.13	5.75	4.62	3.74
Time of Flight, sec	0.0000	0.1434	0.3023	0.4791	0.9760	0.8955
Path, inches — 100 yds	-1.5	0.0	-7.3	-25.5	-57.2	-105.6
Relative to — 200 yds	-1.5	3.7	0.0	-14.5	-42.5	-87.3
Line of Sight — 300 yds	-1.5	8.5	9.7	0.0	-23.2	-63.1

long range tables

Exterior Ballistic Table for Ballistic Coefficient 0.38

		Muzzle	100 yds	200 yds	300 yds	400 yds	500 yds
				RANGE			
Velocity, ft/sec		2100	1895	1704	1529	1372	1238
Energy, ft/lbs per grain		9.79	7.97	6.45	5.19	4.18	3.40
Time of Flight, sec		0.0000	0.1504	0.3173	0.5033	0.7105	0.9410
Path, inches	100 yds	-1.5	0.0	-8.2	-28.4	-63.6	-117.3
Relative to ZERO RANGE	200 yds	-1.5	4.1	0.0	-16.1	-47.2	-96.7
Line of Sight	300 yds	-1.5	9.5	10.7	0.0	-25.7	-69.9
Velocity, ft/sec		2000	1802	1618	1451	1304	1183
Energy, ft/lbs per grain		8.88	7.21	5.81	4.67	3.78	3.11
Time of Flight, sec		0.0000	0.1581	0.3338	0.5297	0.7480	0.9899
Path, inches	100 yds	-1.5	0.0	-9.3	-31.8	-71.0	-130.6
Relative to ZERO RANGE	200 yds	-1.5	4.6	0.0	-18.0	-52.5	-107.5
Line of Sight	300 yds	-1.5	10.6	12.0	0.0	-28.5	-77.5

Exterior Ballistic Table for Ballistic Coefficient 0.39

		Muzzle	100 yds	200 yds	300 yds	400 yds	500 yds
				RANGE			
Velocity, ft/sec		3400	3130	2876	2637	2409	2193
Energy, ft/lbs per grain		25.66	21.75	18.36	15.44	12.88	10.68
Time of Flight, sec		0.0000	0.0920	0.1920	0.3009	0.4200	0.5505
Path, inches	100 yds	-1.5	0.0	-2.1	-8.3	-19.6	-36.9
Relative to ZERO RANGE	200 yds	-1.5	1.0	0.0	-5.2	-15.5	-31.8
Line of Sight	300 yds	-1.5	2.8	3.5	0.0	-8.5	-23.0
Velocity, ft/sec		3300	3036	2788	2553	2330	2117
Energy, ft/lbs per grain		24.18	20.46	17.26	14.47	12.05	9.95
Time of Flight, sec		0.0000	0.0948	0.1979	0.3104	0.4334	0.5685
Path, inches	100 yds	-1.5	0.0	-2.3	-9.0	-21.2	-39.7
Relative to ZERO RANGE	200 yds	-1.5	1.1	0.0	-5.6	-16.6	-34.0
Line of Sight	300 yds	-1.5	3.0	3.7	0.0	-9.1	-24.6
Velocity, ft/sec		3200	2942	2699	2469	2249	2042
Energy, ft/lbs per grain		22.73	19.22	16.17	15.53	11.23	9.26
Time of Flight, sec		0.0000	0.0978	0.2043	0.3205	0.4478	0.5878
Path, inches	100 yds	-1.5	0.0	-2.5	-9.8	-22.9	-42.8
Relative to ZERO RANGE	200 yds	-1.5	1.3	0.0	-6.0	-17.8	-36.5
Line of Sight	300 yds	-1.5	3.3	4.0	0.0	-9.8	-26.4
Velocity, ft/sec		3100	2848	2610	2384	2169	1966
Energy, ft/lbs per grain		21.33	18.01	15.12	12.62	10.44	8.58
Time of Flight, sec		0.0000	0.1010	0.2110	0.3313	0.4632	0.6085
Path, inches	100 yds	-1.5	0.0	-2.8	-10.7	-24.8	-46.2
Relative to ZERO RANGE	200 yds	-1.5	1.4	0.0	6.5	-19.2	-39.2
Line of Sight	300 yds	-1.5	3.6	4.3	0.0	-10.5	-28.4
Velocity, ft/sec		3000	2754	2520	2299	2088	1889
Energy, ft/lbs per grain		19.98	16.84	14.10	11.73	9.68	7.92
Time of Flight, sec		0.0000	0.1044	0.2183	0.3429	0.4798	0.6309
Path, inches	100 yds	-1.5	0.0	-3.1	-11.7	-26.9	-50.0
Relative to ZERO RANGE	200 yds	-1.5	1.5	0.0	-7.0	-20.7	-42.3
Line of Sight	300 yds	-1.5	3.9	4.7	0.0	-11.3	-30.6

Exterior Ballistic Table for Ballistic Coefficient 0.39

		RANGE Muzzle	100 yds	200 yds	300 yds	400 yds	500 yds
Velocity, ft/sec		2900	2659	2431	2213	2008	1814
Energy, ft/lbs per grain		18.67	15.70	13.12	10.87	8.95	7.31
Time of Flight, sec		0.0000	0.1080	0.2260	0.3554	0.4977	0.6550
Path, inches	ZERO RANGE 100 yds	-1.5	0.0	-3.4	-12.8	-29.2	-54.3
Relative to	ZERO RANGE 200 yds	-1.5	1.7	0.0	-7.6	-22.4	-45.7
Line of Sight	ZERO RANGE 300 yds	-1.5	4.3	5.1	0.0	-12.2	-33.0
Velocity, ft/sec		2800	2564	2341	2128	1927	1738
Energy, ft/lbs per grain		17.41	14.59	12.17	10.05	8.24	6.71
Time of Flight, sec		0.0000	0.1120	0.2344	0.3688	0.5170	0.6810
Path, inches	ZERO RANGE 100 yds	-1.5	0.0	-3.8	-14.0	-31.8	-59.1
Relative to	ZERO RANGE 200 yds	-1.5	1.9	0.0	-8.3	-24.2	-49.6
Line of Sight	ZERO RANGE 300 yds	-1.5	4.7	5.5	0.0	-13.2	-35.8
Velocity, ft/sec		2700	2469	2250	2042	1846	1664
Energy, ft/lbs per grain		16.18	13.53	11.24	9.26	7.57	6.15
Time of Flight, sec		0.0000	0.1162	0.2435	0.3834	0.5379	0.7091
Path, inches	ZERO RANGE 100 yds	-1.5	0.0	-4.2	-15.3	-34.8	-64.5
Relative to	ZERO RANGE 200 yds	-1.5	2.1	0.0	-9.0	-26.4	-53.9
Line of Sight	ZERO RANGE 300 yds	-1.5	5.1	6.0	0.0	-14.4	-39.0
Velocity, ft/sec		2600	2374	2160	1957	1766	1590
Energy, ft/lbs per grain		15.01	12.51	10.36	8.50	6.92	5.61
Time of Flight, sec		0.0000	0.1207	0.2532	0.3991	0.5605	0.7396
Path, inches	ZERO RANGE 100 yds	-1.5	0.0	-4.7	-16.8	-38.1	-70.6
Relative to	ZERO RANGE 200 yds	-1.5	2.3	0.0	-9.8	-28.7	-58.9
Line of Sight	ZERO RANGE 300 yds	-1.5	5.6	6.5	0.0	-15.7	-42.5
Velocity, ft/sec		2500	2279	2070	1872	1687	1518
Energy, ft/lbs per grain		13.88	11.53	9.51	7.78	6.32	5.12
Time of Flight, sec		0.0000	0.1257	0.2638	0.4162	0.5851	0.7726
Path, inches	ZERO RANGE 100 yds	-1.5	0.0	-5.2	-18.6	-41.9	-77.4
Relative to	ZERO RANGE 200 yds	-1.5	2.6	0.0	-10.7	-31.5	-64.4
Line of Sight	ZERO RANGE 300 yds	-1.5	6.2	7.2	0.0	-17.1	-46.5
Velocity, ft/sec		2400	2184	1980	1788	1610	1448
Energy, ft/lbs per grain		12.79	10.59	8.70	7.10	5.75	4.65
Time of Flight, sec		0.0000	0.1310	0.2753	0.4348	0.6117	0.8083
Path, inches	ZERO RANGE 100 yds	-1.5	0.0	-5.8	-20.5	-46.1	-85.2
Relative to	ZERO RANGE 200 yds	-1.5	2.9	0.0	-11.8	-34.5	-70.7
Line of Sight	ZERO RANGE 300 yds	-1.5	6.8	7.9	0.0	-18.8	-51.0
Velocity, ft/sec		2300	2089	1890	1704	1534	1380
Energy, ft/lbs per grain		11.74	9.69	7.93	6.45	5.22	4.23
Time of Flight, sec		0.0000	0.1369	0.2878	0.4550	0.6406	0.8470
Path, inches	ZERO RANGE 100 yds	-1.5	0.0	-6.5	-22.7	-51.0	-94.1
Relative to	ZERO RANGE 200 yds	-1.5	3.2	0.0	-13.0	-38.0	-77.9
Line of Sight	ZERO RANGE 300 yds	-1.5	7.6	8.7	0.0	-20.7	-56.2
Velocity, ft/sec		2200	1995	1802	1622	1459	1315
Energy, ft/lbs per grain		10.75	8.84	7.21	5.84	4.73	3.84
Time of Flight, sec		0.0000	0.1432	0.3015	0.4770	0.6721	0.8889
Path, inches	ZERO RANGE 100 yds	-1.5	0.0	-7.3	-25.3	-56.6	-104.2
Relative to	ZERO RANGE 200 yds	-1.5	3.6	0.0	-14.4	-42.0	-86.0
Line of Sight	ZERO RANGE 300 yds	-1.5	8.4	9.6	0.0	-22.8	-62.1

long range tables

Exterior Ballistic Table for Ballistic Coefficient 0.39

		Muzzle	100 yds	200 yds	300 yds	400 yds	500 yds
				RANGE			
Velocity, ft/sec		2100	1900	1714	1542	1387	1254
Energy, ft/lbs per grain		9.79	8.01	6.52	5.28	4.27	3.49
Time of Flight, sec		0.0000	0.1502	0.3165	0.5011	0.7063	0.9341
Path, inches	100 yds	-1.5	0.0	-8.2	-28.2	-62.9	-115.7
Relative to	200 yds	-1.5	4.1	0.0	-16.0	-46.6	-95.3
Line of Sight	300 yds	-1.5	9.4	10.6	0.0	-25.3	-68.7
Velocity, ft/sec		2000	1807	1627	1463	1318	1197
Energy, ft/lbs per grain		8.88	7.25	5.88	4.75	3.86	3.18
Time of Flight, sec		0.0000	0.1578	0.3329	0.5274	0.7436	0.9828
Path, inches	100 yds	-1.5	0.0	-9.2	-31.6	-70.2	-128.9
Relative to	200 yds	-1.5	4.6	0.0	-17.8	-51.8	-105.9
Line of Sight	300 yds	-1.5	10.5	11.9	0.0	-28.1	-76.3
Velocity, ft/sec		1900	1713	1542	1387	1253	1145
Energy, ft/lbs per grain		8.01	6.51	5.28	4.27	3.49	2.91
Time of Flight, sec		0.0000	0.1663	0.3510	0.5563	0.7841	1.0349
Path, inches	100 yds	-1.5	0.0	-10.4	-35.4	-78.6	-144.0
Relative to	200 yds	-1.5	5.2	0.0	-19.9	-57.9	-118.0
Line of Sight	300 yds	-1.5	11.8	13.2	0.0	-31.4	-84.9

Exterior Ballistic Table for Ballistic Coefficient 0.40

		Muzzle	100 yds	200 yds	300 yds	400 yds	500 yds
				RANGE			
Velocity, ft/sec		3600	3323	3065	2821	2590	2370
Energy, ft/lbs per grain		28.77	24.51	20.86	17.67	14.89	12.47
Time of Flight, sec		0.0000	0.0867	0.1808	0.2828	0.3938	0.5149
Path, inches	100 yds	-1.5	0.0	-1.7	-7.0	-16.8	-31.7
Relative to	200 yds	-1.5	0.8	0.0	-4.5	-13.5	-27.6
Line of Sight	300 yds	-1.5	2.3	3.0	0.0	-7.4	-20.0
Velocity, ft/sec		3500	3230	2977	2738	2511	2295
Energy, ft/lbs per grain		27.20	23.16	19.68	16.64	14.00	11.69
Time of Flight, sec		0.0000	0.0892	0.1860	0.2911	0.4055	0.5305
Path, inches	100 yds	-1.5	0.0	-1.8	-7.6	-18.0	-34.0
Relative to	200 yds	-1.5	0.9	0.0	-4.9	-14.4	-29.4
Line of Sight	300 yds	-1.5	2.5	3.2	0.0	-7.9	-21.3
Velocity, ft/sec		3400	3136	2888	2654	2431	2219
Energy, ft/lbs per grain		25.66	21.83	18.52	15.64	13.12	10.93
Time of Flight, sec		0.0000	0.0919	0.1916	0.2999	0.4180	0.5472
Path, inches	100 yds	-1.5	0.0	-2.0	-8.3	-19.4	-36.5
Relative to	200 yds	-1.5	1.0	0.0	-5.2	-15.3	-31.4
Line of Sight	300 yds	-1.5	2.8	3.5	0.0	-8.4	-22.7
Velocity, ft/sec		3300	3042	2800	2570	2351	2143
Energy, ft/lbs per grain		24.18	20.54	17.41	14.66	12.27	10.20
Time of Flight, sec		0.0000	0.0947	0.1975	0.3093	0.4314	0.5650
Path, inches	100 yds	-1.5	0.0	-2.3	-9.0	-21.0	-39.3
Relative to	200 yds	-1.5	1.1	0.0	-5.6	-16.4	-33.6
Line of Sight	300 yds	-1.5	3.0	3.7	0.0	-9.0	-24.3

long range tables

Exterior Ballistic Table for Ballistic Coefficient 0.40

	Muzzle	100 yds	200 yds	300 yds	400 yds	500 yds
RANGE						
Velocity, ft/sec	3200	2948	2711	2485	2271	2067
Energy, ft/lbs per grain	22.73	19.29	16.32	13.71	11.45	9.49
Time of Flight, sec	0.0000	0.0977	0.2038	0.3194	0.4457	0.5841
Path, inches — ZERO RANGE 100 yds	-1.5	0.0	-2.5	-9.8	-22.7	-42.3
Relative to — 200 yds	-1.5	1.3	0.0	-6.0	-17.6	-36.0
Line of Sight — 300 yds	-1.5	3.3	4.0	0.0	-9.6	-26.0
Velocity, ft/sec	3100	2854	2622	2400	2190	1990
Energy, ft/lbs per grain	21.33	18.08	15.26	12.79	10.65	8.79
Time of Flight, sec	0.0000	0.1009	0.2105	0.3301	0.4610	0.6047
Path, inches — ZERO RANGE 100 yds	-1.5	0.0	-2.8	-10.6	-24.5	-45.7
Relative to — 200 yds	-1.5	1.4	0.0	-6.5	-19.0	-38.8
Line of Sight — 300 yds	-1.5	3.5	4.3	0.0	-10.4	-28.0
Velocity, ft/sec	3000	2760	2532	2315	2109	1914
Energy, ft/lbs per grain	19.98	16.91	14.23	11.90	9.87	9.13
Time of Flight, sec	0.0000	0.1034	0.2178	0.3417	0.4775	0.6268
Path, inches — ZERO RANGE 100 yds	-1.5	0.0	-3.1	-11.6	-26.6	-49.5
Relative to — 200 yds	-1.5	1.5	0.0	-7.0	-20.5	-41.8
Line of Sight — 300 yds	-1.5	3.9	4.7	0.0	-11.2	-30.2
Velocity, ft/sec	2900	2665	2442	2229	2028	1837
Energy, ft/lbs per grain	18.67	15.77	13.24	11.03	9.13	7.49
Time of Flight, sec	0.0000	0.1079	0.2255	0.3541	0.4952	0.6507
Path, inches — ZERO RANGE 100 yds	-1.5	0.0	-3.4	-12.7	-28.9	-53.7
Relative to — 200 yds	-1.5	1.7	0.0	-7.6	-22.1	-45.2
Line of Sight — 300 yds	-1.5	4.2	5.0	0.0	-12.0	-32.6
Velocity, ft/sec	2800	2570	2352	2143	1946	1761
Energy, ft/lbs per grain	17.41	14.66	12.28	10.20	8.41	6.88
Time of Flight, sec	0.0000	0.1118	0.2339	0.3675	0.5144	0.6765
Path, inches — ZERO RANGE 100 yds	-1.5	0.0	-3.8	-13.9	-31.5	-58.4
Relative to — 200 yds	-1.5	1.9	0.0	-8.2	-24.0	-49.0
Line of Sight — 300 yds	-1.5	4.6	5.5	0.0	-13.1	-35.3
Velocity, ft/sec	2700	2475	2261	2058	1865	1686
Energy, ft/lbs per grain	16.18	13.60	11.35	9.40	7.72	6.31
Time of Flight, sec	0.0000	0.1161	0.2429	0.3820	0.5351	0.7043
Path, inches — ZERO RANGE 100 yds	-1.5	0.0	-4.2	-15.2	-34.5	-63.7
Relative to — 200 yds	-1.5	2.1	0.0	-8.9	-26.1	-53.3
Line of Sight — 300 yds	-1.5	5.1	5.9	0.0	-14.2	-38.4
Velocity, ft/sec	2600	2380	2171	1972	1785	1611
Energy, ft/lbs per grain	15.01	12.58	10.46	8.63	7.07	5.76
Time of Flight, sec	0.0000	0.1206	0.2526	0.3976	0.5576	0.7345
Path, inches — ZERO RANGE 100 yds	-1.5	0.0	-4.7	-16.7	-37.7	-69.7
Relative to — 200 yds	-1.5	2.3	0.0	-9.7	-28.4	-58.1
Line of Sight — 300 yds	-1.5	5.6	6.5	0.0	-15.5	-49.1
Velocity, ft/sec	2500	2285	2080	1886	1705	1538
Energy, ft/lbs per grain	13.88	11.59	9.60	7.90	6.45	5.25
Time of Flight, sec	0.0000	0.1255	0.2632	0.4146	0.5819	0.7672
Path, inches — ZERO RANGE 100 yds	-1.5	0.0	-5.2	-18.4	-41.5	-76.5
Relative to — 200 yds	-1.5	2.6	0.0	-10.7	-31.1	-63.6
Line of Sight — 300 yds	-1.5	6.1	7.1	0.0	-16.9	-45.8

Exterior Ballistic Table for Ballistic Coefficient 0.40

		Muzzle	100 yds	200 yds	300 yds	400 yds	500 yds
Velocity, ft/sec		2400	2190	1990	1802	1627	1467
Energy, ft/lbs per grain		12.79	10.65	8.79	7.21	5.88	4.78
Time of Flight, sec		0.0000	0.1255	0.2632	0.4146	0.5819	0.7672
Path, inches	100 yds	-1.5	0.0	-5.2	-18.4	-41.5	-76.5
Relative to	200 yds	-1.5	2.6	0.0	-10.7	-31.1	-63.6
Line of Sight ZERO RANGE	300 yds	-1.5	6.1	7.1	0.0	-16.9	-45.8
Velocity, ft/sec		2300	2095	1900	1718	1550	1398
Energy, ft/lbs per grain		11.74	9.74	8.01	6.55	5.33	4.43
Time of Flight, sec		0.0000	0.1367	0.2871	0.4532	0.6371	0.8410
Path, inches	100 yds	-1.5	0.0	-6.4	-22.6	-50.5	-92.9
Relative to	200 yds	-1.5	3.2	0.0	-12.9	-37.6	-76.8
Line of Sight ZERO RANGE	300 yds	-1.5	7.5	8.6	0.0	-20.4	-55.3
Velocity, ft/sec		2200	2000	1811	1635	1475	1332
Energy, ft/lbs per grain		10.75	8.88	7.28	5.93	4.83	3.94
Time of Flight, sec		0.0000	0.1430	0.3007	0.4751	0.6683	0.8826
Path, inches	100 yds	-1.5	0.0	-7.2	-25.1	-56.0	-102.9
Relative to	200 yds	-1.5	3.6	0.0	-14.2	-41.5	-84.9
Line of Sight ZERO RANGE	300 yds	-1.5	8.4	9.5	0.0	-22.5	-61.1

Exterior Ballistic Table for Ballistic Coefficient 0.41

		Muzzle	100 yds	200 yds	300 yds	400 yds	500 yds
Velocity, ft/sec		3300	3049	2811	2586	2372	2168
Energy, ft/lbs per grain		24.18	20.64	17.54	14.85	12.49	10.43
Time of Flight, sec		0.0000	0.0946	0.1917	0.3083	0.4295	0.5618
Path, inches	100 yds	-1.5	0.0	-2.2	-8.9	-20.8	-38.8
Relative to	200 yds	-1.5	1.1	0.0	-5.5	-16.3	-33.2
Line of Sight ZERO RANGE	300 yds	-1.5	3.0	3.7	0.0	-8.9	-24.0
Velocity, ft/sec		3200	2954	2722	2502	2291	2091
Energy, ft/lbs per grain		22.73	19.37	16.45	13.90	11.65	9.71
Time of Flight, sec		0.0000	0.0976	0.2034	0.3183	0.4437	0.5807
Path, inches	100 yds	-1.5	0.0	-2.5	9.7	-22.4	-41.8
Relative to	200 yds	-1.5	1.2	0.0	-5.9	-17.5	-35.6
Line of Sight ZERO RANGE	300 yds	-1.5	3.2	4.0	0.0	-9.5	-25.7
Velocity, ft/sec		3100	2860	2633	2416	2210	2014
Energy, ft/lbs per grain		21.33	18.16	15.39	12.96	10.84	9.01
Time of Flight, sec		0.0000	0.1008	0.2101	0.3291	0.4589	0.6011
Path, inches	100 yds	-1.5	0.0	-2.8	-10.5	-24.3	-45.2
Relative to	200 yds	-1.5	1.4	0.0	-6.4	-18.8	-38.3
Line of Sight ZERO RANGE	300 yds	-1.5	3.5	4.3	0.0	-10.2	-27.6
Velocity, ft/sec		3000	2765	2543	2331	2129	1937
Energy, ft/lbs per grain		19.98	16.97	14.36	12.06	10.06	8.33
Time of Flight, sec		0.0000	0.1042	0.2173	0.3405	0.4752	0.6230
Path, inches	100 yds	-1.5	0.0	-3.1	-11.5	-26.4	-48.9
Relative to	200 yds	-1.5	1.5	0.0	-6.9	-20.3	-41.3
Line of Sight ZERO RANGE	300 yds	-1.5	3.8	4.6	0.0	-11.0	-29.8

long range tables

Exterior Ballistic Table for Ballistic Coefficient 0.41

		RANGE				
	Muzzle	100 yds	200 yds	300 yds	400 yds	500 yds
Velocity, ft/sec	2900	2671	2452	2245	2047	1860
Energy, ft/lbs per grain	18.67	15.84	13.35	11.19	9.30	7.68
Time of Flight, sec	0.0000	0.1078	0.2250	0.3529	0.4929	0.6467
Path, inches — ZERO RANGE 100 yds	-1.5	0.0	-3.4	-12.6	-28.7	-53.1
Relative to — ZERO RANGE 200 yds	-1.5	1.7	0.0	-7.5	-21.9	-44.6
Line of Sight — ZERO RANGE 300 yds	-1.5	4.2	5.0	0.0	-11.9	-32.1
Velocity, ft/sec	2800	2576	2362	2158	1965	1783
Energy, ft/lbs per grain	17.41	14.73	12.39	10.34	8.57	7.06
Time of Flight, sec	0.0000	0.1117	0.2334	0.3662	0.5119	0.6722
Path, inches — 100 yds	-1.5	0.0	-3.8	-13.8	-31.2	-57.8
Relative to — 200 yds	-1.5	1.9	0.0	-8.1	-23.7	-48.4
Line of Sight — 300 yds	-1.5	4.6	5.4	0.0	-12.9	-34.8
Velocity, ft/sec	2700	2480	2271	2072	1884	1707
Energy, ft/lbs per grain	16.18	13.65	11.45	9.53	7.88	6.47
Time of Flight, sec	0.0000	0.1159	0.2423	0.3806	0.5325	0.6998
Path, inches — 100 yds	-1.5	0.0	-4.2	-15.1	-34.1	-63.0
Relative to — 200 yds	-1.5	2.1	0.0	-8.8	-25.8	-52.6
Line of Sight — 300 yds	-1.5	5.0	5.9	0.0	-14.0	-37.9
Velocity, ft/sec	2600	2385	2180	1986	1803	1632
Energy, ft/lbs per grain	15.01	12.63	10.55	8.76	7.22	5.91
Time of Flight, sec	0.0000	0.1205	0.2520	0.3962	0.5548	0.7298
Path, inches — 100 yds	-1.5	0.0	-4.6	-16.6	-37.4	-68.9
Relative to — 200 yds	-1.5	2.3	0.0	-9.6	-28.1	-57.4
Line of Sight — 300 yds	-1.5	5.5	6.4	0.0	-15.3	-41.3
Velocity, ft/sec	2500	2290	2090	1900	1722	1558
Energy, ft/lbs per grain	13.88	11.64	9.70	8.01	6.58	5.39
Time of Flight, sec	0.0000	0.1254	0.2625	0.4131	0.5790	0.7622
Path, inches — 100 yds	-1.5	0.0	-5.1	-18.3	-41.1	-75.6
Relative to — 200 yds	-1.5	2.6	0.0	-10.6	-30.8	-62.8
Line of Sight — 300 yds	-1.5	6.1	7.0	0.0	-16.7	-45.2
Velocity, ft/sec	2400	2195	1999	1815	1643	1486
Energy, ft/lbs per grain	12.79	10.70	8.87	7.31	5.99	4.90
Time of Flight, sec	0.0000	0.1307	0.2740	0.4315	0.6052	0.7973
Path, inches — 100 yds	-1.5	0.0	-5.7	-20.2	-45.3	-83.2
Relative to — 200 yds	-1.5	2.9	0.0	-11.6	-33.8	-68.9
Line of Sight — 300 yds	-1.5	6.7	7.7	0.0	-18.3	-49.5
Velocity, ft/sec	2300	2099	1909	1731	1566	1416
Energy, ft/lbs per grain	11.74	9.78	8.09	6.65	5.44	4.45
Time of Flight, sec	0.0000	0.1365	0.2864	0.4514	0.6337	0.8354
Path, inches — 100 yds	-1.5	0.0	-6.4	-22.4	-50.0	-91.9
Relative to — 200 yds	-1.5	3.2	0.0	-12.8	-37.2	-75.8
Line of Sight — 300 yds	-1.5	7.5	8.5	0.0	-20.2	-54.5
Velocity, ft/sec	2200	2004	1820	1648	1490	1348
Energy, ft/lbs per grain	10.75	8.92	7.35	6.03	4.93	4.03
Time of Flight, sec	0.0000	0.1429	0.3000	0.4732	0.6648	0.8766
Path, inches — 100 yds	-1.5	0.0	-7.2	-24.9	-55.4	-101.7
Relative to — 200 yds	-1.5	3.6	0.0	-14.1	-41.1	-63.8
Line of Sight — 300 yds	-1.5	8.3	9.4	0.0	-22.3	-60.2

Exterior Ballistic Table for Ballistic Coefficient 0.41

		Muzzle	100 yds	200 yds	300 yds	400 yds	500 yds
Velocity, ft/sec		2100	1910	1731	1566	1416	1284
Energy, ft/lbs per grain		9.79	8.10	6.65	5.44	4.45	3.66
Time of Flight, sec		0.0000	0.1498	0.3148	0.4971	0.6986	0.9213
Path, inches	100 yds	-1.5	0.0	-8.1	-27.8	-61.7	-113.0
Relative to	200 yds	-1.5	4.0	0.0	-15.7	-45.5	-92.8
Line of Sight ZERO RANGE	300 yds	-1.5	9.3	10.4	0.0	-24.7	-66.7
Velocity, ft/sec		2000	1816	1644	1486	1345	1224
Energy, ft/lbs per grain		8.88	7.32	6.00	4.90	4.02	3.33
Time of Flight, sec		0.0000	0.1574	0.3311	0.5232	0.7355	0.9696
Path, inches	100 yds	-1.5	0.0	-9.1	-31.1	-68.8	-125.9
Relative to	200 yds	-1.5	4.5	0.0	-17.4	-50.7	-103.2
Line of Sight ZERO RANGE	300 yds	-1.5	10.4	11.6	0.0	-27.4	-74.1

Exterior Ballistic Table for Ballistic Coefficient 0.42

		Muzzle	100 yds	200 yds	300 yds	400 yds	500 yds
Velocity, ft/sec		3400	3148	2911	2687	2473	2269
Energy, ft/lbs per grain		25.66	22.00	18.81	16.03	13.58	11.43
Time of Flight, sec		0.0000	0.0917	0.1908	0.2981	0.4145	0.5411
Path, inches	100 yds	-1.5	0.0	-2.0	-8.1	-19.1	-35.7
Relative to	200 yds	-1.5	1.0	0.0	-5.1	-15.1	-30.7
Line of Sight ZERO RANGE	300 yds	-1.5	2.7	3.4	0.0	-8.2	-22.2
Velocity, ft/sec		3300	3054	2822	2602	2392	2192
Energy, ft/lbs per grain		24.18	20.71	17.68	15.03	12.70	10.67
Time of Flight, sec		0.0000	0.0945	0.1967	0.3074	0.4277	0.5587
Path, inches	100 yds	-1.5	0.0	-2.2	-8.8	-20.6	-38.4
Relative to	200 yds	-1.5	1.1	0.0	-5.5	-16.1	-32.9
Line of Sight ZERO RANGE	300 yds	-1.5	2.9	3.7	0.0	-8.8	-23.7
Velocity, ft/sec		3200	2960	2733	2517	2311	2115
Energy, ft/lbs per grain		22.73	19.45	16.58	14.06	11.86	9.93
Time of Flight, sec		0.0000	0.0975	0.2030	0.3174	0.4418	0.5775
Path, inches	100 yds	-1.5	0.0	-2.5	-9.6	-22.3	-41.4
Relative to	200 yds	-1.5	1.2	-2.5	-9.6	-22.3	-41.4
Line of Sight ZERO RANGE	300 yds	-1.5	3.2	3.9	0.0	-9.4	-25.4
Velocity, ft/sec		3100	2866	2643	2431	2229	2037
Energy, ft/lbs per grain		21.33	18.24	15.51	13.12	11.03	9.21
Time of Flight, sec		0.0000	0.1007	0.2097	0.3280	0.4569	0.5977
Path, inches	100 yds	-1.5	0.0	-2.7	-10.5	-24.1	-44.7
Relative to	200 yds	-1.5	1.4	0.0	-6.4	-18.6	-37.9
Line of Sight ZERO RANGE	300 yds	-1.5	3.5	4.2	0.0	-10.1	-27.3
Velocity, ft/sec		3000	2771	2553	2345	2147	1959
Energy, ft/lbs per grain		19.98	17.05	14.47	12.21	10.23	8.52
Time of Flight, sec		0.0000	0.1041	0.2169	0.3395	0.4731	0.6194
Path, inches	100 yds	-1.5	0.0	-3.0	-11.4	-26.1	-48.4
Relative to	200 yds	-1.5	1.5	0.0	-6.9	-20.1	-40.8
Line of Sight ZERO RANGE	300 yds	-1.5	3.8	4.6	0.0	-10.9	29.4

Exterior Ballistic Table for Ballistic Coefficient 0.42

	Muzzle	100 yds	200 yds	300 yds	400 yds	500 yds
RANGE						
Velocity, ft/sec	2900	2676	2463	2259	2065	1881
18.67	18.67	15.90	13.47	11.33	9.47	7.85
Time of Flight, sec	0.0000	0.1077	0.2246	0.3518	0.4907	0.6429
Path, inches — 100 yds	-1.5	0.0	-3.4	-12.5	-28.4	-52.5
Relative to ZERO RANGE 200 yds	-1.5	1.7	0.0	-7.4	-21.7	-44.1
Line of Sight — 300 yds	-1.5	4.2	5.0	0.0	-11.8	-31.7
Velocity, ft/sec	2800	2581	2372	2173	1983	1804
Energy, ft/lbs per grain	17.41	14.79	12.49	10.48	8.73	7.23
Time of Flight, sec	0.0000	0.1116	0.2329	0.3650	0.5096	0.6682
Path, inches — 100 yds	-1.5	0.0	-3.7	-13.7	-31.0	-57.2
Relative to ZERO RANGE 200 yds	-1.5	1.9	0.0	-8.1	-23.5	-47.8
Line of Sight — 300 yds	-1.5	4.6	5.4	0.0	-12.8	-34.4
Velocity, ft/sec	2700	2486	2281	2086	1901	1727
Energy, ft/lbs per grain	16.18	13.72	11.55	9.66	8.02	6.62
Time of Flight, sec	0.0000	0.1158	0.2418	0.3793	0.5300	0.6956
Path, inches — 100 yds	-1.5	0.0	-4.1	-15.0	-33.8	-62.3
Relative to ZERO RANGE 200 yds	-1.5	2.1	0.0	-8.8	-25.6	-52.0
Line of Sight — 300 yds	-1.5	5.0	5.8	0.0	-13.9	-37.4
Velocity, ft/sec	2600	2390	2190	2000	1820	1651
Energy, ft/lbs per grain	15.01	12.68	10.65	8.88	7.35	6.05
Time of Flight, sec	0.0000	0.1203	0.2515	0.3948	0.5521	0.7253
Path, inches — 100 yds	-1.5	0.0	-4.6	-16.5	-37.1	-68.2
Relative to ZERO RANGE 200 yds	-1.5	2.3	0.0	-9.6	-27.9	-56.7
Line of Sight — 300 yds	-1.5	5.5	6.4	0.0	-15.1	-40.7
Velocity, ft/sec	2500	2295	2099	1913	1739	1577
Energy, ft/lbs per grain	13.88	11.69	9.78	8.12	6.71	5.52
Time of Flight, sec	0.0000	0.1253	0.2620	0.4117	5762	0.7574
Path, inches — 100 yds	-1.5	0.0	-5.1	-18.2	-40.7	-74.8
Relative to ZERO RANGE 200 yds	-1.5	2.6	0.0	-10.5	-30.5	-62.0
Line of Sight — 300 yds	-1.5	6.1	7.0	0.0	-16.5	-44.5
Velocity, ft/sec	2400	2199	2008	1828	1659	1504
Energy, ft/lbs per grain	12.79	10.74	8.95	7.42	6.11	5.02
Time of Flight, sec	0.0000	0.1306	0.2733	0.4299	0.6022	0.7923
Path, inches — 100 yds	-1.5	0.0	-5.7	-20.1	-44.8	-82.3
Relative to ZERO RANGE 200 yds	-1.5	2.9	0.0	-11.5	-33.4	-68.0
Line of Sight — 300 yds	-1.5	6.7	7.7	0.0	-18.1	-48.9
Velocity, ft/sec	2300	2104	1918	1743	1581	1433
Energy, ft/lbs per grain	11.74	9.83	8.17	6.74	5.55	4.56
Time of Flight, sec	0.0000	0.1364	0.2857	0.4498	0.6306	0.8301
Path, inches — 100 yds	-1.5	0.0	-6.4	-22.2	-49.6	-90.8
Relative to ZERO RANGE 200 yds	-1.5	3.2	0.0	-12.7	-36.8	-74.9
Line of Sight — 300 yds	-1.5	7.4	8.4	0.0	-19.9	-53.8
Velocity, ft/sec	2200	2009	1828	1660	1504	1364
Energy, ft/lbs per grain	10.75	8.96	7.42	6.12	5.02	4.13
Time of Flight, sec	0.0000	0.1427	0.2992	0.4715	0.6615	0.8710
Path, inches — 100 yds	-1.5	0.0	-7.1	-24.7	-54.9	-100.6
Relative to ZERO RANGE 200 yds	-1.5	3.6	0.0	-14.0	-40.7	-82.7
Line of Sight — 300 yds	-1.5	8.2	9.3	0.0	-22.0	-59.4

long range tables

Exterior Ballistic Table for Ballistic Coefficient 0.42

		Muzzle	100 yds	200 yds	300 yds	400 yds	500 yds
Velocity, ft/sec		2100	1914	1740	1577	1430	1299
Energy, ft/lbs per grain		9.79	8.13	6.72	5.52	4.54	3.75
Time of Flight, sec		0.0000	0.1496	0.3141	0.4952	0.6951	0.9155
Path, inches	100 yds	-1.5	0.0	-8.0	-27.6	-61.1	-111.7
Relative to	200 yds	-1.5	4.0	0.0	-15.5	-45.1	-91.7
Line of Sight ZERO RANGE	300 yds	-1.5	9.2	10.4	0.0	-24.4	-65.8
Velocity, ft/sec		2000	1820	1652	1497	1358	1237
Energy, ft/lbs per grain		8.88	7.35	6.06	4.98	4.09	3.40
Time of Flight, sec		0.0000	0.1573	0.3303	0.5212	0.7318	0.9635
Path, inches	100 yds	-1.5	0.0	-9.0	-30.8	-68.2	-124.5
Relative to	200 yds	-1.5	4.5	0.0	-17.3	-50.1	-101.9
Line of Sight ZERO RANGE	300 yds	-1.5	10.3	11.5	0.0	-27.1	-73.1

Exterior Ballistic Table for Ballistic Coefficient 0.43

		Muzzle	100 yds	200 yds	300 yds	400 yds	500 yds
Velocity, ft/sec		3300	3060	2833	2617	2411	2215
Energy, ft/lbs per grain		24.18	20.79	17.82	15.20	12.91	10.89
Time of Flight, sec		0.0000	0.0944	0.1963	0.3065	0.4259	0.5558
Path, inches	100 yds	-1.5	0.0	-2.2	-8.8	-20.4	-38.1
Relative to	200 yds	-1.5	1.1	0.0	-5.4	-16.0	-32.5
Line of Sight ZERO RANGE	300 yds	-1.5	2.9	3.6	0.0	8.7	-23.4
Velocity, ft/sec		3200	2965	2743	2532	2330	2137
Energy, ft/lbs per grain		22.73	19.52	16.70	14.23	12.05	10.14
Time of Flight, sec		0.0000	0.0974	0.2026	0.3164	0.4400	0.5744
Path, inches	100 yds	-1.5	0.0	-2.5	-9.5	-22.1	-41.0
Relative to	200 yds	-1.5	1.2	0.0	-5.9	-1.2	-34.9
Line of Sight ZERO RANGE	300 yds	-1.5	3.2	3.9	0.0	-9.3	-25.1
Velocity, ft/sec		3100	2871	2653	2446	2248	2059
Energy, ft/lbs per grain		21.33	18.30	15.63	13.28	11.22	9.41
Time of Flight, sec		0.0000	0.1006	0.2093	0.3270	0.4550	0.5945
Path, inches	100 yds	-1.5	0.0	-2.7	-10.4	-23.9	-44.3
Relative to	200 yds	-1.5	1.4	0.0	-6.3	-18.4	-37.5
Line of Sight ZERO RANGE	300 yds	-1.5	3.5	4.2	0.0	-10.0	-27.0
Velocity, ft/sec		3000	2776	2563	2360	2165	1980
Energy, ft/lbs per grain		19.98	17.11	14.58	12.36	10.41	8.70
Time of Flight, sec		0.0000	0.1040	0.2164	0.3384	0.4712	0.6160
Path, inches	100 yds	-1.5	0.0	-3.0	-11.3	-25.9	-47.9
Relative to	200 yds	-1.5	1.5	0.0	-6.8	-19.9	-40.4
Line of Sight ZERO RANGE	300 yds	-1.5	3.8	4.5	0.0	-10.8	-29.0
Velocity, ft/sec		2900	2681	2472	2273	2083	1902
Energy, ft/lbs per grain		18.67	15.96	13.57	11.47	9.63	8.03
Time of Flight, sec		0.0000	0.1076	0.2241	0.3507	0.4886	0.6393
Path, inches	100 yds	-1.5	0.0	-3.3	-12.4	-28.2	-52.0
Relative to	200 yds	-1.5	1.7	0.0	-7.4	-21.5	-43.6
Line of Sight ZERO RANGE	300 yds	-1.5	4.1	4.9	0.0	-11.7	-31.4

long range tables

Exterior Ballistic Table for Ballistic Coefficient 0.43

		Muzzle	100 yds	200 yds	300 yds	400 yds	500 yds
Velocity, ft/sec		2800	2586	2381	2186	2000	1824
Energy, ft/lbs per grain		17.41	14.85	12.59	10.61	8.88	7.39
Time of Flight, sec		0.0000	0.1115	0.2324	0.3639	0.5075	0.6644
Path, inches	100 yds	-1.5	0.0	-3.7	-13.6	-30.7	-56.6
Relative to	200 yds	-1.5	1.9	0.0	-8.0	-23.3	-47.3
Line of Sight (ZERO RANGE)	300 yds	-1.5	4.5	5.3	0.0	-12.6	-34.0
Velocity, ft/sec		2700	2490	2290	2099	1918	1747
Energy, ft/lbs per grain		16.18	13.76	11.64	9.78	8.17	6.78
Time of Flight, sec		0.0000	0.1157	0.2413	0.3781	0.5277	0.6916
Path, inches	100 yds	-1.5	0.0	-4.1	-14.9	-33.6	-61.7
Relative to	200 yds	-1.5	2.1	0.0	-8.7	-25.3	-51.4
Line of Sight (ZERO RANGE)	300 yds	-1.5	5.0	5.8	0.0	-13.7	-36.9
Velocity, ft/sec		2600	2395	2199	2012	1836	1670
Energy, ft/lbs per grain		15.01	12.73	10.74	8.99	7.48	6.19
Time of Flight, sec		0.0000	0.1202	0.2510	0.3936	0.5497	0.7210
Path, inches	100 yds	-1.5	0.0	-4.6	-16.4	-36.7	-67.5
Relative to	200 yds	-1.5	2.3	0.0	-9.5	-27.6	-56.0
Line of Sight (ZERO RANGE)	300 yds	-1.5	5.5	6.3	0.0	-14.9	-40.2
Velocity, ft/sec		2500	2299	2108	1926	1754	1595
Energy, ft/lbs per grain		13..88	11.73	9.87	8.24	6.83	5.65
Time of Flight, sec		0.0000	0.1251	0.2614	0.4103	0.5735	0.7529
Path, inches	100 yds	-1.5	0.0	-5.1	-18.0	-40.4	-74.0
Relative to	200 yds	-1.5	2.5	0.0	-10.4	-30.2	-61.3
Line of Sight (ZERO RANGE)	300 yds	-1.5	6.0	6.9	0.0	-16.3	-44.0
Velocity, ft/sec		2400	2204	2017	1840	1674	1521
Energy, ft/lbs per grain		12.79	10.78	9.03	7.52	6.22	5.14
Time of Flight, sec		0.0000	0.1304	0.2727	0.4285	0.5994	0.7875
Path, inches	100 yds	-1.5	0.0	-5.7	-19.9	-44.5	-81.4
Relative to	200 yds	-1.5	2.8	0.0	-11.4	-33.1	-67.3
Line of Sight (ZERO RANGE)	300 yds	-1.5	6.6	7.6	0.0	-17.9	-48.2
Velocity, ft/sec		2300	2109	1927	1755	1595	1449
Energy, ft/lbs per grain		11.74	9.87	8.24	6.84	5.65	4.66
Time of Flight, sec		0.0000	0.1362	0.2851	0.4483	0.6276	0.8250
Path, inches	100 yds	-1.5	0.0	-6.3	-22.1	-49.1	-89.9
Relative to	200 yds	-1.5	3.2	0.0	-12.6	-36.4	-74.0
Line of Sight (ZERO RANGE)	300 yds	-1.5	7.4	8.4	0.0	-19.7	-53.1

Exterior Ballistic Table for Ballistic Coefficient 0.44

		Muzzle	100 yds	200 yds	300 yds	400 yds	500 yds
Velocity, ft/sec		3200	2971	2753	2546	2348	2158
Energy, ft/lbs per grain		22.73	19.60	16.83	14.39	12.24	10.34
Time of Flight, sec		0.0000	0.0973	0.2022	0.3155	0.4383	0.5715
Path, inches	100 yds	-1.5	0.0	-2.4	-9.5	21.9	-40.6
Relative to	200 yds	-1.5	1.2	0.0	-5.8	-17.0	-34.5
Line of Sight (ZERO RANGE)	300 yds	-1.5	3.2	3.9	0.0	-9.3	-24.8

Exterior Ballistic Table for Ballistic Coefficient 0.44

				RANGE		
	Muzzle	100 yds	200 yds	300 yds	400 yds	500 yds
Velocity, ft/sec	3100	2876	2663	2460	2265	2080
Energy, ft/lbs per grain	21.33	18.36	15.74	13.43	11.39	9.60
Time of Flight, sec	0.0000	0.1005	0.2089	0.3261	0.4532	0.5914
Path, inches — 100 yds	-1.5	0.0	-2.7	-10.3	-23.7	-43.9
Relative to ZERO RANGE 200 yds	-1.5	1.4	0.0	-6.3	-18.3	-37.1
Line of Sight — 300 yds	-1.5	3.4	4.2	0.0	-9.9	-26.7
Velocity, ft/sec	3000	2781	2572	2373	2183	2001
Energy, ft/lbs per grain	19.98	17.17	14.69	12.50	10.58	8.89
Time of Flight, sec	0.0000	0.1039	0.2160	0.3375	0.4693	0.6128
Path, inches — 100 yds	-1.5	0.0	-3.0	-11.3	-25.7	-47.5
Relative to ZERO RANGE 200 yds	-1.5	1.5	0.0	-6.8	-19.7	-40.0
Line of Sight — 300 yds	-1.5	3.8	4.5	0.0	-10.7	-28.7
Velocity, ft/sec	2900	2686	2482	2286	2100	1922
Energy, ft/lbs per grain	18.67	16.02	13.68	11.60	9.79	8.20
Time of Flight, sec	0.0000	0.1075	0.2237	0.3497	0.4866	0.6359
Path, inches — 100 yds	-1.5	0.0	-3.3	-12.3	-28.0	-51.5
Relative to ZERO RANGE 200 yds	-1.5	1.7	0.0	-7.3	-21.3	-43.2
Line of Sight — 300 yds	-1.5	4.1	4.9	0.0	-11.5	-31.0
Velocity, ft/sec	2800	2591	2390	2199	2017	1844
Energy, ft/lbs per grain	17.41	14.90	12.68	10.74	9.03	7.55
Time of Flight, sec	0.0000	0.1114	0.2320	0.3628	0.5053	0.6609
Path, inches — 100 yds	-1.5	0.0	-3.7	-13.5	-30.5	-56.0
Relative to ZERO RANGE 200 yds	-1.5	1.8	0.0	-7.9	-23.1	-46.8
Line of Sight — 300 yds	-1.5	4.5	5.3	0.0	-12.5	-33.6
Velocity, ft/sec	2700	2465	2299	2112	1934	1766
Energy, ft/lbs per grain	16.18	13.82	11.73	9.90	8.30	6.92
Time of Flight, sec	0.0000	0.1156	0.2408	0.3770	0.5254	0.6878
Path, inches — 100 yds	-1.5	0.0	-4.1	-14.8	-33.3	-61.1
Relative to ZERO RANGE 200 yds	1.5	2.0	0.0	-8.6	-25.1	-50.9
Line of Sight — 300 yds	-1.5	4.9	5.8	0.0	-13.6	-36.5
Velocity, ft/sec	2600	2400	2208	2025	1851	1688
Energy, ft/lbs per grain	15.01	12.79	10.82	9.10	7.61	6.33
Time of Flight, sec	0.0000	0.1201	0.2505	0.3924	0.5473	0.7170
Path, inches — 100 yds	-1.5	0.0	-4.6	-16.3	-36.5	-66.8
Relative to ZERO RANGE 200 yds	-1.5	2.3	0.0	-9.4	-27.4	-55.4
Line of Sight — 300 yds	-1.5	5.4	6.3	0.0	-14.8	-39.7
Velocity, ft/sec	2500	2304	2116	1938	1770	1612
Energy, ft/lbs per grain	13.88	11.79	9.94	8.34	6.96	5.77
Time of Flight, sec	0.0000	0.1250	0.2609	0.4090	0.5710	0.7487
Path, inches — 100 yds	-1.5	0.0	-5.1	-17.9	-40.0	-73.3
Relative to ZERO RANGE 200 yds	-1.5	2.5	0.0	-10.3	-29.9	-60.6
Line of Sight — 300 yds	-1.5	6.0	6.9	0.0	-16.2	-43.4
Velocity, ft/sec	2400	2208	2025	1852	1689	1538
Energy, ft/lbs per grain	12.79	10.82	9.10	7.61	6.33	5.25
Time of Flight, sec	0.0000	0.1303	0.2722	0.4271	0.5968	0.7830
Path, inches — 100 yds	-1.5	0.0	-5.6	-19.8	-44.1	-80.6
Relative to ZERO RANGE 200 yds	-1.5	2.8	0.0	-11.3	-32.8	-66.5
Line of Sight — 300 yds	-1.5	6.6	7.5	0.0	-17.7	-47.6

long range tables

Exterior Ballistic Table for Ballistic Coefficient 0.44

		Muzzle	100 yds	200 yds	300 yds	400 yds	500 yds
Velocity, ft/sec		2300	2113	1935	1765	1609	1465
Energy, ft/lbs per grain		11.74	9.91	8.31	6.92	5.75	4.76
Time of Flight, sec		0.0000	0.1361	0.2845	0.4468	0.6248	0.8203
Path, inches	100 yds	-1.5	0.0	-6.3	-21.9	-48.7	-89.0
Relative to ZERO RANGE	200 yds	-1.5	3.2	0.0	-12.5	-36.1	-73.2
Line of Sight	300 yds	-1.5	7.3	8.3	0.0	-19.5	-52.4
Velocity, ft/sec		2200	2017	1844	1682	1531	1394
Energy, ft/lbs per grain		10.75	9.03	7.55	6.28	5.20	4.31
Time of Flight, sec		0.0000	0.1424	0.2979	0.4683	0.6553	0.8607
Path, inches	100 yds	-1.5	0.0	-7.1	-24.4	-54.0	-98.5
Relative to ZERO RANGE	200 yds	-1.5	3.5	0.0	-13.8	-39.9	-80.8
Line of Sight	300 yds	-1.5	8.1	9.2	0.0	-21.5	-57.9
Velocity, ft/sec		2100	1922	1755	1599	1455	1327
Energy, ft/lbs per grain		9.79	8.20	6.84	5.68	4.70	3.91
Time of Flight, sec		0.0000	0.1493	0.3127	0.4918	0.6886	0.9046
Path, inches	100 yds	-1.5	0.0	-7.9	-27.2	-60.1	-109.4
Relative to ZERO RANGE	200 yds	-1.5	4.0	0.0	-15.3	-44.2	-89.6
Line of Sight	300 yds	-1.5	9.1	10.2	0.0	-23.8	-64.1
Velocity, ft/sec		2000	1828	1666	1517	1382	1263
Energy, ft/lbs per grain		8.88	7.42	6.16	5.11	4.24	3.54
Time of Flight, sec		0.0000	0.1569	0.3288	0.5176	0.7249	0.9522
Path, inches	100 yds	-1.5	0.0	-8.9	-30.4	-67.0	-121.9
Relative to ZERO RANGE	200 yds	-1.5	4.5	0.0	-17.0	-49.2	-99.6
Line of Sight	300 yds	-1.5	10.1	11.3	0.0	-26.5	-71.2

Exterior Ballistic Table for Ballistic Coefficient 0.45

		Muzzle	100 yds	200 yds	300 yds	400 yds	500 yds
Velocity, ft/sec		2900	2691	2490	2299	2116	1941
Energy, ft/lbs per grain		18.67	16.08	13.76	11.73	9.94	8.36
Time of Flight, sec		0.0000	0.1074	0.2233	0.3487	0.4847	0.6327
Path, inches	100 yds	-1.5	0.0	-3.3	-12.2	-27.8	-51.1
Relative to ZERO RANGE	200 yds	-1.5	1.7	0.0	-7.3	-21.1	-42.8
Line of Sight	300 yds	-1.5	4.1	4.8	0.0	-11.4	-30.7
Velocity, ft/sec		2800	2595	2399	2212	2033	1862
Energy, ft/lbs per grain		17.41	14.95	12.78	10.86	9.18	7.70
Time of Flight, sec		0.0000	0.1113	0.2315	0.3618	0.5033	0.6575
Path, inches	100 yds	-1.5	0.0	-3.7	-13.4	-30.2	-55.5
Relative to ZERO RANGE	200 yds	-1.5	1.8	0.0	-7.9	-22.9	-46.3
Line of Sight	300 yds	-1.5	4.5	5.3	0.0	-12.4	-33.2
Velocity, ft/sec		2700	2500	2308	2124	1949	1784
Energy, ft/lbs per grain		16.18	13.88	11.83	10.02	8.43	7.07
Time of Flight, sec		0.0000	0.1155	0.2404	0.3759	0.5233	0.6842
Path, inches	100 yds	-1.5	0.0	-4.1	-14.7	-33.0	-60.5
Relative to ZERO RANGE	200 yds	-1.5	2.0	0.0	-8.6	-24.9	-50.4
Line of Sight	300 yds	-1.5	4.9	5.7	0.0	-13.4	-36.1

Exterior Ballistic Table for Ballistic Coefficient 0.45

		Muzzle	100 yds	200 yds	300 yds	400 yds	500 yds
Velocity, ft/sec		2600	2404	2216	2037	1866	1706
Energy, ft/lbs per grain		15.01	12.83	10.90	9.21	7.73	6.46
Time of Flight, sec		0.0000	0.1200	0.2500	0.3912	0.5451	0.7132
Path, inches	100 yds	-1.5	0.0	-4.5	-16.2	-36.2	-66.2
Relative to	200 yds	-1.5	2.3	0.0	-9.4	-27.1	-54.9
Line of Sight ZERO RANGE	300 yds	-1.5	5.4	6.2	0.0	-14.6	-39.3
Velocity, ft/sec		2500	2308	2125	1950	1784	1629
Energy, ft/lbs per grain		13.88	11.83	10.02	8.44	7.07	5.89
Time of Flight, sec		0.0000	0.1249	0.2604	0.4078	0.5686	0.7447
Path, inches	100 yds	-1.5	0.0	-5.0	-17.8	-39.7	-72.6
Relative to	200 yds	-1.5	2.5	0.0	-10.2	-29.6	-60.0
Line of Sight ZERO RANGE	300 yds	-1.5	5.6	6.8	0.0	-16.0	-42.9
Velocity, ft/sec		2400	2212	2033	1863	1703	1554
Energy, ft/lbs per grain		12.79	10.86	9.18	7.71	6.44	5.36
Time of Flight, sec		0.0000	0.1302	0.2716	0.4258	0.5943	0.7787
Path, inches	100 yds	-1.5	0.0	-5.6	-19.7	-43.8	-79.9
Relative to	200 yds	-1.5	2.8	0.0	-11.2	-32.5	-65.8
Line of Sight ZERO RANGE	300 yds	-1.5	6.6	7.5	0.0	-17.5	-47.1
Velocity, ft/sec		2300	2117	1942	1777	1623	1480
Energy, ft/lbs per grain		11.74	9.95	8.37	7.01	5.85	4.86
Time of Flight, sec		0.0000	0.1360	0.2839	0.4454	0.6221	0.8158
Path, inches	100 yds	-1.5	0.0	-6.3	-21.8	-48.3	-88.1
Relative to	200 yds	-1.5	3.1	0.0	-12.4	-35.8	-72.4
Line of Sight ZERO RANGE	300 yds	-1.5	7.3	8.3	0.0	-19.3	-51.8
Velocity, ft/sec		2200	2021	1852	1692	1544	1409
Energy, ft/lbs per grain		10.75	9.07	7.61	6.36	5.29	4.41
Time of Flight, sec		0.0000	0.1423	0.2973	0.4668	0.6525	0.8560
Path, inches	100 yds	-1.5	0.0	-7.0	-24.2	-53.6	-97.6
Relative to	200 yds	-1.5	3.5	0.0	-13.7	-39.5	-80.0
Line of Sight ZERO RANGE	300 yds	-1.5	8.1	9.1	0.0	-21.3	-57.2
Velocity, ft/sec		2100	1926	1762	1609	1468	1340
Energy, ft/lbs per grain		9.79	8.24	6.89	5.75	4.78	3.99
Time of Flight, sec		0.0000	0.1492	0.3120	0.4902	0.6856	0.8996
Path, inches	100 yds	-1.5	0.0	-7.9	-27.0	-59.6	-108.4
Relative to	200 yds	-1.5	3.9	0.0	-15.2	-43.8	-88.6
Line of Sight ZERO RANGE	300 yds	-1.5	9.0	10.1	0.0	-23.6	-63.3
Velocity, ft/sec		2000	1832	1673	1527	1393	1275
Energy, ft/lbs per grain		8.88	7.45	6.21	5.18	4.31	3.61
Time of Flight, sec		0.0000	0.1568	0.3282	0.5159	0.7217	0.9470
Path, inches	100 yds	-1.5	0.0	-8.9	-30.2	-66.5	-120.8
Relative to	200 yds	-1.5	4.4	0.0	-16.9	-48.7	-98.5
Line of Sight ZERO RANGE	300 yds	-1.5	10.1	11.3	0.0	-26.2	-70.4
Velocity, ft/sec		1900	1737	1586	1447	1322	1214
Energy, ft/lbs per grain		8.01	6.70	5.58	4.65	3.88	3.27
Time of Flight, sec		0.0000	0.1651	0.3459	0.5441	0.7612	0.9983
Path, inches	100 yds	-1.5	0.0	-10.0	-34.0	-74.5	-135.0
Relative to	200 yds	-1.5	5.0	0.0	-18.9	-54.4	-109.9
Line of Sight ZERO RANGE	300 yds	-1.5	11.3	12.6	0.0	-29.2	-78.4

Exterior Ballistic Table for Ballistic Coefficient 0.46

		Muzzle	100 yds	200 yds	300 yds	400 yds	500 yds
				RANGE			
Velocity, ft/sec		3300	3075	2862	2659	2464	2278
Energy, ft/lbs per grain		24.18	20.99	18.18	15.70	13.48	11.52
Time of Flight, sec		0.0000	0.0942	0.1953	0.3041	0.4213	0.5479
Path, inches	100 yds	-1.5	0.0	-2.2	-8.6	-20.0	-37.1
Relative to	200 yds	-1.5	1.1	0.0	-5.3	-15.6	-31.6
Line of Sight ZERO RANGE	300 yds	-1.5	2.9	3.6	0.0	-8.5	-22.7
Velocity, ft/sec		3200	2980	2772	2572	2382	2199
Energy, ft/lbs per grain		22.73	19.72	17.06	14.69	12.60	10.74
Time of Flight, sec		0.0000	0.0972	0.2015	0.3139	0.4351	0.5662
Path, inches	100 yds	-1.5	0.0	-2.4	-9.4	-21.6	-39.9
Relative to	200 yds	-1.5	1.2	0.0	-5.7	-16.7	-33.9
Line of Sight ZERO RANGE	300 yds	-1.5	3.1	3.8	0.0	-9.1	-24.3
Velocity, ft/sec		3100	2885	2681	2486	2299	2119
Energy, ft/lbs per grain		21.33	18.48	15.96	13.72	11.73	9.97
Time of Flight, sec		0.0000	0.1003	0.2082	0.3244	0.4499	0.5858
Path, inches	100 yds	-1.5	0.0	-2.7	-10.2	-23.4	-43.1
Relative to	200 yds	-1.5	1.3	0.0	-6.2	-18.0	-36.4
Line of Sight ZERO RANGE	300 yds	-1.5	3.4	4.1	0.0	-9.8	-26.1
Velocity, ft/sec		3000	2790	2590	2399	2215	2040
Energy, ft/lbs per grain		19.98	17.28	14.89	12.78	10.89	9.24
Time of Flight, sec		0.0000	0.1037	0.2153	0.3357	0.4658	0.6070
Path, inches	100 yds	-1.5	0.0	-3.0	-11.1	-25.4	-46.7
Relative to	200 yds	-1.5	1.5	0.0	-6.7	-19.4	-39.2
Line of Sight ZERO RANGE	300 yds	-1.5	3.7	4.5	0.0	-10.5	-28.1
Velocity, ft/sec		2900	2695	2499	2311	2132	1960
Energy, ft/lbs per grain		18.67	16.12	13.86	11.86	10.09	8.53
Time of Flight, sec		0.0000	0.1073	0.2229	0.3478	0.4829	0.6297
Path, inches	100 yds	-1.5	0.0	-3.3	-12.2	-27.6	-50.6
Relative to	200 yds	-1.5	1.6	0.0	-7.2	-21.0	-42.4
Line of Sight ZERO RANGE	300 yds	-1.5	4.1	4.8	0.0	-11.3	-30.3
Velocity, ft/sec		2800	2599	2408	2224	2048	1880
Energy, ft/lbs per grain		17.41	15.00	12.87	10.98	9.31	7.85
Time of Flight, sec		0.0000	0.1112	0.2311	0.3608	0.5014	0.6543
Path, inches	100 yds	-1.5	0.0	-3.7	-13.3	-30.0	-55.0
Relative to	200 yds	-1.5	1.8	0.0	-7.8	-22.7	-45.9
Line of Sight ZERO RANGE	300 yds	-1.5	4.4	5.2	0.0	-12.3	-32.9
Velocity, ft/sec		2700	2504	2316	2136	1964	1801
Energy, ft/lbs per grain		16.18	13.92	11.91	10.13	8.56	7.20
Time of Flight, sec		0.0000	0.1154	0.2400	0.3749	0.5213	0.6809
Path, inches	100 yds	-1.5	0.0	-4.1	-14.6	-32.8	-60.0
Relative to	200 yds	-1.5	2.0	0.0	-8.5	-24.7	-49.9
Line of Sight ZERO RANGE	300 yds	-1.5	4.9	5.7	0.0	-13.3	-35.7
Velocity, ft/sec		2600	2408	2224	2048	1881	1723
Energy, ft/lbs per grain		15.01	12.87	10.98	9.31	7.85	6.59
Time of Flight, sec		0.0000	0.1199	0.2495	0.3901	0.5430	0.7096
Path, inches	100 yds	-1.5	0.0	-4.5	-16.1	-35.9	-65.6
Relative to	200 yds	-1.5	2.3	0.0	-9.3	-26.9	-54.4
Line of Sight ZERO RANGE	300 yds	-1.5	5.4	6.2	0.0	-14.5	-38.9

Exterior Ballistic Table for Ballistic Coefficient 0.46

	Muzzle	100 yds	200 yds	300 yds	400 yds	500 yds
RANGE						
Velocity, ft/sec	2500	2312	2132	1961	1798	1646
Energy, ft/lbs per grain	13.88	11.87	10.09	8.54	7.18	6.01
Time of Flight, sec	0.0000	0.1248	0.2599	0.4066	0.5664	0.7408
Path, inches — 100 yds	-1.5	0.0	-5.0	-17.7	-39.4	-72.0
Relative to ZERO RANGE 200 yds	-1.5	2.5	0.0	-10.2	-29.4	-59.4
Line of Sight 300 yds	-1.5	5.9	6.8	0.0	-15.8	-42.5
Velocity, ft/sec	2400	2216	2041	1874	1716	1570
Energy, ft/lbs per grain	12.79	10.90	9.25	7.80	6.54	5.47
Time of Flight, sec	0.0000	0.1301	0.2711	0.4246	0.5919	0.7747
Path, inches — 100 yds	-1.5	0.0	-5.6	-19.6	-43.4	-79.1
Relative to ZERO RANGE 200 yds	-1.5	2.8	0.0	-11.2	-32.2	-65.2
Line of Sight 300 yds	-1.5	6.5	7.4	0.0	-17.4	-46.6
Velocity, ft/sec	2300	2121	1950	1788	1636	1495
Energy, ft/lbs per grain	11.74	9.99	8.44	7.10	5.94	4.96
Time of Flight, sec	0.0000	0.1358	0.2834	0.4441	0.6196	0.8115
Path, inches — 100 yds	-1.5	0.0	-6.2	-21.7	-48.0	-87.3
Relative to ZERO RANGE 200 yds	-1.5	3.1	0.0	-12.3	-35.5	-71.7
Line of Sight 300 yds	-1.5	7.2	8.2	0.0	-19.1	-51.2
Velocity, ft/sec	2200	2025	1859	1702	1557	1423
Energy, ft/lbs per grain	10.75	9.10	7.67	6.43	5.38	4.50
Time of Flight, sec	0.0000	0.1421	0.2968	0.4654	0.6498	0.8514
Path, inches — 100 yds	-1.5	0.0	-7.0	-24.1	-53.2	-96.7
Relative to ZERO RANGE 200 yds	-1.5	3.5	0.0	-13.6	-39.2	-79.2
Line of Sight 300 yds	-1.5	8.0	9.1	0.0	-21.I	-56.5
Velocity, ft/sec	2100	1930	1769	1618	1479	1353
Energy, ft/lbs per grain	9.79	8.27	6.95	5.81	4.86	4.06
Time of Flight, sec	0.0000	0.1490	0.3114	0.4887	0.6827	0.8949
Path, inches — 100 yds	-1.5	0.0	-7.9	-26.8	-59.1	-107.4
Relative to ZERO RANGE 200 yds	-1.5	3.9	0.0	-15.1	-43.4	-87.7
Line of Sight 300 yds	-1.5	8.9	10.0	0.0	-23.3	-62.6
Velocity, ft/sec	2000	1835	1680	1536	1404	1287
Energy, ft/lbs per grain	8.88	7.48	6.27	5.24	4.38	3.68
Time of Flight, sec	0.0000	0.1566	0.3275	0.5143	0.7187	0.9420
Path, inches — 100 yds	-1.5	0.0	-8.8	-30.0	-66.0	-119.6
Relative to ZERO RANGE 200 yds	-1.5	4.4	0.0	-16.8	-48.3	-97.5
Line of Sight 300 yds	-1.5	10.0	11.2	0.0	-26.0	-69.6
Velocity, ft/sec	1900	1741	1592	1455	1332	1225
Energy, ft/lbs per grain	8.01	6.73	5.63	4.70	3.94	3.33
Time of Flight, sec	0.0000	0.1650	0.3452	0.5424	0.7580	0.9931
Path, inches — 100 yds	-1.5	0.0	-10.0	-33.7	-73.9	-133.8
Relative to ZERO RANGE 200 yds	-1.5	5.0	0.0	-18.7	-53.9	-108.8
Line of Sight 300 yds	-1.5	11.2	12.5	0.0	-28.9	-77.5

long range tables

Exterior Ballistic Table for Ballistic Coefficient 0.48

	Muzzle	100 yds	200 yds	300 yds	400 yds	500 yds
Velocity, ft/sec	3300	3084	2879	2683	2496	2316
Energy, ft/lbs per grain	24.18	21.12	18.40	15.98	13.83	11.91
Time of Flight, sec	0.0000	0.0940	0.1947	0.3027	0.4186	0.5434
Path, inches — ZERO RANGE 100 yds	-1.5	0.0	-2.2	-8.5	-19.7	-36.5
Relative to — ZERO RANGE 200 yds	-1.5	1.1	0.0	-5.3	-15.4	-31.1
Line of Sight — ZERO RANGE 300 yds	-1.5	2.8	3.5	0.0	-8.4	-22.3
Velocity, ft/sec	3200	2989	2789	2597	2413	2236
Energy, ft/lbs per grain	22.73	19.83	17.27	14.97	12.93	11.10
Time of Flight, sec	0.0000	0.0970	0.2009	0.3124	0.4323	0.5614
Path, inches — ZERO RANGE 100 yds	-1.5	0.0	-2.4	-9.3	-21.3	-39.3
Relative to — ZERO RANGE 200 yds	-1.5	1.2	0.0	-5.7	-16.5	-33.3
Line of Sight — ZERO RANGE 300 yds	-1.5	3.1	3.8	0.0	-8.9	-23.9
Velocity, ft/sec	3100	2894	2698	2510	2329	2156
Energy, ft/lbs per grain	21.33	18.59	16.16	13.99	12.04	10.32
Time of Flight, sec	0.0000	0.1002	0.2075	0.3228	0.4469	0.5808
Path, inches — ZERO RANGE 100 yds	-1.5	0.0	-2.7	-10.1	-23.1	-42.5
Relative to — ZERO RANGE 200 yds	-1.5	1.3	0.0	-6.1	-17.8	-35.8
Line of Sight — ZERO RANGE 300 yds	-1.5	3.4	4.1	0.0	-9.6	-25.6
Velocity, ft/sec	3000	2799	2607	2422	2245	2076
Energy, ft/lbs per grain	19.98	17.39	15.09	13.02	11.19	9.57
Time of Flight, sec	0.0000	0.1035	0.2146	0.3340	0.4627	0.6016
Path, inches — ZERO RANGE 100 yds	-1.5	0.0	-2.9	-11.0	-25.0	-45.9
Relative to — ZERO RANGE 200 yds	-1.5	1.5	0.0	-6.6	-19.1	-38.6
Line of Sight — ZERO RANGE 300 yds	-1.5	3.7	4.4	0.0	-10.3	-27.6
Velocity, ft/sec	2900	2703	2515	2334	2161	1995
Energy, ft/lbs per grain	18.67	16.22	14.04	12.09	10.37	8.84
Time of Flight, sec	0.0000	0.1072	0.2222	0.3460	0.4796	0.6241
Path, inches — ZERO RANGE 100 yds	-1.5	0.0	-3.3	-12.0	-27.2	-49.8
Relative to — ZERO RANGE 200 yds	-1.5	1.6	0.0	-7.1	-20.7	-41.7
Line of Sight — ZERO RANGE 300 yds	-1.5	4.0	4.8	0.0	-11.2	-29.8
Velocity, ft/sec	2800	2608	2423	2246	2077	1915
Energy, ft/lbs per grain	17.41	15.10	13.03	11.20	9.58	8.14
Time of Flight, sec	0.0000	0.1110	0.2304	0.3590	0.4979	0.6484
Path, inches — ZERO RANGE 100 yds	-1.5	0.0	-3.6	-13.2	-29.6	-54.2
Relative to — ZERO RANGE 200 yds	-1.5	1.8	0.0	-7.7	-22.4	-45.1
Line of Sight — ZERO RANGE 300 yds	-1.5	4.4	5.2	0.0	-12.1	-32.2
Velocity, ft/sec	2700	2512	2331	2158	1992	1834
Energy, ft/lbs per grain	16.18	14.01	12.06	10.34	8.81	7.47
Time of Flight, sec	0.0000	0.1152	0.2392	0.3729	0.5176	0.6746
Path, inches — ZERO RANGE 100 yds	-1.5	0.0	-4.0	-14.4	-32.4	-59.0
Relative to — ZERO RANGE 200 yds	-1.5	2.0	0.0	-8.4	-24.3	-49.0
Line of Sight — ZERO RANGE 300 yds	-1.5	4.8	5.6	0.0	-13.1	-35.0
Velocity, ft/sec	2600	2416	2239	2070	1908	1755
Energy, ft/lbs per grain	15.01	12.96	11.13	9.51	8.08	6.84
Time of Flight, sec	0.0000	0.1197	0.2487	0.3881	0.5390	0.7030
Path, inches — ZERO RANGE 100 yds	-1.5	0.0	-4.5	-15.9	-35.4	-64.5
Relative to — ZERO RANGE 200 yds	-1.5	2.2	0.0	-9.2	-26.5	-53.4
Line of Sight — ZERO RANGE 300 yds	-1.5	5.3	6.1	0.0	-14.3	-38.1

long range tables

			RANGE			
	Muzzle	100 yds	200 yds	300 yds	400 yds	500 yds
Velocity, ft/sec	2500	2320	2147	1982	1825	1676
Energy, ft/lbs per grain	13.88	11.95	10.23	8.72	7.39	6.24
Time of Flight, sec	0.0000	0.1246	0.2590	0.4044	0.5622	0.7338
Path, inches — 100 yds	-1.5	0.0	-5.0	-17.5	-38.9	-70.8
Relative to — ZERO RANGE 200 yds	-1.5	2.5	0.0	-10.0	-29.0	-58.3
Line of Sight — 300 yds	-1.5	5.8	6.7	0.0	-15.6	-41.6
Velocity, ft/sec	2400	2224	2055	1894	1742	1599
Energy, ft/lbs per grain	12.79	10.98	9.38	7.96	6.74	5.68
Time of Flight, sec	0.0000	0.1299	0.2702	0.4222	0.5874	0.7672
Path, inches — 100 yds	-1.5	0.0	-5.5	-19.3	-42.8	-77.8
Relative to — ZERO RANGE 200 yds	-1.5	2.8	0.0	-11.0	-31.7	-64.0
Line of Sight — 300 yds	-1.5	6.4	7.3	0.0	-17.1	-45.6
Velocity, ft/sec	2300	2128	1964	1807	1660	1524
Energy, ft/lbs per grain	11.74	10.05	8.56	7.25	6.12	5.16
Time of Flight, sec	0.0000	0.1356	0.2824	0.4416	0.6149	0.8035
Path, inches — 100 yds	-1.5	0.0	-6.2	-21.4	-47.3	-85.9
Relative to — ZERO RANGE 200 yds	-1.5	3.1	0.0	-12.1	-34.9	-70.4
Line of Sight — 300 yds	-1.5	7.1	8.1	0.0	-18.8	-50.1
Velocity, ft/sec	2200	2032	1873	1721	1580	1450
Energy, ft/lbs per grain	10.75	9.17	7.79	6.58	5.54	4.67
Time of Flight, sec	0.0000	0.1419	0.2957	0.4628	0.6447	0.8430
Path, inches — 100 yds	-1.5	0.0	-6.9	-23.8	-52.4	-95.0
Relative to — ZERO RANGE 200 yds	-1.5	3.5	0.0	-13.4	-38.6	-77.7
Line of Sight — 300 yds	-1.5	7.9	8.9	0.0	-20.7	-55.3
Velocity, ft/sec	2100	1937	1782	1637	1502	1378
Energy, ft/lbs per grain	9.79	8.33	7.05	5.95	5.01	4.22
Time of Flight, sec	0.0000	0.1488	0.3102	0.4859	0.6774	0.8860
Path, inches — 100 yds	-1.5	0.0	-7.8	-26.5	-58.3	-105.5
Relative to — ZERO RANGE 200 yds	-1.5	3.9	0.0	-14.9	-42.7	-86.1
Line of Sight — 300 yds	-1.5	8.8	9.9	0.0	-22.9	-61.3
Velocity, ft/sec	2000	1842	1693	1553	1425	1310
Energy, ft/lbs per grain	8.88	7.53	6.36	5.35	4.51	3.81
Time of Flight, sec	0.0000	0.1563	0.3263	0.5113	0.7130	0.9327
Path, inches — 100 yds	-1.5	0.0	-8.8	-29.7	-65.1	-117.6
Relative to — ZERO RANGE 200 yds	-1.5	4.4	0.0	-16.5	-47.5	-95.7
Line of Sight — 300 yds	-1.5	9.9	11.0	0.0	-25.5	-68.1
Velocity, ft/sec	1900	1747	1604	1472	1351	1246
Energy, ft/lbs per grain	8.01	6.78	5.71	4.81	4.05	3.45
Time of Flight, sec	0.0000	0.1647	0.3439	0.5392	0.7521	0.9835
Path, inches — 100 yds	-1.5	0.0	-9.9	-33.4	-72.9	-131.5
Relative to — ZERO RANGE 200 yds	-1.5	5.0	0.0	-18.5	-53.1	-106.7
Line of Sight — 300 yds	-1.5	11.1	12.3	0.0	-28.4	-75.9

long range tables

Exterior Ballistic Table for Ballistic Coefficient 0.50

	Muzzle	100 yds	200 yds	300 yds	400 yds	500 yds
			RANGE			
Velocity, ft/sec	3300	3093	2895	2706	2525	2351
Energy, ft/lbs per grain	24.18	21.24	18.61	16.26	14.15	12.27
Time of Flight, sec	0.0000	0.0939	0.1942	0.3014	0.4161	0.5392
Path, inches — ZERO RANGE 100 yds	-1.5	0.0	-2.1	-8.4	-19.5	-36.0
Relative to — 200 yds	-1.5	1.1	0.0	-5.2	-15.2	-30.6
Line of Sight — 300 yds	-1.5	2.8	3.5	0.0	-8.2	-21.9
Velocity, ft/sec	3200	2998	2804	2619	2442	2271
Energy, ft/lbs per grain	22.73	19.95	17.46	15.23	13.24	11.45
Time of Flight, sec	0.0000	0.0969	0.2004	0.3110	0.4297	0.5571
Path, inches — ZERO RANGE 100 yds	-1.5	0.0	-2.4	-9.2	-21.0	-38.8
Relative to — 200 yds	-1.5	1.2	0.0	-5.6	-16.3	-32.8
Line of Sight — 300 yds	-1.5	3.1	3.7	0.0	-8.8	-23.5
Velocity, ft/sec	3100	2902	2713	2532	2358	2190
Energy, ft/lbs per grain	21.33	18.70	16.34	14.23	12.34	10.65
Time of Flight, sec	0.0000	0.1000	0.2069	0.3214	0.4442	0.5762
Path, inches — ZERO RANGE 100 yds	-1.5	0.0	-2.6	-10.0	-22.8	-41.8
Relative to — 200 yds	-1.5	1.3	0.0	-6.0	-17.5	-35.3
Line of Sight — 300 yds	-1.5	3.3	4.0	0.0	-9.5	-25.2
Velocity, ft/sec	3000	2807	2622	2444	2273	2109
Energy, ft/lbs per grain	19.98	17.49	15.26	13.26	11.47	9.87
Time of Flight, sec	0.0000	0.1034	0.2140	0.3325	0.4598	0.5968
Path, inches — ZERO RANGE 100 yds	-1.5	0.0	-2.9	-10.9	-24.7	-45.3
Relative to — 200 yds	-1.5	1.5	0.0	-6.5	-18.9	-38.0
Line of Sight — 300 yds	-1.5	3.6	4.4	0.0	10.2	-27.1
Velocity, ft/sec	2900	2711	2530	2356	2188	2028
Energy, ft/lbs per grain	18.67	16.32	14.21	12.32	10.63	9.13
Time of Flight, sec	0.0000	0.1070	0.2216	0.3445	0.4766	0.6190
Path, inches — ZERO RANGE 100 yds	-1.5	0.0	-3.2	-11.9	-26.9	-49.1
Relative to — 200 yds	-1.5	1.6	0.0	-7.1	-20.4	-41.0
Line of Sight — 300 yds	-1.5	4.0	4.7	0.0	-11.0	-29.2
Velocity, ft/sec	2800	2615	2438	2267	2103	1946
Energy, ft/lbs per grain	17.41	15.18	13.20	11.41	9.82	8.41
Time of Flight, sec	0.0000	0.1109	0.2297	0.3573	0.4947	0.6430
Path, inches — ZERO RANGE 100 yds	-1.5	0.0	-3.6	-13.0	-29.3	-53.4
Relative to — 200 yds	-1.5	1.8	0.0	-7.7	-22.1	-44.4
Line of Sight — 300 yds	-1.5	4.3	5.1	0.0	-11.9	-31.6
Velocity, ft/sec	2700	2519	2345	2178	2018	1865
Energy, ft/lbs per grain	16.18	14.09	12.21	10.53	9.04	7.72
Time of Flight, sec	0.0000	0.1150	0.2385	0.3712	0.5143	0.6689
Path, inches — ZERO RANGE 100 yds	-1.5	0.0	-4.0	-14.3	-32.0	-58.2
Relative to — 200 yds	-1.5	2.0	0.0	-8.3	-24.0	-48.2
Line of Sight — 300 yds	-1.5	4.8	5.5	0.0	-12.9	-34.3
Velocity, ft/sec	2600	2423	2253	2090	1933	1785
Energy, ft/lbs per grain	15.01	13.03	11.27	9.70	8.30	7.07
Time of Flight, sec	0.0000	0.1195	0.2479	0.3862	0.5354	0.6970
Path, inches — ZERO RANGE 100 yds	-1.5	0.0	-4.4	-15.7	-35.0	-63.6
Relative to — 200 yds	-1.5	2.2	0.0	-9.1	-26.1	-52.5
Line of Sight — 300 yds	-1.5	5.2	6.1	0.0	-14.0	-37.4

long range tables

Exterior Ballistic Table for Ballistic Coefficient 0.50

		Muzzle	100 yds	200 yds	300 yds	400 yds	500 yds
Velocity, ft/sec		2500	2327	2161	2001	1849	1705
Energy, ft/lbs per grain		13.88	12.02	10.37	8.89	7.59	6.45
Time of Flight, sec		0.0000	0.1244	0.2582	0.4025	0.5584	0.7274
Path, inches	100 yds	-1.5	0.0	-4.9	-17.3	-38.4	-69.7
Relative to	200 yds	-1.5	2.5	0.0	-9.9	-28.5	-57.4
Line of Sight	300 yds	-1.5	5.8	6.6	0.0	-15.3	-40.8
Velocity, ft/sec		2400	2231	2068	1913	1766	1627
Energy, ft/lbs per grain		12.79	11.05	9.49	8.12	6.92	5.88
Time of Flight, sec		0.0000	0.1297	0.2693	0.4201	0.5834	0.7604
Path, inches	100 yds	-1.5	0.0	-5.5	-19.1	-42.3	-76.6
Relative to	200 yds	-1.5	2.7	0.0	-10.9	-31.3	-62.9
Line of Sight	300 yds	-1.5	6.4	7.3	0.0	-16.8	-44.7
Velocity, ft/sec		2300	2135	1977	1826	1683	1550
Energy, ft/lbs per grain		11.74	10.12	8.68	7.40	6.29	5.33
Time of Flight, sec		0.0000	0.1354	0.2814	0.4394	0.6106	0.7963
Path, inches	100 yds	-1.5	0.0	-6.1	-21.2	-46.7	-84.5
Relative to	200 yds	-1.5	3.1	0.0	-12.0	-34.4	-69.2
Line of Sight	300 yds	-1.5	7.1	8.0	0.0	-18.4	-49.2
Velocity, ft/sec		2200	2039	1885	1739	1602	1475
Energy, ft/lbs per grain		10.75	9.23	7.89	6.71	5.70	4.83
Time of Flight, sec		0.0000	0.1417	0.2947	0.4604	0.6402	0.8354
Path, inches	100 yds	-1.5	0.0	-6.9	-23.6	-51.8	-93.5
Relative to	200 yds	-1.5	3.4	0.0	-13.2	-38.0	-76.3
Line of Sight	300 yds	-1.5	7.9	8.8	0.0	-20.3	-54.3
Velocity, ft/sec		2100	1943	1794	1654	1523	1402
Energy, ft/lbs per grain		9.79	8.38	7.15	6.07	5.15	4.36
Time of Flight, sec		0.0000	0.1485	0.3092	0.4834	0.6725	0.8780
Path, inches	100 yds	-1.5	0.0	-7.7	-26.3	-57.6	-103.9
Relative to	200 yds	-1.5	3.9	0.0	-14.7	-42.1	-84.6
Line of Sight	300 yds	-1.5	8.8	9.8	0.0	-22.5	-60.1
Velocity, ft/sec		2000	1848	1704	1569	1445	1332
Energy, ft/lbs per grain		8.88	7.58	6.45	5.47	4.64	3.94
Time of Flight, sec		0.0000	0.1561	0.3251	0.5086	0.7079	0.9243
Path, inches	100 yds	-1.5	0.0	-8.7	-29.4	-64.2	-115.8
Relative to	200 yds	-1.5	4.4	0.0	-16.3	-46.8	-94.0
Line of Sight	300 yds	-1.5	9.8	10.9	0.0	-25.0	-66.8
Velocity, ft/sec		1900	1753	1615	1487	1370	1266
Energy, ft/lbs per grain		8.01	6.82	5.79	4.91	4.17	3.56
Time of Flight, sec		0.0000	0.1644	0.3427	0.5363	0.7467	0.9747
Path, inches	100 yds	-1.5	0.0	-9.8	-33.0	-72.0	-129.4
Relative to	200 yds	-1.5	4.9	0.0	-18.3	-52.3	-104.9
Line of Sight	300 yds	-1.5	11.0	12.2	0.0	-27.9	-74.4

Exterior Ballistic Table for Ballistic Coefficient 0.54

		Muzzle	100 yds	200 yds	300 yds	400 yds	500 yds
				RANGE			
Velocity, ft/sec		3100	2917	2741	2571	2408	2251
Energy, ft/lbs per grain		21.33	18.89	16.68	14.67	12.87	11.25
Time of Flight, sec		0.0000	0.0998	0.2059	0.3189	0.4395	0.5683
Path, inches	100 yds	-1.5	0.0	-2.6	-9.8	-22.3	-40.8
Relative to	200 yds	-1.5	1.3	0.0	-5.9	-17.1	-34.3
Line of Sight ZERO RANGE	300 yds	-1.5	3.3	4.0	0.0	-9.2	-24.4
Velocity, ft/sec		3000	2821	2649	2483	2323	2169
Energy, ft/lbs per grain		19.98	17.67	15.58	13.69	11.98	10.44
Time of Flight, sec		0.0000	0.1031	0.2129	0.3299	0.4548	0.5885
Path, inches	100 yds	-1.5	0.0	-2.9	-10.7	-24.2	-44.1
Relative to	200 yds	-1.5	1.4	0.0	-6.4	-18.4	-36.9
Line of Sight ZERO RANGE	300 yds	-1.5	3.6	4.3	0.0	-9.9	-26.3
Velocity, ft/sec		2900	2725	2556	2394	2237	2086
Energy, ft/lbs per grain		18.67	16.49	14.50	12.72	11.11	9.66
Time of Flight, sec		0.0000	0.1067	0.2204	0.3417	0.4713	0.6102
Path, inches	100 yds	-1.5	0.0	-3.2	-11.7	-26.3	-47.8
Relative to	200 yds	-1.5	1.6	0.0	-6.9	-19.9	-39.9
Line of Sight ZERO RANGE	300 yds	-1.5	3.9	4.6	0.0	-10.7	-28.3
Velocity, ft/sec		2800	2629	2464	2304	2151	2004
Energy, ft/lbs per grain		17.41	15.34	13.48	11.79	10.27	8.92
Time of Flight, sec		0.0000	0.1106	0.2285	0.3544	0.4891	0.6337
Path, inches	100 yds	-1.5	0.0	-3.5	-12.8	-28.6	-52.0
Relative to	200 yds	-1.5	1.8	0.0	-7.5	-21.6	-43.1
Line of Sight ZERO RANGE	300 yds	-1.5	4.3	5.0	0.0	11.6	-30.6
Velocity, ft/sec		2700	2532	2371	2215	2065	1921
Energy, ft/lbs per grain		16.18	14.23	12.48	10.89	9.47	8.19
Time of Flight, sec		0.0000	0.1147	0.2372	0.3681	0.5084	0.6590
Path, inches	100 yds	-1.5	0.0	-3.9	-14.0	-31.3	-56.7
Relative to	200 yds	-1.5	2.0	0.0	-8.2	-23.4	-46.8
Line of Sight ZERO RANGE	300 yds	-1.5	4.7	5.4	0.0	-12.5	-33.2
Velocity, ft/sec		2600	2436	2278	2125	1979	1839
Energy, ft/lbs per grain		1501	13.17	11.52	10.02	8.69	7.51
Time of Flight, sec		0.0000	0.1192	0.2466	0.3829	0.5292	0.6865
Path, inches	100 yds	-1.5	0.0	-4.4	-15.4	-34.2	-61.9
Relative to	200 yds	-1.5	2.2	0.0	-8.9	-25.5	-51.0
Line of Sight ZERO RANGE	300 yds	-1.5	5.1	5.9	0.0	-13.6	-36.2
Velocity, ft/sec		2500	2340	2185	2036	1893	1758
Energy, ft/lbs per grain		13.88	12.16	10.60	9.20	7.96	6.86
Time of Flight, sec		0.0000	0.1240	0.2567	0.3990	0.5518	0.7163
Path, inches	100 yds	-1.5	0.0	-4.9	-17.0	-37.6	-67.8
Relative to	200 yds	-1.5	2.4	0.0	-9.7	-27.8	-55.7
Line of Sight ZERO RANGE	300 yds	-1.5	5.7	6.5	0.0	-14.9	-39.5
Velocity, ft/sec		2400	2243	2092	1947	1809	1677
Energy, ft/lbs per grain		12.79	11.17	9.72	8.42	7.27	6.24
Time of Flight, sec		0.0000	0.1293	0.2678	0.4164	0.5763	0.7486
Path, inches	100 yds	-1.5	0.0	-5.4	-18.8	-41.4	-74.6
Relative to	200 yds	-1.5	2.7	0.0	-10.7	-30.5	-61.0
Line of Sight ZERO RANGE	300 yds	-1.5	6.3	7.1	0.0	-16.3	-43.2

long range tables

Exterior Ballistic Table for Ballistic Coefficient 0.54

			RANGE			
	Muzzle	100 yds	200 yds	300 yds	400 yds	500 yds
Velocity, ft/sec	2300	2147	2000	1859	1724	1598
Energy, ft/lbs per grain	11.74	10.223	8.88	7.67	6.60	5.67
Time of Flight, sec	0.0000	0.1350	0.2798	0.4355	0.6031	0.7838
Path, inches — 100 yds	-1.5	0.0	-6.1	-20.8	-45.7	-82.2
Relative to (ZERO RANGE) 200 yds	-1.5	3.0	0.0	-11.7	-33.6	-67.1
Line of Sight — 300 yds	-1.5	6.9	7.8	0.0	-17.9	-47.5
Velocity, ft/sec	2200	2051	1907	1771	1642	1521
Energy, ft/lbs per grain	10.75	9.34	8.07	6.96	5.99	5.14
Time of Flight, sec	0.0000	0.1412	0.2929	0.4562	0.3220	0.8221
Path, inches — 100 yds	-1.5	0.0	-6.8	-23.1	-50.6	-91.0
Relative to (ZERO RANGE) 200 yds	-1.5	3.4	0.0	-13.0	-37.0	-74.0
Line of Sight — 300 yds	-1.5	7.7	8.6	0.0	-19.7	-52.4
Velocity, ft/sec	2100	1955	1816	1684	1560	1445
Energy, ft/lbs per grain	9.79	8.49	7.32	6.30	5.40	4.64
Time of Flight, sec	0.0000	0.1481	0.3073	0.4789	0.6640	0.8639
Path, inches — 100 yds	-1.5	0.0	-7.6	-25.8	-56.2	-101.0
Relative to (ZERO RANGE) 200 yds	-1.5	3.8	0.0	-14.4	-41.0	-82.0
Line of Sight — 300 yds	-1.5	8.6	9.6	0.0	-21.9	-58.0
Velocity, ft/sec	2000	1859	1725	1599	1481	1372
Energy, ft/lbs per grain	8.88	7.67	6.61	5.68	4.87	4.18
Time of Flight, sec	0.0000	0.1556	0.3231	0.5039	0.6989	0.9095
Path, inches — 100 yds	-1.5	0.0	-8.6	-28.9	-62.8	-112.6
Relative to (ZERO RANGE) 200 yds	-1.5	4.3	0.0	-16.0	-45.6	-91.1
Line of Sight — 300 yds	-1.5	9.6	10.7	0.0	-24.3	-64.5
Velocity, ft/sec	1900	1764	1635	1515	1403	1303
Energy, ft/lbs per grain	8.01	6.91	5.93	5.10	4.37	3.77
Time of Flight, sec	0.0000	0.1639	0.3406	0.5313	0.7371	0.9592
Path, inches — 100 yds	-1.5	0.0	-9.7	-32.4	-70.3	-125.9
Relative to (ZERO RANGE) 200 yds	-1.5	4.8	0.0	-17.9	-50.9	-101.7
Line of Sight — 300 yds	-1.5	10.8	11.9	0.0	-27.1	-71.9

Exterior Ballistic Table for Ballistic Coefficient 0.56

			RANGE			
	Muzzle	100 yds	200 yds	300 yds	400 yds	500 yds
Velocity, ft/sec	3100	2923	2753	2589	2431	2279
Energy, ft/lbs per grain	21.33	18.97	16.83	14.88	13.12	11.53
Time of Flight, sec	0.0000	0.0997	0.2054	0.3178	0.4374	0.5648
Path, inches — 100 yds	-1.5	0.0	-2.6	-9.7	-22.1	-40.3
Relative to (ZERO RANGE) 200 yds	-1.5	1.3	0.0	-5.9	-16.9	-33.9
Line of Sight — 300 yds	-1.5	3.2	3.9	0.0	-9.1	-24.1
Velocity, ft/sec	3000	2827	2661	2500	2345	2196
Energy, ft/lbs per grain	19.98	17.74	15.72	13.88	12.21	10.71
Time of Flight, sec	0.0000	0.1030	0.2124	0.3287	0.4526	0.5848
Path, inches — 100 yds	-1.5	0.0	-2.9	-10.6	-24.0	-43.6
Relative to (ZERO RANGE) 200 yds	-1.5	1.4	0.0	-6.3	-18.3	-36.5
Line of Sight — 300 yds	-1.5	3.5	4.2	0.0	-9.8	-25.9

long range tables

Exterior Ballistic Table for Ballistic Coefficient 0.56

	Muzzle	100 yds	200 yds	300 yds	400 yds	500 yds
Velocity, ft/sec	2900	2731	2568	2411	2259	2113
Energy, ft/lbs per grain	18.67	16.56	14.64	12.91	11.33	9.91
Time of Flight, sec	0.0000	0.1066	0.2199	0.3405	0.4690	0.6063
Path, inches — Relative to Line of Sight — ZERO RANGE 100 yds	-1.5	0.0	-3.2	-11.6	-26.0	-47.3
200 yds	-1.5	1.6	0.0	-6.9	-19.7	-39.4
300 yds	-1.5	3.9	4.6	0.0	-10.6	-27.9
Velocity, ft/sec	2800	2635	2475	2321	2173	2029
Energy, ft/lbs per grain	17.41	15.41	13.60	11.96	10.48	9.14
Time of Flight, sec	0.0000	0.1105	0.2279	0.3531	0.4867	0.6296
Path, inches 100 yds	-1.5	0.0	-3.5	-12.7	-28.4	-51.4
200 yds	-1.5	1.8	0.0	-7.4	-21.3	-42.6
300 yds	-1.5	4.2	5.0	0.0	-11.4	-30.2
Velocity, ft/sec	2700	2538	2382	2231	2086	1946
Energy, ft/lbs per grain	16.18	14.30	12.60	11.05	9.66	8.41
Time of Flight, sec	0.0000	0.1146	0.2366	0.3667	0.5058	0.6547
Path, inches 100 yds	-1.5	0.0	-3.9	-13.9	-31.0	-56.0
200 yds	-1.5	2.0	0.0	-8.1	-23.2	-46.2
300 yds	-1.5	4.6	5.4	0.0	-12.4	-32.8
Velocity, ft/sec	2600	2442	2289	2141	2000	1864
Energy, ft/lbs per grain	15.01	13.24	11.63	10.18	8.88	7.71
Time of Flight, sec	0.0000	0.1191	0.2460	0.3815	0.5265	0.6819
Path, inches 100 yds	-1.5	0.0	-4.3	-15.3	-33.9	-61.2
200 yds	-1.5	2.2	0.0	-8.8	-25.2	-50.3
300 yds	-1.5	5.1	5.9	0.0	-13.5	-35.6
Velocity, ft/000	2500	2345	2196	2052	1913	1781
Energy, ft/lbs per grain	13.88	12.21	10.71	9.35	8.12	7.04
Time of Flight, sec	0.0000	0.1239	0.2561	0.3975	0.5489	0.7114
Path, inches 100 yds	-1.5	0.0	-4.8	-16.9	-37.2	-67.0
200 yds	-1.5	2.4	0.0	-9.6	-27.5	-55.0
300 yds	-1.5	5.6	6.4	0.0	-14.7	-38.9
Velocity, ft/sec	2400	2249	2103	1962	1828	1700
Energy, ft/lbs per grain	12.79	11.23	9.82	8.55	7.42	6.42
Time of Flight, sec	0.0000	0.1291	0.2671	0.4148	0.5732	0.7434
Path, inches 100 yds	-1.5	0.0	-5.4	-18.6	-40.9	-73.7
200 yds	-1.5	2.7	0.0	-10.6	-30.2	-60.2
300 yds	-1.5	6.2	7.0	0.0	-16.1	-42.6
Velocity, ft/sec	2300	2152	2010	1873	1743	1620
Energy, ft/lbs per grain	11.74	10.28	8.97	7.79	6.74	5.83
Time of Flight, sec	0.0000	0.1348	0.2791	0.4337	0.5998	0.7783
Path, inches 100 yds	-1.5	0.0	-6.0	-20.7	-45.2	-81.2
200 yds	-1.5	3.0	0.0	-11.6	-33.2	-66.2
300 yds	-1.5	6.9	7.8	0.0	-17.7	-46.8
Velocity, ft/sec	2200	2056	1917	1785	1660	1542
Energy, ft/lbs per grain	10.75	9.38	8.16	7.07	6.12	5.28
Time of Flight, sec	0.0000	0.1411	0.2922	0.4544	0.6287	0.8163
Path, inches 100 yds	-1.5	0.0	-6.7	-22.9	-50.1	-89.9
200 yds	-1.5	3.4	0.0	-12.8	-36.6	-73.0
300 yds	-1.5	7.6	8.6	0.0	-19.5	-51.6

Path, inches / Relative to Line of Sight — ZERO RANGE: 100 yds, 200 yds, 300 yds

long range tables

Exterior Ballistic Table for Ballistic Coefficient 0.56

		Muzzle	100 yds	200 yds	300 yds	400 yds	500 yds
Velocity, ft/sec		2100	1960	1825	1698	1577	1465
Energy, ft/lbs per grain		9.79	8.53	7.39	6.40	5.52	4.76
Time of Flight, sec		0.0000	0.1479	0.3065	0.4769	0.6603	0.8577
Path, inches	100 yds	-1.5	0.0	-7.6	-25.6	-55.7	-99.8
Relative to ZERO RANGE	200 yds	-1.5	3.8	0.0	-14.2	-40.5	-80.8
Line of Sight	300 yds	-1.5	8.5	9.5	0.0	-21.6	-57.1
Velocity, ft/sec		2000	1864	1734	1612	1497	1391
Energy, ft/lbs per grain		8.88	7.71	6.68	5.77	4.98	4.30
Time of Flight, sec		0.0000	0.1554	0.3223	0.5017	0.6949	0.9029
Path, inches	100 yds	-1.5	0.0	-8.5	-28.6	-62.1	-111.2
Relative to ZERO RANGE	200 yds	-1.5	4.3	0.0	-15.8	-45.1	-89.9
Line of Sight	300 yds	-1.5	9.5	10.6	0.0	-24.0	-63.5
Velocity, ft/sec		1900	1768	1644	1527	1419	1320
Energy, ft/lbs per grain		8.01	6.94	6.00	5.18	4.47	3.87
Time of Flight, sec		0.0000	0.1637	0.3396	0.5290	0.7329	0.9523
Path, inches	100 yds	-1.5	0.0	-9.6	-32.1	-69.6	-124.3
Relative to ZERO RANGE	200 yds	-1.5	4.8	0.0	-17.7	-50.3	-100.3
Line of Sight	300 yds	-1.5	10.7	11.8	0.0	-26.7	-70.8
Velocity, ft/sec		1800	1674	1555	1444	1343	1252
Energy, ft/lbs per grain		7.19	6.22	5.37	4.63	4.00	3.48
Time of Flight, sec		0.0000	0.1729	0.3589	0.5591	0.7746	1.0062
Path, inches	100 yds	-1.5	0.0	-10.9	-36.3	-78.3	-139.6
Relative to ZERO RANGE	200 yds	-1.5	5.5	0.0	-19.9	-56.4	-112.3
Line of Sight	300 yds	-1.5	12.1	13.2	0.0	-29.9	-79.2

glossary

Accuracy: The measure of precision in consistently obtaining a desired result. In shooting, the measure of a firearm's ability to place all shots close to the same point.

Action: The mechanism of a firearm by which it is loaded, locked, fired, and unloaded.

Air Resistance: The slowing effect of air on a projectile in flight that causes it to lose velocity as it travels downrange. Also called drag.

Annealing: The application of heat to a metal to change its characteristics. In handloading, the heating of a brass cartridge case after work-hardening to reduce internal stresses that could make the case brittle. Only the neck should be annealed and great care should be taken not to overheat and thus soften the head and rear portion of the case. *See work-harden.*

Alloy: Different metals combined to achieve desired characteristics. Example: cartridge brass is an alloy of copper and zinc.

Antimony: A metallic element (chemical symbol Sb) that increases the strength of lead when combined to form an alloy.

Anvil: A part of the priming system; a fixed metallic point against which the priming mixture is crushed and thereby activated by the striking force of the firing pin.

Ball: Early term for "bullet." Still used in military nomenclature, usually to describe a fully metal jacketed bullet.

Ball Powder: Trademarked name for a double-base, smokeless propellant powder developed by Olin, Inc. Either spherical or flattened spherical in shape.

Ballistics: The science of gun systems and projectiles. Divided into interior ballistics—covering the time between the start of primer ignition and the bullet's exit from the barrel; exterior ballistics—the bullet's motion from barrel exit to target; and terminal ballistics—the bullet's behavior from the moment it enters its target until it stops or exits.

Ballistic Coefficient (BC): Ratio of the sectional density of a bullet to its coefficient of form used to estimate the projectile's ability to overcome air resistance in flight. The higher the BC, the easier the bullet slips through air, resulting in higher retained velocity and less drop.

Barrel-cylinder Gap: The clearance between a revolver's barrel and cylinder.

Battery Cup Primer: A primer whose anvil and primer cup are supported in an outside shell called the battery cup. Shotshell primers are the most common of this type.

Bearing Surface: That portion of a bullet's surface that makes contact with the bore when moving through the barrel.

Bell: *v.* To expand the mouth of a case slightly in order to seat a bullet more easily. *n.* the expanded portion of the case mouth. Also called flare.

Belted Case: Case head type with raised band or belt at the base ahead of extractor groove; a variant of the rimless case. Originally, the belt was the support point for controlling headspace of the cartridge. *See rim.*

Bench Rest: A shooting style in which a solid table or bench and other devices are used to support a firearm when testing for accuracy, removing some human factors so results are more representative of the firearm and/or ammunition. Bench Rest competition has become an important shooting sport where the smallest group wins.

Berdan: Type of component primer with no integral anvil. Anvil is formed in bottom of the case's primer pocket. Common outside North America, it is named after the inventor, Colonel Hiram Berdan, an American. *See primer.*

Black Powder: The oldest successful ballistic propellant; a mechanical mixture of potassium nitrate (saltpeter), charcoal and sulfur. Corned black powder is the product of combining the three components while slightly damp for better blending that improves handling qualities, stability and performance.

Boat Tail: Name given to a bullet type made with tapered base portion to reduce aerodynamic drag. Also "tapered heel."

Body (of a case): The portion of a cartridge case between the head and the shoulder that contains the powder.

Bolt: The locking and cartridge-handling mechanism of a firearm that operates in line with the axis of the bore, moving fore and aft within a receiver. It can contain the firing pin, firing pin spring, extractor(s) and the ejector.

Bolt Thrust: The force on the face of the bolt or breech of a firearm caused by the pressure of burning powder gases.

Bore: The inside of the barrel of a gun of any kind and, in rifled arms, the diameter of the barrel before the rifling is formed.

Bore Sight: To roughly align the sights of a firearm with the axis of its barrel without firing test cartridges. In its most basic form, it requires looking through the bore and centering it on a bullseye. Then, without moving the barrel, the sights are adjusted so they are also centered on the bullseye.

Boxer: The standard American type of primer, named after the inventor of this type of primer, Colonel Edward Boxer of the British Army. The anvil is integral with the primers. *See primer.*

Brass: An alloy of copper and zinc used for cartridge cases. Typical cartridge brass has a copper/zinc ratio of 70/30.

Brisance: The speed at which an explosive material reaches maximum pressure. A measure of the shattering power of an explosive. *See primer.*

Bullet: The missile used in firearms systems. Technically, it becomes a projectile when in motion. Not to be substituted for the term "cartridge." *See also ball.*

Bullet Path: The track followed by a bullet in flight measured Relative to the line of sight.

Bullet Pull: The amount of force needed to extract a bullet from a loaded cartridge. Used by ammunition manufacturers to measure crimp strength and uniformity.

Bullet Puller: A tool for extracting bullets from loaded cartridges. The inertial and collet types are most common.

Burning Rate: A term used to rank the relative rate at which propellants release energy, based on heat production of the material in a fixed-volume apparatus called a calorimeter bomb.

Caliber: (1) The diameter of either a projectile or the bore of a gun. It is the approximate diameter expressed in hundredths of an inch in the English measurement system. A bullet that is 0.451-inch in diameter is 45-caliber. To add a leading decimal (".30 caliber") is technically incorrect. According to the strict definition, such a bullet would only be 0.003-inch in diameter. Frequently compounded with other descriptive words or numbers to create a cartridge name, e.g., 308 Winchester or 30-40 Krag. (2) In artillery, a measure of barrel length equal to the diameter (or caliber) of a specified gun barrel; a "five inch, 38-caliber" barrel would be 38 bore diameters long (5 times 38 is 190 inches or 15.8 feet). (3) In bullet design, a measure of the curvature of the bullet ogive; a 6-caliber bullet ogive would have a radius of six bore diameters.

Cannelure: Circumferential groove(s) around a bullet used to hold lubricant, or around a cartridge case for securing bullet to case where a case mouth crimp is insufficient or not feasible.

Canister Powder: A propellant marketed for hobby reloading. Each propellant lot is held to strict specifications so the handloader will always have reasonably uniform results over time. The term "canister grade" is applied because such propellants are usually packed in containers of suitable size for consumer use.

Cap: *See primer.*

Cartridge: A complete unit of assembled ammunition: case, propellant powder, primer, and bullet. Commonly applied only to rifle and pistol ammunition, but occasionally to shotshells, as in shotgun cartridge.

Cartridge Overall Length: The length of a cartridge from base to bullet tip. Abbreviated "COAL."

Case: The paper, metal, or plastic container that holds all the other components of a cartridge. Informally called hull or shell.

Case Forming: To alter or modify one cartridge case to another of different shape and/or caliber. *Also see wildcat.*

Case Hardening: A heat-treating process that increases the surface hardness of iron alloys. Some case-hardening methods produce distinctive colors as seen on the frames of Colt Single Action revolvers.

Case Trimmer: A small lathe-like device to allow handloaders to shorten cases uniformly and with repeatability.

Case Trimming: Shortening an overly long case by removing metal at the case mouth.

Cast Bullet: Bullets for rifles or pistols cast from molten lead alloys in a mould. *See mould blocks.*

Centerfire (CF): A broad class of ammunition characterized by a centrally located primer in the case head. Also called centerfire. Most modern centerfire cartridges are reloadable.

Chamber: That part of a firearm formed to accept and support the cartridge. In most firearms the chamber is formed at the breech end of the barrel. In a revolver, chambers are located in the cylinder.

Chamber Cast: A casting usually of a low melting-point metal poured in a firearm chamber to more easily measure chamber dimensions.

Chamfer: To form a bevel on the inside of a case mouth, usually by reaming, to remove sharp edges that can make bullet seating difficult.

Charge: The amount of propellant measured into the case in loading. Also refers to amount of shot measured into a shotshell.

Choke: A constriction at the muzzle of a shotgun barrel designed to regulate the spread or dispersion of the shot charge.

Chronograph: A device that measures the velocity of a projectile.

Collimator: In shooting, an optical device used to roughly align sights with the bore of a firearm where sighting through the bore is not practical. *See bore sight.*

Combustion: Burning; in firearms, the chemical process which unites oxygen and other substances in propellants to produce heat and gas. Also called deflagration.

Compensator: A device fitted to the muzzle of a firearm to reduce recoil or muzzle rise. *See muzzle brake.*

Compressed Charge: A charge of propellant whose volume exceeds the usable volume of the case. Compression occurs when seating the bullet; most handloading propellants allow a small degree of compression through elasticity, packing, or some of each.

Components: The individual parts of a cartridge: primer, case, bullet and propellant.

Copper Crusher: Small, solid copper cylinder used in a pressure gun to measure chamber pressure. *See pressure gun.*

Cordite: Trade name for one of the earliest smokeless rifle propellants developed in Great Britain. Cordite has tubular granules that are often as long as the cartridge's powder space. A short-grain version with the trade name "Axite" was developed for handgun cartridges. Cordite is informally (and incorrectly) used to describe any propellant.

Core: The interior portion of a jacketed bullet, usually a lead alloy in sporting ammunition.

Corrosion: The chemical decay of gun metal due to rusting or the etching action of compounds deposited in the bore by corrosive primers or black powder. *See corrosive primer.*

Corrosive Primer: A primer whose combustion products are hygroscopic (attracting moisture) and release weak acids and/or salts. The compounds will rapidly rust a bore unless removed. All component primers made in the U.S. have been non-corrosive for decades.

Crimp: The bending of the case mouth inward to grip the bullet, or to close the mouth of a shotshell case. Two types are used in metallic reloading: a roll crimp is the bending or rolling of the mouth of the case into the crimp groove or cannelure of the bullet. In a taper crimp, the mouth of the case is pressed into the bullet body without bending the case mouth. A neckdown crimp is a variant of the roll crimp that irons more of the case into the crimp groove forming a step.

Crimped Primer (also called a "staked primer"): A primer that has been secured in its pocket by the bending of part of the case over the closed end of the primer. Usually found on military cartridges intended for use in automatic weapons. Unless the crimp is removed, repriming of the case can be very difficult if not impossible.

Cupro-Nickel: A copper-nickel alloy once used extensively for bullet jackets. It was largely replaced by gilding metal because of barrel fouling problems.

Deburr: To remove burrs or roughness sometimes left on case mouth edge during manufacture or by trimming operation. *See chamfer and case trimming.*

Decap: To remove or eject a primer from its primer pocket when preparing a cartridge case for reloading. Usually done by the decapping pin in the case sizing or expanding operation.

Deprime: *See decap.*

Deterrent: Chemical added to propellant granules by either incorporation or coating to achieve a desired rate of energy release. *See burning rate.*

Die: In handloading, a device designed to perform work on a cartridge case or bullet. It can form or reform cases or bullets, seat bullets and apply crimps. The general term "die" implies that it is an interchangeable part of a larger tool. Interchangeable reloading dies mean that one reloading press can be used to reload a wide range of cartridges.

Double-base Powder: Nitrocellulose (smokeless) propellant that uses nitroglycerine as the plasticizer. *See plasticizer.*

Drag: *See air resistance.*

Dram Equivalent: In shotshells, a term used to indicate that a charge of smokeless powder produces the same velocity as a given charge of black powder that would have been expressed in drams. A "3-dram equivalent load" has a charge of smokeless powder that gives roughly the same velocity as a similar load charged with 3 drams of black powder.

Drift: In exterior ballistics, the deviation of a projectile from the line of departure due to its rotation or spin. In casual use, it refers to the effects of crosswinds on the bullet. *See wind deflection.*

Drop: The distance a projectile falls due to gravity, measured or calculated from the axis of the barrel. *See line of departure.*

Duplex Load: **(1)** Two different propellants used to load the same cartridge. There is little or no advantage to duplex loading in small arms and results are unpredictably dangerous. **(2)** A rifle or handgun cartridge loaded with two projectiles. **(3)** A shotshell loaded with two different sizes of shot.

Elevation: The vertical adjustment in a firearm's sights that allows compensation for bullet drop.

Energy: (Specifically, kinetic energy) A projectile's ability to do work by virtue of its mass and motion, expressed in foot-pounds (ft/lbs) in the English system. Found by multiplying the square of the velocity in ft/sec by the weight of the bullet in grains and dividing by 450,400.

Engraving: The marks made on the bullet by the barrel of a rifled firearm.

Engraving Force: The pressure required to completely engage a bullet into a rifled gun barrel. Sometimes called "shot start pressure."

Erosion: The wearing away of the bore of a firearm due to projectile friction, the action of hot powder gases, or both.

Expander Ball or Button: The round steel part of a reloading die that passes through the sized case neck to set the correct diameter needed to hold the bullet firmly.

Expansion Ratio: Relationship of interior case volume to bore volume.

Extruded Primer: A fired primer that has the metal of the firing pin impression forced back into the firing pin hole in the face of the bolt. Also known as cratering. Usually a gun problem caused by excessive gap between breech face and the firing pin, or by a weak firing pin spring. Extruded primers seldom indicate excessive pressure.

Extrusion: Forming or shaping a ductile material by forcing it through a opening. Example: extrusion of large lead billets makes lead wire for bullet cores.

Extruded Propellant: Another term for cylindrical propellant. Formed by forcing damp propellant mix through a die during manufacture and cutting to desired lengths. Often has one or more longitudinal holes through the grains.

Fireform: Using the pressure of normal firing to shape a cartridge case to fit a given chamber. Used in forming many wildcat cartridges.

Firing Pin: The component of a gun's action that strikes the primer to start ignition.

Flake Powder: A smokeless propellant characterized by thin, disc-shaped granules.

Flash Hole: The hole leading from the primer pocket into the body of the cartridge case. Also called the vent.

Forcing Cone: The bevel in the rear of a revolver barrel just ahead of the barrel-cylinder gap. Provides a transition zone to assist the bullet in engaging the rifling.

Form Factor: In exterior ballistics, a multiplier that relates the shape of a bullet to that of a standard projectile used to determine the ballistic coefficient.

Freebore: The cylindrical portion of a firearm barrel between the forward end of the chamber and the origin of the rifling. *See throat.*

Frontal Ignition: Experimental type of cartridge where the primer's flash is directed through a metal tube to ignite the forward part of the powder charge first.

FMJ: Full metal jacket. *See metal case.*

Galling: Metal deposits and/or roughness resulting from friction between a cartridge case and sizing die.

Gas: In handloading, the vapor produced by burning powder that expands rapidly, creating the pressure required to expel the bullet from the barrel.

Gas Check: A sealing device that restricts gas to a desired location. In bullets, a metal, wax, or plastic disk placed under or on the base of the bullet to improve obturation, intended to keep propellant gas from leaking around the bullet as it moves through the gun barrel. A gas check is also used to protect a bullet base from the effects of hot gases

Gilding Metal: A copper-zinc alloy used for bullet jackets consisting of 5 percent zinc and 95 percent copper.

Grain: An English weight measure used to express weight of ammunition components. 7000 grains equal one pound; 437.5 grains equal one ounce. Incorrectly used in referring to a particle, or granule, of powder.

Granulation: The grain size and shape of either black or smokeless powder.

Granule: A single particle of propellant.

Grease Groove: A circumferential groove or cannelure on a bullet used to hold lubricant.

Group: The pattern made on the target by a number of shots fired with one aiming point and one sight setting. Usually measured from the centers of the holes farthest from each other.

Gun Powder: Informal term for propellant.

Half-jacket: A short jacket that leaves some core material in contact with the bore. Also a bullet made with a short jacket.

Handgun: A firearm designed to be fired from one hand without support of the shooter's shoulder. Consists of two classes: pistols and revolvers.

Handloading: The practice of loading or reloading small arms ammunition by hand-powered equipment and methods.

Hangfire: Slang term for a delayed firing, which is any detectable delay in the ignition of a cartridge after pulling the trigger. Can be a chemical delay caused by the cartridge or a mechanical delay caused by a defect in the firearm.

Headspace: The distance from that surface of the barrel or chamber that prevents the cartridge from moving farther forward into the chamber to the face of the breech with the action fully closed and locked. This is the most important dimension governing the safety of the shooter. In handloading, the combination of cartridge case and gun must be considered when considering headspace.

Heel: The edge of the bullet base.

Holdover: The vertical distance above a target required to hit it at ranges greater than the gun's "zero." *See zero.*

Hollow Point (HP): Bullet design feature; an axial hole at the tip of bullet that assists in the expansion of bullets at low velocity.

Hydrostatic Shock: Pressure wave created in water or water-laden material (such as animal tissue) by a bullet's penetration.

Ignition: The combination of chemically produced heat and pressure that initiates propellant combustion to release its stored energy.

Improved: Term used to indicate a cartridge whose propellant capacity has been made greater by reducing body taper and/or increasing the shoulder angle.

IMR: Abbreviation for "Improved Military Rifle," a trademark of the IMR Powder Co. to identify its line of single-base rifle powders.

Jacket: A cover or "skin" applied to a lead bullet to reduce bore fouling. Usually made of gilding metal in the U.S., but copper-clad steel or mild steel are also used in other countries. *See gilding metal, cupro-nickel and half jacket.*

Keyhole: The oval imprint of a bullet that indicates it was not traveling point-on at the time of impact. Keyholes are evidence that the bullet's flight is unstable.

Lands: The raised spiral portion of a rifled bore remaining after the grooves have been cut or formed.

Lead Crusher: A soft lead cylinder used in a pressure gun for obtaining lead units of pressure (L.U.P. or lup). Formerly used to test low-pressure cartridges like shotshells, this system is now obsolete.

Leade: The tapered portion of the rifling just ahead of the chamber that is cut away to clear the bullet and to provide reasonable engraving forces. *See throat and engraving.*

Leading: Lead deposited in the bore from the friction of lead bullets rubbing against the bore, or from gas cutting. A form of metal fouling, some leading is normal. However, excessive leading can destroy accuracy and raise pressures.

Line of Departure (LOD): The projection into space of the axis of a gun barrel. Bullet drop is measured Relative to the LOD.

Line of Sight (LOS): The straight line through the sights of a gun to the point of aim. Bullet path is defined Relative to the LOS.

Loading Block: A block of wood or plastic with rows of holes to conveniently hold and orient a number of cartridge cases during reloading.

Loading Density: Also called the filling ratio. The ratio of the volume of powder charge to the remaining volume of the case after the bullet is seated. Loading density is dependent on the propellant granulation as well as the case volume, bullet shape and bullet seating depth. *See compressed charge.*

Lubricant: Any compound used to reduce friction. Case sizing lubricant is used to reduce friction when sizing cartridge cases. Bullet lubricant is used to minimize leading when firing lead alloy bullets by reducing friction between the lead and the bore.

Lubricator-Sizer: A tool used to simultaneously size and lubricate cast lead bullets. Often contracted to lubrisizer.

Magnum: Originally, a large wine bottle. In shooting, a cartridge of exceptional size or power. First applied to large, bottlenecked rifle cartridges whose profile was reminiscent of wine bottles.

Mean Radius (MR): The average radius of a group of shots from the center of the group. Another method of analyzing accuracy, MR is commonly seen in military contract specifications for accuracy. Extreme spread is more commonly used to measure accuracy in commercial ammo manufacturing and hobby shooting. *See group.*

Meplat: The diameter of the flat or blunt end of the nose of a bullet.

Mercuric Primer: A primer whose primary initiator is mercury fulminate. These primers have been obsolete for nearly a century. On firing, the compounds release minute amounts of metallic mercury. Mercury attacks the cartridge case making it brittle and thus unsuitable for further loading.

Metal Case (MC): Also Full Patched (FP) or Full Metal Jacketed (FMJ). A type of bullet whose lead core is fully encased in jacket material except for an opening at the base that allows core insertion in manufacturing.

Metal Fouling: Bullet material deposited in bore due to friction. More common in very high-velocity rifle cartridges, metal fouling must be removed to prevent corrosion due to the electrolytic action of the copper with the steel barrel. Metal fouling can also be caused by a rough bore at any velocity.

Micrometer: A measuring instrument with a fine screw adjustment for measuring small dimensions. Usually calibrated to read in increments of 0.001 or 0.0001-inch. *See caliper.*

Mid-range Trajectory (MRT): The maximum bullet rise above line of sight between the muzzle and the sight-in range. Also called the maximum ordinate.

Minute-of-angle (MOA): A unit of angular measurement equal to the distance traversed by 1/60th of a degree. Although usually approximated as one inch per 100 yards, it is actually equal to 1.047 inches per 100 yards. MOA is Relative to the range; a "1-MOA" rifle theoretically shoots one-inch groups at 100 yards or two-inch groups at 200 yards.

Misfire: Failure of a cartridge to discharge after the primer is struck by the firing pin.

Mould Blocks: Two "mirror twin" pieces of metal having one or more bullet-shaped cavities in which lead bullets are cast from a molten alloy.

Mushroom: The ability or capacity of a bullet to increase its diameter upon impact for more efficient energy delivery. The name comes from the desired bullet shape after expansion.

Muzzle: The part of a firearm barrel where a fired projectile exits.

Muzzle Blast: The compression wave caused by hot, high-pressure powder gases jetting from the muzzle.

Muzzle Brake: A deflector fitted to a gun muzzle to redirect exiting gases. In small arms, used to reduce "muzzle flip" by directing some of the muzzle gas upward. Also called a recoil compensator or, informally "comp." *See compensator.*

Muzzle Energy (ME): The kinetic energy of a bullet at the muzzle where velocity is highest. *See energy.*

Neck: The portion of a cartridge case that grips the bullet. In a bottlenecked case, that portion of the case in front of the shoulder.

Neck Down or Up: To change the diameter of the case neck during case forming to accept a bullet of a different diameter. Example: the 35 Whelen is a 30-06 case necked up to accept a 35-caliber bullet.

Neck Expansion: Increasing the diameter of a sized case neck by passing it over an expander plug or button. Sets the correct neck diameter.

Neck Ream: Removing excess metal from the inside of a case neck with a rotary cutting tool. Commonly required when forming a short case from a much longer one that leaves more material in the neck walls than desired, e.g., forming the 300 H&H case to 6.5mm Remington Magnum.

Neck Size: To resize part or all of the neck only, leaving the case body unchanged.

Neck Turn: Removing excess metal from the outside of the case neck by cutting or shaving.

Non-corrosive: Cartridges or primers with priming mixture containing no compound capable of rusting or corroding the bore or adjacent parts. All commercial small arms primers made in the U.S. and most military ammunition produced since 1954 has non-corrosive primers. The prudent shooter cleans his firearm promptly when unsure of the primer type fired.

Non-mercuric: A priming mixture containing no mercury compounds.

Ogive: (pronounced "OH-jive") The curved portion of a bullet between the cylindrical shank section and the tip. Also, the radius of this curve, usually expressed in calibers.

Oil Dent: A depression in a cartridge case formed during resizing, usually at the shoulder, because too much lubricant is present.

Overbore Capacity: A common (but imprecise) term referring to a cartridge case that has excessive case volume compared to its bore volume. Generally used when case volume is so large in relation to the bore diameter that only very slow burning powders will give satisfactory performance.

Parallax: The condition in telescopic sights that exists when the reticle (crosshairs) does not lie exactly in the image plane. Excessive parallax makes the shooter's eye position very critical if repeatable accuracy is to be obtained. Most low-power scopes have the parallax pre-set at 100 to 150 yards; high-magnification scopes (10-power and up) commonly have an adjustable objective to correct for parallax at various distances.

Paper-patched Bullet: A bullet wrapped with a paper "patch" commonly used in older black powder cartridges. Derived from the even older cloth patch used to wrap a muzzle-loader ball. The patch helped seal the powder gases to reduce bore leading and was an evolutionary step towards today's metal bullet jackets.

Pierced Primer: A primer that has been punctured at the firing pin impression. Most often caused by a defective firing pin, a weak firing pin spring or excessive clearance between the firing pin and breech.

Pistol: a class of handgun characterized by having part of the barrel enlarged to accommodate the cartridge for firing.

Plasticizer: A chemical added to nitrocellulose to facilitate forming it into propellant granules. Alcohol and/or ether are the plasticizers in single-base propellants. In double-base propellants, the plasticizer is nitroglycerine. *See propellant.*

Plinking: Casual target practice commonly at informal targets. Shooting for fun where no one keeps score.

Point of Aim: **(1)** The point at which a gun's sights are aligned. **(2)** the spot where the shooter aims to put his bullet on target. Example: at ranges beyond the rear sight's maximum adjustment, a shooter may have to hold the sights on an auxiliary point of aim above the target to have the bullets fall in the bullseye.

Point Blank Range (PBR): The horizontal distance from the gun muzzle to a zone target can be hit without the shooter adjusting the point of aim higher. PBR for a target of two-inch diameter is much less than for a six-inch target. Maximum Point Blank Range (MPBR) is the farthest distance at which the rise and drop of the bullet path Relative to line-of-sight does not exceed the target diameter.

Powder: An informal term for a chemical ballistic propellant. *See propellant.*

Powder Bridging: A blockage that may occur in the drop tube of a powder measure or a funnel. The powder granules interlock and wedge together creating a "log jam" of propellant. Most common with long, cylindrical granules, bridging can be overcome with proper charging techniques.

Powder Measure: A mechanical device that dispenses propellant charges by volume, or a motorized device linked to an electronic scale. The latter "reads" the weight value from the scale and stops dispensing when a pre-set propellant weight is reached.

Powder Scale: A mechanical or electronic device used to accurately weigh bullets or propellant charges. For cartridge reloading, it is usually graduated to permit weighing to units as small as 1/10th grain. *See grain.*

Powder Trickler: A mechanical accessory usually of the auger type that dribbles a few granules at a time for precision weighing with a powder scale.

Pressure: The force exerted by burning propellant in the chamber of a gun. Expressed normally as the peak pressure in pounds per square inch (psi) or copper units of pressure (CUP).

Pressure Gun: A fixture for measuring chamber pressure generated by firing a cartridge. Essentially a gun barrel fitted with a pressure-sensing device. There are two classes of sensing devices: mechanical (crusher), and electronic (piezo-electric transducer) system.

Primer *(also informally, "cap," derived from the percussion caps used with some muzzleloading arms):* In a centerfire cartridge, the small metal cup containing a percussion-activated mixture used to ignite the propellant powder. The primer is seated in the primer pocket in the base of the cartridge case. In a rimfire cartridge the priming mixture is contained within the hollow rim of the case. *See anvil, Berdan, Boxer, brisance and battery cup.*

Primer Flipper: A two-piece metal or plastic tray for orienting and turning primers to facilitate loading of primer tubes in semi-automated equipment.

Primer Indent: Depression made in a primer by the firing pin. Also called the firing pin impression.

Primer Leak: The unintended release of propellant gas between the circumference of the primer and the primer pocket, usually due to a damaged primer pocket. Also used to describe similar leakage within the firing pin impression, usually due to a rough or improperly shaped firing pin. Circumferential leaking can occur in a high pressure condition sufficient to deform the case head, increasing the diameter of the pocket and loosening the primer.

Primer Pocket: The cavity in the head of a centerfire cartridge case made to hold and support the primer.

Primer Pocket Reaming: A cutting operation that properly profiles the primer pocket. It may remove a military primer crimp or remove excessive radius at the bottom of the pocket.

Primer Pocket Swaging: Cold-forming to remove a military crimp from the edge of the primer pocket.

Primer Punch: The rod in a priming tool that pushes the primer into a cartridge case.

Primer Tool: A specialized tool that performs only the priming operation.

Progressive: (1) A characteristic of chemical propellants describing how they release energy. During burning, the energy release is controlled to provide the proper force on the bullet for a desired performance goal. (2) A form of automated reloading press that performs several operations at once to increase production rate.

Projectile: A bullet or other object projected by application of force and continuing in motion by its own inertia.

Proof Cartridge: A special, high-pressure cartridge used to test a new or repaired firearm for strength and safety, usually about 20-25 percent higher pressure than normal maximum pressure.

Propellant: The term applied to chemicals that drive a projectile. The fuel in modern gun systems. Divided into two basic types: smokeless and black powder. Smokeless propellants consist primarily of nitrocellulose and may have other fuel materials like nitroglycerin. Black powder is a mechanical mixture of sulfur, charcoal, and saltpeter and is now used primarily in muzzleloading guns. *See ball powder, flake powder and extruded tubular powder.*

Protruding Primer: A primer that partially backs out of the primer pocket on firing, commonly indicating low firing pressure and/or excessive headspace.

Ram: The large moveable shaft of most metallic ammunition reloading tools that performs work on a cartridge case.

Ream: To remove metal from a cavity with a rotary cutting tool.

Rebated rim: A cartridge case type whose rim is smaller than the largest body diameter. Examples: 284 Winchester, Winchester and Remington short magnums, and 50 Action Express.

Recoil (informally, kick): The backward thrust of a gun in reaction to the bullet or shot charge being propelled forward.

Reloading Press: A force-multiplying device used in reloading ammunition. Usually has some form of mechanical advantage to reduce effort in resizing or reforming cases. The basic types are commonly identified by comparing the shape of the frame to the shape of letters of the alphabet. "O" types are most common today, but "H" and "C" types were also manufactured.

Remaining Energy: The residual or "downrange" energy of a projectile at a given point on its trajectory.

Remaining Velocity: The residual speed of a projectile at a given point on its trajectory.

Reticle: The aiming indicator at the focus of a telescopic sight. May consist of straight or tapered lines (crosshairs), dots, posts, or some combination thereof. Some reticles have auxiliary marks for range estimation. Often incorrectly spelled "reticule."

Revolver: A class of handgun characterized by a moving part separate from the barrel, the cylinder, in which cartridges are held for firing.

Rifling: Spiral grooves cut or impressed into the bore of rifles and pistols in order to make the bullets spin, providing gyroscopic stability in flight to the target.

Rim: A feature at the base of most cartridge cases. A rim can control the position of the cartridge in the chamber and/or facilitate cartridge extraction. *See rimless and rimmed.*

Rimfire (RF): Cartridges that carry their priming mixture within a folded, hollow rim. This ammunition type is not reloadable.

Rimless: A case head type; actually a misnomer. Rimless cases have a rim but it is the same diameter as the case body so it does not protrude. An undercut extraction cannelure or groove provides a place for the extractor to grip. Example: 30-06 Springfield.

Rimmed: A case head type whose rim protrudes beyond the case body, typically becoming the primary headspace control surface. Example: 30-30 Winchester. In British cartridges, this case type is called flanged.

Round: A military term for one complete cartridge.

Round Nose: Bullet design feature; a blunt nose shape.

Rupture *(also separation):* In ammunition, a failure or break in the wall of a cartridge case allowing gas to escape.

SAAMI: Sporting Arms and Ammunition Manufacturers Institute. The industry organization that establishes firearms and ammunition standards in the United States (www.saami.org).

Sabot: From French for "shoe." In modern small arms usage, a lightweight carrier in which a sub-caliber projectile is centered to permit firing in a larger caliber barrel. Most sabots are the discarding type, falling away from the bullet after exiting the gun barrel.

Seating Depth: The depth to which the base of the bullet is seated below the case mouth. Hard to directly measure, proper seating depth is established by the cartridge overall length (COAL), which is easily measured with a caliper. *See cartridge overall length.*

Sectional Density (SD): A bullet's weight in pounds divided by the square of its diameter in inches. Also known as weight per cross-sectional area.

Semi-wadcutter (SWC): A handgun bullet style that is transitional between round nose and wadcutter designs. A SWC has the sharp shoulder of a wadcutter for cutting clean holes in paper targets combined with a reduced-diameter, extended nose that affords better stability at longer ranges. *See wadcutter.*

Shank: The cylindrical section of a bullet between the nose section and the base. The shank usually defines the bearing surface that makes contact with the rifling.

Shell Holder: The interchangeable part of a reloading press that holds the head of the cartridge case centered on the ram. *See ram.*

Shock: *See hydrostatic shock.*

Shock Wave: A wave of compressed air resulting from a rapidly moving object, an explosion or, in the case of modern firearms, very rapid burning of propellant materials.

Shot: Metal spheres used for multiple projectile ammunition such as shotshells. Traditionally made of lead alloys, environmental concerns and resulting government regulation have caused the development of lead-free shot made from steel, tungsten, bismuth, and other low-toxicity metals.

Shoulder: The sloping or rounded portion of a bottleneck cartridge case between the neck and the body.

Sighting in: Firing a firearm to determine its point of impact at a specified range and adjusting the sights so the point of impact has the desired correlation to the point of aim.

Single-base Propellant: Nitrocellulose propellant made without the addition of any other highly nitrated chemical such as nitroglycerine. *See double-base propellant.*

Sizing: *Also resizing.* Reducing a fired cartridge case to dimensions that allow easy chambering in a firearm of the appropriate caliber. May be full length, partial, or neck sizing. Bullets are also sized or reduced in diameter by passing through a die.

Slug: A large, single projectile, often bearing external pre-cut rifling, intended for adapting shotguns to hunting larger game such as deer. Also a slang term for bullet. As a verb, "to slug" means forcing a soft lead cylinder through the bore of a gun for determining internal barrel dimensions.

Small-base dies: Special resizing dies for rifle cartridges that reduce the case body diameter near the head more than conventional resizing dies. Commonly used when reloading for semi-automatic and slide-action rifles that lack the camming power of a turn-bolt action.

Smokeless: *See propellant.*

Soft point (SP): Bullet design feature in which a portion of the lead alloy core is exposed at the tip of a jacketed bullet, allowing it to increase its diameter on impact for better stopping power.

Spent: In shooting, a cartridge or component thereof which has been fired.

Spherical Propellant: A registered trademark of Hodgdon Powder Company used to describe propellants having round or semi-round grains. *See ball propellant.*

Spin: The rapid rotation of the projectile caused by the spiral rifling in the bore that stabilizes the bullet during flight.

Spire Point: A pointed bullet with a conical nose section. The line from the shank to the point is nearly straight.

Spitzer: Bullet design feature from German for "point." A bullet with a pointed nose. The line from the shank to the tip is arched or ogival.

Stabilize: To spin a projectile around its long axis rapidly enough to resist forces that can move it from its point-forward in flight. *See spin.*

Swage: To cold-form applying pressure to a metal part contained in a closed die.

Throat: The transitional zone in the bore of a rifle or pistol barrel between the chamber and the rifled portion. Consists of freebore and leade. However, some throats do not have freebore. *See leade and freebore.*

Time of Flight (TOF): The elapsed time, in milliseconds, of a bullet's flight from muzzle to a given range.

Trajectory: The curved path of a projectile between gun muzzle and target Relative to the line of sight (LOS).

Transducer: An electronic sensing device that develops a voltage directly proportional to the force (pressure) applied to it. In ammunition testing, it is mounted in a test barrel over the chamber perpendicular to the bore axis to electronically measure firing pressures.

Twist rate: The rate at which a bullet is rotated in-bore by rifling. Usually measured by the length of barrel required to rotate a bullet one complete turn (ex: one turn in ten inches). Low numbers (1-in-8) indicate a "fast twist" and higher numbers (1-in-38) indicate a "slow twist."

Upset: **(1)** The tendency for a bullet to become more cylindrical on firing due to pressure, friction and/or inertia. Also known as "slugging up." **(2)** The expansion on impact of a hunting bullet. *See mushroom.*

Velocity: The speed of a projectile, usually measured in feet per second (ft/sec) at a given range.

Vernier Caliper: A simple slide-type precision measuring tool. "Vernier" refers to the readout mechanism. The dial caliper is now more popular because its numerical readout permits faster reading and is less prone to user errors in reading the values. Electronic calipers are even easier to use.

Wad: A disc of paper, felt, cork, plastic or other material used primarily in shotshells to separate propellant from shot. Can be over-powder, filler or a combination of these.

Wadcutter: A cylindrical, sharp-shouldered bullet designed to cut a clean round hole in a paper target for maximum score in competition; most commonly used in revolvers.

Web: That part of a cartridge case between the bottom of the primer pocket and the interior of the case. The web is pierced by the flash hole.

Wildcat: A cartridge formed by altering an existing commercial case to make a style that is not available from ammunition companies. Industry dimensional and pressure standards do not exist for wildcat cartridges.

Windage: The amount of sight correction, left or right, applied to compensate for horizontal deflection of a projectile induced by wind drift or minor sight-mounting errors. *See drift.*

Wind Deflection: Lateral change in the path of a projectile due to crosswind effects.

Work-hardening: The increase in hardness of metal due to repeated flexing or stress. In reloading, continued sizing of a case can work-harden the metal until cracks appear. *See annealing.*

Working-up: The process of developing a safe maximum load by starting with a lower powder charge and increasing it in small steps only after firing and checking for signs of pressure at each point along the way. Accuracy may also be evaluated by firing at a target. Often, best accuracy occurs before reaching the maximum load.

Yaw: A situation where a bullet rotates about its axis at a small angle to the line of flight. In yaw, a bullet's tip is normally on the axis of the path but the base is spiraling around that axis. The spin of the bullet causes it to settle into stable flight with both tip and base on the same path axis, usually within 40 to 100 yards for a rifle. Without the influence of forced stabilization from rifling or another source, yaw will grow into an end-over-end tumble.

Zero: More correctly, "zero sight adjustment." That adjustment of a gun's sights that will place a properly aimed shot at the desired point of impact at some range with a given load in the absence of wind. The basis from which subsequent sight adjustments are made. As a verb, it is synonymous with "sight in," as in, "I want to zero my rifle for 150 yards."

Zero Range: The downrange distance where the bullet path exactly coincides with the line of sight (LOS). Each gun/load combination has two zero ranges—one near the muzzle as the bullet rises through the LOS and another at some greater distance where the bullet descends through the LOS.